TECHNOLOGY COMMERCIALIZATION MANUAL

Strategy, Tactics, and Economics for Business Success

TECHNOLOGY COMMERCIALIZATION MANUAL

Strategy, Tactics, and Economics for Business Success

By

Melvin J. DeGeeter, Ph.D.

ISBN 1-58961-162-4

ABOUT THE AUTHOR

Dr. DeGeeter has over 15 years experience in research and program management while with The Upjohn Company and Monsanto. He was Director of Industrial Relations or Technology Transfer at Texas A&M, Indiana University and the University of Illinois at Champaign-Urbana. He is a visiting lecturer at the University of Illinois where he teaches a course on technology commercialization at the graduate and MBA levels. He has also presented the course at the University of Helsinki. Dr. DeGeeter is founder and owner of Med-Launch^{SM}, a limited liability company focused on technology assessment, development and deployment for the healthcare industry. He has served on boards of companies and incubators and as Regional Vice President for the Association of University Managers.

ACKNOWLEDGEMENTS

The author wishes to thank Jon Outland for assistance in preparing the Technology Pricing Model^{TM} software and Leah Pettit for her suggestions, comments and editing of the manuscript. Thanks are also extended to the author's professional acquaintances that offered content suggestions and ideas. He is especially indebted to his wife, Priscilla, for her advice and understanding during the preparation of the manuscript.

TECHNOLOGY COMMERCIALIZATION MANUAL
Strategy, Tactics and Economics for Business Success

"Successful asset commercialization is a complex process dependent upon numerous inputs that are skillfully managed to establish appropriate and prudent strategic and tactical plans that are effectively and efficiently executed."

TOPICS

- Introduction to technology commercialization and technology based companies
- Structure of the technology transfer organization and related econometrics
- Technology sources - technology transfer, acquisition, commercialization or licensing offices

- Role of Incubators, Clusters, Research Parks and Consortia
- Intellectual property protection and management
- Technology assessment, valuation and pricing
- Technology development and management
- Commercialization and marketing strategies and tactics
- International considerations for technology transfer or commercialization
- Negotiation strategies, methods, and resources
- Capital acquisition and sources
- Company formation or business structure of technology based firms
- Examples of agreements for select situations in the commercialization process

BENEFITS

- Increase awareness of technology commercialization models and related econometrics.
- Learn how to increase the value of an asset through intellectual property protection, identifying and establishing strategic alliances and program management.
- Increase awareness of evaluation methodology to make prudent and informed decisions regarding technology/asset value to receive the best return on technology asset (ROTA).
- Develop understanding of negotiation strategies and tactics.
- Experience the process of technology assessment and enactment of preferred contracts.
- Participate in negotiating win-win licenses to maximum benefit to the contracting parties.
- Gain hands on knowledge through situation analysis and exchange of experiences.
- Exposure to the strategy and tactics related to capital acquisition
- Receive information necessary to form and operate a business.

DELIVERABLES

- Information - textbook with which to generate knowledge
- Experiences - situation analysis, guest speakers(s)
- Model documents - invention disclosure, asset exchange, license agreements, etc.
- Technology Evaluation Software (TES^{TM}) - phased technology evaluation
- Technology Pricing Model (TPM^{TM}) software - negotiation tool to establish contract terms
- Worksheets - business assessment and formation and technology evaluation
- Glossary of business terms - related to technology commercialization
- Questions and answers - collection of frequently asked questions
- Resources - Extensive list of references, publications and related web sites

CONTENTS

THE FOLLOWING ADDENDA ARE AVAILABLE AT NO COST WITH THE PURCHASE OF THIS BOOK. SIMPLY COMPLETE THE "ADDENDA, CASE STUDIES AND PRESENTATIONS REQUEST FORM" ON THE LAST PAGE OF THIS BOOK.

ADDENDUM I - GLOSSARY OF TERMS

ADDENDUM II - REFERENCES AND RESOURCES

ADDENDUM III - FORMS AND AGREEMENTS
    FORMS
    AGREEMENTS

ADDENDUM IV - SOFTWARE
    TECHNOLOGY EVALUATION SOFTWARE (TES - I) - PHASE ONE
    TECHNOLOGY EVALUATION SOFTWARE (TES - II) - PHASE TWO
    TECHNOLOGY PRICING MODEL (TPM)

CASE STUDIES/SITUATION ANALYSIS AND POWERPOINT PRESENTATIONS FOR EACH MODULE ARE AVAILABLE FOR A FEE. SEE "ADDENDA, CASE STUDIES AND PRESENTATIONS REQUEST FORM" ON THE LAST PAGE OF THIS BOOK.

Over 100 situation analysis are available for Modules I through IX. Highlights from each Module are summarized in over 1200 PowerPoint slides which can be adapted to individual needs.

ADDENDA, CASE STUDIES & PRESENTATIONS REQUEST FORM

The "ADDENDA, CASE STUDIES AND PRESENTATIONS REQUEST FORM" is the last page of this book. Simply photocopy or cut out form, complete, fold as trifold with address visible, tape together and mail to the address provided.

MODULE I – INTRODUCTION

- **Definitions - technology transfer, intellectual property and financial**
- **Information resources**
- **Trends-future**
- **Cultures - government vs. university vs. industry, public vs. private**

A review and discussion of technology transfer terms, metrics, office organization, intellectual property definitions, protection methods and strategies, and monitoring of asset protection will be provided. Discussion centers on the growth of technology in contrast to growth of the business sector(s) and the associated economic process.

Technology transfer/commercialization operations

- **Policy and ethics**
- **Brokers/agents/technology transfer office**
- **Incubators/science and technology parks/research parks**
- **Relationships/network**
- **Organization comparisons - government, corporate, university**
- **Knowledge base - knowledge is power**
- **Transfer organization – management, operations**
- **Technology sources**

Information related to variations in policies or practices for government, corporations, universities, and individuals is examined and reviewed. Focus is on differences and similarities that affect the transfer process.

INTRODUCTION

HISTORICAL PERSPECTIVE

For nearly three decades, America witnessed the decline of its industrial prowess. Industry after industry was lost to foreign competition, productivity growth trailed that in Europe and Japan, and our technological superiority in a number of industries was and still is threatened. How did the world's most powerful industrial machine after World War II fall into such a sustained period of economic decline and how did we begin to reverse the trend?

Over the past several years, American industry finally came to recognize the strategic importance of technology to our economic well-being. Moreover, we benefited from an increased focus on quality and the value-added activities that keep a company competitive in its industry. Government, industry, and academia rededicated themselves to reclaiming our previous position of preeminence in the global economy. A fundamental element of industrial competitiveness is the effective development and commercialization of technology, in short, the management of technology.

The technology commercialization process requires: 1) assessment of intellectual property; 2) identification of business partners, licensees or alliances with interests, technology, marketing and management that are of mutual benefit; 3) analysis of strengths and weaknesses of alliance candidates; 4) investigation of strategies and plans for best tactical alliance e.g. start-up vs. existing company; exploration of industry and market trends; 5) knowledge of the competitive market place; and 6) communication and negotiation between client and alliance candidate.

CHALLENGES
History

A few pertinent statistics will serve to dramatize the magnitude of the problem. In 1980, the U.S. held 40.4 percent of the world market for high tech manufactures. By 1990, its market share had slipped to 35.9 percent. During the same period, Japan's market share rose from 18.4 percent to 29.2 percent [6]. The particularly disturbing part is this decline occurred long after problems with U.S. global competitiveness had been well publicized yet, at the time, the U.S. was unable to reverse the trend. Although the U.S. still maintained a positive trade balance in high technology industries, the trend then was downward in six of seven high technology sectors.

It is often said that the U.S. leads in the development of new technology but it is trailing in the development of associated commercial products. Royalties and license fees received from foreign countries or individuals for technology sold as intellectual property have averaged almost four times the amount paid to foreign countries or individuals by U.S. firms for access to their technology. U.S. receipts from such technology licensing efforts totaled $1.9 billion in 1989 with Japan being the largest consumer, accounting for 47 percent of the 1989 sales. From 1984 through 1988, the U.S. entered into three agreements for the transfer of technology to Japan for every single transfer of technology from Japan to the U.S. [5]. The U.S.'s inability and/or shortsighted unwillingness to commercialize its technology were at least partially responsible for its deteriorating trade balance.

The U.S.'s inability and/or shortsighted unwillingness to commercialize its technology were at least partially responsible for its deteriorating trade balance

Clearly, the numbers all indicated the U.S. needed to do a better job of managing its technological resources. The National Research Council (NRC) points out in 1989, U.S. industry expended $64 billion on research and development but less than $1 million on studies to learn how to manage this effort more effectively [4]. Unfortunately, most M.B.A. and other management programs gave little, if any, consideration to the management of technology-intensive industries and companies.

Solutions

Technology commercialization is a complex endeavor and some basic considerations need to be addressed. The following are examples of these considerations: 1) whenever an asset or technology is if not "sold or accepted" before development it may not be market worthy; 2) technology is great but solutions are better; 3) products come after market applications - not before; 4) intellect is more important than intellectual property; 5) a company is not a company just because it is start-up, revenue, profits are needed; 6) the idea must be effectively described; 7) ideas need to be protected (legal protection is available to an inventor from idea through commercialization and includes the use of patents, trademarks, trade secrets, mask works and/or copyright); 8) careful estimation value of invention and understand the difference between pricing and valuing product (learn how to estimate commercial and financial worth of an idea, assess market value, and price a product); 9) when licensing is of interest ask if it is desirable or essential; 10) find a licensee, negotiate a license, develop domestic and international license agreement, as well as alternatives to manufacturing and marketing for the invention; 11) review the steps in developing a business plan, including market analysis, sales forecasting, staffing, cost projections, projected financial statements, financial requirements, and investors or financial providers; 12) structure the organization to grow or design legal and structural aspects when starting a business and plan for future growth of product lines, profits, and personnel and 13) when commercializing inventions consider alternative strategies and tactics to reach the marketplace including licensing, joint ventures, and corporate venturing.

The technology-based organization has many challenges. In this chapter, trends to be considered and methods to gather information on related technology and criteria to measure successful achievements are described. It is imperative that technology-based business employees work as a team to acquire, consolidate and evaluate information related to the corporate goals and business interests. Information will be key to successful commercialization of an asset.

ACADEMIC RESPONSE

Fortunately, industry and academia alike finally came to recognize the serious deficiencies in the traditional methods of educating students and managing companies. Business schools began adding courses in the management of information systems, manufacturing, and technology in general, and in various quality management topics. Where once many MBA programs sought to eliminate or circumvent the production/operations management requirement, this has now become one of the most popular areas of emphasis.

A contributing factor in B-schools' change of heart were new accreditation standards by the American Assembly of Collegiate Schools of Business (AACSB), the principal accrediting agency for business schools in the U.S. The new standards provided B-schools with the freedom to revise their curricula to create integrated, cross-functional courses. Under the new standards, B-schools had to define who their customers were and provide a mission statement detailing how they intended to serve them [6]. This new flexibility allowed B-schools to better differentiate their programs to address the needs of their respective markets as well as their own strengths.

Another new academic response that has received considerable attention is the advent of the Management of Technology (MoT) degree. Programs developed, in response, to a recognized need for a new approach to management education for America's technology intensive industries. In 1978, Fusfeld noted, "The management of technology is, in fact, the only functional area which is not represented by a discipline within any management school [1]." This deficiency has now been remedied. Note that MoT herein means the management of technology, not management and technology or even management technology. Why do we want to manage technology or, why is technology so important that it should be accorded its own management practice? To answer this first define the term. A good definition is "technology is comprised of all the products, tools, processes and methods that are used in the creation of goods or the performance of services". Dr. Robert M. White, past president of the National Academy of Engineering wrote: "Technology is now universally recognized as the engine of economic growth" [7]. Technological innovation generates increases in productivity, keeps companies competitive, and ultimately enables increases in the standard of living. It is precisely through doing a better job of managing technology that we can create an improved standard of living for all of our citizens.

Managing technology has become a critical activity for all firms, not only those in high technology industries. In today's competitive environment even "low-tech" products are often manufactured using "high-tech" processes. The effective management of technology requires an understanding of both the business and technical aspects of technology development and deployment. While the study of how to manage technical activities has been around for much longer, the interdisciplinary field of MoT is rooted in a 1987 report by the NRC. Where once concerned primarily with the management of the R&D function and human resources management pertaining specifically to scientists and engineers, modern MoT includes the study of manufacturing and process technology as well as the new product development process. The field also focuses on strategies for evaluating and acquiring externally developed technology in addition to traditional concerns with internal technology development [2].

In a 1987 report, the NRC identified eight general technology management activities in which America's technology intensive companies needed to improve if they were to regain their competitive edge:

1. integrating technology into the overall strategic objectives of the firm;
2. getting into and out of technologies more efficiently;
3. assessing and evaluating technology more effectively;
4. developing better methods for transferring and assimilating new technology;
5. reducing new product development time;
6. managing large, complex, and interdisciplinary or inter-organizational projects, programs, and systems;
7. managing the organization's internal use of technology; and
8. leveraging the effectiveness of technical professionals.

These are interdisciplinary problems that cut across traditional subject boundaries. Therefore, the NRC recommended that MoT programs be designed to confront these needs directly using problem focused, cross-disciplinary educational experiences [3, 4]. The usual subject-oriented approach to education (i.e. finance, marketing, engineering, manufacturing), which is emulated in the structure of most firms, leads to fragmented and poorly coordinated business strategies. The problems involved in developing and implementing new technology in products and processes, in commercializing new technology, and in managing competitive technology intensive firms transcend the narrow disciplines in which managers and engineers were previously educated. Thus, MoT is a highly applied field, the theoretical foundations of which are now being explored.

Is there a real difference between M.B.A. programs (even "techno" ones), engineering management programs, and management of technology programs? Yes. Many M.B.A. programs are still general management programs with more of a financial, accounting, and analytical emphasis than a strategic management emphasis. An engineer in an M.B.A. program might just as likely find himself or herself sitting next to an art history major who works for a department store (my own recollection) as someone who shares common interests and experiences. This attempt to be all things to all people does not serve the professional from a technology intensive firm well at all. Engineering management programs, on the other hand, present merely a narrow subset of MoT.

The management of technology is more than just the management of the technological operations of an organization. It is more than engineering management, R&D management, or manufacturing management. It is not just about strategic planning, resource allocation, or numerous other business functions. It is all of these and more! It is about understanding and appreciating the role of technology in today's technology intensive organizations and, more importantly, it is about enhancing and making strategic and effective use of a firm's technological capabilities to support business objectives. And this, after all, is what competitiveness is all about.

GENERAL STATISTICS

Ideas do not always lead to products that are sold to the public. In fact, few ever make it to market. Recent survey results indicate the following:

- 7% of conceived ideas or intellectual property (IP) are worth pursuing;
- 27% of pursued (IP) gets patented and licensed;
- 32% of developed IP ending in products gets manufactured;
- 50% of manufactured IP survives in market for two or more years.

The overall success rate for commercializing IP is estimated to be less than 1% (approximately 0.3%); therefore it is not prudent to expend limited resources and time pursuing ideas that lack compelling evidence concerning both market and technological merit. However, for some corporations IP that is generated in support of established product lines, the success rate is higher, ranging from 2% to 10%. The likelihood of commercial success may be greater if: the technology produces an operative, cost-effective benefit significant to at least some people; and thorough patent/literature search reveals strong claims that are likely to be patentable and enforceable.

Ultimately most organizations agree that the most important activity in the technology commercialization process is "marketing" the asset to potential licensees and/or investors. For example, it has been reported that patents obtained by Dow Chemical have been of varied value. The patents' value to the business was as follows: 33% were used in the current business, 29% had a place in the company's future business and 38% were of little value. The need to effectively and efficiently evaluate an invention at the time of disclosure is also evident when considering the cost to obtain patents. Protection costs will very likely increase over time leading to increased emphasis on the initial evaluation of a disclosure. It has been reported that 12 academic institutions in the U.S. spent greater than one million dollars for patent counsel and patent applications and seven of the top twenty-four were land grant universities. More academic and government organizations are utilizing a 3rd party for all or part of protection and transfer activities.

DEFINITIONS

There are numerous organizations, individuals and agencies involved in technology commercialization. The focus of each varies from serving government agencies to commercial entities designed to promote business development based on technology. As a result of the varied backgrounds and multidisciplinary nature of the transfer process terminology is often confusing. Therefore language and terminology consistency is necessary to avoid interpretation differences as technical and business discussion progress. A glossary of terms and words related to technology commercialization and related business activities is presented in the glossary section of this publication.

There does not seem to be a preferred definition of the term technology transfer or commercialization. Initially it would be prudent to consider select words.

Technology has varied meanings depending on the situation or individual. For example, technology eras might be described as follows: '50's - atomic energy; '60's - space exploration; '70's - energy technologies; '80's – computers; '90's - computer networks; '00's – information age. Greater technological gains are seen in "new areas such as information technology and technology evolves as people better understand their own methods. Technological advances can cross boundaries from one task to another e.g. nuclear science - from bombs to power plants.

Transfer or exchange might be accomplished via one or more of the following methods: sale, placement in the public domain, franchise, partnership/joint venture/alliance, market or distribution arrangements, grant of rights to manufacture or produce, assignment, license or philanthropic/gift arrangements.

Examples of phrases that are used to reflect the transition from discovery to public use are: laboratory to marketplace, individual to consumer, idea to utility, research to market, origin to market, idea to public acceptance or acceptable return on investment. Numerous definitions for the term technology transfer or commercialization have been suggested by individuals when asked to define technology commercialization or transfer. Several are as follows with more presented in Exhibit A:

- conveyance of the stewardship of a technology to the most reliable and responsible steward for that technology at its particular stage of development;
- an individual or organization transferring to another individual or organization the knowledge required to effectively and efficiently makes use of a specific technology for a specific application. (Technology is transferred by interaction and collaboration between scientific, engineering, and technical personnel, not by attorneys and/or licensing professionals. License agreements, assignments and the like transfer rights, not technology);
- the business transactions or processes, such as patent licenses or start-up companies, by which innovations are moved from one place (such as a university), development stage or application to another place (such as a company) for a commercial purpose; and
- the successful introduction of scientific concepts and technologies into the public sector to benefit people and business.

TECHNOLOGY COMMERCIALIZATION AS A BUSINESS VENTURE

The commercialization of technology requires multidisciplinary characteristics and approaches. There are distinct differences between the provider of technology from a research institution with numerous types of technology and commercialization by a corporate entity that is focused on a more distinct and interrelated R&D focus. However, there is some commonality in methods and procedures designed to contribute to assessment and valuation of technology in both a public and private environment. See Exhibit B.

The academic organization must take into account the technology portfolio is financed largely by the taxpayer and must assume the industrial community is eager to acquire technology. In turn, successful transfer from the academic institution must, and often does, enhance corporate America's competitiveness in global economy.

Universities in the U.S. are world leaders in basic science because there is a workable balance between federal control and academic freedom so one must improve the university's ability to contribute to the well of basic knowledge.

Embarking on an academic-corporate business relationship involves consideration of the following: re-socialization of faculty (faculty may be reluctant to establish relationships, whether real or perceived, might affect academic freedom; cultural changes so industrial linkages and transfer to industry will be rewarded; changing the infatuation with basic science, publishing and peer review to support for applied research; making university research more relevant to industry; examination of basic thrust; research is currently guided and directed by science policy makers at
federal and state levels (centralized government planning and control of university research has failed in eastern Europe).

A business with product sales to the consumer uses the return on investment as one of several measures of success. When technology is involved it may be more appropriate to base success on the return on technology asset (ROTA). To maximize ROTA it is necessary to manage technology and its core application(s), develop and execute strategic technology, establish a management plan, integrate information about markets and market demand with R&D efforts, maximize scope and enforceability of intellectual property protection, source and acquire complementary technology and identify collateral technology applications (CTA). Collateral technology applications enable one to fully utilize a technology asset, generate increased revenues in a profitable manner and capitalize on the core technology asset. It is usually prudent to integrate CTA's into technology management plans early to gain greater protection and acquire non-competing income through licenses. The earlier CTA's are identified the greater the value.

In some cases, the transition from inventorship to entrepreneurship to market is the business model of choice. An underlying belief is that "as soon as a better mousetrap is built it is wise to move to market fast". This transition is difficult to achieve due to numerous factors such as, capital limitations, rapid technology change, short product life cycles and complex regulatory environment. Therefore, more new products and services create their own markets rather than meet existing demand. Remember technology "push" is more likely to lead to successful break-through than "market pull" However, the "push" situation requires significant investment in securing public acceptance since need is not clearly known or established.

Success of a business venture is not only dependent upon the technology but the asset can lead to some key business advantages. As a result an asset provider and purchaser will need to address such strategic questions as: what competitive advantage through exclusive rights can be attained?, can the current applications be expanded?, how mature is the technology?, is there a need for continued technical assistance from the provider?, what ability to make necessary commitments exists i.e. time; too tied to day-to-day operations vs. long range planning and management?, are there cultural differences between the parties?, what is the technical capacity and capability of the purchaser? And how compatible is the technology for the purchaser's current product line and business objectives. For example, a large company seeks to maintain market dominance whereas a small firm might be trying to fill a market niche and the differences in company strategy will affect how business related to technology or asset acquisition is enacted and conducted.

MISSION/OBJECTIVES

Mission of organizations may differ depending on the type of institution. Academic institutions may not be as concerned about income when compared with corporations or companies. For example a mission statement for a university might include: 1) promote relationships, communication and collaboration; 2) strengthen interaction; 3) encourage support and development of research with commercial potential and 4) conversion of research results into new products and processes. A corporate mission statement may include the same goals as those for a university but would also include a goal to secure reasonable compensation.

In this era of complex products that often involve multiple components, the cultivation of relationships may lead to: sponsored research; "generic" research partnerships; licensing; transfer of unclaimed government sponsored proprietary research; and/or new venture creation.

STRATEGY

The strategy involved in the commercialization process will vary with the technology and the owner intent. However, as a strategic plan is developed the following will need to be taken into account for any asset: ownership, protection, research and development, value, market, financial and management considerations. Technology transfer in a global market involves technology or products that may be in various phases of transition from discovery to market; such as - innovation, development, production, market, and distribution phase. Regardless of the phase an asset is in there are a series of events that can be applied to the asset in question. Expenses will vary with the service provider. Therefore the projected expense for each phase is for purposes of demonstration and may not be the cost for a select service provider. These events are presented in figure one.

The technology commercialization process can be divided into a series of phases; strategic plan, implementation, follow-up and consumer acceptance. Within each phase there are numerous activities that must be addressed in successful commercialization of the asset. An outline of the process is as follows:

28

Phase I - Strategic Plan
 a. Technology identification
  1. Review program
  2. Define research and/or transfer objectives
  3. Prepare and review invention disclosure
 b. Technology transfer plan
  1. Determine technical value and scope
  2. Establish market value and scope
  3. Examine past and existing collaboration and agreements
  4. Identify stage of technology development
  5. Establish preferred cooperator and/or procedures for transfer
  6. Identify alternative collaborators, licensees or approaches
  7. Estimate financial requirements
  8. Establish intellectual property protection plan
  9. Prepare project prospectus
  10. Identify preferred and alternative corporate relationships
  11. Select interfaces; i.e., government, industry, academia, foundations, individuals
  12. Identify participants in transfer, roles and responsibilities

Phase II - Implementation
 a. Intellectual property protection
  1. Establish standard procedures
  2. Monitor progress
  3. Seek collaborator or licensee financial and advisory support or commitment to accept responsibility subject to proper concurrence
  4. Factor outcome into implementation plan and agreement negotiations
 b. Introduction of technology to potential collaborators
  1. Descriptor letter
  2. Follow-up to letter
  3. Scientific meetings
  4. Business meetings
  5. Verbal exchange
 c. In-depth technology and business review
  1. Establish mutual interest and goals
  2. Assess commitment and scope
  3. Define proposed relationship
  4. Initial discussion of terms
  5. Establish and solve concerns
 d. Finalize agreement
  1. Set diligence criteria and consequences
  2. Establish fair and satisfactory business arrangement
   i. Fees
   ii. Royalty
   iii. Goods, equipment, services, exchanges, etc.
   iv. Equity or combination of cash and equity
  3. Agree on "boilerplate" terms
  4. Prepare publication plan
  5. Establish communication plans and procedures
  6. Set payment schedule(s)

Phase III- Follow-up
 a. Define milestone dates monitor and communicate as required

b. Assure proper and timely reports
c. Identify intellectual property and monetary needs, i.e., extensions, filings, maintenance fees, etc.
d. Set-up fee, royalty, payment, etc. schedules
e. Maintain corporate relationship to evaluate technology transfer success, problems, etc.

Phase IV- Consumer acceptance
a. Consumer need(s) met
b. "Product" changes or improvements identified
c. Future needs or innovations developed

Figure one. Asset assessment activities diagram.*

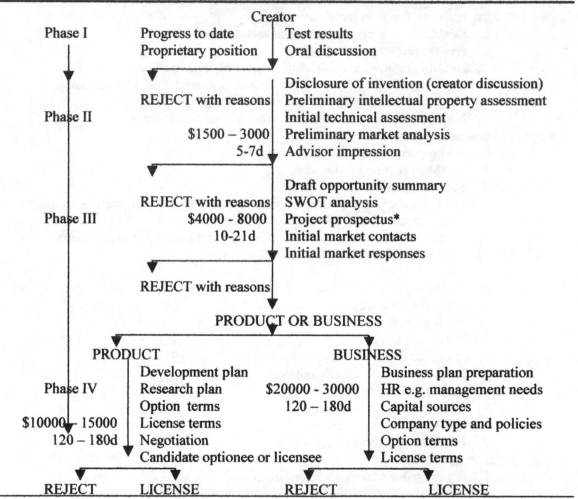

Phase I	Creator	
	Progress to date	Test results
	Proprietary position	Oral discussion
		Disclosure of invention (creator discussion)
	REJECT with reasons	Preliminary intellectual property assessment
Phase II		Initial technical assessment
	$1500 – 3000	Preliminary market analysis
	5-7d	Advisor impression
		Draft opportunity summary
	REJECT with reasons	SWOT analysis
Phase III	$4000 - 8000	Project prospectus*
	10-21d	Initial market contacts
		Initial market responses
	REJECT with reasons	

PRODUCT OR BUSINESS

	PRODUCT		BUSINESS
	Development plan		Business plan preparation
Phase IV	Research plan	$20000 - 30000	HR e.g. management needs
	Option terms	120 – 180d	Capital sources
$10000 – 15000	License terms		Company type and policies
120 – 180d	Negotiation		Option terms
	Candidate optionee or licensee		License terms

REJECT   LICENSE   REJECT   LICENSE

* Expenses are for illustration only and will vary with service provider.

ECONOMETRICS

Econometrics is the criteria employed to assess the commercialization or transfer process. Metrics can reflect success or failure and be used to provide a measure of success or performance by personnel involved in the transfer program. The economics and related metrics can also be used as objective means to report progress, measure success or justify a transfer or commercialization program. Of course the ultimate value is to establish the return on investment or return on technology asset.

Technology managers need to emulate entrepreneurs not banks. A technology manager needs to be market driven not cost driven. Cost cannot be a significant part of an intellectual property's valuation.

There is always a need to design some form of accountability for the technology commercialization activity. Metrics will depend on the goals and objectives of the organization. In certain situations the asset portfolio may have expanded beyond the interests of the company and the financial commitments to protect the assets are exceeding budgets or there may be an interest in seeking a benefit from the sale or licensing of such assets. On the other hand, academic institutions usually are not involved in the late stage development and commercialization of products. However, public organizations, which are funded to a large extent by public funds, do have a responsibility to make new technology available to the public and the return on asset may not be as important as the actual transfer to the public through a relationship with a commercial entity. Individual criteria can be designed to reflect specific achievements. However, it is often valuable to combine select criteria into ratios or design formulas in which multiple criteria are combined to define an endpoint for the commercialization process. These criteria may or may not be weighted as to relative value to the overall formula. Examples of such criteria or econometrics are presented in Exhibit C.

Remember that there will be individual and institutional responsibility involved in the commercialization process. Certain success or achievement criteria may be applicable to the individual, some to the unit and others to the institution. It is important to carefully select the criteria for the situation or need, secure agreement within the organization and make them a part of the personnel, unit and institution review process.

INDIVIDUAL PERFORMANCE ASSESSMENT

There will also be a need to establish performance criteria for the individual responsible for commercialization of technology. These performance criteria are necessary for effective management and reward programs that lead to employee satisfaction, retention and procurement. If there is a desire to establish benchmarks determines if it is to improve or monitor progress.

Some key considerations when establishing personnel performance criteria are to remember that an activity differs from an outcome, publication is an activity, commercialization is an outcome and control can be difficult to maintain. Objectives and what is measured need to be explicit; is it jobs, cooperative agreements, licenses, options, money, etc.? If multiple goals are established, there must be multiple measurements that are related to the select goals. Define how measurements are ranked and what are the priorities.

Set standards of conduct rather than try to differentiate a good deal from a not-so-good one. Arrangements pursued thoroughly, intelligently, and creatively (professionally) can be distinguished from those that are not. Evaluate people on qualities, not dollar amount or number of arrangements. Each disclosure is different so the evaluation process cannot be too rigid, but based on a fair comparison of what came in vs. what went out. Use customer satisfaction surveys of researchers and licensees. However, be aware that researchers may have some very unreasonable expectations. Therefore it is incumbent upon the licensing person to educate the researchers about the variables affecting licensing results using internal and external historical data.

Evaluation of individual performance when licensing intellectual property might be as follows:

Objective factors
- Annual licensing targets which were negotiated with the incumbents (number of licenses)
- Revenue acquired and projected from licensing agreements
- Initiation of disclosures – hard to quantify
- Number of patents filed, number of patents actually written, number of patents in the portfolio

Econometrics
- Disclosures received
- Due diligence assessments completed
- Patent committee actions
- Patent protection activities (legal prosecutions)
  - Patents filed
  - Patents abandoned
- Contacts made for marketing purposes
- Scheduled meetings with faculty/clients on campus
- Documents written for patent program
- Closeout reports prepared on IP from grants
- Funding proposals involving IP which were reviewed
- Licenses granted
- Number and $ value of research projects funded and related to licenses

Subjective evaluation factors
- Effectiveness in evaluation of inventions
- Patenting of inventions
- Marketing
- Negotiation of agreements
- Post-execution follow-up
- License de-activations
- Service to university faculty/staff/inventors
- Supervision (if applicable)
- Special projects

TECHNOLOGY COMMERCIALIZATION OPPORTUNITIES

Innovation abounds all over the world. The challenge will be to recognize the importance of discovery either as a result of current or future world needs. When a market exists and discovery is directed toward that need, it may be easier to achieve market entry but there may be more competition due to multiple efforts to meet a need. If discovery is truly serendipity, a market may be more difficult to establish and enter. Public education, perception and acceptance may be critical under these circumstances. All of these factors provide the innovative scientist, entrepreneur or business man a host of possibilities to advance science and business for the well being of the public and ultimately economic development and return for the commercial entity.

In addition, effective technology commercialization is becoming more and more dependent upon innovative ways to enhance value of an asset. Application of problem solving and critical thinking methods can lead to better and broader protection, novel designs, utility, structure, composition, etc., identity of existing or future competition all of which increase value and create better or new opportunities. Several methods can be effectively applied such as TRIZ, an acronym meaning "Theory of Inventive Problem Solving". Additional information on TRIZ and critical thinking are presented in Exhibit D and in Module III, Exhibit E.

SOURCES OF TECHNOLOGY

Financial and organizational commitment has made the U.S. one of the most innovative and outstanding economic nations. A creative environment leads to numerous discoveries. Some discoveries are made as part of an employee – employer role in which the discovery benefits the business focus of the company and is retained by the company to enhance the firm's value. Other, discoveries are associated with individual creativity or the research focus of organizations such as, universities or government agencies that make the discovery available at no charge to the public. In other cases, rights to the discovery are assumed by private or public organizations that may continue to research, develop and/or market the discovery. On the other hand, certain intellectual property within a corporation may not fall within the current business focus of the company, or the company may want to engage in external relationships to commercialize products based on the intellectual assets or the company may merely want to transfer the asset to other parties. The marketing of these discoveries provides an opportunity and challenge for technology transfer units or businesses designed to commercialize this intellectual property.

There are numerous organizations that provide services for these technology transfer units or organizations. The services range from information or databases to education of technology transfer personnel. Examples of organizations that maintain databases in which information on the technology transfer process is presented are; The Association of University Technology Managers (AUTM), Technology Transfer Society (TTS), Licensing Executives Society (LES), law firms, and United Sates Patent and Trademark Office (USPTO). Examples of organizations that maintain databases in which information on new technology are; Knowledge Express, Community of Science, Technology Access, U Ventures, and Yet2.com. Other firms offer asset management services and software. For example, Inteum, Inc., markets software for management of intellectual property and technology commercialization.

ACADEMIC INSTITUTIONS

The university environment is a rich environment for expertise and discovery. Federal and state funds support the scientific and educational communities from which intellectual assets originate. With the advent of the Bayh Dole Act, these institutions assumed more responsibility for making those creations available to the public. Based on past results, it is projected that for each $2M spent on research there is one disclosure of invention.

In addition to inventions or patentable subject matter, copyright authors abound at the same organizations. The software and hardware developments are of interest to the public and are often made available to the public through the technology transfer process as are trademarks, know-how and plant materials. Trade secrets are not as prominent in the academic communities due to a focus on publication for the benefit of the public.

Technology transfer units exist at many of the larger universities or federal agencies. Most technology transfer offices have Internet home pages in which assets available for purchase or license are presented. In some cases search engines are available for selection of specific areas that one is interested in. Generally these organizations also have web sites in which research opportunities and related expertise are presented.

Brokers/Agents

These organizations give the asset provider assistance with commercialization of property. A broker or agent may accept the technology on a contingency basis, pay for services basis or a combination of the two. Whenever one engages such a service, it is prudent to conduct a review of the organization to assess how successful they have been with similar technology in the past. Often these organizations will be able to provide a good review, assessment and valuation of the asset; however, be alert to scams in the invention broker business arena.

Consortia/ Institutes/Trade Associations

Universities, businesses and government agencies have established collaborative arrangements to more effectively and efficiently support basic research. In some cases, trade associations are sponsoring research designed to benefit the members of the association. Some of these collaborations encourage inclusion of new members or solicit membership at the time of formation. In the case of the trade association and in some cases for the consortia, there may be newly discovered technology for which a commercial entity is needed for effective development and commercialization.

Government agencies/laboratories

Although government agencies such as the federal laboratories often focus on governments needs and directives, there are numerous opportunities for the business community to cooperate with the agencies in application of government discoveries or conducting research to address corporate needs or both In addition, many government programs exist at the local, regional, state and federal levels for the support of research and economic development.

Industry

In some technology-based companies, there are divisions within the firm responsible for corporate units that are involved in licensing and/or technology acquisition. These units may have assets available for acquisition or commercialization. There is no doubt that many of the licensing offices are involved in structuring alliances or joint ventures involving technology and markets of mutual interest.

Individuals

An individual seldom possesses adequate knowledge or capital to effectively commercialize a new technology. The complexity of the technology, development and/or today's market results in the need for many individuals to combine their efforts with a commercial entity to effectively enter the commercial market.

Inventors Association

Often, the individual or group of individuals with ideas or early stage prototypes desire to interact with other inventors to acquire the benefit of other's experiences. Organizations such as the Inventors Association are designed to provide support for these inventors and, in some cases, to provide a database from which one can select assets of interest for acquisition and/or development.

Incubators and Research Parks

Incubators are usually multi-tenant facilities that provide basic services for the entrepreneurial start-up business. The incubator administration provides or arranges for business advice and guidance as well as resources such as secretarial, communication, and other support structures to minimize cash outlay. Since the objective is usually to expand the local economic development, the incubator often receives support from the local communities. Technology commercialization opportunities requiring new relationships may appeal to the local and regional investment or business community that may provide advantages to either the sole business or collaborative business venture. Numerous websites exist and address the services, advantages and benefits of incubators, research parks, consortia, centers, etc. See Addendum II, References and Resources.

The research park is usually a business setting in which growing or mature businesses locate. The park offers the amenities desired by the technology based businesses. These may be support businesses or services such as shipping, day care, banking, packaging, health and medical services, and legal and accounting. Personnel interaction among these research park business residents often contributes to job satisfaction and corporate development. The park is also the site of innovation and potential assets or technology for commercialization.

ACADEMIC - INDUSTRY COMPARISON

There are two primary approaches to academic-industry relations for technology transfer or commercialization: licensing and sponsored research.

LICENSING

Licensing is often from the academic institution to another party whereas corporate licensing between and among industrial organizations is also an important source of revenue. Responsibility for licensing resides with licensing office personnel or patent management firms contracted to commercialize the asset. The focus is on license marketing and royalty revenue. In most cases, licensing competencies are limited to legal and/or technical expertise. The academic institution often retains the rights to intellectual property. Licensing issues or conceptions are:

1. *Questionable profitability* due to: a) high cost of licensing to both parties as the result of legal fees for patenting, b) staff costs for licensing administration, c) time or opportunity costs (due to 2-4 yr waiting period for patent application to issue during which aggressive business development is difficult), d) marketing and search costs (very costly for academic organizations to promote technologies; (High cost prevents bidding and limits pursuit of technological options and potential licensees), e) substantial costs associated with transferring knowledge to a separate entity (especially tacit knowledge), f) lack of seed capital infrastructure (Financial markets and availability of seed capital for technological ventures), and g) hard to accurately predict market value of a license, therefore, royalty rates tend to be set too low.

2. *Not attractive to industrial firms* because: a) licensing firms must accept high levels of risk associated with disclosure which makes academic technology less attractive (however, corporate risk aversion varies substantially), b) for high-tech, non-disclosure is imperative to commercial success but the high risk of disclosure associated with academic research is a major deterrent, c) established firms are less interested in highly specialized markets with limited demand than are new start-ups (academic technologies often represent these types of opportunities), and d) the nature of academic technology or inventions tends to be core/basic/radical which are often of little interest to established firms since they do not complement or enhance existing products or markets and are more applied, process-oriented or incremental, and e) often succumb to the "not invented here" syndrome (corporate researchers tend to reject research results from outside for a variety of reasons);

3. *Licensing offices often represent lost opportunities* because; a) they "sit" on too much intellectual property, b) incentives focus on achieving a few licenses with large corporate partners, c) focus is on easy licenses which usually are downstream/applied research d) much of the technology is radical or basic and is difficult to market, (however, basic technologies are potentially more profitable and therefore, least profitable technologies get most attention), and e) core competencies of licensing are legal/technical, not business/entrepreneurial (licensing offices become intellectual property repositories); and

4. *Intellectual property rights and patents can also decrease in their relevance* as a result of: a) rapid technological change which makes patent time lags intolerable, b) increasing importance of know-how and tacit components indicate poorer enforceability of intellectual property rights and c) mixed inventorship and integration of multiple components confuses intellectual property ownership.

CONTRACT OR SPONSORED RESEARCH

Contract or sponsored research usually involves the search for large corporations or government sponsors, subjugation of basic research aims to applied objectives of sponsor, or the requirement that corporate research conducted in the academic institution have a corporate sponsor. Academic scientists are frequently required to bring or procure sponsorship or government grants when hired. Problems with contract/sponsored research often cited are:

1. not profitable - recent data indicates that only about 10-14% of academic research expenditures originate from this type of relationship;
2. shifts paradigm of academic research from basic research to applied research;

3. breeches barrier between academic freedom and commercial incentives - research contracts cannot be conceptualized as pursuit of knowledge unaffected by external political or commercial incentives (It's research for different reasons or motivations);
4. imposes undesirable or unacceptable limitations such as nondisclosure, limited publication, etc. on academic institution that grows out of firm's need for privacy and proprietary ownership; and
5. is unattractive to firms because contracting firms must accept high levels of risk associated with disclosure within "loose" environment of academic environment; hence, associations with academic institution are less attractive, especially if a firm exposes its own technological property.

There are reasons for the academic institution to consider entrepreneurial technology commercialization methods some of which are as follows:

1. technological entrepreneurship can be more profitable than licensing or contract research. However, there is an opportunity cost associated with both the academic institution's capital and technology commercialization resources. Incentive will be to maximize return from these resources, subject to maintaining and upholding other objectives, values, and imperatives of the institution; and
2. technology entrepreneurship lacks doleful effects of sponsored research, because research pursued will focus on basic research. This is due to the fact that basic research embodies a much greater opportunity for profit from radical innovations. The academic organization will be in a stronger intellectual position to exploit its own technological opportunities.

There may not be any other entity with specific capabilities to utilize the information as well or at all. This is not entirely dependent on transfer cost, as specific competencies may not exist outside the academic institution. A faculty member's involvement in management of a venture has been identified as a key element in success of a new technology venture.

Licensing and contract research present little or no opportunity for close managerial involvement of original inventor. Entrepreneurship offers a unique solution to this parameter:

1. Universities have long-term interests (radical or basic innovations take longer to develop and become profitable than incremental ones). Many traditional financial markets are less interested in pursuing them. Universities due to their historical development and incentive structure have greater interest in long-term investments and tend to be more interested in basic or radical technological opportunities.
2. Social benefit of competing technological paradigms is not internalized by the firm: however, this social benefit is somewhat internalized by the University indicating the University has stronger incentive to pursue competing technological opportunities, especially radical or basic ones. New technology increasingly empowers/enables smaller and smaller ventures with competitive advantage vis-à-vis larger, more established firms.
3. Increased faculty demand that intellectual property rights to their innovations be made economically relevant. Some faculties even make their right to pursue technological entrepreneurship a condition of their employment. Academic organizations find it more difficult to enforce a false separation between researchers and implementation and returns from their research.

In summary, factors limiting exploitation of entrepreneurial technology commercialization within the academic setting are lacking of entrepreneurial competency (offices are often designed to obtain and utilize legal/technical competencies not entrepreneurship); administrative decentralization (administrative structure is designed so no single functional unit can assume responsibility for maintaining institutional objectives and maximizing revenue; mind set against entrepreneurship arising from traditional academic paradigm and satisfying behavior and lack of investment capital or a research focus primarily in areas with little or no commercial opportunity or little or no advanced research (such as teaching institutions)

It is difficult to determine the extent to which entrepreneurship offers a viable solution to many of the problems. Alternatives to licensing and sponsored research are rapidly increasing and traditional academic issues deserve attention and analysis.

TRENDS AND CHALLENGES

Often, the product is not yet well defined and/or the need not well developed; therefore, focus is on the technology and not the resources required producing or supporting the asset. As a result, the market efforts are fraught with risk and unknowns, which impact negotiation, price, value and investment.

The advent of the information age and technological advances has led to numerous management challenges. A brief synopsis of select challenges is as follows:

1. *Corporate objectives/goals.* High technology may alleviate or alter certain ways to accomplish objectives but still requires expertise to market, service and train.
2. *Timing/market entry.* Accelerated change is becoming common for technology and the customer. It is not a matter of keeping up but how to anticipate the future for high technology businesses.
3. *Information and knowledge.* Communication skills and information accumulation and assessment become higher priority as competition and change modify markets.
4. *Product complexity.* High technology is often comprised of components that are combined into a system hence ownership and inventorship varies, alliances become crucial to success, legal issues are more prominent, contracts and negotiation complexity are increased, financial challenges arise and effective relationships become more crucial.
5. *Product support.* Problem solving of complex technology is more difficult and requires new or modified means to address and implement the complexity (Servicing high technology products often differs from those for low technologies).
6. *Marketing.* Marketing high technology is often one of "push" rather than "pull" hence methods of marketing and expenses differ. The Internet is a reliable system comprised of loosely connected and imperfect parts that work because nobody is in control - shakes up our centralist notions of hierarchy. The challenge is how to market via the "web mall"
7. *Capital.* Introduction of high technology is risky so investment commitments are more difficult to acquire.

On the other hand, the emerging information age along with increased availability of capital and public interest in new technology provides a unique opportunity for the pursuit of science and technology.

The impact of information age has and will continue to affect economic and social relationships. Information is the backbone from which good decisions are made. Acquisition of information and data along with focused and structured presentation of these data and information provides those involved in technology commercialization the basis from which to make good business decisions. It is no longer always the physical, facility or tangible assets that are most valuable to a business but more often the intellectual assets. Hence, more focus and financial commitment are being made to protect these assets.

The Internet offers three characteristics that impact business; 1) inexpensive world wide accessibility that is simple, affordable and available in a common language or with on-the-spot translation capability; 2) anonymity due to the difficulty to trace "visitors" or people with whom one is doing business and ability to encrypt communication and 3) sheer size and openness.

The WW Internet user population in 2002 was 605M with 183M in the U.S. and Canada. [8] Therefore, it is and will continue to be difficult to control or enforce Internet issues by local or national governments. The large firm may be easy to chase but the massive number of individual and small business users operating out of homes or in countries with no extradition treaties will be difficult to find much less shut down. Financing is available; however, many small businesses do not need to increase their debt.

The Internet is also an expanded marketing and distribution channel as well as efficient communication and advertising medium for certain products. Emergence of numerous companies that make money on the Web is evidence of the opportunities afforded business by the Internet. A decade ago one in four small businesses in the U. S. conducted business with a computer; today three of four use a computer and this trend is expected to increase.

Small companies are growing in nearly every sector of the business community whereas large company growth has slowed. For example, in a recent poll, over 68% of small businesses expected to grow in the late 1990's early 2000's. Outsourcing for such needs as services, products, technology expertise is increasing. This trend is reflected in the number of firms downsizing or "rightsizing" and establishment of joint ventures, partnerships and "virtual" companies.

A large number of new businesses are started in the home but it is difficult to determine how many of these businesses stay home based. Alternative arrangements are being made for the work force; for example more employers offer "flex hours" and there is an increase in the number of employees who work from the home. Job sharing is also on the increase, which provides the employee, added flexibility and experience while allowing the employer the security of having a workforce available, more of the time.

More "angel" capital is being invested in small business than venture capital. Debt financing is on the increase and as a result many small businesses never go public. Recently small-cap stocks have tended to outperform large-cap stocks.

FUTURE

There are several key factors that influence the transfer and commercialization of an asset and will continue to be emphasized in the future. A few of the more important are as follows:

1. *Communication.* Diffusion of information about new technology is predominantly a process of communication. Anything that impedes communication within the organization, as well as within the environment it interacts in, will jeopardize successful implementation of the technology within an organization.
2. *Financial.* A primary concern is fiscal justification in terms of returns on investment and irreversibility of the investment, where adoption requires investments in unsalvageable products. The payback period and significance of the payback are intrinsic to the justification.
3. *External.* The decision to adopt technology is heavily influenced by environmental factors. These are events occurring in the industry, market, country and world, within which the organization interacts.
4. *Human.* Ultimate users of new technology must do something different from what they have done in the past. They must change their behavior patterns. A consequence of this is that it cannot be expected that recipients will respond to new technology quickly. They must not only assimilate facts relevant to the technology, but also change behavioral patterns that would lead them to use the technology. Also, it is human nature to resist ideas, especially those originating from outside of the organization, and this can lead to myopia or tunnel vision. A clear implication is that technology transfer requires time,

patience and opportunities to experiment (become familiar with) a new technology.

5. *Corporate.* The decision to adopt technology is also heavily influenced by organizational factors. Organizations are more likely to be willing and able to adopt technologies that offer clear advantages, do not drastically interfere with existing practices, and are easier to understand. Adopters look unfavorably on innovations that are difficult to evaluate or which benefits are difficult to see or describe.

6. *Technology.* The decision to adopt technology is influenced by the technology itself. This is a fundamental truth. All other factors being equal, if the technology fails to live up to the expectations of the eventual users, then implementation will not be successful.

With the increased emergence of small businesses and downsizing of large businesses there is increased capability to change, and more emphasis on mergers, joint ventures and partnerships among the business community. These smaller enterprises and start-ups have the capability to interact and react in a more expedient manner than the larger enterprise; hence windows of opportunity close and open more often. Time to market has always been important but the successful business of the future will be more proactive than reactive. The importance of quality information will increase.

As intangible assets become more important to the business entity, interest in protection of such assets will increase. There will be additional emphasis on protection strategy and methods for protecting and enhancing the value of these assets for the creator and business. Channels for securing such protection are becoming overloaded and the process becoming more expensive. In certain types of businesses the life cycle of a products or window of opportunity comes and goes swiftly; therefore it becomes more and more important for government agencies to expedite the approval processes in order to encourage business formation, development and growth.

Global business interaction will lead to a need for national governments to enact and enforce appropriate laws, to enable the technology business ventures some level of security and trust in the nations legal structure to initial and conduct business in that nation.

The emphasis on product life cycle, time to market, small business formation, and potential return on assets will impact the technology transfer offices at academic institutions that are the source of much of the innovations.

Technology in a final product often originates from several sources within, between or among creators, or institutions. This trend will increase as expertise is focused on specifics and multi-disciplinary or multi-institutional teams are formed or expanded. As a result, the transfer organization within a "technology generator institution" may need to spend more time on the management of the asset base in order to enhance value due to appropriate identity and protection of the institutions intellectual property. Marketing and licensing focus may or may not reside within the same transfer office. Strategy and tactics generally differ between the service provider role to faculty and creators and the technology and discovery marketing role of a technology transfer office. Financial and efficiency factors need to be addressed by these organizations as the business environment changes.

As the complexity of technology and the commercialization process increases, the academic, business and government communities will need to consider the following to assure efficient and effective introduction of discoveries to the consumer market and acceptance by the consumer. They are:

- early relationships;
- investor affiliation;
- company alliances and divestitures;
- international emphasis;
- local/regional/city/state alliances;
- legal/legislative/regulatory impact;
- time/personnel commitment;

- team – multidiscipline;
- technology consolidation;
- competitive - time to market;
- public perception and education;
- information assembly and restructuring;
- "think tanks"/"brain-storming"/"blue skying";
- renewal through "guided entrepreneurs" (education coupled with experience);
- major forces of change will continually restructure world economies managing; continuous change will be a challenge. (Wealth will not be measured by fixed assets but in terms of knowledge intensive value and intangible intellectual property); and/or
- must decrease barriers and increase incentives.

Intellectual property (IP) changes will lead to:

- improved technology transfer between countries due to stronger IP laws
- higher IP value and worldwide business leveraging due to trade agreements
- increased cost will increase for global and domestic protection
- IP management competency will be needed for competitive advantage.

When embarking on the commercialization of technology it is important to remember time to market is crucial in the competitive business environment. It is important to remember more than technology must be considered in the process. Technology can be overemphasized and perfected beyond what the consumer needs. Focus should be on existing technology and not resources that give rise to it. Too often the process is relatively passive with excessive dependence on others all of which results in lost opportunities.

Successful asset commercialization requires: 1) market need orientation; 2) focus on an entire suite of technological resources including intellect behind the technology; 3) a "champion" for the technology; 4) business and financial know-how by the transfer individual or team and 5) assertive, opportunistic, proactive, market development. Success breeds and fosters further innovation the technology transition process organization.

Effective technology commercialization requires that the parties involved understand change and adapt to changes that impact the commercialization process. Examples of these changes are presented in table one.

In the future it will be necessary to address the question "If old skills and assets are liabilities and if rapid change is possible and people are assets should one spend 70% of the budget on training?"

CONCLUSION

Individuals involved in technology transfer or commercialization must: be proactive; emphasize and perfect marketing skills; understand differences between government, academic, and corporate institutions; be aware of government initiatives and regulations; focus on the competitive edge not the cutting edge; exercise effective communication with emphasis on demand driven publicity, networks, and database quality and management; practice efficient and effective "deal making"; conduct well planned negotiations and enact win-win relationships. Questions and answers related to technology commercialization in general are presented in Exhibit E.

Table one. Contrast of relationships - past and future.

PAST	FUTURE
Assets are physical	Assets are intangible
Plant is asset	Plant is liability
Land, labor, capital limits	Imagination limits
Competition	Collaboration
National	Global
Standardized/mass production	Customization
Management/leadership control	Commitment
Command	Consensus
Attack	Team
Cost/growth	Quality/imagination
React to change	Initiate change
Intermediation	Distinct mediation
Fixed calendar	Flexible

REFERENCES

1. Fusfeld, A.R., 1978, How to put technology into corporate planning; Technology Review, May 1978, p.51-55.

2. Morone, J., 1993, Winning in High Tech Markets: The Role of General Management; Harvard Business School Press, 1993, 292p.

3. National Research Council, 1987, Management of Technology: The Hidden Competitive Advantage; National Academy Press, Washington, D.C., 31p.

4. _____, 1991, Research on the Management of Technology: Unleashing the Hidden Competitive Advantage; National Academy Press, Washington, D.C., 40p.

5. National Science Board, 1991, Science and Engineering Indicators - 1991; NSB 91-1, U.S. Gov't Printing Office, 1991, Washington, D.C.

6. Sheridan, J.H., 1993, A new breed of M.B.A.; Industry Week, Oct 4, 1993, p.11(5).

7. White, R.M., 1993, as reported in Graham, D.M., 1993, Sea Technology, July 1993, p.7

8. Scope Communications Group, 2003,http://www.nua.ie/surveys/

EXHIBIT A - TECHNOLOGY TRANSFER DEFINITIONS

(EXAMPLES)

- Etymology: Greek *technologia* - systematic treatment of an art;
- Practical application of knowledge especially in a particular area;
- A capability given by practical application of knowledge;
- A manner of accomplishing a task especially using technical processes, methods, or knowledge;
- Specialized aspects of a particular field of endeavor;
- Bridging the gap between the innovator and the exploiter of technology; The process by which the ability to do something is joined with the capacity to do it;
- Selling anything that can't be nailed down;
- Technology is information embodied in a device, the production, use or sale of which may be restricted by law. "Technology transfer" grants to another party (a) access to the information, and/or (b) the right to make, use or sell the device;
- The marketing and successful placement of technology;
- The facilitation of the transfer of the technological know-how and the legal rights from the developmental area to the commercial sector. It is this need that gives employment to the many individuals who work with scientists to license their devices. There is no perfect economy where scientists can make one telephone call, name their price/ terms and get a contract/ check the next day;
- The dissemination of all the information necessary so that one party may duplicate the work of another party. The information is of two types, technical (engineering, scientific, standards) and the second is procedural (legal, non-disclosure agreements, patent rights, licensing);
- The process by which existing knowledge, facilities or capabilities developed under federal R&D funding are utilized to fulfill public and private needs;
- Occurs any time you have two people trying to accomplish a common goal, and the working toward that goal would enable one or the other party to gain information by virtue of the exposure to methodologies or ideas exchanged when two people join forces and expose each other to new ideas;
- The movement of technological and technology related organizational know-how among partners (individuals, institutions, and enterprises) in order to enhance at least one partner's knowledge and expertise and strengthen each partner's competitive position;
- Communication and permission to use previously proprietary and/or restricted technological understanding;
- The formal and legal transfer created technology to the end user for the purpose of technology commercialization and economic impact for a particular Industry. This transfer should be given a period to (transferred ownership's) maybe 25 years and final transferring after 50 years. Any form of default will result in the revocation of the technology transfer to initial owners. Products/Services created and owned by a parent organization that may be (private, public entities, government, individuals or professional groups) are termed as technology services providers. The results of studies, product models and commercialization services to market are owned mechanisms assigned to the creators of the technology;
- Identifying priority needs of industry and the marketplace, collaborating with experts and laboratories to identify a technology or combination of technologies to meet those needs and facilitating R&D investment to develop commercially-viable products;
- Sharing an invention or innovative use of an existing product with another party, be it a government agency, individual or organization;

- The practical application of knowledge gained through theoretical research to a specific production problem. Transfer is applying this application of technology to areas of endeavor not related to the initial implementation. Lasers erasing graffiti, aerospace titanium in artificial joints, aerospace composites for architectural features in saltwater environments are some examples. This also includes overcoming all the political, cultural, personal, training, economic and maintenance issues along the way;
- Technology commercialization is a more correct term. Many of the technology transfer efforts in the States have been less than successful because the emphasis was on transfer. A federal lab, for instance, might be very happy to transfer technology to another lab. Generally, the transfer is only beneficial when it results in products or services that can purchased;
- The provision of rights and knowledge (know-how, show-how, trade secrets, etc.) from one party to another, for commercial (make, use, sell), research or other use by the receiving party;
- Matching a user's technical need with appropriate information.
- An interchange of "know how" or the transferring of new information and skills from one who has it to one who wants it;
- Moving technology from the research and development stage into practical usage or commercialization-implying creative adaptation to a new use;
- The successful application and/or adaptation of a technology developed in one organization to the meet the needs of one or more other organizations;
- The sale or barter of intellectual property related to technology by its inventor or early developer to an implementer or manufacturer for purposes of commercialization;
- Technology transfer is an umbrella term that encompasses the range of processes from most passive to most active: info transfer (what universities do so well); intellectual property protection (allows for legal transfers); technology development; lassoing resources; technology integration; and technology adoption through to the sale of new or innovative products or processes based on a new application of scientific knowledge or technology (and increasingly on innovative business structures);
- The range of processes, from knowledge transfer to product or process commercialization, that facilitate the development and adoption of knowledge and technology; or
- The relationships between innovators and developers of technology that result in new products or new process developments.

EXHIBIT B - ORGANIZATION CONSIDERATIONS/OPTIONS

ASSET DEVELOPMENT AND DEPLOYMENT UNIT

AREAS OF FOCUS
- COMMUNICATION /INFORMATION EXCHANGE
- ACCESS TO ASSET PROVIDER
- FUNDING
- PARTNERSHIPS AND ALLIANCES

SERVICE PROVIDER-INDUSTRY INTEGRATION MODEL
- RESEARCH AND DEVELOPMENT
- DEVELOPMENT
- MARKET SUPPORT
- DEPLOYMENT
- PROTECTION
- SERVICE

GOVERNANCE

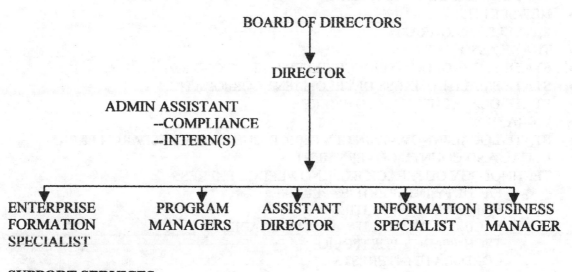

BOARD OF DIRECTORS

DIRECTOR

ADMIN ASSISTANT
--COMPLIANCE
--INTERN(S)

| ENTERPRISE FORMATION SPECIALIST | PROGRAM MANAGERS | ASSISTANT DIRECTOR | INFORMATION SPECIALIST | BUSINESS MANAGER |

SUPPORT SERVICES
- STATISTICS
- BUSINESS
- LAW
- CLINICAL TRIALS
- SCIENTIFIC
- FACILITIES
- LIBRARY/INFORMATION
- ENGINEERING/COMPUTER SCIENCE
- CENTERS/INSTITUTES
- CORPORATE DEVELOPMENT

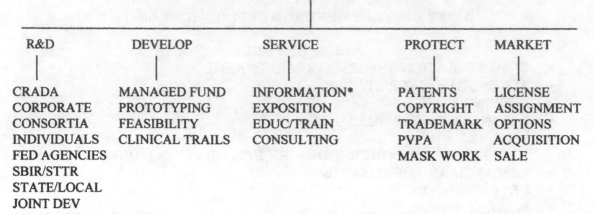

IP ASSET DEVELOPMENT AND DEPLOYMENT UNIT*

R&D	DEVELOP	SERVICE	PROTECT	MARKET
CRADA	MANAGED FUND	INFORMATION*	PATENTS	LICENSE
CORPORATE	PROTOTYPING	EXPOSITION	COPYRIGHT	ASSIGNMENT
CONSORTIA	FEASIBILITY	EDUC/TRAIN	TRADEMARK	OPTIONS
INDIVIDUALS	CLINICAL TRAILS	CONSULTING	PVPA	ACQUISITION
FED AGENCIES			MASK WORK	SALE
SBIR/STTR				
STATE/LOCAL				
JOINT DEV				

* Each of the Units will also require or provide support in the development and deployment process.

INFORMATION EXCHANGE
(AWARENESS/COMMUNICATION)

- WORLD WIDE WEB - HOME PAGE
- NEWSLETTER
- SATELLITE PROGRAM
- TRADE ASSOCIATIONS
- STATE TECHNOLOGY/SERVICE/EXPERTISE EXPOSITION
- STATE SMALL BUSINESS DEVELOPMENT CORPORATION
- STATE DEPARTMENT OF COMMERCE
- LIBRARIES
- STATE/LOCAL INNOVATION CENTERS, INCUBATORS, RESEARCH PARKS
- LOCAL AND COUNTY GOVERNMENT
- TECHNOLOGY OUTREACH E.G. KNOWLEDGE EXPRESS
    - FACULTY INTERESTS/EXPERTISE
    - UNIVERSITY FACILITIES
    - FACILITY CAPABILITY AND AVAILABILITY
    - TECHNOLOGY PORTFOLIO
    - CORPORATE INTERESTS

TECHNOLOGY COMMERCIALIZATION OPTIONS

	Equity/Royalty	Start-up Companies	
Institution		Technology	Technology
From Which		Management	Development
Asset		Office	Corporation
Originates		(non-profit)	(for-profit)
	License	Assign	
	Sell	Gift	
	Collaboration	Partnership	

ORGANIZATION BY DISCIPLINE (EXAMPLE)*

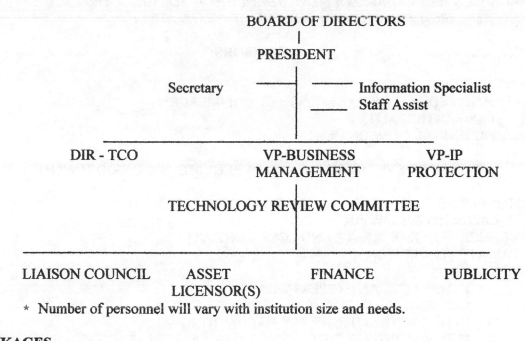

BOARD OF DIRECTORS

PRESIDENT

Secretary ———— ———— Information Specialist
———— Staff Assist

DIR - TCO   VP-BUSINESS   VP-IP
     MANAGEMENT   PROTECTION

TECHNOLOGY REVIEW COMMITTEE

LIAISON COUNCIL   ASSET   FINANCE   PUBLICITY
     LICENSOR(S)

* Number of personnel will vary with institution size and needs.

LINKAGES
- DEPARTMENT OF COMMERCE
- TRADE ASSOCIATIONS
- SMALL BUSINESS DEVELOPMENT CENTERS
- REGIONAL FEDERAL LABORATORIES
- REGIONAL/LOCAL SERVICE FIRMS
- INCUBATORS
- CITY/COUNTY GOVERNMENT
- LOCAL/REGIONAL BUSINESSES
- FINANCIAL INSTITUTIONS
- INSTITUTES/CENTERS (SERVICE/SCIENCE)
- LEGAL AND PATENT COUNSEL

BENEFITS/ADVANTAGES
- CENTRALIZED
- CONSOLIDATED
- COMBINED EFFORT AND EXPERTISE
- BASIC AND APPLIED EMPHASIS
- STRATEGIC ALLIANCES
- FEDERAL SUPPORT PROCUREMENT
- BUSINESS DEVELOPMENT
- FINANCIAL COMMITMENT AND PROCUREMENT

QUERIES
- TOTAL SPONSORED RESEARCH
- INTELLECTUAL PROPERTY QUANTIFICATION
- PEOPLE AND FINANCIAL COMMITMENT

TECHNOLOGY MANAGEMENT - MISSION

"ENHANCE ECONOMIC DEVELOPMENT THROUGH ACADEMIC, GOVERNMENT, AND/OR INDUSTRY RESEARCH AND TECHNOLOGY COMMERCIALIZATION"

SPONSORS

PROVIDER INSTITUTION
STATE AND FEDERAL DEPARTMENTS OF COMMERCE
INDUSTRY PARTICIPANTS
LOCAL/REGIONAL GOVERNMENTS

IP ASSET DEVELOPMENT AND DEPLOYMENT CONSIDERATIONS

COMMON INFO BASE - USEFUL, STANDARDIZED, EFFICIENT
POOL EXPERTISE/NETWORK
INFLUENCE FEDERAL, STATE AND LOCAL INITIATIVES
MODULATE PERCEPTION
EDUCATION
1. INTELLECTUAL PROPERTY LAW
2. CONTRACT LANGUAGE
3. INTELLECTUAL PROPERTY VALUATION
4. FEDERAL INITIATIVES
5. POLICY - CURRENT/FUTURE
ECONOMIC DEVELOPMENT
TECHNOLOGY ALLIANCES
CONSORTIA
INDUSTRY/GOVERNMENT/UNIVERSITY RELATIONSHIPS
BUSINESS FORMATION
CAPITAL FORMATION AND INVESTMENT
GENERAL ISSUES
1. INVENTOR/CREATOR
2. STUDENT INVENTOR
3. LOCAL/ CITIZEN INVENTOR ASSISTANCE
4. INDIRECT COSTS
5. PUBLIC VS PRIVATE FACILITIES - SEC REQUIREMENTS
CONFLICT OF INTEREST AND COMMITMENT
INTELLECTUAL PROPERTY TRANSFER
1. MATERIAL
2. KNOW-HOW
3. COPYRIGHT
4. MARKS
INTELLECTUAL PROPERTY/PRODUCT AWARENESS
1. FACILITIES
2. EXPERTISE
3. TECHNOLOGY
4. RESEARCH SERVICES
MARKETING/PUBLIC RELATIONS

EXHIBIT C - ECONOMETRICS

ECONOMETRICS ASSOCIATED WITH A
TECHNOLOGY COMMERCIALIZATION ORGANIZATION

Service or product	Intellectual property definition
Objectives/goals/functions	Financial
Economic development	Public benefit
Relationships/awareness	Internal
External	Policies
Intellectual property assets	Assign to university
Managed by third party office	Financial considerations
Revenue distribution	Expense recovery procedures
Equity management	Scope of responsibility
Sponsored research	Corporate
Non-corporate	Patents
Copyright	Plant material
Marks	Types of transactions
Sale - with or without conditions	Assign - with or without conditions
Option	License
Gift	In kind
Stock	Non-corporate
Accounting	Compliance
Corporate sponsored research	Payment schedule
Reporting	Intellectual property
Review/comment	Responsibility for protection
Notices	Option
Duration	Term/extension
Payment	

COST VS. REVENUE ECONOMETRICS

Cost Oriented Environment	**Revenue Oriented Environment**
Budget Policy	Consideration
Break-even	Break-even analysis
Profit	Profit
Patent expense	Patent expenses
	Royalties
	Fees
	In-kind contributions
	Equity
	Sponsored research
	Gifts

Service Oriented Environment

Number of transactions compliance	Types of transactions complaints
Disclosures turnaround time	Transactions contacts
Sponsored research	

TECHNOLOGY COMMERCIALIZATION - OFFICE ACTIVITIES

- Facilitate technology transfer through effective program planning and appropriate relationships within and outside the institution
- Negotiate license and agreement terms which are acceptable to all parties
- Acquire financial and technical support for product development to enhance commercial value of technology while balancing cost/benefit of development process
- Enhance and manage current scientist, technology and corporate information bases

"DATA BASE" CONSIDERATIONS

Scope - needs vs. desires	Maintenance
Flexibility	Updates
User friendly	Service
Report generation	Documentation
Create or purchase	Expansion potential
Time to design and create	Number of sites, linkages, users
Cost	
Site manager, trainer	

COMMUNICATION

Contacts- letters, phone, fax, e-mail	Accountability
Home page	Creators
Faculty	Units
Corporate	School
Other	Department
Presentations	Center/institute/consortia
Corporate contacts	Administration
Who	Follow-up
When	Monitoring
Follow-up	Records - discovery, litigation, continuity
Topic	Internal management vs. external reporting

INTELLECTUAL PROPERTY ASSETS ARE THOSE THAT SOMEONE CONTENDS HAVE COMMERCIAL POTENTIAL

Software/multimedia	Marks
Plant material	Trade dress
Patentable matter	Art/music/sculpture
Know-how, show-how	Video
Trade secrets	Microchip architecture

INTELLECTUAL PROPERTY METRICS

Disclosure of invention
    Number disclosed
    Number accepted
Provisional patent application
    Date
    Cost
Patent application
    Date
    Cost
    Office action
    Date
    Response
    Cost
Patents allowed
    Date
Fee payment
Patents issued
    Date
    Reissues
    Continuation
    Continuation in part
    Foreign applications
    Plant variety protection
Copyright
Invention
Know-how
Plant material
Marks
Trade dress
Research and development commitment
    Number of projects
    Compensation/ project
    Total sponsored R&D funds

Disclosures
Disclosures/number of scientists
Disclosures/amount of research funds
Licenses
    Copyright
    Mark
    Plant material
    Patent
Options
    Number
    Compensation
Infringement
    Number
    Expenses
Revenue
    Total
    Income/agreement
    Income/asset
    Income/scientist
    Income/license
    Royalty income
    Fee income
    IP protection reimbursement
Expenses
    Expense/license
    Expense/scientist
    Expense/year

LICENSE TERMS RELATED TO FINANCIAL CONSIDERATION

Credit toward royalty
Fees
In-kind compensation
Milestones payment
Minimum royalty
Maintenance fees

Performance criteria
Reports
Running Royalty
Upfront payment

EXHIBIT D – GUIDING CRITICAL THINKING

Generic Questions	Specific Thinking Processes Induced
Explain why _____ (Explain how _____)	Analysis
What would happen if ?	Prediction/hypothesizing
What is the nature of _____?	Analysis
What are the strengths and weaknesses of _____?	Analysis/ inferencing
What is the difference between _____ and _____?	Comparison-contrast
What is _____ happening?	Analysis/inferencing
What is a new example of _____?	Application
How could _____ be used to _____?	Application
What the implications of _____?	Analysis/inferencing
What is _____ analogous to?	Identification/creation of analogies and metaphors
How does _____ affect _____?	analysis of relationship (cause/effect)
How does _____ tie in with what we learned before?	Activation of prior knowledge
Why is _____ important?	Analysis of significance
How are _____ and _____ similar?	Comparison-contrast
How does _____apply to everyday life?	Application to real world
What is a counter argument for _____?	Rebuttal to argument
What is the best _____, and why?	Evaluation and provision of evidence
What is the solution to the problem of _____ ?	Synthesis of ideas
Compare _____ and _____ with regard to,	Comparison-contrast & evaluation based on criteria
What do you think causes _____? Why?	Analysis of relationship (cause/effect)
Do you agree or disagree with this statement: _____?	evaluation and provision of evidence
What evidence is there to support your answer?	evaluation and provision of evidence
What is another way to look at _____?	Taking other perspectives
What does _____ mean?	Comprehension
Describe _____ in your own words.	Comprehension
Summarize _____ in your own words.	Comprehension

(Following is for information only. Seek legal or accounting advice for your specific situation)

1. What are pitfalls related to technology transfer?

Many inventors think they can do it all on their own. They must cover all of the potential targets and not give up too soon. It often takes a long time to be successful; so don't expect an overnight success. Several key pitfalls are:

  a. unwillingness to share with others who have the ability to help maximize the value of their intellectual property (IP) by licensing and/or commercializing it. (That is not prudent because at the moment they own 100% of nothing whereas if the IP where well managed, it might be worth substantially more);

  b. trying too quickly to sell/license the IP without completing the technical and business feasibility; hence value and commercialization plans are absent or inaccurate;

  c. marketing and promoting the IP "package" when not well prepared and effectively presented to license candidates;

  d. in certain situations inventors fail to engage qualified experts when it is necessary to do so; or

  e. having unrealistic compensation expectations, thereby not knowing when to say "yes" or "no" to an offer.

2. What are the pros and cons for securing legal and patent counsel assistance when new discoveries are being transferred or commercialized and when should they be involved?

It is not uncommon for an inventor to approaches Patent Counsel or seeks legal advice early even though asset evaluation is often rather superficial at this point. Individuals often develop dislike or ill feeling when legal bills are presented and technology is not well accepted in the market or slower developing than at first projected. If Legal Counsel could direct or offer access to tools for individual to assess an asset prior to significant legal or patent expense; Counsel would probably achieve a long term relationship that might be more profitable than a short term relationship that goes sour due to inadequate upfront assessment so be sure to ask for such help. Most business recommendations are to involve the legal profession when contract is near conclusion. This approach may not be beneficial. Counsel with background in technology commercialization which covers more than intellectual property might benefit creator due to more efficient use of time and better deal making.

3. What types of questions need to be raised if a technology transfer/commercialization effort wants to provide an incentive program to employees? You would like to: 1) determine if there has been an increase in the incentive practice and 2) obtain details on existing or planned programs.

Examples of information to request are outlined below:

  a. Has your organization implemented, or is it considering implementing, an incentive compensation system for its technology transfer employees?

  b. Do/will all members of the Technology Transfer organization receive incentive compensation, or just a select group ("professionals," managers, etc.)?

  c. On what basis is a) the distribution amount calculated and b) the corresponding allocation made (e.g. pool as % of total program income, % of individual deal, % of base salary if organization/personal goals achieved, other)?

  d. Who makes the allocation decision?

  e. Does/will your incentive compensation program distribute any shares of equity, actual or "phantom," received as partial consideration for a license transaction to a University based start-up company to your employees?

f.   Is the amount of incentive compensation for the Technology Transfer organization or the individual limited/capped?

g.   Has a "vesting" period been established which triggers the opportunity to obtain incentive compensation? If so, how much time must the employee be on staff prior to program participation?

h.   If the individual leaves the Technology Transfer organization, will the individual be able to receive "earned" incentive compensation after their departure (note: presumes that the incentive compensation is based on individual deals and/or equity participation)? If so, a) is this only possible if the employee is "vested" and b) does this last in perpetuity or is it for a finite period of time after departure?

i.   Have you received any negative feedback from the faculty, administration, or other employees due to the incentive compensation system or have there been any other ramifications?

j.   Can you quantify a) your ability to attract/retain high caliber professionals since your implementation of the incentive compensation program and b) your organization's growth/increase due to the same?

4. Is technology transfer a competitive venture?

Yes, investors have finite funds and those with similar technologies vie for the same investor in many cases. Government laboratories will become major competitors with universities in transfer of technology. These labs have large $20B research budgets (as high as $20B), 100K scientists and hold many patents (i.e. 28K). Currently few American companies take advantage of federal research. Private and public institutions are advertising in technology transfer news publications and via the Internet. These same firms also preview their technology and research as they attempt to formulate key relationships designed to move discoveries to market.

5. What is the Bayh-Dole Act, what prompted it, and why is it important to university technology transfer?

Enactment of the Bayh-Dole Act (P.L. 96-517), the "Patent and Trademark Act Amendments of 1980" on December 12, 1980 created a uniform patent policy among the many federal agencies that fund research. Bayh-Dole enables small businesses and nonprofit organizations, including universities, to retain title to materials and products they invent under federal funding. Amendments to the Act also created uniform licensing guidelines and expanded the law's purview to include all federally funded contractors. (P.L.98-620)

Critical pressures prompted the Bayh-Dole Act in 1980. Congress perceived the need for reliable technology transfer mechanisms and for a uniform set of federal rules to make the process work. One major impetus for the bill was the lack of a capability on the part of the federal government to transfer technologies for which it had assumed ownership. Hundreds of valuable patents were sitting unused on the shelf because the Government, which sponsored the research that led to the discovery, lacked the resources and links with industry needed for development and marketing of the inventions. Yet the government was unwilling to grant licenses to the private sector. The few federal agencies that could grant patent title to universities were over regulated with conflicting licensing and patenting policies. Technology transfer under those conditions was operationally prohibitive for universities and made them reluctant to enter the technology arena.

Since U.S. industry also was not inclined to brave government bureaucracy to license patents from universities or from the government, limited technology transfer was accomplished by the publishing of research results, training of students for the workforce and some extension programs established by the land-grant universities. The benefit to U.S. industry of such an unstructured process is undocumented and highly speculative.

The stability provided by the Act, its amendments and clear implementing regulations has spurred universities to become involved in transfer of technology from their laboratories to the marketplace. The ability to retain title to and license their inventions has been a healthy incentive for universities. Such incentive is needed, since participation in patent and licensing activities is time consuming for faculty, and must be done in addition to research and teaching priorities. The number of U.S. patents issued to universities has increased sharply since Bayh Dole was passed.

6. How has the Bayh-Dole Act influenced university technology transfer over the last decade and what are the results?

Bayh-Dole gave universities control of their inventions. By placing few restrictions on the universities' licensing activities, Congress left the success or failure of patent licensing up to the institutions themselves. That foresight has been rewarded by skillful and committed university professionals who have shown that licensing embryonic inventions can be successful. The keys are inventors motivated to engage in the process and a licensing relationship built on partnerships with industry. This model is now emulated by the federal laboratories.

The success of Bayh-Dole in expediting the commercialization of federally funded university patents is reflected in the statistics. Prior to 1981, fewer than 250 patents were issued to universities per year. Slightly over a decade later, almost 1,600 were issued each year. Of those, nearly 80% stemmed from federally funded research. In addition, the number of universities participating in the patenting effort has increased to the point that in 1992, 200 universities had at least one patent issued annually.[1]

Core technologies, likely to spark whole new industries, often result from university patents. This potential makes the contributions of the university sector to the national patent pool so significant. Examples range from the biotechnology to the laser industry. Stanford's Cohen-Boyer patent on basic gene splicing tools is at the heart of the entire biotechnology industry. The Axel patents, from Columbia University, provided a new process for inserting genes into mammalian cells to make protein. A host of new pharmaceutical products resulted from this invention.

The Atomic Force Microscope, invented at the University of California, Santa Barbara, is the most advanced atomic microscope in existence. The invention has not only significantly improved our ability to study the structure of molecules important in biology and medicine; it also helps scientists comprehend the subtle details of physiological and chemical processes as they occur in real time.

The field of Magnetic Resonance Imaging, as we know it today, has its roots in research at the University of California, San Francisco. This University-developed technology was first disclosed in the mid 1970s. Later university work in this area and productive partnerships with industry have led to continual advancement in the field. Today, Magnetic Resonance Imaging is a staple in modern medical care.

University gross licensing revenues of approximately $200M in 1991 and $250M in 1992,[2] are a striking indicator of how many university-owned patents have become marketplace products or are in the process of development by industrial companies. Bayh-Dole has enabled laboratory advances to become a significant factor in U.S. industrial growth.

7. How many research universities have technology transfer offices and what do they do?

It is not known exactly how many universities are engaged in technology transfer activities. One indicator is that over 230 U.S. universities and nonprofit research institutions are represented in the Association of University Technology Managers (AUTM). Among those universities that are active, one can observe a variety of structures and sizes. More significant than the structure of those officers, however, is their mission.

The mission of university technology transfer/licensing offices is to transfer research results to commercial application for public use and benefit. The office seeks and receives reports of inventions from investigators; reports the inventions to sponsors; decides whether to elect title for inventions

---

[1] AUTM Survey, compiled annually by Ms. Kathleen Terry, State University of New York at Buffalo
[2] AUTM Licensing Survey, 1993.

developed with external funding; files patent applications; markets those patents to industry, and negotiates and administers license agreements. The technology transfer office is also responsible for oversight of patent prosecution, recording of income and disbursements, and yearly reports to the government.

The major effort of the office is to find companies which have the capability, interest and resources to develop embryonic technologies into useful products. Once a match is found, a license agreement is negotiated to ensure that the company will be diligent in its efforts and will provide a fair financial return to the university - one that reflects a portion of the university's contribution to the return the company receives.

Technology transfer operations are generally also involved in negotiating material transfer agreements. Under such agreements, investigators share research materials (cells, cells lines, reagents, or other organisms) with colleagues in other universities or industry. Technology transfer experts also review the intellectual property terms in sponsored research agreements with industry (in some cases actually negotiating these agreements in conjunction with the university's Contracts and Grants office). Importantly, the professionals in the office are also a resource to the campus on a wide variety of intellectual property matters.

8. How does university technology transfer work and what do universities license?

The major steps in technology transfer are: disclosure of inventions; record keeping and management; evaluation and marketing; patent prosecution; negotiation and drafting of license agreements; and management of active licenses. University technology transfer is mainly a system of disclosure, patenting, licensing and enforcement of patents and licenses.

The disclosure document contains information about the invention, the inventors, the funding sources, anticipated bars to patenting (such as publications), and other data (such as likely candidates for licensing). The licensing staff or a university committee, who make a preliminary decision about ownership and the invention's potential commercial value and patentability, reviews the disclosure. The technology transfer office takes action to insure that the newly disclosed intellectual property will be handled in compliance with federal and university policies.

The next step is to seek an opinion on the patentability of the invention or to file a patent outright. The technology transfer office then markets the invention to industry. A nonconfidential summary is sent to companies that are likely to be interested. If a company expresses interest, it will be asked to sign a secrecy agreement (to protect patent rights) prior to receiving confidential information from the university. If the company continues to be interested after reviewing the confidential information, an agreement with the company is negotiated. This can be a letter of intent; an option; or a license.

In conjunction with any one of these options, a research agreement may be negotiated to continue work on the invention at the university. Most university inventions are embryonic and require further research and development before they are ready for the market place. Thus, there is a high level of risk for the licensee - a fact that is taken into account in the licensing negotiation.

Technology transfer offices have many different "customers" with sometimes conflicting objectives. For instance, customers may consist of the:

a. faculty/inventors, who often have expectations of research opportunities, income, public utilization and fame;

b. private sector, with expectations of securing commercially viable technology at a fair price;

c. university administration, which expects the office to be self-supporting and wants to prevent conflicts of interest;

d. governing board, which needs assurance that the university's name and reputation are protected in its industrial relationships;

e. taxpayers, with expectations that the office will manage state and federal resources in an effective and nondiscriminatory manner; and

f. sponsoring agency which insists on compliance with provisions of the Bayh-Dole Act.

In addition, the technology transfer office has the critical task of insuring that the missions of the university - education, research and service - are not compromised by the business interest emerging from the technology licensing function.

9. How is value realized in the transfer process?

License fees and royalties are determined by arm's length negotiations between licensor and licensee. Fees and royalty rates are rarely large because most of the technology is in early stages and risky, thus requiring considerable investment to transform it into a marketable product. There are, however, a few technologies that have clear commercial applications and have large potential markets. In such cases, the university can negotiate larger fees and higher royalty rates. The deciding factors are: the type of technology, its stage of development, the size of the potential market, the profit margin for the anticipated product, the amount of perceived risk, the strength of the patents, and the projected cost of bringing a product to market.

To place this in perspective, license fees rarely reach into the six figures for a single patent, but more often range from a few thousand to a few tens of thousands of dollars. Royalty rates range from less than one percent (for some process technologies) to perhaps eight percent (for a patented compound with a significant market). The majority of royalty rates are in the 3% to 6% range, based on net sales.

The marketing process itself sets the value of the technology -- how interested are the prospective licensees. Other factors that play a role are the estimated dollar value of the research which led to the discovery; the projected cost of development needed to complete the product; the scope of the license (exclusive vs. nonexclusive; U.S. vs. worldwide; narrow vs. multiple fields of use, etc.) and royalty rates for similar products.

Beyond such general considerations, many organizations seek to accomplish several basic goals in development of the package of considerations: a) the licensee should fund the patent application either through an up-front fee for reimbursement of costs already incurred or through a requirement to reimbursement of ongoing expenses; b) the license agreement should include ongoing considerations to the organization (a royalty); c) required minimum annual royalties after a specified period of time regardless of actual sales; and d) performance milestones to assure that the technology enters the market. This "formula" hopefully assures that the technology is developed to completion and put in the stream of commerce, assures a fair return to the organization, and assures that the technology is returned to the university should the licensee not pay the minimums or achieve the specified performance milestones.

10. What factors influence university decisions to license patents either exclusively or non-exclusively?

University decisions on whether to license a patent only to one company or to a number of companies are based on several factors. However, universities are generally most influenced by two major determinants: (1) what kind of licensing is most likely to lead to rapid commercialization; and (2) what kind of licensing is in the public interest.

Patents which are broad in scope and can be used in multiple industries, or patents that are so basic that they form the building blocks for new technologies are most likely to be licensed non-exclusively, or by fields of use. An exclusive, "field-of-use" license is a way to protect a market for a company while enabling the university to identify more than one licensee to assure public utilization of the technology in all markets.

Stanford University's Cohen-Boyer patent is an example of a basic patent that was licensed to all companies needing it. Non-exclusive licensing is preferred by universities when the technology can be used to foster product development in many fields of use. For example, if a technology will be of greatest benefit to the public if it becomes an industry standard, the university will make it readily accessible to all interested parties.

Universities most frequently will grant exclusive licenses to patents that require significant private investment to reach the marketplace or are so embryonic that exclusivity is necessary to induce the investment needed to determine utility. Frequently, these are new drugs requiring time-intensive and capital-intensive development or they are technologies that have only a tenuous link between the workbench and production. As such, they require a company willing to dedicate financial backing and the creativity of its own scientists on a long-range basis.

At the final call, the decision to license on an exclusive or non-exclusive basis is inevitably driven by market interest. Not only does the interest relate to the value of the invention, but also to the investment required to develop new products and the risk associated with that technology.

11. To whom do universities license and what role does the start-up company play in technology transfer?

Universities license technology to a broad spectrum of organizations and individuals, ranging from the large for-profit corporation to a small non-profit research institute. For example, a license may be given to a multi-national pharmaceutical company for a new application of a known drug because that company may hold the patent on the compound. A non-exclusive license may be granted to a number of computer hardware and software firms to incrementally improve product lines. A royalty-free license may be granted to another non-profit research institute to enable a researcher to practice the invention for research purposes. Included in these examples must also be a license to an early stage firm whose founding purpose was to commercialize the technology. While these kinds of licenses are probably the riskiest in terms of eventual commercialization and subsequent payoff, those licensee companies are sometimes the most effective at transferring the technology for the public good.

Universities search for the licensee most capable of commercializing the technology. Examples of criteria used in identifying the licensee are: financial and technological resources; "fit" within the company business plans; previous experience, and marketing capabilities. Desire of the licensee to commercialize the technology and the relationship of the inventor to the licensee are also important. Commercialization of technology is not dependent only on intellectual property rights such as patents, but also on the ideas and know-how of the inventor. Therefore, the ability of the inventor to relate to the licensee is often a key factor in a license transaction.

When an entrepreneurial inventor is involved, the licensee may be a early stage company formed around the technology. These entrepreneurial ventures may bring with them a myriad of potential conflict of interest issues which must be resolved before a license is consummated. Nevertheless, they often are the most desirable because they have several of the key licensing components: desire by the licensee to make the product/technology a success, and involvement by the inventor in assuring success. One other factor in licensing to early stage companies is that these companies make that technology their business, whereas in established companies the technology must compete for resources with other development projects.

12. Why is it not feasible to select licensees through a competitive bidding process?

Most academic-developed technology is "sold" rather than "bought". This means that considerable investment is required to present, persuade, and tailor specific arrangements to the needs of the licensee. Usually, the task is to find at least one capable and interested company, rather than choosing among several candidates. It is generally impossible to bring the interest of several prospects to a head at the same time, as would be required for a meaningful competitive bidding process. Also, tailoring to special industry needs makes the competitive bidding useless. Yet, such tailoring is especially necessary in the case of small business firms to which universities are required to give preference for technology developed with federal funding.

Many universities cannot afford the full patent application expense. Therefore they seek prospective licensees to cover patenting expenses as part of a license agreement. The confidentiality required to prevent loss of rights in pre-filing negotiations makes competitive bidding difficult, especially when loss of patent rights through publication is imminent.

Normally universities contact several prospective licensees and pursue the most promising ones. Should there be more than one, universities will decide in favor of the one best able and diligent to develop the technology, not necessarily by the one who will pay the most. Where time and circumstances permit, universities may showcase technology available for licensing, through publications, databases, and technology shows. More satisfactory results probably would not be achieved through a formal competitive bidding process. Because of the extra time and effort required in bidding, together with the inevitable reduction in flexibility, the result almost certainly would be fewer licenses and thus fewer university technologies being productively commercialized.

13. Why do universities sometimes license to foreign companies, and to what extent have federally assisted technologies been licensed to foreign companies on an exclusive basis?

When universities seek potential licensees, they begin close to home -- with companies within the same state or region. This makes sense because the company often needs to have access to the inventor as a consultant to assist in the development process. Such interaction is easier if distant travel is not required. Universities consider licenses to foreign companies in those instances where all attempts to identify a domestic licensee have failed. If a thorough investigation of all possible licensees in the United States results in failure, should the university seek foreign licensees or close the file? There are many foreign companies which are leaders in their fields and thus, also, are potential licensees. In some cases, such as in equipment for the paper drying industry, the only prospective licensees may be foreign companies. Many of what appear to be local and U.S. based companies are, in fact, "foreign"; they may have been purchased by a foreign corporation (as is the case with Genentech) or they may be a U.S. based subsidiary (as is the case with Miles, Inc.). The fact is that many companies are multi-national and have U.S. offices and factories.

The choice of licensee is best made on the basis of whether a company has the capability and resources to develop the technology and to bring it to market effectively. Since university technology is not a fully developed product, it is less a question of choosing among various qualified companies than finding any company willing and able to take a license. Thus if a foreign company makes a reasonable proposal and is capable of developing and marketing products based on the invention, the university will generally grant that company a license.

Nevertheless, universities should be extremely cautious in considering foreign licensees, especially if the research was funded by the U.S. government. For those inventions, all exclusive licenses require the licensee, including foreign companies, to manufacture products substantially in the U.S.

The recent GAO survey of thirty-five top NIH and NSF grantees showed that during 1989 and 1990, only eighteen of the one hundred ninety-seven exclusive licenses for NIH/NSF-funded inventions went to foreign companies (less than 10%). An additional eleven were granted to U.S. subsidiaries of foreign corporations.[3]

14. What is the relationship between patents and publications?

In order to obtain a patent, the inventor must fully disclose his/her invention. Thus, in some ways the act of patenting insures publication. At the same time, publication of the details of an invention prior to filing a patent application can result in the loss of patent rights in most countries. The U.S. is an exception since it permits an inventor to obtain a patent if a patent application is filed within one year of the date of publication which first disclosed the invention.

Some scientists are concerned that the desire to obtain protection may cause publication to be delayed for long periods, slowing the exchange of scientific information and thus scientific progress. While this may be true in industry, it does not appear to occur in academia where publication delays

---

[3] *"University Research-Controlling Inappropriate Access to Federally Funded Research Results", May 1992.*

for patent purposes are rare. When they do occur, it is usually for less than three months. In fact, if a faculty member starts the patent filing process at the same time as submitting a manuscript for publication, it is likely that the patent application will be filed (in three months) long before the manuscript is published (in six months).

For university scientists, the right of unfettered publication of data - in journals, other written media, through oral presentation at public meetings - is a basic principle of academic life. Patents protect this form of public discourse in science. It is not a matter of having to choose between patents and publications; both are feasible and frequently desirable. But if there is a choice, it is the faculty who makes the call.

15. Why is it not desirable to dedicate all federally-assisted inventions to the public via publication, rather than patenting some of them?

An argument has been made that inventions resulting from federally funded research should be dedicated to the public, by publishing the details of the invention in literature available to the public. The thought is that since taxpayers paid for the invention they should have free access to it. In reality, taxpayers could only reap benefit of the invention if they had large financial resources, sophisticated technical skills and the personal interest in practicing the invention. Further, this scenario would require inventions that are ready to go to production stage. In today's complex technological environment, federally funded research is rarely ready to go into production when universities are ready to license it. Such development is often time consuming and costly.

Taxpayers do benefit from inventions by having access to a broad range of products developed by a predominantly competitive marketplace. New drugs are a prime example. If the invention has been dedicated to the public through publication, no commercial firm would devote extensive resources to developing the first commercial application, knowing that any of their competitors can step in and reap the profits of commercial exploitation once the invention has been proven. Patents, and the seventeen-year exclusive position they provide to the inventor, or to the inventor's designee, are necessary for successful commercial development of inventions.

16. What potential financial conflicts of interest could arise at universities in the technology transfer process, and what steps have universities taken to deal with them?

Universities are concerned about four primary issues in a conflict of interest between the academic researchers' duties to the university and their involvement with industry in technology transfer.

a. Conflicts of time and commitment - an over involvement of the investigator with the company to the detriment of teaching and university research obligations. Most universities have regulations regarding the faculty member's time obligations to the university. For example, some universities state that the "academic year salary" covers 80% of the faculty member's time during the nine months of the academic year. Faculty are free to consult "up to 20% of the time" (usually understood to be one day per week) during the academic year. Payment for the "summer months" is often under a separate, negotiated arrangement. The issue is further controlled by regular reporting of the investigator's consulting and other outside commitments.

b. Misuse of university resources on the company's behalf - this includes university facilities, equipment, supplies and involvement of graduate students and other paid researchers. University policies should make it clear that work done at the university must be publishable in the open literature and that any intellectual property such as data, patents and software, developed with university resources belongs to the university. In addition, periodic reports to research sponsors assure that grant money is used for legitimate research ends. Periodic performance review by academic administration and an "appeal path" for employees further controls the process.

c. Confusion in ownership of intellectual property - The question: "Who owns Professor X's patent?" could become a common source of dispute, unless there are clear university policies and definitions within research agreements of the sponsor's rights. University policies commonly state that the university owns all patents and software developed using university facilities or developed under a sponsored research agreement. Industrial sponsors are commonly granted first options to license patents arising from the research, and the federal government is granted a nonexclusive license to patents from federally funded research.

d. There may be potential or perceived conflict of interest where an inventor holds an equity position in a company, which the university has licensed to market and distribute the invention. Most universities believe that bringing such financial holdings into the sunlight, through public disclosure, is preferable to a hard and fast rule prohibiting the taking of equity altogether.

Universities also understand that potential unethical conduct may arise from an investigator's financial interest in a company. Universities have separate rules in place to prevent, discover or sanction fraudulent activities. Scientific misconduct, however, is not to be equated or confused with conflicts of interest.

17. Why is there sometimes joint federal and industrial participation in university research projects?

Increasingly, the federal government encourages the development of collaborative relationships between itself, industry, and academia. New partnerships are fostered through the Defense Reinvestment Act, programs at the National Institutes of Standards and Technology, the Environmental Protection Agency and the Department of Energy. Collaborative relationships are expected to promote economic development, job creation, technology transfer and innovation.

Federally funded projects can indeed benefit from the practical industrial perspective. The research can be enhanced by industry's interest in the application of the research to solving practical problems and creating new or better products. Industry scientists have substantial expertise in many federally funded research areas. Thus, collaboration between research at the university and development at the company facilitates the transfer of new technologies to the commercial sector. The resulting leveraging of funds and expertise benefits all parties and the public.

In certain programs, federal agencies require applicants to present a technology transfer plan as part of their funding proposal. In these cases, universities seek potential licensees while the research is in progress. Gaining company participation at that early stage increases the likelihood that the company will grasp the commercial potential of the research and will help move inventions to the marketplace.

Universities increasingly try to foster ties with industry. This can be a win-win situation; industry extends the scope of its R&D, and university investigators extend their limited research dollars and gain access to the expertise of industrial scientists. Bringing industry interests into university projects also contributes to placement of university graduates in industrial settings where their education and training is effectively used.

Some state governments are also promoting industry-university ties. For instance, the Texas Higher Education Coordinating Board makes biannual awards of approximately $60 million to researchers at state universities in the Advanced Technology Program. Receipt of state funds under this program is contingent upon industry participation in the research project.

18. Do universities apply different policies and procedures to inventions assisted by industry funds than to those assisted by federal funds?

Universities generally apply the same policies and procedures to all inventions made at the institution, whether they result from federal or industrial funding. Of course, the university must comply with certain government reporting and licensing requirements of the Bayh-Dole Act for inventions resulting from federally funded research. Nonetheless, university policies emphasize the university's responsibility to manage all its inventions for the public benefit.

When an invention results from industrially funded research, the sponsoring company is often granted the first opportunity to obtain a license to commercialize the invention. If joint industrial and federal funding is involved, the company's rights are subject to the institution's obligations to the federal government. Whether or not federal funds are involved, the university insists on license terms that require the company to be diligent in developing the invention. If the company does not comply, the university generally reserves the right to terminate the license or to grant licenses to other companies. In this way, a company can be prevented from "shelving" an invention that might replace or compete with one of its existing products.

19. When is it appropriate for license rights to future federally assisted inventions to be committed to an industrial sponsor?

When both federal and industrial funding support a research program, it is appropriate to grant an industrial sponsor the right to receive licenses to subsequent inventions. The regulations implementing the Bayh-Dole Act specifically recognize this possibility. It is also possible for two separate research projects to contribute to a single invention. If one project is sponsored by industry and one by the federal government, the industrial sponsor can be given rights to the invention.

It is, however, considered inappropriate to grant an industrial sponsor the right to exclusive licenses to future federally assisted inventions which result from research that the company does not fund.

Perhaps the most fundamental boundary is that universities should not grant to a single industrial sponsor the rights to federally assisted inventions from the entire institution or major units such as departments, centers and laboratories. The granting of rights must be specific to the scope of work funded.

University action in the management of inventions is guided in part by their mission: instruction, research, and public service. It is within this mission that universities undertake federally assisted research. The administration of invention rights arising in this research is further bounded by the implementing regulations of the Bayh-Dole Act. For example, the Act specifies that manufacture of products based on the technology should be done substantially in the United States. This is good public policy, but it also makes good business sense. Companies often express a concern about the government's march-in rights under the Act. These rights, again, are appropriate public policy and would likely be applied only when a company's pricing is abusive -- a condition which the marketplace is more likely to correct first.

It is within this framework of principles, institutional mission and federal regulations that universities determine what rights to grant to industrial sponsors.

20. How much income is derived by universities from licensing federally assisted inventions, and how is that money used?

The 1992 GAO survey of thirty-five top NIH and NSF grantees showed that for the two-year period 1989 and 1990, those universities received a total of $113M from licensing of which $82M was for licenses of NIH/NSF funded inventions. To place these figures in context, the invention income was less than 1% of the research support provided to universities by NIH and NSF.

The Association of University Technology Managers (AUTM) gathered 1991 - 1992 data from U.S. and Canadian institutions engaged in technology transfer. 98 U.S. universities provided gross figures on their royalty income. For 1992, royalties amounted to $172M. This figure needs to be adjusted for legal fees, amounting to $37M. In addition, the survey does not translate into dollar terms the amount of staff time expended to manage the process. Such figures tend to be meaningless in the abstract, lacking the context of institutional, federal and industry funding which provided the basis for the invention disclosures.

In reality, licensing income is small in comparison to the total university budget or even in comparison to the university's sponsored research budget. Even at the schools with the most licensing income those percentages rarely exceed 3 - 5%, and at most schools the percentage is less than 1 - 2%.

How do universities use royalty income? The answer is the same at all U.S. universities - income from licenses flows back into research or teaching. According to federal law, the universities must share licensing income from federally funded inventions with the inventors. The balance of income can be used to cover the costs of the technology transfer program and to support teaching and research at the university. While the specific percentages vary from institution to institution, the typical royalty sharing policy provides, after expenses, about 1/3 of net income to the inventor 1/3 to the inventor's department, and the university's general research fund receives the final 1/3.

21. How can success in technology transfer be measured?

There are many ways to measure success in technology transfer, but since this is a new field, success indicators are not yet uniformly established. Various measures include: the number of inventions disclosed; the number of patent applications filed, patents issued, and licenses consummated; the amount of licensing income, and the number of commercial products produced and sold. Some institutions track the number of industrial interactions and research projects funded as a direct result of marketing initiatives. Others point to spin-off industries and related incubation facilities, which tend to grow next to highly innovative businesses or academic institutions. Silicon Valley and Route 128 are well known examples.

More intangible, but nonetheless significant indicators include: an institution's capability to retain entrepreneurial faculty and attract outstanding graduate students; its reputation for innovation; the enhancement of research; and the promotion of the institution's name. And the marketplace impact of university originated products and technology is unquestionably a major component of success.

Marketplace products are recognized by the public as a tangible outgrowth of its support of basic research. An example of the impact of university technology transfer on the marketplace is found in the biotechnology industry. This entire industry - and ten of thousands of new jobs it created - is based upon university research. The Cohen-Boyer patent licensed by Stanford University is used by all biotechnology companies. In addition, many of these companies were founded to develop university inventions, whether related to specific genes, monoclonal antibodies or potential drugs.

22. Why do universities retain title to inventions?

Universities are unique environments. They are the cumulative product of decades of social investment. Their land and physical plant may have been granted or gifted by state governments or individuals. Their tremendous value to the public is exemplified by the fact that they are traditionally tax-exempt. Their activities are supported by a mix of state, federal and private investment. The pact between universities and the public demands accountability for use of resources which have been provided at public expense, and imposes an obligation upon universities to ensure that the public receives benefit for its investment. This is one factor in some universities' reluctance to sell patent title to industry. Other factors also play a role:

   a. the value of the American research university is in the reservoir of its scientific experience and the accomplishments of its faculty and students. Ensuring continued use of unique discoveries within the classroom and laboratory is indispensable to maintaining the quality of the research university. By maintaining control of their patents, universities allow both commercial use plus contributions to the universities' collective intellectual experience;

   b. by nature the university is a dynamic environment with faculty and students freely interacting with one another. Cross-fertilization of ideas may result in multiple inventions with obligations to different funding sources. By retaining title to patents, universities are in a position to equitably apportion the right to use patents among the contributing organizations;

c. the link between technology creator and product developer is crucial for successful commercialization. The product developer most often does not have the knowledge to work with the basic inventions that result from university research. By retaining patent title and licensing those patents to industry, universities establish a partnering relationship that allows ongoing interaction between the source of the idea and those with the expertise to bring it to the marketplace;

d. by retaining title to patents, universities can require licensees to make diligent efforts toward commercializing those patents. Patents not used must be surrendered to the university so that an alternative licensee may be found. Universities can ensure that new product opportunities are not wasted by companies without the resources, resolve or capability to achieve commercialization; or

e. incentive to invent is as important to the university scientist as it is to the industrial scientist. A technology transfer program structured around royalty-bearing licenses, rather than patent title assignment, helps motivate university scientists to pursue break-through discoveries.

23. Why are universities a vital link in the chain from creation of knowledge to development of products?

The valuable results of research which provide advances in technology are usually the result of the curiosity of a researcher who is asking "Why is this so?" or "Where could that lead?" What makes universities unique is the fact that they provide a rich diversity bringing together multiple disciplines, with a broader focus than product-specific industries. Most importantly, universities train and nurture the next generation of scientists and engineers which will carry with them to industry the ability to link creative knowledge with product development. The university provides the environment to nurture the pursuit of knowledge; i.e. library, laboratory, resources, equally curious colleagues and students.

However, this knowledge often needs further work even to begin to determine its usefulness as a contribution to a product or service. Industry is reluctant to support research which is not directed toward immediate financial return. The university provides a proving ground on which to take next steps toward commercialization.

The majority of university research is sponsored by government agencies and is not targeted to specific commercial markets or end products -- it is, by definition, basic research. However, since it is the nature of research to identify and test new ideas, its results often lead to the expansion of scientific knowledge as well as to the development of new technologies and products which benefit the public.

24. Why is it important to encourage university inventors to participate in the patenting process and how are they motivated?

Universities make a considerable investment each time they decide to patent an invention. Their resources include the faculty inventor's time and energy, and the outlay of dollars required by the patent application process. Commitment and support from the faculty is essential for successful technology transfer activities by their institution. Beyond the actual patenting stage, however, the path from an invention to final product or service in the marketplace is usually long and expensive. During this stage, the scientific knowledge of the inventor needs to feed into the process, to assure smooth and continued progress.

In addition to royalty income, faculty recognition by peers is important. In some schools the preparation of material to obtain a patent and the successful completion is given weight in the tenure and promotion process. This investment in time and money will not be made without incentives. In fact, the Bayh-Dole Act deliberately grants those incentives, to the inventor and the universities. Beyond the gratification of bringing technology to public use, the institution needs to recover its investment. The inventor hopes to generate research funding in the short term and possibly receive license fees to use for future research support. It is important to recognize that without such incentives, many inventions may not get carried through the necessary steps and a commercial opportunity will be wasted. This wasting of ideas is a drain on the economy, irrespective of whether it was public or private funding which led to the initial invention.

Many faculty researchers were not exposed to the idea of intellectual property, patents, copyrights, trademarks, etc., during their early academic careers. They may have misconceptions and apprehension about the patenting process. One common misconception is that the public benefits only when research is rapidly published and provided equally to all interested parties. Another is that only industrial researchers should obtain patents.

Many universities provide outreach programs to potential university inventors to dispel these misconceptions and to allow inventors and their laboratories to benefit from their ideas. Encouraging faculty to participate in the process of patenting may increase their understanding of the benefits of protecting the valuable technology. Involving inventors in the process of marketing the technology is helpful in broadening their outside interests. In this manner, the inventor gains an insight into new potential sources of research funding as well as the benefits of commercialization.

Not all faculties will agree that their involvement in commercialization activities is appropriate. Some contend that commercialization taints the university and detracts from its mission. They believe that technology transfer should be accomplished through more traditional methods, such as the education and training of students and the broadest dissemination of knowledge through publications.

Change is inevitable and change will be affected by success of the commercialization efforts. Yet, participation in such activities should always remain an option, and should remain consistent and focused on the mission of academia.

MODULE II - INTELLECTUAL PROPERTY PROTECTION

- **Intellectual property**
- **Records/laboratory notebooks**
- **Disclosure - abstracts/seminars/posters, forms/process, government notification**
- **Exchange - bailment/material transfer**
- **Overview**
- **Plant variety protection**

Emphasis is on records, asset transfer and disclosure before protection is obtained. Laboratory book procedures, material transfer arrangements, options, etc are reviewed and discussed. Intellectual property identification and related methods for protection are examined from a global perspective. Strategy and tactics along with financial commitment are reviewed and case studies examined.

Intellectual property - patent

- **Description**
- **Protection strategy**
- **Time/cost**

Patent definitions, strategy and processes are reviewed. Expenses and key decision dates are presented as part of the commercialization strategic planning.

Intellectual property – copyright, marks, secrets

- **Description**
- **Protection strategy**

The Internet and copyright protection in the information technology age for the business enterprise has become a key issue in business strategic planning. Absence of clear protection law and legal decisions adds to the risk of an emerging business. This section addresses various ways to protect copyright, multimedia, courseware, and video and audio assets.

INTRODUCTION

The intellectual property assets of the new or growing business often form the core of the enterprise, are the basis for investment and enhance one's competitive position. It is imperative that these assets are well protected. Protection can vary and can be strategically planned to provide a cascade of protection that maximizes the duration of asset protection. The following is designed to provide information on strategic planning and means to implement these plans for the benefit of the business.

It has been said that corporate America is leaving lucrative technology assets on the table meaning the value of intellectual property may be overlooked by U.S. and European businesses. The projected value of these assets is based on the projection that U.S. companies ignore technology assets with a value of ~ $115 billion. This is based on the fact that 60% of $550 billion spent on R&D over the past 5 yrs is spent on in-house technology development; hence greater than 35% of resulting patents go unused. One reason for this loss is that patents do not fit into company's core business; however, patents do represent assets that can bolster profits & maximize return on R&D investment. Thirty three percent of one hundred seventeen respondents were interested in licensing unused intellectual property but many were unaware of companies that are dedicated to licensing services and if they did know only seven percent had been involved with external service providers. Ninety percent of survey respondents consider patents a large part of the R&D process and eighty percent had been involved in patent litigation. Seventy one percent felt they had wasted resources developing technology already patented by other companies and forty two percent carried out regular patent audits. Ten percent used patents to block competitor's product development. Sixty-six percent believed patents measure value of innovation. Patent activity is highest in chemical, pharmaceutical and electronics industries. Patent fees presented herein are subject to change; so check with patent counsel or the patent office for current charges.

Strategic intellectual property plans

Intellectual property can be protected in numerous ways depending on the property. In certain cases multiple methods of protection might be selected. The following are examples of terms associated with material that could be a candidate for protection: patent, trademark, copyright, mask work, trade secret, trade dress, plant variety protection and know-how. Protection might also be achieved through secrecy or confidentiality arrangements, disclosure documents, or provisional patent applications. All of these will be addressed in this chapter. A combination of these means of protection may also be advisable. It is usually best to perform a risk-benefit analysis before embarking on a select route of protection. Intellectual property assets can provide a variety of benefits to their owners. Accordingly, they should be used as a strategic tool in corporate planning. Often, however, individuals and companies do not understand why they should obtain and enforce intellectual property rights, even if they have been told that they should do so. For example, it is not uncommon for an established company; even one with in-house patent counsel, to have dozens of patents without knowing what value each one contributes to the company. This is an unfortunate result, and tends to result in corporate legal departments and outside counsel being viewed as cost centers rather than value-producers.

In order to maximize return from its investment in intellectual property, a high technology company should take a prospective, rather than reactionary, view of intellectual property. For example, the company should not make isolated decisions concerning whether particular inventions deserve patent protection, but should consider each invention in the context of other related factors, such as whether other modes of protection (e.g., trade secret and copyright) might protect the invention nearly as well at much lower cost, how the invention fits in with the overall direction of the company, the market life of the invention, other upcoming candidate inventions that might be more worthy, and whether the company would ever assert the patent against a potential infringer. In other words, a reasoned, comprehensive and forward-looking cost-benefit analysis should be used rather than a knee-jerk reaction.

Similarly, a company should anticipate possible intellectual property disputes as far in advance as possible. That may entail periodic searches of federal records to learn of the patent and copyright activities of competitors, seeking licenses from those developing interesting technologies before the company has a specific need for such technology, and designing around the patents held by parties known to aggressively assert their patent rights.

In order to achieve this strategic planning, one of two types of education must take place. Either company management must obtain a robust understanding of intellectual property, or counsel with broad intellectual property experience must learn the direction and goals of the company. Only when a company has someone available who understands both business and legal aspects of intellectual property protection can strategic planning concerning such intellectual property occur.

PRE-PROTECTION

PRE-DISCLOSURE

There is often a delay from the time of discovery until official protection unless the discovery is kept as a trade secret. Employees in technology-based company should be informed of the company policy and procedures related to any creations made while a company employee. Instructions on the maintenance of laboratory notebooks, laboratory equipment outputs and electronic data should be made available to each employee. It may be beneficial to provide company notebooks and an intellectual property liaison service to assist the employee with the discovery and protection process.

The technology-based company policies and procedures usually require administrative approval before publication of technical results. In the academic environment written and oral publication is the primary interest of the academic employee. Therefore there is need to inform the academician of the impact of publication on intellectual property protection. Numerous methods are available to inform including seminars, home pages, brochures and "networking".

EXCHANGE/TRANSFER

With the emergence of emphasis on multidisciplinary teams across and within companies, the consolidation of several technologies or components to create a system or workable product and the emphasis on exchange of novel material it becomes important for the technology based company, government agency, individual or academic institution to enact appropriate agreements as the exchanges take place. Any time a proprietary asset is exchanged it is important to have some type of "paper trail" in which the terms of the exchange are clearly presented. Legal counsel can prepare the documents but the appropriated business or intellectual property units in the corporate, academic or government organization should establish the expectations and business terms. Examples of such agreements are material transfer or bailment, discussed below. Others, including alpha or beta test, clinical trial, and inter-institutional are discussed in subsequent chapters.

Material Transfer Agreement (MTA)

Material transfer agreements are means by which one can transfer proprietary material to another party without transferring any proprietary rights. There are several forms of MTAs, one of which is when payment is exacted to cover the costs of providing the material. Avoid charging more than cost, because then one may run the risk of establishing a first sale bar date if a patent application for the material has not been filed. Universities as well as nonprofit research organizations and commercial companies use material transfer agreements to control their downstream rights to the materials and may legally charge something for the materials as long as it is not excessive and is intended to cover their cost.

Bailment

Another form of MTA that can be used is the bailment agreement which is used for proprietary material which is not likely to be patented because it is a biological material which will be used as a research tool leading to development usually of diagnostic kits within a year or two and then the products from its use will then be subject to a royalty under the bailment agreement.

Bailment is an exception to university policy in that it requires that a trade secret be maintained, i.e., limited access to the biological material. A bailment requires the recipient to exercise a certain degree of care over the transferred material but at least the same degree of care that they would exercise over their own material of a similar nature. Some universities prefer to use a biological materials license agreement instead of a material transfer agreement.

When a University accepts material and it is subject to a bailment agreement there may need to be an exception to University policy, to maintain it as trade secret. The question is the degree to which to which the recipient must comply. It is also the responsibility of the university to also restrict its distribution. It may require a sign-off of a university official to make the exception to policy regarding publication restriction and maintenance of what amounts to a trade secret.

Agreements with bailment for unpatented, published biological materials can be enacted. Bailment does not always deal with proprietary objects. For example, a bailment is created when cars are parked in a public parking lot for a fee or when clothing is taken to a dry cleaner.

PROTECT OR NOT DECISION

Some rules of thumb as to whether or not to seek protection are:

1. if invention gives a unique advantage in functionality or cost effectiveness;
2. if patent provides value as a licensable asset or values as right that can be asserted to defend against a patent infringement claim;
3. if numerous ways exist for a accomplishing the same function at approximately the same cost, then any patent granted on an invention will be of limited value since competitors can adopt one of the alternative schemes for accomplishing the same function;
4. if invention is designed to engineer around a shortcoming of another product, the probability of eliminating the problem by a redesign of the other product should be considered; and
5. the overall commercial life span should be considered-securing protection on a product with a short life cycle can be wasteful.

In summary, keep a detailed analysis of the inventive process or a copy of a manuscript: 1) provide drawings, graphs, etc to support data in the document, 2) complete literature and patent searches and identify material that might be considered as prior art and provide a one-paragraph summary of each item, 3) include potential competitive researchers or organizations, 4) identify possible interested parties; and 5) have the disclosure form witnessed by a non-inventor.

LABORATORY NOTEBOOK

The laboratory notebook is often considered to be the most significant document related to an invention. Any enhancement of scientific record(s) enhances a notebook's legal value. There are several standards that should be considered in maintaining a good notebook. Although there may be a tendency to impose extensive legal considerations when maintaining the notebook they should not carried to the point that they detract excessively from scientific considerations.

STANDARDS

The seven primary standards that are considered important when maintaining a valid notebook are: authenticity, reliability, chronology, comprehensiveness, interpretation, corroboration and convenience.

1. **Authentic.** In order to establish authenticity a single author should make all entries. If a second person makes and entry be sure to identify that the entry is by another person and be distinctive. Remember, the Laboratory notebook is the primary and comprehensive source of experimental results.

2. **Reliable.** Reliability is established by entering data on consecutive pages in black and indelible ink. No entries should be obliterated with something like "white out " or erased. Instead a single line should be placed over the item to be corrected and a signature and date place in the margin by the person making the change. It is best to try to avoid non-contemporaneous corrections.

3. **Chronology.** Chronological, day-to-day consistent entries add credibility to the notebook. Data entry must be associated with a date. Entries should be on the date work was undertaken and completed. If there is a need to make an entry other than date of experiment both dates should be entered. Each page should be signed and dated as experimental work described thereon is completed. Relevant experimental data not available contemporaneously can be added; provided the entry is dated & initialed in a manner which makes clear when & how much information was entered.

4. **Comprehensiveness.** The source of all materials used in experiments, scale up, production, and should be identified. Include a detailed account of ancillary activities even if indirectly related to reduction to practice i.e. lot numbers, ordering reagents, date of purchase, storage conditions, special equipment, other supplies, and any analytical information that is available along with intended use such information. Record the disposition of all products and provide references to general procedures stated. Cross reference as much information as possible i.e. disposition of multiple products, intermediates, etc. Also, provide supplemental information i.e. analytical results obtained by others.

5. **Interpretation.** Use scientifically recognized terms i.e. acronyms, abbreviations, and specialized terminology. Remember not everyone who reviews the document will be aware of personal acronyms or abbreviations. Standard English narrative is best with economical use of time. In other words avoid verbosity. Follow standard practices throughout once they are established.

6. **Corroboration.** Each page needs to have a notation that states language similar to the following "Read and understood this _____ day of _____ ". The signature of the party who acts as a witness should follow. The witness should be someone not directly connected to the research but capable of understanding the significance of it. If verification of procedures is undertaken identify who is verifying including sample transmittal, analytical or biological evaluation, etc.

7. **Convenience.** Data should be monochromatic entries. Xerographic and microfilming do not differentiate color. Allow generous margins and be sure each page is identified with its research notebook and page numbers at the top of the page. If sensible, a page should reflect one day's work on one project.

8. **Physical exhibits.** It may not be convenient to attach photographs, samples or spectral data to the notebook; and if not possible maintain another cite where these data are held and identify the cite in the labbook. Be sure that a witness examines and dates and signs the exhibits.

9. *Research records.* Records submitted by an inventor are considered to be "self serving" and must be "corroborated". This corroboration is simple and cheap and needs to be completed in a routine manner. The witness might be one's manager. Select witnesses who are not likely to be co-inventors and schedule regular witnessing sessions e.g. every two weeks. Be sure records are detailed enough so the experiment can be repeated or the outcome is clear. An example of a poor record is:" The concentration of XYZ protein was 100 mg/l". When the facts are gathered, what really happened was: "RIA's were badly inconsistent, so we disregarded them. We determined total protein to be 200 mg/l by Bradford assay using albumin standard, and we estimated 50% of the total protein was XYZ by visualization of a stained gel. Based on those figures, XYZ concentration was calculated to be 100mg/l." A good rule of thumb is to follow the golden rule: "If you transferred into XYZ project, how much would you want to know about this experiment?"

INVENTION DISCLOSURE

When the invention has been conceived and reduced to practice it is usually prudent to complete an invention disclosure. The disclosure can be a guide for the inventor as they assess what they contend might be an invention. Remember that it is not necessary to always reduce an invention to practice if there are historical or current data that would allow one skilled in the art to produce the conceived invention. Also invention can occur without repeated studies, as might be the case for scientific publications that require statistical support for conclusions drawn.

Inventors should prepare a written disclosure that includes at least:

1. a statement of the objects and advantages of the invention;
2. a discussion of the prior art known to the inventor;
3. detailed description of invention including sketches, drawings, or photographs where appropriate; and
4. a discussion of all variations on the invention.

The invention disclosure should be complete and accurate to ensure the application is properly prepared and to minimize cost. See the sample invention disclosures in Exhibit C.

Records are important to prove priority (i.e. who is entitled to the patent) when two parties are trying to patent the same invention and to overcome certain prior art references. Date of invention is the filing date of the patent application that is treated by the patent office as the official date of invention. The patent office will therefore search for prior art dated before the filing date. In some cases prior art can be overcome by swearing behind it i.e., by proving that the actual date of invention was prior to the date of the reference. Proof is best provided by documentation – all inventors should keep an accurate notebook of the development of fan invention. Entries should be in ink, and signed by a witness who understands the technology involved in the invention and who is not a co-inventor.

PATENT COUNSEL

Intellectual property counsel should be sought that is familiar with the scientific field in which the invention has been made. At the first meeting provide a summary & overview of the discovery. Have three copies of prior art, your patent search file, clear and distinct figures, drawings, etc. The first meeting should be designed to determine if you feel comfortable with the attorney and the firm that might represent your intellectual property interests.

PROTECTION METHODS

At the time a decision is made to protect and asset there is a need to examine the background of the invention including ownership, authorship, inventorship in addition to financial and technical sources associated with the invention. Corporate, academic and government policies differ as to ownership. If government funds are involved there may be certain requirement, restrictions or limitations that apply to the intellectual property or technology. These factors impact the strategy for a particular technology. Be familiar with or have someone employed who is acquainted with the Bayh Dole Act, General Agreement on Tariffs and Trade (GATT), and any other restrictions or requirements that might be associated with financial or asset providers to a project from which technology is discovered or developed.

The GATT agreement was designed to establish commonality among countries of the world. An underlying contention was that "Patents shall be available - without discrimination as to the place of invention". Prior to GATT some felt that U.S. law discriminated against foreign inventors since a patent had to be filed at the time of discovery or invention whereas in the U.S. a patent application could be filed up to one year after discovery and the priority date was the date of discovery. Hence the date of discovery, and documentation thereof, was important. Abolition of that discrimination caused U.S. inventors to lose some of the advantages they had taken for granted.

The date of invention (priority date) to which a patent applicant is entitled is important when determining when publication occurred relative to discovery (publication can constitute disclosure and hence patent application will usually need to take place within one year after publication. In the event patent infringement is suspected it may be necessary to establish the original date of discovery or when the public was first made aware of the invention or product. Interference claims will also be dependent on the documentation of the discovery date and related diligent pursuit of patent protection.

PRE-PATENT

If worldwide patent is desired, it is necessary to avoid disclosure prior to filing a patent application. Alternatively, in the U.S. a patent application can be filed within one year after disclosure. In either case it is important to understand what constitutes disclosure. Any dissemination of enough information to allow someone skilled in the art to be in a position to conceive and reduce to practice the proposed invention constitute adequate disclosure that can be considered as prior art when determining whether or not to file a patent application. Examples of publication or disclosure are presented in table one.

Table one. Public disclosure – publication meaning or dissemination of work.

- Thesis upon deposit
- Awarded grants (government); unless request to maintain confidentialitity made
- Intra-company distribution
- Speeches and handouts
- Distribution of single vs. multiple copies implying limited publication
- Material received by request as a result of the Freedom of Information Act

Several protection methods to consider prior to the preparation and filing of a patent are as follows.

Confidentiality
Confidentiality, secrecy or non-disclosure agreements are a matter of timing. It is necessary to maintain confidentiality until patent application filed & advisable to continue until a patent issue. The

reason is that a patent application may be changed one or more times before it issues and therefore it may be important to delay disclosure of information that could impact the business if not part of the issued patent. In some cases one can disclose material that is not closely related to the invention but does provide information and data that is business related and which can be used in assessing preliminary interest in an asset. Individuals, brokers, investors, and service providers often see a lot of similar technology and may be hesitant to sign confidentiality agreements at the first contact and information exchange. The following are examples of points to consider when deciding whether or not confidentiality is necessary, the extent information should be held confidential and select conditions related to confidentiality: 1) stage of product development; 2) compounds in product need to be kept confidential; 3) name of collaborators are not to be disclosed; 4) collaborator arrangements/terms or materials need to be held secret (i.e. promotion material); 5) web sites must be secured for material exchange; 6) employee confidentiality agreements or training programs in place; 7) need to assure all documents and emails exchanged are labeled as confidential; 8) manage dissemination of secure information on a "need to know" basis; 9) do vendors or suppliers need to commit to maintain select items confidential; 10) how long must items be held confidential (3-5 years is normal but 25 years might be preferred depending on the project); 11) how are rights to intellectual property dispersed (may belong to client, may be result of using service provider's proprietary technology or knowledge or may require innovation for success); and 12) be prepared to offer good reasoning for confidentiality and negotiate for necessary terms.

Registered letter

The invention is described in writing and sent to a friend, attorney or yourself. This method affords no legal protection since the judicial system recognizes only a patent.

Disclosure document

A disclosure document provides legal support for the approximate date of the invention. It does not relieve one from proving earlier invention date and diligent pursuit of the invention if someone files a patent application for the same invention after a disclosure document is filed. The document should contain; 1) a description of the invention including text and drawings, 2) individually numbered pages, 3) one original and one copy of the document signed and submitted by the inventor and 4) a self-addressed envelope and check for $10 sent to Box DD, Assistant Commissioner of Patents, Washington, DC 20231.

No prototype is required to accompany the document. The PTO keeps the original, stamps the copy with an identity number, date of receipt and returns a copy to the submitter. The PTO does not examine the disclosure document. The disclosure document is retained by the PTO for two years; unless a request to retain longer is made when a related patent application is filed. This request for extended retention must be in a separate letter, not with the application.

Provisional Patent Application

The provisional patent application (PPA) was the result of an international treaty called the "General Agreement on Tariffs and Trade (GATT)" that took place in 1994. GATT added a new dimension to the patent strategy and process. It is now possible to file a provisional patent application in order to establish a priority date. The provisional is not examined but requires identification of the inventors and can include only a copy of a manuscript or material describing the invention. The cost is not as much as would be incurred for a patent application. Although the provisional patent application may require less time and cost to prepare and file one needs to consider the consequences if it fails to include critical elements that may be included at the time patent claims are drafted for the full patent application. Failure to include key elements would void the priority date and if publication occurred during the time between filing the PPA and filing the PA others could conceive and reduce to practice in the interim, hence influencing the value of the full application and increasing the potential competitive position of the technology and product.

Features of the PPA are: 1) it applies only to utility patents; 2) an invention description is required along with preliminary drawings if they support the description; 3) no oath or declaration from the inventor is required; 4) no claims or detailed drawings are required; it allows one to claim an early priority date; and 5) places invention in "patent pending" status. A formal application, PCT and U.S., must be filed within one year after filing a provisional application. Provisional patent application requirements, features and considerations related to a non-provisional patent application are summarized in tables two, three and four. Prices change so check with the patent office for actual cost.

Table two. PPA requirements (a priority document for an application filed later).

- Written description of invention that provides
  - Enablement
  - Best mode
- Drawing where necessary
- Fee $80/$160 (small/large entity)
- Inventor's names
- Complete application must be filed within a year after the provisional application
- The provisional is reviewed for compliance, but no more. The current filing fee is $80/$160 for a small entity/large entity. This type of application is useful if time is critical and a filing date important.

Table three. Items to consider when filing a provisional patent application (PPA).

- Preference may be to file a "complete application" that requires as much time and legal effort as a full application
- Starts irrevocably one year clock for filing full applications including PCT applications
- Could increase costs; need to review PPA when patent is filed to assure completeness
- File PPA if best mode presented and file patent one year later but be aware of consequences
- Filed with PTO but not examined
- Filing date for U.S. PPA is accepted for the PCT application
- PPA can be merely a manuscript

Table four. Provisional patent application features.

- No claims
- No oath
- No examination
- Reduced filing fee
- Automatic abandonment at 12 months
- Minimal legal and formal requirements
- Establish an early filing date
- Applications kept in confidence by office
- Parity with foreign applicants
- Filing does not start 20-year term
- Provides one year to:
  - Further develop invention
  - Determine marketability
  - Acquire funding
  - Seek licensee
  - Seek manufacturer

PATENTS

A patent is a grant from the U.S. government of the right to exclude others from making using importing, offering for sale, or selling the patented invention throughout the U.S. and its territories for a period of 20 years after the patent issues. These same conditions apply to patents in nearly all countries other than the United States.

The patent is a contract between the inventor and the government. The inventor discloses the invention to the public; in return the government gives the inventor the right to exclude others from practicing the invention for a limited time. The benefit to the public is the knowledge gained from the disclosure and such knowledge provides a base for additional innovation. A common misconception is that the grant of a patent gives its owner the right to make, use, import, and offers for sale or sell the invention. It only gives the owner the ability to exclude others from making, using, importing, offering for sale or selling the invention. The patent owner may be forbidden from using the invention, usually due to the existence of another patent, or sometimes due to other legal restrictions.

Components of a patent are specification and claims. Specification is a written description of the invention, including drawing if appropriate, sufficient to teach one of ordinary skill in the art how to make and use the invention. Claims are one or more one-sentence definitions of the invention. The scope of protection of the patent is determined by the claims.

Remember when discussing patents to: 1) refer to the one who developed the invention as an inventor; 2) not refer to what an inventor invented as the patent (an inventor may have invented an invention but an inventor did not invent a patent. The government "developed" the patent system); and 3) not talk about renewing a patent (patents cannot be renewed but trademarks can be renewed). Copyright was renewable under the 1909 Copyright Act but not under the 1976 Act.)

OWNERSHIP

The formality of a patent application as a prerequisite to protection actually makes patent ownership issues significantly more straightforward than copyright ownership issues. Nonetheless, patent law does raise several ownership issues that can trap the unwary.

Original Ownership in Inventors

Under United States patent law, patent ownership resides originally in the inventors. Thus, it is critical to obtain an assignment from each of the inventors if patent ownership is to be lodged elsewhere. United States law requires assignments, grants, or conveyances of patents, patent applications, or interests therein to be made in writing and to be recorded in the Patent and Trademark Office in order to be valid against any subsequent purchaser or mortgagee. This requirement is not considered by courts to be a mere formality, but instead is seen as a viable defense to an infringement claim.

It is not always a simple matter to determine who the actual inventors are for patent law purposes. In short, a person must have contributed to at least some portion of the novel subject matter in at least one of the claims in a patent application to be considered an inventor for that application. The situation becomes yet more complex if, in the process of "prosecuting" the application in the Patent and Trademark Office, the claims are amended. In this instance, inventorship may need to be changed to reflect the subject matter of the amended, as opposed to original, claims.

Joint Owners

Patents may be jointly owned, either by the inventors or by assignees of the inventors. Absent a contractual agreement to the contrary, joint owners need not obtain any consent from one another to practice the patent, and need not account to one another for profits derived thereby. Joint venturers and others contracting with regard to patent rights must be cognizant of this when drafting patent ownership clauses.

Employees and Shop Rights

Typically, inventors who are employed by United States companies have signed agreements by which they are obliged to assign rights in patents and patent applications to their employers. In general, state law rather than federal law governs such ownership rights in patentable inventions. As detailed above, some states limit the extent to which employers may claim such rights. Even if an employee is under no such obligation to assign rights to an employer, the employer may nevertheless be able to claim "shop rights" that are equivalent to a non-exclusive, royalty-free, non-transferable license to the invention.

Assignor Estoppel

Under this patent law doctrine, once a patent owner transfers ownership of the patent, it is estopped from later contending that the assigned property is valueless, i.e., invalid.

Remedies

In the event of willful infringement, a defendant may be liable for treble damages. The statute of limitation for patent infringement is a running period of 6 years; that is a suit can be brought for infringements occurring only in the 6 years prior to filing the suit. Imported foreign goods that infringe a U.S. patent can be enjoined from importation and sale in the U.S. Also non-patented goods made overseas by a process or method covered by a U.S. patent can be enjoined form importation and sale in the U.S. A U.S. patent affords no rights in foreign countries. Such protection requires a patent in each foreign country.

TYPES OF PATENTS

In the United States there are three kinds of patents -- design patents, utility patents, and plant patents.

DESIGN PATENT

Design patents in the U.S. have a term of 14 years. The design patent provides protection for appearance or ornamental design of objects e.g. clothing, jewelry or furniture. If revisions are made a new filing is required. The fee for filing is relatively low, small entity is $165 and large entity is $330. No maintenance fees are required. Patent counsel fees for preparation and filing may range from $3000 - $5000.

UTILITY PATENT

The term of a utility patent depends on when the patent application was filed. If the patent issued from an application filed prior to June 8, 1995, the term is the later of; 1) 17 years from the date of issuance of the patent, or 2) 20 years from the first U.S. filing date for the patent. If the patent issued from an application filed on or after June 8, 1995, then the term is 20 years from the first U.S. filing date for the patent. This complicated rule for the term of a utility patent is the result of the transition from the old term (17 years after issuance) to the uniform term prescribed by The General Agreement on Tariffs and Trade (GATT) (20 years after filing). It applies to all patents still in force on June 8, 1995.

Utility patent features are; 1) protects the function or method of the invention, 2) usually more complicated document than a design patent; 3) requires a detailed explanation of use, 4) is usually more difficult to obtain, and 5) is more expensive than a design patent, $370 and $740 for a small and large entity, respectively.

PLANT PATENT

The utility, design and plant itself can be patented. The variety name cannot be the trademark name since it is available for public use; however, a trademark series name can be protected. For example, if rose varieties are neon red, neon yellow, & neon pink; the trademark neon cannot be protected but if the series is labeled as "starlight"- neon red rose or "starlight ^{TM}"-neon red rose protection can be secured. The plant must be asexually produced; hence all resulting plants are genetically the same e.g. cuttings, layering, budding, grafting, tissue culture or division. Other requirements are the same as for any patent. It must be new or novel, non-obvious, not publicly known (no prior art) or disclosed, offered for sale, or sold more than one year prior to filing a patent application.

Plant characteristics must be clearly distinguishable from existing varieties. Examples of such characteristics are:

1. environmental conditions i.e. habitat, soil;
2. immunity from disease;
3. color of flower, leaf, fruit or stems;
4. flower;
5. productivity including ever-bearing qualities in the case of fruit;
6. storage qualities;
7. perfume; and
8. form and ease of asexual reproduction.

An inventor invents or discovers and asexually produces any new "variety" The inventor must recognize the novelty and distinctness & proceed to produce asexually the plant. For example, A discovers a peach tree in A's yard. For ten years A cared for and cultivated the tree and then B visits A & recognizes that the tree is a new & distinct variety. B gets the okay from A to take cuttings from the tree and produces several successive generations of the peach tree. If B files a patent B is the inventor because B recognized the novelty and distinctness. Excluded from protection are propagated tubers e.g. artichoke & Irish potato because part of plant that is asexually reproduced is the same part sold as food and plants found in an uncultivated state or wild state e.g. desert or tropical rain forest plants. The plant patent term is the same as for other patents, 20 years from the time the application is filed. The patent is administered by the USPTO. Only one claim is allowed.

Recent court action reduced the appeal of plant patents making a plant utility patent preferred when compared with the patent of a plant itself. The US Court of Appeals ruled that a plant patent could be infringed by a plant that merely has similar characteristics to patented plant. The decision requires the plant patent owner to prove the accused variety actually was derived asexually from plant material representing patented variety. Since there is a need to "distinctly claim" plants, inventors often claim seeds that are deposited and then use a mixture of structural and functional terms in the patent application. The current fee for filing a plant patent is $400 and $800 for a small and large entity, respectively. Plant patent protection can be controversial. Public and private relationships are often involved in the propagation of plants and the supporters i.e. farm organizations or seed trade associations that often support research at public institutions desire "free" exchange of germ plasm in return for the support. If licenses are awarded there is concern about royalty vs. royalty free licensing and exclusive vs. non-exclusive licensing. Supporters will prefer royalty free and non-exclusive in order to make sure varieties are available to the public who they represent.

SEARCHES

A search of literature and patent office records to attempt to locate prior patents and art relevant to the inventions. It helps determine the chances of obtaining a patent and provides knowledge of other relevant art. A search usually takes 3-6 weeks and costs $500-$1000. All pending patent applications are held in secrecy therefore it may not be possible to locate some pre-issue information and if the discoveries are cutting edge there may not be any relevant information.

PATENT REQUIREMENTS

A patent application must be filed in the name of the true inventor or inventors. All inventors must be named and only inventors can be named. Others cannot be named even if it might be desirable to do so. An inventor is one who aided in both conception and implementation even if only on paper. Inventorship is not the same as co-authorship. In addition to filing the application with the patent office an oath or declaration of inventorship is filed along with a filing fee.

In the United States two approaches are possible for the protection of an invention in the face of a statutory bar such as the on-sale bar or the publication bar: filing a patent application or filing a provisional patent application.

No U.S. patent will be granted on an application if the invention was disclosed in a printed publication anywhere in the world more than a year before the filing of the application. Furthermore, no U.S. patent will be granted on an application if the invention was sold or offered for sale in the U.S. more than a year before the filing of the application.

If interest exists for protection in countries other than the U.S. remember the patent application should be filed prior to any public disclosure of the invention.

The US Patent Office publishes a good brochure about patents entitled General Information Concerning Patents and information is available at the U.S. Patent Office web site. In all cases, it is advantageous to file a patent application sooner rather than later.

There are three requirements that must be met to obtain a patent: 1) must be patentable subject matter (i.e. it must be a new and useful process, machine, manufacture, or composition of matter, or any new and useful improvement thereof); 2) must be novel i.e. not have been previously developed by another inventor; and 3) even if invention is novel in the sense that it has not been done exactly before, it must further be non-obvious to one having ordinary skill in the applicable art in view of what the technology has taught in the past.

INVENTIONS THAT CAN BE PATENTED

The question "What is patentable?" is a complicated one. In order to be patentable, an invention must pass four tests:

1. the invention must fall into one of the five "statutory classes" of things that are patentable: processes, machines, manufactures (that is, objects made by humans or machines), compositions of matter, and new uses of any of the above;
2. the invention must be "useful". One aspect of the "utility" test is that the invention cannot be a mere theoretical phenomenon;
3. the invention must be "novel", that is, it must be something that no one did before; and
4. the invention must be "unobvious" to "a person having ordinary skill in the art to which said subject matter pertains". This requirement is the one on which many patentability disputes hinge.

DISCOVERIES THAT CANNOT BE PATENTED

Nebulous concepts, ideas, or statements of intended results, without teaching how to apply the ideas or accomplish the results, are eligible for patent protection. Laws of nature (e.g. gravity), as opposed to applications of such laws; mathematical algorithms; general methods of doing business, and mental processes are also not subject to patent shelter.

NOVELTY REQUIREMENTS

Once patentable subject matter is found the invention is tested for novelty under a countries patent law and is entitled to a patent unless: 1) the invention was known or used by others in this country, or patented or described in a printed publication in this or any foreign country before the invention thereof by the applicant for patent, or 2) the invention was patented or described in a printed publication in this or a foreign country or in public use or on sale in this country, more than one year prior to the date of the application for patent in the U.S., or 3) the applicant did not invent the subject matter sought to be patented.

In the U.S. an inventor has a one-year grace period to file a patent application after the invention is considered to have become publicly known in various ways. The one-year period commences when the invention is put into public use, or is put into commercial use or is sold or offered for sale. Any patent or printed publication in existence anywhere in the world more than one year before the filing date of an application will bar a patent. A public use, a sale, or an offer for sale by the inventor or anyone else in the U.S. more than one year before applying for a patent will also bar a patent.

"OBVIOUS" AND "UNOBVIOUS" DEFINITION

There is much misunderstanding over what "unobvious" means in the context of U.S. patent law. The level of unobvious required to render an invention patentable is a function of the particular art area containing the invention. An experienced patent attorney or agent will often be able to give some indication of the likelihood of a particular invention being held obvious or unobvious. In some cases the unobvious part of an invention (the part that renders the invention patentable) is simply identifying the problem, even if the solution is obvious once the problem has been identified.

Sufficiently non-obvious means the invention would not readily have occurred to a person having ordinary skill in the art to which the invention pertains. For example, if right hand threaded bolts already exist in the market, in most cases marketing left hand threaded bolts would be obvious adaptation of the known prior art or if antibody labeled with alkaline phosphatase is known and horseradish peroxidase is known, then it is likely antibody labeled with horseradish peroxidase would be an obvious adaptation of the known prior art.

The test for obviousness of an invention under the patent law is: 1) the scope and content of the prior art are to be determined; 2) differences between the prior art and the claims in issue are to be ascertained; and 3) the level of ordinary skill in the pertinent art resolved. Such secondary considerations as commercial success, long felt but unsolved needs, failure of others etc. might be utilized to enlighten circumstances surrounding the origin of subject matter to be patented.

Determination of unobvious is an extremely complex factual and legal question and inventions may seem obvious when viewed in hindsight. If uncertainty exists after your assessment patent counsel may have good suggestions and/or solutions.

ALGORITHMS OR COMPUTER SOFTWARE

If a novel and unobvious algorithm or piece of computer software has been created, and patent protection is sought, the next step should be to consult one or more patent attorneys or patent agents who are experienced in securing patents on inventions involving algorithms or software. In the U.S. the mere presence of software in an invention does not automatically render it unpatentable. It is commonplace for inventors to obtain patents in inventions composed largely or nearly entirely of software.

Inventors have been getting strong patent protection for software-intensive inventions for decades, essentially by being thoughtful about the wording and claim-drafting style of the patent applications and as long as the claims of the patent do not attempt to monopolize a mathematical algorithm or a law of nature.

To test the patentability of software inventions consider the following two-step process.

1. Does the software involve a mathematical algorithm? If not, the invention comprises patentable subject matter? and
2. If the software does involve a mathematical algorithm, is the algorithm "preempted"? That is does each claim as a whole, including all of its step or apparatus elements, merely recite a mathematical algorithm or method of calculation? If so, the claim does not recite statutory subject matter. (That is if a mathematical algorithm is merely presented and solved by the

claimed invention and is not applied on any manner to physical elements or process steps recited in the claim, the invention is not patentable.) For example, if the end product of a claimed invention is a pure number, the inventions are not patentable or a program, which only converts binary coded decimal numerals into pure binary numerals, is not patentable.

Delete the mathematical algorithm in issue from the claim and if the remainder of the claim language covers patentable subject matter, then the claim with the algorithm represents patentable subject matter.

An example of a nonpatentable software claim; a method of displaying data in a field comprising the steps of calculating the difference between the local value of the data at a data point in the field and the average value of the data in a region of the field which surrounds said point for each point in said field, and displaying the value of said difference as a signed gray scale at a point in a picture which corresponds to said data point.

An example of a patentable software claim would be if the method of the claim above; wherein said data is X-ray attenuation data produced in a two-dimensional field by a computed tomography scanner.

TIME LIMITS

Before making plans for the timing of the filing of a patent application, any inventor should seek advice of competent Patent Counsel. The time periods described here represent only a few of the factors that will influence how quickly a patent application should be filed.

Under U.S. patent law, a patent will not be granted to an applicant unless the application is filed less than one year from the date that the invention was sold or offered for sale within the United States.

Yet another condition imposed under U.S. patent law is that the patent will be denied unless the application is filed within one year of the date the invention was described in a printed publication anywhere in the world.

These requirements are cumulative in the sense that either of those two events, occurring more than a year ago, will be a bar to patentability. Thus, if the invention has been described in a printed publication anywhere in the world, or if the invention has been sold or offered for sale in the United States, then it is prudent to pay close attention to the dates on which those events occurred, and to make sure to consult with competent counsel long before the expiration of the one year grace period.

Numerous other factors influence the timing of the filing of a U.S. patent application and one of the most important is a business decision related to stage of development and market entry. There is always the possibility that someone else has filed or will soon be filing a patent application on the same subject matter. The sooner you file, the more likely it is that you will prevail against someone who has filed or is about to file.

If there is interest in obtaining patent protection in countries outside the United States, then it is imperative to seek advice of competent counsel in advance of any public disclosure, offer for sale or sale of the invention. In many countries outside the U.S., public disclosure of the invention at any time prior to the patent application may bar the grant of the patent. Therefore it may be prudent to get a patent application on file prior to public disclosure, offer for sale or sale.

Several options exist for securing worldwide patent protection. The most common is what is usually termed as a PCT patent application. Others are filing via the European Patent Office (EPO), or Paris Union convention (PC). Each process has its advantages and disadvantages depending on the type of invention, needs, strategies or intentions of the inventor or company involved. Patent application features are presented in table five and figures one through six.

Table five. Features of a PCT patent application.

- file in native language
- file in country of which inventor is resident or citizen
- called international patent application
- fee dependent on length of application and number of countries
- no design or trademark coverage
- designate Canada, PCT countries, EPO countries, Australia, Japan, etc.

Examples and comparison of U.S. and non-U.S. patent protection strategies and tactics are presented in figures one through six.

Figure one. Comparison of PCT* and PC**.

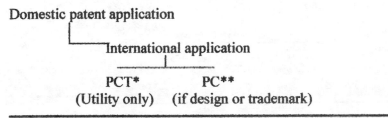

Domestic patent application

International application

PCT*   PC**
(Utility only)   (if design or trademark)

* PCT – Patent Cooperation Treaty ** PC- Paris Union Convention (100 Years old) Allows patent applicants in member countries to receive benefit of filing date of 1st filing in a member country if foreign application is filed within 1 year of filing in member country. No search information is provided and allows design and trademark applications.

Figure two. Impact of GATT on divisional patent applications.

(Application matures from a family or line of earlier applications, as has often been the case in U.S. practice with an almost routine filing of continuation applications)

File A+B	Restriction/	Appeal	Issues		Expires
June 7, 1990	Elect A		June 9, 1995		June 9, 2012
Old law		File Div B	Issues	Expires	
		June 7, 1995	Jan 1, 1999	Jan 1, 2016	
New law		File Div B	Issues	Expires	
		June 8, 1995	Jan 1, 1999	June 7, 2010	

Figure three. PCT timeline.

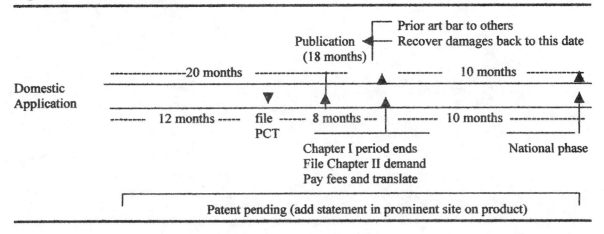

Prior art bar to others
Recover damages back to this date

Publication
(18 months)

Domestic
Application

----------20 months---------- ---------- 10 months ----------

--------- 12 months ----- file ------ 8 months --- --------- 10 months --------------
PCT

Chapter I period ends   National phase
File Chapter II demand
Pay fees and translate

Patent pending (add statement in prominent site on product)

Figure four. Key features of the general agreement on tariffs and trade (GATT).

20 year patent term

  <u>Applications filed before June 8, 1995</u> – longer of 20 years from filing or 17 years from issue.

  <u>Applications filed after June 8, 1995</u> - 20 years from filing

- Eliminates "submarine" patents
- Changes continuation-in-part practice
- Shortens life of many patents

<u>Existing patents in force on or after June 8, 1995</u> – term will be adjusted to the longer of 17 years from issuance or 20 years from the earliest effective filing date. If prosecution was less than 3 years the patent will automatically receive a patent term extension.

Old law

Filed	Issued	Expires
June 7, 1995	Jan 1, 1999	Jan 1, 2016
		17 years from issue

Effective term = 17 years

New law

Filed	Issued	Expires
June 8, 1995	Jan 1, 1999	June 8, 2015
		20 years from filing

Effective term = 16.5 years

Figure five. EPO patent process*.

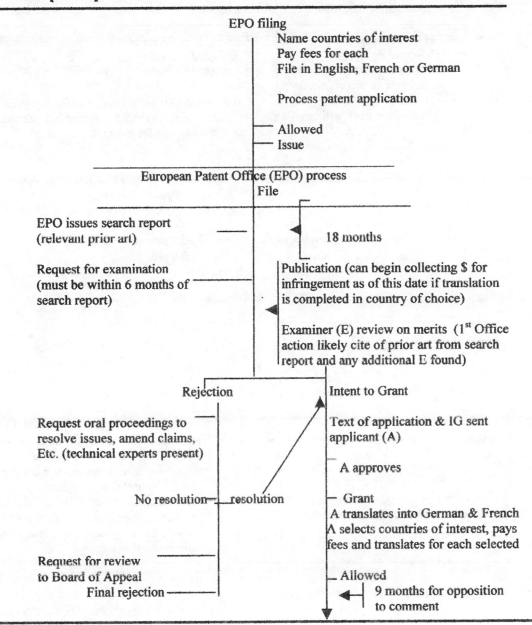

*EPO established in 1978 is not part of Euopean Union; members of one may not be members of the other.

Figure six. U.S. patent application process.

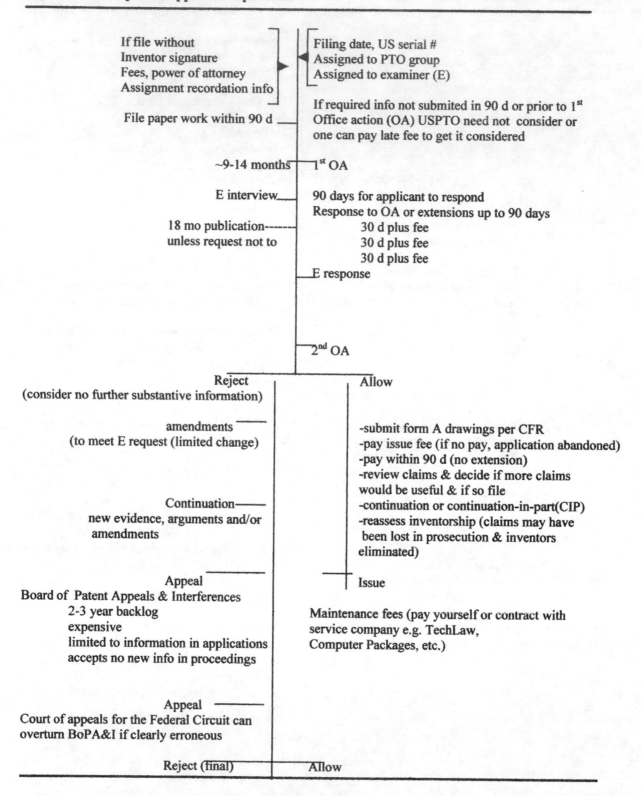

If file without
Inventor signature
Fees, power of attorney
Assignment recordation info

Filing date, US serial #
Assigned to PTO group
Assigned to examiner (E)

File paper work within 90 d

If required info not submited in 90 d or prior to 1st
Office action (OA) USPTO need not consider or
one can pay late fee to get it considered

~9-14 months — 1st OA

E interview — 90 days for applicant to respond
Response to OA or extensions up to 90 days

18 mo publication------
unless request not to

     30 d plus fee
     30 d plus fee
     30 d plus fee

E response

2nd OA

Reject | Allow
(consider no further substantive information)

amendments ——
(to meet E request (limited change))

-submit form A drawings per CFR
-pay issue fee (if no pay, application abandoned)
-pay within 90 d (no extension)
-review claims & decide if more claims
would be useful & if so file
-continuation or continuation-in-part(CIP)
-reassess inventorship (claims may have
been lost in prosecution & inventors
eliminated)

Continuation——
new evidence, arguments and/or
amendments

Appeal —— | Issue
Board of Patent Appeals & Interferences
    2-3 year backlog
    expensive
    limited to information in applications
    accepts no new info in proceedings

Maintenance fees (pay yourself or contract with
service company e.g. TechLaw,
Computer Packages, etc.)

Appeal ——
Court of appeals for the Federal Circuit can
overturn BoPA&I if clearly erroneous

Reject (final) | Allow

PROSECUTION

The first substantive response from the patent office takes 12-18 months from the filing date. Usually few if any claims are allowed by an examiner in the first office action. Time from filing to issue is typically 2-3 years, 3-5 years for biotechnology and software, if no major problems are encountered.

While a patent is pending it is held confidential by the patent office. After a patent, issues a patent notice should be applied to all patented articles whether made by the patent owner or a licensee. Notation can be "patent" or "pat" along with the patent number. Prior to issue and after filing for a patent, articles can be marked as "patent pending" or "patent applied for" even if a provisional patent application has been filed.

ECONOMICS

The freedom of contracting partners to determine patent ownership as they fit also makes it incumbent upon them to determine in advance which parties are to pay for such patent rights. Acquisition of existing third-party patents, prosecution of patent applications for new inventions, and payment of maintenance fees on a large portfolio of issued patents may all entail significant expenditures, and it is generally considered prudent to match the relative contribution of each party toward these costs with the relative benefit to be obtained by each party.

The filing fee for a small business is half that for a large business (more than 500 employees) and varies with the number and type of claims. Currently preparation and filing fees for design and plant patents can range from $5,000 - $7,000 and for a utility patent with numerous claims $8,000 - $13,000. Additional patent expenses must also be taken into account as plans for patent protection are established. Examples of activities and fees are:

- patent search fees; $175-$300;
- patent search analysis and opinion; $650 - $1,200;
- professional drawings by expert draftsperson; $75-$250 per page;
- patent prosecution: 90% of all patents receive one office action one to ? office actions = Counsel time, $150-$250/hour; and
- once a U.S. patent is allowed an issue fee must be paid and maintenance fees are due to keep the patent in force. Maintenance payments are required every 4 years. Fees are to be submitted to the PTO 3.5, 7.5 and 11.5 years after a patent issues. The current fee for small/large entities is 3.5 = $440/$880; 7.5=$1010/$2020; 11.5=$1550/$3100. Fees for international filings vary with country and can be more expensive than in the U.S. It is necessary to examine these charges when establishing protection strategy and related budgets. See Exhibit A.

In summary, patent protection charges will be dependent upon the type and complexity of the patent and fees will increase over time. Although anyone can file a patent application it is recommended quality Patent Counsel be involved since the issued patent may become a significant asset for the business venture. United States patent information is available from the Patent and Trademark Office at http://www.uspto.gov. For references to international web sites and additional sources of information see Addendum I, "Glossary of Terms and Addendum II, "References and Resources".

PATENT INFRINGEMENT

A patent is a property right that permits patentee to exclude others form infringing the inventions claimed in the patent.

Direct

The most common form of infringement is direct infringement which occurs when someone not permitted by the patentee makes, sells offers for sell or uses the patented invention in the U.S. or imports a patented article into the U.S. The law of infringement applies to patents that claim products (such as machines or compositions of matter) and to patented processes (such as those for use of a product and those for making a product). A patent claiming a process for making a product is also directly infringed if that patent process is practiced outside the U.S. and the product is then imported into the U.S. The importation is not an infringement if, before importation, the product has been materially changed by later processes or had become a trivial and nonessential component of another product.

Direct Infringement Proof

To prove direct infringement, an accused product or process must have every one of the features of an invention recited in at least one claim of a patent currently in force. Examine closely the wording of the claims. It the accused product or process is exactly as recited in one or more claims, then there is direct infringement.

A particular patent claim might recite features A+B+C+D, referred to as the *limitations* of that claim. The claim for a bicycle might list a frame, a supporting wheel at each end of that frame, a set of pedals operabley connected to one wheel, and a handlebar operabley connected to the other wheel. If a competing bicycle has those features and no additional features, then that competing bicycle is a direct infringement of that patent.

But what if the bicycle has features A+B+C+D+E, with the additional feature being a seat? Would that bicycle still infringe the patent?

Maybe. It depends… patent claims are written in three parts. The *preamble* states generally, in a single word or phrase, what the invention is – for example, "a bicycle", "a nucleotide sequence," or "a method for" doing something. The *body* of the patent lists the limitations of the claimed invention, A+B+C+D and so on. Between the preamble and the body of the claim is *connector*.

The connector is typically a single word or short phrase. The most restrictive connector is *consisting of*. When it is used direct infringement will be found only when an accused product or process has all of the limitations of the claims and no more. So a claim for a bicycle consisting of limitations A+B+C+D will not be infringed by a bicycle with features A+B+C+D+E.

The least restrictive connector is *comprising*. It provides that an accused product or process will infringe a claim if it contains each of the features of the claimed invention, even if it also contains additional features. Therefore, a bicycle containing features A+B+C+D+E (or even A+B+C+D+E+F+G+H) will infringe a claim calling for a bicycle comprising limitations A+B+C+D. Alternative connectors such as *including, containing,* and *characterized by* have been interpreted to synonymous with comprising. Others such as *composed of, having,* and *being* are not precisely defined and may be construed as being synonymous with either "comprising" or "consisting of", depending on the wording of the specification.

A third commonly used connector is *"consisting essentially of"*. That phrase has been defined an intermediate between *"consisting of"* and *"comprising"*. In a patent claim, *"consisting essentially of"* means that a product or process will infringe the claim if it contains all the features recited in the claim and any additional features that do not materially affect the basic and novel characteristics of the claimed invention.

So, even thought a bicycle has the additional feature of a seat, it will still infringe a claim for a bicycle that does not recite a seat if the connector is *"consisting essentially of"* because the bicycle having the additional feature is still a bicycle and has that same basic and novel characteristic of the bicycle called for in the patent claim.

Indirect

One way to indirectly infringe a patent is to induce someone else to infringe the patent. For example, imagine if someone that claims the use of a nonpatented therapeutic agent, such as aspirin, for treatment of a specific condition, such as baldness, by applying an aspirin solution to the scalp. The aspirin itself is not patented; it is the particular method for using it that is covered by the patent.

In such a case, the end user who applies aspirin to the scalp hoping to cure baldness actually infringe the patent directly. However, it is usually not desirable to pursue end users for patent infringement. Typically, the recovery of damages available from an end user does not justify the expense involved in patent infringement litigation. It would be more desirable to sue the company that sold the aspirin and induced the end user by advertisements or by instructions on the package to directly infringe the patent. Therefore, the law provides that the company can be sued for inducing the end user to use the aspirin as a therapy for baldness.

A second type of indirect infringement is contributory infringement. A person contributes to the infringement of a patent when h/she provides an article that is a component of patented product and has no other use. It is also an infringement to export from the U.S. the components of a patented invention to be assembled outside the U.S.

Direct infringement is a necessary component of indirect infringement. In the previous example of using aspirin to treat baldness, if a drug company is to be liable for indirect infringement by inducement, and end user must directly infringe the patent by applying that aspirin to the scalp. It is not necessary to sue the end user to enforce the patent against the indirect infringer. But without a direct infringement, there can be no indirect infringement.

Another way to infringe a patent is to apply for federal regulatory approval for a drug or a biological product that is covered by a patent.

READING A PATENT

An issued patent contains valuable information for the party collecting competitive intelligence. The following remarks pertain to patent number 5,478,814 which is presented in Exhibit B. There are four parts usually associated with a patent: 1) the cover page, 2) a description describing how to make and use the invention, 3) the claims detailing what is protected and 4) drawings if needed to understand the invention.

COVER PAGE (PART I)

The cover page contains information important to the patentee, potential licensees, competitors, attorneys and judges. The number inside brackets is an international notation that appears on all patents e.g. [22] is the filing date. All U.S. patents have a title, the name of the first inventor and a patent number.

Information that may be absent if not pertinent to a particular patent is the assignee, any foreign application priority data and the name of patent counsel who filed the application.

At the top of the page in the upper left corner is the United States Patent and numerical designation [19] and the last name of first named inventor. In the upper right corner is bar code which provides information related to the patent number.

The patent number [11] is unique for the different types of patents. The following are examples of the different numbers for the specific type of patent:

1. Utility patent = seven digits (5,146,634);
2. Design patent = six digits preceded by D or DES (D123,456);
3. Reissue patent (correcting an older patent) = five digits preceded by RE. (RE12,345);
4. Reexamination certificate (patent reexamined because of newly discovered prior art) = seven digits preceded by B1 (or B2 or B3 depending on whether it is first, second or third reexamination (B1 5,123,456);
5. Plant = 4 digits preceded by PP (PP8,901);
6. Defensive publication = six digits preceded by T (T109,201);
7. Statutory Invention Registration (SIR) or H Document = four digits preceded by H (H1,523) (US patent applicant may give up on patent and instead pay USPTO to publish it as a SIR; keeps others from getting a patent on same invention); and

8. Research Disclosure (RD) document (Anyone may pay a British company, Kenneth Mason Publications Ltd., to publish an invention disclosure. Some are anonymous, while others are attributed. Like a SIR, a RD keeps others from getting a patent on the same invention.)

Also at the top of the page is the Date of Patent [45] or the issue date (date when patent is in force) Prior to June 8 1995 all patents expired 17 years from issue date if maintenance fees paid but now filing date of application must be known to determined when patent expires.

A notice appears occasionally. An asterisk prior to date of patent indicates patent's term has been shortened so it will expire on a date that cannot be determined solely on information found there. In the example, the patent will expire no later than the date on which patent number 4,954,084 expires.

Below the black line provides further information. To have the assignee listed on a cover page assignment from inventor to assignee must be recorded with the USPTO. If no recorded assignment the notation is absent from the cover page. The application Number [21] is the serial number assigned by the USPTO to application that became the issued patent. An application number is an eight digit number beginning with 08 or 09 followed by a slash and six numbers e.g. 08/034,151. On the patent cover page two digits to left of slash are omitted and if the first digits to right of slash are zero they are also omitted. In the example, application number 08/034,151 appears as 34,151.

The date the application was filed with the USPTO appears in field [22] It is used to determine expiration and priority dates unless it is related to a previously filed parent application. Generally for application filed after June 8, 1995 patents expire 17 years from issue date or 20 years from filing date which ever is later. If the patent in the example had no parent application it would expire on March 22, 2013.

In addition data related to the application date consist of:

1. Patents parent applications and their outcomes [63]. In the example, the patent has a first parent application filed July 8, 1987 that issued as U.S. Patent Number 4,945,084. A second parent application was filed based on the first parent application on February 27, 1990 and issues as U.S. Patent Number 5,196,405.

2. The present patent was filed as a continuation application of the second parent application on March 22 1993 and issued as U.S. Patent Number 5,478,814. In the example, the priority date is July 8, 1987.

3. Any publication dated less than one year before July 8, 1987 cannot be used to invalidate the patent. The patent will expire December 26, 2012, seventeen years from issue date of December 26 1995 because that is later than July 8, 2007, which is 20 years from the filing date of earliest parent application July 8, 1987.

4. The expiration date issue in the example is complicated because a terminal disclaimer was filed as indicated by the asterisk next to the date of the patent [45]. In the example the patent term was disclaimed beyond the expiration of U.S. Patent Number 4,945,084. Examination of that patent reveals that it expires on July 31, 2007; so expiration of the patent in this example is July 31, 2007.

International Patents

In some cases, an international patent application is filed in accordance with the PCT as an alternative to filing directly with the USPTO. The international patent application eventually enters a national phase at the USPTO. In such a case the eventual patent's cover page does not list a U.S. filing date and related U.S. application data. Instead the following data concerning PCT application will be provided:

1. [22] PCT application filing date;
2. [86] its application number;

3. date it entered USPTO to become prior art reference that could apply against other U.S. patent applications;
4. publication date of PCT application; and
5. [87] PCT publication number.

If the application is filed in a foreign country before the filing date in USPTO or PCT, the patent's cover page will list [30] foreign application priority data showing the date filed, the country in which it was filed and the application number in that country.

The next three items on the cover page provide: the international classification [51], U.S. classification [52] and the field of search [58]. These are related to the subject matter of the invention and fields that the patent examiner searched in examining the patent application. Information regarding that classification system can be found in the Manual of Classification, a publication of the USPTO. Classification information is useful in searching for relevant prior art, such as when trying to invalidate a patent or drafting a patent application is a similar field.

References cited [56] is a list of publications considered by an examiner in deciding whether to grant a patent. The list is important because of legal presumption that invention patentability is based on absence of interference with what is disclosed in them. The first references cited are U.S. patents for which numbers, issue dates, inventors and U.S. classifications are given. Next are the foreign patent documents which may include patents and published patent applications and finally other publications e.g. scientific articles are listed.

Patent examiners are listed by name followed by the patent attorney and/or law firm that prosecuted the application.

The abstract [57] is a short description of the invention and facilitates searches of a patent's subject matter. Following the abstract is line which indicates the number of claims in a patent and how many drawing sheets it contains.

The final item on cover page is a figure representing the patent invention. In the example there is no figure since no drawings were included.

The issued patent is also published in the Official Gazette, a weekly government publication that provides information concerning patents and the USPTO. The Manual of Classification is available at www1.uspto.gov/web/offices/pac/clasdefs/index.html.

DESCRIPTION AND CLAIMS (PART II)

The description includes a specification and drawings that disclose how invention is made and used. Claims are based on the description and set out legal limits of what is protected by the patent. Sometimes it is prudent to draw a picture. A patent is complex with several parts including drawings, specification and series of claims after the specification. The specification describes the invention and how to make and use it. Drawings are included, if necessary, to enhance understanding the invention.

The description is the focal point. It cannot be amended to include new matter after an application is filed. Claims can be amended after filing but only to extent that they claim what is shown in drawings or described in the specification. It is an important section when searching for prior art. If the invention is described in published matter "new" invention is not new; hence, specifications and drawings can be more than or as important as claims.

Claims analysis permits a reviewer to determine the scope of patent protection. It is important for deciding whether a product infringes the patent in question. Claims are useful for ascertaining how to "design around" a patent to avoid infringement.

Drawings can be the basis for claims even if the claim(s) is/are not described in a specification. As mentioned before, drawings are included in a patent for clear understanding of the invention.

A specification describes invention, how it is made and how it is used. It discusses prior art and how the invention overcomes problems leading to its development - parts are (all parts may or may not be included):

- title (same as that on title page);
- statement of patent history (first line discloses existence of prior application on which the present patent is based and fate of the application (abandoned, pending or issued);
- statement that U.S. government has rights in invention (occurs when invention resulted from federally sponsored research);
- field of invention (description of industry or field to which invention pertains (1-2 sentences);
- background of invention (description of problems that remained unsolved by prior art which are addressed by this patented invention);
- review of literature and patents related to the invention;
- summary of invention (Brief overview of how this invention overcomes disadvantages of prior art;
- brief description of drawings (One sentence description of drawings; and
- detailed description of invention (this is the longest section, each invention feature is described along with how to practice it (make and use), examples are presented, it may contain prophetic examples (those conceived as part of invention but not yet performed) and the last paragraph states the invention is not limited to what is described but also includes undescribed equivalents of invention recited in the claims.

CLAIMS - SETTING BOUNDARIES (PART III)

Claims define an invention and can be the most important guidance for competitors who want to steer clear of a patent since they set scope and bounds for court assessment of infringement. Claims follow a set format with unusual grammatical style which is sometimes difficult to understand for the layperson.

The preamble is the first part of a claim that states what invention relates to such as a nucleic acid, a pharmaceutical composition, a method for treating arthritis, a device for accelerating wound healing.

Wording generally does not affect the scope of protection but connecting phrases such as "comprising, consisting of and consisting essentially of" have a tremendous impact on the breadth of a patent.

"Comprising" means an article, device or process containing all features of claimed device as described in a claim will infringe the patent even if the patent infringer contains additional features: e.g. if claim recited a table comprising four legs and a top, then a table with five legs, or with four legs, a top, and a shelf below the tabletop would infringe that patent.

"Consisting of" in claim means patent will be infringed by anything that contains all features of the claimed invention but will not be infringed if it contains additional features; e.g. table with five legs or with a shelf below the tabletop would not infringe a table consisting of four legs and a table top because term "consisting of" significantly narrows a patent claim. Patent attorneys generally avoid it unless they deem it necessary for avoiding a very close prior art.

"Consisting essentially of" is seen occasionally in biological and chemical fields and means a patent claim will be infringed if a potential infringer patent contains all features of claimed invention along with additional features that do not substantially change the nature of the patent claim; e.g. presence of an additive that enhances effect of patented composition such as increasing shelf life or potency would infringe the patent; or addition of an ingredient that changes the nature of the composition; such as something that makes it unsuitable for use as acne medication but makes it suitable for increasing cardiac output would not infringe the patent.

Body of a claim follows the connecting phrase. Elements of the invention are described and how they are related. For example it may be a series of mechanical parts and a description of how they are put together or it may be a series of process steps to make or use something.

To infringe a patent another device, composition of matter or process must contain all listed elements or their equivalents.

Claims can be independent or dependent. An independent claim can exist alone; such as "A nucleotide sequence, comprising---"

A dependent claim refers to previous claims, which may be independent claims themselves or other dependent claims. The dependent claim contains all features of the claim or claims on which they depend and one of more additional features. For example, "The nucleotide sequence of claim 1, which further comprises----"

When a question of infringement or not arises ascertain whether potentially infringing articles or processes are literally included and recited in independent claims. Usually if independent claims are not infringed, assuming they contain connector "comprising", dependent claims will not be infringed. When claims examination fails to indicate literal infringement, it is usually necessary to review the prosecution history of the patent as it was examined in Patent Office ("file wrapper") – allows reviewer to determine whether infringement exists based on equivalents of the claims elements. The "file wrapper" will also include the provisional patent application if one was filed.

TRADE AND SERVICE MARKS

A trademark is a work, phrase, symbol, or sound that serves to distinguish the goods of one entity from the goods of others. A service mark is a word phrase, symbol, or sound that serves to distinguish specific services of one entity from the services of others. A trade name differs from a trademark or service mark. A trade name is a company name or a corporate name used to identify and distinguish a business organization from other companies. This distinction is important because federal registration is valuable for trademarks and service marks, but not for trade names. A trade name may also be a trademark or a service mark) e.g., Xerox Corporation sells XEROX – brand products and provides equipment repair services under the name XEROX.

TRADEMARK OWNERSHIP

The nature of trademarks is quite different from that of patents and copyrights, which are means for protecting the "work product" of a company. Trademarks, instead, protect the goodwill that is generated by the activities of the company, which in turn adds value to the company's work product. Trademarks provide this protection by preventing others from using a similar trademark in a way that would give rise to consumer confusion regarding the source of products or services produced by the company.

While trademarks apply only to goods, service marks are quite similar and protect the goodwill associated with the services provided by a company. For simplicity, the term "trademark" is used herein to denote both trademarks and service marks.

General Trademark Ownership Principles

Some trademark protection arises immediately upon use of a word, symbol or other identifier in a trademark sense, i.e., as an indicator of the source of origin of goods. Recent changes to the law have made it possible to reserve trademark rights when use of a mark is only anticipated, but the general rule is that a mark must be used for "ownership" of the mark to ensue and to be maintained.

Availability of a Mark

In certain circumstances, two or more parties may make simultaneous use of the same trademark. However, in general terms, only one entity can use a trademark in a particular area of commerce, as the very purpose of a trademark is to identify the source of origin of goods. Thus, it is important for any new enterprise to explore the availability of marks that it may wish to use. Trademark searches are available at a variety of levels, and provide commensurate amounts of information. Even though only United States trademark rights may currently be desired, it often is helpful to perform a worldwide availability search to determine the likelihood of any future conflict with senior international users of the mark.

Transfer of Ownership

Unlike patents and copyrights, there are some very important limitations on the transfer of trademark rights. Primary in importance is the requirement that a trademark not be transferred without an associated transfer of the goodwill that the trademark protects. Thus, a trademark owner cannot simply sell its trademark to another bereft of some indication that the company's goodwill associated with that mark will be transferred along with the mark. Assignment of a mark apart from its associated goodwill is known as "assignment in gross" and results in evisceration of rights associated with the mark.

The purpose underlying the prohibition against assignments in gross has been described as being to ensure that the consumer is getting more or less the same thing in buying the product or service from its new maker. (Noting that such products may of course change over time). As with patents and copyrights, transfers of federally registered marks should be recorded in order to be effective against subsequent purchasers not having notice of the assignment.

Retention of Control

Closely related to the requirement of transferring goodwill along with a trademark is the need for a licensor or other contributor of a trademark to retain some quality control over the products or services that are to bear the mark. The reason for this requirement is that a mark placed in the hands of one who has no concern for the quality of goods associated with the mark ceases to convey good will.

Concerns About Marks Becoming Generic

Trademark owners have a special responsibility to ensure that their marks remain distinctive of the goods or services they provide. If a company uses the mark improperly or allows others to do so, the mark may erode in value to the point where it no longer identifies the source of goods, but instead simply identifies a generic type of goods. Once this happens, trademark rights evaporate. Thus, it is critically important for a trademark owner to be ever vigilant that the mark is always used properly, i.e., as an adjective to characterize the generic class of product, rather than as a noun or verb that would suggest that the mark is itself generic.

MARK PRINCIPLES

The first principle for creating a strong trademark is to select a mark that is "distinctive." The more distinctive it is, the more successful a trademark will be in performing its function of distinguishing your company's products or services from the competition. Conversely, a mark that is little more than a descriptive term commonly used in the relevant industry will not lead to clear product distinction and hence will require more resource investment to generate market recognition and can also be difficult to protect against use by others.

Unfortunately, the more a mark describes the product or characteristics of the product, the less protectable it will be legally. The long-term effect of adopting a descriptive name is that competition jumps on the bandwagon and adopts very similar names for competing products, a phenomenon against which the original user has little or no legal recourse given its initial decision to use a legally weak mark.

Therefore, in selecting a mark, attention should be given to what is known as the "spectrum of distinctiveness." The four categories of distinctiveness in which a trademark might fall are arrayed along a spectrum from nondistinctive, legally unprotectable trademarks, to highly distinctive, protectable marks. The four categories are inherently distinctive, generic, descriptive, suggestive, and arbitrary or fanciful.

Inherently Distinctive Marks

Arbitrary or fanciful marks are inherently distinctive and considered to be the strongest marks in terms of legal protectability. An arbitrary mark is a word or term that is in common linguistic use but not in connection with the particular goods at issue. APPLE for computers, KODAK for film, LEXIS for legal databases, SHELL of oil, ZENITH for electronics and IVORY for soap are good examples of such marks. Fanciful marks are coined terms, such as XEROX, or archaic terms that are not particularly well known.

Suggestive Marks

A suggestive mark is one that requires the consumer to exercise imagination in order to determine the nature of the goods. A suggestive mark does not immediately describe the goods or their features, but may suggest or allude to the same. Examples of marks found to be suggestive include RED LOBSTER for restaurant services, CHICKEN OF THE SEA for canned tuna fish, QUEST for hardware and software and HARDCARD for personal computer hard disk drive expansion kits. Not surprisingly, the line between descriptive and suggestive marks is not a bright one: Courts sometimes have difficulty determining if a mark is descriptive and therefore not protectable, or actually suggestive and protectable.

Descriptive Marks

Descriptive marks are considered to be non-distinctive because these marks directly describe a product, its characteristics, elements or qualities. The law presumes that such descriptive phrases must be reserved for use by all competitors to describe their goods to the public. These marks identify one or more ingredients, characteristics, or qualities of the goods or services. Geographically descriptive terms and personal names tend to fall in this category; e.g. SAN DIEGO BAKERY. Marks that are merely descriptive are generally not protectable, since they simply describe some aspect of the goods or services, and do not serve to distinguish them from the goods or services of others.

It is possible to transform a descriptive mark into a truly distinguishing trademark. By sufficient advertising, promotion, and continuous exposure over time, a fair portion of the public may come to assoicat3e a mark solely with products or services from one source. Such a descriptive mark is said to have a "secondary meaning", that is, as a designation of r a particular product or service. Such a mark gives the owner the same rights that an inherently distinctive or suggestive mark gives. An example would be MRS. FIELDS' COOKIES.

Generic Marks

A generic mark is a misnomer and is incapable of functioning as a mark. Since the name of the actual goods and the generic term are the same, a generic term can never distinguish the products of one company from those of any other company providing the same goods. Examples are: "Service Station" for gasoline stations; "Directory Assistance" for telephone directory services; "Yellow Pages " for yellow-colored telephone directory books.

Marks as Verbs, Plurals or Possessives

Do not use a mark as a verb, plural or possessive. Using a mark as a verb; e.g. Xerox that book, may lead to widespread consumer use of a mark as a verb and may put the mark into the public domain as a generic term. Avoid using a mark in possessive sense e.g. "BAND-AID's sticking power is great". This tends to make the public associate the mark with the product and not as an indication of the origin of the product and can lead to public use of the mark for all similar products and services.

Distinguish Marks From Goods or Services

A mark must be properly used in conjunction with other words so there is no reason for the public to assume that the trademark is the generic name of this associated product.

For example, former trademarks that have come to be generic descriptions of the associated goods are "aspirin", "nylon", "escalator" and "shredded wheat". In such cases, often the owner of a mark is too successful in its advertising and has failed to strictly monitor the use of the mark as a proper adjective. The public comes to associate the loosely used mark with all similar goods or services, ultimately causing the mark to degenerate from a brand name into a generic product name.

The owner of a mark can help avoid losing rights in a mark by having it become generic simply by following a trademark with a generic product name; e.g. VASELINE petroleum jelly; XEROX copying machines.

Trademark Availability

It is important to attempt to "clear" the mark or marks for your company's intended use. Nothing can be more frustrating and potentially financially disastrous than to launch a product only to find out that another party owns superior rights in the name of that product and is prepared to enforce those rights in court absent a name change. While this scenario is not absolutely avoidable, prior searching of the mark provides the greatest possible insurance against finding yourself in such a predicament.

In the United States, trademark rights arise as a result of use, not registration. Therefore, it is imperative that any search strategy include a review of unregistered trademarks as well as those that have been registered or may be pending for registration in the U.S. Patent and Trademark Office and/or in the various state trademark offices.

When international marketing is anticipated, search a mark for availability, at least in key markets. Conducting a full search in every foreign country would likely be cost-prohibitive, but more limited, cost-effective search strategies can be developed for major markets.

Trademark Rights Establishment

Once the decision is made to adopt a particular mark, trademark rights must be established before the company will be in a position to prevent others from using similar marks in connection with related goods. A company does not establish trademark rights simply by choosing a trademark or even by advertising the company's intent to use the trademark in the future in connection with the particular product. Likewise, use of the chosen mark as an advertising slogan will not establish trademark rights.

In most jurisdictions around the world, the notable exception of which is the U.S., trademark rights are established only by registration of the trademark with the appropriate authorities. Actual use of the mark is not required. In the U.S. and in British law countries, trademark rights arise to a greater or lesser extent upon use of a mark; however, registration remains important for attaining the best possible protection for the mark.

Trademark Reservation

It is possible, however, to reserve a trademark for future use, by filing an "intent-to-use" trademark application with the United States Patent and Trademark Office. Although the Trademark Office will not actually register the mark until the mark is used, once the registration issues, rights in the mark will date back to the date the "intent-to-use" application was filed.

Using this procedure avoids the all too common dilemma of belatedly learning at the time of product launch that another has begun to use a conflicting mark after you came up with the name but before it was actually used, and hence has superior rights in the mark and can keep you from using the mark on your product.

If one does not take advantage of the "intent-to-use" process for establishing trademark rights in the United States, one may establish rights solely on the basis of use. Once a distinctive trademark is affixed to a product and the product placed in commerce as a genuine commercial transaction, one begins to accrue rights in that trademark for those products. One need never register the trademark with state or federal authorities and as long as use of the mark was continuous one will have protectable rights it can assert against another's use of a similar mark on similar goods.

Trademark Registration

A federal trademark registration is in effect nationwide notice to all users of the registrant's claim in the mark (whether they have actual notice or not). Registration is not required. However, registration has a number of other benefits.

1. Federal registration permits: a) trademark owner to use the ® symbol with the mark; b) suit may be brought in federal court to enforce the owner's trademark rights; and c) after a registration has been in effect for 5 years, the owner is conclusively presumed to have the exclusive right to use the mark;

2. To be eligible for federal registration, a mark must be used in interstate or international commerce;

3. Registration requires completion of an application, and submittal of a drawing showing the mark and 3 samples of the mark as actually used (e.g., labels or packaging with the mark on it);

4. A properly submitted trademark application is reviewed by the Trademark Office to determine whether any of the prohibitions of the present law against registration of the mark apply. Those requirements are phrased in the trademark law as follows: "No trademark by which goods of the applicant may be distinguished from the goods of others shall be refused registration on the principal register on account of its nature unless it:
   a. consists of or comprises immoral, deceptive, or scandalous matter; or matter which may disparage or falsely suggest a connection with persons, living or dead, institutions, beliefs, or national symbols, or bring them into contempt, or disrepute;
   b. consists of or comprises the flag or coat of arms or other insignia of the U.S., or of any state or municipality, or of any foreign nation, or any simulation thereof;
   c. consists of or comprises a name, portrait, or signature identifying a particular living individual except by his written consent, or the name, signature, or portrait of a deceased President of the U.S. during the life of his widow, if any, except by the written consent of the widow;
   d. consists of or comprises a mark which so resembles a mark registered in the Patent and Trademark Office or a mark or trade name previously used in the U.S. by another and not abandoned, as to be likely, when applied to the goods of the applicant, to cause confusion, to cause mistake, or to deceive...;
   e. consists of a mark which, 1) when applied to the goods of the applicant is merely descriptive or deceptively descriptive of them, or 2) when applied to the goods of the applicant is primarily geographically descriptive or deceptively descriptive of them, or 3) is primarily merely a surname."

5. If the Trademark Office finds grounds for not registering a mark, it will reject the application. The applicant may submit arguments by way of an amendment to the original application attempting to refute the Trademark Office's opinion that a prohibition exists;

6. If the application is approved by the Trademark Office, an official notice is published that the mark is pending for registration. This notice permits members of the public to oppose registration of the mark. An opposition (or a request for extension of time to file an opposition) must be filed within 30 days after the notice is published. The opposer must submit evidence as to why the mark should not be registered. The principal grounds for opposition are that the pending mark is considered to be confusingly similar to a mark held by the opposer, or registration will in some other way cause injury to the opposer;

7. If no opposition is filed, or if an opposition is overcome, the application will mature into a registration. Registrations (and renewals of registrations) for trademarks have a term of 10 years; and

8. The registration process normally takes 8-12 months and typically costs $500-$1000.

Though registration is not mandatory in the United States, registration does offer particular benefits to the trademark owner that enhances rights established on the basis of use. The registration provides the owner an evidentiary "leg up" in infringement litigation by creating a presumption of the trademark owner's rights. The trademark owner need not go to the expense and trouble of trying to convince the court of its ownership rights in the mark, as would be necessary if the mark was unregistered. Instead, the burden falls on the defendant to try to establish that despite registration, the complaining party actually has no protectable rights in the mark. These benefits make the registration a powerful tool in convincing others not to use infringing marks.

Trademark registrations are also invaluable in enforcing rights against counterfeiters. Once a trademark registration is recorded with the U.S. Customs Service, Customs will assist the trademark owner by seizing goods entering the country bearing infringing trademarks. Likewise, the penalties, including significant monetary damages, available to a trademark owner under The Trademark Counterfeiting Act, are only available if the trademark in question is registered.

Trademark Rights In the United States

Contrary to law in most of the world, trademark rights in the United States arise as a result of use, not registration. The first user of a mark has the right to exclude subsequent users from adopting a confusingly similar mark on similar goods or services. While exceptions to this rule exist; it is by far the best to select a mark at the outset that will not infringe the rights of others. Under present law, trademark and service mark rights re acquired by actual use of a mark in conjunction with the marketing of goods or services (except for foreign applications under the Paris Convention, under which trademark rights can be created upon the filing of a foreign trademark application). A trademark must be used in association with the goods the mark represents. This can be done by applying the mark on the goods, or on the label attached to the goods, or on packaging containing the goods. Use of a trademark in advertising not accompanying the goods themselves is not trademark usage. Since services are intangible, a service mark cannot be used on services. Proper usage of a service mark includes brochures and advertising relating to the services.

Trademark Notices In the United States

Under common law and federal law, acts or omissions of a trademark owner may cause rights in the mark to be abandoned or the mark to lose its significance as an indication of origin.

A trademark is a proper adjective, and normally should be displayed with an initial capital letter, entirely in capital letters, in italics, or set off by quotation marks. As an alternative the mark can be set off by differences in color or type style from other wording so that the mark stands out for easy recognition. Marks should be prominently placed on goods or packages and should not be abbreviated or changed unless the mark is being permanently changed or a second version of the mark is being adopted; e.g. COCA-COLA and COKE.

Recommendations are that once a mark is federally registered, prominent uses of that mark should be followed by the trademark notice symbol, ®. The ® provides notice to the public that the mark is federally registered, making it somewhat easier to obtain monetary damages in an infringement action. Other forms of proper statutory marking in addition to ® are: REGISTERED IN THE U.S. PATENT AND TRADEMARK OFFICE and REG. U.S. PAT. & TM. OFF. Failure to display one to the above notices results in the owner not being awarded damages or the infringer's profits since the infringer did not have actual notice of the registration.

Unregistered marks should be followed by the superscript ™ for a trademark or ℠ for a service mark. Although not legally required, use of ™ or ℠ will provide public notice of your trademark claims and assist in establishing rights in descriptive marks.

Trademark Rights Abroad

While trademark registration is advisable in the United States, it is absolutely essential in other countries. Registration in the United States does not confer ownership rights abroad. Virtually every country has its own trademark registry and law, and virtually every country awards trademark rights to the first to file a trademark application, not the first to use a mark in that country. If one intends to use a trademark overseas without completing the relatively inexpensive registration process (approximately $1700 per mark per country) it could be disastrous.

This is particularly true in the licensing context: All too often the U.S. trademark owner who has not bothered registering finds that its former distributor has registered the mark in the territory in its own name and can prevent, or at least significantly impede, distribution of the U.S. company's goods in that country. Likewise, it may be impossible to collect royalties on existing licenses if the licensed mark is not registered and the license agreement recorded with the proper authorities.

The registration process varies from country to country and appropriate Legal Counsel should be consulted.

Trademark Notices Abroad

In most countries, trademark notices are not required. However, where such notices are required or suggested the notices rarely take the form of the ®, ™ and ˢᴹ used in this country. Instead other forms of notice are common, such as "MR" for "marca registrada" used in many Spanish-speaking countries.

Trademark Infringement

The question of what constitutes trademark infringement arises with great frequency in managing a trademark portfolio and the test for infringement varies from country to country (and even within jurisdictions), legal counsel familiar with trademark law should be consulted.

Trademark Licensing

The trademark can be a direct source of capital generation. A trademark owner need never actually use a mark itself in order to acquire protectable rights, so long as whatever use is made is through an authorized licensee. It is critical, however, that the trademark owner exercise control over the quality of the goods with which the mark is used.

Failure to exercise quality control may result in an abandonment of the licensed trademark because the trademark will be considered to have lost its significance as a source and quality identifier.

Many trademark licenses today are the result of settlement of a trademark dispute between two unrelated companies. For example, it is common for the parties to agree that one will assign its rights in the disputed trademark to the other and then take a license back so that it may continue to use the mark, but it no longer claims ownership rights in the mark. The danger in such a situation is that both parties' rights in the mark are jeopardized if the trademark owner does not exercise a modicum of control over the licensee's activities in relation to the mark. While the control exercised need not be particularly intrusive, often any such oversight is unpalatable to one or both parties. Trademark licenses should be recorded in writing, although an oral license may be enforceable. The agreement should specify the goods with which the mark may be used and any other use restrictions, the territory of such use, royalties, quality control provisions, termination provisions and the like. The licensee should be precluded from registering the mark in its own name or from taking any other action adverse to the licensor's ownership interest in the mark. Just as each country has its own trademark law, each country also imposes its own requirements and restrictions on trademark licensing. Further, licensing in European Community countries carries with it additional problems with regard to enforcement of territorial restrictions.

Many countries also require that trademark licenses be recorded with the trademark authorities to be effective against third parties and/or for the trademark owner to be in a position to collect royalty payments. Accordingly, it is prudent to have all trademark licenses either drafted or reviewed by trademark counsel prior to entering into such an agreement.

TRADE DRESS

In addition to trademark protection, federal trademark law provides relief more generally against false or misleading representations as to the source of goods or services. One important subset of this general unfair competition law is that of "trade dress" protection, protecting the visual appearance of products, product packaging, service establishments and the like. Historically, this theory of protection has been reserved for the unique appearance of product packaging.

Trade dress protection covers the overall look or appearance of the goods in question, not isolated aspects of that look. To be protectable, trade dress must be 1) nonfunctional and 2) distinctive in the same manner as a trademark must be

TRADE NAME

Trade names or company names, like trademarks, are protectable against use of confusingly similar trade names or trademarks by others. Unlike trademarks, however, the United States has no central registry for recording trade names. In order to register a trade name on the trademark registry, it must be used as a trademark, as a symbol indicating the source of particular goods rather than as the name of a company. Often, the deciding factor as to whether a company name is being used as a trademark or as a trade name on packaging is whether the name is accompanied by the company's address. If so, it is an unregistrable trade name use; if not, it may be a registrable trademark use.

Trade name protection parallels trademark protection. The likelihood of confusion standard applies regardless of whether the names at issue are two trademarks, two trade names or one of each. When adopting a company name it is important to perform a more global search of prior rights than simply checking the corporate names registry in the state of incorporation.

COPYRIGHT

A copyright is a legal right to protect certain creations, or works, of authorship. A copyright gives its owner the exclusive right to do and to authorize any of the following: a) to reproduce the copyrighted work; b) to prepare derivative works based upon the copyrighted work e.g., significant new revisions of a work, or translations of a work from one language to another; c) to distribute copies of the work to the public by sale or other transfer, or by rental, lease, or lending; d) in the case of literary works, to display the copyrighted work publicly e.g., art work; and e) in the case of literary works, to perform the copyrighted work publicly e.g., plays. Note that a "work" is the intangible product of authorship while "copies" are the multitude of material objects in which a "work" can be embodied; the original embodiment of the work is also considered to be a "copy".

Federal copyright law protects writings and other forms of expression from unauthorized duplication, modification, and distribution. For works created by individuals, copyright protection lasts for the life of the last surviving author, plus 70 years; for works created by corporations, copyright protection lasts for 95 years from first publication or 120 years after creation, which ever expires first. The owner of a copyright possesses, among other rights, the exclusive right to do or authorize others to do any of the following: reproduce the work, prepare derivative works based on the copyrighted work, and distribute copies to the public by sale, rental, lease or lending.

Copyright protects only the way an idea is expressed, not the idea itself. A work need not be novel to be copyrightable, but it must be "original" meaning that the expression was not copied from another source.

The Copyright Act provides that copyright protection "subsists" in a work from the moment of its creation, provided that the work is "original" and "fixed" in a tangible form. Although some copyright protection arises automatically when a work is created, to obtain maximum protection place a copyright notice on the work and register it with the U.S. Copyright Office. As a result of numerous treaties, works receive copyright protection in many countries automatically, without a need to register copyrights outside the U.S.

The scope of copyright protection received varies widely from country to country. Within the United States, the proper scope of copyright protection for computer software has not yet been settled. The courts disagree on the scope of protection available for the "look and feel" or "structure, sequence and organization" of a software program.

Copyright protection is easier and cheaper to obtain and lasts longer than patent protection. However, unlike patent protection, copyright gives one no defense if a competitor creates a similar product without copying the work.

PROTECTION

For a work to be considered "original" and therefore copyrightable, it cannot be substantially copied from another work and it must exhibit a modicum of intellectual labor. The requirement of originality does not demand that novelty or invention be present, as is required for patent protection.

A work satisfies the requirement of being "fixed" when the author or someone authorized by the author puts it in a copy or phonorecord that is permanent or stable enough to allow it to be perceived, reproduced or otherwise communicated for more than a fleeting moment.

COPYRIGHT OWNERSHIP

The author of a work is the initial owner of the copyright in that work. In the case of a "work made for hire," the employer for whom the work was prepared is deemed to be the author--and therefore the copyright owner--of the work.

The authors of a work that has been jointly created are the co-owners of the copyright in the work. Any author may exploit the copyright without the permission of the other(s), but absent an agreement otherwise, each author must account to the other(s) for any profits derived from exploitation of the work.

The copyright in a work created by an independent contractor or a consultant will generally be owned by the contractor or consultant, not the one for which it was commissioned. Thus, to obtain ownership of works prepared by independent third parties, one should always secure a written agreement before the work is created in which the consultant agrees that one they work for will own the work and the consultant assigns to employer or contractor any rights in the work that the consultant might otherwise have. The agreement should also contain a strong clause stating that the third-party consultant waives, transfers and agrees never to assert any "moral rights" it may have in the work created, such as the right to be identified as the author of the work and the right to object to any alterations to the work.

"Authorship" under copyright law. Section 201 of Title 17 of the United States Code (the copyright statute) provides that copyright in a work of authorship vests initially in the "author" of the work. "Author" is a legal term of art and the following are examples of author applications:

Individuals

For works created by individuals not acting within the scope of employment of another or acting as a commissioned author (see below), the individual is the "author" of the work and the owner of the copyright, which comes into existence automatically upon creation of the work.

Joint Works

The authors of a joint work are co-owners of copyright in the work. Section 101 defines a "joint work" to be a "work prepared by two or more authors with the intention that their contributions be merged into inseparable or interdependent parts of a unitary whole." Any joint author may exploit the copyright in the joint work without permission of the other author(s), but absent an agreement otherwise, each author must account to the other author(s) for any profits derived from exploitation of the work.

Collective Works

Copyright in each separate contribution to a collective work is distinct from copyright in the collective work as a whole, and vests initially in the author of the contribution. In the absence of an express transfer of the copyright or of any rights under it, the owner of copyright in the collective work is presumed to have acquired only the privilege of reproducing and distributing the contribution as part of that particular collective work, any revision of that collective work, and any later collective work in the same series.

Work for Hire

The "work made for hire" doctrine constitutes the major statutory exception to the fundamental principle that copyright ownership vests in the individual who writes a work. In the case of a "work made for hire" (defined below), the employer or other person for whom the work was prepared is considered the "author", and therefore the copyright owner, of the work.

Section 101 of the Copyright Act contains a two-prong definition of a "work made for hire":

1. a work prepared by an employee within the scope of his or her employment; or
2. a work specially ordered or commissioned for use:
   a. as a contribution to a collective work,
   b. as a part of a motion picture or other audiovisual work,
   c. as a translation,
   d. as a supplementary work,
   e. as a compilation,
   f. as an instructional text,
   g. as a test,
   h. as answer material for a test, or
   i. as an atlas.

Also the parties may expressly agree in a written instrument signed by them that the work shall be considered a work made for hire.

"Employee" Definition

The U.S. Supreme Court recently narrowed significantly the circumstances under which a third party not a regular, full-time employee can be considered an "employee" within the meaning of the first prong of the work made for hire definition.

Example (the CCNV case)

In 1985, the Community for Creative Non-Violence (CCNV) entered into an oral agreement with Reid, a sculptor, to produce a statue dramatizing the plight of the homeless. After the completed work was delivered, the parties, whose agreement did not address copyright in the sculpture, filed competing copyright registration certificates. CCNV claimed copyright under the work made for hire doctrine.

The Supreme Court, noting the divergence that had developed in the lower courts concerning the meaning of the two prong definition of work made for hire, concluded that general common law agency principles must be first applied to determine whether the work was prepared by an "employee" or independent contractor.

If prepared by an "employee", then the first prong of the work made for hire definition governs, and the employer is deemed "author" and copyright owner of the work. If under common law agency rules the hired party does not qualify as an employee, then the work can be a work made for hire if and only if it satisfies the requirements of the second prong of the definition.

Thus, the Supreme Court concluded, contrary to the approach of some of the lower federal courts prior to CCNV, that the two prongs of the work made for hire definition are mutually exclusive. The Supreme Court noted that the following factors are among those that are relevant under rules of common law agency in determining whether a hired party qualifies as an "employee", although the Court noted that this list of factors is not exhaustive, nor is any one factor determinative:

1. the hiring party's right to control the manner and means by which work is accomplished;
2. the skill required;
3. the source of the instrumentalities and tools;
4. the location of the work;
5. the duration of the relationship between the parties;
6. whether the hiring party has the right to assign additional projects to the hired party;
7. the extent of the hired party's discretion over when and how long to work;
8. the method of payment;
9. the hired party's role in hiring and paying assistants;
10. whether the work is part of the regular business of the hiring party;
11. whether the hiring party is in business;
12. the provision of employee benefits; and/or
13. the tax treatment of the hired party.

The CCNV test is to be applied retroactively so as to affect all past and existing relationships among authors and hirers.

Written Assignments From Consultants

The CCNV case significantly narrows the circumstances under which a hired work will be deemed to be a "work made for hire". Most independent computer programmers and computer consultants will probably not fall within the definition of "employee" under common law agency rules. Moreover, software does not fit generally into any of the nine enumerated categories of the second prong of the definition of work made for hire.

Although some programs prepared by independent consultants might be characterized as a "translation" (from one computer language to another, for example), as a "supplementary work" (such as an "add-in" program that works with another program), as part of an audiovisual work (when a consultant creates screen displays, for example), or as a collective work (when a consultant creates a segregable module, such as interface code that is distinct from the main "engine" code), many -- indeed probably a majority -- of computer programs prepared by independent consultants will probably not fall into the nine enumerated categories of the second prong of the definition.

The practical result is that most independent contractors will own the copyright in the work that they produce, absent a written agreement that transfers ownership of the copyright to the hiring party. Alternatively, if the contractor works with employees of the company, the contractor may end up a "joint author" of the resulting work. The contractor would then be free to exploit the copyright in the work without the permission of the company, subject only to a duty to account for profits, and, worse, would be entitled to an accounting of profits from the company for its exploitation of the work.

Moreover, in a "joint work" situation, the contractor will have a termination right after 35 years, but the company will not (since the company's interest in the work is as a work made for hire, for which termination rights do not apply). Conceivably, an independent contractor or his successors could terminate a grant to the company and demand an accounting for any future profits derived by the company thereafter.

In view of the foregoing significant traps and complexities arising from the use of independent contractors, it is crucial that written agreements assigning ownership of the work and all intellectual property rights therein to the hiring party be executed prior to commencement of any work on the project by the independent contractor. Such agreements should also contain clauses obligating the consultant to execute confirmatory assignment documents with respect to specific works of authorship. Such confirmatory assignment documents, which should name the copyrighted work specifically, are necessary for recordation to satisfy the constructive notice requirements discussed above.

To combat the problem of termination rights, the written agreement with the consultant could contain a clause granting the company a right of first refusal to obtain a further grant in the event the first grant is terminated. Conceivably, the agreement could also contain a covenant not to exercise termination rights. Although the copyright statute allows exercise of termination rights notwithstanding such a clause, the clause arguably would give rise to a breach of contract action in such event.

There is a substantial chance, however, that a court would view such clause as circumventing the policies embodied in the termination provisions of the copyright statute and would refuse to allow a breach of contract claim to be based on such a clause.

In view of these risks, insertion of such a clause may only alert the independent contractor to the existence of rights of which he or she might not otherwise have been aware.

Note that the same traps of ownership and termination rights can arise when incorporating code from another company under license if such code was not a work made for hire of such company and is therefore subject to termination rights of a third party individual programmer. Thus, a company licensing code from another company for incorporation into a product should make sure such code constitutes a work made for hire that is not subject to termination rights.

Alternatively, the licensing company could demand a warranty from the other company that no termination rights will arise within the term of the contract that will interfere with use of the acquired code, coupled with an indemnity against damages in the event of breach of the warranty.

Employee Agreements

In addition to obtaining written agreements from consultants, it is a good idea as a precautionary measure to have employees who will invent or produce works of authorship execute an employee agreement upon commencement of employment assigning ownership of all such inventions and works of authorship, and all intellectual property rights therein, to the company.

These agreements can be particularly important if an employee will do some work at home or after hours, as is often the case in the computer industry nowadays, or produce work not within the scope of his or her ordinary employment that may get incorporated into a product of the company (such work would not fall within the first prong of the work made for hire definition because outside the scope of employment).

It should be noted, however, that many states have statutes limiting general assignment clauses and excluding from such clauses certain types of inventions developed on the employee's own time. In view of such statutes, a company should discuss with each employee upon commencement of his or her employment what, if any, work that may relate to the current or future business of the company the employee may intend to pursue on his or her own time. If a potential problem concerning ownership surfaces, counsel should be sought to resolve such issues from the beginning, perhaps in a side letter.

Action for Preservation of Ownership

In view of the principles discussed above concerning ownership, transfers and recordation of copyrights, the following steps should be taken by a company to obtain and perfect title to copyrights:

1. before commencing any work, all employees and consultants should be required to sign written agreements transferring ownership of all works of authorship produced by them, and all intellectual property rights therein. Such agreements should also contain clauses obligating the signatory to execute confirmatory assignment documents with respect to specific works of authorship;

2. the copyright in all works of authorship owned by the company and of significance to the

company should be registered promptly with the U.S. Copyright Office. Section 412 of the copyright statute allows a three-month grace period after first publication of a work in which to register to preserve all the copyright owner's rights. (Note, however, that if a security interest in the copyright is involved, registration of the copyright and recordation of the security interest must be accomplished within one month in order to preserve priority of the security interest.);

3. confirmatory assignment documents specifically naming the copyrighted work by title, at least for those works produced by independent contractors, should be recorded with the U.S. Copyright Office within one month after execution;

4. if independent contractors are used by a company, the company must be aware of the potential difficulty raised by termination rights, even if assignments of ownership are obtained. Careful records should be kept of what code the independent contractor created and what code, if any, employees created, so that in the event termination rights are exercised, the company can segregate the code its employees created and continue to exploit it. Similarly, if a company licenses or purchases title to code from another company for incorporation into a product, it should, if possible, make sure such code constitutes a work made for hire of the licensor/transferor that is not subject to termination rights;

5. exclusive license agreements, which the copyright statute treats as a transfer of part ownership in the copyright, should be recorded with the U.S. Copyright Office within one month after execution;

6. security interests in copyrights should be recorded with the U.S. Copyright Office within one month after execution; and

7. the parties to a transaction should make great effort to anticipate possible new media or uses of the work and to have the agreement clearly set forth the scope of rights granted with respect to such new media or uses.

COPYRIGHT NOTICE REQUIREMENTS
Form

A proper notice of copyright should be placed on all publicly distributed copies of a work. A proper copyright notice consists of three elements: the symbol "©" or any one of the words "Copr" or "Copyright" (the symbol "©" is preferred because of international copyright treaties); the year of first publication of the work (which is not necessarily the current year or the year in which the work was created); and the name of the copyright owner.

In addition, the phrase "All Rights Reserved" should be used to afford protection in certain foreign countries. An example of a proper copyright notice is: © 1994 ABC Company, Inc. All Rights Reserved.

Locations

For books, technical papers and advertising and promotional material, a copyright notice should be placed on the title page, the back of the title page, either side of the front cover or either side of the back cover.

Packaging

A copyright notice should be placed on the front or back side of packaging or containers that display copyrighted material, artwork or designs.

Computer Programs

Each one of the following locations of notice are adequate under Copyright Office regulations:

1. notice embodied in the copies in machine-readable form so that on visually perceptible printouts it appears either with or near the title, or at the end of the work;

2. notice that is displayed at the user's terminal at sign-on;
3. a legible notice reproduced durably, that will withstand normal use, on a gummed or other label securely affixed to the copies or to a box or other container used as a receptacle for the software; or
4. notice that is continuously on terminal display.

Although a notice in any one of these four locations is adequate under Copyright Office regulations, for computer programs it is suggested that one place a notice in all of the first three locations on all copies of computer programs. Regular checks should be made to assure all works for which copyright protection is desired include proper notice.

Registration with Copyright Office

Although registration of a work with the Copyright Office is not required for copyright protection to exist, it is strongly recommend for several reasons:

1. registration is a prerequisite to filing a lawsuit for infringement of any copyrighted work whose "country of origin" (as defined in the copyright statute) is the U.S.;
2. registration is required to cut off certain defenses of so-called "innocent infringers."; a registration certificate establishes in court a presumption that the copyright in the work is valid, which yields certain tactical advantages in litigation;
3. registration is a prerequisite to recording the copyright with the U.S. Customs Service, so that the Customs Service may stop the import of piratical copies of the copyrighted work into the United States; and
4. registration may be required to perfect a security interest in the copyright.

Registration is a prerequisite for recovering "statutory damages" and attorneys' fees. "Statutory damages" are penalties the court may award if the copyright owner is unable or chooses not to prove actual damages caused by the infringement. No award of statutory damages or of attorneys' fees may be made for any infringement of an unpublished work that commenced before the effective date of registration, or any infringement of copyright commenced after first publication of a work and before the effective date of its registration, unless such registration is made within three months after the first publication of the work.

Thus, all works for which copyright protection is desired should be registered with the Copyright Office within three months of first customer shipment. Implement a procedure that ensures that registrations are regular. As a general rule, separate registration should be filed for each new release of a computer program that contains more than just ordinary "bug fixes."

Registration Mechanics

An application for copyright registration is a short form that is easily prepared, and the registration application fee is currently twenty dollars ($20). The owner must also deposit with the Copyright Office two copies of published works. Only one copy is required for unpublished works and most computer programs.

For computer programs published only in machine-readable form, the Copyright Office requires a deposit of one copy of the first and last 25 pages of source code (or 50 pages of source code representative of the revisions in "derivative works"), together with the page containing the copyright notice. The Office will register deposits consisting solely of object code only under a "rule of doubt," which means that the copyright will not be presumed valid by virtue of the registration (as it ordinarily would) in the event of litigation.

Computer programs containing trade secret material can receive special treatment in order to protect such trade secrets. A copyright owner is entitled to protect the trade secrets by submitting, in lieu of the ordinary deposit of the first and last 25 pages of source code, a deposit in one of the following forms:

1. the first and last 25 pages of source code with up to 50% of the material blocked out to protect trade secrets;
2. the first and last 25 pages of object code together with any 10 consecutive pages of source code (with nothing blocked out); or
3. a deposit of the first and last 10 pages of source code (with nothing blocked).

In addition to a source code deposit, the copyright owner of a computer program may elect to deposit, as part of the registration application, material that reflects a representative sample of the screen displays or other audiovisual material produced by the computer program.

The Copyright office does not allow separate registration of the screen displays of a computer program (apart from the code). Rather, only one registration per computer program is allowed. Deposit of identifying material representative of the screen displays or other audiovisual material produced by the program is optional and is not required to assert copyright protection of such material.

Because the Copyright Office's policies with respect to registration of computer screen displays are somewhat complicated and tricky, and because the Office has shown considerable hostility to protecting computer screen displays and other aspects of computer user interfaces, an attorney should be consulted to determine whether to deposit identifying material for the screen displays in each particular case.

COPYRIGHT INFRINGEMENT – LIABILITY

To establish liability for copyright infringement, one must show that someone "copied" all or some portion of the copyrighted work. Because direct evidence of copying is seldom available, the courts have devised an alternative, circumstantial test of copying under which a copyright owner may prove "copying" by someone by showing that he or she had "access" to the copyrighted original work and the other's work is "substantially similar" to the original.

The concept of "copying" is much broader than mere exact duplication of all or some of a copyrighted work. With respect to computer software, for example, copying may be found where someone transfers the program to another medium (such as from a hard disk onto a network), disassembles the object code (see below), translates the program into another language, modifies the program, or creates a competing program that utilizes the "structure, sequence and organization" of the original program.

Literal Copying

Perhaps the biggest risk faced for copyright liability for literal copying is based on vicarious liability resulting from illicit copying of computer software (particularly mass-marketed microcomputer software such as spreadsheet programs) by employees.

A company can be held vicariously liable for its employees' infringing acts if the employees performed the unauthorized copying within the scope of their jobs. Copying as part of activities that are only slightly related to an employee's duties may be deemed to be within the scope of employment for purposes of vicarious liability.

To help avoid vicarious liability, establish and distribute to employees written policies and guidelines concerning unauthorized copying and use of copyrighted materials. The guidelines should make clear to employees that they can be held individually liable for infringing acts, including criminal liability for willful infringements, and that the company may be held liable for the acts as well.

Contractual Grounds

In addition to vicarious liability, companies can be held liable for acts of employees that violate contractual rights. Many copyrighted works, particularly computer programs, are distributed subject to a license agreement, which may be either a "shrink wrap" license (a license that is visible beneath shrink wrapped packaging and that states the user agrees to its terms by opening the package) or an individually signed license. These license agreements may impose restrictions that go beyond what the copyright law would prohibit, such as restrictions on disassembly and reverse engineering, and restrictions on the product's use (such as limiting use to a particular computer).

There is a doubt under current law whether shrink-wrap license agreements are enforceable, and whether in particular some restrictions commonly contained in them are enforceable, the safest course to avoid liability is to obey any restrictions contained in the agreements.

Developing Competing Products

Risks of potential infringement are particularly high if products are developed that compete with a copyrighted product, especially if a company's product is a "clone" of all or a portion of the copyrighted product. For example, Lotus Development Corp. has recently won several lawsuits brought against various developers of clones of the Lotus 1-2-3 spreadsheet product for copyright infringement of the "look and feel" of the Lotus 1-2-3 user interface and command set.

"Clean room" Procedures

Companies often attempt to avoid a claim of copyright infringement while developing a product that competes with a copyrighted product by relying on so-called "clean room" procedures. These procedures attempt to prove that, even if a company's work is substantially similar to the copyrighted work, it is not infringing because the company had no access to the copyrighted work. In other words, the company's work was independently developed.

In the case of computer programs, for example, clean room procedures consist of creating two groups of developers: the specifications group and the coding group. The specifications group is the only group allowed to see the copyrighted computer code, and that group prepares a functional specification from which the coding group creates the new code. The coding group is never allowed to see the actual code of the copyrighted program, but instead sees only the functional specification prepared by the specifications group.

Fair use (Disassembly)

The Copyright Act provides that the fair use of a copyrighted work is not an infringement as long as the use is "for purposes such as criticism, comment, news reporting, teaching, (including multiple copies for classroom use) scholarship, or research". In determining whether the use made of a work in any particular case is a fair use, the factors to be considered include, but are not limited to: 1) the purpose and character of the use, including whether such use is of a commercial nature or is for nonprofit educational purposes; 2) the nature of the copyrighted work; 3) the amount and substantiality of the portion used in relation to the copyrighted work as a whole; and 4) the effect of the use upon the potential market for or value of the copyrighted work. For example "fair use" is the photocopying of selected technical articles on an infrequent basis to keep in a private notebook for reference purposes but this would not be "fair use" if a company made copies and distributed them to its research personnel. Details and means or methods to test for whether or not use is "fair use" are presented in Exhibit D.

Under a newly evolving line of case law, disassembly of a computer program may not be a copyright infringement, even if limited copying is involved in the course of the disassembly. If the copying is "necessary" to learn the ideas of the computer program, the copying may be considered a "fair use." The "fair use" doctrine is a defense to copyright infringement that is used to limit the copyright owner's ability to unfairly use the monopoly power of a copyright.

The difficulty of determining whether copying is "necessary" and the factual nature of the fair use defense make disassembly a treacherous activity. Before embarking on any form of disassembly consult your counsel.

Other Uses of Copyrighted Materials

Care must be taken when using other copyrighted materials to prepare a competing or related product. For example, by writing a computer program to implement a method of trading stocks described in a copyrighted manual, the program author can infringe the manual's copyright. The copyright holder itself had no computer program that implemented the method from which the program author could have copied. Thus, copyright liability may arise from referring to copyrighted materials to develop competing products.

COPYRIGHT TRANSFER

Separate Transfer of Exclusive Rights

Under Section 106, the owner of a copyright in a work has the exclusive rights, among others, to reproduce the work, to prepare derivative works based upon the copyrighted work, and to distribute copies of the work to the public by sale or other transfer of ownership, or by rental, lease, or lending. Under Section 201(d), any of the exclusive "bundle" of rights under the copyright may be "unbundled" and transferred and owned separately.

This area of the law was extremely important during the ascendancy of television as a popular new medium, and again later with the growth of videocassettes, as many contracts were unclear as to whether an assignment of "motion picture" rights included telecasting or videocassette rights. Such issues are once again undergoing close scrutiny in light of the rapid growth of multimedia technology and applications.

Requirement of "a writing"

Section 204(a) provides that a transfer of copyright ownership, other than by operation of law, is not valid unless an instrument of conveyance, or a note or memorandum of the transfer, is in writing and signed by the owner of the rights conveyed or such owner's duly authorized agent. Some courts have held that the requirement of a writing may be satisfied by the owner's later execution of a writing that confirms a prior oral agreement, at least where there is no evidence of any dispute between the parties as to the validity of the alleged oral grant.

However, a recent decision of the Ninth Circuit takes the view that since an oral transfer is not valid in the absence of a "writing", a later written "confirmation" may not be sufficient.

Registration of copyright in a work by a transferee made prior to a valid transfer of ownership is invalid. Wales, 612 Fed. Supp. at 516. Under Section 101, a "transfer of copyright ownership" is defined to include an exclusive license, whether or not it is limited in time or place of effect. Thus, exclusive licenses must be in writing in order to be valid.

Moreover, a lien on a copyright has been construed to constitute a "transfer" within the meaning of the copyright statute. (re Peregrine Entertainment Ltd., 16 U.S.P.Q.2d 1017, 1025; C.D. Cal. 1990). A lien holder is therefore subject to the copyright statute's priority provisions governing conflicting transfers discussed below (and not the priority provisions of the Uniform Commercial Code).

Recordation of Transfer

Section 205 contains provisions for recording transfers of copyrights with the U.S. Copyright Office. Recordation will constitute constructive notice of the facts stated in the recordation only if:

1. the recorded document specifically identifies the work to which it pertains so that, after indexing by the Copyright Office, it would be revealed by a reasonable search of the Copyright Office records; and
2. The copyright in the work has been registered with the Copyright Office.

Priority Between Conflicting Transfer

Under Section 205(d), as between two conflicting transfers, the one executed first prevails if it is recorded in a manner that satisfies the constructive notice provisions, within one month after its execution in the United States (or within two months after its execution outside the United States), or at any time before recordation in such manner of the later transfer.

Otherwise the later transfer prevails if recorded first in a manner that satisfies the constructive notice provisions, and if taken in good faith, for valuable consideration or on the basis of a binding promise to pay royalties, and without notice of the earlier transfer.

Perfection of Security Interests in Copyrights

The Peregrine case changed the general practice for perfecting security interests in a copyright, ruling that in order to perfect a security interest in a copyright, the document granting the security interest must be recorded in the U.S. Copyright Office. The court concluded that the recordation provisions of the copyright statute preempt the provisions of the Uniform Commercial Code with respect to copyrights.

Accordingly, the court further concluded that the filing of a UCC-1 financing statement does not perfect a security interest in a copyright and its related accounts receivable. An important difference exists between the priority provisions of the copyright statute and the priority provisions of Article 9 of the UCC.

Unlike Article 9, the copyright statute priority provisions permit the effect of recording with the Copyright Office to relate back for one month (in the case of transfers executed in the U.S.) or two months (in the case of transfers executed outside the United States).

Under Article 9, by contrast, priority between holders of conflicting security interests in intangibles is generally determined by who perfected his or her interest first.

UCC § 9-312(5) - The Peregrine case raises a number of important problems that should be noted by companies (and counsel representing companies) that lend money to a debtor owning valuable copyrights and that wish to perfect a security interest in such copyrights (see Brinson & Radcliffe, "Security Interests in Copyright: The New Learning," 7 The Computer Lawyer 10; Sept. 1990)):

1. *Accounts Receivable.* The Peregrine court ruled that a security interest in accounts receivable from a copyright is also not perfected unless the security interest in the copyright is recorded in the Copyright Office.
2. *Multiple Recordations.* Because the Copyright Office recordation provisions have no equivalent of the Article 9 "floating lien" in all assets of the borrower (including after-acquired assets), separate recordation must be made each time a new copyright comes into existence.
3. *Multiple Registrations.* The priority provisions of the copyright statute require that the copyright be registered prior to the recordation in order to take priority. Thus, a concurrent flood of new registrations will be necessary to protect security interests in copyrights.
4. *Delay.* The Copyright Office is very slow in both the registration and the recordation processes, which can each take six months or more to complete.
5. *Statutory Grace Period.* Because the copyright statute allows a one-month grace period in which to record in order to have the recordation relate back to the date of execution of the security interest, a lender could, after a transaction, find its interest sub-ordinated to that of an earlier transferee who recorded after the lender but within the grace period.
6. *Risk of Loss of Recordation Priority.* The Copyright Office regulations require very specific things for a document to be recordable. Thus, there is a good chance of making an error in the process, causing the Copyright Office to deny the recordation, thereby missing the grace period and losing the recordation priority.
7. *Incomplete Rules of Priority.* The copyright statute's priority provisions are not exhaustive of all situations -- they do not cover, for example, priority between two unrecorded security interests.

8. ***Different Procedures for Patents and Trademarks.*** Because the reported decisions have consistently ruled that the patent and trademark statutes do not preempt the recordation provisions of the UCC, different procedures must be followed to perfect security interests in patents and trademarks (and trade secrets--a right under state law) than for copyrights.

Termination Rights

Under Section 203, in the case of any work other than a work made for hire, the exclusive or nonexclusive grant of a transfer or license of copyright or any right under a copyright may be terminated by an author or the author's statutory successors within a five-year window beginning 35 years after the grant, or in the case of a grant covering rights of publication, 35 years from the date of publication, or 40 years from the date of execution of the grant, whichever is earlier. In the case of a grant executed by two or more authors of a joint work, termination of the grant may be effected by a majority of the authors who executed it (which may be only one).

Termination is effected by serving an advance notice of election to terminate not less than two or more than ten years before the effective date of termination. As a condition of its taking effect, a copy of the notice must be recorded in the U.S. Copyright Office before the effective date of termination.

Section 203(5) provides that termination rights may be exercised notwithstanding any agreement to the contrary, including an agreement to make any future grant.

In addition to the ownership problems discussed in Section II below, termination rights pose an additional problem when using independent contractors, rather than employees, to create software. If an independent contractor is used, the contractor may terminate transfer of the copyright or any license grants after 35 years. Because termination rights do not apply to works made for hire, the problem does not arise with respect to software written by employees.

Section 203(b)(1) provides that a derivative work prepared under authority of the grant before its termination may continue to be utilized under the terms of the grant after its termination, but this privilege does not extend to the preparation after the termination of other derivative works based upon the copyrighted work covered by the terminated grant. Thus, if an independent contractor prepares software and later exercises the termination right, the company might be unable to create new versions of the software.

Although the 35 year period at which the termination right becomes exercisable will be beyond the commercial life of much software, some "core" technology -- such as UNIX code, for example -- could easily have a useful commercial life long enough to implicate the termination rights. In those cases, consideration of termination rights should be weighed in the decision whether to use independent contractors to create software or other important core technology (the problem of termination rights is discussed further below).

TRADE SECRETS

A trade secret is any device or information that is used in a business and that gives the owner an advantage over others who do not know or use it. Trade secret protection is governed by state, rather than federal law. While the laws of the states vary significantly, more than half of the states have adopted a uniform law of trade secrecy. Because trade secret law is not provided on a federal basis, protection does not extend beyond the borders of the United States.

No formal filings or registrations are required, or are even available, for trade secret protection. However the secret must be useful and the owner must take appropriate steps to inform the recipient of a trade secret of the intent to keep it as secret. Trade secret protection may last indefinitely but is lost when the information becomes generally known to the public.

TRADE SECRET OWNERSHIP

Trade secrets are creatures of state, rather than federal law, and are not subject to the statutory ownership provisions that apply to patents, copyrights, and trademarks. In general, whoever develops information that derives value from the fact that it is not generally known, and takes reasonable steps to maintain the secrecy of that information, is the owner of a trade secret in the information? Where two or more parties jointly develop such confidential information, they are both owners of the trade secret. The doctrine of shop rights applies to trade secrets as it does to patents. (Saunders v. Florence Enameling Co., 9 U.S.P.Q.2d 1066;Ala. Sup. Ct. 1988). Since an owner of a trade secret is not generally under any duty to maintain the secrecy of the information, co-owners are well advised to require the other co-owners to maintain the secrecy of any jointly owned trade secrets.

Ownership Transfer

Trade secrets may be freely licensed or sold, but the caveat always remains that if the secret is disseminated to persons having no duty to the owner to maintain the confidentiality of the information, trade secrecy may be lost. Thus, where it is desired to license a trade secret, the license should include specific requirements constraining the licensee's use and disclosure of the trade secret. Where a trade secret is transferred outright to another party, such restrictions may not be called for, as the transferor retains no interest in need of such protection. Certain trade secret transfers and licenses may give rise to conflicts with federal antitrust and patent laws, and consideration to these possibilities should be given in drafting such agreements.

Patents vs. Trade Secrets

Trade secrecy is in some sense antithetical to the patent law, as patent law is based on disclosure to the public being the quid pro quo for the patent monopoly. Thus, material that must be disclosed in a patent application cannot be protected by trade secret law once the patent document is published. However, United States patent law protects trade secrets in patent applications by retaining confidentiality of patent applications until such time as a patent actually issues. Therefore, if a patent application is rejected by the United States Patent and Trademark Office, no public disclosure results and trade secrecy is preserved. In most other countries, patent applications are eventually published whether or not a patent actually issues from the application. Trade secret owners are therefore well advised to consider whether patent applications disclosing confidential information should be filed at all, and whether such filings should be limited to the United States.

Maintaining Trade Secrets for Software

While trade secrets may protect a great deal of a software company's technology, the current legal environment is not as conducive to maintenance of those secrets as it had been just a few years ago. As more and more software becomes patented, companies are forced to disclose information about their products, either to obtain their own patent or to block someone else from obtaining a related patent.

Secondly, courts have now suggested or directly held that under certain circumstances, it is a "fair use" of a copyrighted work to make copies of the work as needed to understand the ideas and concepts underlying the work (Atari Games Corp. v. Nintendo of Am. Inc., 975 F.2d 832; Fed. Cir. 1992); Sega Enterprises Ltd. v. Accolade, Inc., ___ F.2d ___, 1993 U.S. App.Lexis 78; 9th Cir. 1993). These holdings mean that competitors may legitimately obtain trade secret information by reverse engineering, further lessening the force of trade secrets in software. Nonetheless, a great deal of software technology is still protected by trade secret law.

MASK WORKS

The Semiconductor Chip Protection Act was enacted in 1984 to provide copyright like protection to mask works and semiconductor chip products. Although the Act borrows many concepts from the copyright laws, it stands on its own merits, and is not simply an extension of the copyright laws.

The new Act generally protects a "mask work" fixed in "semiconductor chip product" if certain conditions are met:

1. a semiconductor chip product is defined as the final or intermediate form of any product having tow or more patterned layers of metallic, insulating, or semiconducting material on a piece of semiconductor material and intended to perform electronic circuitry functions (thus, the new law does not protect circuit boards, since circuit boards are not made of semiconductor material); and
2. a mask work is a series of related images, however fixed or encoded, having or representing a predetermined three-dimensional pattern of metallic, insulating, or semiconductor material on a semiconductor chip product and in which each image is essentially a pattern of the surface of one of the intermediate forms of the semiconductor chip product.

A mask work fixed in a semiconductor chip product by or under the authority of the owner of a mask work is protected under the Act if, on the earlier of the date the mask work is registered with the U.S., Copyright Office or the date of the first commercial exploitation of the mask work anywhere in the world, the owner is:

1. a national or domiciliary of the U.S.;
2. a national or domiciliary of the foreign nation which affords U.S. nationals similar protection row; and
3. a stateless person.

Alternatively, protection is afforded to anyone if the mask work is first commercially exploited in the U.S. To commercially exploit a mask work means to distribute a semiconductor chip product embodying the mask work to the public for commercial purposes. The definition of distribution then becomes important. Delineation of distribution might be as follows:

1. To distribute means to sell, or to lease, bail, or otherwise transfer the semiconductor chip product, or to offer to do so;
2. Beta testing – note that an off-site transfer of pre-production units for beta testing probably constitutes a distribution, and may therefore be considered to be a commercial "exploitation";
3. If a semiconductor chip product is not in existence (that is, the mask work has not yet been fixed in the semiconductor chip product), then an offer to sell or transfer a semiconductor chip product does not constitute commercial exploitation unless it is in writing, and in any event does not occur until after the mask work is fixed in the semiconductor chip product. Thus an advertisement, even though it is in writing, offering a new semiconductor chip product for sale does not constitute commercial exploitation until after the semiconductor chip product is actually created; and
4. distribution or importation of a product incorporating a semiconductor chip product, such as a circuit board, is deemed a distribution or importation of that semiconductor chip product.

The Act does not protect works that are not original or embody design that are staple, commonplace or familiar in the semiconductor industry, or variations of such designs, combined in a way that is not original when considered as a whole. Further, the protection of the Act for mask works does not cover any ideas, procedures, processes, systems, and methods of operation, concepts, principles, discoveries or the like, regardless of form.

MASK WORK OWNERSHIP

Exclusive rights in a mask work are owned by: 1) the person who created the mask work, 2) the creator's legal representative in the event of death or incapacity or 3) if the work was made within the scope of a person's employment, the owner is the employer for whom the person created the mask work. This is similar to the "work made for hire" doctrine of present copyright law, but appears to extend further to include mask works created by independent contractors without the need for a written agreement. Alternatively, the amount of control or supervision by the employer may be sufficient to make a contractor an employee" within the intent of the mask work law. However to be absolutely safe, written assignments should be obtained from contractors and recorded until the scope of this definition is adopted by the courts.

The owner of a mask work has the exclusive right to: a) reproduce the mask work; b) import or distribute a semiconductor chip product embodying the mask work; and c) authorize others to do either of the foregoing acts. Two general limitations exist: a) others may exactly reproduce a mask work without infringing if the reproduction is solely for the purpose of teaching, analyzing or evaluating the concepts, techniques, circuitry, logic flow, and organization of the mask work, and they may incorporate the results of such conduct in an original mask work of their own.

This reverse engineering is expected to permit the use of otherwise protected mask works to aid in the production of an original semiconductor chip by another, if that production involves significant toil and investment and therefore is not a "mere plagiarism. Such an effort should be provable by the engineering documentation required to achieve the resulting original chip. The courts are expected to strike a balance in this area on a case-by-case basis.

If an accused infringer adequately assets the affirmative defense of reverse engineering, the legislative history of the Act suggest that the mask work owner can only win an infringement case by proving that the accursed infringer's mask work is substantially identical to the owner's mask work. Normally, the test for infringement is substantial similarity.

Notice

The owner of a mask work may, but is not required to, give notice to others of that fact by affixing the following notice to a mask work and to masks and semiconductor chip products embodying the mask work: a) the words "MASK WORK", or either of the symbols "M" or M within a circle and the name of the owner, or an abbreviation by which the name is recognized or generally know. Unlike a copyright notice, the year is not required. The notice must be affixed in such a manner and location as to give reasonable notice or protection. The notice is not a condition of protection, but does constitute prima facie evidence of notice of protection. Examples of affixation and position are a) a gummed or other label securely affixed or imprinted upon the package or to the container used as a permanent receptacle for the product; or b) a notice imprinted otherwise affixed in or on the top or other visible layer of the product.

DURATION OF PROTECTION

Protection for an eligible mask work begins on the earlier of: a) the date on which the mask work is registered with the U.S. Copyright Office; or b) date on which the mask work is first commercially exploited anywhere in the world. Protection ends 10 years after the date on which protection commenced; however, the Act provides that the term of protection shall actually expire at the end of the calendar year in which the protection otherwise would expire. For example, if the protection for a mask work commenced on January 1, 2000 the protection will not expire on January 1, 2010 but rather on December 31, 2010.

REGISTRATION

The qualifying owner may apply to the U.S. Copyright Office for registration of a claim to protect a mask work if the application is made within 2 years after the date on which the mask work is first commercially exploited anywhere in the world. Registration consists of:

1. completion of Form MX (obtained from the Copyright Office);
2. submission in 81/2 x 11 form or foldable to that size, of a least a 20X (1) composite plot of the mask work, or (2) complete set of plastic overlay color sheets, or (3) a photo of each layer of the work fixed in the chip; and
3. submission of 4 samples of an actual chip embodying the mask work, stored in a chip carrier; and payment of the registration fee of $20.

If a mask work contains trade secrets, special relief can be requested from the Copyright Office form the above deposit requirements.

An action for infringement is barred unless commenced within three years after infringement occurs.

PLANT VARIETY PROTECTION ACT (PVPA)

Certain technology-based companies and research organizations are involved in science and commercialization surrounding plant materials. In addition to patent and trade secret protection one can obtain protection on plant material in another way. The plant variety protection act provides a means to protect sexually reproduced plant material for an 18-year period. The law prevents others engaged in the seed business from selling seed of a protected variety without permission of the variety owner. A protected variety must be novel and clearly distinct by one or more characteristic from all prior varieties of public knowledge; stable in that upon reproduction it will retain its essential and distinctive characteristics; and uniformity so variants are clearly described, predictable and commercially acceptable.

This method of protecting plant material is administered by the United States Department of Agriculture (USDA). Unlike a plant patent this method protects sexually reproduced plants. It affords protection forF1 hybrids & tuber propagated plants. Seed can only be saved for replanting by the farmer on his own acreage or sold for non-reproductive purposes. The term of protection is 20 years unless the plant material is trees or vines in which case the term is 25 years. A certificate of plant variety protection is awarded the applicant. "Essentially derived" varieties & varieties "not clearly distinguishable" from protected variety will infringe.

PROTECTION SUMMARY

The various methods of asset protection are summarized in table six.

Table six. Comparison of intellectual property protection methods.

	Trade Secret	Right of Publicity	Copyright	Trademark	Patent[1]
Subject matter	information	personal identity	works fixed in a tangible medium of expression	symbols	functional features[2]
Protection criteria	not generally known and having value (actual or potential	must be (or have been) a living individual	originality and creativity	used to identify and distinguish goods and services	new, useful and non-obvious
Protection provided Under---	state rights upon development	state rights upon birth	federal rights upon development	common law and state or federal registration	grant by federal gov
Protection period	until made public	death (and possibly thereafter)	author's life plus 90 years[3]	common law: as long as used property; Fed Reg: 10 yrs[4]	20 years from date of filing of application[5]
Infringement Test (Unauthorized)	use or disclosure	use	direct or copying[6]	likelihood of confusion or dilution	make, use, sell, offer for sale, import or sell

1. Functional features are protected by utility patents. In the U.S., non-functional, ornamental features for articles of manufacture may be protected with a design patent. Asexually reproducing plants may be protected with a plant patent.
2. The functional features of processes, machines, manufactured items, or compositions of matter are protected by utility patents.
3. This provides the duration of protection of a copyright for an individual for works prepared after 1/1/78. The term for protection of a work made for hire is 95 years from the date of publication or 120 years from the date of creation, whichever expires first.
4. The 10-year period is renewable if statutory requirements are followed.
5. For a utility and plant patent that had issued before or an application was filed before June 8, 1995 is the longer of 17 years for the issuance of the patent to 20 years from the filing of the application. Design patents last 14 years from the date of issuance.
6. Direct infringement requires evidence of actual copying. Indirect infringement requires access to the work and substantial similarity to the ordinary observer. The test for infringement of a design patent is to compare the claimed design with the accused design and determine whether the designs look confusingly similar to the eye of the ordinary observer.

ENFORCEMENT OF INTELLECTUAL PROPERTY RIGHTS

Typically, companies are motivated by one of four incentives to obtain intellectual property protection. Some seek to reduce the competitive threat against their products. Many are primarily interested in developing a defensive portfolio of intellectual property assets for use in negotiations with competitors, potential business partners or holders of related intellectual property rights. Others look primarily toward additional licensing revenue that intellectual property can provide.

Finally, some software developers seek intellectual property protection to legitimize their technology to customers and investors. The issues that come into play in enforcing intellectual property rights are as varied as the possible goals of intellectual property owners. Presented below are

118

just a few examples of some issues that may motivate intellectual property owners and possible infringers.

OWNER'S VIEWPOINT

A primary consideration of the owner of an intellectual property asset should be the specific goals of the owner with respect to the asset, e.g., blocking competitors from entering the industry, obtaining licensing revenue, increasing the presence of the company within the industry, or building respect among potential investors. The early identification of such goals will help to direct and control activities undertaken to maximize the owner's benefit from the intellectual property asset.

Using the example of a newly issued patent, a typical first step is to determine what level of investigation, if any, the owner wishes to make regarding third parties that may infringe the patent. It may be determined most effective to focus only on known competitors, to investigate only those who seek a license to the patent at issue, to keep a weather eye on the competition from the trade press and trade shows, or to do no investigation whatsoever and just wait for possible infringements to make themselves known.

A preliminary investigation of a possible infringer may involve procurement of possibly infringing products for examination, a search of U.S. and foreign patent offices to determine whether the potential infringer may hold patents or pending applications that may be asserted in retaliation, investigation of the resources available to the possible infringer for defending an infringement claim and possibly searching for invalidating prior art.

Other preliminary considerations include the effect on the patent owner of asserting the patent. In some industries, a bully image may be helpful to the company while in others it may be devastating. Enforcement of a patent puts the validity and enforceability of the patent at risk, and other negative collateral implications may also arise from assertion of patent rights in an adversarial environment.

Once these factors are taken into consideration, it is generally considered desirable to determine a strategy that can be adhered to regardless of future events that may ensue. A company's credibility can be severely damaged if patent rights are asserted prematurely and without conviction. In some instances, threats of suit that are not followed up can lead to a court finding that the company has acquiesced to the alleged infringement.

It is critical that notice to a potential infringer be given very carefully. Some circumstances call for the patent owner simply to put the potential infringer on notice that the patent exists, enclosing a copy of the patent for the potential infringer's reference.

Other situations require that an assertion of an infringement be made in such notice. The patent owner must carefully discuss the situation with litigation counsel familiar with the patent and the industry before sending such notice. It is rarely desirable to make any public statements regarding alleged infringement, at least until suit is actually filed.

If the patent owner is interested in licensing revenue, one technique that is often used after initial investigation indicates infringement is to approach the potential infringer with the choice of a license or litigation. The classic scenario is to present the potential infringer with a draft license and a draft infringement complaint and to assert that at the end of the negotiation session, one of these documents will be operable.

ALLEGED INFRINGER'S VIEWPOINT

More and more companies in the computer industry have experienced the discomfort that comes from being put on notice of possible infringement of an intellectual property right. However, experience has shown that patents, copyrights, trade secrets and trademarks are often asserted far beyond their legal scope, and the strategies available to an alleged infringer are wide-ranging.

A primary consideration for those concerned about being accused of patent infringement is that, unlike copyright law, patent law does not require copying as an element of infringement. In other words, independent creation is not a defense to a patent infringement action. Therefore, preventive legal and factual research is often recommended to reduce the likelihood of innocent infringement.

Many companies schedule periodic patent searches to keep track of the patent portfolios of their primary competitors. It has become commonplace to perform patent searches before embarking on important new technology development projects and before purchasing such technology from third parties.

On the other hand, there are a number of situations in which companies are well advised not to seek information concerning third party patents. Under U.S. law, willful patent infringers may be assessed treble damages and may be forced to pay the patent owner's attorney fees. Thus, there is risk involved in searching for third party patents, especially if the company is not prepared to alter or abandon development plans should a troublesome patent be uncovered. The decision regarding such patent searches should, therefore, be made only after consultation with patent litigation counsel as to the pros and cons for each particular situation.

Willful infringement may also result from receipt of notice of a patent from the patent owner, especially if accompanied by a demand to cease and desist from alleged infringement.

Other circumstances that may result in a finding of willful infringement include possession of a patented product that is properly marked, or even seeing such a product at a trade show or described in the trade press. In short, any situation that triggers a reasonable apprehension of infringement may lead to a finding of willfulness. The most common technique for avoiding a finding of willfulness is to obtain an opinion of competent patent counsel as to non-infringement, invalidity, or unenforceability of the patent at issue.

Courts have imposed fairly strict requirements on such opinions, however. It is therefore imperative that such patent analyses be taken very seriously by client and attorney alike, to ensure that if infringement is ultimately determined, the client will be insulated as much as possible from the detrimental effects of a willfulness finding.

When confronted with notice of a patent, one practical solution adopted by many companies, albeit at some risk, is to simply do nothing in response. Many patent holders are averse to actually asserting their patents in litigation for the reasons discussed above. An important consideration militating against such a strategy, however, is that courts look askance upon parties that simply ignore a patent owner's claim of rights.

Another strategy available to accused infringers is to bring a declaratory judgment action to determine non-infringement. While litigation should generally be considered a last resort, this strategy may be effective where it is deemed important that the court view the accused infringer as the aggrieved party seeking to resolve a controversy affecting the marketing of its products.

The issues of invalidity and unenforceability are available as affirmative defenses to accused infringers. These affirmative defenses are asserted in nearly every patent infringement action.

Finally, the accused infringer's patent portfolio should be considered as an important tool for use in such situations. If the portfolio is of significant size, one or more of the patents may be asserted against the opposition to prompt settlement of the original dispute. Alternatively, the parties may decide to cross-license each other's patents simply to avoid the expense of litigation, regardless of who has the stronger position.

RECORD RETENTION

Since the term of intellectual property protection varies with the type of protection it is important to be aware of the time that records are retained and related statutes. Some relevant information related to record retention is as follows: 1. the patent office keeps file wrappers of provisional applications for 26 years; 2. some law firms keep patent files for 5-8 years after the patent expires, then review and decide whether to keep longer; and 3. some state statutes of limitations for contracts are 12 years. It is always prudent to discuss record retention time with Patent or Legal Counsel since statutes will vary.

For example, files for a patent application that were filed more than ten years ago and abandoned more than five years ago have been subpoenaed for evidence in a third party lawsuit.

MISCELLANEOUS

Although not usually considered to be clear-cut intellectual property protection, officers in a technology-based business might include in their strategic planning unique or advantageous status with respect to regulatory clearance, market position, alliances, import-export capabilities, etc. Frequently successful achievements in these areas contribute significantly to the competitive edge a technology-based company is seeking.

Many technology-based companies consider it beneficial to secure regulatory approval of new products prior to competition since market entry is tied to regulatory approval. In some cases this lead-time affords the company a distinct advantage over the competition. On the other hand, in cases when the technology is clearly new and similar products have never been approved before it could merely pave the way for faster approval for competitor's products. Examples of regulatory agencies and procedures that affect market entry are as follows:

1. Food and Drug Administration (FDA);
2. United States Department of Agriculture (USDA);
3. Environmental Protection Agency (EPA);
4. Occupational Safety and Health Association (OSHA);
5. Good Manufacturing Practices (GMP); and
6. Good Laboratory Practices (GLP).

See Exhibit F for questions and answers related to intellectual property.

IMPORT - EXPORT

Anyone involved in technology commercialization must be aware of the import-export laws that govern commodities and data leaving the U.S. Concerns include the commodity, country and maybe end-user, re-export, etc. It is an export violation to send a commodity to Canada knowing they will re-export it to Cuba, a U.S. export controlled country (Exhibit E).

Licenses are a different matter (provided there are no national security issues and there are substitute commodities). If the Canadian licensee makes and sells products for Canada, exports to Cuba do not violate U.S. export laws. If the Canadian company is importing U.S. components for their product, and no substitutes are available, then there is an export control problem (for re-export).

Official import-export regulations are presented in 15 Code of Federal Regulations (CFR) Chapter III, Part 370. If in doubt contact the field office of the Bureau of Export Administration of the Department of Commerce, discuss the technology or product to be exported and allow them to determine if a specific or general license to export is needed. Forms are available from the Office of Export Licensing, P.O. Box 273, Washington DC 20044 or from district offices.

If still unsure written instructions are desired, submit a letter in which request for classification is made. Always include language in any agreement involving possibility for export to occur that places responsibility for abiding by U.S. export law in the hand of the contractee.

(Fees are subject to change. For more recent fees see www.uspto.gov)

Description	Entity Fee, $ (Large/Small)
Patent Application Filing Fees	
Basic filing fee – Utility	750.00/375.00
Basic filing fee - Utility (CPA)	750.00/375.00
Independent claims in excess of three	84.00/42.00
Claims in excess of twenty	18.00/9.00
Multiple dependent claim	280.00/140.00
Surcharge - Late filing fee or oath or declaration	130.00/65.00
Design filing fee	330.00/165.00
Design filing fee (CPA)	330.00/165.00
Plant filing fee	520.00/260.00
Plant filing fee (CPA)	520.00/260.00
Reissue filing fee	750.00/375.00
Reissue filing fee (CPA)	750.00/375.00
Reissue independent claims over original patent	84.00/42.00
Reissue claims in excess of 20 and over original patent	18.00/9.00
Provisional application filing fee	160.00/80.00
Surcharge - Late provisional filing fee or cover sheet	50.00/25.00
Non-English specification	130.00
Patent Post- Allowance Fees	
Utility issue fee	1,300.00/650.00
Design issue fee	470.00/235.00
Plant issue fee	630.00/315.00
Publication fee for early, voluntary, or normal publication	300.00
Publication fee for republication	300.00
Patent Maintenance Fees	
Due at 3.5 years	890.00/445.00
Due at 7.5 years	2,050.00/1,025.00
Due at 11.5 years	3,150.00/1,575.00
Surcharge - Late payment within 6 months	130.00/65.00
Surcharge after expiration - Late payment is unavoidable	700.00
Surcharge after expiration - Late payment is unintentional	1,640.00
Miscellaneous Patent Fees	
Request for continued examination (RCE) (see 37 CFR 1.114)	750.00/375.00
Processing fee, except in provisional applications	130.00
Request for voluntary publication or republication	130.00
Request for expedited examination of a design application	900.00
Requesting publication of SIR - Prior to examiner action	920.00*
Requesting publication of SIR - After examiner action	1,840.00*
Submission of an Information Disclosure Statement	180.00
Processing fee for provisional applications	50.00
For filing a submission after final rejection (see 37 CFR 1.129(a))	750.00/375.00
For each additional invention to be examined (see 37 CFR 1.129(b))	750.00/375.00
Certificate of correction	100.00
Request for ex parte reexamination	2,520.00
Request for inter partes reexamination	8,800.00
Statutory disclaimer	110.00/55.00

* Reduced by basic filing fee paid.

Description	Entity Fee, $ (Large/Small)

Patent Application Extension Fees

Extension for response within first month	110.00/55.00
Extension for response within second month	410.00/205.00
Extension for response within third month	930.00/465.00
Extension for response within fourth month	1,450.00/725.00
Extension for response within fifth month	1,970.00/985.00

Patent Appeals/Interference Fees

Notice of appeal	320.00/160.00
Filing a brief in support of an appeal	160.00/320.00
Request for oral hearing	280.00/140.00

Patent Petition Fees

Petitions to the Commissioner, unless otherwise specified	130.00
Petition to institute a public use proceeding	1,510.00
Petition to revive unavoidably abandoned application	110.00/55.00
Petition to revive unintentionally abandoned application	1,300.00/650.00
Acceptance of an unintentionally delayed claim for priority	1,300.00
Filing an application for patent term adjustment	200.00
Request for reinstatement of term reduced	400.00
Extension of term of patent	1120.00
Initial application for interim extension (see 37 CFR 1.790)	420.00
Subsequent application for interim extension (see 37 CFR 1.790)	220.00

Patent Service Fees

Printed copy of patent w/o color, delivery by USPS, USPTO Box, or electronic means	3.00
Patent Application Publication (PAP)	3.00
Printed copy of patent w/o color, next business day delivery to PTO Box	6.00
Printed copy of plant patent, in color	15.00
Color copy of patent (other than plant patent) or SIR containing a color drawing	25.00
Certified copy of patent application as filed	20.00
Copy of patent-related file wrapper and paper contents of 400 or fewer pages	200.00
Additional fee for each additional 100 pages or portion thereof	40.00
Additional fee for certification of patent-related file wrapper and paper contents	25.00
Copy of first compact disc in a single order of file wrapper and paper contents	55.00
Each additional compact disc in the single order of section 1.19(b)(3)(i)	15.00
Certified or uncertified copy of document, unless otherwise provided	25.00
For assignment records, abstract of title and certification, per patent	25.00
Library service	50.00
List of U.S. patents and SIRs in subclass	3.00
Uncertified statement re status of maintenance fee payments	10.00
Copy of non-U.S. document	25.00
Disclosure document filing fee	10.00
Local delivery box rental, annually	50.00
International type search report	40.00
Self-service copy charge, per page	0.25
Recording each patent assignment, agreement or other paper, per property	40.00
Publication in *Official Gazette*	25.00
Labor charges for services, per hour or fraction thereof	40.00
Unspecified other services, excluding labor	AT COST
Retaining abandoned application	130.00
Handling fee for incomplete or improper application	130.00
Handling fee for withdrawal of SIR	130.00

Description	Entity Fee, $ (Large/Small)
Patent Enrollment Fees	
Application fee (non-refundable)	40.00
Registration examination fee	310.00
Registration to practice	100.00
Reinstatement to practice	40.00
Copy of certificate of good standing	10.00
Certificate of good standing - suitable for framing	20.00
Review of decision of Director, Office of Enrollment and Discipline	130.00
Regrading of seven or fewer questions	460.00
GENERAL FEES	
Finance Service Fees	
Establish deposit account	10.00
Service charge for below minimum balance	25.00
Service charge for below minimum balance restricted subscription deposit account	25.00
Processing each payment refused or charged back	50.00
Computer Service Fees	
Computer records	AT COST
PCT Fees - National Stage	
IPEA - U.S.	720.00/360.00
ISA - U.S.	750.00/375.00
PTO not ISA or IPEA	1,060.00/530.00
Claims meet PCT Article 33(1)-(4) - IPEA - U.S.	100.00/50.00
For filing where search report prepared by EPO or JPO	900.00/450.00
Claims - extra independent (over three)	84.00/42.00
Claims - extra total (over twenty)	18.00/9.00
Claims - multiple dependent	280.00/140.00
Oath or declaration after twenty or thirty months from priority date	130.00/65.00
English translation after twenty or thirty months from priority date	130.00
PCT Fees - International Stage	
Transmittal fee	240.00
PCT search fee - no U.S. application	700.00
PCT search - prior U.S. application	450.00
Supplemental search per additional invention	210.00
Preliminary examination fee - ISA was the U.S.	490.00
Preliminary examination fee - ISA not the U.S.	750.00
Additional invention - ISA was the U.S.	140.00
Additional invention - ISA not the U.S.	270.00
PCT Fees to WIPO or EPO	
Basic application fee (first thirty pages)	407.00*
Basic supplemental fee (for each page over thirty)	9.00*
Handling fee	146.00*
Designation fee per country	88.00*
International search (EPO)	936.00*

*WIPO and EPO fees subject to periodic change due to fluctuations in exchange rate. Refer to the *Official Gazette of the United States Patent and Trademark Office* for current amounts.

Description	Entity Fee, $ (Large/Small)
Trademark Processing Fees	
Application for registration, per class	335.00
Filing an Amendment to Allege Use under § 1(c), per class	100.00
Filing a Statement of Use under § 1(d)(1), per class	100.00
Filing a Request for a Six-month Extension of Time for Filing a Statement of Use under § 1(d)(1), per class	150.00
Application for renewal, per class	400.00
Additional fee for filing renewal application during grace period, per class	100.00
Correcting a deficiency in a renewal application	100.00
Publication of mark under § 12(c), per class	100.00
Issuing new certificate of registration	100.00
Certificate of correction, registrants error	100.00
Filing disclaimer to registration	100.00
Filing amendment to registration	100.00
Filing § 8 affidavit, per class	100.00
Additional fee for filing § 8 affidavit during grace period, per class	100.00
Correcting a deficiency in a § 8 affidavit	100.00
Filing § 15 affidavit, per class	200.00
Petition to the Commissioner	100.00
Petition for cancellation, per class	300.00
Notice of opposition, per class	300.00
Ex parte appeal, per class	100.00
Dividing an application, per new application (file wrapper) created	100.00
Trademark Service Fees	
Printed copy of each registered mark, regular service, dely. by USPS, fax, or PTO Box	3.00
Certified copy of registered mark, with title and/or status, regular service	15.00
Certified copy of registered mark, with title and/or status, expedited local service	30.00
Certified copy of trademark application as filed, regular service	15.00
Certified or uncertified copy of trademark-related file wrapper and contents	50.00
Certified or uncertified copy of trademark document, unless otherwise provided	25.00
For assignment records, abstracts of title and certification per registration	25.00
Self-service copy charge, per page	0.25
Recording trademark assignment, agreement or other paper, first mark per document	40.00
For second and subsequent marks in the same document	25.00
Labor charges for services, per hour or fraction thereof	40.00
Unspecified other services, excluding labor	AT COST
X-SEARCH terminal session time, per hour	40.00
Fastener Quality Act Fees	
Recordal application fee	20.00
Renewal application fee	20.00
Late fee for renewal application	20.00

Average Costs of Domestic and Foreign Patent Application Procedures[1] (EURO)

Country	Initial Costs[8] Drawing up of a patent application by a patent lawyer — lawyer	Filing of application at national patent office — office	lawyer	Request for examination after prior search — office	lawyer	Examination procedure with 2 office actions + search request — lawyer
Germany	2000	205	500	149	130	800
France	1700	360	500	-	-	500
Great Britain	1500	195	640	150	225	800
Italy	2000	400[5]	450	-	-	-
Spain	1000	560	1000	-	-	800
USA[2]	2500	800(400)	300	-	-	2500
Japan	2400	205	1750	1100	560	2500
European Patent (15 claims) (8 countries)[9]	2000	1549	2000	1431	150	1000
International Patent Application (PCT)[6]	2000	2164	2100	1681	150	1000

Average Costs of Domestic and Foreign Patent Application Procedures[1] (EURO) Cont'd

Country	Payment of fee for grant — office	lawyer	Renewal fee for 1st 5 years — office	lawyer	Total cost in 1st 3 years — office	lawyer	Total cost for 20 years — office	lawyer
Germany	90	130	3rd yr 59 / 4th yr 59 / 5th yr 90	80 / 80 / 80	503	3650	~12000	~4800
France	86	100	2nd yr 29 / 3rd yr 32 / 4th yr 37 / 5th yr 51	29 / 29 / 29 / 29	827	2900	~5500	~3400
Great Britain	-	-	5th yr 75	82	300	3200	~6700	~4500
Italy	70[3]	-	1-3rd yr 70 / 4th yr 37 / 5th yr 47	- / 84 / 84	470	2450	~6200	~3900
Spain	25	170	3rd yr 19 / 4th yr 24 / 5th yr 46	60 / 60 / 68	604	3050	~3400	~4200
USA[2]	1210 (605)[2]	250	3.5 yr 940 (470)[2]	150	2010 (1005)[2]	5550	~8130 (4065)[2]	~6000
Japan	850	350	4th yr 500 / 5th yr 500	180 / 180	2155	7550	~85000	~11000
Europe Pat. (15 claims) (8 countries)[6]	715	180	3rd yr 38	80	4078	5400	~19400	~6800
International Patent Application (PCT)[6]	-	-	-[7]	-	3845	5250	-[9]	-[9]

Footnotes

1. The figures for office fees were supplied by each country by the patent office. Lawyers' fees are based on information given by several lawyers from each country. Both sets of figures correspond to patent applications of average scope and level of difficulty.
2. For certain applicants, referred to as "small entities", the US regulation of fees intends a reduction of 50% for most of the office fees. The following applicants are "small entities":
    - Non-profit-making organizations, e.g. schools, universities, organizations for sport, culture, education etc. These organizations' public welfare status must be recognized and they are not permitted to make a profit in favor of private persons.
    - Small companies, i.e. firms with < 500 employees during the previous business year, including all temporary employees and casual workers.
    - Independent inventors.
    The table shows the costs for large entities, while the costs for small entities are marked in brackets.
3. Repay when patent is granted
4. With (without) examination.
5. No search request
6. Without national phase
7. Renewal fees only in the national phase
8. Costs arising in the initial phase of the procedure
9. Depends on quantity of states in which protection finally sought

EXHIBIT B – PATENT EXAMPLE

[Bar Code]

United States Patent [19[	[11] Patent Number:	5,478,814
Packman	[45] Date of Patent:	*Dec. 26, 1995

[54] HEMORRHOIDAL, OTHER COMPOSITIONS AND METHODS OF TREATMENT

[75] Inventor: Elias W. Packman, Merion, Pa.

[73] Assignee: Norman H. Oksman, Katonah, N.Y.; A part interest.

[*] Notice: The term of this patent shall not extend beyond the expiration date of Pat. No. 4,945,084.

[21] Appl. No.: 34,151

[22] Filed: Mar. 22, 1993

Related U.S. Application Data

[63] Continuation of Ser. No. 485,573 Feb. 27, 1990, Pat. No. 5,196,405, which is a continuation of Ser. No. 70,904, Jul. 8, 1987, Pat. No. 4,945,084.

[51] Int. Cl.^{6} A61K 31/715
[52] U.S. Cl. 514/53; 514/882; 514/946; 514/947; 514/960
[58] Field of Search 514/53; 882, 946, 514/947, 960

[56] References Cited

U.S PATENT DOCUMENTS

Re. 28,011	5/1974	Urbin	424/94.3
3,432,489	3/1969	Nitta et al.	514/53
3,935,310	1/1976	Homan	424/195.1
4,192,866	3/1980	Anderson	424/697
4,613,498	9/1986	Crosby	424/697
4,626,433	12/1986	Gross	424/682
4,912,093	3/1990	Michaeli	514/53
4,945,084	7/1990	Packman	514/53
4,975,281	12/1990	Harwood et al.	424/441
5,196,405	3/1993	Packman	514/53

OTHER PUBLICATIONS

Medium Treatment and New Drug, vol. 6, No. 8, Shinryo 40 Shinyako Ohtaka, Oct. 1969.
American Journal of Surgery, pp. 809-812, Borrers et al. Jul. 1984.

South African Medical Journal, pp. 996-1000, Halter Jul. 1984

Handbook of Non-Prescription Drugs, Hemorrhoidal Products, 7th Edition American Pharmaceutical Assoc., pp. 645-655, Hodes, Nov. 1982.

The Extra Pharmacopeia, 28th Edition, p. 84, Martindale, Dec. 1983.

Remington's Pharmaceutical Sciences, 17th Edition, p. 815, 1985.

The New England Journal of Medicine, pp. 459–460, Solomon Jun. 1986.

The American Journal of Medicine, vol. 83, pp. 1-127, May 1987.

Primary Examiner – Marianne M. Cintins
Assistant Examiner – K. Weddington
Attorney, Agent, or Firm – Weiser & Associates

[57]   Abstract

Hemorrhoidal compositions containing disaccharide polysulfate-aluminum compounds such as sucralfate, above or in combination with other hemorrhoidal products, as an agent effective for alleviating the symptoms of anorectal disease when topically applied to the human skin. Method for alleviating the symptoms of hemorrhoids in humans. Compositions containing disaccharide polysulfate-aluminum compounds such as sucralfate, alone or in combination with antibiotics, antifungal agents, anti-acne agents, or local anesthetics as an active agent effective in promoting the healing of wounds which are not anorectal when topically applied to the surface of a wound. Method for promoting healing at the surface of a wound in humans.

13 Claims, No Drawings

I claim:

1. A therapeutic method for alleviating symptoms of wounded tissue not associated with or caused by high acidity which comprises applying to the wounded tissue a composition which comprises a therapeutic amount of sucralfate as a vehicle for and with a topical, therapeutically active agent, forming a complex between the wounded tissue and the sucralfate, and promoting prolonged adhesion of the therapeutically-active compound to the wounded tissue.

2. The therapeutic method of claim 1, wherein the therapeutically-active agent is selected from the group consisting of an antifungal, an analgesic, an anesthetic, a protectant, a counter-irritant, an astringent, a wound-healing agent, an antiseptic, a keratolytic, an anti-cholinergic, a biocidal and an anti-acne agent.

3. The therapeutic method of claim 1 wherein the amount of sucralfate is from about 0.01% to about 0.1%.

4. The therapeutic method of claim 1 wherein the amount of sucralfate is from about 0.01% to about 25%.

5. A therapeutic method for alleviating symptoms of a wound other than anorectal which comprises applying topically to the wound a composition which comprises a therapeutic amount of sucralfate and a pharmaceutically-acceptable topical vehicle.

6. The therapeutic method of claim 5 wherein the topical vehicle is selected from the group consisting of a cream, gel, paste, foam, aerosol, lotion and an ointment.

7. The therapeutic method of claim 5 wherein the amount of sucralfate is from about 0.01% to about 0.1%.

8. The therapeutic method of claim 5 wherein the amount of sucralfate is from about 0.01% to about 25%.

9. The therapeutic method of claim 5 wherein the topical vehicle is a pulverulent mixture.

10. The therapeutic method of claim 5 wherein the composition also comprises a therapeutic amount of a topical, therapeutically active agent.

11. A suppository for the treatment of hemorrhoids or of an anorectal disease or anorectal disorder which comprises a therapeutic amount of sucralfate and a pharmaceutically acceptable suppository vehicle.

12. The suppository of claim 11 wherein the amount of sucralfate is from about 0.01% to about 0.1%.

13. The suppository of claim 11 wherein the amount of sucralfate is from about 0.01% to about 25%.

This invention relates to a method and medication for the treatment of wounds and lesions. It further relates to a method and medication for the treatment of the symptoms of anorectal disease or irritation and in particular relates to a method and medication for the treatment of hemorrhoids.

Anorectal disease is an annoying and uncomfortable disorder. Hemorrhoids is a common ailment of the anorectal area and may be either or both internal and external. Anorectal disorders are characterized by the signs and symptoms of itching, burning, pain, bleeding, seepage, protrusion, inflammation, irritation, swelling general discomfort and changes in bowel pattern or any combination thereof. Many remedies have been suggested and tried for the alleviation of these ailments with varying degrees of success. Anorectal disease, though rare in other animals, is very common in humans. No human is immune. The vast majority of adults suffer from one or more anorectal symptoms at some time in their life. Anorectal disease has caused an unaccountable number of man-hours to be lost annually in the work place.

Compositions have previously been developed which generally relieve either the itching or inflammation but few have been successful in reducing or completely eliminating both. Thus, the efficacy of these compositions in relieving or curing the symptoms of such diseases is uncertain.

Some of the compositions disclosed to be useful in the treatment of hemorrhoids include a powdered mixture of alum, quinine sulfate and aspirin mixed with petroleum jelly (U.S. Pat. No. 4,613,498); a mixture of oxidase enzymes (U.S. Pat. Re. 28,011); a mixture of the powdered or chipped limbs or roots of the shrub Celastrus scandens (U.S. Pat. No. 3,935,310); a mixture of polyglycerides and ripe berry products of the plant Solanum carolinese to which sublimed sulfur, ammonium alum and turpentine are added (U.S. Pat. No. 4,192,866). Other compositions, which are well known, include those marketed over-the-counter. Non-limiting examples of these numerous products of varying compositions include Anusol, Balneol, Lanacane, Nupercainal, Preparation H and Vaseline.

The FDA has published a monograph relating to Anorectal Drug Products for over-the-counter human use; the proposed monograph was published at Federal Register 45 35576, May 27, 1980. The monograph lists over 75 ingredients which are contained in marketed products submitted to the FDA panel for review. The ingredients are classified as being local anesthetics, vasoconstrictors, protectants, counterirritants, astringents, wound-healing agents, antiseptics, keratolytics and anticholingerics. The composition used in this invention is not listed in the monograph.

It is evident that numerous attempts have been made to solve the problem of the treatment of hemorrhoids and yet no entirely satisfactory solution is yet available. There is a real need for a safe and effective product and treatment for the relief and cure of anorectal disease.

It is, therefore, an object of the present invention to provide a preparation for use in the treatment of anorectal disease and irritation.

It is another object of the present invention to provide a preparation which reduces swelling, inflammation and pain caused or attributable to anorectal disease.

It is a further object of the instant invention to provide a method for treating the symptoms of anorectal disease to control or relieve such symptoms at a wound site.

Another object of the present invention is the relief of the symptoms of anorectal disease, like inflamation, irritation, itching and the accompanying or consequential psychological and/or emotional effects.

Another object of the instant invention is to provide a preparation which combines with damaged tissue, (where such exists) to form a protective barrier over a wound or lesion.

A further object of the instant invention to provide a preparation which forms a protective barrier for a wound and also acts as a carrier for materials such as antibiotics, local anesthetics, antihistamines, antiacne materials and antifungal materials.

The invention provides a method for treating the symptoms of anorectal disease by topically administering to the perianal region of a human body, in an amount effective to control or relieve such symptoms, a composition which is safe and effective and includes as an active ingredient a disaccharide polysulfate-aluminum compound.

This invention provides a composition and a method for treating dermal wounds or lesions which are not caused by conditions of high acidity or chemotherapy.

The composition of the instant invention comprises a disaccharide polysulfate-aluminum compound such as sucralfate in combination with a pharmaceutically acceptable carrier. The composition is typically dispersed in a topical medium as the carrier of choice.

It is known to one skilled in the art that the use of disaccharide polysulfate-aluminum compounds is an accepted medical treatment for peptic ulcer. Such compounds are disclosed in U.S. Pat. No. 3,432,489 to Nitta et al (Nitta), which is incorporated herein by reference. Typical compounds are sucrose polysulfate-aluminum compounds, lactose polysulfate-aluminum compounds and maltose polysulfate-aluminum compounds. The sulfur and aluminum contents are commonly in the range of 7-13% and 11-24%, respectively and, therefore, generally contain 1-4 aluminum atoms per sulfur atom.

Nitta discloses the internal use of these compounds in the treatment of peptic ulcers by oral administration. The disaccharide polysulfate-aluminum compounds are hardly absorbed in the digestive tract. The dosage of the compounds in human beings is disclosed to be preferably between 2 and 12 g per day administered divided into several doses. Each unit dose preferably contains between 500 and 1000 mg of the compound along with the carrier or excipient.

One of the compounds disclosed in Nitta is a sucrose polysulfate aluminum compound referred to in The Merck Index, Merck & Co., Inc., Rahway, N.J., 10th Edition, 1983 at number 8755 as sucralfate. This compound is currently marketed as an anti-ulcerative agent. The disaccharide polysulfate-aluminum complexes are referred to hereinafter for the purposes of simplicity as sucralfate. Sucralfate has been established in the United States Pharmacopeia Official Monograph (USP 23) as fructose and sucrose hydrous basic aluminum complexes. The monograph is made part of this specification. Sucralfate complexes of this type are commercially available for use in pharmaceutical preparations and are intended to be within the scope of the invention.

When, as disclosed by Nitta, sucralfate was administered orally to rats whose pylorus was ligated according to Shay's method, the development of Shay rat ulcer was suppressed. In addition, the development of histamine-induced ulcer in guinea pig was suppressed by the administration of sucralfate.

Nitta also discloses that human patients having gastric or duodenal ulcers were given oral administration of sucralfate. All patients experienced curing effects of the compound.

Peptic ulcer is a pathology characterized by erosion of the mucosa. The mucosa is located anatomically in areas bathed by acid. The major areas where mucosa occurs include the esophagus, the stomach (gastric mucosa) and the duodenum (duodenal mucosa).

Nitta teaches that the pH of gastric juices in the mouse ranges from about 1.0 to 4.0. Sucralfate was shown to have an antacid effect. Therefore, sucralfate is understood to work in areas of high acidity, more particularly at a pH of about 1.5 to about 3.5. The use of acid neutralizing substances such as antacids are contraindicated for administration with sucralfate since such substance would tend to lessen, if not cancel out, the effect of the sucralfate. The literature and medical practice therefore suggest that the benefit of sucralfate is optimally obtained in an acidic medium.

Sucralfate is now recognized by those skilled in the art as being comparable to cimetidine in the treatment of peptic ulcer disease (Borrers et al, Am. J. Surg., 148 (1984) pp 809-12) and in short term duodenal and gastric ulcer healing (Halter, S. Afr. Med. Journal 23 (1984) 996-1000).

In addition, oral ulcers or mucositis which have developed as a direct consequence of treatment of patients receiving chemotherapy or radiation or both have been treated with sucralfate suspension with some success. (Solomon, Cell 351, 459 (August, 1986).

In contrast, the wounds, lesions, inflammations, etc. which are treated in accordance with the instant invention are not associated with or caused by condition of high acidity or by reaction to a chemical agent (chemotherapy).

Anorectal disease, including hemorrhoids, is concerned with three parts of the body, the perianal area, the anal canal and the rectum. The causes of hemorrhoids include predisposing causes such as erect posture, heredity, occupation and diet and precipitating causes such as constipation, diarrhea, pregnancy, anal infection, rectal carcinoma, pelvic tumors, cardiac failure, portal hypertension, coughing, sneezing, vomiting and physical exertion. Hemorrhoids are abnormally large or symptomatic conglomerates of blood vessels, supporting tissues and overlying mucous membrane or skin of the anorectal area. In addition to hemorrhoids, other anorectal disorders which are treated in accordance with the instant invention include anal fistulas and anal fissures.

Essentially, the condition of anorectal disease is not affected by pH or acidity. In fact, the pH within the anorectal region is very different than that which prevails in the stomach. The pH in the human stomach is generally below 4.0 and commonly in the range of 1.0 to about 2.0. Gastric juice analysis has a pH of about 1.0 to 4.0 (see Nitta). The pH in the anorectal region is close to neutrality, typically between about 6 and about 7. The rectal pH ranges from neutral to basic. Therefore, anorectal disease is not associated with low pH or acidic secretion and acid neutralizing materials have no effect on the progression control or retarding of anorectal disease.

It was thus unexpected that the administration of sucralfate aids in the relief of the symptoms of anorectal disease.

The symptoms of anorectal disease which are relieved by the method of treatment and composition of the instant invention include itching, burning, pain inflammation, irritation, swelling, discomfort and bleeding. In addition, the size of a hemorrhoid can be reduced by treatment with the compositions of the invention.

The compositions of the invention are applied topically to the anorectal area to obtain relief from the above mentioned symptoms. Depending on the particular symptom, the administration is on any or all

133

of the regions of the anorectal area including the perianal area or portion of the skin and buttocks immediately surrounding the anus, the modified anal skin area of the anal canal and the mucous membrane of the rectum.

The compositions are applied topically to the involved area until the symptoms are relieved. The compositions are administered once or several times over the course of a single day. The administration is continued for as many days as are necessary to relieve the condition being treated.

The amounts of sucralfate which is administered in accordance with the invention is noteworthy. Particularly, it has been noted in accordance with the invention that the compositions of the invention form a visible complex of the white sucralfate with the inflamed and damage area. Thus the compositions make available prolonged and extended treatment.

In the composition of the invention the sucralfate is present in an amount from about 0.1% to 25% but it can be present in smaller amounts like 0.01% to less than 0.1% or in amounts over 25% to 50%.

The unit dose administered is in the range of from 0.01 to 1.0 g per dose not to exceed about 5 g in a 24 hour period. Preferably the unit dose is from about 0.05 to 0.5 g per dose, although the unit dose can be adjusted upward or downward as warranted by the size of the area being treated.

When an ointment containing 5% sucralfate was applied topically to the anorectal region of subjects suffering from hemorrhoids immediately before and immediately after defecation, the subjects immediately experienced relief from pain. In addition, after 5 days, bleeding and the size of the hemorrhoid were decreased.

It was observed that the white ointment containing the sucralfate adhered to the hemorrhoid even after defecation. No adherence was observed when the same ointment without sucralfate was applied. Thus, this was a visual demonstration that complexing occurred between the sucralfate and the inflamed and damaged area. Unexpectedly, this complex formation occurred in a non-acidic environment.

In another embodiment of the invention the sucralfate is administered to a patient with the symptoms of anorectal disease in conjunction with the administration of a product therapeutically helpful in the symptomatic treatment of anorectal disease. Examples of over-the-counter products which can be administered with sucralfate include but are not limited to, A-Caine, Americaine, Anusol, Balneol, BiCozene, Blue-Gray, Calmol 4, Cortef Rectal Itch Ointment, Diothane, Epinephricaine Ointment, Gentzy Wipes, Hemorrin, HTO Ointment, HTO Stainless, Lanacane, Mediconet, Non-Steroid Proctofoam, Nupercainal Ointment, Nupercainal Suppositories, Pazo, Perifoam, Peterson's Ointment, Pontocaine, Preparation H, Preparation H Cleansing Pads, Proctodon, Rantex, Rectal Medicone Suppositories, Rectal Medicone Unquent, Tanicaine Ointment, Tanicaine Suppositories, Tronolane, Tucks Cream and Ointment, Tucks Pads, Vaseline Pure Petroleum Jelly, Wyanoid Ointment and Wyanoid Suppositories. See also Federal Register, 45 33576, May 22, 1980.

The main pharmacologic agents formulated in the above products include local anesthetics, vasoconstrictors, protectants, counterirritants, astringents, wound healing agents, antiseptics, keratolytics, and anticholingerics. See also Federal Register 45 35576, May 27, 1980. It is within the scope of the instant invention that sucralfate is administered in combination with any or all of these agents. Preferred agents include those known as topical anesthetics, protectants, vasoconstrictors and wound healing agents.

Local or topical anesthetics temporarily relieve pain, burning, itching, discomfort and irritation by preventing transmission of nerve impulses. Non-limiting examples of topical anesthetics include

134

benzocaine, pramoxine hydrochloride, benzyl alcohol, dibucaine hydrochloride, dicylonine hydrochloride, lidocaine, tetracaine and tetracaine hydrochloride. See also Federal Register, 45 35576, May 27, 1980. Preferred are benzocaine and pramoxine hydrochloride which are generally recognized as being safe and effective.

Protectants act to prevent irritation of the anorectal area and water loss from the skin layer by forming a physical barrier on the skin. There is little or not absorption of the protectants. Non-limiting examples include aluminum hydroxide gel, calamine, cocoa butter, cod liver oil, glycerin, kaolin, lanolin, mineral, shark liver oil, starch, white petrolatum, wood alcohol and zinc oxide. See also Federal Register, 45 35576, May 27, 1980.

Vasoconstrictors act to reduce inflammation, irritation and swelling by constricting the symptomatic abnormally large conglomerates of blood vessels. Non-limiting examples include ephedrine and epinephrine. See also Federal Register, 45 35576, May 27, 1980.

In non-prescription hemorrhoidal products, several ingredients are claimed to be effective in promoting wound healing or tissue repair in anorectal disease. Non-limiting examples of wound healing agents include skin respiratory factor (SRF), a water soluble extract of brewer's yeast also referred to as live yeast cell derivative, cod liver oil, vitamin A and vitamin D. See also Federal Register, 45 35576, May 27, 1980.

It is within the scope of the instant invention that sucralfate be administered to a patient having the symptoms of anorectal disease in a separate composition administered in conjunction with the administration of a known composition for the treatment of anorectal disease. Thus, in one embodiment the composition containing sucralfate is administered to the patient immediately before or after the administration of the hemorrhoidal product. In another embodiment the administration of the two compositions is alternated so that several minutes or hours pass before the administration of the second composition.

In another embodiment of the invention sucralfate and other pharmacologic agents used in the treatment of the symptoms of anorectal disease are formulated in the same composition, for example with a wound healing agent, a protectant, a vasoconstrictor, or a local anesthetic or with more than one of these agents.

In a more particular embodiment within the scope of the invention, sucralfate is mixed with an existing product for the treatment of anorectal disease. For example, sucralfate is mixed with Preparation H to obtain a composition of the invention.

It is also within the scope of the instant invention that a pharmaceutical composition containing sucralfate be administered topically to wounds or lesions which are other than anorectal. What is characteristic of these wounds or lesions is that they are of the type which is known to be treated topically.

The wounds or lesions can be caused by infections such as a fungal infection. An example is the lesion caused by athlete's foot. Additionally the wounds or lesions can be caused by allergic reaction, such as that caused by poison ivy, poison oak or poison sumac, or caused by infection or aggravation of another condition such as occurs with acne. The wound can also be caused by physical trauma to the site of the wound to cause a cut, incision or abrasion.

In a particular embodiment of the invention, topical administration of a composition containing sucralfate is used to promote the healing of abrasions such as those which are typically received as a

135

result of physical trauma to joints such as knees, elbows, knuckles, shoulders, hips, shins and the like.

The composition of the invention is applied topically to the involved area until the wound has healed. The compositions are administered once or several times a day for from one day to a week or more until the healing occurs.

In the composition of the invention the sucralfate is present in an amount from about 0.1% to 25% but it can be present in smaller amounts like 0.01% to less than 0.1% or in amounts over 25% to 50%.

The unit dose administered is in the range of from 0.01 to 2.0 g per dose not to exceed about 10 g in a 24-hour period. Preferably the unit dose is from about 0.05 to 0.5 g per dose, although the unit dose can be adjusted upward or downward as warranted by the size of the area being treated.

In a non-limiting example of this embodiment, knee abrasions on basketball players which were caused by falls during a basketball game were treated with an ointment containing 5% sucralfate. The applied white ointment could still be observed on the wounded area 24 hours after the first application. The ointment was reapplied daily. Fusion was stopped after twenty-four hours and good healing occurred over a three-day period.

It was observed that with each topical application of a sucralfate containing ointment to a wound, anorectal or otherwise, the sucralfate formed a visible complex with the tissue associated with the wound. Thus a further embodiment of the invention is the use of the composition containing sucralfate as a carrier composition for an additional pharmaceutical compound or compounds. The sucralfate complexes with the wounded area thereby holding the additional pharmaceutical compound near the wound. In this manner for example, an antibiotic, a steroid, an antifungal agent, a biocidal agent, a local anesthetic or an anti-acne agent or a combination thereof is applied topically to a wound or lesion site in a composition containing sucralfate and is kept in place by the complexing action of the sucralfate with the tissues in the wound or lesion area.

For the topical treatment of the anorectal and non-anorectal wounds the compositions are in the form of ointments, creams, gels, pastes, suppositories, pads, liquids, foams or aerosols or any other composition suitable for topical administration.

In other aspects, the composition of the invention may contain conventional materials and ingredients and conform to pharmacologically accepted formulations.

Carriers into which the active ingredients can be incorporated to produce satisfactory composition are those commonly employed for topical application of cosmetics or pharmaceuticals. Such carriers or vehicles incude lotions, ointments, aerosols, water solutions, creams (preferably of the oil-in-water type), pulverulent mixtures, gelled sticks and the like. Depending on the physical nature of the vehicle or carrier employed, the method of this invention can be practiced by applying such compositions topically in any appropriate manner according to the particular type of carrier employed.

In preparing the desired pharmaceutical form of the present compositions, various additives, diluents and adjuvants can be utilized. These illustratively include perfumes, essential oils, surfactants, ointment type bases, higher fatty acids, propellants, thickening agents, humectants, silicone-type fluids and solid diluents as is known in the art.

The following examples are not intended to limit the invention but are merely illustrative thereof. It is understood that one of average skill in the art would be able to make substitutions, change proportions, make other variations, all within the scope of the teachings and without departing from the spirit of the invention and without undue experimentation.

EXAMPLE 1

Ointment
An ointment was formulated by mixing the following ingredients:

Ingredient	% by Weight
Stearic Acid	07
Cetyl Alcohol	02
Mineral Oil	20
Glycerin	10
Triethanolamine	02
Purified Water qs	100

To this ointment, there is added sucralfate to obtain a 5% final concentration.

EXAMPLE 2

Gel
A gel composition was prepared by mixing the following ingredients:

Ingredient	% by Weight
Samuet	000.3
Purified Water qs.	100

To this gel there is added sucralfate to obtain a 5% final concentration.

EXAMPLE 3

Cream
A cream was prepared by mixing the following ingredients:

5% Sucralfate
qs. Hydrophylic Ointment

EXAMPLE 4

Suppository
A suppository was formulated by mixing the following ingredients:

Ingredient	% by Weight
Polyethylene Glycol 400	10
Polyethylene Glycol 1500	30
Polyethylene Glycol 6000	60

To this formulation there is added sucralfate to a final concentration of 5% and the formulation was formed into the desired shape.

EXAMPLE 5

Ointment

An ointment was prepared by mixing the following ingredients:

Ingredient	% by Weight
Preparation H	95
Sucralfate	5

EXAMPLE 6

Ointment

An ointment was formulated by mixing the following ingredients:

Ingredient	% by Weight
Stearic Acid	7
Cetyl Alcohol	2
Mineral Oil	20
Glycerin	10
Triethanol Amine	2
Benzocaine	6
Sucralfate	5
Purified Water	48

EXAMPLE 7

The ointment of Example 1 containing 5% sucralfate was compared for efficacy against hemorrhoids with the same ointment without sucralfate.

The total number of subjects was 6. All subjects were between 55 and 70 years of age and suffered with external hemorrhoids. Symptomatically, all subjects experienced pain and bleeding during defecation. In addition, each suffered from hemorrhoids sufficiently large that they were readily observed and measured.

Three of the subjects were treated with the ointment without sucralfate and three were treated with the ointment containing 5% sucralfate. The ointment was applied immediately before and immediately after defecation in an amount sufficient to cover the perianal area and the anal canal as a thin covering.

Over a 5-day-period, of the three subjects who were treated with the ointment alone, only one experienced some relief in that there was some reduction of pain and some reduction of bleeding during defecation. The other two subjects had no relief of symptoms and after three days requested a change in treatment because of the lack of relief.

The three subjects who were treated with the 5% sucralfate ointment all reported reduction or absence of pain and reduction or absence of bleeding during defecation. A marked reduction in the size of the external hemorrhoid to almost normal was visually observed. The results are tabulated in the following table.

Subject #	5% Sucralfate	Response		
		Pain	Bleeding	Size/Hem.
1	No	0	0	0
2	No	0	0	0
3	No	+	+	0
4	Yes	++	++	++
5	Yes	++	+++	++
6	Yes	+++	+++	++

Scale 0 = No relief, + = Some reduction, ++ = Significant reduction, and +++ = Complete absence of symptom

EXAMPLE 8

The ointment of Example 5 was applied before and after defecation to a patient suffering from external hemorrhoids as described in Example 7. Relief from the symptoms of pain and bleeding during defecation was obtained and a reduction in the size of the external hemorrhoids was visually observed.

EXAMPLE 9

The ointment of Example 6 was applied before and after defecation to a patient suffering from external hemorrhoids as described in Example 7. Relief from the symptoms of pain and bleeding during defecation was obtained and a reduction in the size of the external hemorrhoids was visually observed.

EXAMPLE 10

Knee abrasions on three adult males, ages 19-21, as the result of a basketball game were treated with the 5% sucralfate ointment of Example 1 as follows.

The wound was cleaned by washing and the 5% sucralfate ointment was applied. The fusion was stopped by the next day in each case. The ointment was reapplied daily. Good healing occurred over a three-day period. Sucralfate could be seen to be present on a wound 24 hours after a single application.

In the above examples, ingredients other than those recited can be added to achieve a desirable pharmaceutical effect. The physical form of the product can be any of those known to the cosmetic art.

The compositions of the invention are administered topically to the site of the wound or lesion once or several times a day depending on the condition which is being treated as is known to one skilled in the art.

This invention provides a composition which is relatively simple to prepare and to apply, and it has been found effective in accomplishing its desired purpose.

Although particular formulations have been shown and described above, modifications may be made, and it is intended in the claims to cover all modifications which come within the spirit and scope of the invention.

140

EXHIBIT C – INVENTION DISCLOSURE CHECKLIST AND EXAMPLES

Answer the following to the best of your knowledge.

1. Is the patent application technically correct?   Yes_____   No_____

2. Does the application disclose all details necessary to enable one skilled in the art to make and use everything in the scope of the broadest claim? See page 2.   Yes_____   No_____

3. Are the best methods for making and using the invention disclosed in the application? See page 2.
Yes_____   No_____

4. Are all the compounds, processes, uses and formulations that were actually made or practiced and that gave positive results included in the scope of the claims?   Yes_____   No_____

5. Have the most relevant references been discussed with the Patent Division? See page 2.
Yes_____   No_____

6. Does any existing information or data appear to contradict any statement or data in the application?
Yes_____   No_____

7. In order to cover all aspects of the invention, should the application include additional claims to intermediates, processes, uses or formulations that are not now expressly claimed?
Yes_____   No_____

8.   Have any limitations critical to operability (such as essential reaction conditions, concentrations, dosages, modes of administration or other necessary conditions) been omitted?
Yes_____   No_____

9. Do the process descriptions cover the full scope of reaction variables?
Yes_____   No_____   N/A_____

10. Can the compounds be made by any commercially significant route other than those taught in the application?
Yes_____   No_____   N/A_____

11. Do the process or method claims include all essential limitations but no non-essential ones?
Yes_____   No_____   N/A_____

12. Should any other facts relating to the invention be considered? See page 2.
Yes_____   No_____

13. Should the inventorship be reconsidered?   Yes_____   No_____

I have read the application text and have answered the above questions to the best of my knowledge and ability.

_____   _____
Inventor   Date

_____   _____
Inventor   Date

_____   _____
Inventor   Date

Disclosed to and understood by me this _____ day of _____, 20__.
Signature:_____

141

Notes

The law requires that the description of the invention in the patent application be complete enough to enable one skilled in the art to which the invention relates to make and use the invention. This requirement pertains not only to every embodiment within the scope of the broadest claim, but also to all intermediates, starting from a known compound or source, used in making any claimed compound. The description must teach how to make the invention and how to use it.

The law also requires that a patent application contain a description of the best mode contemplated by the inventor(s) for carrying out the invention. You, as the inventor(s), should determine what, in your opinion, is the best way to carry out the invention, and that way must be described in the patent application.

A duty of candor and good faith toward the Patent and Trademark Office rests on the inventor(s), on each attorney or agent and on every other individual who is substantively involved in the preparation or prosecution of the application. Information is "material" where (1) it creates, by itself or in combination with other information, a suggestion of unpatentability of a claim; or (2) it supports a position of unpatentability taken by the Patent and Trademark Office which the applicant (inventor) disputes, or it is inconsistent with a position in support of patentability on which the applicant relies. The failure to disclose material information can result in allegations of fraudulent patent procurement being raised against the inventor(s), attorney(s) and others involved in the patenting effort.

Furthermore, the presumption of validity of a patent is strengthened if the Patent and Trademark Office examiner considers the closest prior art before allowing the patent to issue. Therefore, it behooves us to be sure that all of the most relevant prior art is disclosed. You are not required to make a literature search, but you are required to disclose relevant references of which you are aware.

Failure to comply with any of the above requirements may result in invalidation of the patent. In some cases, the penalties may be much more severe, such as money damages against the company and sanctions against the attorney.

INVENTION DISCLOSURE

An invention disclosure should be made when something new and useful has been conceived or developed, or when unusual, unexpected, or unobvious research results have been achieved and can be utilized.

The purpose of this disclosure form is to permit evaluation of your invention to determine whether the invention is patentable and whether commercial development is feasible. The invention should be clearly described so that someone having knowledge in the field of the invention can understand the technical merits of the invention, its usefulness, and possible practical applications. Information that helps evaluators appreciate the invention will increase its ultimate chances for successful patenting and later market development. This is the goal in Section 1-4 of the attached Invention Disclosure Form.

The remainder of the disclosure covers certain general issues that need to be taken into account with every invention. The first is public disclosure of the invention (Section 5), because such disclosure places severe limitations on available patent protection. Non-confidential disclosure of an invention may initiate a one year period within which a U.S. patent application may be filed. If an application is not filed within that time, U.S. law prevents one from obtaining patent protection of the disclosed invention. The patent laws of most other countries are even more strict: the right to patent protection is lost immediately upon public disclosure unless a U.S. patent application is filed prior to such disclosure. Thus, to ensure the possibility of worldwide patent protection, it is important that invention disclosures be submitted for timely review so that a U.S. patent application can be filed before public disclosure occurs.

Determine ownership and licensing rights in the invention. Identification of the financial support used during the development of the invention helps determine whether there are contractual obligations to external research sponsors which provide such support.

Identify all individuals who contributed to the development of the invention. It is important to note that these individuals may not meet the legal criteria for inventorship. Legal inventorship is determined later by a patent attorney at the time claims are drafted and a patent application is filed. All Creators should date and sign this form.

Contents of each page should be witnessed and the witness should date and sign each page in the space provided. (A witness should be knowledgeable in the area of the invention and able to understand the content of the disclosure.)

If hard copy is completed the back of the disclosure sheet or appended sheets may be used if the form space is not sufficient and the form is. You may include, if you wish, additional comments that you or the other inventors may have regarding the invention. **IN NO CASE SHOULD THE FORM BE COMPLETED AND RETURNED BY ELECTRONIC MAIL SINCE THAT MAY CONSTITUTE PUBLIC DISCLOSURE WHICH MAY RESULT IN LOSS OF ALL OR PART OF POTENTIAL FOR PATENT PROTECTION.**

CHECKLIST FOR COMPLETING THIS DISCLOSURE

- Review the Disclosure Guidelines for each Section.
- Review Invention Disclosure and Appendices for completeness of responses.
- Attach the following where applicable
  a. all cited materials
  b. supplemental sheets with typed responses
  c. diagrams
  d. scientific articles and patent search results
  e. one-page non-confidential abstract
  f. Appendix A, if Invention includes software as an essential or major component of Disclosure.
- Complete inventor checklist
- Be sure all required signatures are provided.

INVENTION DISCLOSURE

Submitted by (Contact Person):_____

print or type

Business (if applicable):_____

Address_____

City _____State _____ Zip Code _____

Work Phone: _____Home Phone: _____

Facsimile: _____

A patentable invention may be any new and useful process, machine, manufacture, or composition of matter, or any new and useful improvement thereof. Under patent law, this is also interpreted to include drugs, newly discovered, mutated or genetically engineered microorganisms or plants, new or altered forms of plant life, vaccines, cells, tissue and organ cultures, products of recombinant DNA research, hybrid cell cultures, processes involving microorganisms, monoclonal and polyclonal antibodies, engineered proteins, some computer programs, plants, devices and designs.

1. TITLE OF INVENTION (Brief, but comprehensive, technically accurate and descriptive)

_____

_____

2. FINANCIAL SUPPORT/ CONTRACT IDENTIFICATION: Identify the specific grant or contract number(s) (not the account number) and external sponsors (governmental agencies, industrial sponsors, private agencies, or others) which provided support used to defray costs related to the research from which the invention resulted. Provide the identity of any other sources of support, financial or in-kind, that was associated with the discovery. Identify any future sources of funding and the nature of the work to be performed that is related to the invention. In the case of software indicate the likely hood of future revision, modification and/or improvement. This information is needed to determine whether this invention is subject to any commitments or restrictions arising from the terms of sponsorship. Be specific about <u>all</u> of your research support that led, in whole or in part, to your Invention.

a) Collaboration with other institution(s) (list institutions; if none, so state)

Agency	Contract/Grant ID	Co/Ctr	PI On Grant
_____	_____	_____	_____
_____	_____	_____	_____
_____	_____	_____	_____

b) Federal Funds (if none, so state)

Agency	Contract/Grant ID	Co/Ctr	PI On Grant
_____	_____	_____	_____
_____	_____	_____	_____
_____	_____	_____	_____

Disclosed to and understood by me this _____ day of _____, 20__.

Signature:_____

c) Corporate/Industrial, Foundation, or Private Agency Sponsors (including any gifts; if none, so state)

Agency	Contract/Grant ID	Co/Ctr	PI On Grant
_____	_____	_____	_____
_____	_____	_____	_____
_____	_____	_____	_____

d) University funding sources (i.e. University or other state funding sources, seed grants, bridge grant, faculty start-up/development packages; if none, so state)

Souce	Contract/Grant ID	Co/Ctr	PI On Grant
_____	_____	_____	_____
_____	_____	_____	_____
_____	_____	_____	_____

If work is to be continued, what other funding sources do you anticipate will be used? (If none, so state)

_____

_____

_____

3. PRE-EXISTING WORKS OF THIRD PARTIES: Identify any pre-existing works of third parties which your Invention derives from, integrates or otherwise would be required in order to practice your Invention (if none, so state). Attach additional sheets if necessary.

Patents: _____

Copyrights:_____

Processes/Procedures:_____

Trademarks for Products or Services: _____

Outside sources of materials received under written agreements (e.g. Material Transfer Agreements, contracts, letters, emails) or other sources (if none, so state).

Biological Materials/Equipment or Supplies Computer Programs or Software Received	Source	Date
_____	_____	_____
_____	_____	_____

4. PUBLIC DISCLOSURE/PUBLICATION PLANS: Public disclosure includes abstracts and presentations at scientific meetings (including poster sessions), public seminars, shelving of theses, publications, disclosure to others outside of your organization who have not signed a confidentiality agreement, and use, sale, or offer of sale of the invention. For computer/software inventions provide information related to dispersion of the invention electronically including what was transmitted to others. Identify dates and circumstances of any such disclosures. Also, indicate your future disclosure or publication plans. Accurate information is essential because prior disclosures may affect the chances of securing patent rights. Please carefully consider all events relating to your Invention that fall into the categories below (if none, so state).

Disclosed to and understood by me this _____ day of _____, 20__.

Signature:_____

	DATE (Note whether estimated [E] or documented [D])	COMMENTS (e.g. **Who** involved ? **Place** where it occurred? Confidentiality Agreements in place at time? Name of Journal/Conference)
a) Initial Idea ?		
b) **First** description (conception)?		
c) **First** successful demonstration, prototype, sample (reduction to practice)?		
d) **First** publication of "enabling" information (e.g. abstract, paper, poster session, thesis, letter, news article/release)?	Need date actually available to public if earlier than official "publication date".	
e) Other publications (defined above) of "enabling" information?		
f) **First** oral "enabling" disclosure (e.g. seminar, conference, conversations)?		
g) Other oral (defined above) enabling" disclosures?		
h) **First** offer for sale, public or commercial use, or non-laboratory or non-secret experimental use? (specify which)		
i) Oral presentations, publications or other public disclosures planned in <u>future</u>?		

Attach additional pages if necessary. Add a page number, date, and sign each supplemental page. Have each page witnessed.

Disclosed to and understood by me this _____ day of _____, 20__.
Signature:_____

5. DETAILED DESCRIPTION OF THE INVENTION: Your description should enable anyone having knowledge of the field to understand the Invention. It must show that you have both <u>conceived</u> of an idea and <u>reduced your idea to practice</u>. Include all essential elements (features, concepts, or new results of the invention, whichever is most applicable), their relationship to one another, and their mode of operation. Identify the elements that are considered novel. Also, if the invention is an apparatus, or system, attach drawings or a sketch and indicate if it has ever been built or tested. In the case of software include a flow chart and copies of source code. If source code is extensive submit the flow chart; source code will be required at a later date as the application is prepared.

Describe what is presently available in the field. Identify existing chemicals, devices, software/hardware or processes (and their shortcomings) and list any published material such as patents, commercial literature, scientific articles relating to the invention. Identify the advantages or benefits of the invention over currently available technology, such as efficiency, cost benefit, simplicity, overcoming a defect. Identify possible uses or new uses of the invention (especially important if the invention is a chemical compound). Responses will differ depending on which questions are appropriate for your invention. Use additional pages, attach drawings, manuscripts, papers, or other supporting material to facilitate understanding of the invention.

Type the responses to Sections (a), (b), (c) and (d) on separate sheets (designating each Section with its subtitle) and attach to Disclosure. If your Invention includes software as an essential or major component of your Disclosure, complete Appendix B (attached) also.

a) Commercial application or objective of invention: Develop commentary for the following questions.

    a.   What does it do?

_____
_____
_____
_____

    b.   How does it do it?

_____
_____
_____
_____

    c.   What problem does it solve?

_____
_____
_____
_____

    d.   What markets or applications exist or are foreseen for the Invention? Who will use this product or service? List potential users in order of importance. i.e., 1 equals most important.
          Major users: _____
_____

          Possible other uses: _____
_____

    e.   What is current competition? List existing products or processes that fill a similar purpose.

_____
_____

Disclosed to and understood by me this _____ day of _____, 20__.
Signature:_____

b) Advantages of this Invention over previous approaches: Comment on the following if applicable. If your Invention includes software as an essential or major component of your Disclosure, complete Appendix B (attached) also. Develop commentary to address the following points or queries.

1. What are/is commercial application(s) or objective(s) of your invention?

_____
_____
_____
_____

2. Describe currently available technology used in the field today (methods/approaches/devices/processes).

_____
_____
_____
_____

3. What unsolved problems or disadvantages/shortcomings currently exist in the field?

_____
_____
_____
_____

4. How long did that problem exist before it was appreciated as a problem?

_____
_____
_____
_____

5. How did workers in the field handle, face or avoid the problem?

_____
_____
_____
_____

6. How does your Invention solve or reduce the problem?

_____
_____
_____

7. What technical impact is your Invention likely to have (i.e. marginal improvement, significant change, revolutionary upheaval, create new fields, etc.) and why?

_____
_____
_____
_____

Disclosed to and understood by me this _____ day of _____, 20__.
Signature:_____

8. Can anyone achieve the intended use or application of your Invention <u>without</u> using any of what is new and novel in this Invention Disclosure?

_____
_____
_____
_____

9. Can anyone achieve a similar objective using "prior art" knowledge?

_____
_____
_____
_____

10. Why is your Invention an improvement over currently existing technology?

_____
_____
_____
_____

11. Why is your Invention better than competing products, processes, methods or applications?

_____
_____
_____
_____

12. Will your Invention reduce costs?

_____
_____
_____
_____

13. Will your Invention improve efficiency, accuracy, simplicity?

_____
_____
_____
_____

14. Identify all possible or new uses of the Invention, especially if the technology is a chemical compound or biological material.

_____
_____
_____
_____

15. How will your Invention benefit a licensee? List the most important advantages in order of importance, i.e. 1 equals most important.

_____
_____
_____
_____

Disclosed to and understood by me this _____ day of _____, 20__.
Signature:_____

c) Implementing or constructing the Invention: Describe in detail all of the steps of the best way, process or method (i.e. "best mode") to make your Invention so that you include all essential elements (concepts, methods, new results, features) of that Invention. Describe the relationships of these elements, and their mode of operation. Which of the elements are novel and why? If your Invention has more than one way to achieve its intended use, please state which of these is the "best mode".

_____
_____
_____
_____
_____
_____
_____
_____
_____
_____
_____
_____

d) Stage of development for this Invention. Address the following questions (if applicable) in your commentary. If none or not applicable, so state.

    (1)   What is the Invention's working status?

_____
_____
_____
_____

    (2)   Has the Invention ever been built, tested or prototyped?

_____
_____
_____
_____

    (3)   Is there a computer simulation?

_____
_____
_____
_____

    (4)   Has clinical or field trial testing started? If so by whom?

_____
_____
_____
_____
_____

    (5)   Are there plans for continuing future research and study of the Invention?

_____
_____
_____
_____

Disclosed to and understood by me this _____ day of _____, 20__.
Signature:_____

(6)   What are the limitations to developing your Invention as a product, application or process?

_____
_____
_____
_____

(7)   If there are limitations or disadvantages, can they be overcome?

_____
_____
_____
_____

(8)   Estimate the nature and amount of work that remains to be done before a commercial product/application is obtained.

_____
_____
_____
_____

e) If the Invention has human health or clinical applications, identify diseases or conditions in the U.S.A. affected by the technology (if none, so state). If you have information relevant to other areas of the world, please note this. Provide source of data.

Indication	Patients/year	New cases/yr	Deaths/yr
_____	_____	_____	_____
_____	_____	_____	_____
_____	_____	_____	_____
_____	_____	_____	_____

f) Records to substantiate Invention. Do you have the following items? Indicate yes or no:

(1)   Lab notes and records (___Y ___N)?   Witnessed and dated? (___Y ___N)?
(2)   Rough sketches or diagrams (___Y ___N)? Finished working drawings (___Y ___N)?
(Attach these to your disclosure, especially if Invention includes an apparatus or a system.)
(3)   Dated photographs (___Y ___N)?
(4)   Financial documents (___Y ___N)?
(5)   Other (Y/N)? Please describe

_____
_____

g) Identify the competition. What companies or research organizations may be developing similar technologies or work products that will compete with your Invention?

_____
_____
_____

h) Independent Experts: Do you know independent experts familiar with the technology and its applications in the marketplace that we may contact to obtain additional information?

Name	Address	Phone
_____	_____	_____
_____	_____	_____
_____	_____	_____

Disclosed to and understood by me this _____ day of _____, 20__.
Signature:_____

i) Prepare a key word list related to your Invention:

_____   _____
_____   _____
_____   _____

6. SEARCH RESULTS:

a) You should have conducted a search of the **scientific literature** for information related to your Invention that could be considered "prior art". Attach articles that could be related to your invention.

b) Attach 2-4 **background/review articles** that relate to your technology's future growth, application, breakthroughs expected for the state of the art. Articles that clarify how your Invention <u>does not</u> relate to the "state of the art" can also be useful. Mark relevant sections or add margin notes to insure that the reader grasps relevant points. This helps IPO understand the technology and its potential applications.

c) Conduct a **patent search** using such search sites as http//patent.womplex.ibm.com, http://www.delphion.com or http://www.uspto.gov. Use key words related to your Invention to find relevant patent abstracts and claims. Print the summaries that are relevant and attach them to this Disclosure.

7. NONCONFIDENTIAL SUMMARY: Prepare a one-page draft abstract (Business Opportunity Document example included herewith) that does not include any confidential information (should not be "enabling" to someone skilled in this field). Avoid acronyms and technical jargon, as business decision-makers who read this are not always experts in your technical field.

8. POTENTIAL COMMERCIAL APPLICATIONS OF THE INVENTION/POTENTIAL LICENSEES: Have you been contacted by any party regarding the licensing of your invention? Are you aware of any companies in the field that may be interested in your invention? Are there current plans to use your idea commercially?

a) Are there current plans to use your invention commercially?

_____
_____
_____
_____

b) List any people or commercial entities that you have spoken to or are aware of, that may be interested in this Invention. Provide names and phone numbers if known.

Organization	Name	Phone

c) List any people or commercial entities which you do <u>not</u> wish to be contacted regarding this technology.

Organization	Name

Disclosed to and understood by me this _____ day of _____, 20__.

Signature: _____

9. ADDITIONAL INFORMATION: Please provide any other relevant information, not previously covered, which may provide guidance to the decision-making process and optimal utilization of the technology.

a) Previous marketing effort - If a previous attempt has been made to sell your product, please supply the following information (please include complete results).

Date(s) of marketing effort _____
Number sold _____
Selling price _____
Manufactured by _____
Reason for discontinuing marketing effort. Please list reasons in order of importance.
1. _____
2. _____
3. _____

b) Previous agreements - I have entered into prior agreements relative to this project with:

Individuals / Orgs.	Purpose	Date	Still in effect
1. _____	_____	_____	Y __ N __
2. _____	_____	_____	Y __ N __

c) I estimate the amount of time spent on the development of this idea is _____

d) The actual amount of money spent on the development of this idea is $_____.

e) Legal protection I currently have...

_____ No protection
_____ A patent; Number _____ Issue Date _____ Copy Attached ___ Y ___ N
_____ A provisional patent applied for
_____ A non provisional patent applied for
_____ Preliminary patent search: Date of Search: _____ Copy of findings attached _____
_____ A Disclosure Document with U.S. Patent Office: Date _____
_____ Copyright registration; Issue Date _____
_____ Inventors notebook / Notarized records of invention

10. IDENTIFICATION OF CONTRIBUTOR(S): List below all persons who are believed to have contributed to the conception or reduction to practice of this invention. Include a brief description of what each creator contributed to the discovery. Please provide social security numbers, addresses and phone and/or fax numbers and e-mail addresses where they may be contacted. (Use the back of this sheet if more space is needed.) *Note: The foregoing list should include names of all persons who may qualify as legal inventors. Legal inventorship is a technical question which is determined later by the attorney of record at the time a patent application is filed.*

Disclosed to and understood by me this _____ day of _____, 20__.
Signature:_____

Inventor / Author
Name: _____ Position/other title(s): _____
Citizenship _____ If not US citizen, visa type _____ Nonresident alien (Y/N); _____ Resident alien
(Y/N)
College _____ Department _____
Campus/Work Address (St.)_____ Room No. _____ Zip Code ____
Office Telephone _____ Fax No. _____ Email _____
Current Local Address: _____
Permanent address (include country): _____
Social Security #: _____ % inventive contribution to this Invention: _____

Inventor / Author
Name: _____ Position/other title(s): _____
Citizenship _____ If not US citizen, visa type _____ Nonresident alien (Y/N); _____ Resident alien
(Y/N)
College _____ Department _____
Campus/Work Address (St.)_____ Room No. _____ Zip Code ____
Office Telephone _____ Fax No. _____ Email _____
Current Local Address: _____
Permanent address (include country): _____
Social Security #: _____ % inventive contribution to this Invention: _____

Inventor / Author
Name: _____ Position/other title(s): _____
Citizenship _____ If not US citizen, visa type _____ Nonresident alien (Y/N); _____ Resident alien
(Y/N)
College _____ Department _____
Campus/Work Address (St.)_____ Room No. _____ Zip Code ____
Office Telephone _____ Fax No. _____ Email _____
Current Local Address: _____
Permanent address (include country): _____
Social Security #: _____ % inventive contribution to this Invention: _____

Inventor / Author
Name: _____ Position/other title(s): _____
Citizenship _____ If not US citizen, visa type _____ Nonresident alien (Y/N); _____ Resident alien
(Y/N)
College _____ Department _____
Campus/Work Address (St.)_____ Room No. _____ Zip Code ____
Office Telephone _____ Fax No. _____ Email _____
Current Local Address: _____
Permanent address (include country): _____
Social Security #: _____ % inventive contribution to this Invention: _____

(Add this same information on a separate page for each additional inventor)

Disclosed to and understood by me this _____ day of _____, 20__.
Signature: _____

11. ACKNOWLEDGEMENT OF INVENTION RIGHTS: Each Inventor/Author listed in the foregoing section or in any Supplemental pages, must complete this section.

a) By signing below, the Inventors/Authors acknowledge that _____'s patent policy governs their rights and obligations with respect to the Invention, and agree to abide by such policy. The Inventors or Authors declare the information herein is accurate and complete to the best of their knowledge. Authors of copyrightable works declare, to the best of their knowledge, that such works do not infringe any pre-existing copyright.

Name (print or type)	Signature	Date
_____	_____	_____
_____	_____	_____
_____	_____	_____
_____	_____	_____
_____	_____	_____
_____	_____	_____

b) Any **Principal Investigator** named in Section 2, if <u>not</u> an Inventor listed above, should acknowledge that this Invention Disclosure is being submitted.

_____   _____
Signature   Printed Name

_____   _____
Signature   Printed Name

_____   _____
Signature   Printed Name

Unit Director

_____   _____
Signature   Printed Name

12. COMPLETE

This Disclosure contains a total of _____ printed pages and _____ pages of attachments.
Name of person completing this Disclosure form: _____
Submit completed form (one original and 2 copies) with all attachments, to:

13. DISTRIBUTION: Prepare and distribute copies of the completed Invention Disclosure Form as follows:
        1 original for each Creator's file
        1 original and 2 copies to:

        _____
        _____
        _____

Disclosed to and understood by me this _____ day of _____, 20__.
Signature:_____

SOFTWARE DISCLOSURE FORM

Guidelines for Authors

Dear software developer:

Software can be very valuable. In order to extend benefits of software development efforts you want to do everything possible to reap these benefits quickly and economically. The purpose of this booklet is to help you understand how you can help achieve this goal for your software.

This Guidelines booklet is designed to serve as a complete guide for first-time disclosers/submitters and also to provide experienced submitters a quick-reference/checklist for preparing their submittals. **Section 1** provides instructions for completing the software submittal form. **Section 2** provides a copy of the submittal form that can be copied and used with each submittal. Extra copies of the form are available.

Services, policies, and procedures are continually being made and these guidelines updated accordingly. If the date on this copy of the Guidelines booklet is over twelve months old, check to see if a newer version of the guidelines has issued.

SOFTWARE SUBMITTAL FORM

SECTION 1

This section is designed both to help you prepare your program for submittal and to help you complete the submittal form. This form provides basic information about the submittal and a mechanism for verifying receipt of all information. The text follows the order of items on the submittal form.

Program Acronym and Program Title

If an acronym and a title have been given, please provide both on the submittal form. These will be used unless they infringe on trademarks. In choosing them, allow up to 15 characters for acronyms and up to 180 characters for acronym plus title. For multiple machine versions of any given program, reference the machine version in parentheses at the end of the regular title.

1. Submittal Type

All material is logged in and processed according to the type submitted.

Presubmittal Evaluation

The Presubmittal Evaluation service is optional. This service should be used if you have doubts about the potential value and utility of your program. **For Presubmittal Evaluation you need only fill in those items denoted by * on the form and provide a descriptive summary of the program.** This information helps assess the technology transfer potential for the program. Information about the hardware platform, software requirements and target markets are particularly important in this evaluation.

Initial Submittal

Initial Submittal is a term used to describe a program which has just been assigned a New Technology Number (Tech. #) or is being formally processed as a result of a Presubmittal Evaluation.

Revision/Updates to an Initial Submittal

Revisions or updates are complete replacements for programs and documentation which have been accepted and are already in the inventory. No new Tech.#s are involved. Usually an update reflects some new features or enhancements to the original program as well as some minor additions and corrections. Updates and revisions are processed like initial submittal with the exception that they automatically replace the program and the document in the inventory under the same Tech.#.

When submitting a revision or an update, please provide a list of new or updated features for inclusion in the revised abstract and marketing materials.

NOTE: If during the processing of an initial submittal, more information is needed, or a replacement of the code is necessary, you need not prepare a form for this type of submittal; however, you should include a brief letter which refers to the Tech.# and states the purpose of the additions or corrections.

2. Is this program related to other programs in the inventory?

Programs in the inventory are often updated, revised or ported to new platforms, and for a variety of reasons are assigned Tech.#s which differ from those of previous submittal. If a relationship with other programs, exists describe relationship. *For example: "This program is a new machine version of Tech.# ABC-12345."*

3. Items in the submittal package

This provides a quick check for the items in your submittal.

<u>Complete source code</u> must usually be provided and should be distributed. If not included, state why the program without source code. If it is include that the program is not transferrable without source code, it may not be accepted.

<u>Sample input and output</u> data are also expected for all types of software, so customers can verify results. Sample input an output should be provided in a useful printed or electronic form (i.e., screen dumps, tables, figures, step-by-step examples, sample input an output data files, etc.).

<u>Directory listings</u> help verify the receipt of all necessary files.

One printed <u>copy of the documentation</u> is desired even if the documentation is submitted in electronic form. Customers often prefer to review program documentation before purchasing a program.

<u>The electronic version of the document</u> should include what format it is in and a listing of any significant differences between the printed materials and the electronic documentation. *Example: The printed version consists of a User Manual and a Theoretical Manual; the electronic version consists of a User Manual only.*

4. Media description

In order to verify the correct media with your submittal, describe it here as well as visually label the media with program acronym and format. Be sure this information is included here or on another area of the form or documentation. Table 1 contains the range of media on which programs are accepted. **Please contact us if you have any questions about submittal media. If it is impractical to submit the preferred media, one of the others listed in the table may be acceptable since our computers are networked. Also, an electronic transfer option may be possible.**

PLEASE NOTE: Program documents (i.e., those end users will receive) and to be free of media descriptions since distribution media and format may differ from what you submit. Also, contact us before submitting any media that contains files that are compressed using commercial software.

5. Document description

Succinctly identify each volume of the documentation, program listings will not be included in the distributed document. Listings should not be in published documents unless the program is already in the public domain.

6. Primary contact for technical questions.

The person listed as the primary contact is the person who will be asked to review the draft abstract and is also the person who will be contacted first in case of technical questions. We make every effort to minimize the impact of customer questions and problems on your workload. Well-documented, fully tested code helps keep these questions to a minimum.

Unless you want to directly accessible, it is very important to make sure the document and code are free of names, phone numbers, e-mail addresses, and invitations to make direct contact with you and other authors.

Provide an electronic mail address, fax number and telephone number. *Be sure to check the Yes answer if you are an author.*

7. Who should be credited as authors of this program?

The names of all persons who should be given credit as contributing authors should be listed here along with complete mail addresses. Acknowledgement letters are sent to all authors. If you have checked "yes" to the author question in item 6, you do not need to duplicate that information in this item.

Table 1. Submittal media by platform
(boldface type highlights the preferred submittal media for each type of program)

PLATFORM(S) CARTRIDGES	DISKETTES (low or high density)	9 TRACK TAPES (1600 or 6250 BPI	TAPE

8. Are there any special distribution restrictions or other concerns that we should be aware of?

Our standard distribution restriction is that initial submittals are not for international distribution for a minimum of one year. After this period, with permission from the authoring group, the program is made available internationally.

If more than the standard restrictions are to apply, please identify them.

TECHNICAL INFORMATION

Whether this form is accompanying a presubmittal or a submittal, provide an accurate indication of the types of hardware environments for which this program is suitable, the types of software required in order to use the program, and the scope of the topics addressed by the documentation. The form gives you two options for providing this information. In either case please answer question 9.

For submittals, the preferred is covered in part 10, the optional Quick Reference Supplemental (QRS) Documentation. The other option is more suitable for presubmittals, and involves fully answering the questions in parts 11-13 of the form. Please review the guidelines for both options. Regardless of which option chosen, any information requested in the QRS Documentation outline not already clearly included in the document should be provided in order to minimize confusion and avoid processing delays.

9. Has your program been independently installed and tested by a colleague?

If a colleague has been able to successfully compile, line and execute the submitted code (on a machine other than your development and testing machine) based on the instructions in the submitted documentation, please indicate here.

10. Have you provided the optional Quick Reference Supplemental Documentation?

An outline of the information requested for the Quick Reference Supplemental Documentation appears on the next page. If you submit both an electronic and a hardcopy version of your QRS documentation, it will be included near the front of the documentation and will serve as a convenient place to gather any information needed to clarify, supplement or correct other documents.

If the information requested in the outline is clearly presented in the documentation, state where the information can be found. If it is in a hardcopy document, state which one and the page number. If it is in a "readme" file, state which one.

QUICK REFERENCE SUPPLEMENTAL DOCUMENTATION OUTLINE

Below is a description of where various types of information appear in the program documentation or files, and if necessary, statements which clarify or supplement the information provided in the documentation.

A.   STATEMENT OF PROGRAM'S PURPOSE

B.   EXPLANATION OF METHOD(S), including capabilities and limitations of method(s), and unique or novel features of this program

C.   DESCRIPTION OF HARDWARE REQUIREMENTS (vendor, model, operating system, memory, peripherals, etc.), include a list of any environments which are known to be incompatible

D.   STATEMENT OF SOURCE CODE LANGUAGE(S) USED, including whether program is (a)known to use extensions specific to a particular compiler or (b)known to meet ANSI standards

E.   LIST OF OTHER SOFTWARE REQUIREMENTS (ie., anything which must be linked in or otherwise be available for GUI or graphics capabilities, pre- or post-processing, input/output data, printing, etc.), including vendor names and contact information, when appropriate

F.   DESCRIPTION OF FILES PROVIDED ON MEDIA (including a summary or explanation of their purposes and information about where they need to be installed)

G.   STATEMENT OF SYSTEM LEVEL PRIVILEGES and system-level interactions of installation scripts, command files, etc.

H.   INSTRUCTIONS FOR CREATING AN EXECUTABLE

I.   INSTRUCTIONS FOR INSTALLING THE CREATED EXECUTABLE OR A PROVIDED ONE

J.   INSTRUCTIONS FOR USING PROGRAM (including how to provide input, use various features, and obtain output)

K.   EXPLANATION OF HOW TO VERIFY THAT PROGRAM IS OPERATING CORRECTLY and producing results that the author would expect to see (including location of examples, names and locations of sample input and output files, etc.)

L.   DESCRIPTION OF FORMAT AND LOCATION OF ELECTRONIC/MAGNETIC COPY OF DOCUMENTATION, if available on distribution medium (a description of any differences between electronic and hardcopy versions of the documentation, and the name and version of the word processing package or other tool required to display or print the electronic version)

Include a hardcopy and electronic copy (ASCII) of your QRS Documentation, as well as a hardcopy of any "readme" file to which it refers.

11. What hardware/operating system environments were used to develop (D) or test (T) program? What other hardware is required?

List all the computers/operating systems on which the program was developed or tested. Also are any environments known to be incompatible/inappropriate for the program (example: PCs, MAC, HP-UX or any other specific platforms).

In table 2 is described the capabilities needed to test source code in various programming languages, and create and run test executable when third party software is required.

Indicate whether your program is suitable for any platform with an ANSI standard compiler, or is suitable for all UNIX platforms, etc. However, we still need to know which environments have actually been tested.

12. What software environments are required to compile, link and execute the program?

Before potential users of your program can know whether your software may be of value to them, they need to know exactly what other software is required to run your program.

Provide an executable if your software is specifically designed for personal computers such as the IBM PC or Macintosh, since customers interested in programs for these platforms often prefer to receive an executable in addition to source code.

Provide results of a colleague's test of the submittal media and documentation for quality and completeness.

13. What will the submitted user documentation tell users about this program?

This section of the form is designed to help judge the completeness of documentation. Take time to accurately indicate which topics are addressed. If there are good reasons for not including certain of the requested items, clearly explaining those reasons.

Pay particular attention to the last two items. Either the installation instructions or an early section of the user documentation should tell what type of run-time examples or sample input and output are provided and where they are located.

Table 2. Submittal checkout resources

SPECIFIC MACHINES	OPERATING SYSTEMS	COMPILERS	OTHER SOFTWARE

SOFTWARE DISCLOSURE INFORMATION
This section of the submittal form will provide valuable input into the promotion or marketing process for the program.

14. What are the major "selling points" of this program?

Explain the technical significance of the program. This is an important consideration in determining the amount of resources that will be allocated to preparing the program for inventory.

15. How valuable do you believe this program will be to the following audiences?

If you have already received requests for the program, we encourage you to forward requestor contact information along with your submittal. We will notify the requestors when the program is available.

16. What industries should be targeted in marketing or promotional efforts?

Provide your opinion as to which industries would most likely find application for the program. If the selection doesn't cover what you feel defines the user market, please feel free to identify either a general or a specific user community.

17. What professional societies are you a member of, what trade shows do you attend, and what professional magazines do you read?

Press releases to magazines, publishers, and technical organizations are made to help promote appropriate press coverage for your program. Are there particular places to which press releases should be sent?

ADDITIONAL SUPPORT

The process of checkout and evaluation which takes the program from receipt to inventory is a time consuming labor intensive process. Thus any extra assistance that you can provide will be greatly appreciated and should result in getting the program into the inventory faster and at less expense.

18. Double-check the following:

This item is a checklist which addresses the most common problems encountered during program check-out. Double-checking of the submittal will clear up most of the problems, reduce the time and expense of checkout, will allow the program into the inventory faster and reduce the charge for services.

19. Keywords and subject categories.

Suggest keywords and subject categories for the program. Provide a primary and secondary subject category plus six keywords.

20. Provide a draft abstract for the program.

A draft abstract of the program should include the following:
(a)   1-2 sentences about why the program was originally developed
(b)   a paragraph about the program's theoretical basis
(c)   a paragraph describing the program's primary functional capabilities
(d)   a brief description of the type of user interfaces provided for input and output
(e)   a paragraph which identifies the development platform and source code language(s) and states all hardware and software requirements.

SOFTWARE SUBMITTAL FORM

SECTION 2

The following submittal form can be copied and used with a submittal.

Technology # _____

Program Acronym

Program Title

1.   Submittal Type: (Refer to text for instructions)
        ____ Presubmittal Evaluation
        ____ Initial Submittal
        ____ Revision or Update to an Initial Submittal
        ____ Other

2.   Is this program related to other programs presently listed by company/institution? __ Yes   __ No
        If yes, identify related program and explain differences [new machine version, major new feature].

3.   Items in the submittal package

Y	N	
__	__	Complete source code
__	__	Sample input and output
__	__	Directory listing from submitted code
__	__	Hardcopy documentation
__	__	Electronic copy of the documentation

4.   Media description: [type(s), number of pieces each, and format(s)]

5.   Document description: [number of volumes, publication numbers and format for electronic documentation]

*6.   Primary contact for technical questions. Is this also an author? __ Yes   __ No

        Name _____   Phone _____
        Organization _____   Fax _____
        Address _____   E-mail _____

7.   Who should be credited as authors of this program? [Provide names and complete office addresses]

*8.   Are there any special distribution restrictions or other concerns that we should be aware of?

Disclosed to and understood by me this _____ day of _____, 20__.
Signature:_____

SOFTWARE SUBMITTAL FORM

<u>TECHNICAL INFORMATION</u>

*9.   Has your program been independently installed and tested by a colleague? ___ Yes ___ No

10.   Have you provided the optional Quick Reference Supplemental documentation which answers questions 11-13 [below]? ___ Yes   ___ No   If not, please answer questions 11-13 fully.

*11.   What hardware/OS environments were used to develop [D] or test [T] your program? What peripherals/hardware are required?

*12.   What software environments are required to compile, link and execute the program? [List specific compilers, linkers, libraries and other third party software.]

*13.   What will the documentation tell users about this program?
        ___ background/purpose
        ___ capabilities & limitations of methods used
        ___ hardware needed
        ___ file description
        ___ languages used
        ___ software requirements
        ___ how to create an executable
        ___ how to install a provided executable
        ___ instructions for using
        ___ system privileges required & any other issues of concern to system manager
        ___ how to verify correct operation [i.e., sample data, examples, etc.]
        ___ format & location of electronic documentation, if provided

*14.   What are the major "selling points" of this program for non-NASA users?

        ___ significant new engineering/scientific data
        ___ significantly improved engineering/scientific calculation methods
        ___ the ability to take advantage of significant new computer-based engineering/scientific
            technology and methods [ie., remote sensing, control systems, artificial intelligence, etc.]
        ___ the ability to take advantage of significant new computer networking, graphics, or technology
            [ie., remote processing, graphical user interfaces, graphical visualization of data, relational
            databases, etc.]
        ___ the ability to take advantage of other new computer technology [i.e., interactive or command-
            line versions of modern programming languages; databases and spreadsheets; word
            processing, etc.]
        ___ a modern version of older, but valuable NASA software
        ___ other [please explain]:

Disclosed to and understood by me this _____ day of _____, 20__.
Signature:_____

165

SOFTWARE SUBMITTAL FORM

*15. How valuable do you believe this program will be to the following audiences?

AUDIENCE TYPE	HIGH	MEDIUM	LOW
Industry	___	___	___
Government Agencies	___	___	___
Research Organizations	___	___	___
Universities	___	___	___
High Schools	___	___	___

*16. What industries should TTO target in its marketing or promotional efforts? [check as many as apply]

    ___ aerospace   ___ communications   ___ industries equipment
    ___ automotive   ___ bio/medical   ___ electronics
    ___ chemical   ___ power/energy   ___ computers
    ___ defense   ___ manufacturing   ___ other

17. What professional societies are you a member of, what trade shows do you attend, and what professional magazines do you read?

ADDITIONAL SUPPORT

18. Please double check the following:

    ___ submitted media is readable and in a format which we can read
    ___ media contains all needed files and no extra files
    ___ hardcopy documentation corresponds to the program version submitted
    ___ document has few, if any, handwritten corrections and comments
    ___ data should still be legible after document is copied & put in a three-ring binder
    ___ differences between electronic documentation and printed documentation have been noted under item 5
    ___ any author contact information in code or document is acceptable for our customers to use
    ___ files and document are free of copyrighted items or owner's clearance for redistribution on a cost-recovery basis is provided
    ___ for update, included a list of new features, bug fixes, etc.

19. Please suggest keywords and subject categories.

Keywords: _____ _____ _____ _____ _____ _____

Primary subject category: _____

Secondary subject category: _____

20. Please attach a draft abstract for the program (Business Opportunity Document).

PLEASE NOTE: *Software developed by Company/Institution employees should carry the following copyright notice on the media label, the first screen displayed when the program is executed, and the cover page of the program documentation: **Copyright (year) (Company/Institution) All rights reserved.***

Disclosed to and understood by me this _____ day of _____, 20__.
Signature:_____

CONFIDENTIAL AND NON-DISCLOSURE AGREEMENT
FOR INVENTION DISCLOSURE

Enclosed is a description and other materials pertaining to my idea for processing and review by Company (hereafter called CO). After your research, I understand that CO will send me an independent evaluation and patent search with patentability opinion. It is further understood that:

1. CO will use best efforts to keep this disclosure confidential. Staff and employees have signed a non-disclosure with CO stating they will keep the submission evaluation in strict confidence, unless they receive written permission from me to disclose idea.

2. CO will only use recognized and credible independent evaluators (i.e. Universities, Private Assessment organizations, research Triangle Institute, National Technology Transfer Center, Washington State University, Drake University, University of Wisconsin, Wal-Mart Innovation Network or individuals or firms that have experience in evaluating and licensing institutional assets). These evaluators will follow, as a minimum, evaluation guidelines set forth by CO even though they may have their own procedures in place for the safeguarding of ideas.

3. The various patent attorneys that will be involved in the patentability opinion are obligated to abide by the US Patent & Trademark Office "Canon of Ethics" and various Bar Associations ethical standards.

4. In consideration for this confidential evaluation, I agree to hold harmless CO, its employees, agents and others assisting in my idea, both now and in the future, from any loss or damage arising out of this disclosure and subsequent evaluation.

5. Materials submitted herewith or in the future in connection with my idea may be retained by CO and evaluators, returned to me at my expense, or destroyed after 3 years by CO and evaluators. It is my responsibility to advise you of any change of my mailing address and whether I want materials submitted returned to me.

6. Any assistance beyond this initial evaluation is provided at the option of CO and evaluators and will depend upon the merit of my idea and the availability of staff and resources.

7. CO and evaluators acquire no right or license in my idea by this submission.

THE NAME OF THE PRODUCT/PROCESS IS:

_____

ENCLOSED is my check or money order for the amount of $_____.00 made payable to Company, at _____[address]_____.

I have carefully read this agreement form, understand its contents and agree.

CLIENT   COMPANY

_____   _____
Signature of Client   Signature of Company Official

Date_____   Date_____

Please provide a detailed description of your product. Include information on the size of the device, materials, uses and so forth. Keep in mind that you should provide enough detailed information so that the persons evaluating your idea fully understand the functions and purpose. Attach any photographs you may have, but <u>DO NOT SEND ANY PROTOTYPES UNLESS REQUESTED.</u>

Describe your PRODUCT in both technical and non-technical manner. Use the space below for the non-technical description; attach a technical description on a separate page. Graph paper has been included for any drawings or you may provide your own prepared drawings on a separate paper.)

It is suggested that you have this description notarized if you have no form of protection for your invention. This helps establish the date of conception of your idea. A DETAILED DESCRIPTION IS NECESSARY.

State of _____

County of _____

On this _____ day of _____, 20 ____, before me, _____
_____Notary Public, personally appeared _____
_____ known to me (or proved to me on the oath of _____
_____) to be the person whose name is subscribed to the within instrument, and acknowledged that he (she or they) executed the same.

Witness my hand and official seal.

_____

Notary Public in and for the
State of _____
County of _____
My commission expires _____

Disclosed to and understood by me this _____ day of _____, 20__.
Signature:_____

THE FAIR USE TEST

Although the Fair Use provision is in the Copyright Act, prior to the 1990s, it was seldom invoked outside of academic circles. Until the 2 Live Crew case, Fair Use seemed only to concern itself with making copies for the classroom and using portions of works in academic treatises. The Fair Use provision and the four factors to be considered in a fair use analysis were dramatically fleshed out in the 2 Live Crew case. Here, we look at the fair use provision and the four factors to be used in making a determination of fair use.

> Fair Use Provision of the Copyright Act
> > Factor 1 - Purpose and Character of Use
> > Factor 2 - Nature of Copyrighted Work
> > Factor 3 - Relative Amount
> > Factor 4 - Effect on the Market

The Statutory Decree §107. Limitations on exclusive rights: Fair Use

Notwithstanding the provisions of sections 106 and 106A, the fair use of a copyrighted work, including such use by reproduction in copies or phonorecords or by any other means specified by that section, for purposes such as criticism, comment, news reporting, teaching (including multiple copies for classroom use), scholarship, or research, is not an infringement of copyright. In determining whether the use made of a work in any particular case is a fair use the factors to be considered shall include:

1. the purpose and character of the use, including whether such use is of a commercial nature or is for nonprofit educational purposes;
2. the nature of the copyrighted work;
3. the amount and substantiality of the portion used in relation to the copyrighted work as a whole; and
4. the effect of the use upon the potential market for or value of the copyrighted work.

The fact that a work is unpublished shall not itself bar a finding of fair use if such finding is made upon consideration of all the above factors.

17 U.S.C. § 107 (1988 ed. and Supp. IV). Purpose and Character of Use

This first factor looks at the new work and takes into account the following three sub-factors.

The first sub-factor (1) simply looks at the new work and determines whether it was created primarily as a for-profit venture or was created for a non-profit educational purpose. While not at all determinative, this test indicates that preference will be granted to works that were created for non-profit educational purposes.

The second sub-factor (2) looks to see if the new work is for one of the purposes that are mentioned in the preamble of the fair use provision. It should be noted that this list is not restrictive. However, the burden of showing fair use is somewhat easier if the work is for one of these purposes.

The third sub-factor (3) looks at the degree of transformation accomplished by the new work. In other words, this sub-factor seeks to determine whether the new work merely supplants the original, or whether it adds something new, with a further purpose or different character, thereby altering the first with new expression, meaning or message.

Nature of Copyrighted Work

This second factor acknowledges that some works are more deserving of copyright protection than others. Consequently, this portion of the test looks at the original work and attempts to determine where that work is in the spectrum of worthiness of copyright protection.

Relative Amount

The third factor looks at the amount and substantiality of the copying in relation to the work as a whole. However, the critical determination is whether the quality and value of the materials used are reasonable in relation to the purpose of copying. This is not a pure ratio test in that using a whole work may be fair use in some circumstances, whereas using a tiny fraction of a work does not qualify for fair use in other circumstances.

Therefore, the quantity, as well as the quality and importance, of the copied material must be considered. Some Justices have looked to see that "no more was taken than was necessary" to achieve the purpose for which the materials were copied.

Effect Upon Potential Market

The fourth factor considers the extent of harm to the market or potential market of the original work caused by the infringement. This test takes into account harm to the original, as well as harm to derivative works.

GUIDELINES FOR CLASSROOM COPYING OF COPYRIGHTED MATERIAL
Sections 106, 107 and 501 (a) of the Copyright Act of 1976 (Title 17 U.S. Code)

Section 106. Exclusive rights in copyrighted works

Subject to sections 107 through 118, the owner of copyright under this title has the exclusive rights to do and to authorize any of the following:

1. to reproduce the copyrighted work in copies or phonorecords;
2. to prepare derivative works based upon the copyrighted work;
3. to distribute copies or phonorecords of the copyrighted work to the public by sale or other transfer of ownership, or by rental, lease, or lending;
4. in the case of literary, musical, dramatic, and choreographic works, pantomimes, and motion pictures and other audiovisual works, to perform the copyrighted work publicly; and
5. in case of literary, musical, dramatic, and choreographic works, pantomimes, and pictorial, graphic, or sculptural works, including the individual images of a motion picture or other audiovisual work, to display the copyrighted work publicly.

Section 107. Limitations on exclusive rights: Fair use

Notwithstanding the provisions of section 106, the fair use of a copyrighted work, including such use by reproduction in copies or phonorecords or by any other means specified by that section, for purposes such as criticism, comment, news reporting, teaching (including multiple copies for classroom use), scholarship, or research, is not an infringement of copyright. In determining whether the use made of a work in any particular case is a fair use the factors to be considered shall include:

1. the purpose and character of the use, including whether such use is of a commercial nature or is for nonprofit educational purposes;
2. the nature of the copyrighted work;
3. the amount and substantiality of the portion used in relation to the copyrighted work as a whole; and
4. the effect of the use upon the potential market for or value of the copyrighted work.

Section 501. Infringement of copyright

Anyone who violates any of the exclusive rights of the copyright owner as provided by sections 106 through 118, or who imports copies or phonorecords into the United States in violation of section 602, is an infringer of the copyright.

Agreement on Guidelines for Classroom Copying in Not-for-Profit Educational Institutions With Respect to Books and Periodicals (included in House Report 94-1476)

The purpose of the following guidelines is to state the minimum standards of educational fair use under Section 107 of H.R. 2223. The parties agree that the conditions determining the extent of permissible copying for educational purposes may change in the future; that certain types of copying permitted under these guidelines may not be permissible in the future; and conversely that in the future other types of copying not permitted under these guidelines may be permissible under revised guidelines. Moreover, the following statement of guidelines is not intended to limit the types of copying permitted under the standards of fair use under judicial decision and which are stated in Section 107 of the Copyright Revision Bill. There may be instances in which copying which does not fall within the guidelines stated below may nonetheless be permitted under the criteria of fair use. Guidelines are:

I. Single Copying for Teachers. A single copy may be made of any of the following by or for a teacher at his or her individual request for his or her scholarly research or use in teaching or preparation to teach a class:

- A. A chapter from a book;
- B. An article from a periodical or newspaper;
- C. A short story, short essay or short poem, whether or not from a collective work;
- D. A chart, graph, diagram, drawing, cartoon or picture from a book, periodical, or newspaper;

II. Multiple Copies for Classroom Use. Multiple copies (not to exceed in any event more than one copy per pupil in a course) may be made by or for the teacher giving the course for classroom use or discussion; provided that:

- A. The copying meets the tests of brevity and spontaneity as defined below; and,
- B. Meets the cumulative effect test as defined below; and,
- C. Each copy includes a notice of copyright.

Definitions

Brevity

(i) Poetry:

    (a) a complete poem if less than 250 words and if printed on no more than two pages or,

    (b) from a longer poem, an excerpt of not more than 250 words.

(ii) Prose:

    (a) either a complete article, story or essay of less than 2,500 words, or

    (b) an excerpt from any prose work of not more than 1,000 words of 10% of the work, whichever is less, but in any event a minimum of 500 words. [Each of the numerical limits stated in "i" and "ii" above may be expanded to permit the completion of an unfinished line of a poem or of an unfinished prose paragraph.]

(iii) Illustration:

    One chart, graph, diagram, drawing, cartoon, or picture per book or per periodical issue.

(iv) "Special" works:

    Certain works in poetry, prose, or in "poetic prose" which often combine language with illustrations and which are intended sometimes for children and at other times for a more general audience fall short of 2,500 words in their entirety.

Paragraph "ii" above notwithstanding such "special works" may not be reproduced in their entirety; however, an excerpt comprising not more than two of the published pages of such special work and containing not more than 10% of
the words found in the text thereof, may be reproduced.

Spontaneity

(i) The copying is at the instance and inspiration of the individual teacher, and

(ii) The inspiration and decision to use the work and the moment of its use for maximum teaching effectiveness are so close in time that it would be unreasonable to expect a timely reply to a request for permission.

Cumulative Effect

(i) The copying of the material is for only one course in the school in which the copies are made.

(ii) Not more than one short poem, article, story, essay, or two excerpts may be copied from the same author, not more than three from the same collective work or periodical volume during one class term.

(iii) There shall not be more than nine instances of such multiple copying for one course during one class term. [The limitations stated in "ii" and "iii" above shall not apply to current news periodicals and newspapers and current news sections of other periodicals.]

III. Prohibitions as to I and II Above. Notwithstanding any of the above, the following shall be prohibited:

A. Copying shall not be used to create or to replace or substitute for anthologies, compilations or collective works. Such replacement or substitution may occur whether copies of various works or excerpts there from are accumulated or produced and used separately.

B. There shall be no copying of or from works intended to be "consumable" in the course of study or of teaching. These include workbooks, exercises, standardized tests and test booklets and answer sheets and like consumable material.

C. Copying shall not:

> (a) substitute for the purchase of books, publishers' reprints or periodicals;
> (b) be directed by higher authority;
> (c) be repeated with respect to the same item by the same teacher from term to term.

D. No charge shall be made to the student beyond the actual cost of the photocopying.

Guidelines for Educational uses of Music (included in House Report 94-1476)

Representatives of the Music Publishers' Association of the United States, Inc., the National Music Publishers' Association, Inc., the Music Teachers National Association, the Music Educators National Conference, the National Association of Schools of Music and Ad Hoc Committee on Copyright Revision developed the following:

The purpose of the following guidelines is to state the minimum and not the maximum standards of educational fair use under Section 107 of H.R. 2223. The parties agree that the conditions determining the extent of permissible copying for educational purpose may change in the future; that certain types of copying permitted under these guidelines may not be permissible in the future; and conversely that in the future other types of copying not permitted under these guidelines may be permissible under revised guidelines.

Moreover, the following statement of guidelines is not intended to limit the types of copying permitted under the standards of fair use under judicial decision and which are stated in Section 107 of the Copyright Revision Bill. There may be instances in which copying which does not fall within the guidelines stated below may nonetheless be permitted under the criteria of fair use.

I. Permissible Uses

    A. Emergency copying to replace purchased copies which for any reason are not available for an imminent performance provided purchased replacement copies shall be substituted in due course.

    B. For academic purposes other than performance, single or multiple copies of excerpts of works may be made, provided that the excerpts do not comprise a part of the whole which would constitute a performable unit such as a section, movement or aria, but in no case more than (10%) of the whole work. The number of copies shall not exceed one copy per pupil.

    C. Printed copies which have been purchased may be edited or simplified provided that the fundamental character of the work is not distorted or the lyrics, if any, altered or lyrics added if none exist.

    D. A single copy of recordings of performance by students may be made for evaluation or rehearsal purposes and may be retained by the educational institution or individual teacher.

    E. A single copy of a sound recording (such as a tape, disc or cassette) of copyrighted music may be made from sound recordings owned by an educational institution or an individual teacher for the purpose of constructing aural exercises or examinations and may be retained by the educational institution or individual teacher. (This pertains only to the copyright of the music itself and not to any copyright which may exist in the sound recording.)

II. Prohibitions

    A. Copying to create or replace or substitute for anthologies, compilations or collective

    B. Copying of or from works intended to be "consumable" in the course of study or of teaching such as workbooks, exercises, standardized tests and answer sheets and like material.

    C. Copying for the purpose of performance, except as in I.A. above.

    D. Copying for the purpose of substituting for type purchase of music, except as in I.A. and I.B. above.

    E. Copying without inclusion of the copyright notice which appears on the printed copy.

EXHIBIT E – EXPORT/IMPORT INFORMATION

EXPORT LICENSING GENERAL POLICY AND RELATED INFORMATION
(PART 370 OF 15 CFR)

- Export Administration Act of 1979
- Commodity Control List (CCL) – reviewed at least once every 3 years
- Technical Task Groups (TTG) – comprised of technical experts from various government agencies
- Technical advisor committees (TAC) – input from various sources and welcome recommendations from interested parties

GENERAL LICENSE

- issued by U.S. Dept of Commerce (DOC)
- no application required and no document is granted or issued
- permits export as long as no restrictions apply to individual, company, technology or product
- does not apply to agencies other than DOC SPECIFIC LICENSE
- everything not subject to general license

COUNTRY GROUPS

For export control purposes foreign countries are separated into seven country groups designated by letters (Canada is not in any of the groups and is referred to by name in the regulations)

Q - Romania

S - Libya

T - North America

Northern Area: Greenland, Miquelon and St. Pierre Islands

Southern Area: Mexico (including Cozumel and Revilla Gigedo Islands

- Central America

Belize	Guatemala	Panama
Costa Rica	Honduras	
El Salvador	Nicaragua	

Bermuda and Caribbean Area:

Bahamas	Haiti	Trinidad and Tobago
Barodos	Jamaica	French West Indies
Bermuda	Leeward and Windward Islands	
Dominican Republic	Netherlands Antilles	

- South America

Northern Area:

Columbia	Surinam	Guyana
French Guiana	Venezuela	

Western Area:

Bolivia	Ecuador
Chile	Peru

Eastern Area:

Argentina	Paraguay
Brazil	Uruguay
Falkland Islands	

V - All countries not included in other country groups

W – Hungary, Poland

Y - Abeno

Abeno	Laos	Lithuania
Bulgaria	Latvia	Czechoslovakia
Estonia	Mongolian People's Republic	Union of Soviet Socialist Republics
German Democratic Republic (includes East Berlin)		

Z - North Korea

Vietnam

Cambodia

Cuba

EXHIBIT F – INTELLECTUAL PROPERTY Q AND A (LABBOOK, PATENT, COPYRIGHT, WEBLAW, MARKS, AND TRADE SECRETS)

(Following is for information only. Seek legal or accounting advice for your specific situation)

LABBOOK

1. How will the law be applied?

Inventors outside of the United States will be able to prove a date of invention of January 1, 1996 or later for patent applications filed after January 1, 1996. Over time patent applicants outside the United States will share equal footing with United States inventors with respect to their ability to establish priority dates earlier than the patent application filing date.

As one example of how the law will be applied, laboratory notebooks from an invention first conceived and documented on January 10, 1996, but not filed as a patent application until September 10, 1996, can be submitted to the U.S. Patent Office to overcome novelty rejections based on a reference by another disclosing the invention and published on April 10, 1996. This evidence is offered as proof that the inventor was in a possession of the invention before the publication date of the reference.

However, also based on the GATT legislation, the earliest priority date available to inventors outside the United States is January 1, 1996. Therefore, an application filed on January 10, 1996 will be limited to a priority date no earlier than January 1, 1996 even if the inventors can prove a conception date years earlier. As noted, this disparity will even out over time.

2. What does this change mean to the inventor outside the United States?

Unless procedures are already in place, inventors outside the United States must establish rigorous invention documentation procedures to corroborate statements made to the United States Patent Office. United States courts have held that mere statements of invention and diligence are not sufficient. The inventor must provide corroborating evidence to establish what was done and when it was done. This evidence is preferably documentary in nature and is used to establish a "priority date." Priority date is one of two potential dates; either the date the invention was conceived and reduced to practice prior to patent application filing or the date the invention was first conceived and subsequently worked on diligently until the patent application was filed.

3. When is establishing a priority date earlier than the patent filing date important?

Proof of the priority date is useful in both litigation and patent examination within the United States Patent Office. Proof of conception and reduction to practice is important in litigation in any patent infringement case, when the date of invention is at issue. Invention dates are also important in trade secret misappropriation litigation.

During patent prosecution, evidence of the date of invention can be used to remove references from examination when the references are published less than one year before the patent filing date. Here, the inventor must document conception and diligence from a time prior to the publication date to the time the invention was either reduced to practice or filed as a patent application. Proving the date of invention is also critical in interference practice where the outcome of the proceeding rests upon a determination of which of two or more inventors was the first to invent the claimed invention. Finally, laboratory notebooks and invention disclosures may be used to remove prior art rejections from reissue and re-examination proceedings.

4. How is the date of invention, "the priority date", established in the U.S. Patent Office?

Under the U.S. system, invention begins with the conception of the invention; that is, the formulation of a definite and permanent idea of an operative invention. The inventive process ends when the invention is reduced to practice. Reduction to practice is said to occur when either the invention is reduced to a tangible and useful form or when an enabling patent application is properly filed in the United States or elsewhere. Priority is awarded to the inventor who first reduces the invention to practice or who first conceives of the invention and can prove that he or she has worked diligently on the invention toward reducing the invention to practice until a patent application was filed. Diligence has been held in the courts to mean consistent, mostly daily activity directed toward the goal of reducing the invention to practice. However, even if an inventor can prove conception and diligence in reducing an invention to practice, priority will be lost with proof that the inventors abandoned, suppressed or concealed their invention. Therefore, even under the U.S. patent system, timely filing of a patent application is essential.

5. What type of references can be antedated using corroborating evidence?

"Antedation" refers to the ability of the patent applicant to prove that he or she was in possession of as much of the information in a reference as the Patent Examiner is using to form the rejection. Evidence of prior conception and diligence in reducing an invention to practice is used to antedate patents, published patent applications or printed publications from anywhere in the world.

There are at least four basic exceptions to this rule. First, a reference cannot be antedated with corroborating evidence if the publication date of the reference is more than one year prior to the effective filing date of the patent application under examination. Nor can a reference be antedated if the reference is a patent issuing to the same applicant outside the United States prior to the filing date of the U.S. application where the non-U.S. patent application was filed more than twelve months before the effective date of the United States patent application. Third, one cannot antedate a U.S. patent claiming the same invention as claimed in the patent application under examination if the patent is issued to another inventor. This dispute is managed by an interference proceeding. Finally, an Examiner can refuse to enter evidence introduced to remove a reference from prosecution where the Applicant has previously admitted that the reference was prior art.

6. What form of corroborating evidence is permissible?

Laboratory notebooks, invention disclosures, internal memoranda, monthly reports and laboratory data sheets are all permitted documentary evidence. Invention disclosure forms can be prepared by the inventor to prove the date that the invention was first conceived. Signed and witnessed copies of these forms can be used to establish conception and, in some cases, reduction to practice. While invention disclosures, internal memoranda and monthly reports may be accepted by the Patent Office, they may also be viewed as self-serving. Similarly, laboratory data sheets that were not attached to a laboratory notebook at the time of their preparation may also be considered suspect.

7. Why isn't witness testimony enough to antedate a reference?

Corroboration may take the form of independent testimony; however, when the testimony is provided long after the facts occurred, it may not be well received. In general, original exhibits, drawings, records or photocopies must accompany and form part of the affidavit or declaration by the inventor or their absence must be satisfactorily explained.

In some cases testamentary evidence is enough where the absence of documentary evidence can be adequately explained. When the testamentary evidence is provided solely by an inventor or an interested party without supportive documentary evidence, the testamentary evidence may be viewed as self-serving. Third party testamentary evidence is rarely sufficient to antedate a reference because the third party must be able to swear to facts which would necessarily be documented in a laboratory notebook. Thus, the third party may be called on to swear to dates, details regarding laboratory experiments, results, and details relating to the progress of the invention. It is rare that a third party has first hand information related to these details or was available to view and review the experiments at each stage of the inventive process. The Patent Office is free to conclude that witness testimony is not credible or reliable.

8. What type of corroborating documentary evidence is preferred?

Legible laboratory notebooks are preferred as a corroborating source by the United States

Patent Office because the notebooks represent an unbiased resource for the laboratory worker who is attempting to reduce the invention to practice. The notebooks were prepared contemporaneous with conception and reduction to practice. Thus, there is a presumption that these notebooks are an unbiased and true representation of the data. Notebooks should be signed and witnessed at or near the time of their preparation by someone (a non-inventor, under a duty of confidentiality) who has read and understood their contents. It is possible that a Patent Examiner will not accept notebooks that are not witnessed.

9. How much documentary evidence is needed to antedate a reference?

An applicant is only required to provide evidence of priority with respect to so much of the claimed invention as the references happen to show. Thus, it is not necessary that the laboratory notebook evidence demonstrate each and every fact provided in a particular publication. Rather, the applicant must demonstrate only that he was already in possession of the particular information in a reference that was used to form the novelty or obviousness rejection at the time the reference was published. The Applicant is also permitted to provide evidence demonstrating an obvious variation of the information provided in a reference that is being used to reject the application.

10. When should laboratory data be submitted to the Patent Office to antedate a reference?

Laboratory data, accompanied by the appropriate testimonial proof, must be timely presented. Patent Examiners generally will consider this evidence if it is submitted prior to a final office action. These rules change somewhat if a petition for expedited examination has been filed with the United States Patent Office. After final rejection the Applicant must provide a showing of good and sufficient reasons why the evidence was not earlier presented. Without this evidence, the Applicant may be required to file a continuation application in order to have the evidence submitted into the record.

11. Is it necessary to disclose the date of conception to the Patent Office to antedate a reference during patent examination?

No. Documentary evidence of conception and reduction to practice is enough if it is introduced together with sworn testimony that the dates of conception and reduction to practice or conception and diligence were earlier than a cited reference publication date. Dates can be blocked out of laboratory notebook pages that are introduced into the patent prosecution record. In contrast, interference proceedings and litigation may require disclosure of dates relating to inventorship.

12. What if the data entries are not in English?

At present, there is no regulation in the United States Patent office requiring that laboratory notebook pages be translated into English. It might be possible to submit the pages together with a sworn declaration by the inventor providing a summary of the data pages. At that time, the Patent Office may elect to prepare a translation. Alternatively, the Applicant may elect to submit a formal, certified translation of the laboratory pages. It is likely that Patent Office regulations will be promulgated in this area in the near future.

13. How does the Patent Office determine whether documentary evidence is sufficient to antedate a reference?

The standard of review for interference proceedings is a "preponderance of evidence" standard. This is a higher standard than what is required for routine patent prosecution: however, if the preponderance of evidence standard is used to maintain coherent, legible laboratory notebooks, the Patent Office will be convinced that a proper showing has been made. In general, the Applicant must demonstrate during patent examination that more likely than not the invention was conceived and either reduced to practice or was worked on diligently from the time of conception to the patent application filing date.

14. If a laboratory notebook is preferred, what should it look like?

Preferably, the laboratory notebook is a bound volume. The pages should not be removable. These volumes are commercially available. The research organization or individual orders a series of the volumes, each successively numbered. A numbered book is checked out to an individual scientist for their use and recorded in a central ledger. The notebook includes a designated place for the scientist's name, together with the starting and the ending dates. The individual scientist writes his or her name in the book and enters a starting date. The notebook contains the name of the research organization, a statement regarding the confidentiality of the contents of the volume, an index and consecutively numbered pages. Each page should preferably contain a printed statement such as: "This notebook is considered confidential material and is the sole property of Organization X." There is a place for the scientist to sign and date each page. Also at the bottom of each page is a place for the signature of at least one witness along with printed words stating that the signature indicates that the witness has read and understood the contents of that page. An exemplary page from such a notebook is found at the end of this pamphlet.

15. What should the laboratory notebook contain?

The notebook should contain a legible account of each experiment that is performed. In addition, the notebook should record inventive ideas that may form the basis for proving conception. The recorded experiment should begin with a title or statement of purpose. The methods should be provided in detail at least one time. Later, methods used in similar experiments can reference the original experiment and list changes that have been made to the methods. All preparatory calculations and formulations are listed in the notebook. This includes a record of each animal and what it received or each sample and how it was treated. When abbreviations are used that would be unfamiliar to the average scientist at another organization, a key should be maintained within the notebook to translate the abbreviations. Data results are also incorporated into the volume. A summary of the results should be provided with the data. The level of detail should be sufficient to permit someone to repeat the experiment using only the notebook or resources cited in the notebook.

16. How should the scientists summarize their data in the notebooks?

It is best if the scientists are educated regarding the need to summarize results factually. Where an experiment failed, s simple statement indicating that the experiment will be repeated is enough. When not needed, or not completely true, absolute statements in a laboratory notebook regarding failure, inconclusiveness or the obviousness of a result can be used by the Patent Examiner or, after issuance, by a competitor to argue against patentability.

17. What should the scientist do with photographic evidence or data output from label equipment?

Photographs of animals, electrophoretic gel results and other photographs, together with printed data records including radionucleotide quantitations, and spectrophotometric measurements and readouts should be incorporated into the notebook. This information can be labeled and glued or taped onto a blank page. Remaining blank regions should be blocked out. Dates should be entered next to the data and some explanation should be provided for these entries. Copies of graphical displays of data should also be incorporated into the notebook. In some cases, such as where large autoradiograms are used, the rough data will not fit within the confines of a notebook. In these cases data sheets can be catalogued, permanently labeled, signed and witnessed with reference made within the laboratory notebook regarding interpretations from the data and their location within the laboratory.

18. What if graphical displays are stored on the computer rather than in a notebook?

While this is a trend in many laboratories, retrieval of data from long term computer storage without evidence of duplicate hard copy created at a time the graphical display was made may create problems in the United States Patent Office. Some Patent Examiners recognize that there may be motivation to manipulate data that has been stored electronically and may reject such data. A hard copy stored in laboratory notebook is the best defense against these allegations. Where computer storage is preferred, disks should be archived regularly to document that no change was made to the data. Again, in such a circumstance, the Patent Office may view the archive date as the date of conception or reduction to practice absent evidence to the contrary.

19. What if the scientist is recording data for more than one experiment at time?

Many commercially purchased notebook volumes contain a space stating "continued on page ___" at the bottom of each page and a "continued from page___" at the top of the page to provide continuity and clarity for experimental records that are performed over weeks or months. These can be used to tract the progress of individual experiments. Alternatively, each scientist may employ multiple notebooks; each notebook following the course of a particularly project. This is useful in proving that the scientists worked diligently to reduce the invention to practice. Notes should be made as to incubation times and dates when laboratory animals or reagents are ordered with expected arrival dates. These dates are aids for documenting diligence where, because of the nature of the invention, daily work on a particular invention is not possible.

20. When are the laboratory notebooks signed and dated?

Each entry should be dated and handwritten in pen. The notebook pages should be signed and dated by the scientist as each page is completed. Empty spaces on the pages should be crossed out in pen. The notebooks should be witnessed as soon as reasonably possible. Ideally, the notebooks pages are signed by witnesses on the day when they are completed, after the blank spaces have been crossed out. Practically, the laboratory should initiate regular (preferably bi-monthly) notebook signing sessions to insure that each notebook is up to date. There is a danger that the Patent Office or a court may use the date that the witness has signed a particular page, rather than the date of the scientist's signature. Therefore, prompt review by a witness is important.

21. What if the scientists in my organization prefer to use pencil?

They should stop. Experimental records should be permanent. Each page of a notebook should be written in the same ink to negate arguments that additions were made to the text at a later date. Mistakes should be crossed out in the same pen with the corrected text written next to, and not above, the mistaken entry.

22. What if a scientist wants to correct errors in the notebook at a later date?

If a scientist identifies errors, for example, in the math associated with a particular calculation, the errors can be corrected by crossing out the necessary information and writing in the correct entry. Some explanation should be provided in the notebook to give guidance as to why these changes were made. The changes should be initialized and dated and the changes should be signed and dated by a witness as well.

23. Who should sign a laboratory notebook as a witness?

Individuals signing as witnesses cannot be inventors to the invention. Under United States law, the inventor is the individual who conceived of the invention. Those who reduced the invention to practice are not necessarily inventors. Therefore, a laboratory co-worker, one who is not considered an inventor, may sign each page of the laboratory notebook of another indicating that they have read and understood the contents of the notebook. To prevent arguments of bias, the witness is preferably a laboratory worker who is not working on the same project and still more preferably, the witness is from another research group within the organization, who is familiar with the work in that laboratory and who is under a duty of confidentiality to the organization.

24. Who maintains possession of the laboratory notebooks?

The notebooks are the sole property of the research organization. When a particular scientist leaves the organization, the notebook remains with the organization. Old laboratory notebooks that are no longer needed in the laboratory should be checked into a data storage repository. The individual organization may elect to keep the notebooks in one place and a microfilmed copy of the notebook at a difference location.

PATENT

Most countries use a "first to file" patent system. The first inventor to file a patent application receives the right to exclude others, including those who first invented the same invention, but filed at a later date. Under the United States System, the person who first invents is entitled to exclude others from practicing a claimed patented invention. Until recent GATT legislation, only U.S. inventors were permitted to establish a date of invention prior to the U.S. patent application filing date. Other inventors seeking earlier priority dates could only rely on the earliest patent application filing date established under the Paris Convention. On January 1, 1996, GATT legislation will take effect to allow all inventors, including those outside the United States, to establish a date of invention of January 1, 1996 or later for all patent applications filed in the United States after January 1, 1996. The following includes questions to help understand new legislation. The GATT legislation offers patent opportunities for inventors and assignees outside of the United States who are able to adequately document their inventive process in a manner that is acceptable to the United States Patent Office.

1. If an idea is generated; what should they do next to protect it?

Before an inventor begins spending money on the patent process, they must first verify the marketability or feasibility of the invention. Way too often inventors go down the road of inventing "just knowing their invention will sell" but not having the desire to see whether it won't sell. So the recommended steps to proceeding with the invention process are: (1) begin an inventor's journal and record in writing everything having to do with the invention, (2) complete some good market research and verify the marketability, and (3) begin the patent process.

2. What is a patent?

In the United States there are three kinds of patent -- utility patents, design patents, and plant patents. A patent allows one to prohibit others from making, using, selling, offering for sale or importing into the United States for a period of up to twenty years from the date of filing the application. Most countries of the world have patent systems, although the patent terms and types of patents vary.

In the United States, the term of a utility patent depends on when the patent application was filed. If the patent issued from an application filed prior to June 8, 1995, the term is the later of (1) 17 years from the date of issuance of the patent, or (2) 20 years from the first U.S. filing date for the patent. If the patent issued from an application filed on or after June 8, 1995, then the term is 20 years from the first U.S. filing date for the patent. This complicated rule for the term of a utility patent is the result of the transition from the old term (17 years after issuance) to the uniform term prescribed by GATT (20 years after filing). It applies to all patents still in force on June 8, 1995.

Design patents in the United States have a term of 14 years, while plant patents have a term of 17 years. A common misconception is that the patent gives its owner the right to make, use, import, offer for sale or sell the invention. It only gives the owner the ability to exclude others from making, using, importing, offering for sale or selling the invention. The patent owner may be forbidden from using the invention, usually due to the existence of another patent, or sometimes due to other legal restrictions.

To illustrate this principle, consider the following common case: Person 1 patents an invention. Person 2 later patents an improvement to the invention. In order to make, use, or sell the improved invention, one may need permission from 1 (due to the patent on the original invention), and also permission from 2 (due to the patent on the improvement). For example, suppose person 1's patent has a claim covering apparatus comprising a seat and legs (a chair). Suppose person 2's patent has a claim covering apparatus comprising a seat, legs, and two curved rails (a rocking chair). Someone who would hope to make apparatus comprising a seat, legs, and two curved rails will have to get permission from both person 1 and person 2. Another choice is to wait for person 1's patent to expire; then permission is needed only from person 2. Still another choice is to wait for both patents to expire.

The US Patent Office publishes a good brochure about patents entitled General Information Concerning Patents.

3. What are the different types of United States patents?

The most common type of patent is a utility patent. Utility patents protect function, usually in a device or method. A utility patent may be filed either as a provisional patent application or a standard patent application. The next most common is a design patent, which protects aesthetic appearances. A third, highly uncommon, patent exists. This is a plant patent, which protects asexually reproduced plants such as roses.

4. Why does the law recognize patents?

Patents were designed to reward persons for particular benefits provided to the government and the people with a monopoly. Originally, the "benefits" was loosely defined and the monopoly was not well connected to the benefit provided. In time the "benefit" to be offered became more narrowly defined to require a teaching about something unknown. The monopoly offered as a reward also became more closely related to the benefit. The inventor received a limited monopoly on the subject matter of the teaching (i.e., the invention as described in the claims). The impact of these events still permeate patent law today.

5. What inventions can be patented?

The question "what is patentable" is a complicated one. Here is a simplified answer. In addition, we will discuss some common misconceptions about patentability. In order to be patentable, an invention must pass four tests:
   1. The invention must fall into one of the five "statutory classes" of things that are patentable:
      - processes,
      - machines,
      - manufactures (that is, objects made by humans or machines),
      - compositions of matter, and
      - new uses of any of the above.
   2. The invention must be "useful". One aspect of the "utility" test is that the invention cannot be a mere theoretical phenomenon.
   3. The invention must be "novel", that is, it must be something that no one did before.
   4. The invention must be "unobvious" to "a person having ordinary skill in the art to which said subject matter pertains". This requirement is the one on which many patentability disputes hinge.

Typically inventions are aesthetic designs, functional items, functional methods, or asexually reproduced plants.

Other technical requirements must be met for the patent to issue, relating to the disclosure and form of the claims. Meeting the technical requirements is generally within the ability of a skilled patent practitioner.

6. What is the requirement of "new" or "novel"?

New and novel have the same meaning. Specifically, one's invention is new or novel if the invention is not identical to a single invention found in the prior art. Any public disclosures or offers for sale of your invention more than one year prior to your filing for a patent are prior art. This is called the on-sale bar and is perhaps the single most common reason why an invention may not be new or novel.

7. What is the requirement of "useful"?

An invention that is useful is one that functions. This requirement is to avoid issuance of patents on perpetual motion machines. Some inventions are so advancing of science that many people do not currently have the capacity to understand how the invention functions. Scientific testing can be used to prove that this requirement has been met.

8. What is the requirement of "non-obvious"?

Non-obviousness is anything that is outside the ability of one having ordinary skill in the art. This is a subjective test that is difficult to explain and difficult to apply. In essence, one looks to two or more prior existing inventions to find the part of the invention in question. Typically, this can be found in all inventions. To combine the parts of different inventions there must also be a teaching to make the combination. Typically, this teaching is not present in patentable inventions.

There is much misunderstanding over what "unobvious" means in the context of U.S. patent law. The level of unobviousness required to render an invention patentable is a function of the particular art area containing the invention. An experienced patent attorney or agent will often be able to give some indication of the likelihood of a particular invention being held obvious or unobvious. In some cases the unobvious part of an invention (the part that renders the invention patentable) is simply identifying the problem, even if the solution is obvious once the problem has been identified.

9. Are algorithms or computer software patentable?

If one has invented a novel and unobvious algorithm or piece of computer software, and wishes to obtain patent protection, then one's next step should be to consult one or more patent attorneys or patent agents who are experienced in getting patents on inventions having algorithms or software in them. The law (in the U.S.) is settled that the mere presence of software in an invention does not automatically render it unpatentable. It is commonplace for inventors to obtain patents in inventions composed largely or nearly entirely of software.

Many of the well-known cases in the Patent Office Board of Appeals, and many of the well-known cases in the Court of Appeals for the Federal Circuit, in which the patentability of a software-related invention was contested, are instances not of inventions that were unpatentable subject matter, but rather are instances in which the parties got caught up in disputes over the wording and style of the pending claims. Inventors have been getting strong patent protection for software-intensive inventions for decades, essentially by being thoughtful about the wording and claim-drafting style of the patent applications.

Prosecution of software-intensive patent applications tends to take longer than prosecution of some other types of patent applications, for the simple reason that the examining groups handling the former tend to have large backlogs.

The USPTO web site provides the draft Examination Guidelines for Computer-Related Inventions.

10. Why should one file before the first public disclosure or offer for sale?

Filing a patent application before the first public disclosure or offer for sale permits later filing in foreign countries. It also allows one to mark their product patent pending, which can provide a practical protection when introducing a new product into the market. Another advantage is that people often forget to file a patent application in a timely manner if they do not file the application before bringing the product into the market.

10a. When must a patent application be filed before the first public disclosure or offer for sale?

Almost everywhere in the world, except the United States, a patent application must have a priority date before the first public disclosure. Filing a patent application in any country ascribing to the Patent Cooperation Treaty gives the priority date. One invention may have multiple priority dates.

11. Can one use a priority date from one country in a second country?

Yes. There are two common modes of claiming a priority date. First, a priority date can be claimed in the filing papers if the application is filed in the second country within one year of the priority date. Second, a PCT application can be filed which extends the time to file in other countries up to 30 months from the priority date and in some countries even longer.

12. What benefit is there to waiting to file a patent application?

One can wait up to a year after the first public disclosure or offer for sale to file a U.S. patent application. The principal benefit in waiting is to gain further understanding of the commercial viability of the invention before investing in patent protection. Waiting does risk forgetting to file and forever losing the right to obtain patent protection.

13. What are the basic steps of obtaining a U.S. Patent?

One may conduct a patentability search to determine whether an invention is patentable. Next, a patent application is prepared and filed. The US Patent and Trademark Office, USPTO, examines the patent application and typically issues an Office Action. The patentee can either argue the examiner is wrong or make appropriate corrections in a document called an Amendment or a Response. This Office Action/Amendment process may repeat and typically occurs twice. The examiner then sends out a Notice of Allowance if the applicant successfully defines a patentable invention. The applicant pays issuance fees and files formal drawings and the USPTO issues the patent. Each case may vary, although most cases follow this course.

14. What are the considerations to conducting a patentability search?

A patentability search is not necessary. The reason for conducting a search is to determine whether the invention is patentable and if so what is the likely scope of protection. The principle counter consideration is the financial cost of the benefit. The USPTO will conduct a search upon filing an application.

Often inventors perform their own search of the market and then of patents in a public library. Legal counsel is brought in when quality becomes more important. The inventor should be specific as to what they would like counsel to perform. The search can come with a formal written opinion or simply be copies of the prior art found in the search. Costs vary depending on what the inventor wishes to have the patent attorney perform as does the work involved and the quality of the information received from the patent attorney.

15. What is involved in preparing the patent application?

An inventor describes the invention to a patent professional, attorney or agent, and the professional drafts an application. This is typically done in the first meeting. You should request the firm representing you to sign a non-disclosure/non-compete agreement to protect your interests before disclosing the invention. Contracts are much easier to enforce than Rules of Professional Conduct, fiduciary duty rules or other areas of law that some firms will ask you to rely upon.

The patent lawyer or agent prepares the application based upon the inventor's description and models if available. This application is sent to the inventor for review. The inventor should be sure all information is disclosed and that the content is correct. The professional has the changes made to the application and sends out the application for signatures. The professional files the signed application with the USPTO. Formal drawings may be filed at this time or after the USPTO sends out the Notice of Allowance.

The inventor needs to identify all prior art, related products or methods known to the inventor at the time of filing. These need to be filed or the validity of any patent ultimately received can be jeopardized.

16. What is an Office Action?

The USPTO examines the application and in about 90% of the cases finds reason why the patent should not issue. Most professionals agree that an error, failing to ask for enough protection, occurred in those cases where the application issues without an Office Action. The examiner issues an Office Action usually in 6-9 months, although this timing can fluctuate considerably. The Office Action itemizes and explains the reasons why the application was not allowed. Typically, the USPTO issues two Office Actions before an application is allowed, however, the number of Office Actions may be higher or lower in uncommon circumstances.

17. How does the applicant respond to an Office Action?

The applicant has an opportunity to correct those points the USPTO considers to be basis for rejection/objection. Alternatively or additionally, the applicant can explain why they believe the examiner's assessment of the application is incorrect. The applicant's position is recorded and presented in a document called an Amendment or a Response. The applicant has three (3) months, extendable to six (6) months to file this document. The examiner sends out a Notice of Allowance if the applicant is successful in overcoming all objections and rejections.

18. What happens upon receipt of the Notice of Allowance?

The file is reviewed, formal drawings are made, if this has not already been done, and an issue fee is paid after receipt of the Notice of Allowance. A two (2) month period is provided to do this work. Formal drawings are often delayed until this time to avoid paying the cost until necessary, since not every application is allowed. Although the national average of patents issuing per application is only about 50%, our experience shows competent professionals have a much higher success rate. We believe that pro se applicants and the former practice of submarine patents lower the average.

Non-obviousness is anything that is outside the ability of one having ordinary skill in the art. This is a subjective test that is difficult to explain and difficult to apply. In essence, one looks to two or more prior existing inventions to find the part of the invention in question. Typically, this can be found in all inventions. To combine the parts of different inventions there must also be a teaching to make the combination. Typically, this teaching is not present in patentable inventions.

Under the new 20 Year Patent Term Adjustment rules, a notice of patent term adjustment may accompany the Notice of Allowance. This notice means that your patent term will be lengthened or shortened, depending on delays in promoting timely completion of the prosecution phase. See the 20 Year Patent Term Adjustment FAQs for more information.

19. What are the steps to obtaining foreign patent protection?

Patents provide protection only in the issuing country. When one files a patent application, the USPTO issues a Foreign Filing License. That license specifies a priority date. Foreign patents must be filed within one year of the priority date or the priority date is lost. This one-year window can be extended to thirty (30) months or even longer in some cases with the filing of an application in accordance with the Patent Cooperation Treaty (PCT). Foreign patent applications must then be filed before the expiration of the PCT application.

20. What is the significance of the priority date?

Almost every country in the world requires filing a patent application before the occurrence of a public disclosure or offer for sale. Filing in every country prior to such a disclosure would be cost prohibitive for all. Countries have agreed to treat each application filed in accordance with particular rules as if that application had been filed on the priority date. The practical effect is that one can pursue sales of their invention for up to twelve (12) months before a PCT application needs to be filed and up to thirty (30) months, assuming a PCT application has been filed, before filing in individual foreign countries.

21. What does it cost to get an opinion whether an invention is patentable?

Any answer to a question of what something costs turns on our estimate of the number of hours something will take. The actual number of hours sometimes turns out to be more, and sometimes turns out to be less, than the estimate.

The opinion regarding whether something is obvious (or, what is really the point, patentable) is always necessarily given relative to a particular collection of prior art. And the opinion is nonsense unless it is with respect to particular proposed patent claims, claims that are written to cover the invention. Thus, claims (at least, first-draft claims) have to be written. This would surely cost $200 or more. Claim drafting is, after all, one of the most difficult areas of patent practice. So, unless one has already drafted some claims and are sure they are good claims, one will need to allow for some professional time for claim drafting.

The breadth of the claims that are considered in reaching the opinion is also quite important. Generally speaking, the narrower the claims are, the more likely they would be patentable. On the other hand, if the claims are quite narrow they are also less likely to be economically important, since it is less likely anyone would ever infringe them. This is an area where some inventors get misplaced hopes if the breadth of the claims is not explicitly discussed. An inventor may ask "can I get a patent?" to which the answer can be "yes" so long as the claims are quite narrow (and thus worthless).

The next issue is for you to decide what collection of prior art you wish to have used in forming the opinion. If the collection is small, the time required to form an opinion is small, but the opinion is of limited comfort since there is lots of other prior art out there (probably) which could interfere with getting a patent. If the collection is large, then money was, of course, spent to accumulate the collection. And it takes a long time to consider all of the art in reaching the opinion. But the opinion will provide a higher confidence as to the outcome if a patent application is filed.

One choice is to form an opinion with respect to the particular prior art found by the inventor in the inventor's own search, perhaps conducted online (e.g. via the Internet or Compuserve) or by means of a visit to a patent depository library. The value of such an opinion turns on how confident you are that your search was thorough. Such an opinion might cost $200 or more if delivered orally, and $500 or more if delivered in writing. This assumes you have already drafted your own claims or have already budgeted for professional drafting of at least first-draft claims.

Another choice is to hire experienced counsel to do some online database searching to augment whatever searching the inventor has already done. That would cost $200 or more for professional time and $50 or more for the database charges. The augmented collection of prior art is then compared with the claims and an opinion reached as to patentability. One should consider developing their own in-house capability for searching on the comprehensive online databases such as Dialog, STN, and Orbit. Effective searching in these databases requires keeping up to date through frequent use, so those clients who would search only rarely are perhaps wise to have experienced counsel do the searching.

Still another choice is to have a searcher do an in-person search at the USPTO public search room to augment your search. That would cost at least $500. The augmented collection of prior art is then compared with the claims and an opinion reached as to patentability. Most professional searchers take at least a few days to do searches, while the online searches can be done much more quickly, a factor that sometimes discourages the use of a professional searcher.

There is also the person who wants to get the strongest patent possible. In some bet-the-company situations, it is more important to scour the earth for prior art, before filing the patent application, then it is to save money. When this arises, depending on the particular technology area, conduct online searches, in-person searches by patent counsel at the patent office, and other searches of non-patent literature.

In all of this, it must not be forgotten that:

1. Online searches necessarily only find references that happen to contain the key words that were used in the search. We have seen cases where an online search missed an important piece of prior art, all because it used nonstandard vocabulary. Online searches also have the drawback that they do not contain the figures, yet for some inventions the figures are exactly the best way to pick out the pertinent prior art.

2. In-person searches sometimes miss things. One reason is that the in-person search includes only patents in a particular numerical class, and the class numbers are assigned by fallible humans. A second reason is that even a diligent searcher will sometimes miss a reference among hundreds.

3. No search, no matter how thorough, has any hope of detecting things recently filed with the Patent Office that might make it impossible to get a patent. Patent applications are kept secret (at least for 18 months, and sometimes all the way until issuance) and such non-public applications can nonetheless get in the way of getting a patent.

The cost of a patentability opinion depends on many things including the claim drafting, the online searching, the in-person searching, and the opinion. The answer is anywhere from a $200 - $1000 or more. In some cases it might cost more to reach a patentability opinion than simply to prepare and file the patent application. For some clients, what makes sense is to do some online searching, order up copies of the references, and draft and file a patent application based on what is found. This is done with the knowledge that the patent examiner, who can search references in person looking at the figures, may find prior art that we did not know about. It is also done with the knowledge that the examiner gets to see pending patent applications, and we don't.

Some potential clients ask if they can have a flat rate quoted for a search or for a patentability opinion. The answer is "yes", but we arrive at such a flat rate by the simple step of figuring out the largest amount of time the work is likely to take, and asking to be paid that amount. For most clients, then, the money-saving strategy is to pay us in our usual way, which is by the hour.

22. How was the duration of a patent determined prior to GATT?

Utility patents, prior to GATT, lasted 17 years from date of issuance. The master-apprentice relationship was a seven-year relationship. Custom had it that when an apprentice learned something from his master that was not otherwise known in the trade (i.e., an invention) the apprentice would not practice it for two apprentice periods following the end of his apprenticeship. The master could have developed the invention at the start or at the end of the apprenticeship, making the average time in the middle. Adding half the existing apprenticeship period with the two subsequent apprenticeship periods (3-1/2 + 7 + 7) gave 17-1/2years of a monopoly for the inventor. For convenience sake, the half-year was dropped, giving a 17-year monopoly. Design and plant patents lasted 14 years from the date of issuance (7+7). GATT changed the durations which are now based upon a compromise of time periods from the contracting governments.

23. How important was patent law during the formation of the United States?

The significance of patent laws was recognized by the drafters of the United States Constitution. Article I, Section 8, Clause 8 states: The Congress shall have power ...To promote the progress of science [patent] and useful arts [copyright], by securing for limited times to authors and inventors the exclusive right to their respective writings and discoveries. Promulgation power for most federal law, including trademark law, is not separately set forth in the Constitution like patent and copyright law, but rather is promulgated under the interstate commerce clause. Today, many people would cite the United States patent laws as the reason why the United States is a world leader in technology. The European Patent Office (EPO) and Japanese Patent Office have similar strong patent systems.

24. Did the United States Patent Office believe that all inventions would be uncovered?

Originally, it was believed that there were less than a thousand inventions that could ever be discovered. The number fluctuated somewhat and eventually was abandoned. One interesting result of the belief that we still enjoy today is found in the Library of Congress. The patent office originally required the submission of a working miniature model. Each of these models was to be donated to the Library of Congress, where they can still be found today. The reasoning behind such requirement is so that the Library of Congress would hold an example of every invention. This practice of submitting miniature models was discontinued as the estimated number of total inventions continued to increase and as space decreased.

25. What is the best way to go forward with patent counsel?

In some cases, of course, it is easy to go in person to see the patent counsel and to discuss the costs of the work and the nature of the invention itself. In this modern world of email, faxes, and overnight courier delivery, it is also possible to imagine proceeding without having met one's patent counsel in person. Several things can be said about all of this.

First, one should not send one's invention to any patent professional without getting permission in advance to do so. Most patent professionals necessarily discard such things unread; since there is the possibility the professional will have a conflict of interest due to some existing client. Second, unless prior arrangements are made for encryption (e.g. via PGP) it is unwise to use the Internet to communicate the invention.

Counsel usually conducts a conflict check to see whether or not a new client can be accepted. If the conflict check is clear, then after some discussion by email or telephone payment is requested in advance of a deposit, which is held in escrow to be applied toward the bill to be rendered later. Thus the deposit is a crucial part of the first package sent from the client. Also in the package would be drawings of the invention, text description of the invention, copies of prior art already found, and related materials.

26. What are the tax consequences of spending money to get patents? Are patent lawyer bills tax-deductible?

Before taking steps in reliance on the tax status of an expenditure obtain tax advice from a qualified tax advisor. Here are some general comments to assist you in determining what questions to ask your tax advisor.

Generally speaking, money spent to obtain a capital asset is deductible only through depreciation. Similarly, legal bills expended to acquire an asset with a limited life, such as a lease, are typically only deductible in the same manner as the underlying capital spending.

Under the U.S. tax law, however, research and development expenses enjoy a tax preference in the sense that they can typically be expensed in the year in which the expense was incurred.

Generally, the money spent to obtain patent protection for the inventions resulting from research and development is similarly deductible as an expensed cost in the year in which the bills were incurred. However, correct tax advice depends a great deal on the individual situation, so consult a tax advisor about this subject, and do not rely upon these comments as tax advice.

27. How much does a patent cost? (2003 figures)

Patent application costs are often a heavy burden at first, as it can be several years before an invention becomes profitable. The table "Average Costs of Domestic and Foreign Patent Application Procedures" points out the costs for some larger countries and differentiates between the fees of the patent offices and those of the patent lawyers.

In all countries except the USA, annual fees rise constantly until the final, 20th year, with the result that these are quite substantial towards the end of this period. These high fees are usually less important, however, since the majority of patents are not maintained for longer than 15 years. But if an invention is particularly successful and the annual fees for the corresponding patent are paid until the 20th year, profits are also high enough to make paying the annual fees easier.

While the office fees are fixed, for the purposes of the table, an average for the lawyers' fees had to be found. In each country several patent lawyers' chambers were asked about their respective costing and an average was calculated. A patent application of customary scope and degree of difficulty was then based on this information.

One should also bear in mind that, with the European and International Patent application, only the costs of the European Patent Office and the international authorities are mentioned and not those for the national phase. The costs for the national phase depend on the number of countries selected and maintained and whether there is an examination procedure at the respective patent offices. Such a wide range of possibilities exists here that costs can only be forecast on an individual basis.

28. What is the SPI (Software Patent Institute)?

Whenever the Patent Office considers the patentability of an invention, it searches the prior art. The starting point for such searches is generally patents that have already issued in the same art area. This approach doesn't work very well in software areas because until quite recently many inventors in the software arts labored under the (incorrect) impression that the software content rendered an invention unpatentable; as a result there are large gaps in the body of issued patents leaving many software areas undocumented by patent. The Software Patent Institute is building a database of information documenting the known software "folklore" to assist the PTO and others in researching prior art in the software arts.

29. How long is a patent valid?

Patents issuing prior to June 8, 1995 can last up to 17 years from the date of issuance. Patents resulting from applications that were pending on June 8, 1995 can last up to the longer of: 17 years from the date of issuance or 20 years from the date of filing. Patents resulting from applications filed after June 8, 1995 can last up to 20 years from the date of filing.

30. What is the geographic scope of a patent?

A patent is national in scope. Patents can be obtained in most foreign countries.

31. Can one infringe a patent without having knowledge of the patent?

Yes. Infringement occurs when one practices the invention described in the claims. Knowledge, or lack thereof, is generally irrelevant to issues of liability. Independent development is not a defense. Knowledge of the patent by the infringer, however, can be relevant to damages. Many companies do new product clearance searches to avoid lawsuits.

32. Can I keep some information about my invention a secret?

There is a requirement that the invention be completely disclosed. Failure to disclose will invalidate the resulting patent. One cannot maintain information important to the patent as trade secret if the information was known as of the filing date.

33. What does a Provisional Patent Application (PPA) cost?

Cost to prepare and file most PPAs, is about $850 including the filing fee of $80 for a small entity, $160 for a large entity. Of the $850, some Patent Counsels apply a part of the $850 toward a formal application when filed. Some firms are willing to assist inventors in filing provisional applications, in which case the total cost of the provisional filing includes the attorney's fees.

Many patent firms, generally decline to represent an inventor if the only service desired is the filing of a provisional application. The reason is simple: it is all too easy to file a provisional application which would fail to satisfy 35 USC § 112. (See pitfalls of provisional applications.)

The time and effort that would be required to draft proposed claims, to check the provisional application to be sure it supports those proposed claims, to check for best mode and enablement, and to otherwise pass upon whether the application meets §112, go a long way toward the time and effort required to prepare and file a complete (section 111(a)) application.

If an inventor has already filed a provisional application, and comes to us, we will counsel the inventor to get a complete (section 111(a)) patent application filed right away, just as if no provisional had been filed at all. If someone comes to us with a disclosure and asks us to prepare and file a section 111(a) application, we will generally file a provisional patent application right away based on the disclosure (since there is some possibility that the disclosure satisfies§ 112) and then settle down to preparing the 111(a) application.

34. What does it cost to get a patent?

The cost to get a United States patent is made of several components. These include the cost to prepare and file a patent application, various prosecution costs, and the issue fee. Some of the costs are payable to the Patent Office.

After the patent has issued, keeping the patent enforced requires paying maintenance fees to the U.S. Patent Office after 3 1/2, 7 1/2, and 11 1/2 years. Many of the Patent Office fees are discounted for applicants who qualify as small entities (generally, all individuals and organizations except for-profit businesses with 500 or more employees).

The filing fee, depending on the number of claims in the application, can be anywhere from about $400 to $1,000 or more.

But for most applicants, the main cost item in the patent application is the professional charges by the patent attorney or agent preparing the patent application. A patent application covering something that is very simple and easy to describe can cost the applicant as little as $2,000 to file with the Patent Office.

Other inventions, especially inventions that are very complicated or have substantial electronic or software content, can cost as much as $8,000 or $15,000 to be filed with the U.S. Patent Office.

These costs may seem quite high. However, patents are only intended to protect commercially useful inventions, and patent costs are generally small compared to the costs of turning an invention into product, and then of marketing and selling the product. If you do not have good reason to believe that the profits from the invention will greatly exceed the costs of getting the patent, you probably should not be patenting the invention. (See www.uspto.gov)

35. What does it cost to get an opinion whether my invention is patentable?

An opinion usually requires a search prior to preparation of an opinion. Searches generally cost $300 - $500 and an opinion may cost approximately $500 for a total of $800 - $1000 for the search and opinion. Cost will vary depending on complexity of the invention.

36. What are the USPTO fees for patent matters?

For current fees for intellectual property protection see http://www.USPTO.gov.

37. What are the time limits for filing a patent application?

Before making plans for the timing of the filing of a patent application, any inventor should seek advice of competent advice. The time periods described here represent only a few of the factors that will influence how quickly a patent application should be filed.

Under U.S. patent law, a patent will not be granted to an applicant unless the application is filed less than one year from the date that the invention was sold or offered for sale within the United States.

Yet another condition imposed under U.S. patent law is that the patent will be denied unless the application is filed within one year of the date the invention was described in a printed publication anywhere in the world.

These requirements are cumulative in the sense that either of those two events, occurring more than a year ago, will be a bar to patentability. Thus, if your invention has been described in a printed publication anywhere in the world, or if your invention has been sold or offered for sale in the United States, then you would be wise to pay close attention to the dates on which those events occurred, and to make sure that you consult competent counsel long before the expiration of the one year grace periods.

While these are the two most commonly mentioned so-called "statutory bars" in U.S. patent law (35 USC section 102), they are by no means the only factors that should be taken into account when one decides when to file a patent application (or, when to consult patent counsel). Numerous other factors influence the timing of the filing of a U.S. patent application. For one thing, there is always the possibility that someone else has filed or will soon be filing a patent application on the same subject matter. The sooner you file, the more likely it is that you will prevail against someone else who has filed or is about to file.

The discussion up to this point assumes nothing more than that the inventor is interested in getting United States patent protection. It is important to keep in mind, however, that if there is any possibility that the inventor would want to seek patent protection in countries outside the United States, then it is imperative to seek advice of competent counsel in advance of any public disclosure or sale of the invention.

The reason for this is that in many countries outside the United States, public divulgation of the invention at any time prior to the patent application may bar the grant of the patent. For these reasons it is wise to consider setting a goal of getting the patent application on file prior to any public disclosure or sale.

Even if the invention has not been publicly divulged there are reasons to file a patent application sooner rather than later. Filing the application sooner will help to some extent in prevailing over others who happen to have developed the invention independently and who also file a patent application.

In the United States two approaches are possible to the protection of an invention in the face of a statutory bar such as the on-sale bar or the publication bar: filing a patent application or filing a provisional patent application.

No U.S. patent will be granted on an application if the invention was disclosed in a printed publication anywhere in the world more than a year before the filing of the application. Furthermore, no U.S. patent will be granted on an application if the invention was sold or offered for sale in the U.S. more than a year before the filing of the application. Finally, 35 USC section 102 lists other conditions that will bar patentability and should be consulted prior to any decision to postpone filing a patent application.

For those who are interested in also obtaining protection in countries other than the U.S. it is important to bear in mind that the patent application should be filed prior to any public divulgation of the invention.

In all cases, it is advantageous to file a patent application sooner rather than later.

38. What do the terms "patent pending" and "patent applied for" mean?

They are used by a manufacturer or seller of an article to inform the public that an application for patent on that article is on file in the Patent and Trademark Office. The law imposes a fine on those who use these terms falsely to deceive the public.

39. What rights does a patent provide?

The right to prohibit (see previous question) does not automatically include the right for the inventor to make, use, sell, import and/or offer the invention for sale. Anyone is free, however, to engage in such activities unless there is a law prohibiting it. The prohibitory laws of greatest concern include FDA regulations, firearm and explosives regulations, and patent laws whereby one's invention improves on another's patented invention.

40. Is there any danger that the Patent and Trademark Office will give others information contained in my application while it is pending?

No. All patent applications are maintained in the strictest confidence until the patent is issued. After the patent is issued, however, the Office file containing the application and all correspondence leading up to issuance of the patent is made available in the Files Information Unit for inspection by anyone and copies of these files may be purchased from the Office.

41. May one write to the Patent and Trademark Office directly about my application after it is filed?

The Office will answer an applicant's inquiries as to the status of the application, and inform you whether your application has been rejected, allowed, or is awaiting action. However, if you have a patent attorney or agent of record in the application file the Office will not correspond with both you and the attorney/agent concerning the merits of your application. All comments concerning your application should be forwarded through your attorney or agent.

42. Is it necessary to go to the Patent and Trademark Office to transact business concerning patent matters?

No. Most business with the Office is conducted by correspondence. Interviews regarding pending applications can be arranged with examiners if necessary, however, and are often helpful.

43. If two or more persons work together to make an invention, to whom will the patent be granted?

If each had a share in the ideas forming the invention, they are joint inventors and a patent will be issued to them jointly on the basis of a proper patent application. If, on the other hand, one of these persons has provided all of the ideas of the invention, and the other has only followed instructions in making it, the person who contributed the ideas is the sole inventor and the patent application and patent shall be in his/her name alone.

44. If one person furnishes all of the ideas to make an invention and another employs him or furnishes the money for building and testing the invention, should the patent application be filed by them jointly?

No. The application must be signed by the true inventor, and filed in the Patent and Trademark Office, in the inventors name. This is the person who furnishes the ideas, not the employer or the person who furnishes the money.

45. Does the Patent and Trademark Office control the fees charged by patent attorneys and agents for their services?

No. This is a matter between you and your patent attorney or agent in which the Office takes no part. To avoid misunderstanding you may wish to ask for estimate charges for: (a) the search (b) preparation of the patent application, and (c) Patent and Trademark Office prosecution.

46. Will the Patent and Trademark Office help select a patent attorney or agent to make a patent search or to prepare and prosecute a patent application?

No. The Office cannot make this choice for you. However, your own friends or general attorney may help you in making a selection from among those listed as registered practitioners on the Office roster. Also, some bar associations operate lawyer referral services that maintain lists of patent lawyers available to accept new clients.

47. Will the Patent and Trademark Office advise as to whether a certain patent promotion organization is reliable and trustworthy?

No. The Office has no control over such organizations and does not supply information about them. It is advisable, however, to check on the reputation of invention promotion firms before making any commitments. It is suggested that you obtain this information from the Better Business Bureau of the city in which the organization is located, or from the bureau of commerce and industry or bureau of consumer affairs of the state in which the organization has its place of business. You may also undertake to make sure that you are dealing with reliable people by asking your own patent attorney or agent or by asking others who may know them.

48. Are there any organizations in my area which can tell me how and where I may be able to obtain assistance in developing and marketing my invention?

Yes. In your own or neighboring communities you may inquire of such organizations as chambers of commerce, and banks. Many communities have locally financed industrial development organizations which can help you locate manufacturers and individuals who might be interested in promoting your idea.

49. Are there any state government agencies that can help in developing and marketing an invention?

Yes. In nearly all states there are state planning and development agencies or departments of commerce and industry which seek new product and new process ideas to assist manufacturers and communities in the state. If you do not know the names or addresses of your state organizations you can obtain this information by writing to the governor of your state.

50. Can the Patent and Trademark Office assist in developing and marketing a patent?

The Office cannot act or advise concerning the business transactions or arrangements that are involved in the development and marketing of an invention. However, the Office will publish, at the request of a patent owner, a notice in the Official Gazette that the patent is available for licensing or sale. The fee for this is $25.

51. Can one apply for a patent myself?

Yes, you can apply for a patent yourself. It is called applying pro se. Perhaps one-fifth of all issued U.S. patents were applied for pro se, and some of them are actually well written. Most inventors find, however, that an experienced patent agent or attorney can add value in many ways in preparing a patent application, both in bringing past experience to bear in drafting claim language, and in assisting the inventor in appreciating all the inventive aspects of the invention.
Furthermore, the agent or attorney is likely to be methodical about following and meeting Patent Office due dates, where a pro se applicant might miss a due date at some point during prosecution.

If you wish to explore the possibility of applying for a patent pro se, then a good starting point is Patent It Yourself from Nolo Press. The publisher says the book "is a must for any inventor who wants to get a patent--from the patent search to the actual application. Patent attorney and former patent examiner David Pressman covers use and licensing, successful marketing and infringement." The book is, in fact, good reading even for the inventor who plans to hire patent counsel; it helps the inventor to be a more knowledgeable customer.

52. Can I save money by drafting a patent application myself and then simply paying a patent attorney or agent to touch it up for filing?

We are sometimes asked if the cost of preparing the patent application can be reduced if the applicant prepares a first draft of the application. It is not possible to answer this question in advance, since it is not possible to know whether the draft application which will be prepared by the client will be suitable for use in preparing the final application.

For many draft applications prepared by clients, it turns out to be more expensive for counsel to fix up the application than it would have been for us to prepare it from scratch.

This is not lost on some potential clients, who might ask one to review a client-prepared draft application to arrive at an estimate of the cost involved in making the application suitable for filing. When one considers the extraordinarily varied ways in which a draft application might be flawed, many of which are subtle and take time to find, one may appreciate that simply reviewing an application to arrive at an estimate of the time required to fix it may take as much time as preparing an application from scratch.

It is always helpful for the patent attorney or agent to receive anything and everything the client has written about the invention. And it is helpful to receive it in computer-readable form in case some of it is usable in the patent application. The foregoing discussion is simply meant to emphasize that when the client provides lots of written matter about the invention (which never hurts and generally helps) the result is not so much the savings of money as an improvement in the quality of the patent application that results. Thus, the client should not focus so much on writing a patent application as on gathering and organizing the information that will go into the patent application, especially the description of the invention and the relevant background information about the prior art.

Nonetheless, it is perfectly reasonable for a client or a potential client to want to have some idea what things would cost. Without knowing the particular subject matter involved, a patent attorney or agent can only answer in generalities as to the cost of a patent application. After hearing about the subject matter, the attorney or agent can usually give a more specific estimate of the cost to prepare a patent application.

Costs of pro se and attorney/agent filings compared - If you apply pro se (that is, filing an application yourself, without a patent attorney or agent), the largest single expenditure is typically the Patent Office filing fee of some $300 or more. If you retain a patent agent or attorney you can expect to pay for many hours of that person's time at some standard billing rate, leading to total costs as of filing the application of some higher amount. Depending on the billing rate and the time required it is common for a patent application to cost $2,000-$3,000 at the low end of the scale, or $10,000-$15,000 for a complex application. Patent agents and attorneys vary in billing rates and in billing practices. Some, although not very many, will quote a fixed price for preparation of a (utility) patent application.

53. How can one tell if a Patent Attorney/Agent is legitimate/honest?

Check the US Patent Office's current registry to see if the patent attorney or patent agent is listed: "Roster of Patent Agents and Attorneys". Remember, there is a difference between 'legitimate' and 'good'. Ask the provider for references of other inventor clients, as well as for copies of patents they have filed in your field (for instance, certain patent attorneys specialize in Chemical Patents, Software Patents, etc. - so find the one with technical expertise in your patent technology)

54. How can one order copies of patents, or patent applications?

There are many ways to obtain copies of patents. You can get a copy of a US patent by sending $3 and the patent number to US PTO, Washington, DC 20231. This service takes a few weeks. Many patent offices and private organizations offer quick turnaround of patent copies. See, for example, the European Patent Office and Dialog.

Any inventor can get a copy of the filed application and look at the files. You can have a patent contractor such as Patent Providers get it for you. An inventor can complete a power to inspect form and the contractor can then secure copies for the inventor. The inventor must be named on the patent. If not, the other inventor or patent attorney of record would have to execute a power to inspect.

One can get a certified copy of a PPA from the USPTO. Fax number: 703.308.7048 Required Info: Name and address of person making request; Credit card #, name on PPA and exp. date; PPA number, filing date; name(s) of inventors or assignees, etc. Turn-around time: 9 to 17 days for $15 (normal) or 5 days for $30 (expedited request).

The USPTO site also provides the following info: Patent Application (IA) (For an Issued Patent) - A non-provisional application for a patent includes a written document, which comprises a specification (description and claims), and an oath or declaration; and a drawing in those cases in which a drawing is necessary; and the filing fee. A provisional application provides the means to establish an early effective filing date in a patent application and permits the term "Patent Pending" to be applied in connection with the invention. Claims and oath or declaration are NOT required for a provisional application. Provisional applications may not be filed for design inventions. Applications are scanned upon receipt and copies are produced from the scanned images. Note that copies of applications are available to the general public only for issued patents. Pending applications for patents are NOT open for public inspection; and no information or copies may be obtained without the written consent of the applicant, attorney of record, or the assignee. Copies of applications for issued patents may be ordered by the patent number or by the 8 digit application number.

55. What is the Paris Convention?

The Paris Convention is a treaty, adhered to by about 110 countries, which helps those who wish to obtain patent protection in more than one country. To illustrate how the treaty helps an applicant, consider the inventor who desires to apply for patent protection in countries A and B (both of which adhere to the Paris Convention). If there were no Paris Convention, then for the best chances of obtaining a patent in both countries, the inventor would have to file in both countries simultaneously or nearly simultaneously because the publication of the patent in country A would bar filing a patent application in country B. Because of the Convention, however, the inventor need only file in one of the two countries, say country A, and may postpone filing in country B for almost a year. When the filing is done in country B the applicant merely "claims priority" from the filing in country A, and the patent office in country B will treat the country-B application as if it had been filed on the date in which the country-A application was filed.

The Paris Convention is thus very helpful to inventors, for several reasons:
1. Filing in many countries costs a lot of money. The Paris Convention allows the inventor to defer that cost. What's more, if events during the year lead to a decision to abandon the attempt to get patents, then the Paris Convention allows the inventor to save all the money that would have been spent in the countries other than the first country.
2. Filing in many countries is often time consuming and involved. Often the text of the patent application has to be translated into several languages. It is necessary to engage in correspondence with patent agents or attorneys in each of the countries involved. In the absence of the Paris Convention, an inventor would have to do these things in a hurry, in many countries at once, necessitating large courier bills, lots of faxes, and lots of rush translations.

The Paris Convention allows the translating and international correspondence to be undertaken over the course of a year rather than all at once.

56. What is a priority date for a patent application?

The term "priority date" can mean any of several different things, depending on the context. The "priority date" of a patent application is the date which controls what prior art affects its patentability, whether a statutory bar applies, etc. For many patent applications the priority date is the date on which the patent application was filed with the patent office. In some circumstances a patent application will enjoy an priority date earlier than its own filing date. For example, a continuation or divisional application will enjoy the filing date of the application of which it is a continuation or divisional. Another example is the application which claims priority under the Paris Convention from a counterpart application filed less than one year earlier in another country; such an application has a priority date equal to that of the earlier application. Yet another example is the application which claims priority from a provisional application. Finally, an application may enjoy a priority date by virtue of being a national-phase application arising out of a PCT patent application in which the United States was designated. There are other circumstances in which a patent application will have a priority date differing from its filing date.

57. What is the PCT (Patent Cooperation Treaty)?

PCT stands for the Patent Cooperation Treaty (text), which is adhered to by about 88 countries. PCT patent applications are administered by the World Intellectual Property Organization. The Patent Cooperation Treaty permits an inventor to file what is called a PCT patent application. The Treaty is the result of an effort by many countries to provide some streamlining of patent applications across several countries at once. The US Patent and Trademark Office has additional information about PCT.

58. What benefits flow from a PCT application?

For an applicant who has filed a patent application in a particular country, a PCT application offers a way to postpone having to make decisions about filing patent applications in other countries. If there were no such thing as the Patent Cooperation Treaty, then the only opportunity to postpone making decisions about foreign filing would be the opportunity provided by the Paris Convention.

Under the Paris Convention, someone who files an application in one country is forced to make a decision, within one year, as to whether to file patent applications in other countries which would claim priority from the first application. A PCT application offers a way to extend the time during which a decision must be made about foreign patent filings, for a longer period than the decision-postponement period provided by the Paris Convention.

By filing a PCT application, the applicant can postpone for 20 months (rather than 12 months under the Paris Convention) the decision about whether or to spend the money for foreign patent filings. In addition, assuming that the first application was filed in a country that has adhered to Chapter II of the Patent Cooperation Treaty, it is possible to perform a step called "demanding preliminary examination" which permits postponing the decision about foreign filing (in many countries) until 30 months after the priority date.

The PCT process is helpful to those who don't have enough money to file in several countries, but who expect to have enough money at a later time. A PCT application provides a convenient way to keep the options open for foreign filing for up to thirty months.

Applying for patents in several countries through the PCT system nearly always costs more than applying for patents in the same countries without using the PCT system. Thus, the inventor who is sure that she wishes to file in several countries, and who has enough money now to pay for the filings in those countries, will be saving money by filing directly in those countries (through the Paris Convention) rather than through the PCT system.

59. Why, would anyone file a PCT application?

The answers are simple. First, not everyone knows for sure at the time of the first patent filing which, if any, foreign countries should have patent applications filed. After a year or two the inventor may have more information that makes it easier to know whether to do foreign filings. For example, after a year or two the invention may prove to have great commercial potential in some foreign countries and not others. In particular, the inventor who benefits from having filed a PCT application is the one who discovers between, say 12 and 30 months after the filing date, that it is no longer desirable to perform foreign filing. In this case, when the decision is made to drop the foreign filings the inventor will have saved all the money that would have been spent on foreign filings.

Another possible advantage of a PCT application is that it proceeds on a fixed timetable. The applicant may be sure of receiving a Search Report from the International Searching Authority no later than about 17 months after the priority date of the application. If the applicant demands Preliminary Examination, the examination Written Report will be received no later than about 26 months after the priority date of the application. An ordinary U.S. patent application, depending on the backlog in the examining group handling the application, can sometimes go for more than two years before a first Office Action is received. The PCT applicant can thus get faster feedback from a patent office.

Still another possible advantage of a PCT application (if the applicant is from the US or any of certain other countries) is that the applicant may specify where the Search Report and Preliminary Examination Report will be prepared. For the applicant who wants to know as much as possible about the relevant prior art, this permits drawing upon the searching and examination expertise of a selected patent office. For example, if the priority application is filed in the U.S., an applicant may choose to file a PCT application designating the European Patent Office (EPO) for the search and for examination. This will permit the applicant to have the benefit of the searching expertise of both patent offices.

60. What does it cost to file a PCT patent application?
The cost to file a PCT application is affected by several factors, including the number of countries that are being designated, the particular patent office that is designated to perform the international search, and the number of pages in the application. PCT Application filing may range from as little as $4,000 or as much as $9,000. If a PCT application is to be filed using the US Patent Office as the Receiving Office, the fees are listed in the PTO fee schedule.

61. Which world agency administers the PCT patent application?
PCT patent applications are administered by the World Intellectual Property Organization.

62. What is the ISA (International Searching Authority)?
Each PCT patent application has to be searched by a competent International Searching Authority, generally the US Patent Office or the European Patent Office. The applicant gets to choose the particular ISA that will search a particular PCT application.

63. What is the IPEA (International Preliminary Examining Authority)?
In a PCT patent application in which the applicant has demanded Preliminary Examination, the application has to be examined by a competent International Preliminary Examining Authority, generally the US Patent Office or the European Patent Office. The applicant gets to choose the particular IPEA that will search a particular PCT application.

64. What is the purpose of a PCT application?
The filing of a PCT application gives two principle benefits. Filing a PCT application gives a second priority date. This can be important if the invention has not been publicly disclosed or offered for sale. The PCT application also extends the time one has to file foreign patent applications. This extension is up to thirty (30) months and in some select few countries even longer. The extension is beneficial in several ways. Most importantly, the extension allows one to market the invention and find licenses before incurring more substantial costs.

Additionally, the domestic patent usually issues, if it will issue, before the application must be filed in foreign countries. This saves on filing patent applications that never will issue. This situation further saves on the cost of Amendments, since one knows how one examiner believes the claims should be written to be allowable.

65. What does it cost to file a PCT patent application?
Access Oppedahl & Larson Patent Law home page for estimates. For planning purposes set aside $5000 for preparation and filing and allow $3000 to $6000 per country for nationalization. The cost to nationalize varies by country. Consult your Patent Counsel for exact costs.

66. What happens when foreign patent applications are filed?

Most countries prosecute patent applications in the same manner as the US. There are a few notable exceptions. Canada and Japan permit one to delay the examination (Office Actions and Amendments) up to seven years from the priority date. European countries are typically prosecuted in the European Patent Office (EPO) all in one application. When the EPO allows the application, the application is split into the individual countries and each designated country issues a separate patent. However, the European countries that the applicant desires to receive a patent from must be designated at the time of filing the EPO application. African countries use a process similar to the EPO procedure.

67. What is the key business consideration with foreign patent practice?

Foreign patent practice can be expensive. The underlying business should justify the costs in all cases, but even more so with foreign patent applications in view of the cost. Actively seek marketing avenues and/or licensure/assignments in foreign countries preferably before filing a PCT application, but more importantly before filing in individual countries. Although costs can be considerable, these business opportunities can easily justify the cost of foreign patent protection.

68. What is an International Patent Application?

An international patent application is a patent application filed under the Patent Cooperation Treaty. PCT patent applications are administered by the World Intellectual Property Organization. An international patent application does not, however, lead to an "international patent". It merely leads to the ability to file patent applications in designated countries over a wider range of permissible times than if no international patent application were filed. Other tangible results of filing an international patent application include a PCT publication, a Search Report from the International Searching Authority, and optionally a Written Opinion from the International Preliminary Examining Authority.

69. How much does it cost to file patent applications in countries outside of the U.S. ?

The cost for patent filings varies greatly from one country to the next. For someone who has already filed a patent application in the U.S., the cost to file in Canada, to give one example, is typically under $1,000. In contrast, a filing in Japan, which requires translations, might cost $10,000. In some countries the number of claims influences the cost, in others it is the total page count.

Anyone who is attempting to make a decision about whether to do foreign filings in a number of foreign countries would be wise to seek advice from a patent attorney or agent who has done many filings in foreign countries; an experienced attorney or agent can provide some estimate of the cost of the filings.

70. What is the EPC (European Patent Convention)?

EPC stands for European Patent Convention. This convention has given rise to what is called the European Patent Office (EPO). The European Patent Office offers a way to file a single patent application which can lead to patent coverage in all the European countries that belong to the EPC.

While the European Patent Office has its historical origins in the European Union, it is interesting to note that the European Patent Office formalities can lead to patent coverage in countries that do not belong to the European Union. For example, Switzerland does not presently belong to the European Union, and yet it is possible to secure Swiss patent protection through the European Patent Convention and the European Patent Office.

The countries that belong to the European Patent Office include Austria, Belgium, Switzerland, Germany, Denmark, Spain, France, United Kingdom, Greece, Ireland, Italy, Liechtenstein, Luxembourg, Monaco, Netherlands, Portugal, and Sweden.

For an inventor, the main decision that has to be made is whether to file directly with the country or countries in Europe in which patents are desired, or whether to do a single filing with the European Patent Office. As a first approximation, if it is only desired to get patent coverage in one or

two or three countries of Europe, it may be more economical to file directly with the patent offices in those countries. On the other hand, if the number of countries of Europe in which patent
protection is desired is much greater than just one or two countries, then it would be probably be economical to file directly with the European Patent Office.

For planning purposes, an estimate of the cost of a European Patent Office filing is $10,000.

71. How should one do their own patent searching?

The USPTO site can be searched or other sites as well. IBM had established a search site for U.S. patents, discussed below.

Those who do not find it inconvenient to travel to the United States Patent Office in Crystal City, Virginia, will find that the public search room at the Patent Office, which is available free of charge, can be a very fruitful resource for patent searching. Searching in the public search room of the U.S. Patent Office permits you to see physical patents, complete with the figures. Depending on the technological area being searched, the figures can be very valuable as you attempt to figure out which patents are relevant to your area and which ones are not. The patents are available in physical groupings called "shoes", each of which contains all the patents in a particular subclass. This means that after you have finished looking at one patent you simply flip past it to the next one in the same subclass, without delay. In contrast, some of the other ways of searching patents do not let you look at the figures, and impose considerable delays as you go from one patent to the next.

Another patent searching resource available to the general public may be found in patent depository libraries, located in many major cities around the United States. These libraries contain searching resources that enable you to view the titles of patents located in a particular numerical classification. You can then jot down the patent numbers that might be of interest based on the titles, and then view the patents one by one on microfiche. This approach can be very cumbersome, and runs the risk of missing important patents. For example, there might be a patent that is very important to your research, but that has a title that does not particularly indicate the importance of the patent. Another drawback to depository library searching is that it can be a bit of a waste of time to go through the microfiche slides one by one to find the particular patents on your list.

Yet another way of to do patent searching is through any of several online computer databases. The online pay services offer the advantage that they cover patents issued outside of the US, as well as published patent applications from countries other than the US.

Several databases are available through Compuserve or Dialog. Dialog tends to have a more powerful search engine than that available with the Compuserve patent files. In addition an experienced searcher can get exactly what is needed from Dialog at a lower cost than a comparable search on Compuserve.

It should be appreciated, however, that not all types of searching can be done effectively through online databases. After all, an online database only carries text information and thus does not provide figures. It should also be appreciated that online patent databases differ from one to the next in their geographic coverage, their comprehensiveness, how far back they go, how up-to-date they are, and in other ways.

72. How should one search for patents on the Internet?

The one resource that is free of charge and that many people have found helpful is the IBM patent searching site. The site contains over 26 years of U.S. Patent & Trademark Office (USPTO) patent descriptions as well as images dating back to 1980. The first entries date back to January 5, 1971. You can search, retrieve and study over two million patents. The main advantage of this site is that it is free of charge.

Of course, people doing patent searching do it to solve any of a range of questions. If a person is doing a "novelty search", which is a search intended to determine whether a concept is novel (and perhaps patentable), it is necessary to have access to patent information going back for a period of time that makes sense given the technical area being searched. This often means that one needs to have patent records going back at least 10 years and in many cases 20 or 30 years. Such a body of patent information is so large that it would not be easy for anyone to provide that information for free over the Internet. One can do novelty searches on Dialog, a commercial online database service, by searching databases that contain the full text of U.S. patents, the full text of European patents, and abstracts for patents in many other countries.

Depending on the database and subject matter involved the information extends from the present back to about 1970. Another type of search that some people want to do is an infringement search. This is a search which is intended to uncover any patents that might be infringed by particular proposed device or conduct. Since each patent has an expiration date, such a search typically only requires going back far enough in time to cover all the patents that have not yet expired. In the case of United States patents, this typically requires databases going back 17 years or more.

There are, of course, some searches for which the free resources may be helpful. Examples of online patent resources are:

- IBM site,
- Derwent.
- Dialog Information Services may be reached by telephone at 1-800-3-DIALOG or 415-858-3785 or by telnet to dialog.com. There is a one-time sign-up fee, an annual fee, and online time costs money. Intellectual property databases available on Dialog include the following:

World Patents Index. This is an extraordinarily useful database which provides English-language abstracts of patent filings in numerous countries. (Dialog files 350, 351.)

Inpadoc. This provides legal status and patent family information for filings in many countries. (Dialog file 345.)

Japio. This file details Japanese patent filings, including Kokai filings (Japanese applications laid open for public inspection) that are not abstracted anywhere else. (Dialog file 347.)

U.S. Copyrights. This provides bibliographic information on copyright registrations. (Dialog file 120.)

U.S. Patents Fulltext. The full text of U.S. utility patents is provided. (Dialog files 652-654.)

Trademarkscan. These files detail trademark filings in the U.S. Patent and Trademark Office, in various states of the U.S., and in Canada, Australia, Benelux, Denmark, France, Germany, Ireland, Italy, Liechtenstein, Monaco, Switzerland, the United Kingdom, and the World Intellectual Property Office.

Lexis. To sign up, call 1-800-543-8682 or send email to sales@lexis-nexis.com. Lexis can be reached by telnet to lex.lexis-nexis.com. There is a one-time sign-up fee, an annual fee, and online time costs money. Intellectual property databases available on Lexis include U.S. utility, design, and plant patents in full text.

- Questel/Orbit (WWW, telnet) and STN (WWW, telnet) maintain commercial databases on patents and trademarks.
- The U.S. Patent Office has a bulletin board system and a Web server.
- Compuserve. Compuserve has several databases. An account number and password are needed to use Compuserve which can be reached by telnet to compuserve.com.

73. How can one determine whether a particular patent has expired? (If one is considering selling a product which would infringe on a patent that was issued long enough ago that it might have expired, but not long enough ago that they know that it has expired. How does one determine if this patent is still in force (in which case one would need to license or design around it) or if it has been allowed to expire, in which case it might be used without fear of repercussions?

Several online computer databases help to answer this question. For example, check Dialog file 345, Inpadoc, which contains the legal status of patents. Also examine Lexis file Patents Util. If the patent has expired for failure to pay maintenance fees, an expiration date will generally be shown. Also check Shepard's Patent Citator (found in law libraries). If the patent has expired, the expiration will likely have been mentioned in the PTO Official Gazette. The OG citation will be in the Shepard's volume.

One can also hire a patent professional skilled in searching.

74. How do patents and copyrights compare?

A patent may be contrasted with a copyright in several important ways. A copyright typically covers only the expression of a work, and does not do anything to stop people from appropriating clever ideas that happened to be embodied in that work. In contrast, a patent can sometimes be used to stop someone who looks at a copyright work, extracts the clever ideas from it, and creates a new system embodying those clever ideas. It is only a slight oversimplification to say that if there are clever ideas in your software, and if you wish to protect those clever ideas, you are unlikely to be able to do so through copyright, but may be able to do so through patent.

A U.S. patent is obtained only after preparing a very detailed patent application, and then only after a patent examiner has reached the view that the patent application is allowable. Many patent applications are filed that never yield an issued patent. The patent application process typically costs at least a few thousand dollars and sometimes $10,000 or more, including the fees of a patent attorney or agent.

In contrast, a copyright registration is granted almost as matter of course upon filing a relatively simple and relatively inexpensive copyright registration application.

75. How do patents and trade secrets compare?

There is a tension between the notion of trade secrets and patents. One approach to protecting intellectual property is to hold everything as a trade secret. The decision to apply for a patent includes necessarily a decision to take some fraction of one's trade secrets and to give them away, in return for the grant of a patent.

The decision to apply for a patent does not necessarily require giving up all of one's trade secrets, however. One might have trade secrets on inventions A, B, and C, and applying for a patent on C might not require giving up the trade secret status of A and B. However, to obtain a U.S. patent on C, it is necessary that the application contain (1) enough to enable one skilled in the art to practice C and (2) the best mode known to the applicant for practicing C. This might require revealing A and B in the application. If so, it would probably make sense to seek patent protection on A and B as well as on C. Depending on the time sequence, one could patent an invention and simultaneously keep secret an improved version of the invention. For example, if a patent application for invention A is filed, and if an improvement A+ is conceived after the filing of the patent application on A, the improvement A+ could be kept secret.

If the only patent being sought is a United States patent, then the decision to give up trade secrets to obtain a patent is not, at present, an irreversible one. The reason for this is that a U.S. patent application is kept secret by the U.S. Patent Office until such time as a patent issues. At any point prior to payment of the issue fee, an applicant could is permitted to abandon the patent application, in which case it would remain secret thereafter.

One should keep in mind, however, that the U.S. Patent Office has announced its plans to start a program of publishing patent applications 18 months after filing, thus coming into harmony with the majority of countries having patent systems. This change, if implemented, puts the U.S. applicant in the same position as applicants in other countries, having to make a decision whether to seek a patent or rely on trade secret protection.

At such time as the patent issues, it reveals to the public any and all trade secrets that are contained within it. To review what was said earlier, recall that at the time the patent application was being drafted, the drafter would have included within the application everything required to enable one skilled in the art to practice the claimed invention. This means that the issued patent application will contain not only the exact wording of the invention, but will also contain such other things as are required to enable someone skilled in the art to practice the invention. In addition, when the (U.S.)

202

patent application was being prepared, it had to include the best mode known to the applicant for practicing the invention. This means the issued patent contains not only that which is necessary to enable someone to practice the invention, but also discloses the best mode known to the applicant for practicing the invention.

As mentioned above, the U.S. patent system presently permits an applicant to "have it both ways" regarding patents and trade secrets. If it turns out (after several years of patent prosecution) that patent protection is not available, the applicant can simply abandon the application and retain the trade secrets therein. It is quite different in most countries outside of the U.S., where each patent application is published 18 months after the priority date.

Thus, to give a common example, a patent application might be filed in the U.S. on a particular date, and a counterpart application might be filed outside the U.S., for example in Europe, slightly less than one year afterwards. What happens next is that the European Patent Office notices that the patent application is claiming priority from a U.S. application, and makes a note to publish the application 18 months from the U.S. filing date. Thus, 18 months after the U.S. filing, the European patent application becomes published, and all the trade secrets present in that application are no longer trade secrets. Again, as mentioned above, the U.S. Patent Office has announced plans to begin publishing patent applications.

Before relying on the above discussion, you should find out whether the proposed publication procedures have been finalized. Depending on the country, there are sometimes ways to withdraw an application in advance of the 18-month publication date, thus protecting its trade secrets. Thus the applicant who wants to pursue patent protection outside of the U.S., and yet who wants to maintain trade secret protection if patent protection proves unlikely, has to make a decision about this before the 18 months are up.

For some applicants the 18-month publication is not as great a drawback as it might seem. After all, some inventions get revealed to the public automatically through sales of the patented product, in which case revelation of the product's secrets through the 18-month publication would not make much difference. In any event, the applicant must consider the possibility of loss of a trade secret through issuance of a U.S. patent or publication of a patent application in a country outside the United States.

76. Is it possible to get trade secret insurance?

InsurerCNA of Chicago is now offering TradeSecret, an insurance policy to cover financial losses resulting from theft of trade secrets. This is a welcome development, but like patent insurance, premium rates will be high due to risk uncertainty on the part of the insurer (which for both patents and trade secrets depends greatly on how original the IP being protected is, a technical assessment most insurance companies are not experienced at.

77. How do design patents and copyrights compare?

It is not inconsistent to seek both copyright and design patent protection, depending on the nature of what is being protected. Design patent protection is, of course, available only on articles of manufacture and then only on the novel and ornamental aspects thereof. Copyright protection is available on most articles of manufacture but also on many other works.

The copyright term (in the US) is 70 or 95 years, while the design patent term (in the US) is 14 years. Copyright protection is available without your even having to ask for it, although of course it is prudent to place a copyright notice on the work and to register the copyright with the copyright office.

78. How do I get unique design protection?

Design patent protection is available only after filing a design patent application with the Patent Office, and then only if the application is allowed by the Patent Office after examination.

79. Should I mark my products with the patent number?

Under 35 USC section 287, a patent owner is required to mark goods embodying the invention with the patent number. The owner's failure to mark the product runs the risk that the patent owner will not be able to collect damages from infringers during the time that the product was distributed without patent markings. (This obligation to mark does not apply to a patent that has only method claims.)

A proper patent marking would the words "U.S. Patent" followed by the patent number. Many manufacturers choose to provide a more detailed patent marking, such as "May be covered under one or more of the following U.S. patents...".

The law is always changing in the area of patent marking, and the application of the law is quite specific to the patent claims and to the goods involved, so anyone who is concerned about a particular marking should seek advice of competent counsel.

Carl Oppedahl has published a law review article on patent marking entitled "Patent Marking of Systems," Santa Clara Computer and High Technology Law Journal,
Vol. 11, No. 2, p. 205 (1995).

80. Why are laboratory notebooks important?

Laboratory notebooks are important for several reasons. In the U.S., if two applicants are seeking a patent on the same invention, the patent is not necessarily awarded to the one who filed first, but is sometimes instead awarded to the one who was the first to invent.

Establishing priority of invention often depends on such documentation as laboratory notebooks. An inventor who fails to keep a laboratory notebook runs the risk of having difficulty establishing the date on which the invention was made, and thus may lose out in a priority contest with another inventor.

Laboratory notebooks are also important for other reasons. For example, when one is accused of taking a trade secret from someone else, if a laboratory notebook shows that one was in possession of the contested information before any access to the adversary's information, this helps to negate a claim that the secret was stolen from the adversary.

81. What should I do if I am about to publish something about my invention?

Anyone who is going to publish an article, whether it be in a scholarly journal, the trade press, or elsewhere, would be wise to consider whether such a publication would be a bar to patent protection. For example, where is desired to get patents in countries other than the United States, it would be wise consider filing a patent application prior to the publication. If you are quite sure you will not want patent protection in countries outside of the U.S., and if the only patent protection you think you would ever want is protection within the U.S., then you might take some comfort in the one-year grace period offered by U.S. patent law. In such a case you would mark the one-year anniversary of the publication on a calendar and be sure to file the patent application before the year was up.

However, there are many other reasons why it is wise to file a patent application soon, rather than to postpone it. Even if you are sure there is no reason to rush the patent filing, there are reasons why it is wise not to allow almost the entire year to pass, for example because it takes a while to prepare and file a patent application.

There are other reasons not to postpone filing a patent application. For example, the date you file a patent application sets a limit on the prior art available to the Patent Office in rejecting your patent application. The sooner you file the application, the less prior art is available to the Patent Office to be used to oppose your patent application.

Whenever a publication is imminent, it is wise consider possible patent consequences, and to seek appropriate counsel.

82. What should one do if they are about to sell (or offer for sale) a new product that might be patentable?

Whenever sales of a new product are imminent, attention should be given to the question of whether one or more patent applications should be filed. In particular, if one puts off filing a patent application until after a product has been shipped, this may leave only the U.S. as a place in which patent protection may be gotten, for the reason that many countries other than the U.S. deny patent protection to someone who divulges the invention to the public, prior to filing a patent application.

If you are quite sure you will only want patent protection in the U.S., then you might choose to take some comfort in the one-year grace period offered under U.S. patent law. But there are plenty of other reasons why it may be unwise to postpone filing solely because of the grace period; someone else may be planning to file a patent application on the same invention.

83. How can one find out if a proposed product infringes someone else's patent?

For some technological areas the answer to this question is easy to find, while other technological areas the answer may be very difficult. For example, if a product has been on the market for a very long time, one can have some confidence level that any patent that might have covered it would have long since expired. But the mere passage of a long period of time is not, by itself, a complete assurance that no patent is infringed, for the reason that a patent could issue from a patent application that had been pending before the U.S. Patent Office for a very long time.

Depending on the particular business circumstances, it may be advisable to conduct a patent search for patents that might be infringed, perhaps by searching patents in certain subject areas. Such a search may take place through online public databases, or by an in-person physical search of patents at the Public Search Room at the U.S. Patent Office.

Another way to learn of patents that might require study is to look at patent markings on products made by competitors. Carl Oppedahl has published a law review article on patent marking entitled "Patent Marking of Systems," Santa Clara Computer and High Technology Law Journal, Vol. 11, No. 2, p. 205 (1995).)

Sometimes the business circumstances are such that one can be fairly sure that the only patents that would be of concern are patents held by a particular adversary. In such a case the usual first step is to identify and study all patents (and published patent applications) owned by that adversary.

84. How does one find out if a patent assignee has been changed? How does one send in a change of address to the PTO?

Go to www.delphion.com and check INPADOC. (Delphion used to be the IBM server site.) Bring up the patent. You may see a link that says "Show legal status actions". Click that and it should tell you if any assignments have been made.

As for the change of address, there are change of address (change of correspondence – patent or application) forms on the PTO web site. The address to send them in to is on the form.

85. What is an opinion letter and what is its value?

As the term is generally used, an opinion letter is a document representing a legal opinion given by counsel. The opinion might be on any of a wide range of topics.

In the particular area of patent law, one very important category of opinion letter is an opinion of patent counsel regarding a patent held by an adversary. For example, if one has the misfortune to be the losing party in a patent infringement case, the finding that one is the infringer of a valid patent may leave one liable for damages. In addition, if the court decides that the infringement was willful, the damages may be increased by a factor of up to three. This so called "trebling" of damages only occurs if the infringement was found to be willful. If, however, the infringer had a good-faith belief that the conduct was noninfringing or that the patent was invalid, then this state of mind may negate a finding of willfulness, in which case the damages will not be trebled.

For this reason, when a manufacturer encounters a patent for which some argument might be made that it is an infringer, it is prudent for the manufacturer to seek advice of patent counsel. If patent counsel determines that the patent is invalid or that its claims are not infringed, a decision may be made to memorialize this finding in an opinion letter. As described above, such an opinion letter, if well-founded and well-reasoned, may negate a subsequent finding of willfulness and thus may avoid trebling of damages.

86. What is a Provisional Patent Application? Does it differ from a Disclosure Application? Does it differ from a patent Document?

Effective June 8, 1995, as a consequence of the adherence of the U.S. to GATT, it is possible to file what is called a Provisional Patent Application with the U.S. Patent and Trademark Office. The Provisional Patent Application is intended to be a relatively low-cost way of postponing the cost and effort of drafting and filing a full patent application. The provisional application need not contain claims, and the filing fee is modest ($160 for large entities, $80 for small entities).

The applicant may then wait almost a year before filing a patent application. The twenty-year patent term that runs from the first U.S. filing date does not start with the provisional application, but instead begins only with the date of the subsequent patent application. As a result, one may postpone the start of the 20-year patent term by up to one year by the use of a provisional patent application. The provisional application may serve as a priority document for non-US convention filings.

Under U.S. patent law, the provisional application is subject to the same burdens under 35 U.S.C. § 112 as a patent application. This means that the provisional application must be complete enough to enable one skilled in the art to practice the invention, and means that the application must disclose the best mode known to the applicant for practicing the invention.

These requirements are likely to lead to difficulties for those who file sketchy provisional applications. One who files a provisional application (and who fails to satisfy the requirements of § 112) would be making a mistake to sit back and rely on that application as a justification for waiting eleven months before taking the time and trouble to prepare and file a full patent application.

A second potential drawback of the provisional filing is that it postpones, by a year, any hint or clue from a patent examiner as to whether or not the invention is likely to be patentable. No search report or office action will come during the pendency of the provisional application; they will only be received after the filing of the patent application.

For the applicant who is considering whether or not to file patent applications in countries outside of the U.S., the use of a provisional application virtually guarantees that no clues to patentability will be received from the U.S. Patent Office that might assist in deciding whether or not to spend the money on foreign filing. The applicant who files a patent application (rather than a provisional application) may, in contrast, receive an Office Action before the year is up for making foreign-filing decisions, and the content of the Office Action may be helpful in deciding what to do about foreign filing.

A provisional application differs in many ways from an Invention Disclosure Document. Most importantly, a provisional application establishes a filing date, which serves as the priority date for a patent application filed within one year. In contrast, an Invention Disclosure Document does not provide a priority date for any later-filed patent application, but merely shows that an applicant was in possession of the contents of the Disclosure Document as of the date the Disclosure Document was filed.

A provisional application has a larger filing fee ($160/$80 (large entity/small entity), as compared with $10). Note that if the one-year anniversary of the filing of the Provisional Application falls on a weekend or holiday, the Patent Application that is to be filed within one year has to be filed on the preceding day that is not a weekend or holiday. Stated differently, the time limit for filing a patent application claiming priority from a Provisional Application is often actually less than a year.

87. What's the difference between provisional and non-provisional patent applications?

Regular (non-provisional) Application: The non-provisional application establishes the filing date AND initiates the examination process.

Provisional Application: The PPA only establishes the filing date and automatically becomes abandoned after one year. The filing cost for a provisional is much lower than the regular application, so it saves initial investment when you are not yet ready to enter the regular application process. Filing of a PPA also allows you to use the term "Patent Pending" during the year that the provisional remains in force.

88. What are the advantages of a PPA over a regular application?

The PPA gives you the ability to claim 'Patent Pending' on your invention as soon as the completed application and enclosures are filed, for only a $160/$80 (large entity/small entity), filing fee. In the event you need to quickly obtain a patent filing date, the PPA is a tool that can short cut the time and cost of obtaining your Patent Pending.

If during the year following the filing of a PPA you determine that the invention is commercially viable, and that it justifies the higher cost of formal patent protection, you can later file the more expensive regular application.

The filing of a PPA can allow the immediate promotion of the product or invention for sale with greater protection against having the invention stolen.

The PPA therefore can be used as a strategic business tool to defer the higher regular application costs to a later date - up to one year later.

89. Are there disadvantages to filing a PPA?

Although there are benefits to filing a PPA, it's important to understand the disadvantages of a Provisional application. They include (among others):

a. Provisional applications for patent may not be filed for design inventions;
b. The PPA filing date (priority date) cannot be claimed if the one-year deadline for filing a non-provisional application for patent is missed;
c. You will loose the PPA priority date if the claimed subject matter in the later filed non-provisional application must have support in the provisional application for patent;
d. Amendments are not permitted in provisional applications for patent after filing as they are in a regular application;
e. Failure to file a regular application within one year of filing the PPA will result in the PPA being abandoned; and
f. You will lose your invention priority date for later patent application.

90. Can the PPA automatically become a regular patent?

No. In fact, the PPA only lasts one year, after which time it becomes abandoned. If you want to pursue a regular patent on your invention, you will have to file the regular patent application before the one-year provisional term expires.

91. Are the applications for Provisional and regular patents the same?

The PPA does not require you to include claims. Further, the Patent Office does not review the provisional applications, so the provisional cannot become a regular patent application.

The regular patent application requires that you include all of your claims for the present invention. Regular patent applications are reviewed for merit by the Patent Office.

92. Does one need to first file a Provisional, then later file the regular patent application?

You do need to file the regular application within a year of filing the provisional, assuming that you want to pursue formal patent protection on your invention.

However, it is not necessary to file a PPA before filing a regular application. You can skip the PPA and go directly to the more expensive Regular Patent Application.

93. What does one need to submit to the Patent Office for a PPA?

A PPA will be deemed to have been properly submitted, and a filing date will be provided to the inventors once the PTO receives:

a. a written description of the invention, complying with all requirements of 35 U.S.C. §112 ¶ 1;

b. any drawings needed to understand invention, complying with 35 U.S.C. §113; and

   i. names of all inventors.

   ii. the filing fee of $75.00

   iii. a cover sheet identifying:

      - application as a provisional application for patent;

      - inventor name(s);

      - inventor residence(s);

      - title of the invention;

      - name and registration number of attorney or agent and docket number (if applicable);

      - correspondence address; and

      - any U.S. Government agency that has a property interest in the application.

94. When should a PPA be filed?

The PPA must be filed within one year following the date of first sale, offer for sale, public use, or publication of the invention. But you should be aware that although you are permitted to file a PPA in the US within one year of public disclosure, you may not be granted such invention priority in foreign countries, and may not be able to obtain later patent protection in those countries.

A PPA should also be filed before the occurrence of an event that you feel requires presentation of your product or invention with a 'Patent Pending' status

95. Can one file their own PPA?

Yes. The Patent Office has the necessary forms and instructions to make it fairly easy for an inventor to file their own provisional application.

96. Should one use an attorney to file a PPA?

It is highly recommended that you use the services of a registered patent attorney or patent agent to file your PPA.

97. If it's so easy to file a PPA, why should one invest in a patent attorney or agent?

Although the mechanics of filing a PPA are straight forward, the disclosure of the invention in the provisional application for patent needs to be as complete as possible. If during the one-year period of the PPA you find that additional subject matter needs to be added in the Regular patent application, you will lose the original filing date (priority date) of the PPA.

A patent professional skilled in developing descriptive language may be able to write the PPA description in a manner that would allow it to support a slightly different description in the later filed Regular application.

98. What are the requirements for a Provisional Patent Application? May one file it themselves and save the cost of a patent attorney or agent?

A Provisional Application, to obtain a filing date in the U.S. Patent Office, has to contain the items set forth in 37 CFR § 1.51(a)(2). The requirements of that Rule are summarized here but the reader is advised to consult the Rule personally and to be familiar with it.

The Provisional Application requires a specification satisfying 35 U.S.C. § 112, except that it need not contain claims. In simple terms the specification must enable one skilled in the art to practice the invention, and must disclose the best mode known for practicing the invention. A drawing must be provided if needed to explain the invention, see 37 CFR § 1.81-1.85. The Provisional Application must also identify the inventors who contributed to the subject matter disclosed in the application. The filing fee ($150 or $75) is required. A cover sheet is also required. The applicant is not required to use an official Patent Office cover sheet, but may employ any cover sheet containing the required information, namely the specific identification of the application as a Provisional Application; the name or names of the inventor or inventors, the residence of each inventor, the title of the invention, the name and registration number of the attorney or agent if any, the docket number (if any) used by the applicant, the correspondence address, and the name of the U.S. Government agency and government contract number (if the invention was made by an agency of the U.S. government or under a contract with an agency of the U.S. Government. Suitable Provisional Application cover sheets are available free of charge from the U.S. Patent Office, Washington, DC 20231.

U.S. patent law permits an applicant to file a Provisional Application pro se, that is, without representation by a patent attorney or agent. It is easy to identify some possible pitfalls of failing to consult a competent patent attorney or agent, however. For example, at some later time one would draft claims, for filing in the patent application within the one year period. It might develop, however, that the claims are not supported by the specification of the Provisional Application. To avoid such an unhappy result one might choose to draft the patent claims at the time the Provisional Application is being written, so that one may be sure to include in it whatever is needed to support the claims.

A further pitfall is to wait until the year is nearly expired before consulting competent patent counsel, lulled by a false sense of security from the Provisional Application's one-year duration. It is much wiser to consult competent patent counsel soon after filing the Provisional Application. This permits counsel to review the Provisional Application and, if it is thought to be defective or incomplete another application may be filed promptly, so that one has a filing date that is not too much worse (later) than the filing date of the defective or incomplete Provisional Application.

99. Are provisional patent applications public or are they kept confidential?

All patent applications received at the US Patent Office are kept secret by the Patent Office. The most commonly occurring exception to this rule is that when a patent issues, the application file becomes public. (Note that the entire application file becomes public, not just the issued patent itself.)

Another exception is that if a patent application is referred to by number in an issued patent, the application file becomes public. There are other less frequently occurring exceptions. This is the case for both provisional applications and regular applications under 37 CFR § 111(a).

It has been proposed that the US Patent Office would change its rules on secrecy to be more like the rest of the world. In most countries other than the US, a patent application becomes public 18 months after the priority date.

100. Are provisional applications available for search?

The public searching resources contain no information about pending provisional applications.

101. Does the description in the full application have to be absolutely same as the description in the provisional application to benefit from its priority date?

The law of provisional applications is quite new, dating from just June 8, 1995. It will develop in coming months and years. At present there is no single clear answer to your question. The only answer that is sure at this point is, if a provisional application is to provide a priority date for a claim in a patent application, the application must satisfy 35 USC § 112 with respect to that claim.

102. What is an Invention Disclosure Document and how does it differ from a patent application?

There is a world of difference. A patent application has the prospect of leading to an issued patent; the disclosure document does not. It is extraordinarily easy and inexpensive to file a disclosure document yourself, and there is little need to pay someone else to do it for you. A patent application, on the other hand, is not easy to do yourself, and the Patent Office fee is much higher. Quoting from § 1706 of the Manual of Patent Examining Procedure: The Patent and Trademark Office accepts and preserves, for a limited time, "Disclosure Documents" as evidence of the dates of conception of inventions. A paper disclosing an invention and signed by the inventor or inventors may be forwarded to the Patent and Trademark Office by the inventor (or by any one of the inventors when there are joint inventors), by the owner of the invention, or by the attorney or agent of the inventor(s) or owner. It will be retained for two years and then be destroyed unless it is referred to in a separate letter in a related [patent] application within two years.

The Disclosure Document is not a patent application, and the date of its receipt in the Patent and Trademark Office will not become the effective filing date of any patent application subsequently filed. However, like patent applications, these documents will be kept in confidence by the Patent and Trademark Office until a patent is granted.

This program does not diminish the value of the conventional witnessed and notarized records as evidence of conception of an invention, but it should provide a more credible form of evidence than that provided by the popular practice of mailing a disclosure to one self or another person by registered mail.

A Disclosure Document is available to the public when an application which refers to it issues as a patent.

Content of a Disclosure Document. Although there are no restrictions as to content and claims are not necessary, the benefits afforded by the Disclosure Document will depend directly upon the adequacy of the disclosure. Therefore, it is strongly urged that the document contain a clear and complete explanation of the manner and process of making and using the invention in sufficient detail to enable a person having ordinary knowledge in the field of the invention to make and use the invention. When the nature of the invention permits, a drawing or sketch should be included. The use or utility of the invention should be described, especially in chemical inventions.

Preparation of the Document. The Disclosure Document must be limited to written matter or drawings on paper or other thin, flexible material, such as linen or plastic drafting material, having dimensions or being folded to dimensions not to exceed 8 1/2 by 13 inches (21.6 by 33 cm.). Photographs also are acceptable. Each page should be numbered. Text and drawings should be sufficiently dark to permit reproduction with commonly used office copying machines.

Other Enclosures. In addition to the fee described below, the Disclosure Document must be accompanied by a stamped, self-addressed envelope and a separate paper in duplicate, signed by the inventor, stating that he or she is the inventor and requesting that the material be received for processing under the Disclosure Document Program. The papers will be stamped by the Patent and Trademark Office with an identifying number and date of receipt, and the duplicate request will be returned in the self-addressed envelope together with a notice indicating that the Disclosure Document may be relied upon only as evidence and that a patent application should be diligently filed if patent protection is desired.

The inventor's request may take the following form: "The undersigned, being the inventor of the disclosed invention, requests that the enclosed papers be accepted under the Disclosure Document Program, and that they be preserved for a period of two years."

Disposition. The Disclosure Document will be preserved in the Patent and Trademark Office for two years and then will be destroyed unless it is referred to in a separate letter in a related patent application filed within the two-year period. The Disclosure Document should be referred to in a separate letter filed in a pending application by identifying the Document by its title, number, and date of receipt. Acknowledgment of receipt of such letters is made in the next official communication or in a separate letter from the Patent and Trademark Office. Unless it is desired to have the Patent and Trademark Office retain the Disclosure Document beyond the two-year period, it is not required that it be referred to in a patent application.

Fee. A fee of $20 (37 CFR § 1.21(c)) is charged for filing a Disclosure Document. Payment must accompany the Disclosure Document when it is submitted to the Patent and Trademark Office. Be sure to check price as it is subject to change (www.uspto.gov/go/fees)

Warning to Inventors. The two-year retention period should not be considered to be a "grace period" during which the inventor can wait to file his [or her] patent application without possible loss of benefits. It must be recognized that in establishing priority of invention an affidavit or testimony referring to a Disclosure Document must usually also establish diligence in completing the invention or in filing the patent application since the filing of the Disclosure Document.

Inventors are also reminded that any public use or sale in the United States or publication of the invention anywhere in the world more than one year prior to the filing of a patent application on that invention will prohibit the granting of a patent on it. If the inventor is not familiar with what is considered to be "diligence in completing the invention" or "reduction to practice" under the patent law, or if he has other questions about patent matters, the Patent and Trademark Office advises him to consult an attorney or agent registered to practice before the Patent and Trademark Office.

A Directory of Registered Patent Attorneys and Agents Arranged by States and Counties titled ATTORNEYS AND AGENTS REGISTERED TO PRACTICE BEFORE THE U.S. PATENT AND TRADEMARK OFFICE is available from the Superintendent of Documents, U.S. Government Printing Office, Washington, D.C. 20402.

103. What is "patent prosecution"?

Patent prosecution means preparing and filing patent applications, and taking the many subsequent steps involved in progressing toward issuance of an U.S. Patent.

104. What is a divisional patent application?

A divisional patent application is an application claiming priority from some previously filed patent application (called a "parent application") in which more than one invention was disclosed. The divisional application has claims directed to a different invention than that claimed in the parent application.

The most common way that this happens is that the Patent Office rules that your application contains more than one invention, communicating this in what is called a "restriction requirement". The applicant then elects to pursue one of the inventions in that application (the "parent application"), and optionally submits a "divisional application" containing the claims regarding another of the inventions. The divisional application is entitled to the filing date of the parent application as its priority date.

It is not uncommon to receive a restriction requirement identifying several inventions, leading to several divisional applications and several issued patents. Under GATT, if the application was filed prior to June 8, 1995, it is disadvantageous to file a divisional application since the divisional application may end up with a shorter patent term. One option, if the application was filed prior to June 8, 1992, is to use a rule under GATT in which the applicant pays a fee (equal to the cost of a new filing fee) to have the extra invention considered in the same application rather than in a divisional application.

105. What is a continuation patent application?

Under United States patent practice, a continuation patent application is an application which claims priority from a previously filed application. A continuation application is usually filed when the Patent Office has responded to the parent application with a "final" office action (rejecting the claims in the application), but the applicant wishes to revise the claims again.

A continuation application receives the priority date of its parent application. A continuation application is often filed using the file wrapper continuation (FWC) administrative procedure.

A related type of patent application is the continuation-in-part (CIP) application. Under GATT, if the rejected application was filed prior to June 8, 1995, it is disadvantageous to file a continuation application since the result may be a shorter patent term.

One option, if the filing date of the rejected application is prior to June 8, 1993, is to use a rule under GATT in which the applicant pays a fee (equal to the cost of a new filing fee) to have the finality of the rejection withdrawn.

106. What is a CIP (continuation-in-part) patent application?

Under United States patent practice, it is possible for the owner of a pending patent application to file what is called a "continuation-in-part" patent application. A CIP patent application is an application which contains some matter in common with a previous patent application (called the "parent" application), and that also contains new matter, and which was filed at a time when the parent application was pending.

If such an application issues as a patent, then the patent has a sort of a blurred priority date. It is possible that some claims of the patent enjoy the priority date of the parent application, while other claims might enjoy only the filing date of the CIP application as their priority date.

107. What is an FWC (file wrapper continuation) patent application?

"File Wrapper Continuation" is a term specific to the U.S. Patent Office, and is a continuation patent application which claims priority from a previously filed application.

It is easier (from the paperwork point of view) to file than other continuations since it is effectively simply a request that the Patent Office reuse an application file already in its possession.

108. What kinds of patent search services does a patent firm offer to its clients?

There are several kinds of searches with varying cost. The only way to know which kind of search to do is to talk with the client and to determine what the client's needs are, of course. Categories of searches include:

Assignee search. Sometimes what a client needs is a list of all patents owned by a particular company, or a list of published patent applications for a company. Those searches are easy for those who are fluent in the databases. Well-known online databases have search fields for the assignee of the patents. The databases will have variant spellings of company names, however, so the experienced searcher will take steps to try to pick up all the variants. The steps that are taken are different depending on the particular database being searched. Searches can be done for patent documents in dozens of countries. The cost can be anywhere from $10 to $100 or more.

Novelty Search. The question is, "is my invention patentable?" Part of the effort to answer that question is the novelty search, which tries to answer the question "has someone done this before?" In such a search, it does not matter how old the patent is. One difficulty is that the online databases go back only to about 1970 at the furthest and sometimes a relevant patent will be older than that. Sometimes a novelty search is done as a "traditional search" (see below) and sometimes it is done online, or as a combination of the two approaches.

Infringement Search. The question is, "will proposed machine X infringe any patents?" In such a search, one generally is not interested in patents that are so old they have expired. Sometimes one is only interested in whether the machine will infringe patents owned by some particular company, which often makes the search much easier. Sometimes these searches are done by "traditional" means, and other times by online searches. Once it has been determined the category of search that is desired by the client, the next step is to figure out what type of search to do. Types of searches include:

Traditional search. One kind of search is what we might call the "traditional" search. The client tells us the area of interest, we communicate it to a professional searcher in Virginia, the searcher goes to the Patent Office, and searches the physical shoes at the Public Search Room. We receive the results of the search and study it, and give you our opinions. This kind of search is called "traditional" because at many very well known law firms, it is the only way any searching is done. This kind of search can be very helpful in cases where the figures make it easy to determine which patents are of interest. Such a search depends on the particular searcher doing a good job, and is necessarily limited to issued US patents since the Public Search Room only contains issued US patents. A traditional search often involves paying $500 or more to the professional searcher, and then paying our firm on an hourly basis to render our opinions. Depending on the subject matter and its complexity, the total cost to the client can be $700 or much, much more.

Online search. Another kind of search is the online text search. Somebody will spend some time logged in with one of the online information providers such as Dialog, Orbit, or STN. You plug in key words and find patents mentioning those key words. Depending on the results of the search, you plug in still other key words, or cross-search by patent class or by the names of particular companies that are likely to be active in the area of interest. Again depending on the results, we may expand the search to other online databases.

It is a recursive process that is intended to lead to some level of confidence that the search has found all, or nearly all, of the references of interest in the databases searched. We may then order up copies of the references that were found, and study the copies. This kind of search can find references other than US patents.

For example, it can find published patent applications in countries outside of the US. It can find articles in professional journals and in the trade press. Such a search depends on good luck in selection of the key words that are being used as search terms. Depending on the question that is to be answered (find all patents owned by company A, find all patents on subject matter X) the cost to the client of an online search can be $10 or $100 or $1000 or more. A variant of this kind of search arises if the attorney does not know how to do online searching. The attorney then has someone else do the online search, and the results of the search are then studied by the attorney.

Such searches can be quite unsatisfactory since it is difficult to efficiently perform follow-up searches, to try other words or databases, etc. The searcher does not, generally, know what counts as "finding the right references", but has to consult with the attorney after each search. The attorney does not, generally, know what the other steps are that might be taken to improve the search or to expand or vary it. It is difficult, for some such searches, to arrive at a high confidence level regarding the results of the search.

In-person attorney search. Still another kind of search involves the attorney going in person to the Public Search Room at the US Patent Office. The idea is that the attorney knows exactly what the client needs and the attorney can be quite sure of knowing the quality of the work that is being done. Such a search also may involve a visit to the private search files of the Examining Group in the area of interest, as well as a number of online search sessions. These searches are very expensive and are done only when the client's needs are very great.

109. What is the governing law for patents?

In the United States, the law that governs patents is Title 35 of the United States Code, commonly cited as "35 USC". It incorporates the Patent Cooperation Treaty (discussion, text), and changes made for conformity to the intellectual property provisions of the General Agreement on Tariffs and Trade.

110. Does one need a working model of my invention to get a patent?

In the United States in the 1800's, there was a requirement that the applicant provide a working model of the invention. The requirement that each applicant submit a model was dropped by the late 1800's, although many of the models may now be seen in the Smithsonian and elsewhere and are a fascinating glimpse into the creative efforts of inventors from the past century.

Examiners in the US Patent Office do, to this day, have the power to require submission of a working model in a particular case, but the requirement is imposed very rarely, usually in cases where an applicant claims to have invented a perpetual motion machine.

111. What is an H document? What is an RD document?

An H document is a Statutory Invention Registration (SIR). An applicant for a US patent may, if desired, give up the ability to obtain a patent and instead pay the US Patent Office to publish it as an SIR. The main benefit of this is that it keeps others from getting a patent on the same invention.

An RD document is a Research Disclosure (RD). Anyone who wishes to do so may pay a British company, Kenneth Mason Publications Ltd., to publish an invention disclosure. Some disclosures are anonymous, while others are attributed. Like an SIR, an RD has the effect of keeping others from getting a patent on the same invention.

112. What royalty rate should I expect to receive for my patent?

There is no "standard royalty rate" or "average royalty rate" for a patent. The royalty rate for a particular patent license is simply a function of negotiation between the patent owner and the licensee.

One patent license may have a royalty rate of a small fraction of a percent, while another may be ten percent. What must be kept in mind, too, is that the character of a patent license is strongly affected by its definition of the "royalty base" to which the royalty percentage is applied.
For many patent owners, what is desirable is to figure out the "value added" by the patented invention, and to collect a significant fraction of that value through the royalties.

113. How long does it take to prepare and file a patent application?

The traditional answer is, "you can have fast, cheap, and high quality, and you get to pick any two." There are many circumstances that require preparing and filing a patent application quickly. Examples include:

- a US provisional application was filed almost a year ago and it is desired to file a full (111a) application now to protect US patent rights;
- a US provisional application was filed almost a year ago and it is desired to file a PCT patent application now to protect US and non-US patent rights;
- the inventor is on the verge of disclosing the invention (perhaps at a conference or trade show or in a meeting with a potential licensee) and wishes to file right away to protect non-US patent rights or to prove inventorship;
- the inventor disclosed the invention in a printed publication almost a year ago, and wishes to try to preserve US patent rights;
- the inventor sold the invention or offered it for sale almost a year ago, and wishes to try to preserve US patent rights;
- a full US patent application was filed almost a year ago and it is desired to file corresponding applications in non-US countries to protect patent rights in those countries;
- a patent application was filed in a non-US country almost a year ago, and it is desired to file a corresponding application in the US to protect patent rights in the US;
- a PCT application was filed with a priority date almost nineteen months ago, and it is desired to file patent applications in one or more of the designated countries to preserve patent rights in those countries;

- a PCT application was filed with a priority date almost thirty months ago, and International Preliminary Examination was requested, it is desired to file patent applications in one or more of the designated countries to preserve patent rights in those countries; and

- a US patent is about to issue and it is desired to file a continuation or divisional application before the issue date, so as to preserve patent rights in the US Patent practitioners are accustomed to occasionally having to prepare and file patent applications in a hurry when it is necessary. But it is much better in every way if the patent practitioner is able to start the work with more time to spare. This permits checking the work, revising the application, detecting errors, and obtaining more information from the client if necessary. Any writing project comes out better if the writer is able to put it down for a while and then come back to it and improve it.

Where the subject matter is simple (e.g. an improved mouse trap with three or four moving parts) the preparation of a patent application may take only a few hours. But most patent applications are not simple. A patent application directed to a complicated system of software and electronic hardware may require forty hours of writing, spread out over several weeks. With such patent applications it is essential that the inventors review the draft carefully to see what else needs to be included.

It often happens that upon review of the draft, the inventors identify entire additional aspects of the invention that the attorney or agent was not told about. These aspects have to be included in the application which takes more time. At this point the claims are revised, and it is necessary to revisit the question who the inventors are (which is defined with respect to the claims) and a new inventor may be added to the list. That inventor must review the entire application as well, and perhaps more material is identified that needs to be added.

Where complex subject matter is involved, an experienced and knowledgeable patent attorney or agent can nonetheless sometimes prepare and file an entire patent application in a day or two. It is extremely exhausting to do so, and the attorney or agent generally has to take off a couple of days from work afterwards to decompress. But if there is a rush, perhaps for one of the reasons given above, then it has to be done.

For the person that wants to be able to call upon their patent counsel to do such rush-type patent filings, it is imperative to keep the attorney or agent fully informed about all facets of the client's business at all times. This background is necessary for the attorney or agent to do a good job.

A few categories of patent application filing can sometimes be done quickly, within a few days. These categories include the following:

- a full (111a) application where the previous provisional filing was actually drafted as a full application. In such a case, the attorney or agent checks to see what, if anything, needs to be added, and then refiles the provisional application as a full application;

- a continuation or divisional application where there is no need to add anything to the parent filing. Then the parent application is simply photocopied and refilled;

- a planned US filing where the non-US filing (with a filing date of less than a year ago) already satisfies US law (especially as to the "best mode" requirement of 35 USC § 112. The non-US application is simply photocopied and filed;

- a planned non-US filing where the US filing already satisfies the law of the country of the planned filing. The US application is revised to satisfy the format requirements (metric paper, claim format, etc.) of the country of the planned filing, and is filed; and

- a planned national-phase filing (in response to the 20-month or 30-month due date) based upon a PCT patent application.

114. In some cases the life of a patent is 20 years and in others 17 years; which is correct or are both?

Patents are enforceable only between the date they are granted and the date they expire. There is some minor royalty collecting possible between the time applications are published and the time a patent issues but generally I think this will be fairly unlikely. The patent term for utility patents is "counted" as 20 years from the date of non-provisional application to date of expiration assuming maintenance fees are paid. If you (highly not recommended) "convert" a provisional application to a non-provisional application the 20-year term starts on the filing date of the provisional application (in other words, "conversion" cheats you out of a year). If the Patent Office causes delays that delay your grant, and you don't cause offsetting delays that additionally delay the grant, then on a day for day basis your term will be extended beyond 20 years for the number of days of "net" delay to give you at MOST 17 years of enforceability. PTO delays are very unlikely (unless Congress gets much greedier).

115. Where can one get patent infringement insurance?

Several agencies offer patent infringement insurance. Examples are:

Intellectual Property Insurance Services Corp. (IPISC) - An insurance company that offers patent infringement insurance is Intellectual Property Insurance Services Corp. (IPISC). The company will pay 80% of your legal expenses and pay your legal costs should you be counter sued for patent invalidity. The policy typically covers both U.S. and foreign patents. You can also get this type of insurance for patents that have not been issued (if the application process is underway). There is no deductible, and your financial contribution is 20% of the costs. Limits on protection come in three levels: $100,000, $250,000, and $500,000, per claim, with the respective average annual premiums running

in the neighborhood of $1,555, $2,155, and $3,000, not including state and local taxes and applicable process fees. As the insured, you have control over the litigation; you select the attorney you want to represent you; and you dictate the settlement terms, if there are any. For more info see their web site at www.infringeins.com

Summit Global Partners - Summit Global Partners, Inc. and certain Underwriters at Lloyd's announced 11/98 the creation of a break-through patent infringement policy for pharmaceutical companies and medical device manufacturers. Underwritten by syndicates at Lloyd's in London, this is a policy that, for the first time, provides insured companies with broad based protection for patent infringement claims with coverage available even for enhanced damages attributable to claims for willful infringement. A. J. Renner and Associates, a worldwide leading wholesale broker with expertise in the pharmaceutical and medical device industries, in conjunction with Besso Limited, a London based specialty broker, assisted in the creation of this unique policy.

116. How long should I retain my intellectual property records?

Some relevant information related to record retention:

- The patent office keeps file wrappers of provisional applications for 26 years.
- Some law firms keep patent files for 5-8 years after the patent expires, then review and decide whether to keep longer.
- Some state statutes of limitations for contracts are 12 years.
- Files for a patent application that was filed more than ten years ago and abandoned more than five years ago were recently subpoenaed for evidence in a third party lawsuit.

117. What is an orphan drug?

It is always desirable to have an exclusive market position. One way a drug company can obtain an exclusive market position for a drug is to obtain a utility patent on the drug. The exclusivity lasts for the 20-year term of the patent. This is helpful only if the drug is a newly discovered substance. Thus, while the patent system provides an incentive to discover new substances with medicinal benefits, it provides less of an incentive to investigate possible benefits from the use of an old substance to treat a present-day health problem, since the old substance is not going to be patentable. One possibility is to secure a method patent coverage on the newly discovered use of the old substance, but such coverage is often less strong than utility patent coverage on the substance itself. To provide an incentive to investigate possible new benefits from old substances, the Orphan Drug Law was enacted. This law permits the FDA to grant a seven-year period of exclusive drug approval for a drug which satisfies the requirements of the Orphan Drug Law, namely a drug for a disease or condition which is "rare in the [United] States".

118. What are some relevant web sites and publications related to intellectual property protection?

See the resource directory in the compact disk included with this book.

COPYRIGHT

1. What is a copyright?

The owner of a registered copyright enjoys the ability of blocking the unauthorized copying or public performance of a work protected by copyright. Depending on how old a work is, whether or not copyright was renewed, when the work was published (if at all), and whether or not it is a work for hire, the U.S. copyright term for a work may be 28 years, 56 years, the life of the author plus 70 years, 95 years from the publication date, or 120 years from the date of creation. The reader will appreciate that these terms are much longer than the 17-year or 20-year term of a U.S. utility patent.

2. What are the meanings of letters in circles?

C in a circle (©) represents copyright protection

R in a circle (®) represents a trademark protected by a federal trademark registration.

P in a circle represents a phonograph or other sound recording protected under pertinent portions of the copyright law.

M in a circle represents a "mask work", protected under the mask work provisions of U.S. copyright law.

Another commonly used symbol within a circle is the U within a circle, which has nothing to do with intellectual property, but which indicates that a product has been found to be kosher by the Union of Orthodox Jewish Congregations of America (also known as the "OU").

K in a circle indicates a product is certified as kosher by the Organized Kashruth Laboratories. (U in a circle and K in a circle symbols are registered trademarks, even though they don't have an R-in-a-circle or TM after them.)

3. How do I copyright my software?

The question whether a work is "copyrighted" might, depending on who is talking, mean either of two things. Someone who says a work "is copyrighted" might be trying to say that a copyright registration on the work has been obtained from the U.S. Copyright Office (gopher server, web server). A different person who says a work "is copyrighted" might mean that the work is protected by the U.S. copyright laws. Lots of people say the former, but it is sloppy usage. The latter is more correct. In the United States, an original work becomes protected by the copyright laws from the moment it is "fixed in a tangible medium". This provides several obvious examples of ways that a work could fail to be protected by the copyright laws: the work might contain no originality, or it might not be fixed in a tangible medium. Yet another example is if a work has gone into the public domain, perhaps because the term of copyright has expired or because the owner has dedicated the work to the public prior to the expiry of the copyright term.

From this it becomes clear that the answers to the question "what must I do to protect my software through copyright" is, roughly, "fix it in a tangible medium". This is a fairly simple step, one which probably occurred no later than when the author stored the software on a hard disk or floppy disk. Generally once it is explained that works are automatically copyrighted from the moment the programmer saves the file to disk, the person asking the question restates the question "How may I register the copyright in my software?" We will now address that question.

It is, of course, possible for authors to obtain copyright registrations pro se, i.e., without representation by intellectual property counsel. The U.S. Copyright Office has a circular on software copyright protection. There is the danger, however, that an improperly drafted copyright registration application could fail to preserve the trade secret rights in a work of software. For this reason, authors of computer software are encouraged to seek advice of competent counsel. There is another reason why the software author who is inclined to proceed pro se in applying for copyright protection might be well advised to seek advice of competent counsel. In our experience, it is rare that the only steps needed to attend to a client's intellectual property needs are copyright registration steps. It frequently develops that there are other aspects of the client's business that also require attention. A work may contain material prepared by subcontractors, or material recycled from a previous programming task. The software may call for design patent protection, utility patent protection, or trademark protection. The programmer may have failed to give enough attention to the placement and content of copyright notices. Dozens of other intellectual property issues may present themselves. A consultation with competent intellectual property counsel will improve the likelihood that these other aspects are considered. While there are several reasons to consult intellectual property counsel before filing a copyright registration application on software, it is also in our experience that an author who plans to register numerous similar works will find it fruitful to work with intellectual property counsel on the first one or two registration applications, after which it may be possible for that author to proceed filing subsequent registration applications with minimal assistance of counsel. In other words, it should not be taken as a foregone conclusion that the legal costs for the first copyright registration would have to repeat themselves for subsequent copyright registrations.

4. When must I file a copyright application?

Those who are familiar with the rather strict time limits for filing a U.S. patent application may find it to be a pleasant surprise that under the U.S. copyright law, a copyright application can be filed many years after the initial publication of a work, and still be eligible for a copyright registration. This does not, however, mean that you should put off filing your copyright registration. Stated differently, even though there is no particular time limit for filing a copyright registration application, this should not lull the author into a false sense that copyright registration is unnecessary or that it need not be done promptly. The registration of a U.S. copyright offers many benefits to the owner of the copyright. For example, it creates a presumption that ownership of the copyright is as set forth in the registration. In addition, if you happen to have the good luck that you registered the copyright on a date earlier than the date of an act of unauthorized copying, or under certain other circumstances set forth in the copyright law, then if you prevail in court against the unauthorized copier, you may find yourself eligible for statutory damages and for recovery of attorney's fees.

The damages and attorney's fee benefits that come from registering a copyright in advance of infringement are so great, and the cost of registering a copyright is so small, that it is wise to attend to copyright registrations promptly. Many people successfully file copyright registration applications on their own without the assistance of counsel. However, some authors find it convenient to pay someone else to do it for them, simply to avoid the paperwork. Additionally, those whose authorship is in computer software may wish to retaining competent counsel to assist them in filing registration applications, since filing the application incorrectly could conceivably result in loss of trade secret rights, or, in an extreme case, could result in loss of all copyright rights. For example, there are steps which may be taken in filing a copyright registration application in software which preserve trade secrets that are contained in the software. Additionally, since most software is produced in versions, with each version based in part on previous versions, there are certain disclosures which must, under certain circumstances, be made in the registration application to acknowledge the older content. To give one example, the owner of the dBase programming language came very close to losing all copyright rights in the language due to failure to disclose that portions of the work were based on older works.

5. Can I register a copyright myself?

Many types of copyright registrations are easy and straightforward to do, in which case a layperson can obtain a copyright registration for little more than the $20 and a bit of one's time. In the area of computer software, however, it is often helpful to retain experienced counsel to prepare the copyright application. The reason for this is that for any copyright registration application there is the requirement that the applicant deposit a copy of the work with the Copyright Office (gopher server, web server); the deposit becomes available to the public. In the particular case of software it is possible to deposit less than all of the work, which helps to protect trade secrets. (The Copyright Office has a helpful circular on this subject.) Experience is helpful in determining what, exactly, needs to be deposited with the Copyright Office. Advice of experienced counsel is also helpful in determining whether the application is complete, e.g., whether it needs to disclose previous works upon which the present work is based. Failure to disclose prior works runs the risk that copyright protection will be lost later. Another trap for the unwary is characterizing a work incorrectly as a work-for-hire when it is not; this, too, runs the risk of later loss of copyright rights.

6. What does it cost to register a copyright?

At the time of writing, the filing fee for registering a copyright with the U.S. Copyright Office is $20. The Copyright Office will do a registration on an expedited basis as well, for example if litigation is imminent. An extra fee must be paid and the application has to be submitted to a different address for expedited registration. The factors described above explain why the lawyer's fees in a software copyright registration application are likely to be at least $200-$300, exclusive of copying and courier charges.

6a. What steps are involved in hiring an intellectual property lawyer to register a copyright?

Here are some of the steps that are generally followed when a new client wants to register a copyright. First, determine what, exactly, is needed. Is it really a copyright registration that is needed, or (as sometimes turns out to be the case) a trademark registration or patent application? At the same time, Counsel will do a conflict check to see if accepting the new client would present a conflict with respect to any existing clients. Assuming that it is indeed a copyright registration that is needed, then find out what it is that needs to be registered - software, a videotape, a sculpture - and then determine what needs to be deposited. This might require a photocopy, a photograph, or some other type of copy, depending on the type of work.

It is also a good idea to review the types of information the Copyright Office is going to want to know. How, for example, did the applicant come to own the work? In the case of software, is there a written agreement between the programmer and the applicant? Was the work published? If so, when? Another step is to establish the correct form of copyright notice to be placed on the work. Counsel usually will ask for money in advance, which is held in escrow and applied toward the cost of the professional services.

Notice
7. What constitutes a satisfactory copyright notice?

There are two popular misconceptions which it is important to dispel: One misconception is that under the Berne Convention it does not matter whether a copyright notice is correct or not. It is also important to dispel the misconception that it does not matter, under the Berne Convention, whether a copyright notice has been placed on a work.

This misconception has its origin in the fact that, prior to the 1978 Copyright Act, publication of a work without a proper copyright notice often resulted in a complete loss of copyright rights. The 1978 Copyright Act provided for the salvaging of copyright rights if certain efforts were taken to cure the failure to mark with copyright notices. After the 1978 Act, the United States adhered to the Berne Convention. Under the Berne Convention, the absence of a copyright notice does not necessarily lead to the automatic loss of all copyright rights. It does not, however, follow from this that an author can place an incorrect copyright notice without any risk of harm flowing from the notice being incorrect. As will be discussed below, certain defects on a copyright notice might still jeopardize the copyright rights of an author.

Having said all this, let us return to the original question, which is what constitutes a proper copyright notice. A proper copyright notice is (1) the C in a circle symbol (©) or the word "copyright" or the abbreviation "Copr.", (2) the copyright date, and (3) the name of the copyright owner. Each of these three elements will be discussed in turn.

The symbol. As is well known to computer programmers, the ASCII character set does not include the © symbol. (It is noted that the extended character set used in the World Wide Web does provide a © in many browsers.) It is not uncommon for programmers to attempt to approximate this symbol by means of a "(C)". Until such time as the courts have interpreted the copyright law in the way that it approves of this approximation, we cannot advise the use of "(C)" as a proper copyright symbol. Thus, where the character set is limited to ASCII, it is suggested that in a copyright notice the word "Copyright" be spelled out in full, or that the abbreviation "Copr." be used instead.

The date. The copyright date is perhaps the most important trap for the unwary. One of the purposes of the copyright date, under U.S. copyright law, is to assist members of the public in identifying works which are so old that the copyrights have expired. To do this, a member of the public would take the copyright date appearing in the notice, add to it the number of years of the copyright term, and thereby arrive at a conclusion as to when the copyright would have expired. In the case of computer software, it is commonplace for the work to include original matter from many different dates including original work dating from any of several different years. Consider what would happen if the most recent year were the only year used in the notice. A member of the public would then be led to the conclusion that the entirety of the work is protected by copyright starting from that year and ending at the end of copyright term. But if part of the work dates from a previous year, then its term expires one year earlier than the rest of the work. This could mislead members of the public in the sense that they would incorrectly think that none of the work could be copied until the end of the term that is based on the date in the notice, when in fact part of the work would have entered the public domain one year earlier than the end of that term. There have been court cases where judges have stricken all of the copyright rights in a work due to such incorrect statements in the copyright notice. Because of this, it is wise to ensure that nothing in the copyright notice would mislead the public regarding the end of the copyright term. If only one year is to appear in a notice, it should be the oldest year, associated with the oldest of the matter in the work. In other words, if one must err it should be in the direction of omitting newer years, not older years. Another approach is to put a range of years. For example, if the oldest matter in the work dates from 1991 and if the newest matter dates from 1994, the notice might say copyright 1991 to 1994 and the name of the owner.

This problem of listing multiple years in a copyright notice is not unique to computer software. Any work that is regularly updated, such as a dictionary or almanac or encyclopedia, will contain items dating from many different years. If you look at such a work you may expect to see at least one copyright notice, and many different years in the notice or notices.

The copyright owner. The third element required in the notice is the name of the copyright owner. The intention is that the members of the general public would, by contacting the entity in the notice, be capable of reaching the actual owner of the rights. Thus, the copyright law is not so strict as to require that the precise legal owner be listed in the notice. If you have some question as to the name that should appear in your copyright notice, we suggest you seek advice of counsel.

Even though copyright notices are not required under the Berne convention, there are numerous benefits that flow from being consistent and thorough in application of copyright notices. Some of these benefits are legal, in that certain rights may be stronger with the notice in place, while other benefits are more practical--if notices are prominently displayed, this may dissuade would-be wrongdoers from making unauthorized copies of the work.

For these reasons, we generally recommend that a detailed review be made of the manner in which a particular client's software is used. We often suggest a copyright notice on the medium by which the software is distributed (e.g., a floppy disk or CD-ROM), a notice that appears when the software is executed, and at least one notice that appears within the executable code in a way that would become visible if someone were to attempt to disassemble or reverse-compile the software. As a separate issue, it is noted that many software works are distributed with user manuals or other documentation, and we often suggest that such materials should also bear appropriate copyright notices.

8. Is there information other than the standard copyright notice that can be included with the notice?

In select situations one may want to include any of the following on a copyright notice:

Copyright 20__ [company or individual]   All Rights Reserved.; or
© 20__ [company or individual]   All Rights Reserved.; or
Copr 20__ [company or individual]   All Rights Reserved.

Examples of additional language follow.

For Published Works: This document is protected by copyright, and contains information proprietary to XYZ. Any copying, adaptation, distribution, public performance, or public display of this document without the express written consent of XYZ is strictly prohibited. The receipt or possession of this document does not convey any rights to reproduce or distribute its contents, or to manufacture, use, or sell anything that it may describe, in whole or in part, without the specific written consent of XYZ.

Authorization to photocopy items for internal or personal use, or the internal or personal use is granted by XYZ.

Faithful reproduction with acknowledgment welcomed.

For Unpublished Works: This work is confidential. The receipt or possession of this work does not convey any rights to reproduce or disclose its contents, in whole or in part, without the specific written consent of XYZ.

For Unpublished Technical Materials and Software: This {Document or Program} is confidential and a trade secret of XYZ. The receipt or possession of this {Document of Program} does not convey any rights to reproduce or disclose its contents, or to manufacture, use, or sell anything that it may describe, in whole or in part, without the specific written consent of XYZ.

For Published, Licensed Software: This program is furnished under a license and may be used and copies made only in accordance with the terms of that license and with the inclusion of the above copyright notice. This program or any other copies of it may not be provided or otherwise made available to any other person. No title to or ownership of the program is hereby transferred.

For Systems Housings: The devices within this product contain information proprietary to XYZ, and any copying, adaptation, distribution, public performance, or public display without the express written consent of XYZ is strictly prohibited.

For Media: The information and programs on this media are proprietary to XYZ, and any copying, adaptation, distribution, public performance, or public display without the express written consent of XYZ is strictly prohibited.

For Media Containers: The media within this protective container contains information proprietary to XYZ, and any copying, adaptation, distribution, public performance, or public display without the express written consent of XYZ is strictly prohibited.

Criminal Liability Warning: Any reproduction of the {Document of program, etc.} without the express written permission of XYZ is a violation of the copyright laws and may subject you to criminal prosecution.

9. Is there a conflict between trade secrets and copyrights?

Most computer software contains trade secrets. The programmer prepares the software in source code, but the software distributed to customers is generally mere executable code. The internal format and structure of the executable code is relatively uninterpretable by humans, which to some extent protects trade secrets contained in the source code.

Prior to the 1978 Copyright Act, the filing of a federal copyright registration application carried with it the sense that the work to be registered must have been "published". Under that Copyright Act works were divided into unpublished and published works, and only the latter were protectable by federal copyright law. Thus, the mere act of asserting federal copyright protection arguably represented an admission that the work had been published. What's more, the applicant was required to deposit a copy of the protected work with the Copyright Office (gopher server, web server). These two factors prompted some anxiety among programmers that seeking copyright protection might count as a tacit admission that there were no trade secrets in the software. The impression was that a programmer could not have it both ways -- that a work protected by copyright did not, by definition, contain trade secrets.

Regardless of the possible ambiguity that existed prior to 1978 for those who wanted to have both trade secret and copyright protection in software, programmers will be relieved to know that the potential ambiguity is no longer present. Under the 1978 Act and under the associated copyright rules that have been promulgated by the Copyright Office, it is possible for the author of computer software simultaneously to assert trade secrets in the source code, and to assert copyright rights in the source code (and in executable code).

10. What is a mask work?

A mask work is a creative work protected under the Semiconductor Chip Protection Act. Although nowadays few chip makers worry about it, there was a time several years ago when semiconductor chip makers were concerned that a competitor would knock off a semiconductor chip by purchasing one of the chips, removing the semiconductor layers one by one, photographing the layers, and using the photographs to generate replicas of the chip. The Semiconductor Chip Protection Act was intended to allow chipmakers to register the masks, which would then provide certain remedies against copiers. The protection is thus a copyright-like protection.

It turns out that there have been virtually no lawsuits brought under the Semiconductor Chip Protection Act, and a very few mask work registrations have been filed. We believe this is because people who are attempted to knock off someone else's integrated circuit nowadays typically have easier ways to do it than by photographing layers and making photographs of the layers. Thus, the Semiconductor Chip Protection Act protects against a type of infringement that is no longer a day-to-day economic threat.

The U.S. Copyright Office has a circular about mask work protection.

11. How may I do copyright searching on the Internet?

The U.S. Copyright Office has circulars How to Investigate the Copyright Status of a Work and The Copyright Office Card Catalog and Online Files.

It is possible to search federally registered copyrights for free on the Internet. The Library of Congress maintains a database of registered copyrights.

It is not always possible to get through to that database, and the search engine is of limited versatility. For that reason, the firm Oppedahl & Larson often does copyright searching through a database available on Dialog. The database, called US Copyrights (File 120), has the normal powerful Dialog search engine and is generally available.

12. How may I learn if the copyright on a work has expired?

It is not easy as a general matter to determine if the copyright on a work has expired. If the work is old enough, you may be able to take the year in the copyright notice, note that it is long enough ago, and conclude that the copyright has expired. Under the Berne Convention, however, it is not even necessary to place a copyright notice on a work to secure copyright protection, thus there is not necessarily a date anywhere on the work. You are then reduced to having to find some other way to date the work. A helpful starting point may be found in Laura Gasaway's table entitled "When Works Pass Into The Public Domain". See also the U.S. Copyright Office's circular "How to Investigate the Copyright Status of a Work".

13. What is the Berne Convention?

The Berne Convention (text) is a treaty regarding copyright which has been adhered to by most of the countries of the world. From the point of view of the United States, one of the most important effects of the U.S. adhering to Berne is that it is no longer fatal to copyright protection for the owner to fail to place a copyright notice on the work.

14. How is it determined who owns software? What is the work-for-hire doctrine?

Under U.S. law, it may be generally stated that the copyright in software (like that in any other work) is owned by the programmer (author) in the absence of a writing transferring ownership, and in the absence of a work-for-hire relationship. This presents a trap for the unwary company that, for example, hires a programmer consultant who is not a full-time employee of the company. Even if the company paid for the work, the company is not, generally, the owner of the copyright in the software, absent some written agreement on the subject. (Note: if this subject matters to you, seek advice of competent counsel!)

For those who wish to learn more about the work-for-hire doctrine in connection with computer software, it may be helpful to study the case of MacLean v. Mercer, which is the leading appellate court case on the subject.

15. What is the governing law for copyrights?

In the United States, the law that governs copyrights is Title 17 of the United States Code, commonly cited as "17 USC". It incorporates the Berne Convention.

16. What is the WIPO (World Intellectual Property Organization)?

The World Intellectual Property Organization is the organization that, together with PCT departments within the patent offices of countries that are signatories to the Treaty, administers the PCT (Patent Cooperation Treaty) program.

17. What is GATT (General Agreement on Tariffs and Trade)?

The General Agreement on Tariffs and Trade is a treaty to which the U.S. and many other countries are signatories. Its purpose is to free international trade and reduce tariffs. GATT has been revised several times; each revision is called a "round". The latest, or "Uruguay" Round of GATT requires signatories to protect intellectual property and provide similar protection of intellectual property owned by nationals and foreigners. (Texts of the treaty, the implementing legislation) Adherence by the U.S. to GATT has brought about numerous changes to the U.S. Patent System that bring U.S. patent law into closer harmony with the patent systems of other countries. See http://www.patents.com/copyrigh.sht.

18. What does a copyright protect?

Copyright law protects creative expression, not fact, idea system or method of process or operation. Expression may be found in product design, written expression, traditional artistic works, and other original works such as literary, dramatic, musical, and artistic works such as poetry, novels, movies, songs, computer software and architecture.

19. Do I have to register my works to get a copyright?

No. Your work is protected by a copyright at the moment you create it in a tangible form (written copy, recorded music, filmed movie, digital data saved on a computer disk). However, if you wish to bring a lawsuit for infringement of a U.S. work, you will have to register your work with the Copyright Office.

20. How can I get my copyright registered?

The US Copyright Office will provide certificates to authors who apply for a copyright certificate. You may get application forms from the U.S. Copyright Office.

21. How do I register a copyright?

You will need to submit a completed application form, a non-refundable filing fee of $30, and a non-returnable copy or copies of the work to be registered. Use the forms obtained from the US Copyright Office. It generally takes 8 months after submitting your registration application before you receive your certificate.

22. What part of my creation does copyright law protect?

Copyright law prevents copying of expression. Facts and ideas are not protectable under copyright law.

23. How long is a copyright valid?

The duration of a copyright depends on when the author acquired the copyright. Currently, the duration for individuals is life of the author plus 70 years, or the case of a joint work, the term lasts for 70 years after the last surviving author's death, whichever is longer. If a company is the author, the duration is 95 years from the year of first publication or 120 years from the year of creation, whichever expires first.

24. What type of protection does a copyright give?

Copyright laws protect against copying. The copying does not need to be exact for infringement to be found. A substantial similarity is enough. Independent development is a defense.

25. What is the geographic scope of protection of a copyright?

Treaties provide for substantially worldwide protection.

26. What is proper copyright notice?

Notice has three parts. First, a word, abbreviation, or symbol designating copyright (copyright, copr, or ©). Next, the name of the author. Finally, the year in which the work was completed. Multiple years indicate multiple years of completion (i.e. continuing editing). Use of the words "All rights reserved" provides protection in a couple of South American countries.

27. Can a company be considered the author?

A company can be considered the author of works done within the scope of an employee's duties. Such work by an employee by which the company is considered the author is called "work for hire". A company under certain circumstances can be considered the author of works of independent contractors. Companies can also become the owner of copyrights through assignments.

28. Can I license or sell my copyright?

Yes. Just like patents or trademarks (or any other property), any or all of the rights of ownership in a copyrighted work may be transferred by the owner to another party. Usually, a legal agreement outlining the transfer accompanies the license or sale.

29. If I write a book how can I copyright it?

You already own the copyright as soon as you placed it in tangible form. Just inscribe the word "Copyright" or the familiar "c"-in-a-circle...or both...at the beginning of your book, followed by the year of first publication and the name of the author....e.g., Copyright 2002 Donald Kelly. Simple enough, but it's prudent to also register your right with the US Copyright Office. This puts your work in the public record and gets you a certificate of registration...also simple enough, and inexpensive enough. Registration will be necessary should you ever have to go to court.

Also if the copyright is registered within three months of the work's first publication, the owner may be entitled to (1) statutory damages and (2) attorneys fees in an infringement suit which are not available to unregistered copyrights.

"Statutory damages" for all infringements of any one work shall be in a sum of no less than $750 and no more than $30,000 (instead of actual damages). 17 U.S.C. 504(c)(1). If "willful" infringement is found, the amount of statutory damages may be increased up to $150,000. 17 U.S.C. 504(c)(2). Since "damages" are often times difficult to prove in a copyright infringement case, having additional "remedies" such as statutory damages and attorneys fees can be determinative whether or not to proceed against an alleged infringer.

Federal registration is also prima facie evidence of the validity of the copyright if registered within five years of the first publication.

30. What are the differences between creativity and copyright?

Most people have seen the word "copyright" hundreds of times. It usually appears at the end of sports telecasts and movies and at the front of books and magazines. The word conveys this generally understood message: Don't use this material without our permission.

No message could be simpler, it seems, but there are often serious questions about what exactly it is that can't be used.

Ideas vs. Expression

A copyright protects an author's tangible expression--the author's particular choice of words and the selection and arrangement of the material. It does not protect the ideas the author expressed. No one can claim an idea and prevent others from writing about it.

This basic rule operates a little differently for works of fiction than for non-fiction, although the goal is the same: don't let authors impede the progress of knowledge by monopolizing ideas that should belong to everybody.

Copyright Rights

Copyright is a federal law that gives authors control over their creations. The author has the exclusive right to determine who, if anyone, can make copies of a poem, book, article, essay, letter, marketing brochure or other work. Authors don't have to do a thing to get this right--it's automatic. The instant your pen, typewriter or printer produces something original--not copied from someone else--it is protected under the copyright laws.

An author also has the exclusive right to:
1. sell or distribute the work;
2. display the work;
3. perform the work; and
4. prepare adaptations of the work (derivative works).

The copyright owner can sell all or part of these rights to others. For instance, a novel's author may sell the exclusive right to make copies to a publisher and the exclusive right to make adaptations to a movie company.

Fiction

If you write a work of fiction--a play, novel, poem or short story, for example--your words can't be copied without violating your copyright.

But the underlying idea--for instance, a police story or an unrequited romance--is not protected by copyright. Similarly, the central idea or theme of a novel or short story can be used by others without the copyright owner's permission.

A fictional work's setting--for instance, romance on a French island in 1920--doesn't come within the copyright statute. Nor does the work's plot--the sequence of events by which the author expresses an idea--unless it is truly original. Very few plots are that original. For instance, if you write a novel about a spunky heroine who triumphs over adversity in the Civil War, you have the right to control your words but not the story line. Anyone else is free to write a novel with a similar character and plot. Many authors rebel at the idea that others can use their plot lines, but the alternative would let authors tie up basic plots for decades, to the detriment of the arts.

Other aspects of fictional works that aren't subject to copyright protection are:

1. events, scenes, situations or details that necessarily follow from the theme or setting stock characters--standard types such as the silent, strong cowboy or hard-drinking private detective;
2. facts from the real world used in the work;
3. the writing style and individual words and phrases--for example, the terse style of Ernest Hemingway or the new words and phrases in George Orwell's 1984 such as "newspeak" and "I love big brother"; and
4. literary devices--for instance, flashbacks and alliteration.

Despite this long list of unprotected aspects of a fictional work, an author might be able to win in court if enough of them together showed up in a later work by someone else.

31. What are some examples of Works Protected by Copyright?

This article discusses written works, but copyright also protects such creative expressions as:

music	computer software	videos
art	databases	web pages
photography	pantomimes	sound recordings
sculpture	choreographic works	toy designs
motion pictures	architectural designs	

Before 1989, a work that had not yet been published (widely distributed on a relatively unrestricted basis) was automatically protected by copyright. But once it was published, it had to carry the familiar copyright notice (e.g., © Copyright 1996 by Nolo Press). Since March 1, 1989, copyright notice has not been required, which means the automatic copyright continues until the copyright period expires. Nevertheless, it helps to have a copyright notice on a work in case a wrongful user claims innocence (that he or she did not know the work was protected) in a lawsuit filed by the copyright owner.

In addition to including a valid copyright notice with the material, a copyright owner can obtain significant additional protection for the work by registering the copyright with the U.S. Copyright Office. Then, if someone uses the work without permission--called copyright infringement--the copyright owner can file a lawsuit in federal court.

32. What does copyright protect?

Copyright, a form of intellectual property law, protects original works of authorship including literary, dramatic, musical, and artistic works such as poetry, novels, movies, songs, computer software and architecture. Copyright does not protect facts, ideas, systems, or methods of operation, although it may protect the way these things are expressed. See Circular 1, section What Works Are Protected.

Copyright protects any creative work that is fixed in a tangible medium of expression, including crafts, poetry, flow charts, movies, CD-ROMs, video games, videos, plays, paintings, sheet music, recorded music performances, novels, software code, artwork, sculptures, photographs, choreography and architectural designs.

Copyright protects a work if and to the extent it is original--that is, independently created by the author. A work does not have to be novel, and its quality, ingenuity and aesthetic merit do not matter. So long as a work was independently created by its author, it is protected by copyright even if other similar works already exist.

To be protected, a work must also be the result of at least some creative effort on the part of its author. There is no hard and fast rule as to how much creativity is enough. As one example, a work must be more creative than a telephone book's white pages, which involve a non-discretionary alphabetic listing of telephone numbers rather than a creative selection of listings.

33. When does copyright protection begin?

A copyright comes into existence the moment an author fixes his work in some tangible form--for instance, the moment a book or article is typed, handwritten or dictated, or when a sculpture first takes shape. No further action need be taken. Because of this rule, caution dictates that all types of creative expression be considered protected by copyright law unless there is good reason to know that it isn't.

Virtually any form of expression will qualify as a tangible medium, including a computer's random access memory (RAM), the recording media that capture all radio and television broadcasts, and the scribbled notes on the back of an envelope that contain the basis for an impromptu speech. If an expression is not recorded, however, it is not protected. For example, an extemporaneous poetry reading or musical jam session will not qualify for copyright protection unless they are recorded as they happen.

34. What do you do if you want to use material from the Internet?

Each day, people post vast quantities of creative material on the Internet--material that is available for downloading by anyone who has the right computer equipment. Because the information is stored somewhere on an Internet server, it is fixed in a tangible medium and potentially qualifies for copyright protection. Whether it does, in fact, qualify depends on other factors that you would have no way of knowing about, such as when the work was first published (which affects the need for a copyright notice), whether the copyright in the work has been renewed (for works published before 1978), whether the work is a work made for hire (which affects the length of the copyright) and whether the copyright owner intends to dedicate the work to the public domain. To be on the safe side, you should assume that all material posted on the Internet is protected by copyright and can't be used without the copyright owner's permission. If you want to download the material for use in your own work, you should track down the author of the material and ask for permission. The only exception to this advice is for situations where you want to use only a very small portion of text for educational or non-profit purposes. (See The Fair Use Rule)

35. What is not covered by "automatic" copyright?

Even if you don't put that little © on your work, you automatically get a copyright the instant your work of expression becomes fixed in a tangible medium. Theoretically, this means that you own the copyright, and no one may copy, distribute, display or make adaptations of the work without your permission.

The problem comes if someone infringes on your copyright. Then, suddenly, the protection is no longer automatic. It's up to you to file a lawsuit in federal court and to convince the judge to order the other party to stop the infringement and compensate you for your losses.

What's more, even though you own the copyright, you can't file your lawsuit unless you have registered the copyright with the U.S. Copyright Office. Until you register, there's nothing you can do to stop the infringement. You may be thinking, "Big deal--I'll register if and when someone infringes on my software and I need to file a lawsuit." But if an infringement occurs, you'll want to register in a hurry so you can file your suit--and "expedited registration" costs an extra $330.

Statutory Damages

There is another--even more compelling--reason to register, and as soon as possible after the software is published: As a practical matter, if you haven't registered, it may not worthwhile for you to bring a lawsuit against an infringer.

Federal lawsuits usually cost a hellish amount of money in lawyer fees and litigation costs. This means that to make a copyright infringement lawsuit worthwhile, you must be able to pry a lot of money loose from the other party.

But it is often very hard to show exactly how much monetary damage a copyright infringement has caused. So even if you can prove infringement, you may not be able to show very much in the way of actual damages. This means that you might end up spending $50,000 on legal fees but recover only $40,000 in actual damages. In other words, relying on the recovery of actual damages creates a substantial risk that you will lose money bringing the suit.

But if you registered the work before the infringement began or within three months of the date the work was published, you may be entitled to recover from the infringer, in addition to your actual damages:

Attorney fees and court costs, and "statutory damages"--special damages of up to $100,000 per infringement--without having to establish what damage you actually suffered.

36. With the advent of massive amount of digitized material has value of copyright declined?

We are living in the midst of a revolution in the way information is stored and transmitted. Most writings, photographs, sounds and graphics can now be transformed into digital form, stored in computers and transmitted over computer networks. More written works are probably now available online than in all the libraries of the world.

It sounds great to the millions of people who have access to all this information from an office or home computer. But authors and other copyright owners are fearful it might not be so good for them. Quite simply, they are afraid that digital copies are too easy to steal.

These fears are not unfounded. Many online users have the mistaken idea that anything available online can be freely copied or distributed without permission. Copyright infringement--unauthorized copying and distribution of protected works--occurs every second in the online world. Indeed, unauthorized copying has become so ubiquitous online that some have declared that copyright is dead--that is, has ceased to be a useful way to protect authors.

But to borrow from Mark Twain, reports of copyright's death are greatly exaggerated. Copyright is a very flexible instrument, and it has adjusted to new technologies time and again. The fact is that the copyright laws have never prevented individuals from making unauthorized copies. What copyright has done, and will continue to do even in the online era, is to deter the big boys--businesses that make money from publishing or broadcasting--from stealing others' work.

37. Are lawsuits really keeping infringers in check?

In increasing numbers, authors and other copyright owners are suing those who copy their work online without permission. Because they're afraid of being sued, publishers are seeking permission to reproduce authors' works online and are making sure that publishing agreements for new works address what's become known as "electronic rights."

Large commercial online services like America Online and CompuServe, and operators of much smaller electronic bulletin boards (BBSs), have all been sued for copyright infringement. For example, 140 music publishers sued CompuServe, alleging that subscribers had uploaded and downloaded more than 550 music compositions. CompuServe agreed to pay $500,000 in damages and to work with the publishers to help them license their work to online users. (Frank Music Corp. v. CompuServe, Inc., No. 93 Civ. 8153 (S.D.N.Y. 1993).)

In another highly publicized case, Playboy magazine sued a BBS operator for copyright infringement, claiming that subscribers to the BBS had uploaded and downloaded at least 50 copies of photos taken from the magazine without permission. The BBS operator was held liable even though he claimed he was not aware of his subscribers' copying. (Playboy Enterprises, Inc. v. Frena, 839 F. Supp. 1552 (M.D. Fla. 1993).)

As a result of these lawsuits, commercial online services and many BBS operators are now actively trying to prevent copyrighted material from being placed on their systems without permission, and quickly removing it when they find it.

The copyright laws have even had an impact on the Internet; a collection of hundreds of computer networks that is the online version of the Wild West. Copyrighted photos and other materials have been removed from the Internet when copyright owners complained. And the creator of a World Wide Web site on Elvis Presley removed it all when the Presley estate complained it violated its copyright and other intellectual property rights.

38. What are factors related to copyright ownership?

The copyright in a protectable work is initially owned by the work's author or authors. But a person need not actually create the work to be its "author" for copyright purposes. A protectable work created by an employee as part of his job is initially owned by his employer--that is, the employer is considered to be the work's author. Such works are called "works made for hire." Works created by nonemployees (independent contractors) who sign work for hire agreements may also be works made for hire.

Like any other property, a copyright can be bought and sold. Transfers of copyright ownership are unique in one respect, however: authors or their heirs have the right to terminate any transfer of copyright ownership 35 years after it is made.

1. What are the exceptions to the rule that the creator of a work owns the copyright?

Copyrights are generally owned by the people who create the works of expression, with several important exceptions:

a. If a work is created by an employee in the course of his or her employment, the employer owns the copyright.

b. If a work is created by an independent contractor, but that independent contractor performs her job under the direction and control of the person or organization paying for the work, the work is owned by the controlling person or organization.

c. If the work is created by an independent contractor who is not under the direction and control of the person or organization commissioning the work, and the independent contractor signs a written agreement, the commissioning person or organization owns the copyright only if the work is

   i. a part of a larger literary work, such as an article in a magazine or a poem or story in an anthology;

   ii. part of a motion picture or other audiovisual work, such as a screenplay;

   iii. a translation;

   iv. a supplementary work such as an afterword, an introduction, chart, editorial v. note, bibliography, appendix or index;

   vi. an instructional text;

   vii. a test;

   viii. answer material for a test; or

   ix. an atlas.

Works that don't fall within one of these categories constitute works made for hire only if created by an employee within the scope of his or her employment. If the creator has sold the entire copyright, the purchasing business or person becomes the copyright owner.

2. Who owns the copyright in a joint work?

When two or more authors prepare a work with the intent to merge their contributions into inseparable or interdependent parts (for example, several writers who work on every part of a book together, rather than breaking the job into discrete parts), the work is considered joint work and the authors are considered joint copyright owners. The U.S. Copyright Office considers joint copyright owners to have an equal right to register and enforce the copyright. Unless the joint owners make a written agreement to the contrary, each copyright owner has the right to commercially exploit the copyright, provided that the other copyright owners get an equal share of the proceeds.

3. Can two or more authors provide contributions to a single work without being considered joint authors?

Yes. If at the time of creation, the authors did not intend their works to be part of an inseparable whole, the fact that their works are later put together does not create a joint work. Rather, the result is considered a compilation. In this case, each author owns a copyright in only the material he or she added to the finished product.

4. What rights do copyright owners have under the Copyright Act?

The Copyright Act of 1976 grants a number of exclusive rights to copyright owners, including:

a. reproduction right--the right to make copies of a protected work

b. distribution right--the right to sell or otherwise distribute copies to the public
   right to create adaptations (or derivative works)--the right to prepare new works based on the protected work, and

c. performance and display rights--the right to perform a protected work such as a stage play, or to display a work in public.

5. Can a copyright owner transfer some or all of their specific rights?

Yes. When a copyright owner wishes to commercially exploit the work covered by the copyright, the owner typically transfers one or more of these rights to the person or entity who will be responsible for getting the work to market, such as a book or software publisher. It is also common for the copyright owner to place some limitations on the exclusive rights being transferred. For instance, the owner may limit the transfer to a specific period of time, allow the right to be exercised only in a specific part of the country or world, or require that the right be exercised only on certain computer platforms (those with UNIX operating systems, for example).

If a copyright owner transfers all of her rights unconditionally, it is generally termed an "assignment". When only some of the rights associated with the copyright are transferred, it is known as a "license." An exclusive license exists when the transferred rights can be exercised only by the owner of the license (the licensee), and no one else--including the person who granted the license (the licensor). If the license allows others (including the licensor) to exercise the same rights being transferred in the license, the license is said to be non-exclusive.

The U.S. Copyright Office allows buyers of exclusive and non-exclusive copyright rights to record the transfers in the U.S. Copyright Office. This helps to protect the buyers in case the original copyright owner later decides to transfer the same rights to another party.

39. When is a work considered to be in the public domain?

When a work becomes available for use without permission from a copyright owner, it is said to be in the public domain. Most works enter the public domain because their copyright has expired. But some works published before 1989 became public domain material because they didn't carry the proper copyright notice (a notice is no longer required to maintain a copyright). Also, many works published before 1964 have entered the public domain because the copyright owners did not renew their copyright under a law that was in effect at that time.

Under a recent change in the copyright laws occasioned by the GATT (General Agreements on Tariffs and Trade) treaty, works of foreign authors that fell into the public domain in the U.S.

because they failed to comply with certain formalities required by U.S. laws (such as a valid copyright notice before 1989) have had their copyrights restored.

To determine whether a work is in the public domain, you first have to find out when it was published. Then you can apply the periods of time set out earlier in this section. If the work was published before 1978, you will also need to check with the U.S. Copyright Office to see whether it was renewed. As a general rule, you should assume that every work is protected by copyright unless you can establish that it is not. You can't rely on the presence or absence of a copyright notice (©) to make this determination, because a notice is not required for works published after March 1, 1989. And even for works published before 1989, the absence of a copyright notice may not affect the validity of the copyright.

Material that is not protected by copyright is in the public domain--free for anyone to use without permission. The public domain includes:

1. material no longer protected by copyright, including anything published in the United States more than 75 years ago;
2. material in which no copyright ever existed, such as materials printed by the U.S. government;
3. ideas, including procedures, processes, systems, methods of operation, concepts, principles and discoveries; and/or
4. facts--scientific, historical, biographical or news of the day.

40. Does copyright protect an author's creative ideas?

No. It is very important to understand that copyright protects only the form in which ideas are expressed (such as a novel, sculpture or software code)--not the ideas or facts underlying the expression. For instance, copyright may protect a particular song, novel or computer game about a romance in space, but it cannot protect the underlying idea of having a love affair among the stars.

Similarly, copyright does not protect facts--whether scientific, historical, biographical or news of the day. Thus, the facts that an author discovers in the course of research are in the public domain, free to all. This is so even if the author spends considerable time and effort discovering previously unknown facts. Copyright only protects fixed, original and minimally creative expression, not the information upon which the information is based.

41. Does copyright protect what I say in an online forum or seminar?

Technically it does, as long as your words are your own and no one else's. But remember that only your words are protected--not any bright ideas that you share with your online audience. Also, a legal doctrine known as fair use may allow others to use your words for educational or news purposes. (See The Fair Use Rule)

42. What is unique about nonfiction material?

The rules are a little different for non-fiction works, because it is harder to show that an author's expression in a non-fiction book was copied. Non-fiction works, by definition, deal with facts which themselves are not protected.

Copyright does not protect facts that an author discovers in the course of research, even if an author spends considerable effort conducting the research. Nor does it protect the author's interpretation of facts--theories or hypotheses about what the facts show, or the book's physical and visual attributes, including choice of typeface style and size, spacing and juxtaposition of text and illustrations.

But as long as the facts are described in a unique way, the expression will be protected even if the facts aren't. Scientists Stephen J. Gould and Lewis Thomas, for example, have written books about science whose language transcends the facts they are based on. The distinctive prose in their books receives far more protection than that of a run-of-the-mill scientific treatise.

The more that writing transcends the mundane and purely functional, the more copyright protection it will receive.

For instance, consider an unadorned factual account of Paul Revere's famous midnight ride during the Revolutionary War that contains the following:

"On April 18, 1775, the Boston minutemen learned that the British intended to march on Concord with a detachment of 700 men. Paul Revere arranged for a signal to be flashed from the steeple of the Old North Church in Boston. Two lanterns would mean that the British were coming by water, and one, by land."

Copyright would not be of much use to the author of this passage. If anyone else wrote a brief factual account of Paul Revere's ride, it would necessarily have to contain sentences looking very much like those in this paragraph. If the author sued, alleging a copyright violation, the law's policy against granting an author a monopoly over facts would mean that a court would likely rule that there was no copyright violation.

In contrast, copyright would protect a highly creative work containing essentially the same facts about Paul Revere's ride.

Consider this:

> Listen, my children, and you shall hear
> Of the midnight ride of Paul Revere,
> On the eighteenth of April, in Seventy-five.
> Hardly a man is now alive
> Who remembers that famous day and year.
>
> He said to his friend, "if the British march
> By land or sea from the town to-night,
> Hold a lantern aloft in the belfry arch
> Of the North Church tower as a signal light,
> One, if by land, and two, if by sea."

These stanzas were written by Henry Wadsworth Longfellow over 100 years ago, and the copyright has expired, but let's pretend they were written just the other day.

This verse conveys almost exactly the same facts as the paragraph above, but would be protected because the author's words are embellished and highly distinctive. The sequence of words is not dictated solely by the facts. It is the unique word sequence itself, not the facts, that is the work's main attraction. No one needs to copy this particular word sequence in order to convey the same facts or to write another work of fancy about Paul Revere's ride. A person who copied even the first two lines would probably be found to have infringed on the copyright in the poem.

43. Why provide a copyright notice?

Until 1989, a published work had to be accompanied by a valid copyright notice to receive protection under the copyright laws. But this requirement is no longer in force--works first published after March 1, 1989 need not include a copyright notice to gain protection under the law. Even though a copyright notice is not required, it is still a very good idea to include one. When a work contains a valid notice, an infringer cannot claim in court that he didn't know it was copyrighted. This makes it much easier to win a copyright infringement case and perhaps collect enough damages to make the cost of the case worthwhile. Moreover, the existence of a notice might discourage infringement. And finally, including a copyright notice may make it easier for a potential infringer to track down a copyright owner and legitimately obtain permission to use the work.

44. What is a valid copyright notice?

A copyright notice should contain the:

- word "copyright" or a "c" in a circle (©) or copr;
- date of publication;

- name of either the author or the owner of all the copyright rights in the published work; and
- clause "All rights reserved." -- in the event the copyright is to be enforced in select foreign countries.

45. How long does a copyright last?

For works published after 1977, the copyright lasts for the life of the author plus 70 years. However, if the work is a work for hire or is published anonymously or under a pseudonym, the copyright lasts between 95 and 120 years, depending on the date the work is published.

If the work was published before 1978 and the copyright has been properly renewed, the copyright expires 75 years after date of publication. If the work was created but not published before 1978, the copyright will last until December 31, 2002.

46. Where can I get more information on application forms?

The Public Information Office telephone number is (202) 707-3000. To order application forms, the number is (202) 707-9100. TTY is (202) 707-6737.

47. What is the mailing address?

Copyright Office, Library of Congress, 101 Independence Avenue, .E., Washington, D.C. 20559-6000.

48. What are visiting address and hours of operation?

The Copyright Office is located at 101 Independence Avenue, S.E., Washington, D.C., in the James Madison Memorial Building, Room LM-401, of the Library of Congress. Hours of service are 8:30 a.m. to 5:00 p.m. eastern time, Monday through Friday, except Federal holidays. The nearest Metro stop is Capitol South.

49. Where can I get application forms?

You may get forms from the U.S. Copyright Office in person, by mailing in a request, or by calling our 24-hours-per-day forms hotline: (202) 707-9100. Some public libraries may carry our forms but we do not maintain a list of those libraries. Forms may also be downloaded from our website.

50. When will I get my certificate?

You may receive your certificate of registration within five months from the date of receipt in the copyright Office.

51. Can you provide me with copies of my application and my work?

Contact the Certifications and Documents Section of the Copyright Office (202) 707-6787 or see Circular 6 for details.

52. How can I obtain copies of someone else's work and/or registration certificate?

The Copyright Office will not honor a request for a copy of someone else's work without written authorization from the owner or from his or her designated agent if that work is still under copyright protection, unless the work is involved in litigation. Written permission from the copyright owner or a litigation statement is required before copies can be made available. A certificate of registration for any registered work can be obtained for a fee of $8. Circular 6 provides additional information.

53. I lost my certificate: Can I get a new one?

Yes, we can produce additional certificates for a fee of $8. See Circular 6 for details on how to make such a request.

54. Do you have a list of songs or movies in the public domain?

No, we neither compile nor maintain such a list. A search of our records, however, may reveal whether a particular work has fallen into the public domain. We will conduct a search of our records by the title of a work, an author's name, or a claimant's name. The search fee is $20 per hour. You may also search the records in person without paying a fee.

55. What is mandatory deposit?

Copies of all works under copyright protection that have been published in the United States are required to be deposited with the Copyright Office within three months of the date of first publication. See Circular 7d and the Deposit Regulation 96 202.19.

56. Do I have to register with the office to be protected?

No. In general, registration is voluntary. Copyright exists from the moment the work is created. You will have to register, however, if you wish to bring a lawsuit for infringement of a U.S. work. See Circular 1, section Copyright Registration.

57. Why should I register my work if copyright protection is automatic?

Registration is recommended for a number of reasons. Many choose to register their works because they wish to have the facts of their copyright on the public record and have a certificate of registration. Registered works may be eligible for statutory damages and attorney's fees in successful litigation. Finally, if registration occurs within five years of publication, it is considered prima facie evidence in a court of law. See Circular 1, section Copyright Registration and Circular 38b on non-U.S. works.

Not all the benefits of prompt registration relate to litigation. In fact, early registration can help keep you out of court. That's because an infringer who knows that you could recover substantial statutory damages in court may be more willing to negotiate and settle out of court.

Since registration is so easy, costs only $20 per work and provides significant benefits, it's one of the great insurance deals of all time.

Of course, if what you're publishing probably has no value to anyone but you, you may want to just place a copyright notice on the material and not bother to register. But in most situations, if your work is valuable enough to publish, it's valuable enough to register.

58. Is this the only place I can go to register a copyright?

Although copyright application forms may be available in public libraries and some reference books, the U.S. Copyright Office is the only office that can accept applications and issue registrations.

59. How do I register my copyright?

Registering a copyright registration is a simple process; you don't need an attorney. All you need to do is to fill out a brief application form, which requires some basic information about the work, including: a) title of the work; b) who created the work an when, and c) who owns the copyright.

Send application, a small nonrefundable fee (usually $20) and one or two copies of all or part of the copyrighted work to the U.S. Copyright Office in Washington, D.C.

There are different forms for different types of works (for instance, form TX is for literary works while form VA is for a visual art work). Forms and instructions may be obtained from the U.S. Copyright Office by telephone: (202) 707-9100 or online (http://www.loc.gov/copyright). The U.S. Copyright Office registration currently costs $20 per work. If you're registering several works that are part of one series, you may be able to save money by registering the works together (called "batch registration").

60. How long does the registration process take?

Copyright registration is considered effective on the day we receive all the required elements, although you may not receive the certificate of registration for five months or so.

61. What is the registration fee?

The current filing fee is $20 per application. Generally, each work requires a separate application. See Circular 4.

62. Can I make copies of the application form?

Yes, you can make copies of copyright forms if they meet the following criteria: photocopied back-to-back and head to head on a single sheet of 8 1/2 by 11 inch white paper. In other words, your copy must look just like the original.

63. What is a deposit?

A deposit is usually one copy (if unpublished) or two copies (if published) of the work to be registered for copyright. In certain cases such as works of the visual arts, identifying material such as a photograph may be used instead. See Circular 40a. The deposit is sent with the application and fee and becomes the property of the Library of Congress.

64. How can I know if my application for registration is received?

If you want to know when the Copyright Office receives your material, you should send it by registered or certified mail and request a return receipt from the post office. Allow at least five weeks for the return of your receipt.

65. Can I find out what is happening with my registration?

Copyright registration is effective on the day we receive the appropriate form, copy or copies of the work, and the $20 filing fee. The current processing time is about five months. Generally, a certificate of registration or, in the event we need further information, a letter or telephone call from our office, will be received during this time period. We are not able to provide status information for submissions that were received less than five months ago. If it is imperative that you have this information sooner, you may pay the appropriate fees and request that the Certifications and Documents Section conduct an in-process search. The current in-process search fee is $20 per hour.

66. Do I have to send in my work? Do I get it back?

Yes, you must send the required copy or copies of the work to be registered. These copies will not be returned. Upon their deposit in the Copyright Office, under sections 407 and 408, all copies, phonorecords, and identifying material, including those deposited in connection with claims that have been refused registration, are the property of the United States Government.

67. May I register more than one work on the same application? Where do I list the titles?

You may register unpublished works as a collection on one application with one title for the entire collection if certain conditions are met. It is not necessary to list the individual titles in your collection, although you may do so by completing a Continuation Sheet. Published works may only be registered as a collection if they were actually first published as a collection and if other requirements have been met. See Circular 1, section Registration Procedures.

68. What is the difference between form PA and form SR?

These forms are for registering two different types of copyrightable subject matter that may be embodied in a recording. Form PA is used for the registration of music and/or lyrics (as well as other works of the performing arts), even if your song is on a cassette. Form SR is used for registering the performance and production of a particular recording of sounds. See Circular 50 and Circular 56a.

69. Do I have to renew my copyright?

No. Works created on or after January 1, 1978, are not subject to renewal registration (see Circular 15). As to works published or registered prior to January 1, 1978, renewal registration is optional after 28 years but does provide certain legal advantages. For information on how to file a renewal application as well as the legal benefit for doing so, see Circular 15 and Circular 15a.

70. Can I submit my manuscript on a computer disk?

No. There are many different software formats and the Copyright Office does not have the equipment to accommodate all of them. Therefore, the Copyright Office still generally requires a printed copy or audio recording of the work for deposit.

71. Can I submit a CD-ROM of my work?

Yes, you may. The deposit requirement consists of the best edition of the CD-ROM package of any work, including the accompanying operating software, instruction manual and a printed version, if included in the package.

72. How do I protect my recipe?

A mere listing of ingredients is not protected under copyright law. However, where a recipe or formula is accompanied by substantial literary expression in the form of an explanation or directions, or when there is a collection of recipes as in a cookbook, there may be a basis for copyright protection. See FL 122.

73. Does copyright now protect architecture?

Yes. Architectural works became subject to copyright protection on December 1, 1990. The copyright law defines "architectural work" as "the design of a building embodied in any tangible medium of expression, including a building, architectural plans, or drawings." Copyright protection extends to any architectural work created on or after December 1, 1990, and any architectural work that on December 1, 1990, was unconstructed and embodied in unpublished plans or drawings. Architectural works embodied in buildings constructed prior to December 1, 1990, are not eligible for copyright protection.

74. Can I register a diary I found in my grandmother's attic?

You can register copyright in the diary only if you are the transferee (by will, by inheritance). Copyright is the right of the author of the work or the author's heirs or assignees, not of the one who only owns or possesses the physical work itself. See Circular 1, section Who Can Claim Copyright.

75. Do you have special mailing requirements?

Our only requirement is that all three elements, the application, the copy or copies of the work, and the $20 filing fee, be sent in the same package. Many people send their material to us by certified mail, with a return receipt request, but this is not necessary.

76. Can foreigners register their works in the U.S.?

Any work that is protected by U.S. copyright law can be registered. This includes many works of foreign origin. All works that are unpublished, regardless of the nationality of the author, are protected in the United States. Works that are first published in the United States or in a country with which we have a copyright treaty or that are created by a citizen or domiciliary of a country with which we have a copyright treaty are also protected and may therefore be registered with the U.S. Copyright Office. See Circular 38a for the status of specific countries.

77. Who is an author?

Under the copyright law, the creator of the original expression in a work is its author. The author is also the owner of copyright unless there is a written agreement by which the author assigns the copyright to another person or entity, such as a publisher. In cases of works made for hire (see Circular 9), the employer or commissioning party is considered to be the author.

78. What is a work made for hire?

Although the general rule is that the person who creates the work is its author, there is an exception to that principle; the exception is a work made for hire, which is a work prepared by an employee within the scope of his or her employment; or a work specially ordered or commissioned in certain specified circumstances. When a work qualifies as a work made for hire, the employer or commissioning party is considered to be the author. See Circular 9.

79. Can a minor claim copyright?

Minors may claim copyright, and the Copyright Office does issue registrations to minors, but state laws may regulate the business dealings involving copyrights owned by minors. For information on relevant state laws, consult an attorney.

80. Do I have to use my real name on the form? Can I use a stage name or a pen name?

There is no legal requirement that the author be identified by his or her real name on the application form. For further information, see FL 101. If filing under a fictitious name, check the "Pseudonymous" box at space 2.

81. What is publication?

Publication has a very technical meaning in copyright law. According to the statute, "Publication is the distribution of copies or phonorecords of a work to the public by sale or other transfer of ownership, or by rental, lease, or ending. The offering to distribute copies or phonorecords to a group of persons for purposes of further distribution, public performance, or public display constitutes publication. A public performance or display of a work does not of itself constitute publication." Generally, publication occurs on the date on which copies of the work are first made available to the public. For further information see Circular 1, section Publication.

82. Does my work have to be published to be protected?

Publication is not necessary for copyright protection.

83. How do I get my work published?

Publication occurs at the discretion and initiative of the copyright owner. The Copyright Office has no role in the publication process.

84. Are copyrights transferable?

Yes. Like any other property, all or part of the rights in a work may be transferred by the owner to another. See Circular 1, section Transfer of Copyright, for a discussion of ownership.

85. Do you have any forms for transfer of copyrights?

There are no forms provided by the Copyright Office to effect a copyright transfer. The Office does, however, keep records of transfers if they are submitted to us. If you have executed a transfer and wish to record it, the Copyright Office can provide a Document Cover Sheet, which can help to expedite the processing of the recordation. See Circular 12.

86. Can I copyright the name of my band?

No. Names are not protected by copyright law. Some names may be protected under trademark law. Contact the U.S. Patent & Trademark Office, (800) 786-9199, for further information.

87. How do I copyright a name, title, slogan or logo?

Copyright does not protect names, titles, slogans, or short phrases. In some cases, these things may be protected as trademarks. Contact the U.S. Patent & Trademark Office at (800) 786-9199 for further information. However, copyright protection may be available for logo art work that contains sufficient authorship. In some circumstances, an artistic logo may also be protected as a trademark.

88. How do I protect my idea?

Copyright does not protect ideas, concepts, systems, or methods of doing something. You may express your ideas in writing or drawings and claim copyright in your description, but be aware that copyright will not protect the idea itself as revealed in your written or artistic work.

89. How long does copyright last?

Under the current copyright law, the duration of copyright is generally the life of the author plus 50 years. Before 1978, the duration of copyright was 28 years plus a renewal term of 47 years, and this term still applies to some pre-1978 works. Even for new works, however, there are some variables, as in the case of works made for hire. Consult Circular 15a for a fuller discussion on the duration of copyright.

90. How much of someone else's work can I use without getting permission?

Under the fair use doctrine of the U.S. copyright statute, it is permissible to use limited portions of a work including quotes, for purposes such as commentary, criticism, news reporting, and scholarly reports. There are no legal rules permitting the use of specific number of words counts, a certain number of musical notes, or percentages of a work. Whether a particular use qualifies as fair use depends on all the circumstances. See Circular 21 and FL 102.

91. How much do I have to change in my own work to make a new claim of copyright?

You may make a new claim in your work if the changes are substantial and creative -- something more than just editorial changes or minor changes. This would qualify it as a new, derivative work. For instance, simply making spelling corrections throughout a work does not warrant a new registration: Adding an additional chapter would. See Circular 14 for further information.

92. How much do I have to change in order to claim copyright in someone else's work?

Only the owner of copyright in a work has the right to prepare, or to authorize someone else to create, a new version of that work. Accordingly, you cannot claim copyright, no matter how much you change it, unless you have the owner's consent. See Circular 14.

93. How do I get my work into the Library of Congress?

Copies of works deposited for copyright registration or in fulfillment of the mandatory deposit requirement are available to the Library of Congress for its collections. The Library reserves the right to select or reject any published work for its permanent collections based on the research needs of Congress, the nation's scholars, and of the nation's libraries. If you would like further information on the Library's selection policies, you may contact: Library of Congress, Collections Policy Office, 101 Independence Avenue, S.E., Washington, D.C. 20540.

94. What is a Library of Congress number?

The Library of Congress Card Catalog Number is assigned by the Library at its discretion to assist librarians in acquiring and cataloging works. For further information call the Cataloging in Publication Division at (202) 707-6345.

95. What is an ISBN number?

The International Standard Book Number is administered by the R. R. Bowker Company (908) 665-6770. The ISBN is a numerical identifier intended to assist the international community in identifying and ordering certain publications.

96. What is a copyright notice? How do I put a copyright notice on my work?

A copyright notice is an identifier placed on copies of the work to inform the world of copyright ownership. While use of a copyright notice was once required as a condition of copyright protection, it is now optional. Use of the notice is the responsibility of the copyright owner and does not require advance permission from, or registration with, the Copyright Office. See Circular 1, Notice of Copyright for requirements for works published before March 1, 1989 and for more information on the form and position of the copyright notice.

97. How do I collect royalties?

The collection of royalties is usually a matter of private arrangements between an author and publisher or other users of the author's work. The Copyright Office plays no role in the execution of contractual terms or business practices. There are performing societies and other collective right societies that distribute royalties for their members.

98. Somebody infringed my copyright. What can I do?

A party may seek to protect his or her copyrights against unauthorized use by filing a civil lawsuit in Federal district court. If you believe that your copyright has been infringed, consult an attorney. In cases of willful infringement for profit, the U.S. Attorney may initiate a criminal investigation.

99. Is my copyright good in other countries?

The United States has copyright relations with more than 100 countries throughout the world, and as a result of these agreements, we honor each other's citizens' copyrights. However, the United States does not have such copyright relationships with every country. For a listing of countries and the nature of their copyright relations with the United States, see Circular 38a, International Copyright Relations of the United States.

100. How do I get on a mailing list?

The Copyright Office does not maintain a mailing list. Important announcements and new or changed regulations and the like are published in the Federal Register. Most will also appear on the Copyright Office website on the Internet.

101. How do I protect my sighting of Elvis?

Copyright law does not protect sightings. However, copyright law will protect your photo (or other depiction) of your sighting of Elvis. Just send it to us with a form VA application and the $20 filing fee. No one can lawfully use your photo of your sighting, although someone else may file his own photo of his sighting. Copyright law protects the original photograph, not the subject of the photograph.

102. How do I get permission to use somebody else's work?

You can ask for it. If you know who the copyright owner is, you may contact the owner directly. If you are not certain about the ownership or have other related questions, you may wish to request that the Copyright Office conduct a search of its records for a fee of $20 per hour. Additional information can be obtained from Circular 22.

103. When is copying okay and what is the 'Fair Use' Rule?

Sooner or later, almost all writers quote or closely paraphrase what others have written. For example: Andy, putting together a newsletter on his home computer, reprints an editorial he likes from a daily newspaper. Phil, a biographer and historian, quotes from several unpublished letters and diaries written by his subject. Regina, a freelance writer, closely paraphrases two paragraphs from the Encyclopedia Britannica in an article she's writing. Sylvia, a poet, quotes a line from a poem by T.S. Eliot in one of her own poems. Donnie, a comedian, writes a parody of the famous song "Blue Moon" he performs in his comedy act.

Assuming the material quoted in these examples is protected by copyright, do Phil, Regina, Sylvia, Andy and Donnie need permission from the author or other copyright owner to use it? It may surprise you to learn that the answer is "not necessarily."

Under the "fair use" rule of copyright law, an author may make limited use of another author's work without asking permission. The fair use privilege is perhaps the most significant limitation on a copyright owner's exclusive rights. If you write or publish, you need a basic understanding of what is and is not fair use.

Uses That Are Generally Fair Uses

Subject to some general limitations discussed later in this article, the following types of uses are usually deemed fair uses:

1. Criticism and comment--for example, quoting or excerpting a work in a review or criticism for purposes of illustration or comment.
2. News reporting--for example, summarizing an address or article, with brief quotations, in a news report.
3. Research and scholarship--for example, quoting a short passage in a scholarly, scientific or technical work for illustration or clarification of the author's observations.
4. Nonprofit educational uses--for example, photocopying of limited portions of written works by teachers for classroom use.
5. Parody--that is, a work that ridicules another, usually well-known, work by imitating it in a comic way.

In most other situations, copying is not legally a fair use. Without an author's permission, such a use violates the author's copyright.

Violations often occur when the use is motivated primarily by a desire for commercial gain. The fact that a work is published primarily for private commercial gain weighs against a finding of fair use. For example, using the Bob Dylan line "You don't need a weatherman to know which way the wind blows" in a poem published in a small literary journal would probably be a fair use; using the same line in an advertisement for raincoats probably would not be.

A commercial motive doesn't always disqualify someone from claiming a fair use. A use that benefits the public can qualify as a fair use, even if it makes money for the user.

For example, a vacuum cleaner manufacturer was permitted--in its advertising--to quote from a Consumer Reports article comparing vacuum cleaners. Why? The ad significantly increased the number of people exposed to the Consumers Union's evaluations and thereby disseminated helpful consumer information. The same rationale probably applies to the widespread practice of quoting from favorable reviews in advertisements for books, films and plays.

Copying From Unpublished Materials

When it comes to fair use, unpublished works are inherently different from published works. Publishing an author's unpublished work before he or she has authorized it infringes upon the author's right to decide when and whether the work will be made public. Some courts have held that fair use never applies to unpublished material.

As you might expect, publishers, authors' groups, biographers and historians were highly critical of this view. They got Congress to amend the fair use provision in the Copyright Act to make clear that the fact that a work is unpublished weighs against fair use, but is not determinative in and of itself. If the other fair use factors favor fair use, it can be permissible to use part of an unpublished work without permission. This is particularly likely where the use benefits the public by furthering the fundamental purpose of the copyright laws--the advancement of human knowledge. For example, a court held that it was a fair use for a biographer to use a modest amount of material from unpublished letters and journals by the author Richard Wright. (Wright v. Warner Books, Inc., 953 F.2d 731 (2d Cir. 1991).)

When Is a Use a 'Fair Use'?

There are five basic rules to keep in mind when deciding whether or not a particular use of an author's work is a fair use:

Rule 1: Are You Just Copying or Creating Something New?

The purpose and character of your intended use of the material involved is the single most important factor in determining whether a use is a fair use. The question to ask here is whether you are merely copying someone else's work verbatim or instead using it to help create something new. The Supreme Court calls such a new work "transformative." The more transformative your work, the more likely your use is a fair use.

Rule 2: Don't Compete With the Source You're Copying From

Without consent, you ordinarily cannot use another person's protected expression in a way that impairs (or even potentially impairs) the market for his or her work. Thus, if you want to use an author's protected expression in a work of your own that is similar to the prior work and aimed at the same market, your intended use isn't likely a fair use.

For example, say Nick, a golf pro, writes a book on how to play golf. Not a good putter himself, he copies several brilliant paragraphs on putting from a book by Lee Trevino, one of the greatest putters in golf history. Because Nick intends his book to compete with and hopefully supplant Trevino's, this use could not be a fair use. In effect, Nick is trying to use Trevino's protected expression to eat into the sales of Trevino's own book.

An interesting example is when a teacher copies parts of books for students to use. In one recent case, a group of seven major publishers went to court and stopped a duplicating business from copying excerpts from books without permission, compiling them into "course packets" and selling them to college students.

Rule 3: Giving the Author Credit Doesn't Let You Off the Hook

Some people mistakenly believe that they can use any material as long as they properly give the author credit. Not true. Giving credit and fair use are completely separate concepts. Either you have the right to use another author's material under the fair use rule or you don't. The fact that you attribute the material to the other author doesn't change that.

Rule 4: The More You Take, the Less Fair Your Use Is Likely to Be

The more material you take, the less likely it is that your use will be a fair use. However, to preserve the free flow of information, authors have more leeway in using material from factual works (scholarly, technical, scientific works, etc.) than to works of fancy such as novels, poems and plays. This is true especially where it's necessary to use extensive quotations to ensure the accuracy of the information conveyed.

As a general rule, never quote more than a few successive paragraphs from a book or article, or take more than one chart or diagram. It is never proper to include an illustration or other artwork in a book or newsletter without the artist's permission. Don't quote more than one or two lines from a poem. Many publishers require their authors to obtain permission from an author to quote more then a specified number of words, ranging from about 100 to 1000 words.

Contrary to what many people believe, there is no absolute word limit on fair use. For example, it is not always okay to take one paragraph or less than 200 words. Copying 12 words from a 14-word haiku poem wouldn't be fair use. Nor would copying 200 words from a work of 300 words likely qualify as a fair use. However, copying 2000 words from a work of 500,000 words might be fair. It all depends on the circumstances.

Rule 5: The Quality of the Material Used Is as Important as the Quantity

The more important the material is to the original work, the less likely your use of it will be considered a fair use.

In one famous case, The Nation magazine obtained a copy of Gerald Ford's memoirs before their publication. In the magazine's article about the memoirs, only 300 words from Ford's 200,000-word manuscript were quoted verbatim. The Supreme Court ruled that this was not a fair use because the material quoted (dealing with the Nixon pardon) was the "heart of the book ...the most interesting and moving parts of the entire manuscript," and that pre-publication disclosure of this material would cut into value or sales of the book.

Determining whether your intended use of another author's protected work constitutes a fair use is usually not difficult. It's really just a matter of common sense. There is no more commonsensical definition of fair use than the golden rule: Take from someone else only what you wouldn't mind someone taking from you.

104. Should I enforce my copyright rights?

The fact that an author has the legal right to control a work isn't the end of the story, of course, as anyone who has used a VCR or a photocopy machine readily understands. Enforcing this right can be difficult.

If someone violates (infringes) an author's rights under the copyright law, the author may sue in federal court, demanding compensation for economic loss and a stop to further harm. Unless the author has already taken certain steps, however, the lawsuit will likely cost far more than the author will win.

To make a lawsuit economically feasible, the author must have: placed a copyright notice on the work (the little c and a name and date), and registered the work with the U.S. Copyright Office. Once this is completed, the law gives the author a much better chance to win a substantial amount of money from the infringer.

105. How are copyrights enforced? Is going to court necessary?

In the event someone violates (infringes) the exclusive rights of a copyright owner, the owner is entitled to file a lawsuit in federal court asking the court to:

1. issue orders (restraining orders and injunctions) to prevent further violations;
2. award money damages if appropriate; and
3. in some circumstances, award attorney fees.

Whether the lawsuit will be effective and whether damages will be awarded depends on whether the alleged infringer can raise one or more legal defenses to the charge. Common legal defenses to copyright infringement are:

1. too much time has elapsed between the infringing act and the lawsuit (the statute of limitations defense);
2. the infringement is allowed under the fair use doctrine;
3. the infringement was innocent (the infringer had no reason to know the work was protected by copyright);
4. the infringing work was independently created (it wasn't copied from the original); or
5. the copyright owner authorized the use in a license.

106. How does international copyright protection differ from U.S. copyright?

Copyright protection rules are fairly similar worldwide, due to several international copyright treaties, the most important of which is the Berne Convention. Under this treaty, all member countries (in excess of 100--including virtually all industrialized nations) must afford copyright protection to authors who are nationals of any member country. This protection must last for at least the life of the author plus 70 years, and must be automatic without the need for the author to take any legal steps to preserve the copyright.

In addition to the Berne Convention, the GATT (General Agreement on Tariffs and Trade) treaty contains a number of provisions that affect copyright protection in signatory countries. Together, the Berne Copyright Convention and the GATT treaty allow U.S. authors to enforce their copyrights in most industrialized nations, and allow the nationals of those nations to enforce their copyrights in the U.S.

107. What about copyrights in Cyberspace?
How Copyright Works

While browsing on an electronic bulletin board, you come across an interesting article on dog training. Thinking it might be of interest to the members of your dog owners' club, you download it, print it out and reprint it in the next issue of your club's newsletter.

Congratulations -- you've probably just violated federal law.

Don't worry, you won't be hauled off to the federal pen. The law you ran afoul of is copyright law, which gives authors, composers and others who create works of expression certain rights over their creations.

You would probably think about copyright rules if you wanted to republish a chapter of a book, a play or a song you liked. But they're easy to overlook when you're dealing with electronic media. These bits of information fly around so rapidly and can be reproduced so easily that it's hard to remember that someone out there probably owns the right to determine when and how copies are made and used.

All works of original expression have at least one thing in common: they are protected by copyright as soon as they are created and fixed in a tangible medium. For the most part, once an expression is entered into a computer in a form that can be read on screen or routed to a printer, it is considered fixed in a tangible medium, even if it is never printed out or saved to a disk. A copyright notice -- that little © followed by the year and the author's name -- is not required, but is recommended to remind people that the author claims a copyright.

The author of the expression owns the copyright, unless there has been a formal written transfer of that ownership or the expression is created as a work for hire or paid for by an employer. So a person who enters an expression into a computer for other people to see usually owns the copyright on that expression.

What does owning a copyright on an expression mean? Simply, that no one else can copy, distribute, display or adapt that expression without the copyright owner's consent. This consent may be given for free, for a fee or on the condition that an appropriate attribution be given. It is always a good idea, if you send material into cyberspace, to explicitly state the conditions for its use and reproduction.

As a starting point, therefore, you can assume that you control the right to use any expressions that you author and put online. The important corollary is that any expressions you find online are probably controlled by someone else and shouldn't be used without permission.

Copyright protects expression, not ideas or facts. For instance, information in a telephone book or a weather summary can be freely used. On the other hand, the expression used in an essay on telephones or a creative explanation of weather systems is protected by copyright even though the underlying data and ideas aren't.

Copyright law doesn't mean that you can never quote something interesting that you find online. The "fair use" rule allows you to use a small portion of an expression to comment on it or for an educational purpose. But if you want to use the expression for commercial gain, the fair use exception probably won't apply unless the portion you use is extremely small in relation to the entire expression.

It's extremely difficult to apply the fair use rule to new forms of expression such as the discussions that take place in "cyberspace" -- for example, on Internet "newsgroups" or the conferences on online services such as America Online and CompuServe. A hundred people may each contribute a few lines to a discussion. If you want to use a big chunk of the conversation, must you get every contributor's permission? Theoretically, yes, because each contributor owns copyright in his or her words. However, since none of the contributions has any significant commercial value by itself, it's hard to see where the copyright owners would be harmed if the entire conversation were used without their individual permissions. Nevertheless, people whose words are used without their permission may be angry about it. It is always better to ask.

Also copyright is not the only law to be concerned about when launching words onto the information highway. You should also avoid:

- invading a person's privacy
- falsely accusing someone of committing an immoral or illegal act, and
- using a trademark or service mark that is already being used by someone else.

108. Can a teacher videotape for the classroom and if not what are some cautions?

As educators find that books and lectures don't impress or excite today's image-saturated youth, televisions are becoming as common in the classroom as blackboards. There is even a special closed-circuit television network just for high schools.

Given the widespread availability of videocassette recorders, many teachers need to know if and when they may legally tape educational TV programs off the air and show them to their students.

The Legal Rules

Television programs, like most other types of expression, are protected by federal copyright laws. This means that as a general rule, a TV program can legally be taped and shown to students only with the copyright owner's permission.

Fortunately, the Copyright Act contains a special exception for educational uses of copyrighted materials. Under what is known as the "fair use" rule, someone other than the copyright owner may make limited use of a copyrighted work without permission for purposes such as teaching, research, scholarship, criticism, parody and news reporting.

To help educators determine when off-air taping is and is not a fair use, a set of very concrete guidelines was created by a committee comprising representatives from educational organizations and copyright owners. These guidelines (known officially as "Guidelines for Off-Air Recording of Broadcast Programming for Educational Purposes") do not have the force of law and have never been tested in the courts. Many producers do not agree with them, and many teachers aren't thrilled either, because they offer only limited, temporary access to broadcast materials. However, most copyright experts believe that taping that falls within the guidelines is permissible and would be upheld as a fair use if challenged in court.

The guidelines apply only to off-air taping by nonprofit educational institutions, including all public schools and most private schools and colleges. The guidelines do not apply to for-profit language or trade schools.

The basic rules are that only programs broadcast to the general public may be taped. This includes all programs broadcast to homes and schools. The guidelines do not apply to programs available only from cable television services such as Showtime, HBO, The Disney Channel, C-Span and ESPN.

A classroom teacher who wants a particular program taped should ask the school to tape it. The tape may be shown only during the first ten consecutive school days after it is made, and only in a classroom or similar place devoted to instruction. A tape may be shown to several classes if appropriate.

A limited number of copies may be made from each off-air recording. Each copy is subject to all the provisions governing the original recording.

The tape may not be altered in any way. For example, tapes may not be edited to create an anthology or compilation.

After the ten-day classroom use period expires, the tape may be used only for evaluation--that is, to determine whether it should be bought or licensed for permanent inclusion in the teaching curriculum. Not later than 45 calendar days after the tape was made, it must be destroyed.

The guidelines do not discuss whether or not a teacher may record a program at home for school use. It seems likely, however, that the practice is permissible so long as all the other guidelines are followed.

No independent organization enforces these guidelines. Schools that want to document their compliance should make and keep records of teacher requests, dates of taping, times shown and number of copies made.

Beyond the Guidelines

The guidelines don't cover many common situations. For example, they say nothing about the legality of keeping a taped program more than ten days, or taping a cable channel offering.

That does not necessarily mean that such uses could not be permissible under the fair use doctrine. To determine whether or not a particular use is a fair use, four rather vague factors must be considered:

1. the purpose and character of the use;
2. the nature of the copyrighted work;
3. the amount used; and
4. the effect of the use on the present or future market value of the work.

In fact, you'll probably know what to do if you just remember that a use that takes money out of a copyright owner's pocket is probably not a fair use. Thus, off-air taping beyond the scope of the guidelines is probably not a fair use if the program's producer makes videotapes available to the schools or the public for purchase or rental, because off-air taping reduces the market for such tapes. This is particularly true where videotapes are made available to schools at special discounts. If videotapes are not available, limited off-air taping might be a fair use, but no one knows for sure because no court has considered the question.

Taping beyond that permitted by the guidelines may be permissible for programs broadcast on PBS (Public Broadcasting System) stations. Producers of many PBS programs permit educational institutions to tape their programs off the air and show them for longer than ten days--sometimes for years. This is not true for all PBS programs, and the scope of the use allowed varies from show to show. Contact the educational or public service coordinator at your local PBS station for information about exceeding the guidelines for any particular PBS program.

More Information

The Association for Information Media and Equipment (AIME), a trade association for film and video producers, publishes a copyright information packet ($7.50) and videotape ($17) for schools. AIME also answers educators' questions about copyright and electronic media. Call (800) 444-4203

The Copyright Handbook, by Stephen Fishman (Nolo Press), discusses the fair use rule, and other aspects of copyright law, in detail.

What, Me Worry?

Theoretically, a teacher or school that makes unauthorized videotapes is in violation of the copyright law and runs the risk of being sued for copyright infringement. But as a practical matter, it is highly unlikely that a television producer would ever sue a school or individual teacher.

Most unauthorized use is never discovered, after all--there are no copyright police roaming the nation's classrooms.

In any case, a lawsuit is just too expensive. In the past 200 years, only a handful of copyright infringement suits have been brought against educators, and there is only a single reported court decision on videotaping, which involved large-scale, systematic taping by an educational consortium in New York. Probably the worst that would happen is that the producer would send the school a nasty letter and demand some payment.

Fear of getting caught, of course, isn't the only reason to obey the law. Schools have a special responsibility to set an example of obedience to law. And from a purely practical point of view, schools are an important market for producers of documentaries and other educational works. If instead of buying copies of a program, schools simply taped a telecast and made as many copies as they chose, producers would lose money and be less likely to create new educational works.

109. Could one be sued for using somebody else's work? How about quotes or samples?

If you use a copyrighted work without authorization, the owner may be entitled to bring an infringement action against you. There are circumstances under the fair use doctrine where a quote or a sample may be used without permission. However, in cases of doubt, the Copyright Office recommends that permission be obtained.

110. Without patenting the software, can you prevent others from marketing similar software to interact with your line of products, even if they don't refer to the line of products by its trademarked name?

Yes, you can. Software can be protected under copyright law. Copyright protection does not require registration or proper notice. (There are great benefits to such acts, but they are not necessary.) One form of proof for copyright infringement is access plus substantial similarity. The answer to your question is that you can prevent somebody from marketing a similar product without patent protection.

"If it doesn't have a copyright notice, it's not copyrighted."

This was true in the past, but today almost all major nations follow the Berne copyright convention. For example, in the USA, almost everything created privately and originally after April 1, 1989 is copyrighted and protected whether it has a notice or not. The default you should assume for other people's works is that they are copyrighted and may not be copied unless you know otherwise. There are some old works that lost protection without notice, but frankly you should not risk it unless you know for sure. It is true that a notice strengthens the protection, by warning people, and by allowing one to get more and different damages, but it is not necessary. If it looks copyrighted, you should assume it is. This applies to pictures, too. You may not scan pictures from magazines and post them to the net, and if you come upon something unknown, you shouldn't post that either. The correct form for a notice is: "Copyright [dates] by [author/owner]" You can use C in a circle © instead of "Copyright" but "(C)" has never been given legal force. The phrase "All Rights Reserved" used to be required in some nations but is now not needed.

"If I don't charge for it, it's not a violation."

False. Whether you charge can affect the damages awarded in court, but that's essentially the only difference. It's still a violation if you give it away -- and there can still be heavy damages if you hurt the commercial value of the property.

"If it's posted to Usenet it's in the public domain."

False. Nothing modern is in the public domain anymore unless the owner explicitly puts it in the public domain (*). Explicitly, as in you have a note from the author/owner saying, "I grant this to the public domain." Those exact words or words very much like them. Some argue that posting to Usenet implicitly grants permission to everybody to copy the posting within fairly wide bounds, and others feel that Usenet is an automatic store and forward network where all the thousands of copies made are done at the command (rather than the consent) of the poster. This is a matter of some debate, but even if the former is true (and in this writer's opinion we should all pray it isn't true) it simply would suggest posters are implicitly granting permissions "for the sort of copying one might expect when one posts to Usenet" and in no case is this a placement of material into the public domain. It is important to remember that when it comes to the law, computers never make copies, only human beings make copies. Computers are given commands, not permission. Only people can be given permission. Furthermore it is very difficult for an implicit license to supersede an explicitly stated license that the copier was aware of.

Note that all this assumes the poster had the right to post the item in the first place. If the poster didn't, then all the copies are pirate, and no implied license or theoretical reduction of the copyright can take place. (*) Copyrights can expire after a long time, putting something into the public domain, and there are some fine points on this issue regarding older copyright law versions. However, none of this applies to an original article posted to USENET. Note that granting something to the public domain is a complete abandonment of all rights. You can't make something "PD for non-commercial use." If your work is PD, other people can even modify one byte and put their name on it.

"My posting was just fair use!"

See other notes on fair use for a detailed answer, but bear the following in mind: The "fair use" exemption to copyright law was created to allow things such as commentary, parody, news reporting, research and education about copyrighted works without the permission of the author. That's important so that copyright law doesn't block your freedom to express your own works -- only the ability to express other people's. Intent, and damage to the commercial value of the work are important considerations. Are you reproducing an article from the New York Times because you needed to in order to criticize the quality of the New York Times, or because you couldn't find time to write your own story, or didn't want your readers to have to pay for the New York Times web site? The first is probably fair use, the others probably aren't.

Fair use is almost always a short excerpt and almost always attributed. (One should not use more of the work than is necessary to make the commentary.) It should not harm the commercial value of the work -- in the sense of people no longer needing to buy it (which is another reason why reproduction of the entire work is generally forbidden.)

Note that most inclusion of text in Usenet follow-ups is for commentary and reply, and it doesn't damage the commercial value of the original posting (if it has any) and as such it is fair use. Fair use isn't an exact doctrine, either. The court decides if the right to comment overrides the copyright on an individual basis in each case. There have been cases that go beyond the bounds of what I say above, but in general they don't apply to the typical net misclaim of fair use. It's a risky defense to attempt. Facts and ideas can't be copyrighted, but their expression and structure can. You can always write the facts in your own words.

"If you don't defend your copyright you lose it." -- "Somebody has that name copyrighted!"

False. Copyright is effectively never lost these days, unless explicitly given away. You also can't "copyright a name" or anything short like that, such as almost all titles. You may be thinking of trademarks, which apply to names, and can be weakened or lost if not defended. You generally trademark terms by using them to refer to your brand of a generic type of product or service. Like an "Apple" computer. Apple Computer "owns" that word applied to computers, even though it is also an ordinary word. Apple Records owns it when applied to music. Neither owns the word on its own, only in context, and owning a mark doesn't mean complete control -- see a more detailed treatise on this law for details. You can't use somebody else's trademark in a way that would unfairly hurt the value of the mark, or in a way that might make people confuse you with the real owner of the mark, or which might allow you to profit from the mark's good name. For example, if I were giving advice on music videos, I would be very wary of trying to label my works with a name like "MTV"

"If I make up my own stories, but base them on another work, my new work belongs to me."

False. Copyright law is quite explicit that the making of what are called "derivative works" -- works based or derived from another copyrighted work -- is the exclusive province of the owner of the original work. This is true even though the making of these new works is a highly creative process. If you write a story using settings or characters from somebody else's work, you need that author's permission.

Yes, that means almost all "fan fiction" is a copyright violation. If you want to write a story about Jim Kirk and Mr. Spock, you need Paramount's permission, plain and simple. Now, as it turns out, many, but not all holders of popular copyrights turn a blind eye to "fan fiction" or even subtly encourage it because it helps them. Make no mistake, however, that it is entirely up to them whether to do that. There is one major exception -- parody. The fair use provision says that if you want to make fun of something like Star Trek, you don't need their permission to include Mr. Spock. This is not a loophole; you can't just take a non-parody and claim it is one on a technicality. The way "fair use" works is you get sued for copyright infringement, and you admit you did infringe, but that your infringement was a fair use. A subjective judgment is then made.

"They can't get me, defendants in court have powerful rights!"

Copyright law is mostly civil law. If you violate copyright you would usually get sued, not charged with a crime. "Innocent until proven guilty" is a principle of criminal law, as is "proof beyond a reasonable doubt." Sorry, but in copyright suits, these don't apply the same way or at all. It's mostly which side and set of evidence the judge or jury accepts or believes more, though the rules vary based on the type of infringement. In civil cases you can even be made to testify against your own interests.

"Oh, so copyright violation isn't a crime or anything?"

Actually, recently in the USA commercial copyright violation involving more than 10 copies and value over $2500 was made a felony. So watch out. (At least you get the protections of criminal law.) On the other hand, don't think you're going to get people thrown in jail for posting your E-mail. The courts have much better things to do than that. This is a fairly new, untested statute.

"It doesn't hurt anybody -- in fact it's free advertising."

It's up to the owner to decide if they want the free ads or not. If they want them, they will be sure to contact you. Don't rationalize whether it hurts the owner or not, ask them. Usually that's not too hard to do. Time past, ClariNet published the very funny Dave Barry column to a large and appreciative Usenet audience for a fee, but some person didn't ask, and forwarded it to a mailing list, got caught, and the newspaper chain that employs Dave Barry pulled the column from the net, pissing off everybody who enjoyed it. Even if you can't think of how the author or owner gets hurt, think about the fact that piracy on the net hurts everybody who wants a chance to use this wonderful new technology to do more than read other people's flamewars.

"They e-mailed me a copy, so I can post it."

To have a copy is not to have the copyright. All the E-mail you write is copyrighted. However, E-mail is not, unless previously agreed, secret. So you can certainly report on what E-mail you are sent, and reveal what it says. You can even quote parts of it to demonstrate. Frankly, somebody who sues over an ordinary message would almost surely get no damages, because the message has no commercial value, but if you want to stay strictly in the law, you should ask first. On the other hand, don't go nuts if somebody posts E-mail you sent them. If it was an ordinary non-secret personal letter of minimal commercial value with no copyright notice (like 99.9% of all E-mail), you probably won't get any damages if you sue them. Note as well that, the law aside, keeping private correspondence private is a courtesy one should usually honor.

"So I can't ever reproduce anything?"

Myth #11 (I didn't want to change the now-famous title of this article) is actually one sometimes generated in response to this list of 10 myths. No, copyright isn't an iron-clad lock on what can be published. Indeed by many arguments, by providing reward to authors, it encourages them to not just allow, but fund the publication and distribution of works so that they reach far more people than they would if they were free or unprotected -- and unpromoted. However, it must be remembered that copyright has two main purposes, namely the protection of the author's right to obtain commercial benefit from valuable work, and more recently the protection of the author's general right to control how a work is used. While copyright law makes it technically illegal to reproduce almost any new creative work (other than under fair use) without permission, if the work is unregistered and has no real commercial value, it gets very little protection. The author in this case can sue for an injunction against the publication, actual damages from a violation, and possibly court costs. Actual damages means actual money potentially lost by the author due to publication, plus any money gained by the defendant. But if a work has no commercial value, such as a typical E-mail message or conversational USENET posting, the actual damages will be zero. Only the most vindictive (and rich) author would sue when no damages are possible, and the courts don't look kindly on vindictive plaintiffs, unless the defendants are even more vindictive. The author's right to control what is done with a work, however, has some validity, even if it has no commercial value. If you feel you need to violate a copyright "because you can get away with it because the work has no value" you should ask yourself why you're doing it. In general respecting the rights of creators to control their creations is a principle many advocate adhering to. In addition, while more often than not people claim a "fair use" copying incorrectly, fair use is a valid concept necessary to allow the criticism of copyrighted works and their creators through examples. But read more about it before you do it.

111. What is a good summation of copyright protection?

Almost all things are copyrighted the moment they are written, and no copyright notice is required.

Copyright is still violated whether you charged money or not, only damages are affected by that.

Postings to the net are not granted to the public domain, and don't grant you any permission to do further copying except perhaps the sort of copying the poster might have expected in the ordinary flow of the net.

Fair use is a complex doctrine meant to allow certain valuable social purposes. Ask yourself why you are republishing what you are posting and why you couldn't have just rewritten it in your own words.

Copyright is not lost because you don't defend it; that's a concept from trademark law. The ownership of names is also from trademark law, so don't say somebody has a name copyrighted.

Fan fiction and other work derived from copyrighted works is a copyright violation.

Copyright law is mostly civil law where the special rights of criminal defendants you hear so much about don't apply. Watch out, however, as new laws are moving copyright violation into the criminal realm.

Don't rationalize that you are helping the copyright holder; often it's not that hard to ask permission.

Posting E-mail is technically a violation, but revealing facts from E-mail you got isn't, and for almost all typical E-mail, nobody could wring any damages from you for posting it. The law doesn't do much to protect works with no commercial value.

Might it be a violation just to link to a web page? That's not a myth, it's undecided, but there is some discussion of linking rights issues.

WEB LAW

1. When am I violating copyright on the Internet?

The Internet, inarguably one of the most remarkable developments in international communication and information access, is fast becoming a lair of copyright abuse. The notion of freedom of information and the ease of posting, copying and distributing messages on the Internet may have created a false impression that text and graphic materials on World Wide Web sites, postings in "usenet" news groups, and messages distributed through e-mail lists and other electronic channels are exempt from copyright statutes.

In the United States, copyright is a protection provided under title 17 of the U.S. Code, articulated in the 1976 Copyright Act. Copyright of a creative work extends 50 years beyond the lifespan of its author or designer. Works afforded copyright protection include literature, journalistic reports, musical compositions, theatrical scripts, choreography, artistic matter, architectural designs, motion pictures, computer software, multimedia digital creations, and audio and video recordings. Copyright protection encompasses Web page textual content, graphics, design elements, as well as postings on discussion groups. Canada's Intellectual and Industrial Property Law, Great Britain's Copyright, Designs and Patents Act of 1988, and legislation in other countries signatory to the international Berne Convention copyright principles provide similar protections.

Generally speaking, facts may not be copyrighted; but content related to presentation, organization and conclusions derived from facts certainly can be. Never assume that anything is in the "public domain" without a statement to that effect. Here are some copyright issues important to companies, organizations and individuals. - LINKS: Even though links are addresses and are not subject to copyright regulations, problems can arise in their presentation. If your Web site is composed using frames, and linked sites appear as a window within your frame set, you may be creating the deceptive impression that the content of the linked site is yours. Use HTML coding to ensure that linked external sites appear in their own window, clearly distinct from your site. Incidentally, you may wish to disavow responsibility for the content of sites to which you provide links.

Work for hire: While copyright ordinarily belongs to the author, copyright ownership of works for hire belong to the employer. The U.S. Copyright Act of 1976 provides two definitions of a work for hire: 1. a work prepared by an employee within the scope of his or her employment; or 2. a work specially ordered or commissioned for use as a contribution to a collective work, as a part of a motion picture or other audiovisual work, as a translation, as a supplementary work, as a compilation, as an instructional text, as a test, as answer material for a test, or as an atlas, if the parties expressly agree in a written instrument signed by them that the work shall be considered a work made for hire. U.S. Copyright Office documentation further states, "Copyright in each separate contribution to a periodical or other collective work is distinct from copyright in the collective work as a whole and vests initially with the author of the contribution."

Employee activities: Just as making bootleg tapes of recorded music and photocopying books are illegal activities, printing and distributing contents of Web pages or discussion group postings may constitute copyright infringement. And companies may be liable for such activities conducted by their employees using company computing or photocopying equipment. However, the law does not necessarily prohibit downloading files or excerpting and quoting materials. The doctrine of fair use preserves your right to reproduce works or portions of works for certain purposes, notably education, analysis and criticism, parody, research and journalistic reporting. The amount of the work excerpted and the implications of your use on the marketability or value of the works are considerations in determining fair use. Works that are not fixed in a tangible form, such as extemporaneous speeches, do not qualify for copyright protection. Titles of works, and improvisational musical or choreographic compositions that have not been annotated, likewise cannot be copyrighted. Names of musical groups, slogans and short phrases may gain protection as trademarks when registered through the U.S. Patent & Trademark Office.

Protecting your own works. Although copyright automatically applies to any creative work you produce, you can strengthen your legal copyright protection by registering works with the U.S. Copyright Office. Doing so establishes an official record of your copyright, and must be done before filing an infringement civil lawsuit in Federal district court. Registration costs $20. For information, visit the Copyright Office Web site at <http:// www.loc.gov/copyright> or call (202) 707-3000; TTY is (202) 707 6737. If you appoint an independent Web developer to create and maintain your Web site, make sure through written agreement that you retain the copyright to your Web content. Place a copyright notice on each of your Web pages and other published materials. Spell out the word "Copyright" or use the encircled "c" symbol, along with the year of publication and your name, as shown in this example: Copyright 1998 EditPros marketing communications If you're concerned about copyright protection in other nations, add: "All rights reserved." Along with your copyright notice, include an acceptable use policy, announcing to your readers how they may use the material. You may allow Web visitors, for example, to download and print pages for their own use, but may prohibit them from distributing those materials to others without your permission. You may wish to decline permission to download graphics or sound files that you created.

How to stay legal. If you'd like to share the contents of an interesting Web page with your company employees, describe the page and tell them the URL address of the Web site so they can look for themselves. And if the latest edition of a business newspaper contains an article you'd like to distribute to your 12 board members, either ask the publication for permission to make copies, or buy a dozen copies of the newspaper. Retention of value through sales of that newspaper, after all, is what copyright law is intended to protect.

2. May I freely copy, print, and email things I find on the Web?

The Internet is the sort of place where it is extraordinarily easy to copy things, although it must not be forgotten that ease of copying did not start with the Internet. The cassette recorder made it easy to copy record albums. The photocopier made it easy to copy printed works. The videocassette recorder made it easy to copy movies. Floppy disks made it easy to copy computer software. In any of these media, the fact that something is physically easy to copy something does not mean that it is legal to copy it, or morally acceptable to copy it.

Absence of a copyright notice does not mean it is okay to copy something. Under U.S. copyright law, for example, any original work fixed in a tangible medium is automatically protected by copyright regardless of whether any copyright formalities are done. Under the Berne Convention the absence of a copyright notice does not mean that a work is not protected by copyright.

Clearly one way to solve the problem is the simple step of obtaining the permission of the copyright owner. Yet another way is to confine one's copying to items that are in the public domain, for example because they were created hundreds of years ago.

Obtaining permission is a more difficult task than one might think. Suppose you see a web site that contains something you wish to copy, and suppose you obtain permission from the webmaster of that site to copy it. Does this mean you may post it on your web site without fear of liability? The answer is no, unless it happens that the webmaster is in fact the owner of all rights in the work you wish to copy. Can you be sure the work was not copied (in an unauthorized manner) from someplace else?

If not, then permission from the webmaster does not put you in the clear. The legal system does, however, permit some kinds of copying if it is done without the permission of the copyright owner. Under U.S. law, for example, even if the copyright owner has not given permission, it is still okay to copy something so long as the copying falls within what is called "fair use". Regrettably for those who are eager to copy things, it is not easy to say for sure what is or is not fair use. Legal factors that are taken into account include: the portion of a work being copied (copying a small portion is more likely to be fair use than copying a large portion); the effect of the copying on the market for the item being copied (if the copying activity makes people less likely to buy the item, then the copying is unlikely to be fair use); and the use to which the copied matter is put (quoting for use in literary criticism or for educational purposes is more likely to be fair use than some other uses).

If you see something on the Web and are tempted to copy it, why not just put in a link to it?

For example, Internic has a policy according to which domain names are registered, and the policies are posted on Internic's web site. If I am tempted to copy the policy into my web site, why not just put in a link to the place where the policy may be found?

It is clear that the law will evolve in this area. Perhaps after some years of experience with the Web, courts will decide some cases that will provide guidance as to what is fair use and what is not. No discussion of copyright and the Web would be complete without at least a mention of the notion of "implied license". For example, when I use my web browser to view a site, I am necessarily copying information from that site to the screen of my computer. Many web browsers have "cache" capabilities, in which case I am also necessarily copying the information into the cache as well. Most browsers have the capability to print what is on the screen, so if I print it I am automatically making a copy of it on paper.

As years go on the courts will develop the notion of implied license in connection with the Web, but it is clear that there is some sort of implied license that is automatically granted by anyone who sets up a web site and makes it open to the public. The implied license surely includes those things we think of as "normal" web activity -- viewing web pages, clicking on links, seeing the web text on the computer screen. What must not be forgotten, though, is that such an implied license is by no means a grant that permits members of the public to do whatever they may please with the material found on a web site. To draw analogies, the person who publishes a book is not granting to the public the right (via implied license) to photocopy the entirety of the book and to sell the copies. The musician who releases a compact disk is not granting an implied license to set up a facility for copying the CD's and selling the copies.

Common sense suggests that if a webmaster has placed a Copyright notice so that visitors to a web site see it, then the webmaster probably is trying to communicate to the public that the contents of the site are not to be freely copied in all ways. Of course, as mentioned above, the absence of a copyright notice does not mean a site is not protected by copyright. As will be appreciated from the above discussion it is impossible, of course, to answer the "may I copy this?" question in general. If you care about copying some particular item you should consult competent counsel for advice.

May I scan any image I wish and post it on my Web site? The short answer is "no".
While it is physically and technically easy to scan images out of books and magazines, and to place computer-readable (GIF and JPG) copies in one's web site, the fact that it is physically and technically easy does not make it legal or moral. See the discussion above regarding copying works of others into one's web site.

The safest course of action is to obtain permission from the copyright owner before posting a scanned image into your web site. Suppose you take a photograph yourself -- can you freely scan it and put it on your web site? Even this sort of photograph can cause trouble. If it is a photograph of someone else, it is safest if you obtain a "model release" from that person releasing you from liability for use of the photograph. From the above discussion it should be clear that if you really care about this you should seek advice of competent counsel.

3. May I use images from the Web sites of others?

Before the Web came along, the only way a publisher could make use of images from others was by physically copying the images into the work being published. The above discussions regarding the copying of text or images address such copying. But the Web allows a new and quite interesting way of using the images of others, namely the "IMG" hypertext reference. It is physically and technically easy to include an IMG reference in your web site, giving a URL (address) located on somebody else's web site.

The use of an IMG reference to somebody else's web site is intriguing. Suppose your web site is on a machine in which you are charged "per megabyte" for its use by visitors. Then when a visitor to your web site views one of your pages, and if the image on your page is an IMG reference pointing to somebody else's web site, the visitor's browser will obtain the image from that web site. It won't run up your bill.

Or suppose your web site is on a machine that has only a slow (narrow bandwidth) link to the Internet. Then if a visitor to your web site views a page of yours that contains an IMG reference to some other web site, the visitor's retrieval of the image won't slow down your link. It will slow down the link of that other web site instead.

There are practical reasons why you might not wish to use IMG links to images on the web sites of others. The image might be changed without your knowing it, leading to an unpredictable result for visitors to your web site. The image might be deleted from its web site, leaving a gaping hole in your web page.

But in addition to practical reasons why you might not wish to use IMG links to the web sites of others, there are legal reasons, and that is the purpose of this discussion. Consider one case that really happened. A fellow noticed that two of his favorite cartoon comic strips were posted daily on a web site hosted by the distributor of the strips. He looked closely at the distributor's web page and determined the IMG URL addresses containing the actual strips. He then made up his own web page saying something like "here are my two favorite comic strips" in a header, followed by the two IMG references. A visitor to his web page would see the header and the two strips.

The next thing that happened was, of course, that lawyers got into the picture. This fellow got a letter saying that he was violating the distributor's copyrights by his placement of the comic strips onto his page. He posted an article in a usenet group asking for comments about the letter.

One commenter said that the distributor's conduct in making its strips available as image files on the Internet amounted to placing them in the public domain, so that anybody who wished could do anything they please with the images. Common sense suggests that this cannot be so; the publisher of a book, in a world in which there are photocopiers, is not giving permission to the world to make copies of the book.

One commenter pointed out that it is technologically possible to reduce unauthorized IMG references, for example by programming the server so that it will provide the requested image file only if the previously accessed page was the distributor's page that might normally contain the image.

Such an approach has several drawbacks, chief among them that it only works if the browsing client being used by the visitor happens to provide what is called a "referrer" header; not all do this. Another drawback of this approach is that it makes every image request take longer. The way this particular story ended was that the fellow chose to delete the IMG references entirely, and to use instead more commonplace HREF references so that a visitor to his site could click on the HREF references and reach the distributor's web pages. As a result, we will never know what would have happened if the case had been decided in court.

Clearly the safest course is to avoid the use of IMG references except in the special case where permission has been obtained from the owner of the site having the image file.

4. May I freely link to the Web sites of others?

This is a question that has led to heated discussion in various Internet discussion groups in recent months. As will become clear, however, most of the disputes turn out to be semantic; once the definitions of certain terms are agreed upon most of the disputes disappear. The question seems easy enough to state: is there any legal or ethical impediment to setting up a link to someone else's web site?

A first difficulty comes if one succumbs to the temptation to rephrase the question as "is a URL copyrightable?" The person who phrases the question this way triumphantly states that the answer is "no" and thus that anyone who wishes may place any URL into any web site without having to answer to anyone else. A URL is rather like a telephone number or a street address. Arguably it is no more protectable by copyright than a telephone number, due to its primarily functional quality. So indeed the answer to the question "is a URL copyrightable?" is "no". But the world is filled with legal constraints on behavior in addition to those that come from the copyright laws. If you post a sign saying "call this telephone number to reach a chronic liar", then unless the person at that telephone number is indeed a chronic liar, you will be subject to legal liability for libel. And it will be no defense at all that the telephone number was uncopyrightable.

Having discerned that the question "is a URL copyrightable?" is irrelevant, how can we arrive at an answer to the original question? An important step is to figure out what kind of link we are talking about. The previous section discusses a somewhat esoteric kind of link, the so-called IMG link. For the reasons discussed in that section, it seems prudent never to make an IMG link to someone's web site without getting permission first.

But the fact is that if you were to study several hundreds web sites, you would find that the links from one web site to another are virtually all so-called HREF links, and that virtually none of them are IMG links. An HREF link is the kind we are all accustomed to. It is a region on the screen which, when selected by the visitor, causes the present screen to be erased and causes an entirely new screen to be loaded. The words "previous section" in the previous paragraph are an HREF link -- they cause the screen to be loaded anew with the text of the previous section.

So now for clarity let us redefine the question as "may I freely set up HREF links in my web site, to the web sites of others?" As will be clear in a moment, the short answer to that question is "yes". (Except in the case of framing, discussed below.)

The general rule proposed and set forth here, that one may freely set up non-framed HREF links to the web sites of others, is a rather reassuring rule since it happens to comport well with common practice and with common sense. The designers of the World Wide Web intended that it would be precisely that -- a web. One of the hopes and goals of the designers was that after the passage of some years, a meaningful fraction of the sum total of human knowledge would be on the Web, and that it would be fully cross-linked. The idea was that while you might not find the answer to your question on the first web page you encountered, after a few rodent movements you would find the answer, as one web page led you to another, and another, eventually finding your answer.

Such a result -- a web of knowledge -- is only possible if people feel free to set up any and all HREF links that might come to mind. A person who steadfastly objects to any and all HREF links to his or her web site is missing the point of the World Wide Web. Having said this, it is important to acknowledge that the proposed rule cannot be taken as a justification for setting up all imaginable links. A few fact patterns will illustrate.

A couple of months after our firm opened this web site to the public, we happened upon a web site in Massachusetts that had a link to the place in our web site where the most recent article of our firm newsletter appeared. The Massachusetts web site explained that its purpose was to provide web capability to those who could not afford it. As an example, the site invited readers to look at our newsletter. The clear message was that our law firm could not afford its own web site, and that this

Massachusetts site was kindly providing a way for our firm newsletter to be seen by the public. We asked the site operator to delete any mention of anything in our web site, and he complied. Suppose someone was to set up a link to our web site, saying, "Click here to reach a web site of chronic liars". Assuming that our firm is not a bunch of chronic liars, then the link libels our firm. A court would not hesitate to order the party setting up the link to delete it. Suppose someone were to set up a link to our web site, saying "See how prolific we are? We wrote all this!" The result would be someone taking credit for the work of others; stating it differently, they would be passing off our work as theirs. In the US, this would probably give rise to liability under the Lanham Act.

Framing. More recently a change in the capabilities of commonly used browsers has given rise to a way in which HREF links can lead to disputes. The new capability is that of "frames". A web author can cause a page to be divided into "frames", each of which can receive an HTML-constructed window of information. On most web sites that use "frames", the web designer provides all the content in each of the frames. Typically a small frame to the left is used as a menu, and a large frame in the center and right of the screen contains the main body of text, all of which originates from the same web site.

The controversial sites using "frames" are the sites that place advertising or editorial content in small frames around the edge of the screen, and that set up the main frame, in the middle of the screen, to contain HTML text from some other web site. In one site that recently drew controversy, the main screen contained content from MSN and from other news sources, while a frame across the bottom contained a banner advertisement.

This sort of frame-linking can lead and has led to disputes. The content provider whose content is in a middle frame might find itself juxtaposed with advertisements for products or services which it opposes. A conservative content provider might find itself juxtaposed with a liberal advertisement, or vice versa. There is also the danger that a web visitor might be misled as to the origin of the content in the middle frame, thus possibly giving rise to a claim under the Lanham Act (part of the US federal trademark law). It might appear that the web operator is passing off someone else's content as their own. And in any event the web operator could be deriving advertising revenue from the effort of others.

This article suggests that one should do "frame" links to the web sites of others only after obtaining permission to do so.

But again let us try to keep reality in view. The vast majority of HREF links on the Web are not libelous and do not pass off one's work as another's. Most HREF links are quite clear to the visitor, who has no difficulty perceiving that by clicking on a colored line of text, she is going to a different web site. Such a user is also aware that by clicking the "back" button she can return whence she came. Most of these links give rise to no legal liability at all. Even if there is no legal requirement that the person setting up an HREF link (at least, a non-libelous, non-misleading, non-framed link) obtain permission from the owner of the site linked to, is there at least a moral requirement? Isn't it somehow "good form" to contact a webmaster to say that an HREF link is proposed or has been set up? To this the answer we offer is this: If you are quite confident that you are not doing anything wrong in setting up a non-framed HREF link, then you probably are not doing anything wrong. Millions of HREF links have been set up in the World Wide Web, and the sky has not fallen and common sense has prevailed. Nonetheless, if you have any misgiving or doubt about a particular link, then the ethical thing to do is to write to the webmaster and ask if there is any objection. This will give the webmaster an opportunity to view the page containing the link, and to consider whether there is any reason to object to it. A couple of additional examples may help to illustrate the common-sense aspects of this proposed rule.

Suppose that someone has set up a web site, and has not publicized it in any way. Suppose further that there is no choice but to make the site public, so as to permit testing of the site by means of visits from other countries. Then the person who stumbles on the URL for this site should, as a courtesy, ask if there is any reason not to link to the site. Setting up a link to the site might interfere with the testing, for example. One Internet discussion group about a year ago contained a posting from a fellow who operated a web site for a nonprofit organization relating to some particular educational needs. On his site, he had laboriously compiled federal laws relating to the subject of the web site; the laws were contained in a series of sub-pages. What prompted his posting was that another site (operated, if I recall correctly, by a competing non-profit organization) had set up HREF links to the sub-pages in such a way that this fellow's effort would go unrecognized. The inattentive visitor might not even notice having passed from one web site to the next.

This fellow wondered what his options were? Could he compel them to drop their links to his sub-pages?

It wasn't exactly traditional passing off. The site never exactly said they had compiled these laws, for example, but merely had a link to the laws as provided on these sub-pages. Quite a few participants in this Internet discussion group had no difficulty figuring out the right answer. This fellow should simply plaster the name of his non-profit organization all over the sub-pages. And at the end of each of his sub-pages, he should put in a link to his own main page. The result is that now the competing organization is directing its visitors to his own web site. Linking to something other than a home page. There are some webmasters who say that they don't want people linking to anything but their home page. Webmasters who say this might be motivated by any of several concerns:

1. The webmaster might want to be able to change around the internal structure of the web site at will, thus perhaps denying responsibility for the trouble that is caused to others when the change causes links to break.
2. The webmaster may feel strongly that a visitor to a sub-page ought to be forced to read the contents of the home page first.
3. The view suggested here is that a webmaster should be prepared for the possibility that members of the public may set up bookmarks to subpages, and that other HTML authors may set up links to subpages. Since this sort of bookmarking and linking can and will happen, the webmaster should be courteous to those visitors and HTML authors. The webmaster, upon moving a page, should have the courtesy to supply a "forwarding" page that lets the visitor know the new page URL. The webmaster should lay out each page with the expectation that bookmarks and links will be made to any and all possible locations within each page and sub-page. (On the Oppedahl & Larson site a copyright notice and disclaimer is provided on each page and sub-page for this reason, and each page and sub-page has a link that returns to the top of the page or to the home page, again for this reason.).

In general, of course, it is desirable for one's site to be the subject of links from other sites. Most people who create web sites hope that lots of people will visit, and links from other sites promote this goal.

5. Someone has set up a link to my Web site without my permission -- what can I do?

The first question would be, why do you care? Does the link cast you or your site or your organization in a bad light? Does it lead to a situation where someone else is taking credit for your work? For these or other reasons, as discussed in the previous section, you may have a legitimate gripe. Before you spend money on lawyers, though, it is suggested that you try resolving the problem by direct communication. Send an email or a paper letter explaining what you want done. Then if you must, consider retaining counsel, preferably counsel who are familiar with the Internet as well as with intellectual property.

If the link is an IMG (image) reference, consider changing the URL of your image, and put some nuisance image in the place of the original URL for the image. That should discourage people from using your image without your permission.

But generally unless there is some special reason to the contrary, you should be pleased if someone sets up a regular (non-framed HREF) link to your web site.

6. How may I keep people from taking things from my Web site?

There are a number of steps which the operator of a web site may take to attempt to minimize the extent to which others take things from it. The simplest is not to post on the web site. Another is to use the access controls built into the web server to limit the range of IP addresses that are permitted to enter the site. Still another is to set up password protection, so that only certain persons are permitted access to your site.

As will be appreciated, however, such suggestions would be of no help to most web site operators. Most web site operators want their web sites to be available and open to the world at large. Thus we can recommend some other steps that may dissuade others from taking things from you. These steps include: filing copyright registrations, placing copyright notices and related notices on your web site, obtaining trademark registrations, placing trademark notices on your web site, and seeking patent protection for whatever there may be in your web site that is patentable.

7. How do I obtain a domain name?

In general terms, you obtain a domain name by making application to a domain name registration authority. For example, to obtain a domain name that ends in .com or .org or .edu, you make application to Internic, whose designated representative is Network Solutions, Inc. Internic by no means handles all domain names, however; domain names that end with two-letter country codes are administered by other authorities.

Prior to making application to the registration authority, you must find someone who operates a domain name server (DNS), who will agree to provide domain name service for your domain name.

In addition, assuming you plan to use your domain name for email, you need to find someone who operates a mail exchanger (MX), who will agree to provide email service for your domain name.

Finally, assuming you plan to use your domain name for a web site, you need to find someone who offers an HTTP server, who will agree to provide equipment hosting your web site. Often it is convenient to purchase all three services from the same Internet service provider, but nothing about how the Internet works requires that you do so. At Oppedahl & Larson, for example, we use Panix for all three services.

Having obtained at least your DNS service and having tested it (see a description of this process in an article in the New York Law Journal) then you may submit an application to the registration authority. Once the domain name is granted to you, then you should make careful note of the due dates (if any) for payment of maintenance fees (see a discussion of this in another article in the New York Law Journal).

8. How do I protect myself from loss of my domain name?

The protective steps to take to keep from losing your domain name differ depending on which organization administers your domain name. If your domain name ends, for example, in .com or .org or .edu, then what matters to you are the policies of Internic, whose designated representative is Network Solutions, Inc. NSI has published various policies with which you must be familiar, and which are discussed in articles by Carl Oppedahl that have been published in the New York Law Journal. Another article that is a must-read was published in Network World. Among other things, it is wise to obtain a trademark registration for the domain name immediately if one has not already done so. You should check to be sure that your registration authority has correctly listed who owns your domain name (on rare occasions an unscrupulous internet service provider will list itself as the owner). You should also check the record to be sure it lists up-to-date postal, email, and telephone contact information for you. Finally, if your registration authority (e.g. Internic) charges maintenance fees, then you should make note of when your maintenance fees are due, and make inquiries if for some reason you do not receive reminders from your registration authority.

9. What is the correct format for a URL on a business card?

There seems to be three common styles for giving URLs:

257

1. http://www.patents.com/
2. URL: http://www.patents.com/ (note the space before the http://)
3. <URL: http://www.patents.com/ > (note space before http:// and after the trailing "/")

The last is kind of ugly and probably best left for email and other computer-readable forms of communication. Clearly, anybody who knows what "http:" means should have no trouble making sense of any of the three forms. The most important thing is to be sure that the printer doesn't insert spurious spaces, or make periods into commas, or the colon into a semicolon, or misprint / as a \.

Most people leave off the ending /, but it is good to provide it. Most widely-used web browsers are programmed to supply it (along with the "http://" if necessary) if omitted by the user. (Those who are printing business cards can be sloppy about leaving off the http:// or the / but those who are writing html text must be very careful about such things.)

If you want to label things on your business card (like "phone:" and "fax:" and "email:") then use "URL:" for the URL.

Note that an email address becomes a URL in this way: mailto:webmaster@patents.com.

10. What is the correct format for a URL when provided in computer-readable form, for example in an email or news posting?

The goal is to provide text which someone else's mail or news reader can easily parse into URLs to make it easy to click on the URL as a browser link. For this, the third form above is appropriate. Note the space before the closing ">" which is required. If you employ the first or second forms, keep in mind that the URL must have a space before it and a space after it. (A common blunder is to place the URL at the end of the sentence, contiguous with a period, thus tricking the reader's browser into including the period as part of the URL, which then guarantees that the browser will not reach the desired page.)

11. Don't those Web search engines violate the copyright laws?

An indispensable resource on the Web are the search engines such as Alta Vista, Lycos, Yahoo, and Infoseek. These engines search the World Wide Web, reading one web page after another and constructing concordances permitting later retrieval of the URLs of web sites containing words of interest. It has been suggested by some that this concordance construction, which necessarily involves copying information found in the web sites, might violate the copyright rights of the web site owners.

It is not possible, of course, to state as a general rule whether such sites engage in activity that gives rise to copyright liability, since each engine is programmed differently and the retrieved information is stored differently in each site. And in any event there have been no court decisions on this topic. But it is quite easy to imagine a court concluding that mere concordance extraction, without more, would be "fair use" or would fall within the implied license that any web site operator grants to its visitors.

12. Can other people copy my email or news postings?

Any original work which you fix in a tangible medium is protected by copyright. The copyright laws of most countries reserve to the copyright owner the exclusive right to make copies of such a work or to distribute it. Upon hearing this, the reader might wonder how usenet news groups (which involve copying one's writings to thousands of news servers around the world) could possibly be legal. The answer is that when one posts to a usenet group, one is giving permission to those who operate news servers to propagate the posting in the way that news servers propagate postings.

Similarly if one sends email to an email discussion group, one is giving permission to the computer that remails the items to remail the items. And of course one who posts material on a web site is impliedly giving visitors permission to view the site on their web browsers.

It would be a mistake, however, for someone to think that because it is easy to copy things from the Internet, it is always legal to do so. Similarly it would be a mistake to assume that because a person who posted news or opened a web site granted permission to the public to do certain things, that the permission extends to all kinds of copying. This writer has heard of CD-ROMs being offered for sale that contain the entirety of the news postings in particular usenet groups, and it is difficult to see how this could be legal in the absence of permission from those who published the articles.

13. What are the basics of copyright?

Copyright is a legal device that provides the creator of a work of art or literature, or a work that conveys information or ideas, the right to control how the work is used. The Copyright Act of 1976--the federal law providing for copyright protection--grants authors a bundle of intangible, exclusive rights over their works, including the right to reproduce, distribute, adapt or perform those works.

An author's copyright rights may be exercised only by the author--or by a person or entity to whom the author has transferred all or part of her rights. If someone wrongfully uses the material covered by a copyright, the copyright owner can sue and obtain compensation for any losses suffered.

14. Why bother with registering software copyrighting?

If you publish computer software, the single most important legal protection available to you is the federal copyright law. But many software authors don't take advantage of its protections, and risk finding themselves virtually at the mercy of infringers--all because they don't send in a simple registration form as soon as the software is published.

15. How are copyrights enforced? Is going to court necessary?

In the event someone violates (infringes) the exclusive rights of a copyright owner, the owner is entitled to file a lawsuit in federal court asking the court to:
1. issue orders (restraining orders and injunctions) to prevent further violations;
2. award money damages if appropriate; and
3. in some circumstances, award attorney fees.

Whether the lawsuit will be effective and whether damages will be awarded depends on whether the alleged infringer can raise one or more legal defenses to the charge. Common legal defenses to copyright infringement are:
1. too much time has elapsed between the infringing act and the lawsuit (the statute of limitations defense);
2. the infringement is allowed under the fair use doctrine ;
3. the infringement was innocent (the infringer had no reason to know the work was protected by copyright);
4. the infringing work was independently created (that is, it wasn't copied from the original); or
5. the copyright owner authorized the use in a license.

MARKS

1. What is protectable under trademark law?

A trademark is anything that indicates source, sponsorship, affiliation, or other relation of a product or service to a business. The specific identity of the business does not need to be known.

2. How long does a trademark or service mark last?

Trademark protection lasts as long as the trade dress or trademark indicates source. This generally means that the protection lasts as long as the trademark or trade dress is being used with some exceptions. Registrations require renewal.

3. What type of competition does trademark law prohibit?

Trademark law prevents consumer confusion as to the source of products or services. (i.e., good will). There is a second minor trend that trademarks are like property and diminishment of value is basis for an infringement action.

4. What is the geographic scope of protection of a trademark?

Common law trademarks, i.e., unregistered, exist in the area in which the mark is being used or is known. State registrations exist throughout the state. Federal registrations exist throughout the country. First in time is first in right. Thus, two or more users may all have the same rights in different locations if the first user did not promptly obtain a federal registration.

5. How important is federal trademark registration?

Federal registration is a must to avoid future expansion problems due to geographic scope issues.

6. What is a trademark?

A trademark is anything that indicates source, sponsorship, affiliation or other business relationship of the goods or services. Start with the notion that an indicator must be perceived through one of the five senses. This includes taste, touch, smell, sight and sound. Some senses lend themselves to interaction with trademarks better than others, but all are capable of doing so. Currently, the following have been registered as trademarks:

Sight - Single words, word strings, slogans, logos, letters (e.g. initials), numbers, drawings/pictures, devices, product configurations, single colors, and multiple colors

Sound - Chimes, many of the items listed under sight are also spoken

Smell - Fragrance

Taste - None known to the authors of this material

Touch - Product configurations

The types of indicators that can function and be protected as trademarks are very much in development. The true test is whether "it" is capable of indicating a single source, sponsorship, affiliation or other business relationship, regardless of whether or not the exact entity(ies) is(are) known.

7. What is the difference between a trademark and a service mark?

Trademarks and service marks are distinct in whether the mark is used with goods or services. The manner of fixing the mark is of significance in seeking a federal registration. There is some difference on how the mark is associated with the goods or services. Goods commonly have labels, where services have no place to put a label. For nearly all other practical purposes trademarks and service marks are treated the same.

8. What are common law, state registered, and federally registered trademarks?

A common law trademark is a trademark that has not been registered with the state or the federal government. Common law rights arise upon use or recognition. Such trademarks are at a distinct disadvantage. See question: "What is the geographic scope of protection of a trademark?"

A state registered trademark is a trademark that has been registered at the state level.

A federally registered trademark has been registered with the federal government. To obtain a federal registration the applicant must use or intend to use the trademark in interstate commerce.

9. Why should I federally register my trademark?

A business can have its expansion efforts limited if it fails to obtain a federal registration. See Question "What is the geographic scope of protection of a trademark?" on the About TM's page. A federal registration provides prima facia (i.e. rebuttable) evidence of exclusive rights in the mark. After five years of registration the rights become incontestable (i.e. non-rebuttable), eliminating nearly every defense to trademark infringement. This aspect can save tens of thousands of dollars if litigation is ever needed and may help the avoidance of litigation all together.

Infringing goods and services may be impounded by the U.S. Customs with a federal registration. A federal registration provides constructive notice of the holder's trademark rights, allows one to proceed in federal court (if necessary), and provides for special statutory remedies.

These benefits are obtained for the nominal cost of obtaining and maintaining federal trademark registrations.

10. How do trademark rights protect the owner?

Trademark infringement occurs when another uses a confusingly similar trademark. An infringer is trying to reap benefits from or shed responsibility for their actions on the trademark holder. Thus, the trademark laws protect the owner from diversion of sales or market-place responsibility as a result of a competitor's bad acts.

11. How do trademark rights protect the public?

Trademarks indicate source, sponsorship, affiliation or other business relationship, and are used to prevent consumer confusion. As a result the public uses trademarks so they know who made the product or who stands behind the service. Trademarks are in essence the proper name, much like your given and surnames, and are used to know exactly who is providing this product to the customer. The benefits flowing to the customer include consistency of quality and character so that the customer does not need to open the packaging on each product to know the quality of what is inside.

12. What is the importance of a trademark as a commercial asset?

A trademark is much like a proper name, just like your proper name includes your given and surnames. It is the identifier of the product or service in that it separates the associated goods and services from all other competing goods and services, just as your name distinguishes you from other people. When considering the importance, try to find a single advertisement anywhere that does not include at least one trademark on the advertising.

Consider the confusion that would be present if people did not have given and surnames. We would only be able to refer to each other as "hey you." This would hardly be helpful when you want to know where the person can be found. "Where is hey you?" Consider how you would tell someone which brand to purchase or give a referral without using a trademark. Trademarks are critically important assets and should be protected as such.

13. Can a business be prevented from expanding if it does not obtain a federal registration?

Yes. A company cannot use its trademark outside the area of geographical protection if another already has the rights outside that area. See Question "What is the geographic scope of protection of a trademark?"

14. What is federal trademark infringement?

Trademark infringement occurs when a new comer or junior user adopts a trademark that is likely to be confused with the senior user's trademark. To determine whether a likelihood of confusion exists, courts consider factors such as: Strength of the mark, similarity between the marks, proximity of the goods in the marketplace, actual confusion, intent of the junior user, relatedness of the goods, degree of care exercised by the customer and other such factors. The key is whether there is a likelihood of confusion. Fifteen percent (15%) confusion is typically considered too much confusion.

15. Why should I conduct a trademark search?

A trademark search seeks to determine if there is a conflict with another's trademark. The search is performed without taking any unnecessary action that may place any prior trademark owner on notice of an infringement problem. A search also helps avoid filing a trademark application that will not issue. Whether to conduct a trademark search is a business decision that should be based on the uniqueness of the trademark and whether the trademark will actually be in use within nine months of filing the application.

A search of the federal trademark records can be conducted relatively quickly. A more extensive search of federal, state and common law trademarks can be conducted in days. Please note, however, that no trademark search can be totally complete.

16. Why should I involve an attorney?

Anyone who did not know all the answers to the commonly asked questions found in this homepage needs those answers and likely the answers to the less commonly asked questions. It is worth some expense in hiring a professional so that the questions that should be investigated and answered are properly handled.

A poorly prepared trademark application will cost a minimum of $245.00 in a second filing fee and potentially the trademark rights may also be lost. Paying an attorney not only saves a hassle, but may well save more than the immediate financial cost of paying the government fee a second time.

While extensive knowledge is available at your fingertips on the internet, the experience necessary to decipher, understand and apply such knowledge is not. Law school and apprenticeship type training is often easier to purchase than to undergo. These are serious matters that are based upon complex legal issues. An understanding of the material can be obtained quickly, but competent working knowledge takes years of experience.

17. What is the strength of different marks?

The strength of a trademark is its ability to distinguish the goods or services of one from the goods or services of another. Generic marks have no strength as trademarks. The strength of all other trademarks is a function of the uniqueness of the mark compared to the goods or service coupled with the level of consumer recognition of the trademark.

18. What is acquired distinctiveness or secondary meaning?

Acquired distinctiveness and secondary meaning are different terms for the same thing. To be treated as a trademark a mark must have a certain quantum of distinctiveness. That distinctiveness can be inherent in the mark, i.e. inherent distinctiveness, or be developed in the minds of the consumers, i.e. acquired distinctiveness. Acquired distinctiveness may be thought of as consumer recognition of the trademark as an identifier of source, sponsorship, affiliation or other business relationship.

19. Do trademarks need acquired distinctiveness before a registration may be sought?

No. Trademarks do not even have to be used before a trademark registration may be sought. See Question "Do I have to be using the trademark before seeking a registration?" on the Application Procedure page.

To be registered on the principal register all trademarks must have a certain quantum of distinctiveness. Marks that are neither generic nor descriptive of the goods or services are said to have enough "inherent distinctiveness" to be registered without proof of "acquired distinctiveness".

Descriptive and special case trademarks can be registered on the supplemental register without proof of acquired distinctiveness, although the rights offered are nominal. Descriptive and special case trademarks can be registered on the principal register upon proof of acquired distinctiveness (which is presumed after the trademark has been on the supplemental register for five years).

20. What marks need to have acquired distinctiveness before they are considered trademarks?

The following marks need proof of acquired distinctiveness before they are considered trademarks: 1) marks that describe the goods or services, 2) foreign terms that translated are descriptive in nature, 3) single colors, 4) surnames, 5) misspellings of descriptive terms, 6) product configurations (usually) and 7) geographically descriptive marks.

21. How can acquired distinctiveness be proven?

Acquired distinctiveness can be proven either directly or indirectly by any evidence that would be admissible in court.

22. How can trademark rights be lost?

The common methods for losing trademark rights are: stopping use of the trademark, allowing the trademark to become generic, failing to prosecute infringements, improper licensing of the rights, improper assignment of the rights, and/or too significant of a change in quality or character of the goods or services.

23. Can I take steps to avoid abandoning my trademark rights?

Most methods by which a trademark can be abandoned are easy to avoid. The attorney involved in preparing and filing the trademark application should provide the applicant with simple to follow guidelines. Such information is available upon request and is provided to all of Angenehm's clients without a request.

24. How can I avoid abandoning the trademark through an assignment or license agreement?

Licenses and assignments should always be done by an attorney that routinely practices in trademark law. Attorney's that do not typically practice in trademark law need to be extra careful to avoid the pitfalls that can lead to malpractice. Be extremely careful when incorporating an existing unincorporated business.

25. Can trademark rights be recovered once lost?

Yes. Each situation is so unique that a single answer as to how the rights may be recovered is not possible here. Specific legal advice should be sought in such situations.

26. Do I have to be using the trademark before seeking a registration?

In most states you do need to be using the trademark before applying for a registration. The federal system includes two types of trademark registrations when considered based upon use. One where use is required and one where the applicant intends to use the trademark.

27. What are the types of federal trademark applications?

The Intent-to-Use application may be filed if the applicant has a bonafide intent to use the trademark. Intent-to-Use applications need to be converted to a standard registration within a certain time period or the intended trademark will be considered abandoned.

The federal system also provides for filing a standard application based upon actual use.

28. What is the procedure for a federal Intent-to-Use application?

An Intent-to-Use Application begins with a conflict check by a competent patent attorney or patent agent. Once it's determined that there is no conflict with existing trademarks, an application is prepared and filed with the US Patent Office.

In about 6-9 months the federal government will issue either an office action or a Notice of Publication. An office action records the examiner's objections to or rejections of the application on various legal grounds.

An amendment or response is usually prepared if an office action issues. Such documents seek to overcome the objections/rejections issued by the government. The "office action and response/amendment process" may occur a couple of times. If successful, a Notice of Publication will issue and the mark will be published for opposition. Anyone who believes they may be harmed by registration of the trademark may oppose the registration. A Notice of Allowance will issue if nobody opposes registration of the trademark. If the amendments/responses are not successful, the application is abandoned.

At any time throughout this process an affidavit alleging use may be filed to change the application into a standard application. Additional charges apply if the affidavit is not filed prior to the issuance of the Notice of Allowance.

Affidavits supporting the applicant's intention to use the trademark need to be filed at regular intervals if use has not been alleged prior to issuance of the Notice of Allowance. Failure to file sufficient affidavits or expiration of 36 months (prior to filing the statement alleging use) results in abandonment of the application.

Once the statement alleging use is filed the application is converted into a standard application.

29. What is the procedure for prosecuting a standard federal application?

A Federal Trademark Application begins with a conflict check by a competent patent attorney or patent agent. Once it's determined that there is no conflict with existing trademarks, an application is prepared and filed with the US Patent Office.

In about 6-9 months the federal government will issue either an office action or a Notice of Publication. An office action records the examiner's objections to or rejections of the application on various legal grounds.

An amendment or response is usually prepared if an office action issues. Such documents seek to overcome the objections/rejections issued by the government. The "office action and response/amendment" process may occur a couple of times. If successful, a Notice of Publication will issue and the mark will be published for opposition. Anyone who believes they may be harmed by registration of the trademark may oppose the registration. A Notice of Allowance will issue if nobody opposes registration of the trademark. If the amendments/responses are not successful, the application is abandoned.

A certificate of registration issues if nobody opposes registration of the trademark. Between the fifth and sixth years the applicant must submit an affidavit or declaration of continued use. A trademark registration lasts indefinitely with the continued filing of an affidavit with the statutory fee on each tenth anniversary thereafter.

30. What are trademarks and service marks?

A trademark is a distinctive word, phrase, logo or other graphic symbol that's used to distinguish a manufacturer's or merchant's products from anyone else's. Some examples: Ford cars and trucks, Kellogg's cornflakes, IBM computers, Microsoft software. In the trademark context, "distinctive" means unique enough to reasonably serve as an identifier of a product in the marketplace.

For all practical purposes, a service mark is the same as a trademark--except that trademarks promote products while service marks promote services. Some familiar service marks: McDonald's (fast food service), Kinko's (photocopying service), ACLU (legal service), Blockbusters (video rental service), CBS's stylized eye in a circle (television network service), the Olympic Games' multi-colored interlocking circles (international sporting event).

A trademark or service mark can be more than just a brand name or logo. It can also be a shape, letters, numbers, a sound, a smell, a color or any other non-functional but distinctive aspect of a product or service that tends to promote and distinguish it in the marketplace. Titles, character names or other distinctive features of movies, television and radio programs can also serve as trademarks or service marks when used to promote a service or product. Finally, the distinctive packaging of a product is protected under the federal trademark statute (the Lanham Act) as trade dress, although trade dress can't be placed on the federal trademark register.

31. How do trademarks differ from copyrights?

The copyright laws protect original works of expression, but specifically do not protect names, titles or short phrases. This is where trademark protection comes in. Under state and federal laws, distinctive words, phrases, logos, symbols and slogans can qualify as trademarks or service marks if they are used to identify and distinguish a product or service in the marketplace.

The trademark laws are often used in conjunction with the copyright laws to protect advertising copy. The trademark laws protect the product or service name and any slogans used in the advertising. The copyright laws protect any additional literal expression that the ad contains.

32. Can corporate and business names be protected under trademark laws?

Generally not. Names for businesses are commonly called "trade names." A business's trade name is the name it uses on its stock certificates, bank accounts, invoices and letterhead. When used to identify a business in this way--as an entity for non-marketing purposes--the business name is subject to some protection under state and local corporate and fictitious business name registration laws, but it is not considered a trademark (thus is not entitled to protection as such).

If, however, a business name is also used to identify a product or service produced by the business, it may qualify for trademark protection if it is distinctive enough. For instance, Apple Computer Corporation uses the trade name Apple as a trademark on its line of computer products, and Nolo Press, Inc. uses Nolo as a service mark for its online people's law services.

Although trade names by themselves are considered trademarks, they may be protected under federal and state unfair competition laws if a competing use is likely to lead to customer confusion.

33. What types of trademarks receive protection?

As a general rule, trademark law confers the most legal protection to names, logos and other marketing devices that are distinctive--that is, memorable because they are creative or out of the ordinary (inherently distinctive), or because over time they have become well known to the public.

Trademarks said to be inherently distinctive typically consist of:
1. unique logos or symbols;
2. made-up words ("coined marks"), such as Exxon or Kodak;
3. words that invoke imaginative images in the context of their usage ("fanciful marks"), such as Double Rainbow ice cream;
4. words that are surprising or unexpected in the context of their usage ("arbitrary marks"), such as Time Magazine or Diesel for a bookstore; and
5. words that cleverly connote qualities about the product or service ("suggestive or evocative marks"), such as Slenderella diet food products.

By contrast, trademarks consisting of common or ordinary words are not considered to be inherently distinctive and receive less protection under federal or state laws. Typical examples of common or ordinary words are:
1. people's names (Pete's Muffins, Smith Graphics);
2. geographic terms (Northern Dairy, Central Insect Control); and
3. descriptive terms--that is, words that attempt to literally describe the product or some characteristic of the product (Rapid Computers, Clarity Video Monitors, Ice Cold Ice Cream)

As mentioned, it's possible for ordinary marks to become distinctive because they have developed great public recognition through long use and exposure in the marketplace. A mark that has become protectable through exposure or long use is said to have acquired a "secondary meaning." Examples of otherwise common marks that have acquired a secondary meaning and are now considered to be distinctive include: Sears (department stores), Ben and Jerry's (ice cream) and Park 'n Fly (airport parking services.)

34. Aren't there marks that aren't protected by the trademark laws?

Typically referred to as "generic marks," these marks are the equivalent of common words used to describe the type of product rather than a brand of the product. For instance, assume that a new cellular telephone manufacturer calls its product "The Cellular." Because the term "cellular" is the descriptive name for the product itself, it cannot legally be considered a trademark or service mark.

However, if the term "cellular" were used on a facial creme, it would be considered suggestive, and therefore distinctive, in that context.

Some marks that start out distinctive become generic over time, as the public comes to associate the mark with the product itself. When this happens, the mark loses protection as a distinctive trademark. Aspirin, escalator, and cellophane are all examples of distinctive marks that lost protection by becoming generic. The Xerox mark was in grave danger of losing protection because of the common use of the term as a noun (a Xerox) and a verb (to Xerox something). To prevent this from happening, Xerox launched an expensive campaign urging the public to use "Xerox" as a proper noun (Xerox brand photocopiers).

35. How is trademark ownership determined?

As a general rule, a trademark is owned by the business that is first to use it in a commercial context--that is, the first to attach the mark to a product or use the mark when marketing a product or service. Once a trademark is owned by virtue of this first use, the owner may be able to prevent others from using that (or a similar) trademark for their goods and services. Whether this is so depends on such factors as:

1. whether the trademark is being used on competing goods or services (goods or services compete if the sale of one is likely to preclude the sale of the other),
2. whether consumers would likely be confused by the dual use of the trademark, and
3. whether the trademark is being used in the same part of the country or is being distributed through the same channels.

In addition, under a number of state laws known as anti-dilution statutes, a trademark owner may prevent a mark from being used if the mark is well known and the later use would dilute the mark's strength--impair its reputation for quality or render it common through overuse in different contexts (even if it is unlikely that any customers would be confused by the second use).

Acquiring ownership of a mark by being the first to use it is not the only way to own a trademark. It is also possible to acquire ownership by filing an "intent-to-use" (ITU) trademark registration application with the U.S. Patent and Trademark Office. The filing date of this application will be considered the date of first use of the mark if the applicant later actually puts the mark into use within the required time limits (between six months and three years, depending on whether extensions are sought and paid for).

36. How do trademarks qualify for federal registration?

Registering a trademark with the U.S. Patent and Trademark Office (PTO) makes it easier for the owner to protect the trademark against would-be copiers, and puts the rest of the country on notice that the trademark is already taken.

To register a trademark with the PTO, the mark's owner first must put it into use "in commerce that Congress may regulate." This means the mark must be used on a product or service that crosses state, national or territorial lines or that affects commerce crossing such lines--such as would be the case with a catalog business or a restaurant or motel that caters to interstate or international customers. Even if the owner files an intent-to-use (ITU) trademark application, the mark will not actually be registered until it is used in commerce (as defined above).

Once the PTO receives a trademark registration application, it determines the answers to these questions:

Is the trademark the same as or similar to an existing mark used on similar or related goods or services? Is the trademark on the list of prohibited or reserved names? Is the trademark generic - that is, does the mark describe the product itself rather than its source?

If the PTO answers all of these questions in the negative, it will publish the trademark in the Official Gazette (a publication of the U.S. Patent and Trademark Office) as being a candidate for registration.

Existing trademark owners may object to the registration by filing an opposition. If this occurs, the PTO will schedule a hearing to resolve the dispute. Even if existing owners don't challenge the registration of the trademark at this stage, they may later attack the registration in court if they believe the registered mark infringes a mark they already own.

37. What does trademark registration accomplish?

If there is no opposition, and use in commerce has been established, the PTO will place the mark on the list of trademarks known as the Principal Register if the mark is considered distinctive (either inherently or because it has acquired secondary meaning). Probably the most important benefit of placing a trademark on the Principal Register is that anybody who later initiates use of the same or a confusingly similar trademark will be resumed by the courts to be a "willful infringer" and therefore liable for large money damages. However, it is still possible to obtain basic protection from the federal courts for a trademark without registering it.

If a trademark consists of common or ordinary terms, it may be placed on a different list of trademarks known as the Supplemental Register. Placement of a trademark on the Supplemental Register produces significantly fewer benefits than those offered by the Principal Register, but still provides notice of ownership. Also, if the trademark remains on the Supplemental Register for five years--that is, the registration isn't canceled for some reason--and also remains in use during that time, it may then be placed on the Principal Register under the secondary meaning rule (secondary meaning will be presumed).

38. How are trademark owners protected?

Whether or not a trademark is federally registered, its owner may go to court to prevent someone else from using it or a confusingly similar mark. To win, the owner must prove that the imitation will likely confuse consumers. If the owner can prove that it suffered or that the competitor gained economically as a result of the improper use of the trademark, the competitor may have to pay the owner damages based on the profit or loss.

If the court finds the competitor intentionally copied the owner's trademark, the infringer may have to pay other damages, such as punitive damages, fines or attorney fees. On the other hand, if the trademark's owner has not been damaged, a court has discretion to allow the competitor to also use the trademark under very limited circumstances designed to avoid the possibility of consumer confusion.

39. Do I have a right to use my name on my business even if someone else is already using it on a similar business?

Yes and no. A mark that is primarily a surname (last name) does not qualify for protection under the trademark provisions of the Lanham Act unless it becomes well known as a mark through advertising or long use--that is, until it acquires a secondary meaning. A trademark is "primarily a surname" if the public would recognize it first as a surname, or if it consists of a surname and other material that is not registrable.

If a surname acquires a secondary meaning, it is off-limits for all uses that might cause customer confusion, whether or not the name is registered. Sears, McDonald's, Hyatt, Champion, Howard Johnsons and Calvin Klein are just a few of the hundreds of surnames that have become effective marks over time.

Under the laws of many states, a person or business who tries to capitalize on his or her own name to take advantage of an identical famous name being used as a trademark may be forced, under the state's anti-dilution laws, to stop using the name if the trademark owner files a lawsuit.

40. How can I find out whether anyone else is already using a trademark I want to use?

A "trademark search" is an investigation to discover potential conflicts between a proposed mark and an existing one. Generally done before or at the beginning of a new mark's use, a trademark search reduces the possibility of inadvertently infringing a mark belonging to someone else. This is extremely important, because if the chosen mark is already owned or registered by someone else, the new mark may have to be replaced. Obviously, no one wants to spend money on marketing and advertising a mark, only to discover it infringes another mark and must be changed. In addition, if the earlier mark was federally registered prior to an infringing use, the user of the infringing mark may have to pay the mark's rightful owner any profits earned from the infringing use.

Usually an attorney or professional search agency conducts a trademark search by checking both federal and state trademark registers for identical or similar marks. Then the searcher checks the Yellow Pages in major cities (nationwide, for a national mark, or regionally, for a mark in regional use), as well as trade journals and other relevant publications. The search report notes all uses of identical or similar marks and the goods or services on which they are used.

Federal lists of registered trademarks are available for searching in book and database forms. For example, the Trademark Register of the U.S. lists all registered trademarks by their product or service classifications. The public can use it at any of the 68 Patent Depository Libraries throughout the country, which are mostly major public or university libraries. The U.S. Patent and Trademark Office also puts out on CD-ROM a federal trademark database called Cassis, available to the public at Patent Depository Libraries. In addition, several private subscription-based companies, such as Dialog, CompuServe, and CompuMark, offer online databases that list federal, state and some international trademarks (including Canada, the U.K. and Japan).

41. What is the significance of trademark symbols--"TM" or "R" in a circle?

Many people like to put a "TM" (or "SM" for service mark) next to their mark to let the world know that they are claiming ownership of it. There is no legal necessity for providing this type of notice, as the use of the mark itself is the act that confers ownership.

The "R" in a circle ® is a different matter entirely. This notice may not be put on a mark unless it has been registered with the U.S. Patent and Trademark Office. The failure to put the notice on a mark that has been so registered can result in a significant handicap if it later becomes necessary to file a lawsuit against an infringer of the mark.

42. When may I use TM and when may I use R-in-a-circle (®)?

Under U.S. trademark law, the R-in-a-circle symbol (®) may only be used in connection with a mark if that mark is a federally registered trademark. By "federally registered" we mean that the trademark owner has not only filed a trademark registration application with the US Patent & Trademark Office, but has been granted a registration. In contrast, the TM and SM symbols may be used freely without respect to whether or not there is a federal trademark registration. If you are offering goods or services, you may freely use the TM or SM symbol to denote trademarks or service marks that you use to indicate the origin of your goods or services.

43. When must I file a trademark application?

Unlike patent applications, which in many cases must be filed in advance of a particular date, there is no specific date by which a trademark application must be filed. Instead, the time constraint is in a different direction. In the United States an ordinary so-called "use" trademark application can only be filed after the goods or services have been in interstate commerce.

44. What is ITU (intent to use)?

A few years ago the U.S. Patent and Trademark Office established a new kind of application called an "intent-to-use" or ITU trademark application. To be able to file this application, the applicant need not have used the mark in interstate commerce (as would be required for a use-type trademark application) but need merely have a good-faith intention to use the mark in interstate commerce. The intent-to-use law does not, however, permit "reserving" trademarks for indefinite periods of time. In particular, an intent-to-use trademark application goes abandoned if the applicant does not perform actual use within a specified time interval after the filing date of the application. "ITU" is also the acronym of the International Telecommunications Union, a body which coordinates policies and technical standards for radio, telephone, and telegraph communications.

45. Can I register a trademark myself?

Just as with copyrights and patents, it is possible to apply for a trademark pro se, that is, without the assistance of counsel. Although the rules for prosecution of a trademark application are somewhat complicated, many trademark registrations have been obtained by applicants who represent themselves before the Trademark Office. Nonetheless, many applicants choose to pay an attorney to represent them before the Trademark Office in obtaining a trademark registration. If you wish to explore the possibility of filing your own trademark registration application, a good starting point is Trademark: How to Name Your Business and Product, from Nolo Press. According to the publisher, this book "shows how to choose a name or logo that others can't copy, conduct a trademark search, register a trademark with the U.S. Patent and Trademark Office and protect and maintain the trademark."

46. What is a good publication from the U.S. Patent and Trademark Office?

The U.S. Patent and Trademark Office publishes Basic Facts About Trademarks, a 20-page brochure containing all necessary forms, information, and fees.

47. What does it cost to file a trademark registration application?

The cost to file a trademark registration application, if you do it yourself, is largely the cost of the U.S. Patent & Trademark Office filing fee. The filing fee increases with the number of trademark classes in which the application is made. If you hire a trademark lawyer to do the work the cost will probably be the lawyer's professional fee, the filing fee (again based on the number of classes), and incidental expenses. The cost (fees and expenses) for the trademark filing averages around $900. The cost does not always end with the filing of the application, however. If the application is opposed by some member of the public, or if the Examiner raises objections, then the response to the opposition or objection takes time and money.

48. What is the governing law for trademarks in the U.S.?

In the United States, the law that governs trademarks is Chapter 22 of Title 15 of the United States Code, commonly cited as "15 USC". (In the referenced document, Chapter 22 is about one-third of the way down the gopher menu.)

49. How may I find out about trademark laws around the world?

For information about trademark laws around the world, the trademark search firm of Thomson & Thomson offers a very helpful International Guide to Trademarks. You may also wish to consult intellectual property counsel in your country of interest. See Web sites of intellectual property law firms and patent agents in countries outside of the United States.

50. The name of my company was approved when I incorporated - Doesn't that mean I am free to use that name as a trademark?

A most common misconception is that if one has a corporate name approved by the Secretary of State (the state agency that regulates corporations) then this means one may freely use the name in commerce. It is simply not so.

The reason that state approval of a corporate name is insufficient, is that the state authorities are only concerned that there not be two identical corporate names. They are not at all interested in making "likelihood of confusion" comparisons. Thus, they will happily allow ABC Distributing Co. and ABC Distributions Co. to exist at the same time, simply because they are not identical. Furthermore, a state agency only cares about one state. This means that there is probably a Mike's Pizza Inc. in most (if not all) of the states.

Another reason why getting approval from a state agency is insufficient is the fact that such agencies only concern themselves with business names, not trademarks. If you wanted to go into business as "Tide Soap Co." you probably would be permitted to do so by the state agency, but the big company that has TIDE as a trademark on its products would take a very different view. Intellectual property lawyers find themselves explaining this from time to time, typically after a client has received a "cease and desist" letter from a company that has been around longer. In many cases the prudent business decision is to give up and use some other name. This has the clear drawbacks that any accumulated goodwill with customers relating to the previous name is often lost, and one must throw away stationery, business cards, and promotional materials and pay to have new materials printed.

In some businesses these costs may be minor enough that there is no good reason to spend money on searching to see if a name is free to use. But for many businesses, it is good planning to conduct a "freedom-to-use" inquiry before making substantial investment in a proposed new name. While the inquiry cannot guarantee the absence of trademark disputes, it can drastically reduce the risks. The client may create a list of proposed names, and experienced trademark counsel can then perform an initial screening of the names using relatively inexpensive online databases. This screening can be done in a matter of minutes by experienced counsel; many clients also have in-house searching capability on Dialog, Compuserve, Questel/Orbit, or STN to perform such screening.

Assuming that one or two proposed names survive the screening, a usual next step is to have a "full freedom-to-use search" done by a well-known trademark search company such as Thomson & Thomson. The results of this search are studied by counsel who can then advise the client of the relative level of risk for the proposed names. Depending on how extensive a search is ordered, freedom-to-use searches may review US federal and state trademark filings, foreign trademark filings, corporate name filings, and databases reflecting usage in trade for which no formal registrations have been made. The results of these searches are studied to evaluate both similarities in the words being used and similarities in the goods or services being offered.

Summary: it is unwise to attach any freedom-to-use significance to approval of a corporate name by a state agency. In cases where it would be a hardship to have to change the name later, it is wise to consult experienced trademark counsel.

51. Can a business entity claim trademark status for a business name (and domain name) when the business is named after a city or geographic region? Would it make a difference if there are already two businesses using that same geographic region name? By way of example, say a NY business calls itself Canterbury Square and there are already 12 regions in Europe called Canterbury Square - can business use of that domain name outside Europe still be protected?

Although it is possible to use a geographic term as part of a trademark, it can be risky. Depending on how the geographical term is used and associated with the product/service by a consumer, it may be entitled to broad trademark rights, little trademark rights or no trademark rights at all.

If the term is used to actually describe the origin of the product or service, it is not entitled to trademark protection unless it acquires secondary meaning (secondary meaning occurs when a business can show that over time it has developed name recognition and goodwill to a mark). For example, if your company produces orange juice in Florida, you would not be entitled to trademark protection for the name "Florida Juice" absent a showing a secondary meaning. An example of a geographically descriptive mark that has secondary meaning is "American Airlines." At bottom, the reason for this rule is that it would be unfair to restrict other businesses in the same region from telling consumers where they are located.

It appears that the business in this case is not using a geographical term in the literal sense. This type of use may be okay as long as reasonable consumers do not actually think that your product or service comes from the geographic region specified. To use the orange juice example again, if you produce orange in Texas using Texas oranges under the name "Florida Juice," not only would you be unable to develop trademark rights to the name, you would also subject yourself to a claim of false

270

advertising because it is likely that consumers will believe the juice is from Florida. On the flip side, if it is unlikely that consumers would think that the product/service comes from the location specified or if consumers would not buy the product based upon its geographical origin (i.e., if the location doesn't indicate a type of quality like orange juice from Florida or pizza from Chicago does), it is possible to develop trademark rights.

The best geographical marks are used in a fanciful or arbitrary manner, meaning there is no literal connection (either actual or perceived by a consumer) between the good/service and the name. A great example of this is Amazon.com, the on-line bookstore. Use of the name Amazon for an on line bookstore works great because it has no connection to the sale of books and it is unlikely that any reasonable consumer would think that the books sold from this store originate in the Amazon region of South America.

If a name is used in a manner similar to the amazon.com example, you are probably in good shape from a trademark standpoint. However, if the use is more closely analogous to the Florida Juice examples, you might suggest that the client rethink their name choice or face an uphill and uncertain battle to secure trademark rights to the name. I hope this information is helpful. If you have additional questions, please do not hesitate to contact me.

52. You have conducted two searches – for the actual name use and the logo. These will be combined for your trademark. Can you file for only one trademark incorporating both? Or do you need to file for two to protect the use of the name as well as the logo?

As a general rule, if you use both the name and design together to present one commercial impression in the marketplace, you should be able to register both elements with one registration fee. If they are used separately and present separate impressions to a consumer, you may have to file two applications with the US Patent and Trademark Office, one for the design and one for the name itself. If you still have questions, you may want to contact a trademark attorney or the PTO's trademark assistance center (703-308-9000).

53. How can you copyright, trademark, patent a phrase or way of expressing an idea? For example, when I see One Minute Manager it usually has the registered trademark along with it even if it is not referencing the book but instead the idea.

Of the different types of intellectual property protection available (including patent, copyright, trademark, trade secret), I believe that trademark protection would be the most applicable to anyone seeking to preserve rights to a short phrase.

Patent rights protect any new and useful machine, apparatus, design or composition of matter. Copyright protects creative works of authorship that are fixed in a tangible form. Trade secrets arise whenever a piece of information that is not generally known that provides a company with a competitive advantage is kept confidential. Trademarks are any distinctive name, symbol or slogan used to identify a company or individual as the source of a product or service being offered in the marketplace.

A good example of these various types of protection would be the Coca-a-Cola bottling company. The Coca-a-Cola name is protected as a trademark, the secret coke formula is protected as a trade secret and advertising copy and other creative advertisement elements and designs are protected under copyright. Coke has chosen not to protect its secret formula as a patent, but that protection would also be available.

As to your specific question, if the phrase in question is distinctive (meaning it is not so descriptive of the good or service in question that it would be unfair to exclude competitors from using the term), and it is used to indicate a company as the source of a product or service, it can be protected as a trademark. Trademark holders can exclude others from using names, symbols or slogans in the marketplace that are considered "confusingly similar" to their trademark.

If you have additional questions, please do not hesitate to contact me. Please note that this information is general in nature and should not serve as a substitute for legal advice.

54. What does "likelihood of confusion" mean when trademark infringement litigation is referred to and what is an example of such infringement?

Parody sometimes seems like an inalienable right - perhaps not uniquely American but certainly well ingrained in our culture. Particularly since the 1950's and the birth of Mad Magazine, taking a shot at the high and mighty has become almost a sport. However, as a recent case involving Budweiser beer points out, the legal system is sometimes asked to be the referee.

Anheuser-Busch Cos. - the brewer of Budweiser - took offense last year when a backyard entrepreneur named Max Bloom developed a potato-shaped pillow he dubbed the Original American Couch Potato. It came complete with an owner's manual to show how one might enjoy a couch potato's lifestyle. The rub came when the slogan "This Spud's For You'" was added to the packaging. Anheuser-Busch apparently was not amused - having spent many years and millions of dollars building brand-name recognition for "This Bud's For You" - and sent a cease-and-desist letter to Bloom.

The primary issue in trademark infringement litigation is usually "likelihood of confusion" - whether ordinary purchasers might be confused as to the source of the products and the affiliation between trademark owners. In this case it was not clear that Anheuser-Busch would be able to show such a likelihood of confusion - or even that Bloom's parody would dilute the value of Anheuser-Busch's famous mark. But in the end Bloom decided he did not have the resources to go at it with Anheuser-Busch; so he decided to switch rather than fight.

The difficulty Bloom found himself in was not unique; coming up with a parody or takeoff of a well-known slogan or name is often a clever way of helping to distinguish a new product in the crowded marketplace. But a court's tolerance of such a marketing campaign is often difficult to predict. For example, a Michigan company called Here's Johnny Portable Toilets used the slogan "The World's Foremost Comedian" and was sued by Johnny Carson. The court ruled there was little possibility of confusion and therefore denied the trademark infringement claim. Nevertheless, the court went on to rule that Carson's right of publicity was violated and ordered the slogan stricken. On the other hand, Jordache Enterprises Inc. got no relief from the court when a jeans maker came out with a line of jeans called "Lardache".

What can one conclude from this somewhat confusing line of cases? Perhaps the safest course of action is to avoid assuming that just because a name or slogan might be a clever parody that there's no potential pitfalls; instead, a careful analysis of the likelihood of confusion and dilution theories should be considered and if the business decision is to proceed, cover the risk with advertising injury insurance.

55. In setting up my website can I use any marks or logos that are available on the Internet?

When Star Trek first launched back in the 1960's, the term "cyberspace" did not even exist. Now, barely thirty years later, it seems like cyberspace is where huge economic battles are being and will be fought. For example, Viacom Inc. - which owns the Star Trek copyrights, trademarks and characters - has been sending out cease and desist letters to the operators of unofficial Star Trek websites who have been posting audio and video clips and scripts from the TV and film series.

The truth is that despite the sometimes expressed notion that if it is available on the internet then it is free for all to use, traditional trademark and copyright principles require the owner of a trademark or copyright to take steps to protect it and control its use. Otherwise the trademark or copyright could be held to be "abandoned". Nevertheless, a number of Trekkies - (a/k/a "The Resistance") have responded by faxing and emailing angry letters to Viacom. This battle is not the first and it will not be the last of its kind. One possible solution: content owners and providers like Viacom can license their copyrights and trademarks to the website operators for a nominal fee; in return the website operators would a post a notice that the images and trademarks are being used with permission of the copyright/trademark owner and can not be re-used without the written permission of that owner.

56. What does one do first to maintain a business identity? a) Register [a prospective] business name with a domain name registering service? or register business name as a tradename first? In other words, if I register a business' name [an idea I have for an online business] with a domain name service & it's not previously registered as a tradename, can it [the business name] then be taken [legally] to be used by someone else?

Three different vehicles for creating and recording part of your business identity exist. Although each of these systems overlap, they are unique. A brief outline of each follows:

1. Trademarks. A trademark is a name, symbol or slogan used by consumers to identify and distinguish your product or service in the marketplace (technically speaking, a name that identifies a service is referred to as a service mark rather than a trademark). A trademark gives you the ability to exclude others from using a name that is confusingly similar to your name and that may result in consumers mistaking another company's products or services for your own. In essence, a trademark or service mark embodies the goodwill that you develop in your products or services in the marketplace.

Generally speaking, the best way to protect a trademark or service mark is to register that mark with the United States Patent and Trademark Office. Although it is possible to secure "common law" trademark rights simply by using a name in the marketplace, federal registration entitles you to nationwide priority to the mark. Before filing a federal trademark application or investing money in marketing a name, many people also choose to have a trademark search performed to better assess the availability of the name as a trademark. Through our web site, nameprotect.com, we offer both an online trademark searching and an online trademark application tool.

2. Trade name/Business Names. In contrast to a trademark or service mark that is used to identify a specific product or service, a trade name is the name that you use to distinguish and identify your company as a whole. As a practical matter, the trade name used to identify the company often functions as a trademark or service mark as well. Well-known examples of trade names that also function as trademarks include Microsoft(R) and Nike(R). A well-known trade name that also functions as a service mark is Allstate Insurance. Trade names that function as trademarks or service marks can be registered with the US Patent and Trademark Office.

In addition to trademark registration, each state has requirements for recording business names. For corporate names, each individual state maintains a corporate name registry. For other types of business names, the individual states and sometimes even county or local governmental units will maintain a fictitious business name system under which any person doing business under an assumed name must file a "doing business as" certificate that identifies the person or persons behind the name. Importantly, as a general rule, a corporate name reservation or fictitious business name filing by itself will not provide its holder with the ability to prevent other similar names from being used in the marketplace.

3. Domain names. Domain names are used on the Internet to locate specific web sites. Domain names are registered on a first come, first serve basis. (You can register a domain name through with Network Solutions -http://www.networksolutions.com-). Because consumers often use domain names to identify and distinguish a company and its products/services, many domain names are also entitled to trademark protection. A well-known example of a domain name that also functions as a trademark is Amazon.com(R). One of the best ways to protect a domain name is to register it as a trademark or service mark with the US Patent and Trademark Office.

Turning to your specific question regarding the proper sequence for protecting your name, the short answer is that there is no one required sequence. Many businesses will perform a trademark search on the name, register the domain name, reserve the corporate name, file a fictitious business name and apply for federal trademark registration on the name all in the same time frame. Because the

273

name you select will ultimately protect the goodwill that you develop for your business, it is very important to make certain that the name is available and that you take the appropriate steps to secure and protect it.

The information is general in nature. It does not constitute a legal opinion on your own specific situation and it should not be used as a substitute for specific legal advice. If you have additional questions, please do not hesitate to contact me.

57. How important is a well-designed logos for the business owner and what are the steps for registration?

It has often been said, "don't judge a book by its cover." However, when it comes to marketing your company's products or services, the image you portray has a very profound effect on the success of your venture. Consumers often judge products by their packaging. It is therefore advantageous to have a well-designed logo to appeal to their senses. A logo is short for logotype, which is an identifying symbol used for advertising.

In order to remain competitive with larger companies, small businesses must have a good product with a very strong package, logo and brand name. Well known logos include Nike's swoosh, Microsoft's Windows design and McDonald's Golden Arches. The goal of packaging is to promote your logo or brand name. This is especially important for products that are usually selected on a brand name basis (such as athletic footwear). This means you will need a well designed logo and strong brand name.

One factor that should be considered when designing a logo is how the logo will appear in the many different settings in which it is used, including magazines, billboards, coupons and packaging. The logo should be distinctive enough to identify your company as the source of the product or service. Once a strong logo is designed, it is advisable to register the logo with the United States Patent and Trademark Office for protection. Before commencing with a registration, a design logo search should be completed to see if the mark would conflict with any currently registered marks with the USPTO. A search is important to ascertain whether there would be a possible infringement of another party's design logo or trademark.

58. You coined a trademark and assigned the trademark to a company. The company consistently uses the trademark as a noun. What logical reason could there be for a company to do this? (They do realize they are using it improperly and persist in doing so.)

It is misuse of a trademark, which will eventually cause them to lose it as a trademark. If you have been paid for your contribution, why worry about their actions? Secondly a trademark is a noun. It doesn't really matter what it's form - - verb, adverb, adjective, etc.

59. If you haven't begun the registration process, you shouldn't be using the TM symbol, right? There is, I believe, an aspect of the law that allows for "priority dates" for using a logo/name as a trademark, but it doesn't automatically give the right to the user of such name to arbitrarily add their own TM symbol if there is no registration, right?

You develop rights to marks in the US through use. The date you first start to use a mark in commerce to identify your company as the source of the product or service is the date you start to acquire trademark rights. Registering your mark at the state and/or federal level provides you with significant advantages (puts people on notice of your rights, allows you to sue infringers under state or federal law, among others) but it is not a prerequisite to developing TM rights.

The TM or SM subscript symbol can be used by any company that is asserting trademark rights to a trademark or servicemark. You do not have to be registered or have even applied for a registration to use this symbol. However, it is illegal to use the circle R symbol unless the mark is federally registered.

60. I just got incorporated into another company. I want to launch a line under the parent company. What are the procedures and cost? Do I have to trademark the name and register it?

There are typically two-main steps in the trademark protection process:

#1. Trademark Research.

A trademark search allows you to better determine whether your trademark is available for your use. Firms usually offer two levels of searching. A preliminary online search for about $35 (one site is http://www.NameProtect.com) and a more comprehensive "Full Availability" search completed by trained researchers.

Some firms offer two different variations of a comprehensive search; a basic search priced at about $175 and an extensive search priced at $275. You would order either a basic or an extensive, but not both.

#2. Trademark Research

Depending on the results of your trademark research, registering a trademark with the US Patent and Trademark Office provides significant advantages.

Estimated costs to protect a trademark would be as follows:

Online preliminary search: $35

Comprehensive research: $175 or $275

Trademark Application Assistance: $65 or $250 attorney fee

Government Filing Fee: $245

61. I registered a dot-com domain name recently for a new e-commerce on European level. Somebody else has a very similar domain name (only 1 dash difference!) in exactly the same business but didn't use (update) his site for the last 3 years. My business will operate in Europe only (But later...Who knows what becomes of it...). The other site is set up for e commerce in US only. I heard that having a domain name is not sufficient. If somebody else has a very similar domain name in the same business and has it trademarked, I could be forced to give up my domain name. Is this true? Do I need to trademark the address? Do I need to trademark it in the USA or is a trademark in Europe sufficient? And how can I, as non-US resident, fill in a form for a trademark? (At the Trademark office, they request a US address for mail and communication).

1. Are trademark rights important? The present domain name dispute policies greatly favor the rights of trademark holders. Thus, anyone who holds a domain name that directly conflicts with a registered trademark runs the risk that the domain name holder will initiate an action against them under ICANN's Dispute Resolution Policy or via traditional trademark law. The best defense to this type of action, other than to create trademark rights of your own, is to show a legitimate, good faith rationale for reserving and using the name.

If you would like to read more about ICAAN's policy, there is information on it at their web site, http://www.icann.org.

2. Trademark protection in the US or Europe? As you suggest in your inquiry, you must seek trademark protection country-by-country. With a few exceptions, there is not international system of trademark protection available at present. Generally speaking, a business will attempt to create trademark rights in the country or countries in which they plan to do business. Aside for the fact that the United States represents a large portion of the global economy, there is no requirement that a company register its trademark rights in the US. The important fact for purposes of a domain name dispute is that the company holds some legitimate rights to the domain name. Having a registered trademark to the domain in at least one jurisdiction would be a real positive.

3. U.S. address? Although you do not need to be a U.S. citizen to seek trademark protection in the U.S., you correctly note that the United States Patent and Trademark Office does require that you list a U.S. address for correspondence purposes. This service, a U.S. address, is provided by some U.S. trademark attorneys.

62. What's the difference between the TM or SM symbol next to a company's name, and a registered mark?

The use of the TM or SM subscript symbol simply means that the entity is asserting trademark rights to the name, symbol or slogan in use. Because you develop rights to trademarks in the United States through use, it is possible to have a trademark without having registered that mark anywhere or even filed for registration of the mark. Thus, anyone is free to place a TM or SM on a name, symbol or slogan that they are attempting to develop rights to. I say this with one caveat; I am unsure whether use of the TM or SM symbol can lead to additional trouble if your mark is found to infringe another entity's trademark. For example, whether your use of the symbol would lead to additional damages in a trademark infringement suit. As a general rule, having an adequate trademark search completed is a good defense to any claim that you have "willfully infringed" on another's mark.

63. A design patent is in effect and good for 14 years. You have also applied for trademarks for your name and tag line. If you were to license your patent, would the licensing rights run out when the patent runs out or would a trademark extend that? If the trademark extends rights, would that change if they changed the name of the idea?

As a general rule, it is possible to license both patent rights and trademark rights which you hold. However, trademarks and patents provide different bundles of rights. A design patent gives you the right to exclude others from using the same non-functional design in the marketplace for a period of years. Once that term of years expires, you no longer have the ability to prevent others from marketing the design under patent law. A trademark provides you the right to exclude others from using a confusingly similar name, slogan or design in the marketplace. Unlike a patent, a trademark rights can be held for as long as you (or your licensee) continues to use the name, slogan or symbol as a trademark in the marketplace.

You might want to discuss the possibility of securing trademark rights to your non-function design (typically called a "trade dress" or "configuration" mark) as a means of extending the life of your exclusive rights to that design.

64. Has any non-profit been made a party to a suit because they owned the trademark associated with a product?

As unseeming as it may be, you are required by case law to police the trademarks that have been licensed to assure that the quality of the licensed goods meet a certain agreed upon standard. As for hiring trademark police to go stores to see if there are illegal goods bearing your trademark, it is matter of building up the value of your trademark by showing that you will enforce it and gain the trust of your licensees who are paying you a royalty. For example, raids were conducted in 1990 or 1991 in Seoul, Korea and San Jose, California flea markets on behalf of a large number of universities and corporations who collectively contributed to a funded private investigation and raid with assistance from local police authorities and Customs. T-shirts, Shoes, Handbags, Software, and Watches were some of the items seized.

A discussion of trademark disputes involving universities has taken place before. Some feel policing their logo is pretty trivial. Others contend there was some good income in university logos. It is often not recognized why universities police their logos.

One, if you don't police it, it may be lost.

Two, it is necessary to protect one's name and reputation. Would Southern Cal like their Trojans logo showing up on a condom? Or Ole Miss on a retirement home?

More seriously, Dartmouth College sued The Dartmouth Review, a very right-wing newsmagazine that had no official connection with Dartmouth, but was started by several Dartmouth students and bankrolled by Bob Buckley (a Yalie), and Jeffrey Hart, a Dartmouth professor. Dartmouth did not want the world to think that the Dartmouth Review reflected the views of Dartmouth College. Unfortunately, Dartmouth lost the case. One of the reasons for the loss was that

Dartmouth had NOT prosecuted for other commercial uses of the Dartmouth name, such as the Dartmouth Co-op and the Dartmouth Bookstore.

One more important point; at the University of California a lot of licensing income was passed up because they had a policy not to trademark anything except the names and logos of the university and its campuses. The reason was that when one gets a trademark, they are "guaranteeing the mark". Hence, they are supposed to actually monitor any manufacture under the mark and guarantee that it meets the quality associated with the mark. Such a responsibility to oversee the quality leads to legal liability.

65. I sent a trademark application to the Trademark office three years ago. I responded to their queries. However, I have not gotten any communication from them about it in over a year. My written requests that they look into that file have been ignored. In 2 verbal conversations with the government's attorney on the case, he has admitted that their last response (over a year ago) and all my subsequent inquiries are logged in - but they can't find the physical file to determine the status of the application - he will have someone find the file (2x). On Monday, I spoke to another attorney there - she is trying to have someone pull the file. What gives? What does one do in this case? Do we have a trademark? There was a very large company who had sent me a letter asking me to withdraw the application because they had something similar in a different category. I refused - but offered to work with them. Oddly enough, I haven't heard from them or the Trademark office on this application since. Coincidence? Any ideas?

The federal trademark application process takes a relatively long time to complete. A good rule of thumb is to budget somewhere between 8 to 12 months from start to finish for the registration process, assuming your application goes through smoothly. If there are problems, the process can take several months longer. In your case, it sounds like another company may have opposed your registration request in what is called an "opposition action." This may be the reason for the delay you have experienced. I would continue to contact the Patent and Trademark Office regarding the status of your file.

66. How may I do trademark research on the Internet?

There are no free-of-charge comprehensive trademark resources on the Internet. A trademark search is often consists of two techniques: online searches with commercial databases and obtaining comprehensive trademark searches from recognized trademark search firms such as Thomson & Thomson. Online databases available through Dialog include trademark applications and registrations in the United States, Canada, and many countries of Europe. Other trademark databases are also available through Compuserve, Questel/Orbit, and STN. A number of companies have set up sites that permit doing trademark searches through a web interface. Examples of service companies are:

Trademark search Atlas at http://www.trademark-search.com
Micropatent's trademark checker at http://www.micropat.com/indextm2.html
Trademarks Online at http://www.trademarksonline.com
TMWeb at http://www.tmweb.com/

67. Where can I get help with trademark selection and registration?

USPTO offers a trademark application form on the Internet and has posted a fairly easy on-line step-by-step method to complete a trademark application. You then print it out & mail it in. Other firms also offer application services via the Internet; some of which are easier to use than others.

The Canadian Trademark Office has posted the trademark database on-line.

Trademark Searches

European and Australian	http://www.IPAustralia.gov
PTO's site (registered)	http://www.uspto.gov
Thomas Register's site (unregistered)	http://www.thomasregister.com

Trademark search online; ($35.00)	http://www.nameprotect.com
Identity Research's AutoMark Registration ($65)	http://www.idresearch.com/register.htm
List of Refused Trademarks	http://oami.eu.int/en/marque/refus.htm
Search trademarks at:	http://www.uspto.gov/tmdb/index.html

Site does not contain information on state, foreign, or common law trademarks. So if a mark is not present on web site, it does not necessarily mean that the mark is not currently being used as a trademark.

Trade Names

Brands & Their Companies	
Canadian Intellectual Property Office	http://cipo.gc.ca/
Catchword	www.catch-word.com
Dotster	http://www.dotster.com/home/
International Trademark Association	http://www.inta.org/
IPM (Intellectual Property Management)	http://www.ipmanagement.com/
Lexicon Branding	www.lexicon-branding.com
Master McNeil	www.naming.com
Metaphor Name Consultants	www.metaphorname.com
Namebase	http://www.namebase.com
NameGuard - business names, domain names; free	http://www.NameProtect.com
NameLab	http://www.namelab.com or http://www.autocognitive.com/
NameTrade	http://www.nametrade.com
Netmark (CTM-Online Search)	http://www.internetmarken.de/ctmohim.htm)
Network Solutions	http://www.netsol.com/en_US/common/error.jhtml
The Name Stormers	http://www.namestormers.com
Thomson and Thomson	http://www.thomson-thomson.com/

PatentPro offers free information and services for inventors at http://www.4patpro.com. TrademarkPRO and CopyrightPRO take users step-by-step through basic information about each, provides the proper forms to fill out, and information on how to fill out the forms. For a nominal fee PatentPRO's on-staff attorneys will review inventor's copyright and trademark applications.

68. What advice would you offer someone who hires employees who have worked in competitor's businesses and have had access to the competitor's trade secrets?

The classic example of a trade secret is the formula for Coca-Cola; the fact that the formula is kept secret gives the Coca-Cola Company a huge advantage over its competition. Often a proprietary process may not be protected by copyright, trademark or patent law, but rather by the law that protects trade secrets. The loss of such a trade secret can be devastating to a business. Legal journals report regularly on lawsuits alleging a theft of trade secrets. A recent case involving Oracle Corp., the database software maker, illustrates one of the ways a trade secrets lawsuit can be avoided.

Recently Informix Corp. sued Oracle and alleged that Oracle tried to steal its trade secrets when it hired eleven of Informix's product development employees. A court granted a temporary restraining order to Informix to prevent its former employees from revealing Informix's trade secrets and from attempting to hire other Informix employees. This case highlights what experience has shown: you are virtually guaranteed to be slapped with a trade secrets lawsuit when you hire a significant number of your competitor's employees.

69. You have registered your trademark in the US, but have interested customers in Australia, Japan and Europe. Is there a means of protecting your trademark without registering in each country and who do you contact to do so?

Unfortunately, there is no international system to protect trademark rights. As a general rule, you must seek trademark protection country by country. One notable exception to this is the European

Community's Community Trademark. As you might imagine, international protection can get quite expensive.

70. I have applied for the Clearance service through NameProtect.com and expect results soon. There was no conflict with official trademarks based on my initial screening search. If the results indicate a common law conflict in the US or Canada, is there legally any rights to the previous common law user of my proposed name even though there is no official trademark by them? How are common law right, if any, enforced? Should I be very worried or just moderately concerned about any potential common law conflicts?

It is important to recognize that rights to trademarks in the United States arise through use in the marketplace. As a general rule, the first to use a distinctive name as a trademark (that is, to help consumers identify and distinguish the company's goods/services) will be granted priority to that name. These rights are commonly referred to as "common law" trademark rights. However, there is an important limitation to these rights. A company will develop common law trademark rights only in the area in which they market their product or service. Courts sometimes define this as the area in which the name enjoys a "sphere of influence." Because of this limitation on common law rights, it is possible for multiple users of the same name to develop common law trademark rights in different geographical regions of the country. The national and international character of our economy in recent years has made this type of concurrent use of a trademark less common, but concurrent use does still occur.

The limited nature of common law rights can be supplemented by a US federal trademark registration. As a general rule, federal registration of a mark will provide the trademark owner with nationwide priority to the mark over anyone who adopts a confusingly similar name after the federal registration is granted. As to pre-existing conflicts, the federal registration holder can "freeze" any existing common law users of the name into their current marketing area.

71. On line trademark are provided by several firms, one of which is NameProtect at http://www.nameprotect.com. They offer a Trademark Clearance service in which they do a trademark and similar name check against the US databases for about $275. Hiring an attorney to process the trademark application would cost about $3 - $4K but money is limited. What would you suggest?

NameProtect.com offers comprehensive search services. They have thousands of businesses and attorneys who rely on their comprehensive research to clear new names for use. You would likely have to perform separate searches for your company name and tag line.

72. How long will it take to get a trademark application approved?

A good rule of thumb is 8 to 14 months from start to finish. NameProtect also offers a referral network of trademark attorneys that will review a search at no charge and provide application services at low, flat fees. They also offer counsel as to which variation of the name, tag line or domain name should be protected.

TRADE SECRETS

1. What are trade secrets?

"Trade secrets" is the legal term for confidential business information. A good nonlegal definition of a "trade secret" is a secret belonging to a business. This information allows your company to compete effectively. Examples of trade secrets include customer identities and preferences, vendors, product pricing, marketing strategies, company finances, manufacturing processes and other competitively valuable information.

Under the Uniform Trade Secret Act, information must meet three criteria to qualify as a trade secret. First, the information must not be "generally known or readily ascertainable" through proper means. Second, the information must have "independent economic value due to its secrecy." And third, the trade secret holder must use "reasonable measures under the circumstances to protect" the secrecy of the information. These requirements are explored throughout these frequently asked questions.

2. Why protect trade secrets?

Failure to adequately protect your company's proprietary information will allow your competitors and ex employees to reduce your profits. The trade secret laws will help prevent such misfortune if your company acts in accordance with its requirements.

Imagine if your top employee left your company. The employee had learned every major area of your company. S/he was an invaluable asset to the company. Now imagine if that employee set up his/her own business in direct competition with you or became an employee of your toughest competitor. You can stop this individual if your company protected its business information properly under the trade secret laws. Proper protection requires action today to be ready for tomorrow.

3. What technology is protectable by trade secrets?

Under the Uniform Trade Secret Act information must not be generally known, not readily ascertainable, have independent economic value due to secrecy, and be the subject of reasonable efforts to protect secrecy. This includes essentially any confidential business information such as customer lists, financial information, employee data, production cost or sales data, and documents memorializing important negotiations.

4. How long is a trade secret protectable?

Information is protectable as long as the information fits the definition of trade secrets. This can be moments or decades.

5. What specific type of protection is offered by a trade secret?

Trade secret law prevents wrongful taking of confidential or secret information. Independent development and reverse engineering by another party are defenses to claims of trade secret theft.

6. What is the geographic scope of protection of a trade secret?

Trade secret protection is a state right. A vast majority of states, including Minnesota, have adopted the Uniform Trade Secret Act. Other states have a law or laws similar to the Uniform Act. Foreign countries have similar laws, although, the particular country should be checked before reliance is placed on trade secrets in a foreign country. The rights will seem to be national or international in scope, since registration of trade secrets is not required and since most states and foreign countries protect trade secrets.

7. How important is trade secret protection?

Trade secret protection is a must for virtually any business. It's most often not addressed until an employee or competitor obtains and uses against you valuable secret information, thereby stealing your sales, customers, technology base, damaging financial information, or other.

8. What is misappropriation of trade secrets?

Trade secret law prevents misappropriation, wrongful taking, of trade secret information. A wrongful taking can occur in a variety of manners. For example, the taking of information would be wrongful when the taking is a: breach of contract, breach of fiduciary obligation, theft, or other legal wrong.

9. What remedies are available when trade secrets are misappropriated?

Control of the information can be recovered along with payment of damages. Attorney fees and/or exemplary (e.g., punitive) damages can be recovered in an exceptional case. Criminal penalties are available in cases of theft.

10. What is the Uniform Trade Secret Act?

Trade secret laws are state granted rights. Minnesota, along with most other states, has adopted the Uniform Trade Secret Act. The Uniform Trade Secret Act attempts to make the trade secret laws the same from state-to-state. These frequently asked questions follow the Uniform Trade Secret Act.

11. What states have adopted the Uniform Trade Secret Act?

Nearly all states have adopted the Uniform Trade Secret Act (UTSA). The UTSA has been adopted by 38 jurisdictions.

12. What is meant by "not generally known?"

Information known to someone or known to non-competitors is still capable of being a trade secret. In fact, more than one competing company can claim trade secret rights in the same information independent of one another. Information generally known to one's competitors is not a trade secret.

Trade secret protection can be lost through publishing the secrets. Be careful in disclosing information if secrecy of the information is important. Trade secrets are often lost through disclosures in the absence of a confidentiality agreement.

13. What is meant by "not readily ascertainable?"

Information that is readily ascertainable is not capable of trade secret protection. The method of manufacturing your product (perhaps a new shoe design) is not a trade secret if someone can learn how to make your product by simply examining the product.

14. What is "reverse engineering?"

Reverse engineering is the determination of someone else's trade secret information via examination and testing of publicly available information. While the amount of effort needed to reverse engineer can show the information is readily ascertainable, this defense applies even when the reverse engineering is difficult and the information is not readily ascertainable. Reverse engineering is a complete defense, since it shows the information, trade secret or otherwise, was properly acquired from public sources of information.

15. What can one do if the information has or may become "generally known or readily ascertainable?"

Your company may still protect the information even if the information is or might become generally known or readily ascertainable. Patents (design and utility), copyright, and trademark laws will provide protection for certain information even when the information is generally known or readily ascertainable. Contracts can also provide rights that exceed the bounds of trade secret law. A decision to pursue patent protection instead of trade secret protection is an involved decision that should be discussed with competent counsel. Such a decision, however, turns in part on your likelihood of succeeding on showing the information "is not generally known or readily ascertainable."

16. What is meant by "independent economic value due to secrecy?"

To be a trade secret the information must have some value due to its secrecy. This criterion is almost always proven when secrecy is proven, since companies typically do not put forth effort in a lawsuit to protect and recover control of valueless information.

17. What is information that is "wealth creating" or "wealth preserving"?

The value of the information may be wealth creating such as your customer list and customer preferences. The value of the information may also be wealth preserving such as knowing which mistakes to avoid. Perhaps your company made a mistake in a marketing strategy. Knowing to avoid the mistake is of value, since it preserves wealth. Your company stands to gain competitively if your competitors make the same mistake. Wealth preserving information and wealth creating information should both be closely guarded secrets.

18. What must one do to protect trade secret information?

A trade secret holder must use "reasonable measures under the circumstances" to protect the confidentiality of the information. The better this step is performed the less likely the trade secret holder will have problems in the future and the future problems will be more easily resolved.

Under this requirement, one may tend to compartmentalize or itemize activities, since any discussion must consider each particular activity separately. To compartmentalize places undue stress on the words "reasonable measures" to the exclusion of the words "under the circumstances." Instead of compartmentalizing, one should consider each specific activity as a single part of a larger whole - that whole being the total circumstances surrounding the treatment of the information. (Example 1).

Example 1:

Assume all employees of a company signed a non-disclosure agreement. Assume that every day those employees promise to never identify a single customer to anyone outside the company. Further assume one other fact completes the whole of the circumstances surrounding the customer list. Every month the board of directors sends a copy of its customer list to all of the company's competitors. The customer list is not a trade secret even though the protective acts outnumber the facts showing lack of protection 2 to 1. The facts showing the entire circumstances are more likely to be interpreted as lack of protection despite the protective efforts.

19. What is the difference between physical security measures and notice measures?

Measures that a company can take are often considered in both notice measures and physical security measures. Notice measures are those measures that put persons who come in contact with the information on notice that the information is to remain secret. Physical security measures are those measures that prevent people who do not need-to-know the information from coming in contact with the information (e.g., confidentiality barriers). Example 1 above shows notice measures, but a complete lack of physical security. Notice measures and physical security measures often overlap even though they are discussed separately below.

20. How important are notice measures?

Recently, a jury was asked whether any of them thought an employee should be responsible for keeping information confidential when the employer had not expressed a desire to keep the information confidential. No juror raised a hand. All those with access to confidential information must be given notice as to what information is to remain confidential. A good use of notice measures involves frequent and clear instruction on confidentiality. Below are some manners in which to express the need for confidentiality.

21. How important is physical security?

In one suit the alleged trade secret holder allowed the employees that smoked to block open a door. The customer list was maintained, unsupervised, on a table next to the door. Visitors to the business were allowed to sit down and pour over the customer list unsupervised. Obviously, the lawsuit concerned recovery of the customer list. The alleged trade secret holder was a publicly traded company.

22. What should one consider when choosing appropriate notice measures?

Pay attention to clarity and regularity of the communications. Don't assume all your employees have a memory as good as your own. Too much assertion of confidentiality is better than not enough. Excessive assertions will indicate that confidentiality is extremely important to the company. Choose procedures that will be easy to show to a court (i.e., leave a paper trail wherever possible). Remember the jury that wanted the employer to clearly express to the employee the manner in which the employee was to behave. And finally, don't overlook providing notice to non-employees.

23. What notice procedures may be used?

Any communication that identifies either what information is confidential or how to handle confidential information will work as a notice measure. Employee handbooks, newsletters, and signs are common examples. These communications do not need to be cold or stale, but may be dressed up in the form of Thank Yous, Slogans, or even graphically presented. Creativity in the mode or manner of expression does not need to be suppressed and may improve the ability of the listener to remember.

The number and types of procedures are limitless. The goal here is to express to everyone orally, in writing, through actions, and any other methods of communication which information is to be confidential. Choose those procedures which are most easily assimilated into your business. Not all procedures are necessary, since two or three carefully chosen procedures may be enough. Several specific examples are discussed below.

24. How should one use non-disclosure agreements?

Non-disclosure agreements should be signed before a person sees, hears or otherwise learns confidential information of the company. In the case of a new employee, the agreement should be signed before the first day of work. If they sign after they start working or otherwise obtain access to the information, they should be given something of value in exchange for their signature (this may be necessary to make the contract binding). The agreement may contain, in addition to a non-disclosure provision, a provision requiring the employee to not compete with the employer for a period of time following the termination of employment. Non-disclosure agreements are not used with just employees, but rather anyone who has access to the confidential information.

A distinction needs to be made between agreements which have been read and those which have not. An agreement that has not been read may provide contract rights, but does not provide significant notice value. Agreements in Minnesota may also need to specify specific types of information that needs to remain confidential. Vague contracts provide little, if any, notice. Consider agreements for everyone who may have contact with sensitive information. Give the signer of the agreement a copy and place the other in the file.

Signed contracts, along with audits, are perhaps the most powerful tools in trade secret law. Beyond notice, contracts can be used to broaden the trade secret holder's rights and provide basis for asserting misappropriation (i.e., breach of contract). A well prepared non-disclosure/ non-compete contract is a must. Court's seem to decide for trade secret holder's in the presence of a contract and against the holder in the absence of a contract.

25. Should the company formally adopt a confidentiality policy?

The company should adopt a statement of policy. The policy may provide that: "information not generally known or readily ascertainable that would have value if it was secret will be maintained secret absent a greater need to the contrary. All situations where there is doubt as to how to treat particular information will be construed in favor of treating the information as secret. The company will determine those times when such information will not be treated confidential on a case-by-case basis." The company should adopt this or a similar statement.

26. How should documents be marked?

Most computer systems will automatically print "confidential" on each page once properly programmed. A rubber stamp stating "confidential" can be placed on each person's desk that commonly sees confidential material. Consider the use of red ink with such a stamp. A clear marking of "confidential" on a document provides very good notice.

27. How can one use positive and negative reinforcement?

Oral and written admonishments and instruction should be used with persons not properly following confidentiality procedures. More serious sanctions should be applied when the infractions are more serious.

Rewards may be given out to those who find actual and potential information leaks. This may include a reward for blowing the whistle on others failing to follow confidentiality procedures. Employees often have a better understanding on the particulars of how information is treated in the company than management. Reward the sharing of their knowledge.

28. How can one use written acknowledgments?

Memorandums expressing the need to treat information confidentially and requiring an acknowledgment by the employee's signature should be regularly distributed. The memorandums should include a statement that the employee recognizes and will follow the company's confidentiality procedures. The more the memorandum explains the procedures and identifies the protected information, the greater the value of the memorandum. The signature can be used to verify that all employees have signed and returned the memorandum. Provide a copy to the signer and keep the original in the file.

29. What should be done at meetings?

Meetings should regularly include a statement regarding confidentiality. You might wish to mention that specific information on the company is not to be given out or ask if anyone is aware of potential leaks. You may wish to have counsel speak to your employees at such a meeting.

30. When should discussions be held with individual persons?

At minimum, discussions about confidentiality should be held at the beginning of the relationship, periodically throughout, e.g. annual reviews, when a problem occurs, and at the termination of the relationship. Each discussion may include a signed statement that the confidentiality procedures were clearly explained to them, that they will follow the procedures, that they will return all information to the company when they no longer need it for the business with the company and that if they ever desire to disclose or use information that might be confidential they will request the company's permission first.

31. What should one consider when choosing appropriate physical security measures?

With physical security measures, like notice measures, one needs to pick those measures that are right for one's own business. Determine how information flows into, through and out of one's company. Place physical security barriers wherever reasonable. Seek to preclude access by all those who do not have a need-to-know the information. The more comprehensive the security measures one uses, the less likely one will encounter a breach in security. Moreover, if a security problem develops, one will be in a better position to recover the sensitive business information. Consequently, over-protection is better than under-protection.

32. What physical security measures may be used?

One may use any physical security measure that restricts access of the information to those who have a need-to-know the confidential information. The information cannot be taken by those who cannot gain access to the information. Below are some suggested physical barriers.

33. What are some procedures for direct control of the information?

The location of information should be separated into different areas (e.g., file cabinets, rooms or buildings). Only people that have a need-to-know the confidential information should have access to the relevant area and hence the information in that area. As an example, the accounting department or accounting books can be locked up in a room or drawer. Only people having a need for the information should have a key. Signs stating "employees only", "authorized personnel only", "restricted access", "private" or similar phrases will help discourage people from getting into these restricted access areas.

A variant of this procedure is used when out-sourcing. Companies that out-source various portions of their business often separate the confidential information among multiple vendors. No one vendor is given sufficient information to be able to recognize or use the confidential information.

Computers provide several methods by which confidential information can be restricted to those people who have a need-to-know the information. Passwords are one method. Separate computer systems are another. A computer system may give off a warning when someone tries breaking passwords, identifying both the problem and the computer terminal being used.
Confidential information should be put away when not in use. A blanket may be thrown over a machine. A drawer may be closed and locked. The company may require that desks be cleaned at the end of every day.

The disposal of confidential information should be carefully handled. Don't forget that garbage can be inspected by people looking for your information. A shredding machine should be used on confidential documents. Machines built according to trade secret knowledge should be disassembled.

34. How should visitors be treated?

Remember visitors to your company do not necessarily know your procedures. Checking people in with a logbook at the receptionist's desk suggests to the visitor that they will be monitored. Consider recording name, company, date, time, purpose and person the visitor is seeing.

Some companies do not permit visits absent an appointment. This permits the company to schedule visits at times known to all employees and allows everyone to be prepared for the visit.
All visitors to your company should be escorted at all times. The escort should keep the visitors eyes off confidential information, which preferably is maintained out of sight. The escort may wish to ask the person to treat all things they see and hear as confidential.

In large companies visitors are difficult to distinguish from employees. Visitors should wear badges identifying them as a visitor.

Employees should be instructed to approach any non-employee that is not being escorted and offer assistance in finding the person they seek.
Confidentiality agreements may be warranted depending upon the extent of access.

35. How should the premises be controlled during off hours?

Smaller companies often do not enjoy the benefit of having 24-hour in-person security at every door. All doors should be locked when and where in-person monitoring is not possible. Lights that activate based upon movement, cameras, and alarms are also good deterrents both inside and outside the facility. Check these systems regularly. Employees have been known to deactivate these systems for convenience, such as blocking open a door for the convenience of smokers.

36. What is meant by "under the circumstances?"

Reasonable measures under the circumstances include all facts and circumstances surrounding the information and its treatment. Happy, loyal employees are more likely to keep information confidential. Certain types of information in a company may "obviously" be secret. Methods of communicating the information may show secrecy (whisper versus speech). The employer needs to make its desires known though oral and written communications, physical barriers, actions, and any other method of communicating. Protection of trade secrets involves creating an environment of confidentiality. Protection is not simply a checklist of protective measures. Employees are people that will generally act in a manner appropriate for their environment.

37. What is a trade secret audit?

Confidentiality audits are important to conduct at regular intervals. A confidentiality audit is an assessment of the confidentiality procedures in your company and the effectiveness of those procedures. You can begin by preparing an explanation of the procedures in place. From the explanation, counsel will come into your company for a short period of time to gather any remaining information and to physically observe the situation. Based upon all the information from the audit, counsel will prepare a legal opinion and provide you with counsel's thoughts regarding your program. The charge will depend upon the size of the company and the preparation work done before counsel's visit. Larger companies take more effort to analyze than small companies. The legal opinion can be used as persuasive evidence in trial should litigation become necessary.

38. Why is a trade secret audit necessary?

In court, the trade secret holder needs to prove it used reasonable measures under the circumstances to protect its information. The trade secret holder stands in a strong position if they consulted with counsel about protection of its information. Is it reasonable to instruct oneself on the law when counsel is readily available?

The trade secret holder's position is greatly enhanced if they have a recent review by counsel, stating that the measures are reasonable under the circumstances. That is, it is unreasonable to require the company to second guess a legal opinion absent a showing that the trade secret holder knew the legal opinion should not be trusted. Such an exception is very difficult to show, making the opinion very powerful evidence.

39. How does the expense of an attorney impact what is reasonable under the circumstances?

The cost and benefit of using counsel determines what is reasonable. Reasonableness may be judged in view of following the most cost effective alternative.

A company using the information on this web page can greatly minimize the amount of involvement of counsel in arranging the procedures. A well-written explanation of the protection program further minimizes the involvement of counsel. A trade secret holder can be quite organized and minimize the cost of counsel, making the cost quite small.

The benefit lies principally in three areas. First, audits help by preventing problems before they occur, since well-protected information is less likely to be misappropriated. Second, audits help minimize litigation when problems arise, since well protected information is less likely to be challenged in court as to whether it is adequately protected. Third, audits ease an attorney's effort needed to prove one's case, since the information used for the audit and resulting opinion is virtually all the evidence that needs to be submitted on perhaps the most costly-to-prove element of a trade secret lawsuit. The cost savings to the trade secret holder alone in one incident will warrant the cost of a hundred or more trade secret audits. Is it reasonable under the circumstances to not have an audit performed, when the costs associated with the decision greatly exceed the cost of having the audit performed?

MODULE III - INTELLECTUAL PROPERTY EVALUATION

Intelligence

- Sources and collection of intelligence
- Interpretation of information and knowledge generation

Valuation/evaluation/assessment

- Project Prospectus
- Enhancement/improvement
- Acquisitions/alliances
- Tools – PriceAid, Valuate, Technology Pricing Model, TRIZ, Top Index, Financial spreadsheets
- Methods - market value, ROI, 25% rule, etc.
- Factors that may affect value – Regulatory e.g. FDA, USDA, EPA; environmental impact review and approval, public perception
- Information resources

Information, tools and methods for technology assessment and related due diligence are presented and discussed. Case studies are presented to provide "hands on" experience for assessment and preparation of commercialization strategy. This will include review of third party assessment and commercialization services. Emphasis is on factors that affect the development and deployment of technology. Focus is on enhancement of technology value ranging from relationships to acquisitions. The impact and influence of information technologies on communication and multimedia and ultimately technology transfer is examined.

- Licensee-corporate review and evaluation
- Checklist
- Consultants
- Compensation examples

Emphasis is on review of potential licensees and examples of variations in quantity and type of compensation to consider for select types of assets and customary corporate expectations.

INTRODUCTION

The major reason for establishing value is to justify investment. The provider must estimate value in order to justify sale terms and the purchaser establishes value based on the purchaser's business goals and objectives. Successful negotiation is often dependent on the quality of the party's evaluations and win-win relationships.

Remaining competitive in an era of rapid technological change and increasing global competition requires companies to stay current technologically. Yet, many firms find it difficult to invest in new technology. Much of the difficulty companies have in justifying investments in new technology stems from the techniques traditionally used to make capital budgeting decisions. As the provider or purchaser of an asset, one must be aware the pros and cons of strategic considerations that impact the decision-making process as these technology investment decisions are made. In addition to the information that follows examine the questions and answers related to asset management presented in Exhibit K.

TRADITIONAL CAPITAL BUDGETING TECHNIQUES

Net present value (NPV), internal rate of return (IRR) and, to a lesser extent, profitability index and discounted payback period have all become standard methods used by financial analysts, engineers, and managers. It is obvious that the cost of capital and timing of cash flows are important considerations in making business decisions.

So, what is wrong with NPV, IRR, and the other standard items when technology is being marketed? There is nothing wrong with these methods except they are insufficient for evaluating all of the pertinent considerations. Discounted cash flow decision criteria (positive NPV, IRR hurdle rate, etc.) make the cost of capital, and its implicit assumption of technological and market risk, the deciding factor in investment decisions - assuming that all costs and benefits have been appropriately considered. It is easy to find, in these caveats, potential problem areas.

First, in spite of years of business research, the translation of technological and market risk into a cost of capital or discount rate is a "judgment call". As a result one usually falls back on an accountant's calculation of the firm's weighted average cost of capital, which considers the different costs of equity and debt capital. In addition, sensitivity analyses are conducted until the original base case scenario is confounded by extraneous inputs.

The second problem revolves around whether or not all costs and benefits have been "adequately considered". Adequate consideration is more difficult to define for technology that requires further development before the final product is released for sale than it would be for a well-defined product. Costs and benefits are not well known nor is the value of the benefit well defined as yet.

TRUE BENEFIT OF TECHNOLOGY RELATED INVESTMENTS

Cash benefit of increases in capacity, production efficiency, and quality, as well as reductions in operating and maintenance costs attributable to an investment in new technology can be determined. However, seldom are strategic benefits, which result from such investments can be accounted.

First, is the investment required just to remain in the market (for example, required for regulatory compliance)? If so you may not have any choice but to proceed with the investment.

Secondly, how important is the investment to maintain competitive i.e. ability to acquire, or defend, market share? Discounted cash flow analyses includes the benefits of reduced operating costs but they seldom consider opportunity cost of lost business as a result of a competitors' ability to offer a higher quality product at reduced cost. Hence, there may be a very real cost attached to not pursuing an innovation.

Several other strategic considerations exist that are not particularly amenable to economic analyses. Will the investment add to or enhance a firm's core competencies? Will it provide the capability to penetrate new markets with a product or service? Will expanded production capacity provide access to increased sales and enhance the learning curve process which ultimately lowers costs? Is the industry one in which the market perceives technological leadership as important? These and other strategic benefits are seldom considered in discounted cash flow analyses of new technology.

TIMING AND RESPONSIBITY FOR ASSET EVALUATION

Two questions often raised are: "When is there a need to set a value for technology?" and "Who needs to value technology?"

The "when" can be considered from a prospective or retrospective view. Those who want to "market" the asset to another party conduct the *prospective* evaluation and hence value is extracted or determined over a future time period. It must be a win-win arrangement. The *retrospective* assessment usually is required as a result of litigation or adversarial situations. Value is determined at a select point in time with the valuation outcome imposed based on legal statutes imposed by judicial proceedings.

There are many parties who have a need to establish value for technology or an asset. Examples are set forth in table one.

Table one. Examples of parties who evaluate technology.

Conditions	Provider	Purchaser/Partner
	Sellers	Academia, Biotech
	Buyers	Biotech, PharmCo.
Willing	Traders	PharmCo., Biotech, Brokers
	Investors	VC's, Investment Bankers, Corporations, Lenders, Creditors
Unwilling	Acquirers	Investment Bankers
	Buyers or Sellers	Litigators

COMPETITIVE INTELLIGENCE (CI)

CI can play an important role in technology commercialization or transfer. However, to date it has not been extensively used primarily because CI is still an emerging field to which most technology transfer professionals have yet to be exposed. In addition, many technology transfer professionals in universities and nonprofit laboratories have not recognized or accepted the importance doing business in the competitive fray in which their industrial colleagues are mired. Whether it is for due diligence investigations or for negotiating from a position of strength, the nonprofit/government technology transfer professional can benefit from CI.

Any transfer of technology involves at least a technology acquirer (buyer) and a technology provider (seller). The CI needs will differ for the two. Information provided herein and by other sources may therefore need to be considered from both points of view.

CI is both a process and the product of that process. It utilizes public sources of information to develop knowledge about competitors, the market, and the business environment in general. It is not industrial espionage which is often illegally and unethically conducted. It has become somewhat axiomatic to say that 90 percent of the information needed for a key decision is available publicly.

However, publicly available does not necessarily imply published. For example, much information about companies is released in documents filed in relation to lawsuits and regulatory requirements (e.g., SEC filings, environmental impact statements, and Uniform Commercial Code filings, all of which are public documents, but are not published). Experienced CI professionals, like good investigative journalists, are part analyst and part detective.

CI is valuable in virtually all facets of technology commercialization or business especially if equity is a form of compensation involved in the transaction. It encompasses aspects of library/database searching, market research, financial analysis, environmental scanning, technology assessment, and strategic planning. The ultimate goal of CI is to generate a greater awareness of asset value, the business environment in general, and competitor actions to support business planning. Therefore, it is extremely important in the decision-making process related to asset procurement or sale. A definition for CI related to technology commercialization might be that CI is an analytical process in which raw data acquired from public sources is transformed into the strategic and tactical knowledge needed to maintain a competitive advantage, including knowledge of competitors' capabilities, intentions, strengths, and weaknesses; market preferences; and trends in technology, society, and the business environment in general.

The field of competitive, or business, intelligence analysis has grown rapidly and many firms have developed sophisticated competitive intelligence (CI) capabilities to maintain a sustainable competitive advantage. CI as discussed herein includes information related to technology or asset as well as business information. Ultimately, product and business success is due, in part, to the quality of the technology or asset held by the organization.

Collecting Information is only the start. Remember information alone is not worth much. It's what is done with it that counts. However, it is critical that the extent and quality of information gathered is all encompassing. Ten factors to keep in mind as information is gathered are:

1. Trust not a single resource, e.g. search engine, person, and book. Search engines have been reported to find less than 30% of relevant sites;

2. Trust not a single medium, e.g. only primary (interviews or surveys) or only secondary (articles or databases). Not everything is on the web. Talk to people knowledgeable in the select area. The effort is large but critical decisions will be made based on the information gathered; so prudent due diligence is essential;

3. Capitalize on electronic means of communication. A courteous request via non-intrusive e-mail, sometimes with a statement to follow-up may lead to procurement of detailed non-proprietary information, literature and software. May be especially effective if international contacts are of interest and also inexpensive;

4. Include multiple and related keywords. Don't stop with a single key word or phrase. Combine several key words that may be interchangeable (such as car and vehicle) to reduce non-relevant hits, such as "freight car" or "marketing vehicle."

5. Search carefully. Use intelligent agents, such as Firefly (www.fireflydigital.com) or Executive Assistants (www.execmag.com) to help find relevant information, or searchable services such as Business Wire (www.businesswire.com). Rely on "advanced" features that many search engines offer. Learning simple Boolean logic is not difficult; but the challenge is to know which engine uses what type of protocols. Some require spaces between the operators (such as the words "and" or "not" or symbols such as "+"), some don't. Some use their own "logic." Set up a file of the major search engine protocols. Knowing how to use "advanced" searches saves hours of time;

6. Collect information specific for a select asset or need. Survey customers via the company web site in addition to the customary site visitor analysis. Technical details of web site analysis for determining where site visitors have been is addressed by others i.e. http://www.wilsonweb.com/webmarket/traffic.htm. If a survey is planned, test the survey for areas of confusion or inconsistencies. Answers provide a basis for initiating a dialog with

prospective clients. Issues or customer concerns can be identified and general trends or customer demand can be acquired;

7. Be innovative and thorough. If a market assessment and competitive analysis for an industry is needed, select the major publicly-traded companies in the industry and examine their 10K filings with the SEC's on-line Edgar database. Look at industry suppliers and their customers. Be creative by checking out web sites of non-profit special interest groups for that industry;

8. Avoid "paralysis by analysis" syndrome. Windows of opportunity in the high tech world can be shut fast. The luxury of a 3-6 month market study may not exist; however, know "when to say when";

9. Capitalize on conflicting data. Establish a process of constant environmental marketplace, technology and other business issues, monitoring to avoid surprises. Many successful companies rely on scenario development. These companies react quickly in times of crisis...or opportunities. Other successful companies collect extensive information and analyze the buying habits of potential or existing customers. These reams of data are analyzed in near-real time. The amount of data and information needed changes according to circumstances and to strategic and corporate "style." But, timing is often critical, and not only in the world of high tech. Leverage the technological and personal resources that are available to get information needed in a timely manner; and

10. Understand data collected. Remember knowledge is power. Through study, analysis, experience, and common sense convert information to knowledge; but are sure to use the knowledge to make successful business decisions.

Academic interest aside, the objective of most commercial research is to uncover ways of improving a situation. Therefore, the analysis should focus on the implication of the research. The implication, "so what", contributes to the analytical strategy selected and enables one to find relevant information and derive valid conclusions (understanding the information) which enable valid decision-making ("recommendations") all achieved at a reasonable cost and quick enough for a business to maintain a competitive position. Several basic techniques are followed by many organizations in the analytical process and are as follows.

DATA CHARACTERIZATION

Beware of micro-segmentation and generalization to the entire marketplace or a particular niche from too small a sample size. For example, a company had three types of commercial customer, sold multiple varieties and sizes of product through a network of reps with established geographic territories across the U.S. Due to budgetary constraints, the survey conducted was limited to 150 telephone contacts of current and former customers, and included both quantitative (numerical or "choice" answers) and qualitative (open-ended, such as "how can we better meet your needs?"). Altogether there were nearly 130 data points (each open-ended question counted as a single data point) for each survey questionnaire. Some good information was gathered and a set of recommendations developed for change in some of the client's rep compensation policies and a few product improvement suggestions. But, when it came to understanding how to better serve each of the three types of commercial customer, the results were "iffy" at best.

First, the 150 contacts were divided among eight geographic territories, each served by a different sales rep, so each territory had approximately 20 companies surveyed. Now most of these territories had all three types of customer industries, so about seven companies of each type were surveyed per territory...and some were current, some were former customers. Of course, not all of these customers bought all of the client's products in question (nine in all, not counting size...from individual units to cases to pallet loads). Further, climate influenced how the products were used. Ultimately, most of the product type/customer type combinations were represented by fewer than five respondents. This did not account for the differences in sales rep capability and territory composition; hardly a case for imputing statistical significance, although valuable one-to-one information was obtained for the client. The lesson is to avoid segmenting respondent groups too finely if the intent is to generalize to the overall market, especially if there are not enough observations from which to draw valid conclusions.

DATA COLLECTION STRATEGY

An effective way to elicit new information is to intersperse open-ended, "discussion" questions among the "choice" variety. However, it is not easy to quantify narrative or subjective responses. Questionnaire replies, memo (narrative) fields included can be imported into a relational database such as Paradox or Access. Sorting and querying of multiple-choice questions is accomplished in the normal fashion to obtain demographic information, seek out relationship patterns and get a statistical profile of the responses.

Working with narrative responses is certainly less routine than working with numerical or standard text selections. Begin by identifying and listing "key phrases" contained in the narrative fields and list them in lookup tables.

Exercise a level of judgment in assigning key phrases to rambling words. Surveys typically generate 15-20 key phrases per question. Key phrases often overlap in questions that are related. It's important to set up "one-to-many" relationships between each new "key phrase" table and the reference table derived from the original narrative responses. It is necessary to capture multiple key phrases that will be present in many open-ended responses.

Transfer these key phrases to new forms, which will be used to generate reports of the key phrases used. Remember many comments made in response to open-ended questions are more appropriate to a different question than the one asked. For example, for "how can we improve?" a part of the response may refer to competitor strengths and resemble the response to another question asked elsewhere.

Once the key phrases are identified, general categories will emerge. These may be issues such as quality problems, confusion over pricing, inadequate customer service or even your entire value proposition. Some of these will be critical success factors, some of less importance. Assigning key phrases to the general categories allows one to quantify market perception of the firm's performance far more reliably than depending entirely on "choose one" types of questions, where human nature often leads to bias when respondents answer without thinking or not wanting to give a "low score" on a troublesome issue.

Identify Relationships

Studies of grocery shopping habits have shown there is a higher-than-expected correlation between beer and diaper purchases. Why? Young families have not yet reached a "champagne" budget.

Actions Speak Louder Than Words

No matter what people say, their actions are louder than words. Does the survey indicate frequent and usual actions whereas other activities are undertaken infrequently? Compare the "hard" evidence of cash register and other tallies against the local demographics and determine the averages. (See http://www.inc.com/incmagazine/archives/07980861.html)

Be Realistic

Do not let perception override reality. When making improvements, making a psychological "fix" may be cheaper, faster, and better than a mechanical or technological one.

Be Aware of the Inevitable

For example, the aging population in developed countries has a significant impact on healthcare, housing and transportation services and products. What will always need to be addressed? Finally, common sense (or lack of it) must be practiced. For example: fiscal foolishness must eventually return to a rational level. Consumer purchases cannot be legislated or mandated, e.g. who will purchase electric vehicles when the technology is still at the stage that requires 8 hours for recharging, allow travel of 80 miles between charges, and cost $10K more than conventional cars.

Strive for Real-Time Analysis

Data collection and analysis should be on-going and achieved in "near-real" time. Terabyte size data volumes are not needed. Small organizations can adopt many of the large-scale data warehousing and data mining models for PC-based systems.

BENEFICIARIES

If one works a competitive business environment, CI is needed and although nonprofit organizations (universities, laboratories, etc.) are not typically thought of as operating in a competitive environment, they do compete for students, research funding, and personnel. Furthermore, they conduct business with firms that are in highly competitive arenas and, though their needs may not be the same, a certain level of CI would be useful for defensive purposes if nothing more.

Membership in the Society of Competitive Intelligence Professionals (SCIP), the principal CI professional organization, continues to grow at a phenomenal rate. An analysis of the SCIP membership directory suggests that three industries are especially active in CI: pharmaceuticals/biotechnology, telecommunications, and computers. A common attribute these firms have is they are all in highly competitive, dynamic business environments and have considerable resources to devote to the effort. The SCIP membership includes individuals from virtually any industry, including nonprofits, and from small firms as well as large ones.

A branch of CI that is of particular interest to the technology transfer professional is competitive technology intelligence, or CTI. Firms that have a need for CTI are involved in the following activities:

1. *Technologically dynamic industrial environment.* These are firms that operate in industries subject to rapid technological change and in which entirely new or different technologies will be needed within five years.
2. *Technology intensive products and/or processes.* For such companies, technology is an important differentiating factor in product features or pricing strategy. In many instances, the timing of market entry may be important to business success. These firms may also be characterized by a high rate of new product introduction. Pharmaceutical firms face costly and complex regulatory approval of new products.
3. *Possession of extensive R&D portfolios.* These companies are R&D intensive, that is, they have a high ratio of R&D expenditure to sales. They are also firms whose R&D portfolio may contain a high proportion of large, long-range products.

Other candidates for CI are firms with a slow reaction time. There is a tradeoff between reaction time, or agility, and intelligence capability. Good intelligence can eliminate surprises or lessen their impact by affording a better opportunity to respond. If one cannot respond rapidly to changes in the competitive environment, one has to develop more accurate foresight. That requires well-developed skills in CI.

As might be expected, the intelligence needs vary with the individual's position. For example, scientists and engineers need primarily detailed technical intelligence on technical objectives, R&D approaches, manufacturing methods, and technical contacts, while technical managers have a greater need for intelligence related to competitors' program funding plans, R&D strategies, and technology acquisition strategies. Senior executives typically need intelligence concerning business alliances, new products introduced by competitors, and technical breakthroughs, while marketing personnel have a greater need for information concerning competitive product features, product sales, and cost/price data. Finally, policy makers and regulators have their own set of CI needs to help establish rational policy and regulatory requirements. These include information concerning new developments in science and technology, trends in markets, and changing societal needs and preferences.

RESOURCES AND TOOLS
Search Strategy

It is important to link to valuable resources from multiple pages, since search engines value a site based upon the number of links to it from other sites. Different search engines have different criteria and methods of search. A search engine review and relevant strategy web site for select needs are http://www.SearchEngineWatch.com.

One search strategy is by keyword, e.g. META NAME = "Keywords" CONTENT = "Search Firm, patents, inventors, US Patent Office, USPTO, Trademark Office, Patent Office, Patent Attorneys, Patent Law, free advice"

Some use text searches. The more closely this keyword list matches the Search Firm's, and the more of the same buzzwords used, the more likely that anybody finding them will also find a select site.

One favorite search engine, when starting a search, is http://www.dogpile.com. This site presents the same search criteria to multiple search engines, probably including the one that might normally be used, and displays the first results from each. One then has the option to continue with the engine that provides the best results.

Use individual and specialty search engines as needed; however, consult with "starting off" with http://www.dogpile.com for almost all comprehensive Internet searches. It is a multi-engine search engine that automatically queries 13 of the top search engines even though the query is entered only once. Go through the hit list, then enter and exit the sites of the individual search engines as desired. If this doesn't work, then use the specialty search engines.

Most search engines use substantially different programs for searching the Internet and provide very different answer sets. Even the top search engines have not indexed 25-40% of the Internet. Dogpile is a good meta search engine. It is listed on the META SE page along with others; i.e. Inference, Metacrawler and Northernlight. Metacrawler was developed at the University of Washington, and is an example of software-based technology transfer at work.

In the 2001, April 3rd Science, Steve Lawrence and C. Lee Giles estimated that the web has 320 million indexable pages. Coverage and the browsers they examined were:

Search engine	% coverage	95% CI*
HotBot	57.5%	+/- 1.3
AltaVista	46.5	+/- 1.3
Northern Light	32.9	+/- 1.1
Excite	23.9	+/- 0.86
Inforseek	16.5	+/- 1.0
Lycos	4.4	+/-0.42

* CI = Confidence Interval. The authors concluded that the best results from searching are obtained with multiple browsers or a softbot web search intelligent agent.

There are too many to list, and can be gotten to easily via web search engines whose features consist of the following or more, including those listed above.

- *Infoseek* - meta tags (lines of html code that provide info not visible to browsers), common meta tag is "keyword" tag which is emphasis of word or phrase in a page;
- *Site review* - good ranking (excite and Infoseek take into consideration);
- *Paid links* - advertiser bids on search terms, reduces "spaming" of site, examples are goto.com;

- *Hot Bot* - blend of standard search engine technology with Direct Hit (frequency and duration user is at a site), no need for boolean search command e.g. and/or, and search options include domain name, limitations, word filters, and specific data ranges;
- *AltaVista* - one of the largest engines (>150M indexed web pages), friendly but broken links in search returns are issue, options limited, boolean search via key word routing and limited searches by date, can refine search outcome by inclusion or exclusion of Alta Vista terms after 1st outcome and has Q & A feature provided by Ask Jeeves Q&A technology;
- *Excite* - simple result with lot of information covered, calls related terms to external search but limited flexibility; and
- *Google* - text match system that only returns results with terms typed into search field, has popular link features and provides web page caching (saves copies of web pages).

Alta Vista is a good source to search for scientific and technical material as well as product literature. However, relying only on Alta Vista causes one to miss important sites. So begin by conducting a Metacrawler search (http://www.metacrawler.com/). Use that search to identify which search engines produce best results and then use those engines for more complicated queries which cannot be supported by Metacrawler and other search engines which browse on the results of other engines.

Another approach is to store useful sites by profiles. That is, each site connected with commercialization work is stored in a database together with motivations for searching and information on the technology, applications, markets, and industries involved (the profile). A case based examiner allows one to rapidly retrieve sites found useful on prior projects. If it takes between five and 15 minutes to find a highly useful site, the ability to cut that search time to seconds has clear utility. A simple variant of this tool can be made by organizing "favorites" in a browser into appropriate folders. Folders can be attached as e-mails to send to colleagues.

Search engine objectives might be one or more of the following: 1) monitor competition, 2) answer key business questions; 3) solve market queries, 4) check criminal records, and 5) achieve home page recognition.

Resources

The Internet is especially good for government information (laws, regulations, pending legislation) and R&D news (e.g. Steelynx). Steelynx is a website that provides more than 5,000 links to steel making and steel-related technologies. The website provides access to online scientific and reference data. It is a popular site for industry/technology/R&D information and is free. Additional Internet resources are presented in Exhibit A and Addendum II. Consider the Gold edition of the CorpTech Directory of High Technology Companies (CD-ROM) for business and market information.

One can also use an academically-oriented set of databases, FirstSeach (an online OCLC product), that is much cheaper than Dialog (though much smaller, too: 55 databases compared to Dialog's 400+ databases). For specialized searches consider Dialog and Lexis/Nexis (e.g. trademarks; some engineering data).

Other information resources are research data collected directly from federal and university laboratories. Technology agents or brokers can also provide technology assessments for new technologies. In some cases these electronic copies of reports can be stored and accessed using Excalibur.

SRI has a for-profit subsidiary SRI Consulting (SRIC) that has a long-standing department which is well-known for its expertise and quality of its reports and customized market research. It's called the Business Intelligence Center or BIC. There are numerous other service firms i.e. SeePort (See Exhibit C and Addendum II.)

Use some of the old standbys like the Thomas Register. Their web site makes searching their massive database easy.

Concerning CI in general and technology CI in particular, it depends whether tools and techniques or information on specific technologies is sought. If the former, then consider the Society of Competitive Intelligence Professionals (SCIP) Magazine and Journal which is a good source of information. More information is available at http://www.scip.org.

If interest is in intelligence on specific technologies, there are no all-encompassing sources. It is usually necessary to go back to the journals and knowledgeable individuals in the field. For instance, IEEE Spectrum (sent to all IEEE members) is a good source for new developments in electronics related areas; whereas, Science and Nature are the usual sources for new developments in life sciences. However, if trying to keep abreast generally, there are a couple other sources to consider. *Technology Investor* helps build general awareness of new startups and up and coming technologies. In the IT area, there are many useful magazines including *The Industry Standard*. *Wired* is one that is often cited.

Corporate Data

When deciding on a strategy to apply when assessing a relationship several steps should be considered including the following: 1) Identify comparable transactions that would be helpful models; 2) determine if any agreements have been filed with the SEC; 3) determine if confidential treatment has been requested (if not, obtain the information from the SEC; if yes, see if consultants can secure necessary information and 4) identifying contractual terms/approaches that are acceptable to candidate party i.e. licensee, partner, contractee, etc.

Sources of comparable transaction data when conducting a review of a corporation whether they are an asset provider or purchaser are: internal databases, published surveys, public announcements, word of mouth, litigation, and required disclosures. Several activities require disclosure of corporate information and can be good sources of intelligence include; SEC Filings, data related to a public firm or firm going public; items contained in corporate reports and exhibits to the S3 (IPO) or 10K (Annual Report). However, commercially sensitive information can be withheld from public disclosure and may need to be disclosed subject to a confidentiality agreement. Disclosure Information Inc. is the primary contractor to the SEC for corporate filings. It was founded in 1968 and is now a subsidiary of Primark (NYSE/PSE: PMK) Waltham, Massachusetts. Only subscription services are available. The firm is a good source of pre-EDGAR documents. Certain firms have collected corporate information available to the public over time and offer consulting services designed to be useful as part of the intelligence collection plan. These firms will often have deal summaries, company valuations, contacts, and articles on valuation theory. For enactment of significant relationships the services offered can be extremely useful and cost effective.

Examples of ways to access SEC filings are: the Internet, SEC Reading Rooms, or service providers such as Disclosure Information, Inc., Recombinant Capital, Inc., Ernst & Young. An example of a web site with information is Edgar-online. Databases also exist that are designed to help multinationals with tax issues. Company valuation might include examination of the most recent 10Q (SEC) to determine the shares outstanding and share prices. At http://www.nasdaq.com exits a direct link to SEC filings where one can get underlying price data, charting, news items, and analyst reports. Another site that offers good information is http://www.stockmaster.com, which publishes corporate information.

CI DATABASE EXAMPLE (STRATEGY SOFTWARE INC.)

An example of a competitive methodology available for establishing asset value is as follows. This software is titled STRATEGY! and is a PC-based competitive information management system. With STRATEGY!, a company can organize, summarize, analyze and share information about its competition and industry.

STRATEGY! works well in a multi-user environment where it helps a team of users create and maintain a large collective awareness of CI that any of the users can contribute to and learn from. STRATEGY! Can be used in an environment with or without a Knowledge Management System.

Some examples of what is possible:

1. management can easily look up and compare specific information about competition such as their known goals, strategies, product strengths and weaknesses, etc., for strategic planning and review;
2. marketing staff can generate Market Size and Market Share reports;
3. sales people can call up a competitive product comparison matrix in seconds to see the comparative strengths and weaknesses between two or more products;
4. set up "Hot" links to competitors' web sites and other web sites with important information about the current and future competitive landscape; financial reports, market reviews, economic forecasts, or any other public information imaginable; and
5. a comprehensive set of report templates is available to help users generate concise reports with little effort. Any report can be then be viewed on screen, printed, emailed, faxed or converted to an html document to share with all employees on the corporate intranet. See http://www.strategy-software.com.

ANALYSIS TECHNIQUES

The true disciple of licensing or marketing will be the one that can convince someone what the new technology is worth. Experience of the evaluator is critical to estimate future revenue and determine the present value of a technology. Evaluation and subsequent valuation can be as much an art as science. Judgment and experience of the manager is key.

Intellectual property and asset values are often the basis from which a company is established. It is critical that the value be established based on sound financial and market facts or estimates. There are numerous methods and procedures available for use as the value is established. Marketing an idea, technology, product or company will ultimately be based on results of the value assessment.

Most analytical techniques utilized by CI analysts are not indigenous to intelligence analysis per se but come from a variety of disciplines including market research, strategic planning, technology forecasting, futures research, finance, economics, operations research, and other social sciences. Several of the more common analysis techniques grouped according to whether they are predominately qualitatively or quantitatively oriented are presented in table two. Details for the techniques are not presented but it is obvious that numerous techniques are applied in competitive intelligence analysis.

Complete and thorough collection of the facts and information related to an asset can be accomplished by following select guidelines or a checklist developed for the select type of asset. One will want to identify the critical path, scientific or marketing needs and financial commitments necessary for successful exploitation of an asset. See table two.

Table two. Common competitive intelligence analysis methods.

Qualitative Analysis Methodologies	Quantitative Analysis Methodologies
Industry/competitor descriptions	Trend extrapolation
Leadership profiling	Trend impact analysis
SWOT analysis	Market share analysis & forecasting
Vulnerability analysis	Technology substitution analysis
Core competency analysis	Data envelopment analysis
Morphological analysis	Technology state-of-the-art indexing
War gaming	Patent analysis
Political stability forecasting	Precursor trends/analogical prediction
Pattern analysis	Delphi surveys
Structured interviews/expert opinion	Financial ratio analysis
Impact wheels	
Mixed Quantitative/Qualitative Methodologies	
Scenario writing	
System dynamics modeling	

Information compiled, as asset evaluation progresses may include one or more of the criteria presented in table three.

Table three. Information resources and evaluation parameters.

Marketing	Finance
-Potential customers	-Working capital requirements
-Potential market size	-Capital expenditures
-Market shares	-Hurdle rate
-Competitors	**Research and development**
-Convoyed sales	-R&D required for particular
-Consumer preference	development stage of invention
-Expected selling price	-Feasibility of various technological
	alternatives
Manufacturing and production	**Other**
-Working capital requirements	-Trade publications or associations
-Current facility utilization	-Academia
-Labor, material and overhead costs	-Research departments in all fields
-Accounting	-University sponsored "think tanks"
-Preparation of revenue & cost estimates	-Professional consultants or advisors
-General knowledge of books and records	
-Feasibility of various technological alternatives	

Another evaluation process addresses potential variables that impact value some of which are presented in table four.

Table four. Examples of variables impacting asset value.

Variable	Basic research/new technology	Replacement technology
Market identity	potential applications geographical markets potential end users level of specialization	existing markets existing customers
Price	uses of technology potential customer's budgets marketplace constraints supply and demand	price of similar tech
Cost to manufacture	cost to manufacture similar tech equipment needed to manufacture	industry manufacturing costs
Cost to sell	potential market distribution channels	industry selling costs
Cost to develop	development cost to date future R&D needed	industry development costs

Basic research/new technology means the capability to develop acceptable alternative technology including both current and future availability. Also included is what type of value is conferred; i.e. are costs reduced, is there a need for less capital investment and/or does it result in improved customer acceptance. Finally does the technology have the potential to become a standard in the industry?

Replacement technology will involve collection of available information through research in both the replacement technology and new technology environments. Available information may include: revenue, cost and profit expectations, asset utilization, financing, marketing, engineering, manufacturing costs and capacities.

USES AND APPLICATIONS

CI supports virtually any business function. It is an essential component of strategy development and business planning; but CI also supports tactical decision-making which is where it is typically applied.

R&D and strategic technology planning are areas in which CI is of particular interest to the technology commercialization professional from industry, academia, or government laboratories. By incorporating technology-forecasting methodologies, competitive technology intelligence can provide needed background into technology trends and competitor capabilities and needs. New developments in scientometrics, including patent analysis, literature citation analysis, which rely on modern database technology, provide additional insight into the technological landscape. This information is vital to strategic technology planning as well as the licensing and other commercialization activities undertaken by industry, universities, and nonprofit research institutions.

Pricing and cost analysis is another area in which CI is important. Such knowledge is intimately related to strategic planning. For example; can a technology and the resultant product compete on cost, or is there a need to differentiate the product in some other manner? Knowledge of competitors' cost structures and pricing policies are needed; otherwise these decisions are merely unsubstantiated projections. Acquiring this information is a challenge. Cost and pricing data are closely guarded secrets (not to mention charges of collusion if this information were shared). Some knowledge of the manufacturing and other business processes used is essential to such an assessment. Knowledge of the processes employed, the types and sources of raw materials used, and the distribution channels engaged will enable one to begin reconstructing a competitor's cost structure. This knowledge is seldom available in a complete package but must be synthesized by the CI analyst from numerous disparate bits of information.

Traditional market research is designed to try to understand market preferences so that products meeting real needs can be developed. However, an understanding of competitors' marketing strategies not only helps one understand how competitors perceive the market (and confirm or negate one's perceptions), but it may indicate new areas of opportunity and vulnerabilities in strategic or tactical plans. Knowing the market is important. It is equally important to know where, how, and when competitors will attack in that market. As a corollary, intelligence concerning a competitor's marketing plans, including what it does not intend to do, might help one avoid the expense of making preemptive moves in the wrong area.

Societal trends and regulatory activities impact everyone. Anticipating societal needs, which are ultimately reflected in legislation and regulatory requirements, may help minimize any adverse impact on a technology or business and/or future opportunities might be identified.

Technology commercialization is becoming more and more complex and often involves acquisitions or partnerships. CI is often used to contribute to the due diligence investigation conducted after such mergers and acquisitions plans are developed. In addition to providing more than just historical financial data, CI can help assess future prospects for the merger/partner candidate. CI can be even more powerful to develop an understanding of competitors' capabilities, strengths, and weaknesses that could indicate a need for, or the desirability of, some type of technology or business combination. CI can help increase the number of potential asset acquisition candidates or partners thus enhancing the transfer of commercialization process.

Finally, benchmarking is an activity that has been widely championed for analyzing and improving asset development and deployment. While benchmarking, as originally conceived, contemplates the open exchange of information among companies, there are many cases in which an open exchange is illegal, unrealistic, undesirable, or simply impossible (e.g., the target refuses to cooperate). In many cases, there is more than enough publicly available information to allow one to gauge capabilities in selected functions against those of other firms, and CI analysis is how we get it.

CI QUESTIONS

Answers are limited only by absence of questions. However, it is necessary to focus on what is needed. Examples of questions that might be raised are:

1. Who are competitors? Who are potential competitors?
2. What is technical capability of competitors or potential competitors? Will relationships be needed to be successful?
3. How do competitors see themselves and how do they view others?
4. What are the track records of key people at competitors? What are their personalities and how do they make decisions?
5. What are the short and long term trends impacting the industry? How will these trends impact the business? How are competitors likely to respond to these trends?
6. In what areas of technology are competitors or potential competitors focusing? What do developments in these areas mean to one's business? How and when will these developments be implemented in new products?
7. How do competitors market products? What distribution channels do they use? In which markets might they attack us directly? What can be learned from their successes?
8. What markets or geographic areas are likely to be left unserved by competitors? What opportunities might arise for one's firm, and can one acquire the technologies and other resources necessary to capitalize on these opportunities?
9. How will the markets respond to changes in price, distribution, and service?

Each of these questions has a strong technological component. As a tech transfer professional on the provider or acquirer side, it typical to answer questions concerning whom to offer an asset to, where to locate needed technologies and how much to pay for them. It may be necessary to address issues concerning the present state of the art and how rapidly that state of the art is likely to progress. At a higher level, strategic technology planning may dictate a need for information on competitor's technologies and how they were acquired. Seldom are technology transfer/licensing activities of universities and government laboratories kept secret. Keeping abreast of these activities can provide important clues about competitors' technological capabilities, strengths, weaknesses, and new product development plans.

As a technology transfer professional on the provider side (which may be business, academia, or government) it is necessary to know essentially the same information about the firm one is negotiating with in order to develop a reasonable negotiating strategy designed to maximize the compensation received. How badly does the firm need this technology? Where does it fit in their product development plans? If no arrangement is concluded what are the alternatives? How good is the technology compared to the alternatives? Answers to these queries impact the license fee and royalty rate that a licensor may reasonably expect to get. Unfortunately, such negotiations often center around historical or "ballpark" royalty rates, principally because the licensor does not have sufficient intelligence concerning the needs and capabilities of the buyer and the alternatives, or lack thereof, available to it.

PROCESS

There is a well-developed set of tasks, sometimes known as the intelligence cycle, that are typically followed for any CI project. The competitive intelligence cycle or process is comprised of five essential steps as listed and described as follows:

1. CI needs established;
2. data collection;
3. data evaluation;
4. data/information analysis and interpretation; and
5. intelligence reporting and dissemination.

Needs Establishment

As with virtually any business activity or project, preplanning is critical. This step consists of six basic elements:

First, state what must be known. This simple question can be difficult to answer succinctly. The question might be altered to "What decision must be made?" or "What specific question do you seek to answer?"

Second, determine who will make decisions using this intelligence? Is it for the benefit of senior management doing strategic planning or is it to support the tactical decisions of operating managers?

Third, specify the time frame available for analysis. It will do no good to initiate a 4-week intelligence project if an answer is needed tomorrow.

Fourth, identify the analysis framework or data reduction techniques needed to acquire the necessary intelligence. This defines what needs to be accomplished to address the question.

Fifth, identify specific targets for analysis, if applicable. Know the plans of every firm in an industry but plans for only one or two specific competitors are really needed.

Sixth, with the results of the previous elements, determine what specific information is needed to make a valid decision.

Data Collection

First consider the types of analyses selected in examining the CI needs. Data collected must be commensurate with the analysis to be performed. Then identify the most promising sources and data collection strategies to be invoked. Remember, that most of the information required is often available from in-house resources. Therefore, conduct an in-house CI audit to identify internal resources available for the project. For external needs, develop a secondary research plan and once these resources are exhausted embark on primary research to supplement data collection efforts. Search and evaluation forms, tools, methodologies and information are presented in Exhibits E, F, and G and Addenda I, II, III and IV.

Once the search strategy is in place the conduct of the search involves selection of key resources and libraries of information. Search engines and web sites are resources that are employed for the collection of data.

Innovation and markets are no longer local, regional or national. The information age and global focus opens up new markets and also creates new challenges as the transfer or commercialization process takes place. Governments are seeking ways to privatize business in certain countries creating opportunities for the business community; however the business strategy in these cases are complex often requiring critical and experienced expertise to engage and foster international relationships. There are several treaties to which certain countries subscribe for the protection of intellectual property. However, these treaties have various unique features and failure to recognize and adjust the protection strategy. This can influence the value and subsequent commercialization of an asset.

Data Evaluation, Analysis and Interpretation

This is usually the most difficult and often most ambiguous part of any CI project. The analytical framework(s) selected are imposed on the data and information to discern meaning. Data and information, no matter how well collated and organized, do not equate to intelligence. True intelligence must be synthesized from the data and information by assembling it in context and determining what it means. If analytical modeling or simulation is part of the project, it is performed in this step. Finally, the data, information, and model results must be interpreted to assess their implications and impact on the business.

At this stage data collected are organized, verified, collated, and transformed into meaningful input for subsequent analysis. First, it is important to determine reliability of both the data collected and the source of that data. Strive for corroboration wherever possible and try to identify and eliminate disinformation. Then, assess accuracy of the data and its relevance to the project. Various rating schemes have been proposed for these tasks, but generally the simpler the better. Next, assemble the data into information building blocks. This step typically involves collating and organizing the data so that it provides useful input for the analyses. Then, abstract, categorize and store the assembled information for easy retrieval. Finally, identify any gaps in the data by asking the question; "What else is needed to complete the analysis? Patent considerations for this step: First, get non-disclosure agreements signed by anyone to whom the idea is presented to for evaluation. Also do a patent search.

Personal or Self-evaluation

To avoid wasting money on evaluations of already patented inventions one can do their own patent search or pay to have one done. First search the patent information available on the Internet. If the invention is not found online, visit the nearest Patent and Trademark Depository Library and conduct a search. (A complete list of supporting libraries can be found at www.uspto.gov.) Librarians will assist with searches. A search is easy to conduct but not foolproof. If no relevant patents or patent applications that have been publicized are found a judgment call needs to be made as to whether or not one should obtain a professional search or proceed based on the assumption that no prior art exists.

Seldom will any professional searcher conclude that no prior art exists. The fact that an invention cannot be found by searching the USPTO's patents does not mean that the invention is patentable. A complete patentability search must consider all prior art, including earlier products, earlier patents, foreign patents, non-patent literature, and "obviousness." Generally, a professional patent search will almost always ignore everything but a searching of U.S. patents unless a searcher is directed otherwise and paid accordingly. If the invention turns out to be a multi-million dollar winner, competitors or potential competitors will do an exhaustive "prior art" search in an attempt to invalidate the patent.

There are broad ranges of programs for evaluating inventions, from the provider who does it at no cost and who will always tell you to go ahead (and, for a fee, they can help you), to University programs, to very expensive market research firms (often used by large successful corporations). It usually makes sense to incur some upfront cost and either conduct a search or have one conducted by a well respected firm or individual. An underlying objective should be to select a person or organization that has a marketing perspective. Remember, the asset must eventually sell.

If performing a self-evaluation, it might be prudent to examine educational resources, such as, "Millions from the Mind" by Alan R. Tripp or "Innovations, Evaluating Potential New Products" (the PIES-VIII book) by Gerald Udell. However, be aware that self-evaluation may not provide an objective opinion.

A free evaluation form is also available at http://www.patent-ideas.com. The author of this site, Mr. Neustel is also responsible for the National Inventor Fraud Center at http://www.inventorfraud.com that offers suggestions related to selecting service providers.

For about $70 one can order the *"Invention Assessment & CD ROM Program"* with no limit on number of ideas that can be evaluated (http://www.patentcafe.com/kits/assesskit.html). The CD contains 6 Excel spreadsheets that provide numerous evaluation questions. The seventh spreadsheet summarizes and displays a Graphic Performance Report.

Academic Evaluation

One of the bigger university evaluation programs is the Wisconsin Innovation Service Center (WISC) at the University of Wisconsin-Whitewater. An electronic version of their evaluation application can be found at http://www.uww.edu/business/innovate/innovate.htm. The WISC program does a thorough check in return for about $500.

The Center for Entrepreneurship, Hankamer School of Business at Baylor University (hsb.baylor.edu/html/cel/ent/inninvp.htm) is patterned after WISC in that they have many of the same questions on their invention disclosure form. They charge $150 and promise an evaluation based on 33 criteria that are used to create a Critical Value Score, an Aggregate Value Score, and an Estimate of Success. They also explicitly provide "no confidential relationship" between the client and them but will treat the disclosure "with care." The extent and uniqueness of the evaluation resembles the WISC and WIN programs.

Another evaluation program is Wal-Mart Innovation Network (WIN) in the Center for Business & Economic Development, Southwest Missouri State University at Springfield, MO (http://www.walmart.com/win). They do the PIES-VIII evaluation for $175. The client receives a full set of responses to their standardized evaluation and a discussion of what the results mean. PIES-VIII is the 8th iteration of the Preliminary Innovation Evaluation System (PIES) developed by Dr. Gerald G. Udell (and others) at the University of Oregon. WIN's purpose is not to predict commercial success but to detect serious technical or commercial flaws in the idea submitted.

Professional Assessment or Marketing Firm Evaluation

At the very least a marketing evaluation should not only answer the "Will it sell?" question, but, if it's "Yes," give an idea of what price buyer's might be willing to pay and what size the market might be. The professional results might also discuss competitors and their current market shares, depending on the product. In some cases the report might give some indication of what marketing strategy competitors are using. How much are they spending on various media? What is their market channel? Remember the more restricted the problem a product solves, the less reliable this kind of competitor information can be because there is simply no place to get the data. A market research firm is most likely to try to err on the conservative side in this kind of analysis. Using a conservative estimate lowers the risk because projections of profitability at the conservative level will justifiably induce one to proceed.

There are numerous firms that are willing to provide a review of new technology or inventions for a fee. It is well to obtain some background information on the firm and examine references or locate others who have used their services to determine quality of the service.

Another option available is to transfer the intellectual property asset to a company that reviews the property, and determines if they are interested in transferring, developing or licensing the property. Other firms determine interest and require that the asset be assigned to them for commercialization. All service providers receive compensation. An example of service provider's terms and strategy is presented in Exhibit C.

Reporting and Dissemination

The last step in the CI process is perhaps the most important, and often the most poorly performed. Intelligence is useless if it is not available for decision makers to act on. In step one, it was determined who will need to make decisions using the intelligence. It may be prudent to disseminate it to others in the organization that may benefit from having it. But, everyone already suffers from information overload; so don't blanket the entire organization with a report containing information needed only by managers in one division. The mode of disseminating the intelligence product is equally important and must be appropriate for the situation. Various types of intelligence alerts, reports, memos, and the like are often used depending on the nature and importance of the intelligence provided. The CI analyst must consider the background of the users and how they like to receive information. It will do little good to present a voluminous report to a CEO who prefers to be briefed with a 10-minute presentation and provided with a one-page synopsis for future consideration. It also helps to pre-sell the information. Remain in close contact with intended users throughout the intelligence project. Discuss the types of data being collected and the analyses being performed. Make certain intelligence generated is valuable to users so they will eagerly anticipate the report and find it beneficial.

COMPETING TECHNOLOGY IDENTITY

The following example is based on software, but the steps may be relevant for other types of technology.

1. Are there patents in this area?
   - Search by keyword, and by classification if appropriate.
   - Also, if sponsor has relevant patent(s), look for later patents that build on original patent.
   - The IBM Patent Server, now Delphi, is a site to try: http://www.patents.ibm.com.

   Analysis: Identify companies with related patents. They represent potential competitors and potential licensors. One cannot determine whether a product has been successfully commercialized from patents, but a product may be under development, and these are often a beginning point for further research.

2. Are there research articles from corporate researchers?
   - Search journal databases for the subject, and check the author affiliation field.
   - Look for authors from companies.
   - Useful databases for software research are available in most libraries. See INSPEC or Current Contents.

   Analysis: Many companies do not encourage publication by employees, so an absence of articles reveals little. The presence of publications by corporate researchers is another indicator of a company's interest in the relevant area. Again, one cannot necessarily determine whether there is a product in the marketplace, but possible future developments are suggested.

3. Is there mention of the problem that this software is attempting to solve in the technical magazines, trade journals, product announcements, and company press release files?
   - Search trade journal databases for mention of your subject, and review the articles found for mention of specific companies.

- Useful databases on the library gateway: Infotrac Expanded Academic Index, ABI/Inform, Reader's Guide and Periodical Abstracts for consumer products, press releases, search PR Newswire (http://www.prnewswire.com) and Businesswire(http://www.businesswire.com).

Analysis: One reason to include this step, and the patent search, for the software industry, is that large companies are not responsible for all major developments. One cannot just evaluate the products of the top five database companies and be assured of having a comprehensive picture of new developments. Check additional sources to find smaller firms.

4. Check software directories and journals carrying software reviews.

- Libraries may have a software directory database for business application software - ComputerSelect, which is a CD-ROM searchable at libraries. This product also includes some basic software company information and reviews.

- For reviews of consumer products, try the following databases on the library gateway: Reader's Guide, Periodical Abstracts, Newspaper Abstracts, Expanded Academic Index, Wilson Select Full Text, ArticleFirst. For reviews of business application software, try ABI/Inform, Expanded Academic Index, Wilson Select Full Text, or Business Abstracts.

- See also journal databases relevant to specific industries - e.g., for reviews of software used in manufacturing processes, check Engineering Index/Compendex, reviews of medical software, check Medline.

- For industries other than software, there are also product directories. For example, for manufacturers one of the primary directories is the Thomas Register, available at http://www.thomasregister.com.

5. Check software company Web sites.

- Examine product brochures, FAQs and white papers.

- Strategy: Once candidate companies have been identified through the above steps and other knowledge, two types of Web searches may be helpful:

    (A) Locate the Web sites for relevant firms, and use the search feature (if available) to look up relevant keywords. Keywords may be product names, or terms to describe benefits/features/problem being solved by the software.

    (B) Search using NorthernLight, power search feature. This feature allows one to put in keywords, + select words in the URL. For example, look for the phrase project management and the URL for Oracle, to find out what the firm is publicizing about its software for such applications.

6. Commercial online information systems, such as Lexis-Nexis, Dialog, and Dow Jones Interactive, can provide much of the above information as well, and often more efficiently. These services also have information sources not easily accessible elsewhere; e.g., the complete text of market research reports. However, access to such services is available only for a fee.

ETHICS

Earlier it was noted that ethical collection of competitive information is desired, not industrial espionage. Remember, ethical CI is legal CI. At no time in competitive intelligence analysis should one seek to do anything illegal nor there be enticement for anyone else to break any laws.

Any intelligence project requires a good understanding of the kind of data and information being sought. Proprietary or trade secret data may not be obtainable ethically or legally. Furthermore, what sources will be used to obtain the information? Information is an unusual commodity because, unlike tangible property, it can be usurped without depriving the owner of its use. Moreover, the owner may not know that the information was taken and the acquirer may not even realize that they have it. Finally, consider how the intelligence generated will be used. It might be used to guide strategy formulation or to undermine a competitor and engage in unfair competition. The former is ethical and the latter is not.

To help ensure that the CI profession remains an honorable one, SCIP has developed a code of ethics for its membership to abide by. With the passage of the Industrial Espionage Act of 1996, there are also very real penalties for engaging in unscrupulous behavior.

TECHNOLOGY ACQUIRER VIEWPOINT

Why do firms acquire technology from outside? Usually it is to supplement internal technological resources, shorten new product development time, or provide access to new markets. These goals suggest three principal uses for CI by the buyers in the technology transfer process including competition analysis, sourcing needed technology and competition monitoring.

Competition Analysis

The first use of competitive technology intelligence is to analyze the competition. In addition to direct licensing arrangements, companies enter into various types of engagements with universities and government laboratories including CRADAs, research consortia, and so on. Nearly all of this is publicly available information. Information on the technology transfer interests of a competitor, including technology it has licensed, the consortia in which it participates, and alliances it has with laboratories and universities, provides valuable intelligence about that competitor's technology strategy, technical capabilities, and new product development plans.

Sourcing Needed Technology

Competitive technology intelligence (CTI) is also useful for identifying potential sources of needed technology. Keep in mind the bulk of technology transfer occurs inter-company and many firms do not proactively seek to license technology that may be available. Only by keeping abreast of the technical activities of competitors, and noncompetitors who have similar technical needs, will you be able to identify technologies that you can acquire. Conversely, CTI can be used defensively to prevent a competitor from using its patent position or alliances to block you from obtaining access to a needed technological resource.

Competition Monitoring

Lastly, CTI can provide an early warning of technical developments in a fields of interest. More than simply tracking and predicting advances in the state of the art, CTI can identify potentially new competitors who may result from either emerging technologies or changes in business strategy. More than one firm (or even industry) has been blind-sided by the application of technologies originally developed in other industries for other purposes.

TECHNOLOGY PROVIDER VIEWPOINT

As a technology provider, especially on the academic or laboratory side, there is a completely different set of needs for competitive intelligence. Generally, these needs fall into the realm of who will buy the technology? Why will they buy it? And, who else is offering something similar? The following is a list of six uses for CTI by providers of technology. For such organizations, CTI can be used to perform the following activities.

Purchaser Identification

Many, if not most, organizations do a poor job of proactively marketing the technologies they have available for licensing. Some simply issue press releases or send announcements to all firms in an industry and hope that the responses will roll in. Once a technology becomes available, it will have value for only a limited period of time and the window of opportunity closes quickly. Technology transfer must proceed at the speed of technological change; preferably faster. Otherwise, there is a strong likelihood that the technology will have diminished value to a potential receiver, if not become obsolete entirely. Technologies that sit on the shelf provide value to no one. CTI can help assess the market for new technologies and identify potential customers. It can help you learn who else works in the field and might have a need for the technology by answering the question: For whom does it fill a gap, provide a needed enabling technology, or shorten product development time?

Due Diligence on Potential Licensees

Will the prospective licensee be able to fulfill its responsibilities under the anticipated license agreement? Does it have a history of attempting to hide revenues from products developed using licensed technology or might it be seeking a license principally to block a competitor from obtaining the technology? Does the firm have the necessary financial strength to complete the development of a product based on the technology and successfully penetrate the market? Without this ability there will be few royalties.

Value of Technology to Licensee

What, really, is this technology worth to them? How much in research and development expenditures will be saved as a result of licensing the technology from you? What revenues will they likely be able to generate from the use of your technology?

Licensee Performance Criteria

Is the licensee living up to the terms of the agreement? Is it giving a full reporting of revenues generated from the technology?

Identify Potential Collaborators

Frequently, a specific technology or individual patent may not be enabling by itself. What other firms or laboratories may have something to contribute? Can a package of complementary technologies/patents be constructed to provide enhanced value to all concerned?

Identify Possible Patent Infringers

Most people working in this field know they must affirmatively defend their patent position. CTI can help identify infringers. Used proactively however, the first item in this list becomes key -- identifying others working in the field who are potentially future infringers and who might otherwise be looked upon as potential licensees.

If transfer of a technology is preferred and not developed or marketed, there is usually interest in reaching agreement with another party as quickly as possible after disclosure. This attitude is more prevalent in the research institutions than in the corporate environment. If early licensing is preferred, establish a network of contacts in the corporate community who are interested in providing preliminary review of new discoveries. A brief synopsis of the discovery or business opportunity can be prepared that does not disclosure information that would jeopardize asset protection. This document can be submitted to the select group of corporate reviewers for preliminary comment.

INTELLECTUAL PROPERTY RIGHTS AND VALUE

The value of a patent is dependent upon the quality of the patent when allowed. The first part of this section is directed toward patent quality as a result of patent office search for prior art. Next, emphasis is on patent documentation as a source of general business information and technical information for Research & Development. Third, focus is on successful use of Intellectual Property Rights (IPR) as a form of technology transfer in business, and finally an example of how patent information was used to generate a satisfactory commercial conclusion is presented. Remember patents are just one type of intellectual property; others include trademarks, copyright, trade secrets and designs.

Economic Value – Non-infringing Substitutes

Infringement is associated with the validity and quality of issued patents. Key to establishing validity and quality is the search and subsequent reference to search results whether it be by the inventor, legal counsel or patent examiners.

Searches are a part of the patent application review process; however, the extent and quality of the search will impact whether the patent is allowed and if allowed the quality of the resultant patent. The owner of the asset for which patent protection is sought should do all they can to conduct literature and patent searches for prior art. Some contend that examiner's searches may or may not be as thorough as the submitting party might expect. When there is doubt as to the validity or quality of patent office searches there is one strategy that might be used, have both USPTO and PCT searches conducted and the results compared. The initial cost can be minor compared with the cost of litigation or loss of product sales revenue.

Patents and Business

The publication of patent documents ("specifications") is an essential feature of the patenting process throughout the world. Over 35 million patents have been published worldwide to date, and another 1 million new patent specifications appear each year. This makes patents the largest single body of technological information available anywhere, and one that is ideally suited for use as a business information source. In brief, you can use patents to answer questions such as:

- What innovations are likely to hit the market?
- Who are the key organizations and individuals working on these innovations?
- Which industries are most productive?
- Which countries are patenting these technologies?

Patent information should be an essential part of the business information strategy if a company is in any way involved in company and market analysis, and development and/or exploitation of technology.

It may be prudent to know more about a particular company if they are: 1) competitors, 2) potential partners, 3) candidates for take-over or; 4) potential candidates for investment. Patent information can be used to answer questions such as the following:

"Does Company X have a meaningful research program?"
  If a company is serious about its research and protecting its ideas, any inventions will be patented under its own name (or perhaps under another name, such as that of a subsidiary, if it wants to 'hide' its research activity). You can locate these patents by searching patent information sources using the appropriate company name as a search term.

"What type of R&D activity is being carried out by Company X?"
  Patent information sources can help identify the patents filed by Company X, and so find out how many have been filed year on year and in which areas of technology. The results suggest where current R&D efforts are focused, and may indicate company strategy. Changes in patent activity may indicate changes in the underlying R&D, such as an increase or decrease in the amount of money invested in R&D or a shift in the area of research.

"Is Company X research at the cutting edge of a new technology?"
  Insight into "what's hot and what's not" can be gained by analyzing the age of Company X patents, and also references to prior patents ("patent citations'). In general, patent documents which are cited frequently contain information which has made a large impact or information about a new technological advance. When a recent patent cites patents

from several decades ago, it can be concluded that an old technology is still being improved. In contrast, when a recent patent cites other recently issued patents, it is evident that this technology is 'hot'.

"How do I learn more about specific market sectors....?"

Scope of patent information searches can be expanded to obtain similar information for entire markets and industry sectors. The following example provides an illustration of how patent activity acts as an excellent tool for detecting emerging technologies and identifying key players in the marketplace.

In 1975, US patent 3873763 was issued to Philips for an invention called "Disk-shaped record carrier on which information is recorded in the form of an 1975-1978 19 U.S. patents were granted to Sony and Philips for optical disks; 1979-1982 14 U.S. optical disk patents were granted; 1983-1986 49 U.S. optical disk patents were granted - CD players went on sale; 1987-1989 61 U.S. optical disk patents were granted - CD-ROM became available; 1990-1992 over 100 U.S. optical patents were granted to Sony and Philips alone.

"How does patent information help if one is involved in product and process development for commercial application..."

Patent information should be an essential part of any business strategy, whether that business carries out original R&D or not. It can enhance business intelligence by providing:

1. ***Full and practical descriptions of innovations.*** A patent specification must contain enough detail to allow an expert in the same area of technology to recreate the innovation described in the specification - an ideal way of keeping your development team informed.

   Many patents are published with search reports prepared by the patent offices, listing patents and any other literature relevant to the subject matter of the invention. These provide additional information that might benefit business intelligence.

2. ***Data on "state of the art".*** The background information provided in patent specifications often provides an excellent review of the state of the art in a particular area of technology.

3. ***Indications of business opportunities.*** Patents can reveal existing technology for those who have a problem to solve. Business can be developed using licensed patents, avoiding the need for costly research. Patents, filed by individuals rather than companies, are often not in use, and the inventors are happy to license them out to companies who need the solution they offer. Large companies sometimes find that their patented products don't always fit their business strategy. In return for royalties, they may be happy to allow another company to market the invention.

If a business is involved in R&D, there are some additional reasons why patents should be included in business information sources:

1. ***Determine if research is redundant.*** European Community studies have shown that 30% of all R&D activity duplicates work which has already been carried out, amounting to a total cost of more than $65M every day in Europe alone. Patent information can help determine the novelty of an innovation and avoid costly duplication of effort - costly both in terms of wasted effort and possible litigation costs.

2. ***Identify new avenues of research.*** If your original research idea has already been patented, you can still use patent information to identify alternative and improved approaches to your research.

3. *Detect infringement of patents.* If a business holds patent rights, there is a need to watch for any infringement of the patent portfolio in order to maintain its commercial value. New patent applications and grants need to be monitored to check if one's patents have been cited by the patent examiner or inventor. This provides an "alert" to competitors who are closing in on one's technology. An objection can be filed to block the competitor's patent application, or a firm can make other business plans before the competitor becomes a threat.

Irrespective of business type, patents as a business information source have two unique advantages:

1. *Data relevance.* The publication of a patent application is often the first time for publication of that information, because the details of an invention are kept secret before a patent application is submitted. Significant inventions such as the jet engine, television and ductile cast iron were all first disclosed in the patent literature 5-10 years before they appeared in any other literature sources.
2. *Unique information.* Failure to examine patents, can result in missing a large amount of information because 70-90% of patent information is never published anywhere else.

Revenue

Most innovations represent small advances that can significantly affect a particular technology or business activity rather than an outstanding breakthrough. Allowing others to develop your innovations or incorporating those from other sources, can be a profitable activity for everyone concerned with this form of technology transfer.

Licensing can be an effective corporate strategy in situations where competing technologies are fighting to establish themselves as the standard in a global market. This is the case with the domestic video recorder market where in the early days the two prime contenders were VHS and Betamax recording formats. Although Betamax was regarded by some experts as technically superior to VHS, the latter (developed by JVC) eventually dominated the market because of JVC's efficient licensing strategy.

For example, the British Technology Group (BTG) is an international technology transfer company which has built a successful business over 45 years on the basis of patent licensing. Although BTG has no manufacturing facility, the annual sales value of the products currently licensed amounts to approximately $2B. It owns or has rights to over 9,000 patents but does not have any R&D facilities; instead it relies on academic and other sources of commercial R&D results. What it has, however, are almost 500 license agreements with companies, both large and small around the world, which currently generate over $32M per annum.

BTG benefits from the increasing awareness of companies worldwide of the importance of Intellectual Property Rights (IPR) and the effect it can have on their business. The level of awareness is indicated by the number of patents filed each year and has increased dramatically. Between 1983 and 1990 the number of patents filed worldwide grew from 0.8 million to more than double that number. It appears that this trend is set to continue, particularly as organizations realize that patenting their ideas can be used to trade in IPR and not just to defend their product position. Estimates put the value of internationally traded IPR at around $15B and this relates to end product sales of around $300B. Nonetheless, the number of companies that file and use their patents strategically as an intrinsic part of their business are on the increase. However, many companies are unaware of the potential of patenting their developments and optimizing the financial return from their investments.

A good example of a company which demonstrated the value of IPR is Pilkington. In 1960, Pilkington was a small family-owned company that had developed a highly innovative float glass process which dramatically reduced the cost of manufacturing sheet glass. Over the subsequent 25 years it became the world's largest producer of float glass through licensing its technology to other companies. The royalty income from licensing contributed substantially to Pilkington's profits and

311

was part of a sophisticated and well implemented commercial strategy. Once in place, licensing carries very little overheads and income from royalty normally falls straight to the bottom line. In the case of Texas Instruments, it is estimated that between 1987 and 1991, they earned nearly $1B in patent royalties from licensing silicon chip technology and that this provided a major contribution to profits.

The examples given are success stories brought about by an appreciation of the value of patents and the will to use them as part of the company's commercial strategy. This is, however, a two-way street and just as the licensee benefits from licensing, the licensor can benefit similarly by having access to new products and opportunities without the risk of engaging in new product development. It makes little sense to commit to valuable resources to "inventing the wheel", when it has already been done. Many companies, particularly small to medium size enterprises with more limited resources, can use licensing to improve, complement, or extend their product range against ever mounting global competition.

RESOURCES AND SEARCH METHODS

To extract and analyze information from such a large fund of documented knowledge is a daunting task to those unfamiliar with patent literature. However, Thomson-Derwent and the major patent issuing authorities have released a number of products designed to overcome any fear of searching through this collection of data, by helping users gain reader access to, and understanding of, the vital information to be obtained from patents.

Generally the databases include abstracted records from published patents and may be interrogated by keyword searching. As a complement to using classification and keywords, inventor and company names may also be searched. (http://www.derwent.com/)

Patent Information is Priceless

The following is an example of how an inventor used the huge resource of data that is "patent information" to plan, develop and control the growth of an original idea into a successful commercial product.

"I know a man who re-invented the wheel." Mike Burrows is probably best known to the public as the designer of the Lotus bicycle with the monocoque frame, on which Chris Boardman won a gold medal in the 1992 Barcelona Olympics.

Despite his innovative approach to bicycle design, Mike Burrows did not profit himself when his early innovations went into commercial production, partly because he did not get patent protection for many of these ideas. But having learnt the cost of not using patent information with his early ideas, he took a different approach when he set about re-inventing the wheel.

"Reinventing the wheel" is a phrase which has entered the English language as a synonym for wasting time by duplicating effort. It might appear that Mike Burrows was wasting his time when he first came up with the idea of a new type of bicycle wheel with injection-molded plastic spokes. But any invention which is sufficiently new and innovative may be patented – even the wheel.

At the start of a project, many inventors make the mistake of not finding out what has been done before. Mike Burrows quickly learned that to avoid wasting time and money developing a new type of wheel, he needed assurance that someone else had not already invented and patented the idea.

So, he searched Derwent Information's patent sources, and discovered that EDO Sports had already been granted a U.S. patent for a similar idea, plastic 'fiber-flight' spokes for bicycle wheels. A setback, you might think? Not so. Like many major industrial companies, Mike Burrows was able to progress his idea by inventing around what had already been done. He revised his original idea to improve on these earlier patents, and developed a unique and more sophisticated way of re-inventing the wheel.

On June 20th 1994, Mike Burrows filed a patent application, (GB 9412309.8), at the UK Patent Office for a "spoked wheel". When his application is accepted, he alone will have exclusive rights to use, market and profit from his invention.

Using Derwent Information's patent sources, Mike Burrows knows that his application has a significantly improved chance of success. He is fully aware of what has already been patented and has made sure that his invention is new.

Two days later on June 22nd 1994, he unveiled his new "spoked wheel" to the public at the Shimano European Bicycle Design Competition in Cologne, as part of his latest carbon-fiber frame bicycle – the Aero-Road Prototype (AR1). The new wheel had injection-molded plastic spokes, just as described in his patent application.

A Commercial Success. Mike Burrows signed an agreement with Giant, a bicycle manufacturer based in Taiwan, that was selling 1.7 million bicycles every year. Giant started commercial production of the AR1 bicycle with its innovative spoked wheels in 1995, and sold it for £2,000-£3,000. Giant and Mike Burrows are to continue developing his innovative spoked wheel. Their aim is to produce the first 'Aero' wheel at a price comparable to that of standard wheels.

A Cautionary Note. If Mike Burrows had not searched the patent information sources and had stuck to his original idea, none of this might have happened. With any of his new ideas, Mike Burrows now uses patent sources as part of the development process and ensures that he is not wasting his time by duplicating someone else's work. The patent search and review is important since there are over 1,500 new patent applications filed every year relating to bikes and their components alone. The End Result - Mike Burrows now profits from his inventions.

There are, of course, some not so successful stories. In the 1983 America's Cup Race, it was rumored that the Australian yacht had a revolutionary hull design. Despite their best efforts, the media were unable to discover the new features of the Australian yacht in advance. In fact, the details of the new hull could have been obtained 3 months before the race from publicly available patent information sources which described the improved hull in detail.

In the 1970's, Patek-Phillipe, Rolex, Longines and other Swiss manufacturers of wrist-watches could have identified the advances being made by Japanese companies such as Sciko in electronic watches suitable for cheap mass production - if they had monitored the patent literature. Today, with the exception of Swatch, Japanese manufacturers have largely captured the market in cheap wrist-watches and most Swiss companies are confined to the high-end market.

Many attempts have been made worldwide to copy the highly successful portable and foldable workbench known as the "workmate". These attempts were a waste of time - a search in the patent information sources would have shown that the inventor, Ron Hickman, had filed a whole series of patents protecting all aspects of the workmate[1].

Summary

The emerging field of competitive intelligence analysis can and should be an important component of any technology transfer program. CI can provide valuable information to organizations on either side of the technology transfer equation, leading to more complete and rapid evaluations of technological options, better decisions, and more successful technology transfer. Furthermore, CI can be of value to organizations of any size in both the profit and nonprofit sectors of the economy. An organization need not be flush with resources to establish a CI program that will make it more successful. It can start small; first by defining the type of intelligence that will contribute to its success and then determining how best to acquire it. A massive program is not required, or even necessarily desirable.

Keys to successful commercialization of new creations and ideas are determining if they are new and what value can be assigned to the technology. There are numerous ways to determine the value of innovations several of which are:

---

1. *Benefits.* Rank core benefits remembering people, consumers or customers purchase benefits, not products. Place the benefits in order of importance.
2. *Survey.* Conduct a survey and ask the consumer to rank/comment on need/benefit.
3. *Audit.* Implement auditing mechanisms to ascertain what is succeeding and what isn't; then make necessary adjustments.
4. *Re-value assumptions.* Assumptions are made before the conduct of an exercise. Review assumptions as situation changes (nature of product or government regulations may force one to alter make-up of the operation. Ask: a) why do I think this will still work?; b) who needs it?; c) do I like this myself?; d) what about competition?; e) what are the media's thoughts?; and f) how flexible do I need to be with respect to time, work, delays etc?
5. *Analyze.* Be analytical about what has been implemented. Think as laterally as possible about how to measure these adjustments.
6. *SWOT analysis...again!!!* This is a study of: a) S – strengths; b) W – weaknesses; c) O - opportunities and d) T – threats. A SWOT analysis is most beneficial in a group setting (number of ideas with a group will be much more numerous and broader than if done alone).
7. *Prepare thoroughly for failure!* How/why could this fail??? One cannot control every aspect of the business. Attain and maintain total objectivity. (Subjectiveness can break this measurement device down). Some items to "negatively" think about are: a) strikes or industrial action; b) underestimated costs; c) staff training and development shortfalls; d) regulation alterations (changes in the legal system and how it affects you); e) natural disaster (fire, war, cyclone, flood etc.); f) judgment errors; (e.g. product development incorrectly diagnosed) and g) financial problems.
8. *Complete understanding of the business.* This includes policy changes, business developments etc. within and outside a person's control affects profits (pay close attention to those that can be controlled). If many aspects are uncontrollable (such as extending government intervention) consider mergers, diversification or perhaps discontinuation of over-regulated products and services. A relationship between government intervention and profit ratio exists. It is inversely proportional. Protect core interests and apply knowledge learned to diversify into areas that can be controlled.
9. *Protect body and mind.* Take care of yourself (number one) and employees.
10. *Be persistent.* Evaluation and valuation is ongoing. If success is realized consider how to further improve. Competition won't stop.

VALUATION

Smart entrepreneurs and other developers know a few deals will be losses, but will be compensated in other portfolio deals in which they'll make i.e. 110%, 220% and 37%. On average with the losses, they'll still make i.e. 29%, far better than the bank, but there is more management and skill involved. So a couple of losses are just a write-off, a cost of doing business. Total losses (i.e. deals that go to zero) are harder to absorb.

Technology managers need to emulate entrepreneurs not banks. A technology manager needs to be market driven, not cost driven. Again, cost cannot be part of an intellectual property's valuation. Academic and government organizations usually deal with technology that has a relatively low value at the point of initial transfer but might rise rapidly in value in certain cases.

A rigorous valuation using a technique appropriate to very early stage technologies, e.g. the risk adjusted net present value approach, would yield a much higher upfront price than most start-ups would want to pay. Therefore the deal structure/valuation approach generally used provides a low up-front payment but also provides a share in the valuation increase as key development hurdles are progressively met.

One such development milestone is finding a corporate partner, providing for a percentage of such a deal to be paid to the licensor is appropriate. At the time the original license is struck, neither party knows what the value of the partnership will be, so the terms have to be expressed in terms of a percentage of the deal, rather than as a fixed dollar amount.

A product might involve one or more of the following: a portfolio of assets including business support arrangements, intellectual property, conceptual aspects or "gleam in the eye, joint ventures, company divisions or business startup. Also, even though it is difficult, correct valuation or assessment of a given idea must proceed before any other work is done. If an objective review of the facts indicates "No Go", drop the claimed "bright" idea and move on to the next one. Valuation criteria (Exhibit G and Addendum IV), along with assessment forms (Exhibits H, I, and J and Addendum III) are present herein or in the enclosed compact diskette.

Value Definition

Value is the sum of benefits received in exchange for payment. No one buys a product; they buy what they think the product will do for them. The origin of a product is based in part on proven theory, prototype tests, product definition and release, innovative teamwork and individual achievements. Customers consist of buyers, adopters and employers; all of who have varied demands and expectations for a "product".

Science and engineering are processes that create value, but value is the result of using what the processes create.[1] Features enable value, but features are the results of development not the results of use. Do not confuse price (the value in exchange) with utility (the value in use). For non-commodity products value in use is always much greater than the price (a $30 hammer does not break after $30 worth of work). Products deliver value but value results from product use, not product ownership and from benefits of what product does, not from what a product is.

Quality is excellence in implementation, performance and durability but value is performance worth paying for. For example: people buy the results of driving nails, not the quality of steel in a hammer. Value directly implies quality, but high quality that meets no need has zero value. Quality assures that value will last, but quality is not the value. Price defines value to seller but value to the buyer is the sum of benefits.

The intent is to offer value that is recognized; therefore look beyond science and engineering, features, quality, technologies, products and exchange mechanisms to what customer believes product will do for them. Create well-deserved perceptions of value by delivering products that meet needs. If a competitive situation exists, or is anticipated, create preference by emphasizing advantages over alternatives.

Exchanges enable transfer of value. Sustainable exchange relationships always require wins for both sides. Perceptions are the ultimate locus of value. If customers do not understand or believe in the value then it has not been received.

The problem with many valuation schemes is that they are not always applicable to early stage technologies. Professional technology appraisers often use the same appraisal methods that are used for real estate or other hard assets. Examples are cost of replacement, income, and market value approaches. The first two are not suitable for embryonic technologies that are far from a product. The market value approach, in which comparable transactions are used, is based on prices that willing buyers and sellers have negotiated. It also requires knowledge of the market for effective use.

[1]Ashton, W.B., and Stacey, G.S. (1995). Technical intelligence in business: understanding technology threats and opportunities. International Journal of Technology Management, v. 10, n. 1. McGonagle, J.J., Jr., and Vella, C.M., (1990). Outsmarting the competition: Practical approaches to finding and using competitive information. Naperville, IL: Sourcebooks, Inc. and Mignogna R. (1997) Leveraging Technology for Competitive Advantage: Proceedings of the 1997 Technology Transfer Society Annual Conference, July 21-23, 1997, Denver, Colorado.

Real estate appraising and valuation methods of assets in other disciplines may be relevant. In real estate, the Replacement Cost method is considered the least reliable and is frowned on; the technology analogy here may be "sunk costs". The Comparable Sales method is the most widely used for residential property: e.g. 123 John Street sold for $100K, therefore 129 John Street is worth $115K (adjusted up since it has a swimming pool).

Yet, technology doesn't have an intrinsic value such as directly providing shelter or a place to raise children, so it is not really an acceptable method. Technology provides a revenue stream either present or future. The Income Approach is the most accurate and most useful for commercial and income producing property, and probably the most desirable method for technology as well.

Frequently, several of the methods are run and then reconciled or averaged. Concept shopping malls (on blueprints only) and early stage technologies do pose a unique problem because there is no existing income to evaluate, and projections are necessary. How to predict the future? The point circuitously being made is that valuation is as much an art as science. The judgment and experience of the manager is key.

Value and Intellectual Property

Royalty is a return on a valuable asset. It is critical that valuation concepts and factors that affect value be applied to establish the present value of an asset's future stream of economic benefits. The future stream of economic benefits is the amount of net cash flow from use of the property taking into account the cost of doing business and capital investment necessary to sustain cash flow. However, future net cash flow may be impacted not only by management but also by economic climates (they can be cyclical, as well), profitability, and competition and capital requirements. Other factors affecting net cash flow are monetary policies, federal budget deficits and income tax laws. It is important to remember that demand and pricing pressure are related to economic conditions when engaged in setting value.

Profitability is associated with aggregates of cost elements such as; wages, procurement of raw materials, conversion of raw materials, sales efforts and overhead. Also influencing profits are material or labor savings and benefits above those currently available.

The competition impact on value will be due to such factors as alternative products and services, superior technology or commercialization strategy of competitors. As value is established capital requirements need to be considered. Examples are reinvestment needs, plant expansion and equipment needs or enhancements. Duration of positive net cash flow can be as important as the amount so it is critical that one monitor and adjust business strategy based on technological breakthroughs and/or government regulations

Value is related to the amount of future benefits, the potential for the benefits to grow and the duration of benefits. In other words, factors that impact the estimated value are; R&D funds expended stage of development, size of ultimate business, capital needed to develop products, competition, alternatives, threats, proprietary position and other interested parties.

Determining the potential and actuality of intellectual property requires knowledge of the amount of growth rate and timing of benefits, recognition that net cash flows need to be estimated by comprehensive analysis of the market and awareness that forecasting reliability is highly related to stage of technology development. This is depicted in figures one through three.

Figure one. Normal valuation approach at different stages.

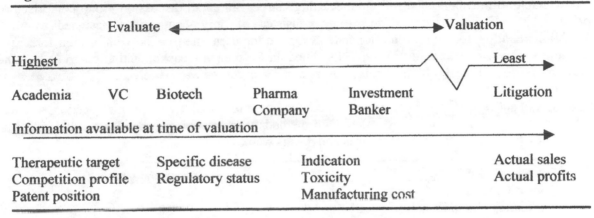

Technology risk

	Academia	VC	Biotech	Pharma Company	Investment Banker	Litigation
Equity	x	xx	x	x	xx	-
Compensation	x	x	xx	-	xx	reasonable royalty
Biz-Model	?	?	x	IRR MIRR	NPV SHARES	lost profit

Figure two. Reduction in risk overtime.

Evaluate ⟵————————⟶ Valuation

Highest   Least

Academia   VC   Biotech   Pharma   Investment   Litigation
                                    Company   Banker

Information available at time of valuation ————————⟶

Therapeutic target   Specific disease   Indication   Actual sales
Competition profile   Regulatory status   Toxicity   Actual profits
Patent position   Manufacturing cost

Figure three. Value vs. Risk.

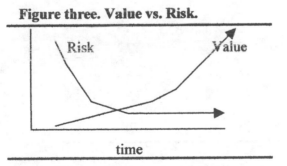

Risk   Value

time

Discount rate is that component of value that compensates the investor for the commitment of capital. These commitments also mean that the investor is giving up other investment opportunities and at the same time assuming new risk.

Also impacting value are factors that affect discount rate such as inflation, liquidity, real interest rates, and risk premium. Inflation can reduce purchasing power of future economic benefits. Liquidity is the difficulty for an investment to be quickly converted into cash. Real interest is sacrificing alternative use of the invested funds (it is the reward for deferring consumption in favor of investment and in real form is usually about 3%). The risk premium is the added amount of return that investors demand for the assumption of risk, e.g., possibility of loss and/or unanticipated variability in earnings. It varies with the type of property and industry.

For example, what is the likelihood that new software products might be competitive technologies that could reduce value? A significant factor that is often overlooked when determining value is whether the technology will form the basis of a product or a business. In the current business environment seldom is a discovery the sole component of a final product. However, the level of contribution to the final product must be taken into account as value is projected.

TECHNOLOGY FORECASTING METHODS
Survey

Although the field of technology forecasting has existed for nearly 50 years, rarely has it been institutionalized in the strategic technology planning efforts of technology intensive organizations. Aside from a number of governmental initiatives, technology-forecasting or foresight techniques have been studied by relatively few. Most technology forecasting, where it was being done, seems to rely primarily on expert opinion or other judgmental approaches rather than trend analyses or other data driven techniques.

A survey of firms involved in technology forecasting was conducted to determine methods most widely applied. To obtain a sampling of workers knowledgeable in the field, a short survey was made available to members of the TechForecasting listserv, an email discussion group comprised of approximately 140 subscribers. The survey consisted of only 4 questions designed to elicit information about the techniques the respondents most often used, the time horizon of their forecasts, their industry, and any software they typically relied on for their forecasting activities. A link to the survey was posted on the TechForecasting listserv and 33 responses were received.

Question 1: What technology forecasting methods do you most often use? For this question, a list of choices from among 10 of the most often cited methods was offered. Respondents could select as many as they found applicable. The choices and results were:

Forecast method	% respondents*
Expert Opinion	88
Technology Trend Analysis (Pearl-Reed & Gompertz)	58
Delphi Technique	48
Fisher-Pry Substitution	30
Nominal Group Technique (NGT)	18
Scenarios	15
Morphological Analysis	9
Relevance Trees	3
Impact Wheel	3
Patent Analysis	3
Other (please specify)	9

*Thirty-three respondents

Resorting to expert opinion (employed by 88% of respondents) was clearly the most widely applied approach in spite of known problems with the bias of individual experts. A distant second and third, though still quite popular, were scenarios (15%) and patent analysis (48%), respectively. The Delphi technique (30%) came in fourth and technology trend analysis (18%) ranked fifth. None of the other approaches garnered more than a handful of votes. The other category received three write-in votes: back casting, essay writing, and help wanted ad trends. The only noticeable correlation was that 3 of the 6 trend analysis users were consultants.

Question 2: What is your industry? The 33 respondents represented panoply of industries from agriculture to venture capital with everything in between including biotech, transportation, telecommunications, academia, government, information technology, environmental, appliances, and others. The sample was too small and the dispersion of responses too great to draw any conclusions concerning which techniques might find greater acceptance in a particular industry.

Question 3: What time frame is the focus of most of your technology forecasting activities? The choices offered for this question were: < 2 years, 2 to 5 years, 5 to 10 years, and > 10 years. The predominant time horizon was 2 to 5 years (61%). This was followed distantly by less than 2 years (18%), greater than 10 years (12%), and 5 to 10 years (9%).

Question 4: What software do you find most useful in your technology forecasting efforts? This open-ended question offered respondents an opportunity to list any software applications that they typically employ in their technology forecasting endeavors. There was no universally popular tool for supporting technology forecasting and, in fact, only a handful of respondents listed any software at all. The software mentioned, with the number of occurrences in parentheses, was: Excel (3), Loglet (technology trend analysis) (2), tfInnovate (technology trend analysis) (1), Decision Explorer (influence diagrams and impact wheels) (1), EC Pro (presumably Expert Choice decision analysis software) (1), Filemaker (1), Microsoft Access (1), Software listed in the back of Joseph Martino's book (1), and Custom Built (1)

The most popular techniques were qualitative in nature. It is unfortunate that problems with bias and misplaced expertise do not diminish use of individual expert opinion for technology forecasting. It is also not surprising that patent analysis was popular since it is a staple of high tech companies, especially larger ones. Conducting such studies is relatively resource intensive (in terms of time and data), but they are easy to conduct and the data are readily available. The timeliness of the patent data – or lack thereof – is the principal drawback to this technique.

The Delphi, which was developed in the mid-1950s, received fairly strong support in the survey. Most of the Delphi surveys being conducted today focus more on the Delphi style of asking a question as opposed to rigorously following the repeated rounds of feedback and re-voting that are characteristic of the rigorous application of the technique.

Note that, in a group of people knowledgeable about technology forecasting, few relied on trend analyses. Whether this is due to the relative difficulty in applying the often cited Pearl-Reed, Gompertz, and Fisher-Pry logistical models, a lack of reliable data, or the absence of knowledge about software that could facilitate such analyses is not known.

Of the remaining techniques, NGT received some support but the others (morphology, relevance trees, and impact wheels) appear to have fallen out of use though each potentially has its place in the assessment of technological alternatives.

It would be expected that, in an era in which R&D is charged with having more of a market focus, the predominant time horizon of interest is 2 to 5 years. Because of the broad dispersion of industries represented with respect to the sample size, there were no significant correlations between industry and time horizon.

Lastly, the death of software cited as helpful in technology forecasting efforts was *Excel, Filemaker, and Access* of course are general-purpose software applications. Expert Choice is a multicriteria decision support tool based on the analytic hierarchy process. Decision Explorer is a general-purpose influence-diagramming tool that can also be used for generating impact wheels. It can be used to help assess technological landscapes. Loglet is a logistical trend analysis tool developed and distributed by the University of Rochester. It is especially helpful for analyzing multiple substitutions using Fisher-Pry techniques. tfInnovate is an Excel add-in that was specifically developed to apply the Pearl-Reed, Gompertz, and Fisher-Pry logistic models to the analysis of technology trends.

VALUE ANALYSIS MODELS ("TOOLS")

There are several spreadsheet type models to provide assistance in project management and related decision-making. One developed by the author, Technology Pricing Model™ (TPM), takes into account a risk benefit analysis, and a comparison of a new project with current projects in the organization based on their net present value and cumulative net present value (Addendum V). Examples of other programs available are Technology Opportunity Potential Index (TOP Index), ProGrid, Theoria Resheneyva Isobretatelskehuh Zadach (TRIZ), sometimes referred to as Theory of Solving Problems Inventively, and Valuate. Additional information on these and other evaluation "tools" is presented in Exhibit E.

The TPM model allows one not only to estimate asset value but also to compare the asset in question with other projects or assets in order to establish priority and fit with existing products, projects or corporate financial expectations. A beta test version of TPM can be obtained by contacting the author of this document.

A simplistic spreadsheet to examine market scenarios can be used to vary factors one at a time or jointly to determine net effect on the bottom line over the life of a contract. Factors that might be varied include but are not limited to: market growth rates, unit prices, and/or patent costs. Sunk costs can be used as a threshold number. If the royalty cannot cover sunk costs charged, then the royalty is not high enough. Present value of future royalties could be the lump sum payment. A spreadsheet is not always a user-friendly tool but once factors are identified it is easy to change to accommodate for situations that increase or decrease marketability.

An analytical tool is necessary to estimate what may occur when prices shift occur in later years of marketing that impact product royalty rate; e.g. market growth decline or acceleration, product sales.

One must differentiate between early stage technology and early stage development. Early stage technology is highly unpredictable as to the outcome therefore one has to assume there will be technical success. It should not be misconstrued for early stage development. It must be incubated to allow growth, and there are no market indicators to make the initial assessment with any clarity. Perceived value of a technology that is not market-driven can make or break the project and at the same time can be fraught with uncertainty.

On the other hand, early stage development has a more market-driven approach. For example, for early stage developments, the market valuation approach works best. In addition, existing competition may already have a market share when considering early stage development.

If over-lapping technologies are involved be cautious, for they can end in bitter reprisals with no monetary gain.

Maturity is when technology (or product) "rolls out," or released for sale. Many factors have to accommodate that "roll out".

When are calculations meaningful? There is a belief that one should predict market share and size assuming that technology development will follow a linear path and lead to a product with hypothetical properties that can be compared with existing products or technology to get market position and share.

However, technology development does not follow a linear path. The analysis may not be meaningful if made too early in the technology or product development cycle. Calculations, even when reasonable, may give royalty rates that are inconsistent with certain industry practices and the general gut feeling of licensees. Rational calculations carry more weight for later stage developments. One can even ask for royalties calculated in a logical way and still not get them.

VALUE DETERMINATION

Value in a license is extracted from upfront fees (cash, stock, research support, past patent costs), ongoing patent costs, milestone payments, annual minimum royalties, sublicense income sharing, earned royalties including a nominal rate and actual royalty after offsets. The basic ways to approach valuation are to:

1. Look back (cost, i.e. sunk, avoided or avoidance (next best alternative))
2. Look around (comparables, i.e. internal reference points, surveys, disclosure-based)
3. Look forward (value i.e. business models)
4. Look to the market (equity appreciation, i.e. initial equity and equity buildup)
5. Look to others (auction)
6. Look no farther (common sense)

Level of effort expended in valuation of technology depends on:

1. Availability of information. Is technology basic research, a new product or replacement product? Is work of other researchers, competitors generally known?
2. Expected value of technology. Is technology a small improvement or major breakthrough?

When basic research or new or early technology is being assessed, several aspects need to be addressed including: a) capability to develop acceptable alternative technology e.g. current and future availability; b) what value is conferred e.g. lower costs, less capital investment, or greater customer acceptance and c) can new discovery be an industry "standard".

Replacement technology information is available in many forms through research in both the replacement technology and new technology environments. Available information may include: revenue, cost and profit expectations, asset utilization, financing, marketing, engineering, and manufacturing costs and capacities.

Quantification of potential variables may also involve a decision tree analysis. An example is as follows:

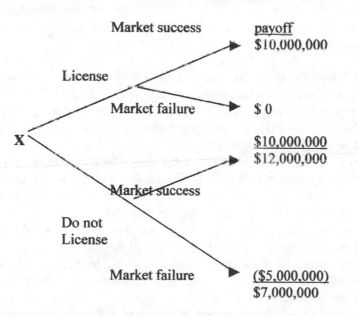

Decision tree analysis may provide insight into determining the value of technology while accounting for possible unknowns. Various scenarios of chain of events are identified and probabilities associated with each potential path are evaluated, ultimately quantifying the potential expected value of any given path.

Important issues that need to be considered are: 1) evolution stage of intellectual property development and hence, time to market; 2) costs associated with additional R&D; 3) success of related technologies; 4) specialized resource requirements; 5) similar market products and outcome of commercialization; 6) NPV based on future estimated earnings (if quantifiable); 7) reason for the valuation; 8) investment to date in the intellectual property; 9) tax credits that may be available; 10) product life cycle; 11) type of entity that owns the intellectual property; 12) financial potential e.g. sales expectations, profit potential and likelihood of success; 13) corporate, technological and production synergy including ability to develop and manage new product and know-how "company fit" and 14) differential advantage e.g. potential for product to be first-on-the-market.

Numerous variables that impact the transfer process and the value of that asset not only exist but also change over time. Among the affecters are: changes in the protection e.g. elimination of certain claims during the examination and approval process of patents leading to fewer and-or less valuable claims to license, new scientific data that may enhance or reduce value of the asset, advent of unrecognized competitors or products into the intended market, change in or unexpected public opinion regarding the technology or product, or new regulatory conditions related to the technology. Remember intellectual property value is difficult to establish until it has a clearly identifiable income potential. Prior to this point the outcome of any valuation is questionable.

Financial Calculation

The financial potential determination consists of estimating new product value, rate of return on investment, discounted cash flow or investor method (the traditional method for determining present value of an annuity. An alternative method that can be used to calculate net present value of a proposed project is:

$$c = r/(1+i)^n \text{ x } a/(1+i)^n \text{ where,}$$

        c = investment outlay;
        r = expected annual cash inflow (before depreciation and after taxes);
        i = rate of return;
        n = expected life of the project;
        a = recoverable asset value at the end of the project (assumed to be zero for the
        present purposes).

If c, r, a, and n are known; i that equates discounted cash flow with investment outlay can be obtained.

This rate is the floor below which the project is not feasible. Alternatively, rate of return (i) is the highest rate that can be paid for funds to finance a project without sustaining an economic loss. For example, assume cost of investment is $758K and cash inflow is $200K. At 10%, the present value of cash inflow is equal to the required investment outlay.

The 10% rate is crucial; borrowing at higher rates would be uneconomical. Rates greater than 10% could be sustained only by higher cash inflow. Generally, with (i) as the denominator and the rates of competing projects as the numerator, the project may be arrayed for screening purposes. Economically viable projects have ratios equal to or greater than "1".

If (i) is set at company's cost of capital, a project is considered acceptable if the net present value of the discounted cash flow equals or exceeds the required investment outlay.

Setting the required investment of each project as the denominator for its present value estimate, all projects with ratios exceeding "1" would be considered satisfactory, and the greater the excess, the more desirable the project.

Numerous factors need to be taken into consideration in setting royalty rate. Cost can be the basis for estimate of the minimum royalty but if royalty rates are to be guides for remuneration they should undergo certain analyses to match returns (royalty) and costs. One needs to account for expected performance of technology as a product relative to the investment in developing it. For licensor, the investment is past and is the sunk cost of the creation.

However, the method of present value is applicable. The formula $r/(1+r)n$ is applied for the present value of $1.00 with $1.00 as the numerator in each of the five years. Multiplying expected royalty by the result in the $1.00 column gives the present value of $200K in each of these years. The amount is rounded off to the nearest thousand dollars. Assume sunk costs are $758K and royalty is 5% of net sales yielding the royalty indicated. At 10 % (i.e. market interest rate), the present value of the royalty amounts to $758K and just pays for the sunk costs.

In this example, present value method determined the "fixed-sum" equivalent of a running royalty. It could also be used to determine trade-off values between rates and dollars. Licensor can take either a running royalty or an equivalent lump-sum payment, which can be invested.

If one assumes a market interest rate of 10%, which is the opportunity cost or rate that is foregone if the licensor elects running royalty. It is the rate of return on the money if taken as fixed sum and invested at the current interest rate. Another example is as follows. A 3% royalty is offered by the licensor. An upfront payment to buy the 2% can be calculated. At 3%, the annual royalty is $120K and the present value amount column calculates to $455K. Difference between the amount at 5% and amount at 3% is $303K; this figure is the dollar equivalent of a 2 point reduction in the royalty rate. It represents the fair amount a licensee could be asked to pay if he wished to have a royalty reduced by 2 percentage points.

Even though mathematical formulas may be available to calculate reasonable fair royalties, agreement is often based on norms for industry, rules of thumb or gut feeling but these do not take into account the uniqueness of new technology, especially its cost, sales potential or profitability.

Some negotiators believe that concern for details hampers discussions. Negotiations can be intense requiring on the spot decisions and executives prefer to have discretion on setting royalties to have room to exercise expert judgment. In any case, one must always be prepared to justify figures to others.

VALUATION METHODS

The analysis applied varies with the type and development stage for the asset in question. Several theories exist for establishing royalty rate including:

1. Investment theory approach in which a select expenditure area such as R&D becomes the basis from which an expected rate of return is established; this method is useful for negotiations as a guideline but may not be best for establishing royalty rate;
2. 25% rule that reflects a desire to obtain 25% of the profit from product sales; however this method requires fair allocation and definition of overhead and expenses as the profit is determined;
3. Multivariate economic modeling of the technology which is complex and sophisticated but may require more time and effort than is necessary for technology that is not yet in final product form;
4. Historical or comparable method which is based on value of similar assets and past arrangements enacted under similar conditions. This method is sometimes called the profit maximization technique that involves shopping the technology to the highest bidder;
5. Cost approach is the cost of reproduction or replacement for a technology or product;
6. Market approach involves determination of sales potential and in some cases could involve exchange tangible or intangible property; or
7. Income approach represents the amount and duration of revenue expected from a technology of product subject to the risk associated with the asset.

Investment Theory (Cost Approach or Expense to Date)

Value in the cost approach to asset valuation is the cost of reproduction or replacement less physical depreciation and functional obsolescence. It can be estimated based on investment into protection and development of intellectual property to date sometimes referred to as sunk costs. Sunk costs are indeed one factor that affects valuation. The technology "seller" has to consider what is sunk into the project in accepting an offer. Even if it is the desired arrangement, it's hard to consider selling something for less than what has been sunk into it because you then lose money. The seller wants a certain yield and earnings.

The technology "buyer" usually could care less how much was invested, but likewise looks at the potential return, yield, earnings, etc. But regardless how reasonable an offer seems to the buyer, if it is below sellers cost, it probably won't fly.

A "valuation" is most accurately reflected by a closed transaction in an arms length transaction between the two parties. So both these considerations need to be met.

Sunk costs should never affect valuation. It is always in a seller's best interest to sell intellectual property at the highest price that the market will pay without any regard to what has transpired in the past. If a seller refuses the best possible deal because the sunk costs were higher, that's an error in judgment. Of course, the seller has to be convinced the best deal has been found, and that may take longer to accept when the sunk costs are too high.

Training one to be emotionally detached from sunk costs is one of the hardest aspects of management. Of course, if there are no better prospects, such discounting may be necessary. Ideally, tech sellers need to realize that in certain deals you have to lose some money, and losing positive integer X [aka $YY, YYY] now is far better than losing 3X when the patent expires. On the other hand, if future revenue is not going to cover sunk costs, then abandon the technology. This method is the selection of a target area, such as R&D, and set an estimated rate of return from that particular investment- royalty rates are then established to reach that expected rate of return. This rationale is useful for selling a particular fee structure during negotiations but may not be best approach to set royalty rate.

25% Rule

The 25% rule was first enunciated by Sam Davis, General Counsel, Research Corporation in a article titled "Patent Licensing" and further discussed in the following articles: Patent Law Institute, 1958 by Goldscheider & Marshall, "The Art of Licensing from a Consultant's Point of View" in Les Nouvelles, 6 1971. This rule is based on empirical observations from a series of worldwide licenses starting in 1959. It represents analysis of a complete IP portfolio involving patents, ongoing know-how, trademarks, and copyrighted product materials. In general, licensors made 20% pre-tax profit and paid 5% royalty which resulted in successful, long term win-win relationships. In "Litigation Backgrounder for Licensing" by Robert Goldscheider, Les Nouvelles, 29, 21-33, March 1994, the royalty revenue was expressed as a % of net sales in a license and royalty rate was 25% times the expected profit margin. This rule can be starting point for negotiation and adjusted up or down depending on the significance of IP portfolio and who bears the principle burden of risk. It may be of limited value in academic licensing negotiations because of the uncertainty of ultimate profitability. The rule is usually important in infringement situations. A fundamental principle of technology valuation is the licensor should receive 25% and a licensee 75% of pre-tax profits from a licensed product.

Generally, the extent of product knowledge is limited when intellectual property is first disclosed or in early stages of development. It is usually possible to estimate the cost of goods, the preferred gross margin for similar products in the select industry and/or the sale price of the product. Industry gross margin norms have been published and can be used in the calculation, if necessary. Royalty is then sale price minus cost of goods or sales times 25% (.25). It is important with this method for setting price to have a clear definition of cost of goods or sales.

For example; "Gross margin" is the dollars remaining after paying "direct" costs of producing the product or service. In addition to direct costs, other costs such as indirect (or operating) costs including engineering costs, selling costs & general & administrative costs exist. "Net margin" is the dollars left after paying these operating costs. (In both terms "profit" can be substituted for "margin".) When expressed as percentages, these are percentages of "sales". A numeric example for a small manufacturer is:

Sales, $	100.0	Engineering expense, $	5.0
Cost of sales,$	50.0	Selling expense, $	15.0
Gross profit, %	50.0	G&A expense, $	10.0
Proposed royalty rate, %	12.5	Net profit, %	20.0

It is imperative when applying the 25% rule to remember that this royalty rate might be appropriate for a product that is market ready. This is seldom the case with technology and one must be prepared to adjust the rate depending on such considerations as stage of development, extent and duration of proprietary position, regulatory approval, license terms (exclusive vs. non exclusive, limited territory vs. worldwide rights, milestones, and up front fees, ease of market entry and size of market). Other factors to consider when determining value are barriers to entry, i.e. relative strength of intellectual property in given market. Stronger intellectual property yields higher profit and other benefits. For example, life cycle of new computer related product is 1-2 years today, whereas the life cycle was longer several years ago. There is no "cook book" recipe; solutions exist but require specialized expertise. Although difficult, correct valuation of a given idea should precede development and deployment activities. If objective review of facts results in "no go" decision, drop the "bright" idea.

Multivariate Analysis (Profit Maximization or Income Analysis)

This analysis a) requires an understanding of both parties' risks and rewards; b) systematically identifies important variables to valuation; c) facilitates negotiations; d) allows creation of computer models to analyze uncertainty and e) allows structure and terms of a license or sale agreement to reflect both parties assumption of risk.

An income or economic analysis that is intended to form the business basis for license terms will encompass inputs from numerous disciplines some of which are depicted in the following diagram:

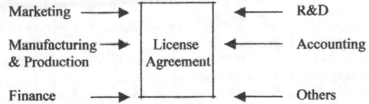

Quantification of technology value generally involves consideration of; 1) availability of non infringing alternatives; 2) useful life of technology and 3) economic impact of technology; e.g. cost savings, total unit sales, cost of sales, operating expenses, capital investment and other measures

The income analysis reflects consideration of the amount, duration and risk associated with revenue flow. Amount of income is the net cash flow or after tax income plus depreciation less additional working capital, capital expenditures and return on other assets employed. Duration is the economic life or period of asset profitability, legal life, physical life, technological life, depreciable life, and pattern of income. Risk considerations are: 1) will you receive expected amount?; 2) will you receive it when expected?; 3) must you invest heavily to get upfront or big payments?; and 4) how long before income realized?.

Present value (PV) calculations are useful to establish asset value and are as follows:

PV = amount ($)/interest rate (%) = present value
PV = amount (1 + growth rate)/(rate - growth rate)
PV = (amount 1/(1 + rate 1)) x (amount 2/(1 + rate 2)) x (amount 3/(1 + rate 3))

Another approach to the income analysis is to calculate net profit potential over the first three (3) years the resultant product is on the market. (If the intellectual property is in the pharmaceutical sector, timing might be 5 to 7 years.) Market penetration models can be constructed for every new product. If the product will be satisfying a clearly untapped, large market (virtually no competition), it follows that revenues and growth will be significant. However, if the market is highly fragmented, entrance and growth patterns will be different but could be predicted. Yet, if the major portion of the market is dominated by a handful of players, then market penetration patterns are going to be very different (rather discouraging).

Historical or Comparables (Industry-Standard or Market Approach)

This method involves; a) use of "what everyone else is doing" as model e.g. existing licenses, established industry royalties, "Rules of Thumb" of formulas and corporate policy; b) identification of alternatives (What alternatives are available? What benefits are conferred by each alternative?); c) determination of economic gains of each alternative; d) comparison of expected economic gains of alternatives; e) determination of potential range of royalty values or selling prices and/or f) identification of "qualitative" issues. This analysis is sometimes called the market approach and often takes into account exchange of comparable property, arm's length exchange, contemporaneous exchange, active and public market influences. This method may not result in true profit maximization.

Even though it is difficult, correct valuation or assessment of a given idea must proceed before any other efforts are performed. Remember valuation concepts and factors affect the ultimate value associated with an asset. The royalty is a return on a valuable asset.

Using the norm for market-segmented royalties based on previous license terms may ignore future problems and opportunities, fails to factor in market changes, does include many variables but in less than an ideal quantitative way, is based on what the market is willing to pay, helps set a standard of fairness (license relationship is usually long term) and forms the basis for start of negotiation. Remember, a departure from the norm is easier to explain.

Market Approach

This method usually is included in a multivariate analysis. However, in certain situations an asset purchaser will want to compensate the provider with tangible or intangible property. Determination of the value of this property is often subjective and will involve consideration of; 1) is comparable property exchanged and what is the value of the exchanged property, 2) is the transaction an arms length one or highly collaborative, 3) is the exchange contemporaneous or phased, and 4) is the market for the asset an active, immediate, well define or public.

Income Approach (Profit Maximization Technique)

The amount of income or net cash flow is the after tax income plus depreciation less additional working capital, capital expenditures and return on other assets employed. Another term for duration is the economic life; such as period of asset profitability, legal life, physical life, technological life, depreciable life or pattern of income. Other criteria included in this valuation method are size of market/expected market share, time to market, competition, and industry growth projections.

This method also takes into account the risk associated with the asset. For example; 1) will the expected amount be received, 2) will it be received when expected, 3) must significant capital be invested upfront or large payments be made to reach market, and 4) how long will it be before income is realized. Another way to address income is to examine items that lead to a discount for royalty; i.e.

development stage (generally closer to market the lower the discount rate), amount or type of competition, barriers to market entry, quality of patent protection, management depth and expertise and level of diversification.

This technique is to "shop" the technology to find highest bid or best marketer. It takes time and often leads to delays, in hopes of finding a better offer. It is less likely to yield true profit maximization in rapidly changing market.

326

PRICE

TYPES OF PAYMENTS
Up-front

Aliases are front end, disclosure, and initial. The upfront payment is usually made upon signing an agreement. This payment is designed to recoup patent, licensing and legal expenses and commands a premium based on importance of technology and market.

Minimum Royalties

These are regular payments to induce development, and/or commercialization activity by licensee. They may be a minimum investment in R&D or milestones. The frequency of payment is related to long vs. short-term development or marketing activities and is often influences by size of company, capitalization of company, etc.

Milestone or Lump Sum Payments

These payments are associated with key events such as regulatory approval, first clinical trial, and market introduction. They can be credited toward royalty.

Running Royalties

A royalty imposed when product reaches market. It is often linked to minimum royalties and is usually required to maintain the license.

Equity/Securities

This type of payment usually is associated with small or start up firms that acquire technology from an academic or government organization or business-to-business arrangements.

PRICING STRATEGY

There are numerous methods available for establishing the price of a technology to be licensed or marketed to others. However, before establishing price one needs to establish the goals and objectives of the organization e.g. academic organizations often are more interested in acquiring sponsored research funds, or in obtaining fees for protection and assurance of commercialization rather than maximizing royalty or the return on the technology asset. Pricing a technology prior to final product definition is often subject to a certain level of uncertainty depending on the stage of development. This, along with the unknown investment required to reach the market, will be taken into account as the price is established.

The price or royalty rate will depend on the amount of upfront money requested, milestone payments, and equity participation by the licensor, clear title or lack of potential infringement to the intellectual property, sponsored research and in-kind contributions.

There is no magic involved in establishing price. Standard economic and financial techniques are used. One must understand economic issues from the perspective of buyer and seller; owners and licensees and avoid the "black box" valuation methodology.

In a recent survey (46 companies reported) many variables were reported to affect royalty; however the most influential factors were: degree of exclusivity, anticipated total monetary return, type of license (patent or know-how), term of license, term and type of obligations assumed by licensee i.e. guarantees, immunity from suit, protection expenses.

Remember, valuation of early stage intellectual property is difficult. The error margins for assumptions are wide and the results of valuation can vary widely. If the asset provider is considered a founder in the company, a better approach would be to negotiate for an equal share of founder's stock in exchange for equity with a license at reduced royalties and payments since, if the technology is successfully developed, your equity will increase in value.

Do not forget that when pricing a technolgy there is an option to "partner" with the licensee, usually a smaller business, and accept equity and/or in combination with royalty in exchange for the asset. This approach is probably more common in business to business relationships than for university to business arrangements. However, in recent years academia appears to be more inclined to accept some level of equity in return for rights to an asset.

There is no single right or wrong way to structure an equity relationship. There is little, if any, control over when equity pays off; even if a product is earning profits.

Will it ever pay off? – like it or not one is a venture capitalist if equity is accepted, so think like a venture capitalist. If a faculty member starts a company they are a partner. Equity may have potential for greater payoff but it is not a sure thing. These decision along with the conflict of interest and commitment policies of the institution will need to be taken into consideration.

Why take equity? The company may be cash poor, your may feel you can receive a higher financial return, spreads technology risk, alternative to license fees and the stock holder has no liability. Before deciding to take equity consider; the faculty member, management team-experience, coroprate commitments, financial resource(s) including stability of funds, amount and track record of the investor, corporate management and value of the technology.

It may be prudent to accept royalty combined with equity. This becomes more common when the technology "pie" is divided e.g. exclusive vs. nonexclusive, field of use, regional vs. worldwide, royalty bearing license is desired and milestone payments, annual maintenance or minimum payments are requested. When accepting equity, establish strong due diligence criteria, and develop specific termination language. It may be advisable to have patent costs reimbursed, get a commitment for research support, or have the faculty member consult and/or serve on scientific advisory board.

In nearly every case involving academic technology, there will be a question of conflict of interest and conflict of commitment. There are several ways to address these issues and the acceptable way will depend on the university and polices of that institution. This is usually not a problem for a business to business relationship.

The questions revolve around institutional as well as individual conflicts. How is equity distributed? Does university administration get equity and only royalty goes to inventors? If so, how is it calculated? Is stock distributed to everyone upon registration or held by university until cash-in is allowed? What is done to assure arm's length stock management to avoid insider trading e.g. is stock held by university treasurer or agent? These are just a few of the questions that arise when a university accepts equity.

Failure rate of start-ups is high (can be greater than 80% in the first five years) so take this into account and monitor the realtionship. Buyouts, joint ventures, or consolidation are highly likely, so one will no doubt be a party to expansion if the firm is successful, which is expected. Consider a request to get "run-up" of stock in a publically traded company if stock is undervalued.

A thumb rule that may apply in an equity arrangement is royalty rate and % equity should equal 10 through the first $2M in financing (2-5% royalty and 5-8% equity with the academic equity position undiluted through the first $2M raised). Technology will need to be core of the business to get this compensation.

Generally the profit sharing might be as follows; investor group, (university and inventor) - 25%; developer - 25%; manufacturer - 25%; and marketer - 25%. These percentages will change depending on the contribution of the parties and there will likely be a need to set aside some equity for the management in the firm. The total value of the arrangement will consist of time to get return on investment, first royalties received, as an owner you need to think like one, development needs-required time and cost and diligence provisions or benchmark payments. In any event you must do diligence and objective evaluation of the arrangement.

Some general figures realted to quantity of stock to seek, although it is highly dependent on the technology "package" are: if lone core to company's business - 10-20%; if add-on to products or product line - 5-10%; if multiple technologies or major licenses needed - 1-5%; and if royalty combined with equity – variable.

Should antidilution be expected – maybe. It will require negotioation. If a low % stock, such as less than 4%, has been offered one might seek antidilution until the initial public offering, or second round of financing, or when greater than $2M is raised.

Generally, the options or equity should vest in 3-5 years. Remember, you might also request the right to purchase additional equity in later funding rounds through credit against royalty. There is always the alternative to equity and that is to get best royalty deal, then seek options or warrants.

AGREEMENT

STRUCTURE - BALANCE RISK

Early stage technology usually is relatively low in value. However, value may rise rapidly. As mentioned before a rigorous valuation e.g. the risk adjusted net present value approach, would yield a much higher upfront price than most start-ups would pay. Therefore, it may be prudent to seek a low up-front payment but also obtain a share in the valuation increase as key development hurdles are progressively met. For example, if development milestone is to find a corporate partner, obtain a percentage of the arrangement.

Another approach is to express terms as percentage rather than as a fixed dollar amount since value is uncertain. It is an accepted theory of licensing, all the way up to patent infringement litigation, that the licensor should receive 25% of the value from selling products based on the technology licensed. The simplest way to do this would be for the licensor to receive a 25% equity stake in the licensee. With appropriate anti-dilution provisions, one can accept equity and waive all other financial components of the deal. The result is that many license arrangements for early stage technology are a combination of equity, future value and shares of future arrangements.

LICENSE ISSUE FEE (LIF)

LIF does not represent a capitalized royalty merely a license issue fee. However, there is an element of capitalized royalties in a license issue fee (seek higher fee when expecting huge sales & profits); but there is also an element of threshold costs (get licensee to pay these threshold costs).

Threshold costs or licensing costs average $30K based on University of California data. Administration costs last for the life of a patent and life of the agreement. These include patent preparation, filing and maintenance costs, and cost for time to draft, negotiate, approve, monitor and administer a license. If intellectual property value is expected to exceed $100K or more, it is prudent to invest capital, $5-10K, for a thorough intellectual property due diligence effort; then construct a fair and equitable arrangement. The LIF should be established based on the analytical analysis (spreadsheet) of the asset. This analysis will have included a sensitivity analysis for different royalty rates and market scenarios. LIF can be payable within X years and/or in increments after signing. It may also be credited against future royalties.

LIF is a way to shift risk related to projected sales from licensor to licensee. A licensee may contend they are bearing all the risk, especially if asked to cover patent costs; but licensor bore risk for some time before invention was even made. Royalties are a way to share in sales. Most licensees will not negotiate on any basis related to "cost to licensor for developing technology". This is sunk cost, and future potential is what matters. The LIF might not be cash but one can use technology as a means to secure further research funding and recover costs of intellectual property protection. In return, asset owners grant first right to negotiate or options to sponsor and delay specific license negotiations until technology is more mature. These types of compensation are in lieu of license issue fees per se.

Why accept securities (stock) in a company? The royalty concept is "give us nothing if unsuccessful or a minimal fee if successful"; whereas, the stock concept is "give us nothing if unsuccessful or a proportionate amount depending upon success".

Amount of equity will depend on one or more of the following; maturity of technology, investment needed from licensee, margins for ultimate product, financial wherewithal of licensee, and importance of the technology to licensee's overall business or revenue stream.

One strategy is to tie payments (milestone fees and/or equity) to success of the company if technology is key to growth of company. Examples of milestones are clinical trials, regulatory approval, working prototype, 1st anniversary of license or product sale, and projected sales volume or sales revenue.

Fee structure strategy is often reversed. The first question asked is; "How much we should charge for this intellectual property whereas it should be; "What is the estimated value of this intellectual property to a prospective buyer?"

The license issue fee even when justifiable is dependent upon negotiation variables. The fee is based on:

1. an array of considerations or variables judged to impact royalty;
2. reasonable estimates or dollar valuations of variables impacting royalty; and
3. weights indicating the relative worth of the variables impacting royalty.

It is a quantity consideration; is consideration of relative importance (importance of a dollar spent on variable); or provides for similar quantities of dollars to have varying degrees of importance for the royalty calculation.

License Issue Fee Scenarios

A LIF might be based on estimated sales when sales plateau, the first three year's average sales, peak sales or final year's sales. Another way to establish LIF is to base it on a cost – plus analysis. All of the revenue estimates for the foregoing methods will be subject to reduction when setting the LIF. In many cases, the estimate will be halved as the figure is established at the outset. Of course, the amount will be dependent on all of the variables previously discussed herein.

Plateau. The plateau may vary but should be established based on several consecutive quarters, months, and years of projected income.

First three year's average. The first year's sales will usually be low since there is little chance that market penetration will be at its maximum the first few years of sales. Therefore, unless one acquires other forms of compensation that offset the reduced LIF this approach is seldom a preferred model. In this case a reasonable LIF is 10% of the projected first 3 years sales. Most business plans include projections for the 1st year of product sales and the assumption is that the sales curve is symmetrical. This approach may not be useful for biotech products not marketed for 6-10 years and further the time value of money or project risk is not taken into account.

Peak sales. Peak sales are an estimate and not always the easiest to reach agreement on. However, a licensor will usually ask the licensee to provide market plans as a part of the conditions for rights to an asset. The estimates, if acceptable to both parties, are good starting points for establishing a figure. Estimate the sales when market penetration peaks or plateaus (3-5 years after market introduction) calculate the average of three years using the year before and the year after the peak). The LIF should be about 50% of the royalty due.

Final year's sales. Although a possible method to set upfront fees this approach is also not very accurate. It is difficult to define the life of a technology much less a product. A realistic percentage is 10-50% of the final year's sales. The problem is that most business plans estimate only the first several years of sales. Further, it is very likely the final year of sales will be the least amount of revenue.

Cost plus. In select situation, a licensor may know or have a good estimate of replacement cost or incurred cost to date. These figures can be verified and, in some, cases an increase justified. This figure then becomes the basis of further negotiation.

Bottom line. No one theory addresses all fluctuations in economic conditions, development, service requirements and investment by the licensing parties. Simplicity and fairness are important features for a long-term workable licensing arrangement.

For the replacement cost situation, the upfront fee will be approximately 15% (MRD-K + MRC-E). MRC-K is modified replacement cost of knowledge, and is determined by asking the researcher, "Knowing what you now know, how long would it take to recreate or invent around this patent?" MRC-E is cost of special lab equipment required by one skilled in the art to recreate this invention and reduce it to practice. For example, if MRC-K is $100K and MRC-E is $50K then the upfront fee is 15% (100K + 50K) = $22.5K. Running royalties must be calculated separately. This is a starting point which may be modified when all other valuation considerations are included. This upfront fee is also traded off in NPV calculations when needed. If a cost-plus basis is used to set the LIF, estimate cost to develop the technology (investigator's salaries, supplies, overhead); add in an inflation factor (3-5%); and account for the amount of the fee to be shared with other parties.

License Issue Fee -Example 1

When establishing a license issue fee several steps are associated with the process. They are as follows.

First, it is presupposed a royalty rate has been selected and the value of know – how, to be transferred, has been determined and whether it is included in the base payment or paid separately. In some cases, negotiators use 5% (or any other industry standard rate) as a starting point & adjust up or down depending on:
   a. importance of technology for end-user, centrality/value of technology for licensee as a product or process (i.e. single product or product line/family);
   b. projected spin-off benefit for other product families or processes for licensee risk (i.e. will not work, patent will not issue);
   c. if company is using asset as part of equity funding strategy, major product line introduction, or revitalization; and
   d. if payments are not all due in advance of offering or introduction, adjust up.

Second, project annual sales for 4-year +/-1 year after product introduction date or revenue on the date when sales are near the projected maximum market penetration.

Third, determine what dollar amount of royalty you expect in that year given projected sales and projected royalty rate.

Fourth, discount that amount to the current value using a high discount rate to take into account market risks involved (usually 25-30%). If the asset is in its infancy and invention the discount might be 40-60% and for low risk with known market & manufacturing established; e.g. an improvement patent, the discount rate might be prime plus 1-15%.

Fifth, the discounted royalty figure is the first cut at a license issue fee. One might add patenting costs (unless such costs are separate items or licensee reimburses separately for out-of-pocket patenting costs.)

Sixth, if the asset will take a long period of time for development, biotech product, estimate sales from comparables/similar products. Then, determine royalty expected at the time of steady market sales. Discount that figure to current value. However, remember that LIF may need to be reduced for an asset requiring extend time before it reaches market but adjust royalty rate to compensate the licensee accordingly. Startups can rarely afford much of a LIF so; 1) establish fair LIF with an increase in royalty rate; 2) adjust or add milestones; 3) secure some equity: 4)

331

request a share of investment development money and/or share what licensee gets from future industry partners.

License Issue Fee-Example 2:
1. Identify what technology (or product) will be when fully developed (i.e. - new heart monitoring devices, software for ultrasound machines, a new gene therapy.)
2. Determine what comparable royalty rates are for technologies in same class (i.e. if the product is software for ultrasound machine, research going rate for medical software applications).
3. Estimate initial payment. Estimate the number of years until a product that produces revenue is on market. Determine fraction of revenue producing product that is the invention. Multiply comparable royalty rate by this number. This is the adjusted royalty rate.
4. Calculate initial payment: Allow company to pay .25 - .50 of adjusted royalty rate per year for the development period and estimate first year's sales of the product. Multiply discounted royalty rate by the estimated first year sales. Multiply this by the number of years until commercialization. If the period is longer than a few years, discount the royalty payments. This is the initial payment. Initial payment should be accompanied by a royalty once product is commercialized. After commercialization, the full-adjusted royalty rate is due.

ROYALTY RATE AFFECTERS

In order to effectively establish a preferred royalty rate, it is necessary to know and understand factors that affect the royalty rate. Some of these factors are as follows:

1. source of technology; University, non-profits, foundations and government are often sources of leading edge technology but due to the stage of development determining value is difficult to establish;
2. upfront payments; when combined with royalty the amount becomes "deal dependent" and involves many factors, all of which can contribute to the flexibility of negotiation. High up-front payments are usually associated with "hot" technology in a developing field. Upfront payments are usually based on current dollar value;
3. exclusive world-wide license; anything else leads to decreased royalty rate;
4. licensor holds no equity in licensee; if equity held rates are usually reduced;
5. credit of upfront payments toward running royalties may contribute toward a higher royalty rate;
6. no significant sponsored research agreements are involved; if no commitment to fund licensor's research royalty rate will be higher but if sponsored research required at licensor facilities rate will be reduced (requirement that a licensee sponsor research as part of a license arrangement is not usually recommended unless the arrangements are separate agreements);
7. overseas licensing; often commands a slightly lower royalty rate;
   status & duration of proprietary position; poor or lack of issued patent(s) protection leads to lower royalty rate;
8. product life cycle; rate will reflect market advantage or lack of;
9. investment in time & capital required to reach market; leaves less profit so royalty rate is less;
10. licensee assumes responsibility for intellectual property protection; (value varies e.g. university need may be greater than corporate need or desire);
11. licensee pledges to assume liability for law suites - leads to lower royalty rate;
12. licensing back technological improvement to licensor can lower value; and hence royalty rate;
13. mandatory sub-licensing by licensee; may produce additional income for licensor but fosters competition and loss of licensee's proprietary position as well as reduced royalty rate;
14. limiting territory, use or product application of the technology; results in reduced market for licensee and will be used to justify lower royalty rate;

15. stronger march-in rights to retrieve technology if licensee does not meet certain milestones - creates risk for licensee and hence desire to pay lower royalty rate;
16. non compete provision that restricts a licensee from marketing products that compete with the licensor or other licensees; limits market size and also royalty;
17. non-exclusivity; depending on situation may or may not make it difficult to license others by licensor but in any event creates potential of competition for licensee who will negotiate for lower royalty rate;
18. equity in lieu of royalty, milestone, upfront, minimum or other payments - so lower royalty rate;
19. elimination of certain claims during the examination and approval process of patents leading to fewer and-or less valuable claims to license;
20. new scientific data that may enhance or reduce value of the asset;
21. advent of unrecognized competitors or products into the intended market; or
22. change in or unexpected public opinion regarding the technology or product, new regulatory conditions related to the technology.

In addition to the foregoing items that contribute to the royalty rate, a survey designed to identify some of the more common factors that are associated with royalty rate led to the conclusions presented in table five.

Table five. Royalty rate – considerations (technology licensing survey).

- economic business decisions drive royalty rates
- beware of "industry norms" (conduct independent evaluation of each license opportunity)
- pharmaceutical "norm"
  - < 2% = process, formulation or software
  - 2-5% = preclinical compounds
  - 5-10% = early stage clinical compounds
  - 10-15% = late stage clinical compounds
- licensing in royalties are lower than licensing out
- company size not an important factor in royalty rate
- little preference for foreign vs. domestic licensee
- if licensing out greater emphasis on established royalty rate
- if licensing in greater emphasis on profit analysis of licensee than on established rates but rates usually higher if profit analysis completed
- percentage rate most preferred - accounts for inflation
- net sales is usual basis for royalty

Royalty arrangements can be extremely complex. A number of issues that affect price and are important to keep in mind during negotiation are as follows.

Derivative Works

A distributor may or may not have a right to create derivative works. If they do have this right, a distributor may want to decrease royalty rate for the revenue received from derivative works. Rationale for this decrease is as derivative works are created original work will represent a smaller and smaller portion of the work as a whole. This same concept will apply where the distributor has the right to merge the original work into other works (e.g., merging a photograph into a collage). If the author agrees with the concept of decreasing royalty, the author should make sure that there is a clear mechanism for determining an appropriate decrease. For example, if the modifications to the work are primarily cosmetic, then the decrease should be small.

Sale Price

Since royalties are usually based upon the sales price of the work, it is important to determine how this price is arrived at. For example, if the distributor is given complete discretion over the price, it would be possible that the distributor could decide to give the work away free, bundled with other products that are being sold. In such a case, the author would receive no royalties. On the other hand, if the author has too much control over price, then this may become intrusive on the exercise of marketing judgment of the distributor. One solution is to require a minimum royalty on each transfer of copies of the work.

Guaranteed Royalties

Amazingly, many royalty arrangements do not require the distributor to sell even one copy. The author may be all too appreciative that the distributor wants to distribute the work that there is no thought that the distributor will make less than a full effort to market the work. However, what if the day after you grant the distributor exclusive rights to market the work that you've spent the last two years developing, the distributor purchases the right to distribute a competitive work that the distributor thinks is better and leaves your work on the shelf? Or worse, what if the distributor's goal was just to get your work off the market so as not to compete with another product that the distributor has? These scenarios are not far fetched and need to be planned for.

One solution is to require minimum royalty payments or sales, as mentioned above. This offers some protection, but it is better to also prohibit the distributor from marketing any competitive product. The definition of what is competitive must be carefully worded.

Sublicensing Rights

Sublicensing rights of a distributor can severely affect royalties earned by the author. For example, assume that you have negotiated a royalty of 15% of the gross revenue received by the distributor on sales. This royalty amount recognizes that the distributor has overhead expenses in addition to the expense of marketing. What if the distributor decides sublicense the work to another company to market. They will now receive 15% of the sales revenue as royalties from the new distributor, and you will only receive 15% of 15%, which only 2.25% of the gross sales price! The solution here is to either prohibit sublicensing or agree that the royalty will be higher (perhaps 50%) for revenues from sublicensing.

Marketing Efforts

It is important to require the distributor to begin marketing the work by some specific date. The work may need further development, and therefore a realistic date should be selected. Additionally, it is very beneficial to require the distributor to spend a certain amount of money on marketing within a specific time period (e.g., $100,000 in the first year).

Royalty Payments

In brief, royalty payments take the following forms: (1) Some cash up front plus royalty payments as sales are made; (2) Some cash up front which represents an advance against royalties earned in the future; and (3) Only royalties as sales are made, with no cash up front. These three forms represent a shift in risk from the distributor to the author. Cash up front represents a risk to the distributor, whereas royalty payments to the author only when sales occur represents a higher risk assumed by the author. The level of rights granted by the author should take into account how much risk either the author or the distributor assumes.

Audit Rights

The author should have clear rights to audit the books of the distributor to determine the accuracy of the royalty payments the author receives. These audits will usually be at the expense of the author, however, the agreement can provide that where the distributor has underpaid, the distributor pays the cost of the audit. There could also be a penalty for such underpayments.

Reversion of Rights

There should be provisions that under certain circumstances rights immediately and automatically revert to the author. For example, if sales fall below a specified level, or if the distributor breaches the agreement rights revert to the licensor.

Arbitration

Lastly, it is often useful to have disputes that arise resolved by arbitration. Arbitrators can be selected in advance, which will facilitate a quick resolution of the issues, which otherwise could be dragged out in litigation, beyond the valuable commercial life of the work. However, arbitration is not a perfect solution, and the terms of the arbitration need to be carefully worked out in advance.

Payment Examples

Several examples of license compensation are presented in tables two through five.

Usual pharmaceutical industry royalty rate ranges differ for not only the stage of the technology but also seem to vary with the type of organization involved in the agreement which is highly correlated with the stage of development. See tables six through eight.

Table six. Biomedical licensing grid.

technology classification	running royalty, %	upfront payment	minimum annual royalty	comments
reagent or process	1-5	recap patent $	$2-10K	
kit reagents	2-10	recap patent $	$2-10	
diagnostics, *in vitro*	2-6	$10-20K or recap patent $	$2-75K	maybe sliding scale for royalty
diagnostics, *in vitro*	3-8%	$10-20K or recap patent $	$2-75K	
therapeutics	4-12	$20-150K	worst case sales scenario X base royalty rate or X (10-30%)	sliding scale for royalty
medical instruments	4-10	$5-150	$5-20K, 1st year $10-50 thereafter	
software	3-15	$10-200K		

Table seven. Value chain for the biotechnology industry.

Component	Academic ($000's)	Early Stage ($000's)	Late Stage ($000's)
Upfront	$30	$4,000	$5,000
Equity		$11,000	$19,000
R&D payments	$351	$16,000	$25,000
Milestone payments	$71	$12,000	$32,000
Advance royalties	$128		
Total	$516	$32,000	$71,000
Royalty Rate		4.7%	9.3%

Table eight. Average royalty rates on sales by R&D stage at signing agreements.

R&D STAGE	BIOTECH COMPANY ◇ UNIVERSITY	PHARMACEUTICAL ◇ BIOTECH COMPANY
Discovery	3.0%	7.0%
Lead molecule	4.0 - 5.0%	9.0%
Pre-clinical	6.0 - 7.0%	10.0%
Phase II or III clinical		15.0%

Considerations that impact compensation demands in a bio-products license are as follows:

- source of technology- university, non-profits, foundations often are sources of leading edge technology that is difficult to establish a value;
- upfront payments combined and amount is "arrangement dependent";
- high end of up-front payments usually associated with "hot" technology in a developing field;
- licenses are exclusive world-wide - anything else decreases royalty rate;
- licensee holds no equity in licensor - if equity held rates reduced;
- no claim of infringement by licensor against licensee - if so up-fronts significantly higher to recapture royalty due licensor;
- credit of upfront payments toward running royalties may be in effect;
- no significant sponsored research agreements are involved - if so rate often reduced;
- overseas licensing often commands a slightly lower royalty rate;
- upfront payments are based on current dollar value;
- status and duration of proprietary position - poorer the protection the lower the royalty rate;
- product life cycle - rate can reflect market position; and
- investment in time and capital required to reach market.

Once all factors that may impact business terms of the license have been addressed the amount of compensation desired should be established. Since royalty is the most common form of compensation and generally is established so licensor shares in the income from product(s) based on some form of intellectual property it is paramount that the rate be established based on the best valuation method(s).

ASSET PRICING EXAMPLES

Shrink-wrapped software pricing for both single and multiple users do not benefit from typical valuation methods (i.e. 25% rule, net present value, etc.) because the software is new, markets are unknown, and any market assessments are in the future or resource limited; yet there seems to be some company immediately calling and wanting a price quote.

Pricing is important, besides knowing a royalty rate, because one can sell software directly, check the price if sold through a distributor, check business plans/equity positions via pricing, etc. This method is empirical. Examples of software pricing are as follows.

5% Solution

The first estimate of the software price is found by taking 5% of the modified replacement cost (MRC). The MRC is the cost it would take the author(s) to recreate the software knowing what they now know after doing the R&D. (Ask for both the time and MRC as a crosscheck). Depending upon your knowledge of the software, immediately ask a few commercial assessment questions such as, "Can we sell this software as a shrink-wrap, now as is? Is a user's manual available? Can we transport this to a more common architecture or platform? Have you embedded other commercially available software in your package? - " If any of these are answered, "No." then ask how much more time and money is required. 5% of the revised MRC is your first estimate of the commercial selling price.

Example: If the MRC were found to be $100,000, the selling price would then be $5,000. (NOTE: The total replacement cost is irrelevant as it includes R&D tangents and dead ends. Although it may be useful in court trials or buyouts where "cost" estimates tend to be on the "up side". The MRC is relevant because if an industrial firm hired the researcher, the researcher could re-create the same software faster and more efficiently than before.)

Market Rules

Determine if any commercial competitors exist. This is not a fully developed market survey, but relies on the researcher as a first cut, as most researchers would not have developed the software if they were aware of commercial products.

No competitors. Applicable to most universities and national labs. More than 50% of the time no competitors exist. The 5% solution is your price. (NOTE: Even if one or two software packages exist the "no competitors" may still apply because competition is not fully developed and the software sold is highly customized rather than shrink-wrapped.)

Highly competitive. Areas include software, such as word processing, spreadsheets, desktop publishing, linear programming, optimizers, etc. Rely on research, as a first cut, and ask, "What competing software is close in price and capabilities?" to determine market "fit" for the software. Get more research later when there is time and money.

Example: The software is priced at $5,000. The researcher indicates that there are two somewhat similar products priced at $8,000 and $7,000. Basic options are: 1) Go for market share and keep the price at $5,000 or 2) Increase the price to $7,000-$7,500 so price is within the commercially acceptable price window. (NOTE: If the competitors are lower at $3,000, a similar logic applies: 1) Go for the high-end market and keep the price at $5,000 or $4,000 or 2) Drop the price to about $3000 and fit within the commercially acceptable price window.)

Multiple users. This entire method, with a discussion of theory, basis, and data is provided in the paper: P. Betten, "Some Guidance on Software Pricing", Proceedings of the Technology Transfer Society, Proceeding of the 1997 Annual Meeting held July 21-23, 1997, Denver, Co., (pp. 217-222). See Exhibit B for details.

Royalty rate should be determined based on the specific technology and market.

However, in some cases it is useful to know what royalty has been paid for a certain type of asset. Examples based on survey results are presented in tables nine and ten.

Table nine. Royalty rates for software copyright and marks.

Product	Royalty rate, %
Fully developed multimedia	40.0
Publisher/distributor to develop	10.0
Algorithms that add to product line	10.0
Hardware needing development	05.0
Licensed trademark	05.0

Whenever possible, up-front monies should be received for cost of early stage technology and early stage development (An arbitrary figure that market itself is best designed to establish).

Table ten. Royalty rates for different types of technology.

Technology	Percent
Automobile manufacturing technology	02.0
Automotive mirror optics	05.0
Basic laser patents	05.0
Bar code scanning	15.0
Blood substitute	03.0
Burn treatment	05.0
Cellular telephone data transmission modem	02.0
Child protection products	06.0
Cytology device	10.0
Disease diagnostic test kits	15.0
Disney toys	12.0
DVD players	03.5
Ergonomic design	03.0
Fire prevention wood treatment	10.0
Flat panel displays	05.0
Hear aid device	02.5
Industrial pipe repair	10.0
Injection molded fans	06.5
Machine vision	05.0
Medical digital scanner	10.0
Pavement texturing	10.0
Plastic lumber	05.0
Pollution scrubber	05.0
Remote metering	05.5
Roofing materials	06.0
Semiconductor manufacturing	05.0
Variable light transmission glass	05.0
Voltage converter	06.0
Water beds	09.4
Used oil refining cents/gallon	06.0

EQUITY - FAIR SHARE

In a 1992 AUTM survey of 1731 licenses; 371 involved equity (21.5%). So equity was becoming "trendy" or a good business venture for univeristies. This trend continued throught 1999. An alternative to equity is to get the best royalty arrangement and then seek options or warrants.

For example, one can have an automatic conversion into common stock based on some valuation event. One could specify something like a 1:2 conversion ratio of preferred to common when the company's value reaches $100MM. But issuer could still issue additional shares in the meantime, thereby making this feature one that mitigates dilution, but doesn't fully prevent it. Plenty of bargaining power is needed to secure this feature.

If common stock is held, a company does well and stock is not over diluted; by the time a company achieves a value of $100 MM, is it likely the investment will be worth more than if one took preferred with a conversion ratio of two common for each preferred. However, if the company failed and common is owned the return will be $0, whereas, the likelihood that after bondholders are paid off, but if preferred stock is held one may receive something from the bankrupt company.

Issues of dividend payments/debt-like features – can still have "debt like" features prior to conversion through the dividend payments of preferred. Dividends can be set up to be paid on a regular basis, to be owed even if the company cannot afford to pay (cumulative dividends) or to be paid by the company only if and when company has cash to declare a dividend (non-cumulative.) Usually start up companies have no cash to pay out and aren't going to have any during their early stages, so dividends are usually paid at the election of the company (i.e. they're not paid.) As with the other points, dividends and how they are paid are subject to negotiation and bargaining power.

If equity is distributed to the originating institution and its employees the organization will need to create appropriate policies for the distribution. Considerations will include conflict of interest and commitment, employee role in company, research support in the employee's laboratory, etc. Examples of queries that might be posed are:

1. Does originating institution administration get equity and only royalty goes to inventors; if so, how is it calculated?
2. Is stock distributed to everyone upon registration or held by originating institution until cash-in allowed?
3. What is done to assure arm's length stock management to avoid insider trading; stock held by university treasurer or agent?

An example of equity distribution as additional financial commitments are made is presented in table eleven.

Table eleven. Anatomy of an equity license arrangement.

Holder	Common stock, M	% of class	Series A preferred stock, M	% of Total class	issued & out-standing, M	% of total issued & out-standing	Options and warrants	Total fully diluted, M	% of fully diluted
Founders	4.5	75	-	-	4.5	50.0	-	4.5	45
Venture fund	-	-	3.0	100	3.0	33.3	-	3.0	30
University	1.2	20	-	-	1.2	13.3	-	1.2	12
Professor	0.3	5	-	-	0.3	3.3	-	0.3	3
Option Plan	-	-	-	-	-	-	1.0	1.0	10
TOTAL	6.0	100	3.0	100	9.0	100	1.0	10.0	100

Equity Examples

When transferring intellectual property, e.g. a discovery of a potential drug, how do you establish value for the purposes of taking equity in a start-up? For purposes of this example assume the academic institution is the 100% owner and the original inventor is not to receive any equity in the start-up.

Consider it as a discounted Net Present Value of what a reasonable licensing fee would be. For example, if a reasonable license fee in the future would be $1M per year and it can be discounted at 5%, then the value to this point is $20M. Then discount this number by the probability that it will actually be a commercial success. For example, in this case one might conclude that it has 1% chance of success and therefore the right value would be $200K for the start-up equity.

Discount rate is that component of value that compensates the investor for the commitment of capital commitments resulting from giving up other investment opportunities and risk assumption

Factors affecting discount rate are: inflation, liquidity, real interest rates and/or risk premium. Inflation can reduce purchasing power of future economic benefits. Liquidity is the difficulty for an investment to be quickly converted into cash. Real interest is sacrificing alternative use of the invested funds (it is the reward for deferring consumption in favor of investment and in real form is usually about 3%). The risk premium is the added amount of return that investors demand for the assumption of risk, e.g., possibility of loss and/or unanticipated variability in earnings. It varies with the type of property and industry. An example is likelihood of competitive technologies that could reduce value, e.g., software products.

FUTURE

Earlier it was alluded to that effective asset evaluation involves continued monitoring of the industry a firm is involved in. some refer to this process as technology forecasting. These projected trends need to be monitored and taken into consideration as an asset is evaluated and a value established.

Members of the World Future Society have forecasted the following for the next 25 years. (September 2002 edition of "The Futurist"):

- By 2020 there will be more than 1B people age 60 or older, ¾ in developing countries
- Nanotechnology; for example, nanomedicine will emerge by 2025; initial focus will be on cardiovascular and cancer areas
- Hydrogen and fuel cell application in automotive and energy areas will be prominent
- Mass customization will be rule for many consumer products
- Water shortages will be rampant over next 2 decades – 3.5 B people will be short of water (10x as many as in 1995)
- Fuel cells will be in common use by 2009
- Aqua culture (fish farming) will overtake cattle ranching as a food source by 2010
- Automated highways which reduce or eliminate personal driving by 2020
- Behavior problems will be solved through improved nutrition and less junk food
- New materials for clothing will enhance human well-being and safety.
-

In the next decade (2002-2012) Battelle expects these new products will be introduced:

- Genetaceuticals – disease treatment through combined genetics and pharmaceuticals
- Personalized computers – hardware and software adapted to personal way of working
- Multi-fuel automobiles – combined electricity, natural gas, gasoline, etc.
- Next generation television – high definition, flat screens for communication, and entertainment
- Electronic wallet –smart card to replace money, keys, license, medical records, etc.

- Home health monitors – automated analysis of vital signs
- Smart maps and tracking devices – Chinese restaurant or the family dog
- Smart materials – sensors to detect stress i.e. bridges or buildings
- Weight control and anti-aging – genetic cures for baldness, nutritionally enhanced food
- Never owned, leased only products – computers and appliances that become obsolete quickly

George Washington University's forecast of emerging technologies and the year they will be in common use and which are now investment opportunities are presented in Exhibit D.

EXHIBIT A - INTERNET INFORMATION RESOURSES
(Also see the resource directory presented in Addendum II)

Web site starting points:

Center for Entrepreneurship, Baylor University	http://hsb.baylor.edu/html/cel/ent/inninvp.htm
Corporate Information: links to >350K co profiles, free/fee	http://www.corporateinformation.com
Company Sleuth – info on publicly traded companies; free	http://www.company.sleuth.com
Convera	http://www.convera.com/index.html
Cyveillance Inc.	http://www.cyveillance.com
Dialog	http://www.dialog.com
Direct Search – web pages and list of lists	http://gwis2.circ.gwu.edu/gprice/direct.htm
EDGAR Online – SEC filings; free & fee	http://www.edgar-online.com
EoMonitor – web site monitoring; free & fee	http://www.javElink.com/cat2main.htm
Hoover's Online - > 50K companies; free & fee	http://www.hooversonline.com
i2 Inc.	http://www.i2inc.com
Insite – Intelligence Data	http://www.iac-insite.com
Knowledge X – IBM product; competitive analysis; free	http://www.knowledgex.com
Kudzukat's People Search – find experts; free	http://members.aol.com/kudzukat/kks_pepl.html
Knowledge Express	http://www.knowledgeexpress.com
Lexis-Nexis – business, law, gov. and academia; fee	http://www.lexis-nexis.com
Logic Team	http://www.logicteam.com
Manning & Napier Information Service	http://www.mnis.net
Mind-It from NetMind - web site tracking; free & fee	http://www.netmind.com
NERAC Inc.	http://www.nerac.com
SRI Consulting	http://www.sriconsulting.com
Steelynx	http://www.steelynx.net
Thomas Register – manufacturers and products; free	http://www.thomasregister.com
Wal-Mart Innovation Network (WIN)	http://www.wal-mart.com/win
WI Innovation Service Center (WISC)	http://www.uww.edu/business/innovate/innovate.htm
Wisdom Builder LLC	http://www.wisdombuilder.com

Job postings

CareerPath.com	http://www.carrerpath.com
Monster.com	http://www.monster.com

EXHIBIT B – TWO MINUTE PRICING METHOD (SOFTWARE)

SHRINK-WRAPPED SOFTWARE PRICING FOR BOTH
SINGLE AND MULTIPLE USERS

Typical valuation methods (i.e. 25% rule, net present value, etc.) do not work because the software is new, markets are unknown, and any market assessments are in the future or resource limited; yet there seems to be some company immediately calling and wanting a price quote. Pricing is important, besides knowing a royalty rate, because one can sell software directly, check the price if sold through a distributor, check business plans/equity positions via pricing, etc. This method is empirical. The 3 steps are:

1) **The 5% Solution**: The first estimate of the software price is found by taking 5% of the modified replacement cost (MRC). The MRC is the cost it would take the author(s) to recreate the software knowing what they now know after doing the R&D.
(Ask for both the time and MRC as a crosscheck). Depending upon your knowledge of the software, immediately ask a few commercial assessment questions such as, "Can we sell this software as a shrink-wrap, now as is? Is a user's manual available? Can we transport this to a more common architecture or platform? Have you embedded other commercially available software in your package? ..." If any of these are answered, "No." then ask how much more time and money is required. 5% of the revised MRC is your first estimate of the commercial selling price. Example: If the MRC were found to be $100,000, the selling price would then be $5,000.

NOTE: The total replacement cost is irrelevant as it includes R&D tangents and dead ends. Although it may be useful in court trials or buyouts where "cost" estimates tend to be on the "up side". The MRC is relevant because if an industrial firm hired the researcher, the researcher could re-create the same software faster and more efficiently than before.

2) **The market rules**: Determine if any commercial competitors exist. This is not a fully developed market survey, but rely on the researcher as a first cut, as most researchers would not have developed the software if they were aware of commercial products.
2A) **No competitors**: Applicable to most universities and national labs. More than 50% of the time no competitors exist. The 5% solution is your price.

NOTE: Even if one or two software packages exist you may still be in the "no competitors" area because competition is not fully developed and the software sold is highly customized rather than shrink-wrapped.

2B) **Highly competitive** areas include software like word processing, spreadsheets, desktop publishing, linear programming, optimizers, etc. Rely on the researcher, as a first cut, and ask, "What competing software is close to yours in price and capabilities?" The intent is to quickly figure where your software fits in the market. More market research can occur later when there is more time and money.

Example: You priced the software at $5,000. Your researcher indicates that there are two somewhat similar products priced at $8,000 and $7,000. Your basic options are: 1) Go for market share and keep the price at $5,000 or 2) Increase the price to $7,000-$7,500 so that the price is within the commercially acceptable price window.

NOTE: If the competitors are lower at $3,000, a similar logic applies: 1) Go for the high end market and keep the price at $5,000 or $4,000 or 2) Drop your price to $3000 or so and fit within the commercially acceptable price window.

3) **Multiple users**. This is hard to explain without figures. There are two distinct regions (market share and highly discounted) essentially, but not always, distinguished by price. The "market share" software is highly competitive (spreadsheets, word processing, etc.), usually costs below $2,000, and is not discounted much for multiple users. The "high-discounted" software packages tend to be unique, costing over $2,000, and very highly discounted. There actually appears to be a gray area on price, from maybe $1000 to $2,500, and the software may be placed in either regime based on other factors. Both follow an "L" shaped curve (single unit price versus number of units sold) with a curve breakpoint occurring at about 10 unit sales. Prices are normalized by the single unit price (normalized price = price per unit sold/single unit price). Averaged out data (error bounds are not provided) and are shown below:

Units sold	Normalized price Market share	Normalized price High discount
1	1.00	1.00
2-5	0.85	0.55
6-10	0.75	0.35
11-40	0.70	0.20
41-60	0. 65	0.15

Example: What's the multiple user discount price for 20 copies? If the software single unit price is selected to be $5,000. Based upon price, the single unit selling price is over $2,000 and therefore placed in the highly discounted software regime. Using the table above and calculation below, the 20 copy price is found to be almost the same as buying 7 copies at full price:

$$P\text{-}20 \text{ copies} = \$5000 (1 + 4 \times .55 + 5 \times .35 + 10 \times .2)$$
$$= \$5000 (1 + 2.2 + 1.75 + 2)$$
$$= \$5000 (6.95)$$
$$= \$34,750$$

___

The entire method, with a discussion of theory, basis, and data is provided in the paper: P. Betten, "Some Guidance on Software Pricing", Proceedings of the Technology Transfer Society, Proceeding of the 1997 Annual Meeting held July 21-23, 1997, Denver, Co., (pp. 217-222).

EXHIBIT C - TECHNOLOGY TRANSFER SERVICE PROVIDER (EXAMPLE)

Contact: Phyl Leah Speser, J.D., Ph.D., President, Foresight Science & Technology, Inc., P.O. Box 6815, New Bedford, MA 02742; Voice: 508-984-0018 ext. 12; Fax: 508-984-0405; phyl@seeport.com; mailto:phyl@seeport.com; See: http://www.seeport.com

Foresight evaluation is based on the following objectives:
1) eliminate technologies with obvious problems (easier to pick losers than winners) i.e.:
   o infringement
   o product already exists
   o end-user demand
   o can it be built
   o competitive given current and emerging alternatives (i.e. price/performance)
2) confirm that someone will license, buy, invest, etc.
3) check markets, estimate market share and potential revenues
4) determine if an entry strategy is feasible.
5) identify technologies that are obvious winners but also recognize that some early stage technologies are difficult to evaluate without some subjectivity

Evaluation takes about 48 hours of labor. About 200 discrete technologies can be evaluated in a year. Forsight in involved in many federal government evaluations. Volume discounts are available. (see http://www.seeport.com/catalog/references/testimonials.htm). Cost is about $4,000. Form and software is proprietary and only used in-house.

The Foresight program consists of seven steps to make the most efficient use of time and money:
1. Preliminary Discussion and Plan Development
2. Secondary (text and data) Research
3. Secondary Research Analysis and Review
4. Interview Guide
5. Primary Research
6. Analysis and Review of all Research
7. Client Report

EXHIBIT D - EMERGING TECHNOLOGIES FORECAST

EMERGING TECHNOLOGIES FORECAST

Technology	Year	Feature
Hybrid vehicles	2007	combination of electric and internal combustion engines
Distance learning	2012	education systems based on computerized teaching programs and interactive TV lectures and seminars
Computer sensory recognition	2009	voice, handwriting, optical recognition
Parallel processing	2015	super computers using parallel processing
Intelligent agents	2007	knowbots, navigators and other intelligent software agents filter and retrieve information
Teleliving	2008	expanded use of embedded processors in common objects and integrated into workplace and home
Expert systems	2012	routine use to help with decision making in management, medicine, engineering, etc.
Computer translation	2018	language translation in real time
Ceramic engines	2022	better heat and wear
Gene therapy	2025	prevent and cure inherited diseases
Optical computers	2012	use of photons rather than electrons to code information so processing occurs at speed of light
Artificial food	2030	synthetic and provides optimal health
Neural networks	2006	computations commonly performed by neural networks using parallel processors
Nanotechnology	2030	microscopic machines with commercial applications
Intelligent transportation systems	2015	computerized highways regulating traffic
High speed trains	2012	high speed rail or mag-lev trains in most major cities in developing nations
Designer babies	2012	offspring avoid inheriting malfunctions and parents design "ideal" offspring
Green business	2015	firms are positioned for long-term sustainability through environment friendly practices
Hypersonic planes	2030	passenger aircraft travel at more than 5X speed of sound
Fusion power	2030	fusion nuclear power used for electricity production
Manned mission to Mars	2022	completed

EXHIBIT E – EVALUATION AND PROBLEM SOLVING METHODOLOGIES

Some of the techniques and methodologies employed in conducting technology or market forecasts are described below. The descriptions explain the rationale on which each technology is based, discuss the ways in which each technology is most commonly used, and indicate whether results are typically quantitative or qualitative in nature. The techniques are categorized by the five different ways people view the future:

1. Extrapolators
2. Pattern Analysts
3. Goal analysts
4. Counter Punchers
5. Intuitors

Each of these approaches has its advantages and shortcomings. However, our experience has been that more valid forecasts result from the use of all five approaches rather than reliance on any one. Thus, in our technology/marketing forecasting projects we normally use at least one technique from each group.

1. Extrapolators believe that the future will represent a logical extension of the past. Large scale, inexorable forces will drive the future in a continuous, reasonably predictable manner, and one can, therefore, best forecast the future by identifying past trends and extrapolating them in a reasoned, logical manner.

Technology Trend Analysis is based on the observation that advances in technologies tend to follow an exponential improvement process. The technique uses early improvement data to establish the rate of progress and extrapolates that rate to project the level of progress at various times in the future. Results produced by this technique are typically highly quantitative. In practice, this technique is typically used to forecast developments such as the speed of operation, level of performance, cost reduction, improved quality, and operating efficiency.

Fisher-Pry Analysis is a mathematical technique used to project the rate of market adoption of technically superior new technologies and, when appropriate, to project the loss of market share by old technologies. The technique is based on the fact that the adoption of such new technologies normally follows a pattern known by mathematicians as the "Logistic Curve." This adoption pattern is defined by two parameters. One of these parameters determines the time at which adoption begins, and the other determines the rate at which adoption will occur. These parameters can be determined from early adoption data, and the resulting pattern can be used to project the time at which market takeover will reach any given level. Results produced by this technique are highly quantitative. The technique is used to make forecasts such as how the installed base of telecommunications equipment will change over time, how rapidly a new chemical production process will be adopted, and the rate at which digital measuring devices will replace analog devices in petroleum refineries, etc.

Gompertz Analysis is very similar in concept to Fisher-Pry Analysis, except that it better models adoptions that are driven by the technical superiority of the new technology. However, customers do not suffer any significant penalty for not adopting the new technology at any given time. Like Fisher-Pry analysis, Gompertz analysis projects adoption by use of a two parameter mathematical model. In similar manner, early adoption is used to determine these parameters and the resulting adoption curve. Results are highly quantitative, and the technique is often used to project adoption of consumer products such as high-definition television, camcorders, new automobile features, etc.

Growth Limit Analysis utilizes a mathematical formulation known as the Pearl Curve to project the pattern in which maturing technologies will approach development limits. This can often be useful to organizations in analyzing maturing technologies, in setting feasible research goals, and in determining the utility of additional development spending. The technique can also be useful in determining if new technical approaches can be used to overcome apparent technical limits.

351

Learning Curve techniques are based on the fact that, as more and more items of a given type are produced, the price of production tends to decrease at a predictable rate. For example, each doubling of the total number of a particular items produced might result in a cost reduction of 15%. In some cases, key technical parameters may improve in a similar pattern. The learning curve phenomenon is reflected as a straight line on log-log graph paper which makes projection relatively simple. Results from the use of this are highly quantitative. The technique can be used for setting price and technical performance targets for developing technologies, particularly in the middle stages of their development.

2. Pattern Analysts believe that the future will reflect a replication of past events. Powerful feedback mechanisms in our society, together with basic human drives, will cause future trends and events to occur in identifiable cycles and predictable patterns. Thus, one can best address the future by identifying and analyzing analogous situations from the past and relating them to probable futures.

Analogy Analysis is based on the observation that the patterns of technical development and market capture for new technologies are often similar to those for like technologies in the past. In applying this technique, forecasters identify appropriate analogies and analyze similarities and differences. Normally, it is desirable to identify more than one applicable example in order to minimize the probability of selecting false or inappropriate analogies. The results from application of this technique are typically semi-quantitative in nature, and are often presented as a range of possibilities rather than a single projection.

Precursor Trend Analysis takes advantage of the fact that, often, the development of one technology lags by a constant period the development of another related one. For example, the first application of technical advances in passenger cars typically occurs approximately four years after their application in race cars. Similarly, the application of new technologies in commercial products tend to follow laboratory demonstration by a relatively constant period. One can, thus, project the status of the lag technology at some future date by observing the status of the lead technology today. This technique also allows the extension of lag technology forecasts by building on forecasts of lead technologies. Results from using this technique are highly quantitative.

Morphological Matrices provide a formal method for uncovering new product and process possibilities. In applying this technique, users first determine the essential functions of the product or process. Next, they list the different means by which each of these functions could be satisfied. Finally, they use the matrix to identify new, reasonable combinations of these means that could result in practical new products or processes. Results of the application of this technique are qualitative in nature. The technique can be used to identify non-obvious new opportunities for a company. This technique can also be used to identify products and processes that competitors might be developing or considering.

Feedback Models provide a means for accounting for the interactions that will connect technical, economic, market, societal, and economic factors as the future unfolds. In using this technique computer models are developed that mathematically specify the relationships between each of the relevant factors. For example, advances in technology may result in improved products that may result in increased sales that may provide more funds for further advance in technology. The results of this technique are highly quantitative, but are often used to examine qualitative consequences of trends, events, or decisions. The technique is most commonly used in the formulation of high level strategies or policy.

3. Goal Analysts believe that the future will be determined by the beliefs and actions of various individuals, organizations, and institutions. The future, therefore, is susceptible to modification and change by these entities. Thus, the future can best be projected by examining the stated and implied goals of various decision-makers and trend setters, by evaluating the extent to which each can affect future trends and events, and by evaluating what the long-term results of their actions will be.

Impact Analysis provides a simple, formal method for taking into account the fact that, in a complex society such as ours, trends, events, and decisions often have consequences that are neither intended nor foreseen. The technique combines the use of left brain and right brain thinking to project the secondary, tertiary, and higher order impacts and implications of such occurrences. Results are qualitative in nature, and the technique is often used to analyze potential consequences of projected technical advances or to determine areas in which forecasting efforts could best be directed.

Content Analysis is founded on the concept that the relative importance of social, political, commercial and economic issues are reflected by the amount of media attention the issue receives. Thus, by measuring, over time, changes in such factors as column-inches in newspapers, time allocated on television, and, more recently, number of items on the Internet, forecasters can project the direction, nature, and rate of change. In the technical arena, this technique can, to some degree, be used to project advances in new technologies, as well as growing market attraction. The results of use of this technique are often displayed in a quantitative format. However, they are typically used only for qualitative analysis.

Stakeholders' Analysis is a formal method for taking account of the influence that various individuals and institutions can have on the way the future develops. It explicitly identifies those people and organizations, internal and external, that have a "stake" in particular decisions, projects, or programs; analyzes the importance that each individual or group assign to these issues; and the relative influence that they may have on developments. The results from this technique are normally semi-quantitative. The technique is often used to test the validity of forecasts that might be impacted by unexpected opposition or support.

Patent Analysis is based on the presumption that increased interest in new technologies, together with conviction of their practicality and appeal, will be reflected in increased R&D activity, and that this, in turn, will be reflected by increased patent activity. Thus, it is presumed that one can both identify new technology opportunities and assess the state of development of given technologies by analyzing the pattern of patent application in appropriate fields. Results from the application are often presented in quantified terms; however, their use in decision-making is normally based on a qualitative evaluation.

4. Counter Punchers believe that the future will result from a series of events and actions that are essentially unpredictable and, to a large extent, random. Therefore, one can best deal with the future by identifying a wide range of possible trends and events, by carefully monitoring developments in the technical and social environments, and by maintaining a high degree of flexibility in the planning process.

Scanning, Monitoring, and Tracking techniques are founded on the observation that, for most new technologies, a finite, often considerable, amount of time is required to bridge the gap between conception and commercialization. Thus, if one is alert, he or she can discern changes in technology, market, and other business factors in time to take maximum advantage of these changes. All three techniques are employed to identify and evaluate developments that might materially impact the organization's operations and strategies. Although the three techniques are similar in many respects, they differ in purpose, methodology, and degree of focus.

- Scanning seeks to identify any trend or event that might impact the organization and is, therefore, by design, essentially unfocussed.
- Monitoring is designed to follow general trends in specified areas and is, thus, more focused than scanning.
- Tracking is designed to carefully follow developments in a limited area and is, consequently, highly focused.

Results from each of these techniques can vary between highly quantitative to basically qualitative. However, in general terms, results are less quantitative in scanning activities and more quantitative in tracking activities.

Alternate Scenarios technique provides a structured method for integrating a number of individual forecasts into a series of comprehensive, feasible narratives about how the future might develop. It provides a vehicle for combining many forecasts in a format that allows decision-makers to effectively relate the implications of the combination of all forecasts. The results from this technique can range from highly quantitative to purely qualitative depending on the objectives of the effort, its organization, and purposes to which it will be put. This technique is typically used to assist executives in critical decision-making. Although a single scenario can be used for making decisions, the use of a series of alternate scenarios allows executives to take account of the fact that the future can never be projected with certainty, and to determine how appropriate flexibility can be built into plans.

Monte Carlo Models are computer models that take explicit account of the fact that all projections of future trends and events are, fundamentally, probabilistic in nature. In this technique, all of the steps involved in the development of a new technology are identified, and their inter-relationships specified in a mathematical model. Numerical values are assigned to the probability of each event occurring in various different ways and to the length of time it will take each event to occur. The model is then run a large number of times to determine the probability of various overall outcomes. The results of the technique are highly quantitative, and the technique can be used to project technology development times and patterns, to allocate resources, and to track the development of emerging technologies.

5. Intuitors are convinced that the future will be shaped by a complex mixture of inexorable trends, random events, and the actions of key individuals and institutions. Because of this complexity, there is no rational technique that can be used to forecast the future. Thus, the best method for projecting future trends and events is to gather as much information as possible and, then, to depend on subconscious information processing in the brain and personal intuition to provide useful insights.

Delphi Survey technique is a method for taking advantage of the talent, experience, and knowledge of a number of experts in a structured manner that allows an exchange of divergent views without direct confrontation. The technique involves initial projections, usually in quantitative terms, of future events. After the initial projections are correlated, participants are asked to explain, anonymously, their differences in a series of follow-up rounds. Results are normally semi-quantitative, and the technique can be used to project future technical, market, and other developments, to uncover fundamental differences of opinion, and to identify non-conventional ideas and concepts.

Nominal Group Conferencing is a formal technique for structuring the input from a number of subject matter experts. The technique is similar in some ways to "brainstorming", but its structure requires all participants to take active part in the process. It also requires participants to use their brains in a series of different ways, i.e., to individually generate new ideas, to silently assess the ideas of others, to jointly examine the implications of new ideas with others, and to formally evaluate a series of options. The results of employment of this technique are typically semi-quantitative. Nominal Group Conferencing is often used to project future developments, to uncover new business opportunities, or to identify new solutions to old problems.

Structured and Unstructured Interviews are methods for gathering and correlating the thoughts and opinions of a collection of experts about how the future will unfold.

- Structured interviews are similar to traditional opinion polls in that the people conducting the interviews know ahead of time the information they are seeking and structure the interview to get this information as efficiently as possible. The use of personal interviews rather than written surveys promotes participation, decreases the probability of misinterpretation, and assists in assessing the qualification of participants. Results are typically quantitative in nature and can be used to project such items as potential market size, rate of technical advance, and general business factors.

- Unstructured interviews, on the other hand, are used when the subject area to be addressed is less well defined. The interviewer begins each session with only a limited concept of how the interview will be structured. In large measure, each question is based on the answer to the previous question. The interview is essentially free form, and the results can be either qualitative or semi-quantitative. This technique is particularly valuable in identifying key issues, clarifying general concepts, identifying additional experts, and formulating future structured interviews and surveys.

Technology Advantage Management is a technique designed to integrate technology, market, and competitive factors in order to gain fullest advantage from advances in technology. New technologies are examined in light of each of these factors using a two-dimensional, nine-element format called the Technology Advantage Matrix (TAM Map). The use of this "map" allows concurrent analysis of each of these factors in terms of business opportunities, organization goals and objectives, and existing and desired programs, resources, and culture. Results range from qualitative to highly quantitative depending on objectives, project organization, and nature of use. The technique is typically used to define strategies, to optimize resource allocation, and to guide cultural change.

TRIZ (http://www.ideationtriz.com)

TRIZ originated in Russia and is translated as "Theory of Inventive Problem Solving". The methodology is based on over 55 years of research, analysis of over 2 million worldwide patents and other sources of technical knowledge. The methodology provides the user a means to control, predict and manage innovation to:

- reduce R&D time and cost
- decrease product development time-to-market
- achieve technological leadership
- dominate or obtaining additional market share
- increase the value of an intellectual property portfolio

TRIZ was developed after extracting 440 patterns of invention and more than 400 patterns of technological evolution (Ideation Process). This knowledge base has been organized so as to provide a user with the ability to generate an exhaustive set of possible Solution Concepts within a short period of time.

@RISK (http://www.palisade.com/html/risk.html)

Another asset management method has been developed by Palisades Corporation and is called @RISK. (The method is based on risk analysis after obtaining full or complete information. Too often decisions are made based on whatever data are available and all possible scenarios are not taken into account. @RISK is a tool that attempts to yield good solutions based on risk analysis.

Resources:

Technology Futures Inc.	http://www.tfi.com/rescon/TF_Techniques.html
International Assoc for Mgnt of Tech	http://www.iamot.org/tfsc/
Washington Post	http://www.washtech.com/calendar/6444.html
Boeing	http://source.asset.com/stars/lm-tds/TechReps/cfrp/CFRP-Definition.html#TOC

EXHIBIT F - DATABASE SEARCH WORKSHEET

Search

			Background Information	
Corporate	Y ___	N ___	Technology number	_____
Literature	Y ___	N ___	Date submitted	_____
Patent, U.S.	Y ___	N ___	Date needed	_____
Patent, U.S. & Int'l	Y ___	N ___	Date completed	_____
Trademark	Y ___	N ___	Project Manager	_____
SIC number	_____		Creator	_____
Classification number (s)	___ ___ ___ ___			

Project Title: _____

	AND	AND	AND	AND	
	CONCEPT 1	CONCEPT 2	CONCEPT 3	CONCEPT 4	EXCLUDE

OR

OR

OR

OR

OR

_____

Comments/Suggestions: _____

_____

_____

Suggestions:
* Divide topic into MAIN CONCEPTS.
* TRUNCATE to retrieve all forms of a term.
* Remember VARIANT SPELLINGS.
* Use OR to broaden the search.
* Use AND to combine terms.
* Use NOT to exclude unwanted terms.

* Use WITH (W#, sometimes ADJ) to link phrases.
* List any authors, journals, organizations or companies pertinent to the search.
* Consult your documentation for a complete listing of controlled vocabulary terms and classification codes.

EXHIBIT G - ASSET EVALUATION CRITERIA
(Also see technology evaluation software, "TES")

LEGAL
In terms of relevant laws, regulations and industry standards (particularly relating to public safety and public risk), this invention will:
- adequately meet all legal requirements.
- meet most legal requirements.
- need further legality and/or safety checks.
- need some major modifications.
- fail to meet the legal requirements.

SAFETY
This invention, process or product will probably be:
- quite safe if used under normal operating conditions.
- safe if used properly and according to instructions.
- safe if the user is properly trained/qualified.
- unsafe unless modifications are made.
- quite dangerous in its present form.

ENVIRONMENTAL IMPACT
In terms of its effects on the environment (e.g. through excessive energy usage, pollution, misuse and/or waste of vital resources, etc) this invention:
- should contribute to an improved quality of life.
- may result in some environmental improvements.
- should have little or no adverse effect.
- could create some minor environmental 'damage'.
- may seriously damage the environment.

REGULATORY/GOVERNMENT APPROVALS
Regulatory approval takes time and this discovery:
- will require FDA drug review and approval
- falls under the approval requirements of USDA
- subject to EIAR guidelines and requirements
- subject to OSHA review and approval
- regulated by import–export law

SOCIETAL IMPACT
In terms of its impact on the welfare of society at large (or on some identifiable part of it), this invention:
- will have considerable benefits to society generally.
- should benefit some sections of the community.
- may be of some benefit to society.
- should have little or no effect on society.
- may have some detrimental effects.

TECHNICAL/FUNCTIONAL FEASIBILITY
Thorough testing, to assess whether or not the invention will work as it was intended to do, shows that it:
- works reliably under all normal operating conditions.
- works satisfactorily if used according to instructions.
- will work if used with care by an expert.
- has some technical problems which need to be solved.
- does not work properly yet.

PRODUCTION FEASIBILITY

In terms of availability of materials, equipment and other resources, and know-how of the technical processes needed, production of this invention has:

- no problems and can start immediately.
- minor problems which may lead to brief delays.
- minor problems, and delays of several months are likely.
- serious problems leading to delays of at least six months.
- many serious problems and cannot start for at least a year.

STAGE OF DEVELOPMENT

This invention, in at least the form of a fully working prototype has:

- no technical problems, and is complete, or almost complete.
- some problems but should be complete within three months.
- some problems but should be complete within six months.
- some major problems and may be complete in nine months.
- an uncertain completion date, but is at least a year away.

DEVELOPMENT COSTS

Total funding needed to cover all likely development costs, and to bring the invention to the point of being ready to market or use, is estimated to be:

- minimal, available, and not cause any cash flow problems.
- light, probably available, with minor cash flow problems.
- moderate, probably available but with servicing problems.
- fairly heavy, not easy to get and hard to service.
- substantial, and fairly difficult to get and to service.

PAYBACK PERIOD

The period needed to recover the overall investment in developing the invention is likely to be:

- under one year.
- one to three years.
- four to six years.
- seven to nine years.
- ten years or more.

PROFITABILITY

Expected revenues from this invention should cover all relevant direct and indirect costs and earn average annual pre-tax profits:

- in excess of 30 percent.
- of between 25 and 30 percent.
- of between 20 and 25 percent.
- of between average bank interest and 20 percent.
- below the current bank interest rate.

MARKETING RESEARCH

The research needed to make the invention 'market-ready', and to properly and accurately determine its likely success in the market, will probably be:

- no problem and therefore inexpensive.
- fairly straightforward and at a reasonable cost.
- moderately difficult and moderately expensive.
- rather difficult and expensive.
- very difficult and therefore very costly.

RESEARCH AND DEVELOPMENT

The technical research and development needed to bring the invention to the stage of being ready to produce is expected to:

- be quite easy.
- be reasonably straightforward.
- show up some problems.
- prove rather complicated.
- be very difficult.

POTENTIAL MARKET

The total market for this type of invention or product would appear to be:

- very large.
- quite large enough to ensure success.
- adequate to give a viable market share.
- just adequate (will need some aggressive marketing).
- very limited (very much specialized and/or local).

PRODUCT LIFE CYCLE

The life cycle of this invention or product is expected to be:

- at least ten years.
- between six and ten years.
- three to six years.
- one to three years.
- under one year.

MARKET OUTLET(S)

The entry into a market will be direct or require intermediaries which may complicate or enhance market size and/or related costs

- no intermediaries so inexpensive
- straight forward and low cost
- moderate difficulty and moderate cost
- rather difficult and expensive
- very difficult and very costly

POTENTIAL SALES

Expected total sales revenue from this product or invention during its expected life cycle is likely to be:

- very large (over $10 million).
- quite substantial ($5 to $10 million).
- most satisfactory ($1 to $5 million).
- adequate ($250,000 to $5 million).
- small (probably under $250,000).

LIKELY TREND IN DEMAND

The market demand for this type of invention or product seems to be:

- growing rapidly.
- growing at a moderate speed.
- growing, but slowly.
- fairly stable.
- falling.

STABILITY OF DEMAND

Fluctuations in market demand for this invention or product are expected to be:

- minor and easily predicted.
- minor to moderate, but fairly easy to predict.
- moderate and usually predictable.
- moderate to large, and difficult to predict.
- fairly large and quite unpredictable.

POTENTIAL FOR PRODUCT LINE EXPANSION

The potential for additional products, models, lines, styles, qualities, price ranges and other variations is:

- excellent.
- quite good.
- uncertain.
- limited, minor modifications only.
- virtually non-existent.

LEARNING

The amount of learning and practice needed for correct and safe use of this invention or product is:

- very little - minimal instructions are needed.
- quite manageable.
- moderate.
- quite considerable.
- extensive and quite demanding.

NEED

The 'level of need' filled by this invention or product (or the 'level of usefulness') is:

- very high.
- high.
- moderate.
- low.
- very low.

DEPENDENCE

The extent to which the sale or use of this product or invention depends on its linkage(s) with other products or processes is expected to be:

- very low - it is quite independent.
- low - it is fairly independent.
- moderate - depends somewhat on other products or processes.
- high - depends heavily on other products or processes.
- very high - can only work with other products or processes.

VISIBILITY

The advantages or benefits of this invention or product to likely users are:

- highly visible and obvious to all.
- fairly obvious to most.
- moderately obvious - some users may need help.
- barely visible - most users will need help.
- not obvious - all users will need a detailed demonstration.

PROMOTION

The costs and effort needed to promote the major features, advantages and benefits of this invention or product are likely to be _____, compared with expected sales.

- very low.
- fairly low.
- moderate.
- somewhat high.
- very high.

DISTRIBUTION

The costs and difficulty of setting up effective distribution channels for this product or invention will probably be _____, compared with expected sales.

- very low.
- fairly low.
- moderate.
- somewhat high.
- very high.

SERVICE

The costs and difficulty associated with providing good after sales service for this product or invention is likely to be _____, compared with expected sales.

- very low.
- fairly low.
- moderate.
- somewhat high.
- very high.

APPEARANCE

In comparison with its competition and/or substitutes, this product's appearance will be

- highly attractive.
- reasonably attractive.
- of average appearance.
- rather lacking in appeal.
- inferior, with little customer appeal.

FUNCTION

Compared with competitors and/or substitutes, the performance of this product, invention or process will be:

- much superior.
- somewhat superior.
- similar.
- somewhat inferior.
- much inferior.

DURABILITY

Compared with competitors and/or substitutes, the durability and reliability of this product or invention is likely to be:

- much superior.
- somewhat superior.
- similar.
- somewhat inferior.
- much inferior.

PRICE

Compared with competitors and/or substitute products, the selling price will probably be:

- considerably lower.
- somewhat lower.
- similar.
- somewhat higher.
- considerably higher.

EXISTING COMPETITION

Competition from existing firms, products, processes or inventions is expected to be:

- virtually non-existent.
- weak at present, but needs careful monitoring.
- moderately strong - need to be alert of potential threats.
- strong enough to be a potentially serious threat.
- very severe, making a viable market share hard to achieve.

NEW COMPETITION

Competitive reaction from new entrants to the industry (i.e. new firms, products etc.) is likely to be:

- slow and weak - no threat to competitive position.
- slow but fairly strong - strategic action needed in the future.
- moderately quick and moderately strong - must be watched.
- fast and fairly threatening.
- fast and posing a serious threat to competitive position.

PROTECTION

An appropriate form of protection (through patent, design registration, trade mark, copyright, license, etc.) :

- has already been successfully taken out.
- is presently being investigated or applied for.
- may be (or will be) investigated in the future.
- has not yet been considered.
- was applied for, but unsuccessfully.

This innovation evaluation provides an overall assessment of the likelihood of a new invention, product or process being technically and commercially successful. It is also intended to determine what aspects of development need more work, more thought, testing or research to chances of success.

If you assign number of 1-5 beginning with the 1st response item the total value for all 34 criteria would be 34, 63, 102, 136 or 170, respectively. You can also determine which items require more serious attention.

It is best to set a standard you are willing to accept and what decision or action accompanies a select standard or score.

EXHIBIT H – IP EVALUATION, VALUATION & PRICE Q & A

(Following is for information only. Seek legal or accounting advice for your specific situation)

1. What information gathering services are most often used?

The results of an informal poll are as follows:

NERAC - 12

DIALOG - 4

University library services - 2

Other – 5 (included in the 'other' category were government sites, big $$$ services, and 1 or 2 people plugging their own services)

2. How long it takes to bring a non-prescription drug such as a painkiller to the market? How should one assess the market potential/valuation of the IP other than use of AUTM's Valuate worksheets.

a. Traditional DCF analysis, per se, is not the greatest way to value a license. OTOH, it's a very helpful mechanism to value only the future cash flows to compare licenses where the timing and size of those flows differs. A recent example...

An individual attempted to license (License #1) a couple of issued patents to an existing, publicly-traded company. The faculty inventor then decides he wants to do a startup. OK. So we take the original license, cash flows, royalty, etc. and mutate them into a license (License #2) we feel is more appropriate for an early stage start-up with little cash. Plug the flows and timings from Licenses #1 and #2 into Excel and compare via NPV. This is a very helpful way to get two completely different licenses to objectively look the same.

The discount rate for early stage projects can be as high as 80%, meaning that anything beyond 3 years out is more or less a crapshoot. The best way to value projects is through real options, but that's pretty hairy for most of us because you cannot get the discount rate right. The internal rates required for research, development, or final commercialization will be different. You can, however, look for comparables in terms of like companies. If your licensee is publicly traded you can get the betas (and therefore back into a semi-valid DCF analysis) through available sources like Yahoo!

However, that all the valuation in the world is worthless if you don't have a licensee with which to share all your nifty valuation calculations. In the end, the value of a technology is only what the market will pay for it. The rest of the analyses are for you to convince yourself that the market should listen to you...

If the compound has to go through clinical trials, then the compound will generally take the length of the patent term until it reaches the over-the-counter market. While patent rights are in effect it would be unlikely to make it a non-prescription compound.

b. You may be looking at this in a somewhat ineffective way. Valuate, as well as other methods that use discounted cash flow analysis (DCF) are not appropriate tools for most early stage University developed technologies, other than to establish an upper bound on valuation. The reasons are two fold:

1. Valuate assumes, and most other DCF users assume also, that the discount rate should be adjusted for "risk" of the project. This is both theoretically and practically flawed. I will not restate what the financial literature has discussed at length, but will point out that "risk" as used in DCF refers to a specific type of financial risk, akin to beta in stock market models. It has nothing to do with project risk, which should be addressed outside DCF calculations.

2. If you have an early stage project (for instance, a new diagnostic marker or a drug lead with in vitro data only), it is very difficult to predict the course of development, the ultimate product market, patient group, cost of goods etc. The models are only as

good as the data that go into them, so if you really have no good idea regarding relevant inputs, you will then have little confidence in the outputs from the models.

It is for reasons like these that the licensing of early stage technologies is an art as much as a science. Late stage stuff is easy. You know the remaining hurdles, you know the payoff, so what you negotiate is the split of financial rewards (well, it's not quite that easy ..) With early stage, you frequently do not even know where the development will end up. You don't know the scope of patent claims that will ultimately be allowed. You don't know the financing/reimbursement environment 5 years out.

c. Consider relying less on valuation, and more on finding prospective licensees. You can do a 5-minute back of the envelope calculation that will tell you whether you should put any time in at all (assume the best case for everything, what is the value then?)

3. How should one establish intellectual property value?

a. There is a lot of uncertainty for those inventions not yet on the market, and some consultants make a living out of evaluating technology.

For technology not yet on the market (if it's on the market then you have your royalties as an estimate), a simple, easy method is just to tally up the patenting (and maybe copyright costs - although they are much smaller) costs of your IP portfolio. This method doesn't tell you the value of your intellectual property (IP),just what you spent to protect it.

You also might want to estimate the replacement cost (i.e. the R&D funding) to create the invention. Most researchers know the cost of their project, although not all of the R&D may be related to the invention. If you have a lot of inventions, this approach may be impractical.

The valuation of intellectual property assets--even the recognition that they ARE assets, is a hot area. An excellent starting point is the book that came out in the U.S. this January called "Intellectual Capital: The New Wealth of Organizations" by Thomas Stewart, a reporter for Fortune Magazine who has been watching the field grow for several years. It was published in the states by Doubleday/Currency, which claims on the title page to have a branch in Sydney (and Auckland). The appendix compares and contrasts a dozen methods proposed by economists and accountants and even a licensing specialist or two (Wes Anson, in particular). Although the focus is on recognizing IC in companies, much of the thinking and extensive references are very relevant to universities.

b. The valuation must be based on the following:

1. *Cost to date of the IP.*
2. *Estimate of net profit potential over IP's first three (3) years on the market.* If the IP relates to a product in the pharmaceutical sector, the timing might be five to seven (5 to 7) years.

   Market penetration models can be constructed for every new product. If the product will be satisfying a clearly untapped, large market (virtually no competition), it follows that revenues and growth will be significant. However, if the market is highly fragmented, entrance and growth patterns will be different but could be predicted. Yet, if the major portion of the market is dominated by a handful of players, then market penetration patterns are going to be very different (rather discouraging.) Experts make a fairly good living doing this type of work.

3. *Barriers to entry,* i.e. the relative strength of the IP in the given market. The stronger and tighter the IP, the higher the profit and other benefits. The life cycle of a brand new computer related product is about one to two years, max today. Several years ago, products had a significantly longer life cycle.

366

These are some of the factors. Unfortunately, there is no "cook book" recipe for this issue. Solutions exist but require specialized expertise. In short the important issues that need to be considered (not in order of importance) are:

- evolution stage of IP,
- similar market products and outcome of commercialization,
- NPV based on future estimated earnings (if quantifiable),
- The reason for the valuation,
- The investment to date in the IP,
- tax credits that may be available,
- commerciality of the IP, and
- the type of entity that owns the IP.

With reasonable probability you can get fairly close. Frankly, IP is not valued until it has a clearly identifiable income potential and only then. Prior to this point the outcome of any valuation is questionable.

4. When you are transferring your intellectual property (let's say a discovery of a potential drug) how do you go about valuing it for the purposes of taking back equity in a start-up. Also assume that your institution is the 100% owner and that the original inventor is not going to be part of the equity in the start-up.

Consider it as a discounted Net Present Value of what a reasonable licensing fee would be. For example, if a reasonable license fee in the future would be $1,000,000 per year and that it can be discounted at 5%, then the value to this point is $20,000,000. Discount this number by the probability that it will actually be a commercial success. For example, figure this hypothetical at a 1% chance of success and therefore the right number would be $200,000 for the start-up equity.

Valuation of early stage intellectual property is an iffy proposition. The error margins for assumptions are wide and the results of valuation can vary widely. If your employer is considered a founder in the company, a better approach would be to negotiate for an equal share of founders stock in exchange for your equity with a license at reduced royalties and payments since, if the technology is successfully developed, your equity will increase in value.

A common theme in the propaganda promoting S.507 is that the act of inventing is valueless. Large companies seem to feel that contribution of producing an invention has value. This is a common rationalization used to denigrate the inventor's contribution. Historically the market has assigned a value to the inventive process which is usually from 1% to 10% of the factory wholesale.

5. How do I assess what technologies I have?

There are a number of ways to assess the technologies, but one of the key aspects is to determine what kind of *real* improvement the technology provides over existing technologies and how close the technology is to being commercially viable; i.e. what quantifiable benefit does it provide for cost, time savings, complexity, etc. and how entrenched is the existing technology in the market. In a capital intensive field, the last point can be incredibly important. Normally it is prudent to complete two technical and business feasibility studies for every promising Intellectual Property (IP).

The first study is exploratory yet complete enough to establish if the subject IP warrants further investigation and allocation of resources. If the IP passes the first test, then determine what requirements the IP needs to satisfy and by when in order to take another, more thorough look at its technical and business merit. Upon successful completion of these two hurdles, the subject IP is considered worthy of its own business plan for development, manufacture and/or commercialization.

A majority of IP would never pass this phase if they were to be evaluated correctly, thereby wasting valuable, scarce resources that could have been better applied to the truly worthy IP. Develop your own proprietary templates to minimize such pitfalls and significantly increase the likelihood of correct IP evaluation.

MODULE IV – MARKETING

Overview

Market Analyses

- Test market/focus groups
- Enhancements
- Regulatory
- Perception
- Customer profile
- International considerations-legal, cultural, tax, government differences, contract terms

A variety of factors affect the marketability of a technology and numerous means are available for use in analyzing the market. Discussion addresses these means and benefits of each. Focus is also on items to consider when engaging in asset transfer to countries, regions or areas outside the site of origin.

Marketing

- **Strategy** – Research, value enhancement, alliances, acquisitions, market identity
- **Methods** – Presentation, business opportunity document, meetings, networks, agents, databases, transfer and capital provider association
- **Solicitation** - how to; "sales force" timing, process

The transfer process requires identification of candidate purchasers of technology and techniques to solicit and engage individuals or firms in initial discussion. Emphasis is on candidate selection and methods for presentation of ideas, technology or products to select commercialization candidates.

Marketing Worksheet

A market-planning tool designed for technology projects or "products" in which technology features are identified for presentation to select clients.

INTRODUCTION

Getting new technology to market is risky. It takes creativity to be successful. Marketing challenges for technology are numerous. The following is a brief synopsis of several of these challenges:

- high technology may alleviate certain ways to accomplish objectives but expertise still required to market, service and train;
- accelerated change is becoming common for technology and the customer, so it is not a matter of keeping up but how to anticipate the future for high technology businesses;
- communication skills and information accumulation and assessment become higher priority as competition and change modify markets;
- high technology is often comprised of components that are combined into a system (think acquisition and exploitation); hence, ownership and inventorship complexity is increased;
- alliances become crucial to success;
- legal issues are more prominent;
- contracts and negotiation complexity are increased;
- financial challenges arise and effective relationships become more crucial;
- problem solving of complex technology is more difficult and requires new or modified means to address and implement the complexity (Servicing high technology products often differs from those for low technologies);
- marketing high technology is often one of "push" rather than "pull "(hence, methods of marketing and expenses differ);
- introduction of high technology is risky so investment commitments are more difficult to acquire;
- the Internet is a reliable system comprised of loosely connected and imperfect parts that work because nobody is in control which shakes up centralist notions of hierarchy (The challenge is how to market via the "web mall");
- technological illiteracy exists as a result of inability or unwillingness to think in terms of the technological basis of products & markets;
- importance of technology is often not part of strategic planning;
- short-term & financial operations are emphasized rather than long-term technology-based corporate development;
- need to synchronize time periods (technological change takes 5-10 years but conventional corporate plans are 3-5 years;
- legal and/or patent issues are increasing - 1) it takes numerous pieces of intellectual property to build something useful, 2) outsourcing, morality & ethics are new and the legal system never intended to deal with these issues, 3) behavior & culture should set the tone of right and wrong (courts are for criminals; do not want them to dictate personal behavior), 4) time scale of legislative courts is at least an order of magnitude off from hi-tech (takes 12 months to get contract in place for a 6 month product life cycle), 5) courts do not have skills needed to understand issues involved; "blind judge for a beauty contest", 6) billions of dollars are spent on reactive legal maneuvering, and 7) international intellectual property protection and litigation quality varies;
- intellectual property estate - focus is on "packaged" or "bundled" assets, a "one-stop-shop" concept to avoid complicated transactions, importance of "time to market" vs. "time to acceptance" reflecting consumer perceptions or demand, desire for "real-time", site diagnosis, nanotechnology, etc., and the dynamics associated with "windows of opportunity" (capitalize on licensing and cooperative research opportunities - act now); and
- audit - schedule external and on-going internal technology and contract reviews.

Marketing technology often requires persistence and marketing skills over and above those necessary for effective product marketing. Technology is usually not as need driven and the market not as well defined. Therefore, the individual that presents the asset to a potential purchaser or partner needs to be a talented technical and businessperson. The methods employed to solicit and engage a partner vary with the type of technology. Employ as many options as possible as a relationship is being sought.

Henry Grunwald, Editor and Chief of Time Magazine have identified several relevant basic personal attributes that affect marketing success. They are: 1) ask good questions and listen carefully to the answers; 2) build your life on a foundation of basic values; 3) great negotiators think their way into others persons mind; 4) talent without humility is a gift not worth having; and 5) see setbacks as obstacles to be overcome.

Many companies today have a tough sell. It isn't due to lack of a competitive edge, product quality or superior service. It's just that the selling points of these particular products and services are hard to grasp or complex in nature. Communication often is the most critical characteristic involved in successful introduction of unique technology to the marketplace. Marketing is defined as the science of making and keeping satisfied customers at a profit in a competitive environment. The components of marketing are:

1. Strategy - fundamental directions that create a context for effective product and tactical marketing;
2. Tactics - the visible and audible part of marketing, including advertising, public relations, brochures, trade shows, and sales presentations; and
3. Product - behind-the-scenes homework done to define the messages, methods, and plans to be used by tactical marketing.

Technology transfer or commercialization units in academia and government agencies need to not only market the technology to external organizations but must also convince the creators or providers of technology that their services are valuable and effective for the transfer or commercialization of the asset.

Exploding choice and unpredictable change requires new marketing - not more but better marketing. A marketer must be an integrator who commands credibility. Relationships are key to success. Ultimately marketing's assignment is to serve customers real needs and to communicate the needs to the organization.

The goal of marketing is to own the market, ownership means domination. Ownership allows one to broaden or narrow the market, which can result in substantial earnings and a powerful market position.

It is important to note that new technology increases one's capacity to deal with a customer in a unique way. This variety plus service yields customization and hence, customer satisfaction. Also note that markets are influenced by fads and new technology. The marketer must anticipate and capitalize on these new forces.

Benjamin Disraeli once said, "As a general rule the most successful person is the person with the best information". Information yields knowledge so be diligent in the pursuit of knowledge. In the field of technology commercialization several suggestions are to be an active reader of trade periodicals; read every book that has been written on the industry; contact retired mentors; interact with successful or retired people in the field - call or write them for ideas and advice; meet for breakfast or take successful people to lunch; talk to customers (Ask what is being conducted properly and what can be performed better); if the firm does not have all of their business, ask why not and ask what can be done to get more of their business; talk to suppliers - suppliers are meeting with the competitors. (What are the supplier's opinions of your strategies compared to your competitors?); actively study competitors (Visit their stores or offices. Read their ads and sales literature? Talk with them at trade shows or conventions.); converse with employees, friends and spouse. (Seek their counsel.); visit franchise operators in your field. (Are franchisees doing innovative things that could be modified and adapted to your business?); and utilize the World Wide Web.

It is possible that innovation has occurred and money is in place; however, one of the major issues that often exists is the strategy and process of selecting and soliciting the market outlet for a select technology or product. Examples of issues that these decisions involve addressing are small company or large company; market ability; liability/trust; control; failure/ risk; time to market/acceptance; compensation; partnering; services; and expertise, people or management. Several factors related to the technology influence interest by potential purchases such as time to market, competition global reach, regulatory requirements, risk possibilities. In the end marketing is critical and leads to success or failure.

There are two marketing premises that a successful marketing organization must consider; 1) knowledge-based and 2) experience-based marketing.

Knowledge-based Marketing

Knowledge-based marketing is more institutional oriented and requires an organization to master a range of knowledge; 1) the technology with which it competes; 2) market competition; 3) customers; 4) new sources of technology that can alter the competitive environment; and 5) the organization's capabilities, plans, and way of doing business.

In order to be successful knowledge-based marketing must; 1) integrate the customer into the design process to guarantee a product that is tailored not only to customer need and desires but also to the customer's strategies; 2) apply niche thinking to use the organization's knowledge of channels and markets to identify segments of the market the organization can own; and 3) develop an infrastructure of suppliers, vendors, partners and users whose relationships will help sustain and support the organization's reputation and technological edge.

Experience-based Marketing

Experience-based marketing emphasizes interactivity, connectivity and creativity (close encounters with customers, competitors, internal and external technologies). With experience-based marketing technology and marketing not only fuse but also "feed" on each other, resulting in a reshaping of both customer and organization. This leads to the integration of the customer into the company and allowing the company to "own": 1) the market, 2) customization, 3) dialogue, and 4) molding a product into a service and service into a product.

Remember knowledge is power and can yield the competitive edge. Be an active seeker of specific industry knowledge. The expertise obtained will save time and money as well as accelerate progress toward goal(s). Also, it is important to recognize that getting new technology to market is risky and it takes creativity to be successful.

INTERNAL MARKETING

DEFINITION

The technology transfer or commercialization unit that services an organization is responsible for identifying assets with commercial potential, determining the asset's commercial potential and managing the transfer of select technologies.

Internal "clients" are the faculty, staff, and scientific community in the firm or organization. These asset providers must be convinced that the transfer unit has the capability to achieve successful transfer or commercialization of their discoveries.

STRATEGY AND PROCEDURES

Many scientists are not familiar with intellectual property identification and protection. Therefore, the transfer specialist must provide a means to recognize a discovery and then to effectively disclose the invention. Educating and training the scientific community is one way to increase knowledge of intellectual property disclosure and management. This can be achieved by information sessions or seminars. Departmental meetings are another way to acquaint the scientific community with intellectual property and the service role of a technology transfer unit.

It is also important to encourage disclosure by staff members so be sure to include them in the education process. Staff, oftentimes, is familiar with solving short-term needs, modifying existing instrumentation, or solving problems through minor alterations in hardware or software. These modifications or alterations can be very valuable.

Often scientists, whether in private or public organizations, have an incentive to be creative merely due to their curiosity and desire to provide an impact in their areas of expertise. In addition, departmental management also wants to establish an image of creativity since public and private funds tend to "follow the creativity". Hence, the technology transfer professional may want to establish a program in which select department management are assigned to the technology transfer liaison group. These managers then educate departmental personnel, encourage disclosure by departmental faculty, scientists and staff, assist the technology transfer unit with initial review of disclosures and also provide a continuum between the technology transfer office and the inventor/creator. It is important to note that competition in the scientific community is at times intense. Some inventors do not want others in the department or outside the department to become aware of their scientific progress for numerous reasons. Therefore, as part of the "internal marketing" it is necessary to assure creators that disclosure to peers or potential competitors will not take place. It is recommended that the technology transfer professional ask the disclosing party to identify parties that should not have access to the disclosure. This information can be included in the invention disclosure form.

Another way to secure comments from industry or scientific personnel as to the value of an invention that is believed to be protectable and which has perceived market value is to prepare a description of the invention without disclosing proprietary information. The opportunity profile can be designed for individuals involved in asset acquisition, licensing or commercial development who are employees of corporations, government organizations, or academia. In some cases, the reviewer might be a potential licensee or collaborator who gets a preview of new discoveries that may be of interest to their organization. It is important; however, not to limit the external market to only those selected for the initial review of the invention or asset.

The transfer professional or agent must take proper steps to gain and maintain the confidence of the source of assets. A hesitancy to disclose and a tendency to question capability of transfer personnel are the consequences of confidence loss. It is important to remember that the service provider's success is dependent upon the quantity and quality of invention disclosures.

EXTERNAL MARKETING

Marketing to parties outside the organization in which an asset is disclosed can be challenging. The reasons are many and are related to the fact that technology usually requires significant development before the product is released to the consumer market. Market planning is critical (Exhibit A). Awareness of technology is fostered via methods such as the following:

1. information dissemination via scientific publications, local press releases, trade magazines, Internet;
2. workshops and/or briefings designed to establish early familiarity of potential customers with the novel technology;
3. laboratory visits to demonstrate the advantages or benefits of the asset;
4. personnel exchange in which scientists, development specialists etc. get "hands on" experience with the technology so they become internal champions;
5. technical assistance to create a sense of partnership and to train or educate the asset purchaser;
6. cooperative research in which the technology provider and potential purchaser provide certain capabilities which when "pooled" leads to efficient and effective development or market

introduction. This approach can reduce the time to develop and enhance the transition from development to market;

7. sponsored research often allows the sponsor to get an early view of the technology and often leads to a license assuming the development proceeds on schedule and the results support the value of the technology to the sponsor Sponsors usually seek options to research outcomes from projects they fund; and

8. licensing is the ultimate in marketing and represents a successful transfer of a technology to another party (license terms vary and will be discussed in chapters five and seven).

MARKET RESEARCH

Knowing the value of an asset is only the start. Once the value is determined it is necessary to locate a buyer or partner. Do you tap into your network, seek professional help or identify a potential buyer or partner in some other way? It might be appropriate to use several means to identify and select a partner or buyer.

DATABASES - LICENSABLE TECHNOLOGIES

The following are sites or organizations that maintain databases of technologies which are for sale or which are sought. Examples are:

- Academia
  1. U Ventures
  2. Association of University Technology Managers (AUTM)
  3. Individual universities
- Government
  1. Department of Energy (DOE)
  2. National Aeronautics and Science Association (NASA)
  3. United States Department of Agriculture/Agricultural Research Service (USDA/ARS)
  4. Environmental protection agency
  5. National institute standards and technology (NIST)
  6. DOE/NIST energy inventions
- Federally funded research
  1. NIST federal research in progress
  2. Federal agency SBIR programs
  3. Federal agency STTR programs
  4. USDA TekTran
  5. NASA Tech Briefs
- Intellectual property list service organizations
  1. Knowledge express data systems
  2. KPMG
  3. PWC
  4. U Ventures
  5. Corptech
  6. Bioscan
  7. TINS high tech (TX)
  8. Research centers
- News
  1. Comtex business news
  2. Technology Access reports
- Scientist profiles

1. R& D Magazine
2. Scientific publications

Additional market information resources are presented in the resource and reference directory that accompanies this text.

LOCAL SOURCES

Technological developments at an academic institution and in local businesses are often of interest to the local business community operating under a directive to enhance economic development. These people are often willing to serve as sounding boards for review of technology or product ideas. In the case of smaller business, these discussions can provide input from local businesspersons and result in support from the community that strives for local economic development.

TRADE ASSOCIATIONS

Members of trade associations are committed to select business areas. The membership is comprised of suppliers of technology, services, and products. These business commitments and interests consolidated into a single association offer the asset provider a rich forum to explore or expand relationships and an efficient means to increase awareness of technology, expertise or needs of the asset provider. More and more associations are "pooling" resources and investing in research and development at select institutions. As a result, the Association and/or consortia of association members become the partner with the asset provider and the contractual relationship can become complicated due to varied interests of the multiple parties.

GOVERNMENT REVIEWS AND REPORTS

Several government agencies such as the Department of Energy and laboratories have programs in place to provide assistance in evaluation and development of technology. There are also numerous government-sponsored reports that are available to the public that can be examined as one embarks on the evaluation and entry into new markets. Nearly all patent offices around the world have intellectual property information available on their web sites.

DEMOGRAPHIC INFORMATION (GEOGRAPHIC LOCATION)

Customs, economic conditions, product manufacture and distribution processes, and public vs. private business practices must be taken into consideration, as strategic plans are made for worldwide market entry. These considerations need to be assessed early if a technology is to be purchased or licensed and diligence criteria are established based on markets and projected income. Business and/or regulatory consultants are well equipped to provide such information but be sure the firm also provides valid interpretation of the information. Careful review of prior customers and familiarity of management and staff with your area of need is critical to assure quality results coincide with legitimate time and cost commitments.

PROFESSIONAL SEARCHERS

The advent of the information age has enabled one to access more information but also leads to acquisition of massive amounts of data to examine. Professional search, information or consulting firms are usually good resources to conduct specified searches or conduct focus groups that would benefit from the technology commercialization process. In addition, many universities have library and information departments that are interested in student education or providing search services to the public.

TECHNOLOGY PORTFOLIOS

It is often necessary to determine status of competition or identify technology that might be of value if it were combined with a new technology being developed for commercialization. Most technology transfer agents or university technology transfer offices advertise the technology available for license and indicate the stage of development and protection and the technology being sought. A brief description is usually provided for each asset. In a competitive analysis, one should search these publications as well to determine who might be the competitors, and who might be seeking assets similar to what one might be developing.

PUBLISHED RESEARCH OR STUDIES

A very reliable source of information is the creator or author of an asset or scientist working in the area related to the technology being commercialized. They usually are well aware of the scientific advances because of interactions with peers on both a national and international scale. Some of this information is available in published form but to be at the cutting edge much exchange takes place before publication. Attendance at scientific meetings or creation of a scientific advisory team can be a very good way to get the most current information. Certainly a thorough review of the literature is also necessary.

MARKET ANALYSIS

There are five traits that make a technology or product easy to introduce: 1) easy to distribute; 2) simple technology; 3) unique: 4) obvious benefit and 5) retail price is at least four times manufacturing cost.

With all of the background data in hand what is the market like and do you know all of the factors that will impact that market? How do you set the price for the asset or product and what should the price be? The competitive analysis, test market or focus group studies will need to be taken into considerations as the desired compensation is established. The whole purpose of the information gathered thus far is to use it to establish fair and reasonable compensation figures that will lead to win-win relationships.

COMPETITION

A competitive analysis for early stage technology is somewhat arbitrary until the product is well defined. The reliability of the analysis should be recognized at the time of the analysis. Since this early analysis may not reflect the market, it becomes imperative the collection of data and analysis be an ongoing activity as the project progresses toward final product definition. On the other hand, a market universe can be determined and projections can reflect the erosion of the universe if research and development results alter the criteria established for determining the product originally defined. Competitive analysis involves careful and focused knowledge collection and subsequent analysis of the data. Any market analysis will require an estimate of the window of opportunity and when the window is open or more importantly when it may close.

TEST MARKET

As a technology matures to product stage it may be necessary to subject it to test market analysis. This may involve oral surveys or actual presentation of product to the customer. Adequate sample selection, size and analyses of the results become critical as key decisions may be made based on the outcome. Test market activity is usually of more value when a new technology is developed and an obvious need is not being fulfilled. However, in any case, product design, public acceptance and perception will be critical factors to assess for any new product.

FOCUS GROUPS

Surveys, much like test marketing, are conducted with the projected customer market. Failure to select the correct customer population and limitation of sample size can have disastrous effects on the decision making process. Careful strategic and tactile planning needs to be followed as the focus group effort are enacted. In some cases, focus groups concentrate on physical reactions and voice reflection as indicators of reaction to questions or products. It is important to consider the way a focus group test is to be carried out. It will depend on the product.

SURVEYS

A less expensive method to acquire data is to survey the market. The design of the survey usually requires input from individuals or companies trained in the conduct of surveys. Language and questions influences responses. Numerous firms offer to conduct surveys and may have survey data available for purchase. In some cases, you may want survey data held confidential which can be arranged with firms that carry out a survey.

TECHNOLOGY ENHANCEMENT

How are enhancements, revisions or new derivatives of a technology marketed and what value is given to the new developments? If new developments are included in a license, it is important that clear definition of the type of developments for which rights are to be granted be precisely defined. Unless the developments are closely related to the technology or product, it is best to establish value and price when the development is known. Agreements can be structured to provide future developments at a reasonable price common for the industry. Often there may be more than one component to a system and in the "suite" may be assets for which royalty is due another party. This stacking of royalty can lead to excessive payment to creators or owners of a technology and need to be addressed in the negotiation of a license. Some technology is developed based on a core technology for which rights are required to practice the invention being licensed or sold. It will be necessary to take this into account as the price is established for a technology and what type of license may be enacted for rights to the background technology.

TECHNOLOGY STAGE AND LIFE CYCLE

There is always a reluctance to assume risk in the licensing process and when pricing an asset that is not market ready there will be a need to adjust the price for the risk assumed in completing the development. Often a small investment might move the technology forward and a significant return on investment realized. However, if such funds are not available or interest does not exist, one must recognize that the added risk will be reflected in the royalty rate negotiated. Royalty payments will also be related to the life cycle or sales volume of a product. Royalty for products with short life cycles can be graduated or agreements can contain language that allows revision of the royalty based on sales volume, income, net sales, etc.

REGULATORY

If at the time a technology is priced, the regulatory clearance is completed, underway or even if regulatory officials have commented on the technology, more of the risk are known and should be taken into account as royalty, fees, equity, etc. are established. In addition, during the development process and prior to market introduction, there is always the possibility the regulatory requirements may change; hence pricing strategy needs to take into account the clearance requirement that exist for a particular technology.

Failure of a patent to issue with the claims intact and that are the basis for the license will lower the technology value and will need to be reflected in the compensation offered the licensor or owner of the asset. Agreements often are designed to alter royalty rate in the event patents do not issue within a defined time period.

PUBLIC PERCEPTION

Public perception - real or imagined - can have significant impact on the introduction and acceptance of new products by the commercial sector. Any anticipated hindrances to market acceptance will lead to adjusted compensation. It can be beneficial if the licensee or owner of the asset has some data or indication of consumer desire and acceptance. On the other hand, the parties may agree to establish a publicity program in cooperation to introduce new technology to the commercial community.

CUSTOMER PROFILES

Generally the licensor or owner of a technology is not as aware of the customer profile as is the firm or individual that is acquiring the asset. Failure to examine the customer profile by the technology provider or request a market plan from the technology purchaser can result in licensor-licensee issues when the agreement is underway and in force. Although royalty may be the same regardless of the field of use or areas in which a licensee has rights to market, there is a definite need to address the extent of a licensee's market commitment.

BUILD A SALES FORCE

Although technology commercialization seldom requires a large office complex, the success of the office is dependent on clear objectives and quality personnel. Goals and objectives will vary with institutional policies and objectives. More time and effort is required in situations that lead to partnerships and joint ventures. Partnerships and equity in place of royalty or in combination with royalty in the university environment leads to unique challenges that the personnel must address. Communication, persistence, perseverance, technical curiosity and understanding and innovation are just a few of the traits required of personnel involved in technology commercialization.

The technology commercialization office often has a large responsibility. There are some preliminary guidelines that would suggest the number of projects per person should not exceed twenty. However, this may be dependent on the infrastructure and support services made available to the technology manager. These services would include an information specialist to gather data or evaluation support. The services maybe in-house or contract services.

Numerous criteria exist to monitor progress. These criteria will usually reflect the goals and objectives of the organization. In some cases, it is the number of arrangements enacted to correspond with the desire to provide a public benefit; whereas in other cases the objective may be the financial return on technology asset. Econometrics consist of various ratios, some of which are designed to monitor progress and success of technology commercialization enterprise.

ALTERNATIVE METHODS FOR DIFFERENT KINDS OF TECHNOLOGY

One of the challenges in technology transfer is to apply different evaluation and marketing methods to different technology assets. The software, multimedia, courseware process will differ from a pharmaceutical or engineering asset. A corporate entity may by much farther along with development or even be approaching market entry whereas the university technology usually requires developmental investments.

Pricing the asset will reflect the stage of development and models for pricing take into account the variations in the asset.

TECHNOLOGY VS. FINAL PRODUCT MARKETING

There are always certain unknowns with technology still in the research stages. As more becomes known through continued development and up to market entry or even beyond, the risk associated with the asset is reduced. It is imperative the technology manager do as much as possible to identify these questions that may arise in order to be prepared to address them as marketing goes forward. Public perception or opinion may be key to successful marketing entry even when technically the asset is without fault. The genetic engineering areas are good examples of how the public may need to be educated and have a higher comfort level before introduction of a new product. The strategic plan can address this issue if recognized ahead of time.

Any planning needs to take into account cyclical situations that may impact successful marketing of a technology. The educational market may make purchasing decision in the spring in order to prepare for the fall school programs, whereas other industries may make purchasing decision based on fiscal year. In addition, significant investments may not be related to purchases but may need to be incorporated into the companies budgeting process as much as a year in advance. A good technology manager will recognize unique features of a market and take then into account as the strategic planning process goes forward.

HIGH VS. LOW TECHNOLOGY MARKETING

As previously indicated marketing high technology is a challenge. The less that is known about a new product from the consumer's perspective the greater the hesitancy to purchase it. The information age is certainly providing effective means to distribute information but highly complicated technology will continue to be carefully examined before purchases are made. If a need exists market entry is simpler; however often times high technology may be fulfilling a need but it may not be as obvious a need as what low technology might be satisfying. The strategy for introducing such technology to a licensee or the market will vary. High technology may alleviate or alter certain ways to accomplish objectives but expertise to market, service & train is still required.

Another factor that must be considered in the commercialization process is the impact of regulatory approval. A dedicated effort is often required to track and secure approval from the Food and Drug Agency, Department of Commerce, United States Department of Agriculture, etc. It is critical that these agencies be involved early in the development process if approval is required. Often times a university is not prepared to conform to the approval requirements nor is the university intent on securing such approval due to the differences in objectives between the academic and business environments.

IDENTIFYING CANDIDATE PURCHASERS

Whenever someone commercializes a technology they are always looking for the best partner. What is best for one technology may not be best for another. Certainly the characteristics of the asset are taken into account as the search for licensees or partners is pursued. Candidate purchasers must be thoroughly examined especially if they are small enterprises that do not have a track record or are not as financially stable as the larger enterprise. The smaller business may be a preferred candidate due to expertise, ability to complete development and commitment to complete development in a shorter time period. Time to market has to be a prime consideration as the technology is marketed to potential licensees.

TECHNOLOGY PURCHASER SOLICITATION AND QUALIFICATIONS

The phrase "The first impression is the most important" is also true when marketing a technology. External technology providers are also competing with the technology purchaser's "in house" technology developers. This is referred to as the "not invented here" feeling. Know-how to get a potential client's attention and create a favorable first impression is essential in getting the technology to market.

SOLICITATION METHODS AND SERVICES

How should technology be advertised for sale? It will depend on the particular asset, the quantity of assets being marketed and whether a partnership is sought or if a "baton" is to be passed to another party and relying on them to commercialize the asset. It is usually beneficial to target market. Select a preferred contact and commence with information and soliciting interest.

Home pages have become one method of making others aware of an asset; there are organizations that post technology that is available and businesses that focus on technology commercialization. If technology is still in the research stage, it is likely that research collaboration or sponsorship may be preferred and no need exists to enlist someone else to assume responsibility for the transfer or commercialization. However, if an international partner is sought there may be good reasons to associate with a party familiar with the politics, government requirements and business details that may be unfamiliar to the asset provider. Establish a means to advertise the asset, attend trade shows, direct contacting, consider brokers or agents, work one's contact network and in some cases attend scientific meetings. Remember there is a lot of competition in business. There is a need to be just a bit better than the competition. There is always a possibility that knowledge of the competition's technology may also lead to interest in combining assets to enhance value, pool expertise and compete more effectively.

There is no doubt that successful marketing requires a buyer and prior to the purchase a "champion" or interested individual is needed. However, how do you find such an individual when marketing a technology? Several considerations should be taken into account: stage strategy for there may be a need to enlist interest from more than one party as the process progresses forward; establish an alliance with an innovative "networker"; create a true partner profile in which the criteria and characteristics of a champion are identified and which are necessary for success and contact multiple candidates to partner with or champion the asset.

When first initiating contact with potential buyers or licensees is established, several key points should form the basis of the early stages of a negotiation process. Be certain the outcome is of mutual benefit and, if not the case, at the outset present reason(s) why the asset will be of mutual benefit. Start simple. The initial exchange is to establish interest and details can follow. Set benchmarks and focus on go/no go decisions or key issues to resolve at appropriate times in the process. Involve the lawyers after key terms are identified. An exchange of a term sheet is an effective way to get key points or potential issues "on the table". It may be possible to simultaneously have legal and business questions addressed and integrated at some later time in the negotiations.

Generally the parties involved in asset exchange, sale or procurement are interested in expeditious market entry. Hence, as marketing proceeds there are several interactive approaches that might be considered. Several are: consolidation of several assets or define an asset "package" or intellectual property estate; consider an exchange of expertise; share or encourage access to each others instrumentation or equipment; jointly establish quality assurance criteria and enable the parties to design and make improvements to the asset in question.

Regardless of events that impact the marketing process, there are several areas that need to be monitors throughout the process that might be considered "watch outs" or caution signals including but not limited to; capitalization changes of the purchase; maintaining focus on issues and process advancement; alteration in the intellectual property portfolio protection; and influence or impact of wall street and politics.

Several key "ingredients" contribute to success in the evaluation, valuation, and marketing of technology. They are as follows:

1. manage process as a business strategy;
2. treat technology suppliers and customers as stake holders and make them partners;
3. know thyself: technology, management, strengths and goals;
4. establish performance assessment criteria - if you don't someone will;
5. benchmark - set goals, adopt new strategies, techniques and/or best practices;
6. know your technology - but scan the horizons;

7. capitalize on opportunities in licensing, cooperative research - act now; and
8. add passion to technology commercialization - key components are technology, capital and management.

In summary, when managing the marketing process emphasize partnership mentality, establish a team of champions, assure frequent communication, think long-term but have short-term successes in mind, maintain a market need orientation, focus on an entire suite of technological resources plus intellect behind technology, be assertive and opportunistic, practice proactive market development that tends to breed and foster innovation.

GUERRILLA MARKETING

A popular concept surrounding effective marketing today is what is called guerrilla marketing. Guerrilla marketers realize that their prospects are constantly bombarded with offers and are very aware of prospect priorities. Eight factors are taken into account:

1. State of economy – In a weak economy, target existing customers more than prospects and get referrals and follow-up business;
2. Competitive scene – Competitive intelligence is extensive in today's marketing; capitalize on it;
3. Latest technology – Critical for creation of more marketing tools, exposure to public and business;
4. News of the day – Stay current with best media;
5. Marketing budget – Stay within it but market actively not expensively;
6. Clutter of other marketing materials – Sophisticated techniques are being used by all and customer get it all; take into account in strategic planning;
7. Know difference between clever marketing message and motivating marketing message – if the message makes prospects laugh but does not get them to act one has failed; and
8. Commit to a plan – have patience and restraint when making changes.

Marketing is not an event but a process that takes time, money and energy.

MARKETING EXPERIENCES

Concepts and examples of "lesson learned" when introducing new technology or products are as follows:

1. Do not assume the public understands new product - Example: Kimberley Clark felt they had winner with Avert; tissues with vitamin C derivative incorporated to reduce spread of germs. Problem: If introducing product based on new technology or a new scientific basis take lots of time to educate consumer.
2. Test new products under real market conditions - Example: Computerized modeling may work in select situations but nothing substitutes for a live customer who decides to buy or
3. Not under actual sales conditions. Case: Nabisco's inadequate testing of graham cracker cereal after making flavor change. Flavor may have been better but cereal sank to bottom of bowl and turned to a glob. Simple market testing would have identified the problem.
4. Look over shoulder when test marketing - Example: Nestle carefully test marketed its new cookery line of low salt, low sugar, low fat foods but execs failed to appreciate that Campbell Soup and other competitors had strategically lowered their prices in the test market areas. Result: Test results were poor and product never fully launched Conclusion: Closely monitor competition during test and at outset of launches; smart competition will undermine the launch.
5. Do not penalize a manager that "Pulls plug" - Situation: Once money is expended it is hard to say no to management, champions and executives. Example: RJR Nabisco invested $325M in

Premier, a smokeless cigarette with poor taste and hard to light. High-level reputations were at stake and spending continued even though smokers enjoy smoke they create.

6. Do not put all trust in advertising agencies - Situation: Most agencies operate in best interest of clients but if agency is hungry and manger of a new product has too much decision making power a problem can arise – aim to please overrides common sense. Suggestions: Ask for straight answers and long-term relationship depends on good answers and suggestions. Be wary of agreeable agency. Insist product manager justify decisions to peers who objectively review test results.

7. Do not combine price promotions with new product launches - Situation: Rebates or low prices skew sales results in critical early months of introduction. Suggestion: When prices rise to normal levels customers return to former product choice and brand loyalty will be hard to establish. Strategy: Test new product a several price levels; then choose one that promises the greatest long-term return on investment. Never waste time testing a product at a price below which you cannot afford to sell it.

8. Be cautious about "cause related" marketing - Situation: Product linked to socially popular concerns such as environmental causes and health fads. Results: Most products flop although Paul Newman's salad dressing and pasta sources are successes. Reason: Niches are usually narrow and social concerns change rapidly and unexpectedly.

9. Avoid associating a new product with a negative image - Example: Gillett's For Oily Hair Only shampoo flopped because consumers don't want to confess in checkout line they have greasy hair - Gillett learned and named its fast selling disposable razor Good News (the name says little about the product but it is undeniably positive).

10. Stay close to customers after launching new product - Situation: Snapple kept up with what customer wanted by talking and surveying its customers and introducing one iced tea after and other in the early '90s. This communication capability is advantage for small to mid size companies. But Quaker Oats, upon purchase of Snapple, relied on unwieldy committees far removed from consumer and marketplace and market share fell.

11. Never sacrifice uniqueness - Example: Tempting to tinker with a winning product to take advantage of a trend – Example: Alka Seltzer fell into trap by trying to market a pill instead of its well-established dissolvable tablet. In process it sacrificed brand recognition to epitomize the unique plop, plop, fizz, fizz commercial. Result: It became and also ran with competition from Bayer and Tylenol. When Alka Seltzer switched back to the dissolvable tablet market share soared.

MARKETING COMMUNICATION TACTICS

The solution to bridging the communications gap with prospective customers under these circumstances is easy. Turn the intangible into tangible and simplify the complex. As you'd expect, that's easier said than done. One must consider the following tactics:

1. *Make it real.* Why do your customers do business with your company? Most likely, it goes far beyond one product or service. It's something harder to grasp like trust, confidence, convenience, quality, prestige or attitude.

   Professional service firms know this all too well. However, it's also true with staples like shampoo and tennis shoes. The first mistake businesses often make is failing to appreciate the role of emotions on their business relationships. The second is going overboard and trying to communicate them all in their marketing efforts. For front-line marketing salvos, focus on one feeling that must be present for a customer relationship to happen, and then deliver it in a way your future customers can grasp.

   For instance, Michelin sells tires, but they lead off with something intangible because it's a deciding purchasing factor with their customer base. That's safety. What makes it tangible is cute babies in tires with the tagline, "Because so much is riding on your tires." An analogy in insurance would be John Hancock's, "Real life, real answers."

2. *Map the buyer's experience.* Good sales people overcome objections. Good marketing anticipates the objections in the first place. If the business has a long sales cycle or demanding customers, marketing can be a salesperson's best friend. Begin by analyzing the entire customer experience and determine what conditions must be met before they'll become a customer? Then formulate strategies and tactics that meet each condition before they grow into an objection.

Saturn Corp. is a master at this. They studied the entire experience of buying a car and used it to take a different approach at every stage; from how cars are marketed to the way customers should be treated. In just the one area of "haggling" alone, they turned a negative into a positive with no-hassle buying. It makes sense now that dealers all over the country are doing it, but remember it was Saturn who had the fortitude to be first.

If the company is selling something complex and the message isn't getting through, revisit customers. Their behavior leading up to the purchase holds the answer.

3. *Own a word.* While one may not be able to do anything to alter a product's intangibility or complexity, one usually has great latitude with the marketing. The goal, as always, is to get through to people and solicit a reaction.

Successful marketers of complex products and intangible services simplify their pitch by seizing a word or phrase to represent their offerings to the marketplace. It's the wellspring of marketable ideas that are dramatic and memorable.

For example, Southwestern Bell turned a bunch of added phone features into an easy to understand consumer offer by packaging and labeling it "the works". Sprint struck a chord with a dime. Federal Express created a new market with "overnight."

Owning a word applies regardless of company size, business complexity or type of asset i.e. intangible or tangible. The goal is to become world-famous. Claim a word or phrase that is easily remembered and conveys essence of a product's appeal.

Expect more intangible and complex products and services due to specialization in search of a competitive edge in a global marketplace. The ability to articulate that point of difference will be critical and will determine not only the success or failure of one's communications but the company as well. If this is applied to marketing methods, techniques, and practices for marketing and selling new technologies it becomes obvious that success depends on how well one:

1. determines the real markets and what one must do to reach the,
2. identifies and circumvents market and industry barrier, and
3. learns concepts such as market segmentation and product positioning.

The bottom line might read as follows: "Marketing is critical and marketing is everything." Further information related to marketing is presented in the form of questions and answers in Exhibit B.

EXHIBIT A – MARKET PLANNING WORKSHEET

MARKET PLANNING WORKSHEET

In working with small and home based businesses over the years there are six fatal flaws that doom a product or service to failure. They are:

1. The product or service is a mystery to consumers. No one is quite sure what it does.
2. The product doesn't have a market. There just aren't enough people willing to buy it
3. The identified market is too broad to reach on a small budget. "Everybody" isn't a market any business can reach.
4. The products' benefits aren't clearly stated.
5. The company owners don't understand the market's needs or buying habits.
6. The company owner isn't clear about what their ads or mailing should accomplish.

To avoid these fatal flaws, consider the following worksheet. It is appropriate to use for any size business and any type of product or service. Use it to gather thoughts and facts before launching a new business, introduce a new product or service, or launch a new advertising or direct marketing campaign. Be sure that anyone involved in developing marketing strategy or marketing literature has a copy of the completed worksheet.

MARKETING WORKSHEET*

Name of product or service:

_____

Description of Product or Service (What it does, what it's used for):

_____
_____

Describe the individuals or businesses to whom product is to be sold:

_____
_____

Describe why they would want to use this product or service:

_____
_____
_____
_____
_____
_____
_____
_____

Describe the benefits of this product (the SPECIFIC problems the product or service solves or SPECIFIC advantages it offers to the customer):

_____
_____
_____
_____
_____
_____

List selling features (e.g., color, weight, dimensions, size, capabilities, etc.):

Features The product/service	Features Competition's product/service
_____	_____
_____	_____
_____	_____
_____	_____
_____	_____
_____	_____
_____	_____
_____	_____

Which are the MOST IMPORTANT differences between the product and the competitions' products?

_____
_____
_____
_____
_____
_____
_____
_____

Is this a totally new product or service?   Yes_____ No_____
Do you sell other similar products or services?   Yes_____ No_____
Do you sell any other products or services?   Yes_____ No_____

How are you planning to sell this product or service? (Check all that apply)
_____Through the mail
_____Through your own retail store(s)
_____Through sales calls to the end-user
_____Through telemarketing calls to the end user
_____Through paid advertising
       __ trade or general circulation magazines   __ TV
       __ trade or general circulation newspapers   __ radio
       __ Yellow pages
_____Through word-of-mouth advertising
_____Through your own contacts and networking
_____Through Window signs to attract walk-in trade
_____Through In-store displays
_____Through Seminars or Conferences discussing the product or service
_____By bidding on jobs
_____Through online classified advertising or Web sites
_____Other (specify)

How do people learn about and buy this product or service now?
_____Through the mail
_____Through retail stores
_____Through sales reps
_____Through telemarketers
_____Through paid advertising
       __ trade or general circulation magazines
       __ trade or general circulation newspapers
       __ TV
       __ Radio
       __ Yellow pages
_____Through word-of-mouth advertising
_____Through contacts and networking
_____Through Window signs to attract walk-in trade
_____Through In-store displays

_____Through Seminars or Conferences
_____Through a bidding process
_____Through online classified advertising or Web sites
_____Other (specify)

What is the objective of this marketing or advertising literature? (i.e., bring in direct sales, bring in leads, etc.)

_____
_____
_____

Who makes the buying decisions--the actual user, purchasing department, department head, other?

_____
_____
_____

Is this product or service now available?   Yes____   No ____

The information presented herein are suggestions and are not intended to be all inclusive since the type of technology/product will require careful development of the queries to pose for a select technology.

EXHIBIT B – MARKETING Q AND A

(Following is for information only. Seek legal or accounting advice for your specific situation)

1. How should one assess the technologies they have?

There are a number of ways to assess the technologies, but one of the key aspects is what kind of "real" improvement the technology provides over existing technologies and how close the technology is to being commercially viable. For example, "What quantifiable benefit does it provide for cost, time savings, complexity, etc?" and "How entrenched is the existing technology in the market?" In a capital-intensive field, entrenchment of competition can be incredibly important. Some evaluators complete two technical and business feasibility studies for every promising Intellectual Property (IP):

    a. the first study is exploratory yet complete enough to determine if the subject IP
       warrants further investigation and allocation of resources; and

    b. if the IP passes the first test, determine what requirements the IP must satisfy and by when
       in order to justify another, more thorough examination of technical and business merit.

Upon successful completion of these two hurdles, the IP is considered worthy of its own business plan for development, manufacture and/or commercialization. A majority of IP would never pass this phase if they were to be evaluated correctly, thereby wasting valuable, scarce resources that could have been better applied to the truly worthy IP.

2. How does one find a prospective market for these?

Go through a number of channels; however, this is heavily based on primary research and covering all of the potential markets.

Successful asset review will include identification and evaluation of the potential market opportunities, present market entrants and their relative strengths/weaknesses, unmet customer needs, environmental and other regulatory trends, etc. It is a clear, objective road map. Once you know who the key players are, then it is much easier to approach them.

A very important element in this selection of market candidates is to be creative, innovative and practical.

3. How should one approach a prospective buyer?

Obviously, there are some right and wrong ways, but most of it comes down to finding the right person and then approaching them in a professional (yet promotional) manner.

There are many innovative and practical ways. However, once you identify an interested party, you must provide them with the "right stuff" or you just closed the door (at least for a while) with said company.

The right presentation includes the professional development of a promo package, which provides a prospective party with easy to understand, clear and compelling evidence of the merit of said IP and why they should seriously consider it. If it is possible, have available working, functional prototype products for evaluation.

4. Should one find an "agent" to help find buyers?

Agents have their place, but usually the answer determines on how much help you need, based on your own capabilities; i.e. if the applications or industries that you are targeting are broad, an outside perspective can be very helpful. The issue is also - when do you need something more than an "agent"? Agents may not have the time or incentive to go beyond a somewhat basic search for a licensee or partner and don't have the resources to cover licensees overseas or in industries outside of their traditional expertise.

Once you know the relative value of your IP, then you must determine if you have in-house the required resources for commercializing the subject IP. In today's fast changing business environment, it is probably to one's advantage to get expert assistance instead of trying to learn and do everything yourself. That is, time is probably much more valuable than the cost incurred to hire an expert.

It is important to team-up with an agent using the "Win-Win" principle. The basic question needs to be: "What's in for all of us?" not only "What's in for me?"

Find an agent who a) is qualified, b) clearly believes in the value of the IP (you will never sell anything that you do not believe in), c) knows that they will be 'fairly" compensated if and/or when the IP is commercialized, etc. and d) is capable to contribute toward improving, fine-tuning and fortifying your IP and respective products (this requirement is rather rare to find but you should always try.) That is, always look for a product designer or development engineer or marketer or salesperson not just a salesperson.

5. Should one "tailor" their technology to a potential buyer?

The technology should be tailored to a commercial application insofar as it is possible. This usually means the technology is tailored to a group of buyers, yielding a higher valuation of the technology, especially in a competitive bidding situation.

The above promotion package must be tailored first to a specific market segment and then further custom-tailored to the needs of a specific prospect. It is very similar to the development of a resume or CV.

6. How should one approach negotiation of contract terms?

Make sure you have someone on your side that knows a thing or two about negotiations and has done their research on past cases with similar technologies/licenses.

Successful negotiation is both a science and art. The more you know about the prospective party's needs, desires, business objectives, etc., etc. the better you are going to be. Also, you must have a very clear picture of your own expectations, bottom line requirements, etc., etc. You might consider putting these negotiations in the hands of experts otherwise you risk loss of a potential deal and/or leaving money "on the table".

7. What are the pitfalls of technology commercialization?

Many inventors think they can do it all on their own...The main thing is to cover all potential targets and not give up too soon. It can often take a long time to be successful; so don't expect overnight success. Examples of individual faults are:
   a. unwillingness to share with others who have ability to help maximize the value of IP by licensing and/or commercializing it. Wanting everything for themselves is foolish because at the moment they own 100% of nothing whereas if the IP where managed by the right people, it could be worth more;
   b. trying too quickly to sell/license the IP without completing correctly technical and business feasibility (phase one.) So, value is unknown;
   c. promotional packages for licensing the IP are poor;
   d. failure to engage qualified experts when absolutely necessary; and/or
   e. having unrealistic royalty expectations, thereby not knowing when to say "Yes" to an offer.

8. You want to market new educational software for delivery of educational and training material.... The questions are: How should you market this idea to the business community? What businesses and which people in the respective companies do you need to contact to make my pitch?

The basic rules of marketing may not apply. If you have a new concept for a band-aid, the "basic rules of marketing" would dictate that one broadcast the features and benefits to all band-aid manufacturers. A proper licensing strategy is to find the one "best" prospect. Know who the final customer is, how many there are and how you will reach them.

"Getting to know" is completed in early stages of invention ...not the marketing stage. (Otherwise, why pursue the invention?) How you will reach the final customer is the job of your licensee.

Clarify difference between manufacturing (and marketing) your own "product", or marketing your "concept" to manufacturers. The "concept" buyer is just an intermediate step to the final customer. The concept buyer (manufacturers/licensees) is your "customer" and may have a totally different list of objectives than the consumer (final customer). Selling to the concept buyer differs from satisfying needs of the consumer. They will be responsible for the needs of the others in the "food chain". If your project does not meet the criteria of the manufacturer, the sales force of the manufacturer, and the retailer ...you are dead meat!

The sales force of the manufacturer is the most difficult (and most important) group to please (read that as "motivate") ...They sometimes have requirements for products that defy the laws of gravity. Satisfy them; and you have a winner.

The consumer is the easiest ...just examine what they buy! ... However, if your project doesn't offer the correct profit margin or incentive for the salesperson you should pack up and pull out immediately!

There is no formula for this ...every company is structured differently. The best strategy is to reach the highest officer of the company. Many times they (or their assistant) will recommend you to the correct person within the company. If the CEO is out of reach, ask to speak to the head of marketing or commercial development.

Note that once you reach them, do not send them your patent number or a copy of the patent. Save that for later. Establish interest first.

9. You have just finished testing the prototype of a new heat exchanger, and are trying to find out what is needed to commercialize this heat exchanger. What should you do?

Get free publicity, and see what develops. To get free publicity:

a. Develop a list of all trade journals whose readers would be interested in the new product. Try for several journals - maybe as many as 25;

b. Phone advertising departments of these journals, and ask for a media kit. They will have a couple of sample journals;

c. Read journals to determine if they have a new products section;

d. Write a new product news release using the samples as your guide. Do not write this like an ad. It must be news. Mention "For more information contact _____";

e. Call the new products editor and ask what kind of photo is preferred if the media kit does not contain instructions for new product news releases. Usually this is a 5 by 7 black and white, but check. Also, this gives one an opportunity to get the name of a contact. Send release to this person; and/or mail all releases simultaneously (This is important since old news is no news).

10. What makes a great ad?

It works, the phone rings your web site gets hits and buyers come to purchase. Poor advertising is clearly a disappointing experience. After spending hard-earned ad dollars with high hopes, you get only a hit in the face with a complete lack of response.

Three ways to make an ad a moneymaker:

a. What means the most to the best prospects?
- What is offered that the prospective customer will value most?
- State "best bet" benefit clearly and prominently in ad.
- If plenty of ad space or radio time, repeat the benefit at least three times.

b. Inform the prospect of what is wanted. Ads that don't come right out and ask for the sale usually fall short.

- Tell prospect to buy
- Why they should buy
- How they should buy
- When to buy
- Examine pricey ads designed for big companies. They almost always tell exactly who they think needs the product or service, which store or web site it can be bought from, how to get to that location, what kind of credit cards or financing is accepted, and when offer will begin and end.

c. Pick your advertising media carefully.
- Don't advertise a specialty service for a particular industry in a daily newspaper unless the city is dominated by that particular industry.
- Chose a trade publication that specifically targets that industry

11. How do you know if a business should be advertised on the Internet?

If the following points are relevant to your interests Internet advertising may be applicable:
- advertising in email newsletters is powerful and affordable,
- it is not hard to reach one million readers a week for $100, and
- buy low-cost ads are available with several quality e-zines.

A business is perfect for Internet advertising if:
- product or service can be sold to people all over North America and world,
- business can be marketed to those who love to get information, and
- prospects are people who own a computer or use one at work.

12. You are negotiating a license arrangement involving a product that has been released for sale. The licensor has asked the licensee, who will assume responsibility for sales, to describe marketing efforts. As the licensee how would you respond to the licensor?

Three types of efforts are relevant; 1) perfect the design and prove it is needed; 2) find a distribution network and sell to a limited market; and 3) establish widespread distribution:

a. *Prove the product will sell.*
i. Identify distribution channels - Sales agent, wholesaler, distributor, retail store, vendor, etc. (Expect to spend 10-30% of your time seeking distribution channels);
ii. List key elements of the selling situation - identify the sales cycle (time to complete sales process from authorization, requisition, and approval of purchase);
iii. Read trade magazines and visit trade shows – compare with similar products; price point, sales cycle, target market, etc.;
iv. Compare distribution channels for similar products; and
v. Establish contacts in distribution network by attending trade shows, direct contact with buyers and marketing people at key distributors – may need to contact 25-30 organizations before a commitment is made.

b. *Find a distribution network to sell in a limited market.*
i. Compare your product with other competing and non-competing products;
ii. Goal is to earn the most money for the least effort;
iii. Factors to consider are; minimum order size, terms, shelf space, promotional budgets, packaging appeal and price discounts;
iv. Start with a small distribution network; succeed and then expand;
v. Secure publicity but remember that is okay for TV but may not satisfy a distributor that seeks package not demonstration as selling appeal;
vi. Distributors want assurance product will sell; so set up introductory stage – promote, demonstrate, give extra long payment terms, frequent restocking services and other services to get distribution network on board; and

vii. Limit to one market at outset – probably cannot afford more than one.
c. *Establish widespread distribution.*
    i. Pre-sell distribution networks – begin when product invented;
    ii. Focus on personal contacts – will minimize advertising for product launch; and
    iii. Secure feedback and adopt good suggestions – it gets orders.

13. You are about to embark on marketing your technology. What would a common scenario be for the marketing efforts?

Consider the following activities:
- identify markets and customers,
- define value and place in customer language,
- establish marketing actions,
- create communications,
- perform marketing actions,
- follow up with personal contact,
- negotiate agreements, and
- manage and monitor relationships.

14. You are soliciting a licensee who will be responsible for completing development and then marketing a life science technology. What business considerations should you be aware of as you select a licensee?

Additional details would be useful e.g. what segment of the life science industry would be involved, however, the following should be examined:
- small business, start-up, or large company,
- competitive advantage through exclusive rights,
- expansion of applications,
- technology maturity,
- need for continued technical assistance,
- compatibility of technology with small vs. large firm strategies (small firm capabilities),
- ability to make necessary commitments - time (too tied to day-to-day operations vs. long range planning and management),
- cultural differences,
- technical capacity, and
- full cost recovery vs. partial cost recovery.

MODULE V - TECHNOLOGY MANAGEMENT AND SPONSORED RESEARCH

Program Management

- **Strategy and tactics necessary for effective technology development and deployment**
- **Management techniques**
- **Management tools and methods - Project prospectus (GANTT or PERT or WBS or CPM networks)**

Focus is on consolidating information from earlier sessions into the actual management of technology in the development phases. Brief examination of methods for project management including GANTT, CPM, WBS and PERT networks in the management process is discussed.

Sponsored Research

- **Sources of sponsors**
- **Solicitation strategy and tactics**
- **Government programs, SBIR, STTR, ATP, CRADA**
- **Strategic alliances**
- **Clinical or field trials**

In addition to project management there is an important need to manage the entire program that will consist of numerous activities not directly related to research associated with a specific technology. These might be public relations, regulatory requirements, clinical trials, capital procurement, etc. Emphasis in this section is on the management of all activities associated with the asset commercialization.

INTRODUCTION

Asset management requires knowledge of multiple areas leading to a need for expertise to be provided by others. Successful asset management is dependent, in some cases, more on personnel selection, team managing and communication than on actual technology management. A small, although not insignificant, component is sponsored research.

In the case of technology developed as a result of funding wholly or in part by others, or made up of components provided by others, and hence owned by others, there is a distinct need to enact a management and monitoring plan. If federal funds are involved, there are reporting requirements for the duration of income related to the technology. A technology based company usually develops a patent defense strategy and may have a "stockade" of patents surrounding a core patent but, in any event, whether a single or stockade approach is taken it will be necessary to have an in-house or external unit manage the portfolio to assure that no protection lapses. In addition, it will be necessary to monitor other technology–based companies that may infringe the patent portfolio. This same requirement exists for any other intellectual property.

The following are examples of areas that must be considered when managing a technology development and marketing program:

- **Intellectual property** - ownership, inventorship, strength and combinations of assets necessary for the final product;
- **Manufacture, production and distribution** - interim manufacture or final product; inventory and shipping, business to business vs. business to consumer, vendor, etc.;
- **Stability** - duration, conditions affecting, features e.g. time release or color change when chemical released;
- **Safety and toxicity** - administration range, method of delivery, range of safety;
- **Regulatory** - Environmental impact, Food and Drug Administration, Food Additive Petition, Underwriter's Laboratory (for electricity uses), etc.;
- **Market** - projections, timing, life cycle, product acceptance, or channel;
- **Capital** - development/market expenses, cost analysis, payback, return on investment; profit margin, joint venture, venture capital or non venture capital;
- **Legal** - contractual arrangements, liability, intellectual property protection and litigation;
- **Public relations** - advertising, press releases, trade shows, or magazines, publications; and
- **Personnel** - who, when, expertise, numbers, cost.

TECHNOLOGY MANAGEMENT - BUSINESS CONSIDERATIONS

OVERVIEW

Technology management involves more than just return on investment or selecting and purchasing or selling assets that quickly pay for themselves. The key is to leverage technology to realize ongoing benefits. It is important to recoup investment as soon as possible, but what are the benefits after payback? In addition, technology often needs time for growth, market penetration or market acceptance. Therefore, be prepared to establish management strategy that reflects the "think big but start small and grow". See Exhibit G for relevant questions and answers.

It is easy to examine past and current budgets and then establish and justify investment based on past experiences and known or expected return on investment. These views are short term and may not be in line with objectives of the organization. Do all that is possible to stay on schedule by tracking, measuring and refining benchmarks. Prepare a 3-5 year strategic plan; determine the plan's components and where they fit in the plan. Preselling others on the "return on investment" prior to and during a project may contribute to implementation and post sale success. Measure both soft and hard-dollar benefits i.e. cost savings, time to market, purchaser satisfaction (key value i.e. inventory reduction, decreased personnel), risk avoidance, support cost and purchaser goodwill. Return on investment cannot replace more important metrics like profit and revenue, which are valid end points. The items presented in figure one are examples of the other criteria that need to be addressed as technology or product programs are designed and managed to meet organizational objectives.

Figure one. Examples of criteria to measure when managing development programs.

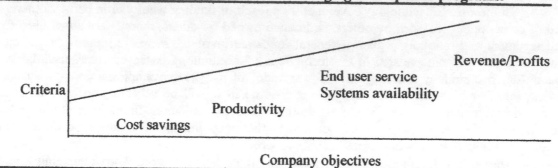

Company Management

The objectives of company management are to complete projects on time, on budget and in sync with corporate strategy to avoid the alternatives of "months late", "way over budget" and totally irrelevant". However, achieving these goals is not simple. First, one must understand the corporate "climate" (mission, goals, strategies and tactics) and second, be prepared to justify plans and have them critiqued thoroughly before implementation.

Managing the Portfolio

Project-portfolio management is simple. Ensure that projects support the organization's strategy; that concurrent projects don't overlap or worse oppose each other; and that resources (people, tools, equipment) are allocated efficiently and effectively.

List the projects and establish how well they are aligned with the company's overall strategy. Establish a decision tree approach in which; 1) project managers decide if a prospective project aligns with company strategy, 2) determine if the project align with the company's technology plan, 3) consider availability of resources required, and 4) subject proposal to a financial ROI analysis. Devote as much time and energy to project approval as to the projects themselves. See Exhibit E.

Senior Management

Some companies are establishing a Project Management Office (PMO) made up of senior executives, to review all project proposals over a certain dollar value, compare them with the organizations overall strategy, and approve or disapprove. Company PMO executives have different reasons for establishing a PMO. In a survey conducted by Interthink Consulting Inc., Edmonton, Alberta (CFO-IT Spring 2003) involving 180 PMO executives, 30% wanted a consistent approach, 28% desired to establish a single point of contact for project management, 25% wanted to prevent project failures, and 20% felt it was needed to support strategic initiatives. Less than half felt the PMO was a significant component of project success and 12% said the PMO made no real contribution to success.

Software Tools

Software vendors offer products that are designed to help manage, track, evaluate prioritize and generally improve projects. These range from PC-based tools for the individual i.e. Microsoft project to Web-based suites that serve an entire enterprise, i.e. Changepoint, Fortera, ITCentrix, Niku, Primavera, Pacific Edge, PlanView and Prosite. The market for project management software is currently worth about $1.5B with sales growing 15% per year according to Dennis Byron, market analyst at IDC (http://www.idc.com/).

Other software packages, i.e. Primavera's TeamPlay, are targeted to the senior executives and provided different views for people in different job functions. For example, it will let senior management track progress toward completion. It is important to understand the statement: "We have 80% completed but have 80% of the work yet to do." History indicates that if a project is 20% off at 20% of its life cycle, it will never catch up so it is critical to "flag" the problem early.

Savvy Management vs. Sexy Technology

Advocates of PMO are standards groups, professional associations, and consultants – those who stand to benefit from such a change. For example, Project Management Institute (PMI) in Newtown Square, PA offers project management guidelines and certification called Project Management Professionals (PMP). More than 50K people have received PMP certification. Microsoft, in January 2003, chose the PMP certifications program as the standard for its entire Services group, which has over 12,000 employees.

Others like Tom DeMarco contend that project management fails because of failure to set deadlines, often by senior executives, who often are in a competition to set unrealistic expectations, and lack to accountability. However, another hurdle in project management are contract issues that lead to delays and legal problems. The key is contract language and terms. However, this is just another reason to engage in effective project management so negotiations do not lead to project failure.

A project with a 12-month deadline is completed in 14 months. Is it late? Depends. Competitors project may be completed in 15 months. But how do you get these kind of data?

1. *Get the numbers.* Secure data from completed projects; i.e. timing, cost, quality, size and complexity. This will yield a means to do a "before" and "after" assessment.
2. *See software interdependencies.* Software is not linear but geometric. Doubling the size of a software project yields a 4-6 fold increase in data points. Take this into accounts as changes to a project are made i.e. new features, requirements or resources to an IT project.
3. *Recognize that talk is not cheap.* Break projects into small pieces that can be handled by teams of 3-5 people especially if international. Communication is critical.
4. *Benchmark performance.* Macro, industry-wide data is great BUT project data is needed. For example, how much time is needed to install a payroll system? If unknown, examine the competition.
5. *Measure progress.* Use data and productivity to measure process and identify systemic problems not just to punish individuals.
6. *Monitor performance quickly.* Do so in real time, not quarterly or monthly. Allows one to track budget, reliability, functionality and complexity and to make changes at onset of problems rather than after problem is too far along to recover and regain expected schedule.

MANAGEMENT TECHNIQUES

A good project coordinator or manager is essential for successful management of a complex project. The individual needs to be a good communicator with sound management and technical skills. As previously indicated, there are numerous tools available for a project or product manager. There will be a need to establish a core team made up of representatives from each component necessary for commercialization of the asset. On occasion consultants or advisors will need to be engaged to provide advice or confirm decisions or projections of the team.

As a project progresses there will be a need to exchange material and commit to tests outside the originating organization. Any exchange will require agreements between or among the parties to protect the parties from loss of asset value and to reduce liability as much as possibility. Material exchange, beta test, research or clinical trial agreements will require that a recipient abide by terms in order to conduct R&D with the asset. Terms include, but are not limited, to data and/or tissue rights, liability, compensation, confidentiality, termination and reporting terms (See Addendum III for agreement examples).

PROJECT MANAGEMENT TOOLS (WBS, PERT, CPM and GANTT)

These acronyms stand for Project Evaluation and reporting Technique (PERT), Critical Path Method (CPM) and a scientific management matrix developed by Henry Gantt (GANTT). Before attempting to use these tools, the project's information must be assembled in a certain way. The project planning process consists of the following:

1. setting the project start date;
2. setting the project completion date;
3. selecting the project methodology or project life cycle to be used;
4. determining the scope of the project in terms of the phases of the selected project methodology or project life cycle;
5. identifying or selecting the project review methods to be used;
6. identifying any predetermined interim milestone or other critical dates which must be met;
7. listing tasks, by project phase, in the order in which they might be accomplished;
8. estimating the personnel necessary to accomplish each task;
9. estimating the personnel available to accomplish each task;
10. determining skill level necessary to perform each task;
11. determining task dependencies;
    - which tasks can be done in parallel
    - which tasks require the completion of other tasks before they can start
12. project control or review points; and
13. performing project cost estimation and cost-benefit analysis.

WORK BREAKDOWN STRUCTURES (WBS)

The development of a project plan is predicated on having a clear and detailed understanding of both the tasks involved, the estimated length of time each task will take, the dependencies between those tasks, and the sequence in which those tasks have to be performed. Additionally, resource availability must be determined in order to assign each task or group of tasks to the appropriate worker. One method used to develop the list of tasks is to create what is known as a work breakdown structure.

A WBS is a hierarchic decomposition or breakdown of a project or major activity into successive levels, in which each level is a finer breakdown of the preceding one. In final form a WBS is very similar in structure and layout to a document outline. Each item at a specific level of a WBS is numbered consecutively (e.g., 10, 10, 30, 40, 50). Each item at the next level is numbered within the number of its parent item (e.g., 10.1, 10.2, 10.3, 10.4). The WBS may be drawn in a diagrammatic form (if automated tools are available) or in a chart resembling an outline.

The WBS begins with a single overall task representing the totality of work to be performed on the project. This becomes the name of the project plan WBS. Using a methodology or system life cycle (analysis, design and implementation) steps as a guide, the project is divided into its major steps. The first phase is project initiation; the second major phase is analysis, followed by design, construction, testing, implementation, and post-implementation follow-up. Each of these phases must be broken in their next level of detail, and each of those, into still finer levels of detail, until a manageable task size is arrived at. The first WBS level for the life cycle would be:

WBS number	Task Description
1.0	Project initiation
1.1	Draft project plan
2.0	Analysis phase
2.1	Plan user interviews
2.2	Schedule users interviews
3.0	Examination and test
4.0	Design
5.0	Test
6.0	Implementation
7.0	Post implementation review

Tasks at each successively finer level of detail are numbered to reflect the task from which they were derived. Thus, the first level of tasks would be numbered 1.0, 2.0, 3.0, and so forth. Each of their subtasks would have a two-part number: the first part reflecting the parent task and the second part, the subtask number itself, such as 1.1, 1.2, or 1.3. As each of these, in turn, decomposed or broken down into its component tasks, each component receives a number comprised of its parent number plus a unique number of its own.

A manageable task is one in which the expected results can be easily identified; success, failure, or completion of the task can be easily ascertained; the time to complete the task can be easily estimated; ant the resource requirements of the task can be easily determined.

PROJECT EVALUATION AND REVIEW TECHNIQUE (PERT)
Overview

PERT is becoming a necessary approach for controlling the many events that contribute to the success or failure of projects involving multiple activities. Development and optimization of a PERT program improves the chance for successful results. The critical path and most critical single event become key to a successful project.

A PERT program is used to define the key events and the sequence in which they must be completed in order to accomplish an objective. Originally developed in the 1950s to expedite the successful completion of the Polaris missile project, PERT has gained widespread acceptance in engineering, biological and computer industries.

Historically, development, operations, purchasing and implementation of a service or product were relatively simple. Only a few manufacturers, options, and participants were familiar with the project and knowledge was widespread. Today, however, initiating new services or introduction of new products require well-planned programs. These plans must encompass the sequence of events from the time the project is initiated through the useful lifetime of the product.

A PERT chart is used to graphically show the required sequence of events. Once these events have been defined, individual responsibilities are assigned for completing the tasks. If a large project is to be successfully completed, many various individual skills will be required. Often, some of this expertise can be found in-house. However, when something is being attempted for the first time, it is often a very wise investment to bring in some outside assistance.

Once the program has been initiated, the PERT chart is an extremely useful tool for monitoring progress and adjusting the schedule of events as required. Periodic progress meetings should be held. If it is properly utilized, the PERT will help keep the program on course and optimize the chances for achieving or exceeding the desired results.

In the entire sequence of events defined in a PERT chart, one critical path stands out as the most important but the critical activity may change during the term of the project or product depending on the activity and status of the project.

For example, in certain situations purchases are required during which justification for vendor, price, product and bid specifications and site visits are necessary with a formal purchase order. While the exact format varies, several steps must be completed before a purchase order is issued. The purchase must be justified. This includes a benefit-risk analysis. For large capital expenditures, a specific protocol for approvals must be complied before a purchase order can be issued. Knowing what is required and how to present the information are key to having the purchase request approved. Utilizing the PERT chart during the pre-purchase period can expedite the program, minimize confusion and prevent emotion from affecting the decision. Finally if there is adequate justification, and priority is high enough, the purchase order is issued.

As a project progresses from conception to product, numerous activities are undertaken some of which are dependent upon successful completion or progress of others. The complexity of the process varies with the type of technology and product. Critical events during the transition from conception to market introduction and sale term are monitored to assure successful market introduction and sales. Certain events will be subject to subcontracted to independent parties. Key to the success of these critical events as well as most other events in the PERT chart, is to agree on who will be responsible for each step well before one reaches that point in the program and what resources are required to accomplish defined activities.

Generating too much enthusiasm and placing unrealistic demands on inexperienced personnel can have very damaging results. It may be best to spread the program out over a longer period of time. The start-up phase of the PERT chart is initiated with an initial meeting, which is attended by the key personnel who will work on the project (project team). At this meeting, objectives are defined for the start-up time period along with projections for later stages.

In addition, responsibilities for quality assurance and project monitoring are defined. If these responsibilities are only verbally communicated, they may break down at a later date. It is a good habit to simplify these procedures and confirm them in writing to avoid confusion at a critical time later on. It is possible that project team personnel will change over time depending on the activities being pursued at different stages of development.

At the conclusion of each phase or key decision point, the project team should meet to review the results of the first six months. A written report should be presented at this meeting summarizing these results, with comments on what should be done in the future to make the next new modality's start-up even more successful.

This initial results report should also make specific recommendations for what should now be done to optimize results with the new modality. Perhaps additional in-services are warranted. Perhaps there should be a change in staffing patterns. Possibly an option that was overlooked initially should now be engaged or purchased. These and other alternatives should be studied and action should be taken on the recommendations in the next phase of the PERT chart.

Implementation, marketing, services and sales channels are constantly changing. One should make a continued effort to monitor and implement new ways to apply this new technology, methods or outlets to realize a products fullest potential. In addition to seeking advanced training that may be required, it is important to periodically conduct basic review sessions for new personnel. Properly implementing new technology and providing upgrades to customers can expand usefulness and lifetime of a product or service. Thus, one can begin the justification of a new purchase or relationships during the project. A PERT chart serves as a management tool aid but does not provide a conclusion for an ongoing cycle of events

In conclusion, which event in the PERT chart has the greatest impact on the results that are obtained? Very simply, it is the event that was least effectively accomplished. For example, if ideal bid specifications were written, but a purchase order was never issued, obviously issuing a purchase order becomes the most important step. If however, the "best system" was purchased but was improperly installed, then that step becomes most important. It is the step that is left out, or poorly done, that will cause the most problems.

With the sophistication and unique characteristics of each new technology or product, it is becoming unrealistic for any one person to be expected to successfully accomplish each individual event in a PERT chart the first time they perform the task. In order to achieve desired results from new, high technology equipment, the time and talents of many individuals must be properly coordinated. In addition to drawing on in-house expertise, properly utilizing the experience of others is becoming an increasingly necessary and worthwhile investment.

Implementation

Program evaluation and review technique (PERT) charts depict task, duration, and dependency information. Each chart starts with an initiation node from which the first task, or tasks, originates. If multiple tasks begin at the same time, they are all started from the node or branch, or fork out from the starting point. Each task is represented by a line which states its name or other identifier, its duration, the number of people assigned to it, and in some cases the initials of the personnel assigned. The other end of the task line is terminated by another node which identifies the start of another task, or the beginning of any slack time, that is, waiting time between tasks.

Each task is connected to its successor tasks in this manner forming a network of nodes and connecting lines. The chart is complete when all final tasks come together at the completion node. When slack time exists between the end of one task and the start of another, the usual method is to draw a broken or dotted line between the end of the first task and the start of the next dependent task.

A PERT chart may have multiple parallel or interconnecting networks of tasks. If the scheduled project has milestones, checkpoints, or review points (all of which are highly recommended in any project schedule), the PERT chart will note that all tasks up to that point terminate at the review node. It should be noted at this point that the project review, approvals, user reviews, and so forth all take time. This time should never be underestimated when drawing up the project plan. It is not unusual for a review to take 1 or 2 weeks. Obtaining management and user approvals may take even longer.

When drawing up the plan, be sure to include tasks for documentation writing, documentation editing, project report writing and editing, and report reproduction. These tasks are usually time-consuming, so don't underestimate how long it will take to complete them.

PERT charts are usually drawn on ruled paper with the horizontal axis indicating time period divisions in days, weeks, months, and so on. Although it is possible to draw a PERT chart for an entire project, the usual practice is to break the plans into smaller, more meaningful parts. This is very helpful if the chart has to be redrawn for any reason, such as skipped or incorrectly estimated tasks.

Many PERT charts terminate at the major review points, such as at the end of the analysis. Many organizations include funding reviews in the projects life cycle. Where this is the case, each chart terminates in the funding review node.

Funding reviews can affect a project in that they may either increase funding, in which case more people have to be made available, or they may decrease funding, in which case fewer people may be available. Obviously more or less people will affect the length of time it takes to complete the project.

CRITICAL PATH METHOD (CPM)

Critical Path Method (CPM) charts are similar to PERT charts and are sometimes known as PERT/CPM. In a CPM chart, the critical path is indicated. A critical path consists that set of dependent tasks (each dependent on the preceding one) which together take the longest time to complete. Although it is not normally done, a CPM chart can define multiple, equally critical paths. Tasks which fall on the critical path should be noted in some way, so that they may be given special attention. One way is to draw critical path tasks with a double line instead of a single line.

Tasks which fall on the critical path should receive special attention by both the project manager and the personnel assigned to them. The critical path for any given method may shift as the project progresses; this can happen when tasks are completed either behind or ahead of schedule, causing other tasks which may still be on schedule to fall on the new critical path.

GANTT CHARTS

A Gantt chart is a matrix which lists on the vertical axis all the tasks to be performed. Each row contains a single task identification which usually consists of a number and name. The horizontal axis is headed by columns indicating estimated task duration, skill level needed to perform the task, and the name of the person assigned to the task, followed by one column for each period in the project's duration. Each period may be expressed in hours, days, weeks, months, and other time units. In some cases it may be necessary to label the period columns as period 1, period 2, and so on.

The graphics portion of the Gantt chart consists of a horizontal bar for each task connecting the period start and period ending columns. A set of markers is usually used to indicate estimated and actual start and end. Each bar on a separate line, and the name of each person assigned to the task is on a separate line. In many cases when this type of project plan is used, a blank row is left between tasks. When the project is under way, this row is used to indicate progress, indicated by a second bar which starts in the period column when the task is actually started and continues until the task is actually completed. Comparison between estimated start and end and actual start and end should indicate project status on a task-by-task basis.

Variants of this method include a lower chart which shows personnel allocations on a person-by-person basis. For this section the vertical axis contains the number of people assigned to the project, and the columns indicating task duration are left blank, as is the column indicating person assigned. The graphics consists of the same bar notation as in the upper chart indicates that the person is working on a task. The value of this lower chart is evident when it shows slack time for the project personnel, that is, times when they are not actually working on any project.

A PLANNING METHOD – THE PROJECT PROSPECTUS

Once an idea is conceived and reduced to practice or even at the time of conception and there is interest in further research and development or commercialization, a strategic plan should be developed. The strategy will be dependent upon numerous aspects related to the potential product. Hence, the strategy and plans will vary. The sooner the project prospectus is developed the better, since the intellectual property involved may be the basis of the company or the only asset held by the individual and any loss of protection may significantly affect the value of the asset. In addition, the mere nature of research, development and commercialization involves numerous activities that are interdependent (See Exhibits A and B for criteria to consider for effective research and development management). This interaction needs to be identified and factored into plans since one affects the other. There are several criteria that are common across the scope of products and technologies. These can be addressed in a project prospectus designed to serve as a template for project management. The items include the following:

1. *Project title.* This should be a clear and concise description of the project. It may become the title applied to such areas as intellectual protection activities, initial correspondence with external parties, and shared internally. A clear title should be general enough to not disclose critical or inventive aspects of the technology, so if presented publicly it does not result in a disclosure which can be considered as prior art by a patent examiner in the event patent protections is ought. Even if no protection is intended, there may be a period of time until marketing commences in which one will not want to limit the information until market entry. Therefore, certain words in the tile may be too informative to those familiar with the technology or even the source of the information.
2. *Department.* In certain situations it will be useful to identify the origin of the discovery or product or technology, since there will be an ongoing monitoring of the project and accountability as the project grows and matures within the organization. Accounting may include financial as well as progress accountability for the particular unit or department involved.

3. ***Project coordinator(s).*** Project or team leaders will be established at the outset of the project and these may change over time or additional leadership added to a project. This section provides a means to identify these individuals so proper contacts can be established and administrative responsibilities assigned.

4. ***Project initiation date.*** This is the date the project is officially initiated. It may be a past date or the current date and serves as the date from which expenses and achievements are measured. This date allows one to monitor time and related cost to develop useful and reliable project econometrics for current or future use as more or similar projects emerge.

5. ***Current date.*** The date that entries are made into the project e.g. today's date.

6. ***Summary.*** Outlining goals, status, timetable for significant events, budget and budget concerns or issues. The summary is a brief concise presentation of the project. It is updated and made available to appropriate people as the project progresses or for reporting purposes. Since it is a dynamic document, it is expected that this summary will be modified as key events are completed.

7. ***Project goal.*** The project goal is a concise definition for the project. A proper focus, agreed to by the project participants, provides a basis from which to apply management principles and prevent divergence that may not be appropriate. On the other hand, the goal may need to be redressed as the project progresses and new knowledge is obtained.

8. ***Product description.*** At the time of discovery or in some cases even as the project progresses, the technology may be known but the definition of the product may be elusive until more detail is known. In order to plan and embark on the development and commercialization path, a definition of the final product needs to be determined. On the other hand, there will be cases in which the need is defined and a product developed to meet that need and then the ideal product definition can be well defined. Any deviations from the ideal then affect other project criteria.

9. ***Product stage.*** Most development and commercialization programs can be divided into several stages. The completion of a stage may be a milestone event or merely completion of key research and development event, which impacts other activities. Staging a project provides other parts of the company an overview so corporate management can implement or adjust management plans designed to influence owners or capital providers. As projects progress, these stages also provide the project leadership a means to assess progress, reward personnel, justify financial expenditures or address capital needs and inform administration.

10. ***Project progress and plans.*** Details of the project activities represent the activities of numerous individuals or groups dedicated to certain responsibilities. In a small company early in the research, development and commercialization process, or when the number of activities is limited due to the type of product, the list of criteria involved in the project may be short and the team may be small, as one or two people. The following are examples of project criteria that might be considered for a biological type project: intellectual property, publications, presentations, efficacy, safety-toxicity, formulation-pharmacy, manufacture or production, regulatory, and international issues or challenges. In each case, a history of activity to date is included along with future plans. Investment to date in the form of time, personnel and cost is estimated if not known. These "sunk costs" provide a basis from which to determine the overall cost when the project is completed, product is released for market or expenses to recover in the event of licensing.

   a. ***Intellectual property.*** Any activity that has occurred, which may influence the protection of intellectual property, is taken into account. A strategic and tactical plan is designed to assure that information is exchanged as the project progress that may affect the protection process or scope. In addition, those responsible for protection are informed and preferably a member of the team, so protection needs and plans can be identified and implemented as efficiently as possible. Financial needs and commitments will need to be taken into account.

b. ***Publications/presentations.*** Publication impacts the project in numerous ways. Publication may be considered as prior art if it appears prior to patent pursuit, it might constitute premature disclosure of information relative to market entry or it might be designed to coincide with market entry. Therefore, good communication between or among those intending to publish and the project leadership is critical.

c. ***Efficacy.*** All projects will have some criteria necessary to assure effectiveness or utility of the discovery or product being developed. These can be identified and appropriate protocols developed from which to formulate the critical path or respective milestones for the various activities. It is prudent to consider the successful achievements as well as the research that has been completed for results, which were not as expected, since the factors that were not successful provide valuable insight and knowledge to the project.

d. ***Safety/toxicology.*** Oftentimes, safety and toxicity information is secured later in the research stage but in certain instances it may be acquired even in absence of detailed and extensive protocol or full-scale research efforts. Knowledge of regulatory requirements is often needed if the new product is gong to be subject to regulatory approval. Regardless of whether such information is required by a regulatory agency, any and all observations regarding the safety of a product should be obtained for the benefit of the company.

e. ***Formulation/pharmacy/metabolism/residue analysis.*** There is a need to blend and mix various ingredients in most new products even when not engaged in an official well planned experimental design, there may be instances in which knowledge is obtained that could be taken into account as other protocols are designed. However, there will usually be defined requirements that a regulatory agency requires for these variables.

f. ***Manufacture/control scale-up.*** Any knowledge obtained that will enhance the production effort will be valuable. Scale-up of a laboratory process is often the most critical phase of a project. Therefore, details become critical for not only the large-scale production but for the protection and efficacy activities.

g. ***Regulatory.*** One of the most time consuming activities in a project is regulatory clearance. It is imperative those responsible for regulatory activities be associated with the project as early as possible, if the project will require such support. Often times there is reason to inform the public and regulatory officials of product benefits and educational materials based on publications and research results need to be compiled and made available to the public.

h. ***International.*** In all of the foregoing activities there is a need to be aware of the international aspects that may influence the development and commercialization process including but not limited to the import export law, intellectual property protection differences, regulatory requirements, product use and administration variations, environmental considerations, and customer or consumer preferences or differences.

11. ***Target dates for key decisions (network).*** A good technology or project manager will employ project management "tools" to manage the project in which the activities of the project are presented. These tools might be either a GANTT chart format or a critical path form such as PERT (project evaluation and reporting technique).

12. ***Market considerations (estimate).*** There may not be much market information available for early stage projects. The person responsible for the commercialization will need to begin to acquire such information as soon as possible to make informed decisions regarding the value of the asset, and to change projections as new data are acquired either

from searches or from researchers. Several criteria that can be considered are the following: finished goods cost; possible selling price; percent gross profit; market universe; market potential; and competition or comparison with the "product" being pursued.

13. *Project financing.* Lastly, all of the foregoing activities must be taken into account as the project is capitalized according to acceptable plans. In the event the technology or product is licensed, all of this information will be useful to establish value and for use as negotiations progress.

VALIDATION PLANNING

This is a way to organize various activities that culminate in validation of a specific project, product or system. Plans are tailored to specific management requirements of a project. No generic plan or template exists.

Plan or Not

There is no requirement that a program or project plan be established but the more complex the project the more valuable a plan can be in providing structure to the effort. In today's business environment nearly every technology development and marketing program consists of numerous intricate activities. Benefits to a plan include:

1. *Structuring validation activities* – tasks are identified, organized and executed to minimize project timeline and maximize benefit from resources e.g. materials, equipment, personnel and funds;
2. *Building familiarity with project* – helpful to both internal and external personnel;
3. *Introducing management to a project* – helps management with overview of nuances, monitoring progress, and understand business aspects especially when budgets and schedule information are included;
4. *Initiating regulatory interaction* – aids in conveyance of anticipated scope of effort to inspectors and ease regulator concerns about possible oversights. Especially useful if validation approach is novel or potentially controversial;
5. *Soliciting bids for outside contractors* – since plan delineates full scope of a project, validations services contractors can use it to provide bids for some or all tasks and useful if site is a manufacturing contract site and clients are solicited;
6. *Creating framework for later validation efforts* – if building a first Current Good Manufacturing Practices (CGMP) facility Validation Management Plan (VMP) can serve as foundation for validation programs since templates methods and procedures are already formulated;
7. *Developing resource for managing activities* – plan can define formats structures and approval for those companies that have yet to establish a validation program, including benefit to outside contractors;
8. *Easing protocol preparation* – may insert specific details from plan into validation protocols; reduces time and cost of protocol preparation; and
9. *Defining procedures* – especially useful for developing first time procedures especially if needs is for calibration or training (identification of Standard Operating Procedures (SOPs) at early stage alerts management to resources needed for timely SOP development).

Types of Plans

Plans vary with the activity or need. Examples of plans are the following:

1. *Corporate plans* – overall program for corporation. If large company includes multiple products at multiple sites. Corporate plans tend to be general and might be considered more of a validation policy statement than an actual validation plan.
2. *Site plan* – focuses on single site and varies with size of site e.g. firm with multiple production and developmental activities for a large firm.
3. *Single project of facility plan* – can be useful in facility design when new facilities involved.
4. *Product based plan* – may be similar to project or facility plan but focus is on single product.
5. *Activity focused validation plan* – task oriented e.g. cleaning, sterilization or analytical method.

Master Plan Size

A master plan might consist of 30-50 pages. It should be readable in a single setting (90 minutes). If the origin is in a multinational organization it might be more general and be considered as a validation policy or position statement, which addresses a specific subject broadly. In this case, the master plan may introduce subordinate plans.

Plan Author

The individual who authors the plan should possess knowledge of the project and be sufficiently well versed in validation requirements and project management. A single author who is an employee, consultant or employee of a service company should be responsible. Knowledge of state and federal regulations is useful if not required. The author should remain with the project and not be replaced or changed in order to maintain continuity.

Writing the Plan

Preparation for the plan should start as soon as project objectives are established and should correspond with project designing and initiation. It is important to keep in mind that a plan is dynamic and subject to change as activities progress.

Plan Preparation

Examples of items that might be included in a plan are: facility diagram, process description, product description, equipment list, utility list e.g. water for injection, storage tank, distribution system and separate equipment within it, controlled environment requirements e.g. HVAC or similar systems, process or quality controls, project schedule, financial projections, market information.

The parts of the plan would include but not be limited to:

1. Introduction – what, where, why, who, and how of project,
2. Descriptions – facility, process and product(s)
   a. Facility
      - Sketch or drawing of overall facility layout with important equipment and classified environments shown
      - Not mechanical drawing but overview
      - Visual rather than written
   b. Process
      - Important steps and the proper sequence
      - Written narratives, annotated block diagrams or process flow diagrams
      - Include critical parameters
   c. Products
      - Types, production volume batch sizes, formulation important features; e.g. color, viscosity and flavor and packaging

- Operating safety
- Handling issues
- Stability concerns
3. System definition

MASTER PLAN OVERVIEW
Content

A master plan consists of an introduction, project description, facility process and product descriptions, and scheduling and staffing. An overview of a master plan follows:

1. *Introduction.* Scope location timing with responsibility assignment for protocols, SOPs, reports and other documentation preparation, and approvals; frequently includes validation SOP or policy statement.

2. *Project description.* Concise but complete description of entire project; materials, product(s) to be manufactured; layout and flow of personnel, materials and components' description of utilities and support systems; and brief description of processes to be performed and products to be made in facility.

3. *Facility process and product descriptions.*
   a. Automation. Computerized information laboratory automation and process control systems in sufficient detail to delineate validation requirements
   b. System definition. List of systems, processes, and products to be qualified or validated; lists equipment, systems and products in matrix format that describes the extent of validation required.
   c. Acceptance criteria. Protocol requirements and acceptance criteria with emphasis on quantitative criteria.
   d. Project specific issues. Included when elements of validation require greater clarification or emphasis; e.g. as computerized systems, cleaning systems isolation technology and lyophilization.
   e. Document formats. Formats for protocols, reports and procedures, especially for new and first time facilities and contractors providing services
   f. SOPs (new or existing). Necessary to operate facility, highlighting number of procedures required operating and maintaining the facility.

4. *Scheduling/staffing.* Staff needed to finish validation effort in plan plus preliminary schedule of required activities to help estimate appropriate staffing requirements.

Intellectual Property Management Systems

All the packages have their strengths and weaknesses. The office responsible for intellectual property management divides responsibilities differently and weight different functionality differently (for example, reporting flexibility versus built-in foreign patent deadline tracking versus data import functionality versus financial analysis capabilities). Any office looking for a system will want to find the package that has the strengths that best correspond to their office's needs. The following are programs used by some offices:

1. AIMS-Pro - built on Filemaker. An "open" system, meaning customers can customize it on their own, with security restrictions, (http://www.knowligent.com/).
2. Aurigin - offers tools for strategic IP valuation (http://www.aurigin.com/corproot.htm)
3. CPI - serving primarily the corporate/legal market. Offers an annuity payment service (http://www.computerpackages.com/
4. DEALS db (http://www.inteum.com) - a significant upgrade is in the works, migrating from FoxPro to an updated client/server system.
5. InfoEd - originally developed for keeping track of sponsored research and now handles technology transfer as well. More web-based (http://www.infoed.org/)
6. MyIP - new offering by UK. Jeremy Kirkpatrick jerrykirkpatrick@easydatabase.co.uk

7. PATTSY - primarily serves corporate/legal clients, but used at some academic sites (www.opsolutions.com)
8. PCMaster – primarily corporate/legal market (http://www.masdata.com/index.cfm)
9. TechTracs by KSS - out of NASA. 4D db platform (http://www.knowledgesharing.com)

TEAM FORMATION

A solid asset management program will include multidiscipline capabilities. Creating and managing a team is a challenge. Merely referring to a collection of employees as a team doesn't make them one. The first question to ask is: Is this a team or a group? Each has a purpose. Typically, a team shares leadership and is interdependent, meaning they depend on each other for information, services or products to achieve a team goal. A leader (manager, supervisor) spearheads a group; members work on their own most of the time with little or no dependence on other members to do their job. There may be a group effort but it is not a team. Expectations for a group are not the same as for a team. Determine whether it is a group or team effort and then proceed.

FOUNDATION

The most successful teams invest time in laying the foundation to create a common framework for everyone. The building blocks are in the team infrastructure and team dynamics. Get started by addressing the following: What is the purpose of the team, the function in relation to the business goals, the actual team goal? Recently these questions were posed to a newly formed team of 17 people and 17 different perspectives were answered. Don't assume everyone will respond the same they probably will not, so be sure everyone understands the goal(s) and then initiate discussion.

FOUR DEVELOPMENT STAGES

The stages for team development are: forming, storming, norming and performing. Explain that the team will progress and digress depending on multiple variables such as turnover and change. Ask the team which stage of development they see themselves and what needs to occur to move to a higher level.

TEAM "PULSE"

Taking the team pulse can happen in a couple of different ways. One is through an initial team survey that generates data on how members perceive team function and interactions. A survey will include topics such as commitment, trust, communication, and conflict resolution. Administer the survey at least quarterly to determine progress and team development priorities. Another way to take a team "pulse" is to have periodic frank discussions about what is working and what is not. Practice regular, informal conversations that keep communication channels open.

ASSESS

Identify a tool to assess behavior work style of each team member. This exercise invariably illuminates each member's style preferences, their team contributions, and gives everyone information to adapt and work together more effectively. For most people, this creates an "ah ha" experience that is pivotal in fostering understanding and communication.

PROACTIVITY

Don't wait until there is conflict to establish a team charter. A charter, generated by team members, should specify guidelines and behavioral boundaries. This will set expectations and clarify what is acceptable and intolerant behavior. Make it clear that the charter can always be amended. Be sure everyone has a copy. Review it on a regular basis and go through it carefully with a new team member.

COMMON SKILLS

Be sure everyone has a common skill base for communication, conflict resolution, problem solving, giving and receiving peer feedback. Teams with these common skill sets are much more productive than teams without them. Technical expertise is only half of the success quotient.

EXPECTATIONS

Are the expectations of team members and the leader clearly communicated? This goes beyond job descriptions. For example, what do people expect to get out of working together as a team, i.e., expression, creativity; what can be expected of their contributions?

UNIQUE TALENTS AND CONTRIBUTIONS

Each team member brings value to the team. Point out or showcase various abilities. Take time in a meeting to recognize one or two members. Be sure everyone receives equal recognition.

DIALOGUE VS. MONOLOGUE

Build dialogue, extinguish monologue. Aim toward two-way interaction, exchange of ideas, and developing new insights in regular communication. Invite members to ask about others reasoning or thinking and explain how they think of or see a situation.

TEAMBUILDING

Initially consider a series of team sessions that incorporate the suggestions above with team building activities. Once the team is grounded, have quarterly or bi-annual team building sessions. The type of team building varies from classroom experiential to rope climbing, and needs to match the culture and challenges of the team. There are hundreds of activities that are metaphors for what goes on or doesn't go on, in the team experience. Whatever the choice, be certain there will be valuable learning and fun.

ENJOYMENT

Laugh together. Laughter is a common language the entire team will understand. So legitimize levity among team members. It will lessen stress and build a bond. Create times for people to laugh together and loosen up. This will also stimulate creativity. Consider some of these ideas: start a meeting with a relevant joke or funny story; show a clip of a comedy video-tape (or sports bloopers) that pertains to a current challenge.

CELEBRATE

Provide a continental breakfast or bring in lunch and celebrate for no special reason than to say thank you to the team. Don't expect employees to gather after work hours. Most people have family obligations and personal commitments.

TECHNOLOGY DEVELOPMENT MANAGEMENT RESOURCES

The technology management process requires one to; assess intellectual property e.g. project prospectus format; identify business candidates based on interests; acquire technology as needed and identify and establish strategic alliances; analyze strengths and weaknesses of alliance candidates; investigate strategies and evaluate plans for best tactical alliance e.g. start-up vs. existing company; explore industry and market trends; evaluate competitive market place; initiate meetings between client and alliance candidates; and evaluate acquisition and alliance candidates. Sources of assistance are:

1. Energy-related inventions program (ERIP) - a program offering free technical evaluation by the national institute of standards and technology and financial support by the U.S. Department of Energy.

411

2. Small business innovation research programs (SBIR) a federal procurement program for small R&D firms that are developing innovative technologies.
3. State and local sources of assistance programs that provide assistance to inventors and entrepreneurs; such as small business development centers, innovation or incubation centers, and technical assistance centers.

The closer a project is to market (phase of development and marketing) the greater the value. An example of these phases is presented in figure two.

Figure two. Development and market stages or phases.

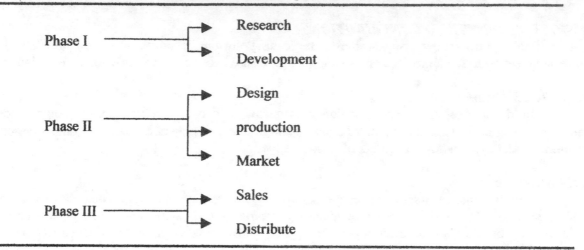

Other considerations in the valuation process, which are associated with the stage or phase of development, include regulatory approvals. Examples are: investigational new drug (IND) or investigational new animal drug requirements (INAD), new drug applications (NDA), new animal drug application (NADA), environmental protection agency's (EPA) environmental analysis report and unique product launch requirements such as public education in the case of biotechnology or novel sales and distribution channels.

There are several types of relationships that need to be taken into account in establishing value that affect value. These alliances or activities may not be directly related to the technology but contribute to value due to risk reduction or value enhancement. Examples of such variables are: 1) partnerships or strategic alliances designed to bring technology to market; 2) manufacturing or production relationships; 3) continued or real time competitive intelligence acquisition designed to make a product better and cheaper; 4) worldwide protection of intellectual property and licensing; and 5) electronic telecommunications involving wireless communications, e-commerce and information access and restructuring.

COMMERCIALIZATION STRATEGIES

LICENSE
Startup or existing firm (business or product) - most technology commercialized from educational institutions is licensed to another party or parties. License may be exclusive or nonexclusive and be; for limited periods of time, for specific fields or applications, limited to manufacture or sale, restricted to certain areas of the country or world along with various combinations of the foregoing.

ASSIGNMENT

An assignment is defined as the transfer of title or ownership, in patent rights, in the form of a written assignment document. The assignment can be in return for certain commitments on the part of the assignee.

SALE

A sale is the transfer of an intellectual property asset to another party subject to agreed on compensation. The sale may or may not involve assignment of title and all rights to the purchaser.

MARKETING/DISTRIBUTION

Parties that are only interested in marketing and distributing the property best achieve certain technology commercialization. In these cases, a producer or manufacturer produces the product and the sales responsibility resides with the individual or firm that enters into the marketing/distribution agreement.

FRANCHISE/VENDOR

Although most research institutions do not enter into franchise arrangements, it is an option for the corporate community. A product may fit with an existing product line and franchises are in place or it may be appropriate to establish a franchise type organization to disperse new technology. The advent of the virtual corporation concept and information age may result in more interest in this method of new technology dispersion.

JOINT VENTURE/STRATEGIC ALLIANCE(S)

As companies downsize and seek greater flexibility to react to market changes and demands, there is increased interest in collaboration as reflected by joint ventures, and strategic alliances. In addition, the product of today is usually a complex unit consisting of multiple components owned by several parties; hence, the need to establish an alliance that benefits all parties.

INDUSTRIAL RELATIONS

The goal of any relationship will be to establish a win-win collaboration. The selection of a partner is usually designed to clearly establish needs and then selectively target alliances that would result in a relationship that would benefit both parties.

The technology transfer process is often best accomplished if corporations agree to sponsor research and then, license the resultant intellectual property. This early corporate interest usually means there is a recognized need or desire for the asset. The transition from discovery to market is more efficient and timely when parties collaborate in the research stages of the project. The downside of early relationships is that an asset is usually not well defined and therefore, establishing value is not easy to do.

The objectives of a relationship might be one or more of the following: 1) increase scientific knowledge; 2) improve transfer of technology to public domain; 3) obtain an industrial view of our research emphasis; 4) acquaint students with industry; 5) maintain academic freedom: 6) obtain financial support; and/or 7) work on unique state of the art problems of the industry.

Of course, goals are achieved only if the contributions of the respective parties are mutually beneficial. Some of these factors might be: similar objectives/goals, reputation or achievement; skills or resources; stability; past/current relationship; local vs. non-local company; domestic vs. worldwide; research requirements, i.e. GMP, GLP, etc.; or market emphasis and ability. If material is exchanged set up an agreement related to the exchange (Exhibit B).

Further examples of what the parties might contribute to the relationship are: new technology/proprietary position; enhancements/to make industry technology better; solutions to

413

specific problems; testing/evaluation/measurement; new relationships - access to experts in field; better communication or access to students for new employees.

It is important to recognize that proposals need not be as extensive for corporate sponsors as usually prepared for government agencies. However, corporations are very familiar with PERT networks and GANTT charts as means for project management. A successful applicant from the academia will present proposals that "fit" with what the scientific and management communities in a corporation. Successful collaboration will be achieved when the two parties respect each other and interaction and communication at this stage is crucial at this point in a relationship.

The initial contact between potential collaborators would be designed to share goals or accomplishments as they relate to industry goals. Focus will need to be on reaching the person who will profit most and is charged for research in order to establish a "champion" for each party involved in the relationship. Initially there will be a need to determine major interests or problems that might exist and assess funding potential. Of course, both collaborators will be interested in the flexibility of each other to make decisions and the level of expertise available to create the 'win-win " relationship. The alternative to the expertise assessment will be the identification of "gaps" that might exist and for which other relationships might be required in order to assure success.

RESEARCH PROPOSAL

A successful research proposal process will depend on several key tactics. First of all the question will be what to emphasize in the proposal. Generally, the initial proposal should be a short, simple, and positive document in which the project idea, product, etc. is presented. In addition, emphasis should be on the benefit to company, the timetable and cost. The initial exchange of information of the proposal depends on the outcome of these initial discussions. If proprietary information is to be exchanged enact a secrecy/disclosure agreement (Addendum III).

Once there is evidence of interest, a final R&D plan can be developed in which details related to the following are addressed: objectives, procedures, decision/key dates, deliverables (e.g. reports), personnel, regulatory, benefits and a budget. It is usually beneficial to provide at a GANTT or PERT network when presenting the proposal.

Eventually the parties will begin to enter into contract or agreement discussions. Remember this phase takes time, requires well-defined policies, must address all issues, requires a well-defined budget and is most advantageous if perceived as benefits presented to company.

Other contractual considerations or issues that should be addressed are: responsibilities of the respective parties; budgets-indirect costs; deliverables; commingling of funds; background technology; other agreements: e.g. confidentiality, materials exchanges or consulting; inventions and licensing intentions, and/or publication rights.

In summary, when entering into cooperative relationship one should know the client or prospective partner, be creative and flexible; make yourself available for timely discussion; be enthusiastic; encourage communication; establish who is accountable for select activities and address publication rights that are expected whether or not interest exists. As indicated earlier, the party seeking a collaborator will selectively target "key" industrial cooperators. The proposing party should exhibit confidence and enthusiasm while encouraging questions and criticism.

SPONSORED RESEARCH (SOLICITOR VS. SPONSOR VIEWS)

Consider objectives before embarking on a sponsored research relationship. Is it to increase scientific knowledge, improve transfer and commercialization of technology to public domain, obtain an industrial view of research emphasis, acquaint students with industry in the case of an academic institution, maintain academic freedom, obtain financial support or work on unique state of the art problems of industry?

What are the preferred characteristics of a sponsor? If goals are similar one will want to assess the reputation and achievements of the sponsor and determining if the scientific skills and resources to be committed to the project will enhance the chances of success. A partner or sponsor needs to show evidence of business stability. Relationships should be based on past experiences and assessment of a current relationship if one exists. In some instances, it makes a difference if the sponsor is a local or non-local company or if it is a domestic or foreign. All of the foregoing is of little value if the company does not have the experience and capability to market the resulting asset.

On the other hand what is industry looking for in a partner and what can a research institution provide sponsor? Some of the contributions are: new technology and proprietary position, enhancements/ to make industry technology better, solutions to specific problems, testing/evaluation/measurement, new relationships - access to experts in field, better communication, access to students for new employees.

What will the initial contact involve? It should include the following: share goals and accomplishments, relate to industry and academic goals, reach person who will profit most and is in charge of research, determine major interests or problems, assess funding potential, evaluate flexibility, and determine existing expertise or "gaps".

The research proposal should be short, simple and positive. It should contain the project idea, product description, and benefits to company, timetable and cost. Discussion should be with "key" industrial cooperators and presented in a confident and enthusiastic manner designed to encourage questions and criticism with commitment to revise if necessary.

The final research and development plan should contain objectives, procedures, decision or key dates, deliverables (e.g. reports), personnel, regulatory, benefits and budget. It is usually beneficial to present the activities budget and personnel commitment in the form of a GANTT chart or PERT network for concise and definitive review.

CORPORATE SOLICITATION

For purposes of this discussion the contractor might be personnel in an academic organization who are seeking corporate support.

Sponsor Solicitation

All responsible parties seeking sponsorship may submit a request for sponsorship, which will be considered. Large organizations often require that a proposal be submitted, or one must respond to a "Request for Proposal (RFP)", for a project.

Refining art of proposal writing and submission is learning about a buying organization, analyzing its RFP, composing the proposal, and following through on the evaluation process.

Before beginning to analyze the RFP, research the buying organization to determine what its strategic goals and objectives are. Start with the buyer's Web site to learn and understand the organization's needs. Examine annual reports or mission statements, which not only outline the organization's philosophy, but also provide the buzzwords and phrases that the company lives by. Learn about its geographic locations, number of employees, and what types of operations the organization is engaged in.

Press releases and articles about the company may also be found on the Web site and may give insight into recent strategic moves, acquisitions, and partnerships with other firms. Remember knowledge is power.

Complete and Thorough

With a clearer picture of the organization, a contractor should sift through the RFP and organize information. If it requires network certification, make a note of it. If it requires "knowledge of" versus being "well-versed in" a particular programming language, this should be noted and reflected in the proposal.

Make sure every question asked is answered and respond to every information request, no matter how insignificant. The easiest way to eliminate a proposal is to point to information that has not been supplied.

A contractor should make a list of the buyer's requirements as specified in the RFP. This should be used as a checklist in putting together your proposal. In addition, make a list of questions and inquiries of items to clarify with the buyer. RFPs aren't always clear and all-inclusive.

Although arduous, responding to an RFP can, however, help a contractor ensure that all parties are clear on the scope of work. This is particularly important if the contractor is selling something other than his time. For instance, project-based work often demands an RFP so that the deliverable is clearly defined. Don't be afraid to make inquiries and clarify things. Few take the time to ask questions, and this can often eliminate a proposal.

While going through the RFP, highlight buzzwords, key phrases, and acronyms that the buyer uses. These may be used to describe networks, systems, processes, and languages. Be sure to feed these words and phrases back to the buyer in your proposal.

Speak the same language that the buyer speaks. Phrases and verbiage in the RFP also give clues as to how the buyer will make the selection. The RFP can ensure reasonably consistent decision criteria across vendors and allow for group input and recognition of needs.

Clarity

A proposal should be written with clarity and brevity. Proposal responses must be specific and address the business requirement or problem. Responses must be discrete, articulating solution capabilities that will avoid 'scope creep' and/or implementation failure. A corporate proposal is usually not as long or as a proposal to a federal agency.

One of the best methods to present for clarity and brevity is to include key points in a bulleted format wherever possible. In addition, use charts, matrices, and graphics, which are easier to read than ordinary text. Assume the proposal will be perused, rather than read. Heavy paragraphs of text intimidate readers and will lose their attention.

Obtain winning proposals to use as models. An excellent place to find these is at federal and government agencies. Inquire with the government agency or office about how to obtain a copy of a winner's proposal. This information is normally in the public domain and is available for anyone to view.

Follow-up

Follow-up is critical. A contractor should focus the follow-up processes on key decision-makers of the project or task. It is more productive to ask about the process and keep close ties with those driving the process.

Identifying the main decision-makers is key. Early in the proposal process determine who is on the selection team. Depending on the organization and its procurement policy, this information may be difficult or easy to attain. The "buying" organization should at least give the contractor a contact to send questions and inquiries to.

A good contractor will also develop a contact schedule and stick to it. This means marking a calendar for dates to contact key persons during the selection process and sticking to the schedule.

By phone, e-mail, or in person, a contractor should politely inquire about the proposal review process and offer the decision-maker an opportunity to ask questions or clear up any concerns. This strengthens the relationship between buyer and contractor and improves the odds of award.

No matter how much the RFP has been analyzed or the proposal refined, nothing beats the human factor. Good relationships will help keep the proposal on track and in the right pile. There is no substitute for good relationship-building techniques, they help ensure one makes the short list and wins the award.

INTELLECTUAL PROPERTY (IP) RIGHTS IN SPONSORED RESEARCH

Generally, universities grant research sponsors an option to be the first to acquire a license to any university IP or joint IP developed under the agreement. The option can be for terms to be mutually agreed on or can provide a range of business or financial terms. Specific financial terms are avoided because the value of the IP cannot be determined until it is created. In some cases, the license terms will reflect the sponsor's contribution to joint IP. If the sponsor declines their option, they are often granted a non-exclusive, royalty-free license to use the IP for internal research and development only. It is important to remember that the term "right to refuse" will require that the sponsor will have the right to match or exceed any offer made by a non-sponsoring party; hence, it may be better to consider other terms to assure flexibility in the event the sponsoring party decides not to acquire the research outcome during the option period. Such a commitment makes it difficult for the sponsored institution to solicit interest by third parties, since there is no assurance that the third party will receive any rights after spending time and money on conduct of the necessary due diligence and evaluation of the research and resultant IP. Anytime proprietary material is involved or invention is possible enact agreements (See Exhibits A, B, C and F).

The tax code requires that non-profit contractors grant intellectual property rights to a sponsoring party on the same terms that they would grant those rights to non-sponsoring parties. With respect to the grant of rights in an option the not for profit organization, which is the case for most academic organizations, it is necessary to note that rights granted at other than fair market value may be considered an abuse of the tax-exempt status of organizations that obtain their exempt status under sec 501C 3 of the Code.

The IRS logic is that the sponsor of the research benefits from the tax-exempt status of the organization in conducting the research. While that is acceptable when the research serves a broader public purpose it may not be when rights pass to the Sponsor without additional benefit based upon the value of the rights within a fair market context. In this instance, the non-profit institution may be acting as an inappropriate tax shield for the corporation and that action, conducted in a regular and usual fashion, may jeopardize the tax-exempt status of the Non-Profit. To lose tax-exempt status from licenses accounting for a minor part of the business, the academic institution conducts would be unfortunate. This line of reasoning does not apply to organizations whose tax-exempt status arises from Sec 115.

Another tax issue that must be considered when a non-profit organization offers IP rights to a sponsor is Revenue Procedure 97-14, which implements certain aspects of the Tax Reform Act of 1986. The procedure deals with facilities financed with tax-exempt bonds and spells out certain "safe harbors" for activities in such facilities that will not constitute "private business use" that would jeopardize the tax-exempt status of these bonds. Most state and many private university facilities are financed with tax-exempt bonds so "private business use" is a real issue.

Section 5.02 of Revenue Procedure 97-14 provides that an agreement for basic research supported by a corporate sponsor is not "private business use" of a facility financed with tax-exempt bonds if: 1) any license of the resulting technology to the sponsor is at a price no less than the price that would be paid by any non-sponsoring party for those rights; and 2) the price paid for the license is determined at the time the technology becomes available.

The private business use of buildings financed by tax-exempt bonds can result in the bonds being declared taxable, causing a problem for the bondholders. The IRS conducts detailed audits of universities and non-profits looking for evidence of private benefit and private business use of buildings financed with tax-exempt bonds.

Contract terms will also influence the rights of each party who receives the contract. For example, most sponsored research arrangements have a section in the contract that addresses commercial rights to the research outcome. Even though the outcome is unknown, the parties attempt to establish key intellectual property and business terms that they are willing to give up or expect in return for the sponsorship. Examples of key items are; terms exclusive or non exclusive rights to the results, right to use data, royalty free or royalty due along with a range or maximum royalty that might be charged, right to acquire or refuse the outcome from the research, rights to materials or test procedures development and whether these rights are for commercial or internal use, publication schedule as it relates to intellectual property protection, etc. Numerous factors affect the extent of rights to be granted including but not limited to level of financing, indirect cost rate, material or expertise exchange, qualifications to manufacture and sell by the sponsor, commingling of funds from government or corporate sources, use of intellectual property from sources other than the sponsor, origin of and contributors to the research protocol, policies of the institutions involved regarding rights to intellectual property, etc. Although government and foundation grants are often considered to be free of significant obligations on the part of the recipient, there is a need to be aware of contractual or policy requirements. For example, most government grants are subject to Bayh Dole legislation. In some cases, foundations or non-profit associations seek rights to participate in the transfer of assets resulting from the grant or even share in the resulting revenue.

GOVERNMENT RESEARCH PROGRAMS AND THE BUSINESS COMMUNITIES

There are numerous government programs designed to enhance technology transfer and economic development. The requirements and solicitation schedules vary for the respective government agencies. Therefore, anyone interested in presenting proposals to these agencies must understand current requirements and procedures to seek funds. Check with agency Internet sites for details.

SBIR AND STTR PROGRAMS
Small Business Innovation Research (SBIR) and Small Business Technology Transfer (STTR) programs are designed to harness the innovative talents of the nation's small technology companies for the benefit of the agency and countries economic strength.

The US Small Business Administration plays an important role as the coordinating agency for the SBIR program. It directs the 11 agencies' implementation of SBIR, reviews their progress, and reports annually to Congress on its operation. SBA is also the information link to SBIR. SBA collects solicitation information from all participating agencies and publishes it quarterly in a Pre-Solicitation Announcement (PSA). The PSA is a single source for the topics and anticipated release and closing dates for each agency's solicitations. For more information on the SBIR Program, contact: US Small Business Administration Office of Technology 409 Third Street, SW Washington, DC 20416 (202) 205-6450. Also see Appendix III for questions and answers related to SBIR and STTR.

Small Business Innovation Research (SBIR)
SBIR is a highly competitive program that encourages small business to explore their technological potential and provides the incentive to profit from its commercialization. By including qualified small businesses in the nation's R&D arena, high-tech innovation is stimulated and the United States gains entrepreneurial spirit as it meets its specific research and development needs.

SBIR targets the entrepreneurial sector because this is where most innovation and innovators thrive. However, the risk and expense of conducting serious R&D efforts are often beyond the means of many small businesses. By reserving a specific percentage of federal R&D funds for small business, SBIR protects the small business and enables it to compete on the same level as larger businesses. SBIR funds the critical startup and development stages and it encourages the commercialization of the technology, product, or service, which, in turn, stimulates the U.S. economy.

Small businesses must meet certain eligibility criteria to participate in the SBIR program:

- American-owned and independently operated;
- for-profit;
- principal researcher employed by business; and
- company size limited to 500 employees.

Each year, ten federal departments and agencies are required by SBIR to reserve a portion of their R&D funds for award to small business. They are as follows:

- Department of Agriculture;
- Department of Commerce;
- Department of Defense;
- Department of Education;
- Department of Energy;
- Department of Health and Human Services;
- Department of Transportation;
- Environmental Protection Agency;
- National Aeronautics and Space Administration; and
- National Science Foundation.

These agencies designate R&D topics and accept proposals. Following submission of proposals, agencies make SBIR awards based on small business qualification, degree of innovation, technical merit, and future market potential. Small businesses that receive awards or grants then begin a three-phase program.

- Phase I is the startup phase. Awards of up to $100,000 for approximately 6 months support exploration of the technical merit or feasibility of an idea or technology.
- Phase II awards of up to $750,000, for as many as 2 years, expand Phase I results. During this time, the R&D work is performed and the developer evaluates commercialization potential. Only Phase I award winners is considered for Phase II.
- Phase III is the period during which Phase II innovation moves from the laboratory into the marketplace. No SBIR funds support this phase. The small business must find funding in the private sector or other non-SBIR federal agency funding.

Small Business Technology Transfer Program (STTR)

STTR is a relatively new small business program that expands funding opportunities in the federal innovation research and development arena. Central to the program is expansion of the public/private sector partnership to include the joint venture opportunities for small business and the nation's premier nonprofit research institutions.

STTR is a competitive program that reserves a specific percentage of federal R&D funding for awards to small business and nonprofit research institution partners. Small business is often where innovation and innovators thrive but the risk and expense of conducting serious R&D efforts can be beyond the means of many small businesses. Conversely, nonprofit research laboratories are instrumental in developing high-tech innovations. But frequently, innovation is confined to the theoretical, not the practical. STTR combines the strengths of both entities by introducing entrepreneurial skills to high-tech research efforts.

Small businesses must meet certain eligibility criteria to participate in the STTR Program:

- American-owned and independently operated;
- for-profit;
- principal researcher need not be employed by small business; and
- company size limited to 500 employees (No size limit for nonprofit research institution).

The nonprofit research institution must also meet certain eligibility criteria:

- located in the U.S.;
- meet one of three definitions;

- nonprofit college or university;
- domestic nonprofit research organization; and
- federally funded R&D center (FFRDC)

Each year, five federal departments and agencies are required by STTR to reserve a portion of their R&D funds for award to small business/nonprofit research institution partnerships:

- Department of Defense;
- Department of Energy;
- Department of Health and Human Services;
- National Aeronautics and Space Administration; and
- National Science Foundation.

These agencies designate R&D topics and accept proposals. STTR is a three-phase program. Following submission of proposals, agencies make STTR awards based on small business/nonprofit research institution qualification, degree of innovation, and future market potential. Small businesses that receive awards or grants then begin a three-phase program.

- Phase I is the startup phase. Awards of up to $100,000 for approximately one year fund the exploration of the scientific, technical, and commercial feasibility of an idea or technology.
- Phase II awards of up to $500,000, for as long as two years expand Phase I result. During this period, the R&D work is performed and the developer begins to consider commercial potential. Only Phase I award winners is considered for Phase II.
- Phase III is the period during which Phase II innovation moves from the laboratory into the marketplace. No STTR funds support this phase. The small business must find funding in the private sector or other non-STTR federal agency funding.

Getting Started in SBIR and STTR

First, review the current solicitation. For most of the agencies the SBIR and STTR solicitations list all the research topics under which the agency is seeking Phase I proposals, and also contain detailed information on the parameters of the SBIR and STTR programs and how to submit a proposal. There may be more than one solicitation per year depending on the agency. Solicitations are available electronically. It is possible to register and receive notices of solicitation.

Second, to resolve questions, it is also usually possible to contact the agency help desk or see the agency Q&A web page. There are usually means provided by the agency to get answers to technical questions as well.

SBIR/STTR "Fast Track"

Some departments offer SBIR and STTR programs, which feature a "Fast Track" process for SBIR/STTR projects that attract outside investors who will match Phase II funding, in cash, contingent on the project's selection for Phase II award. Projects that obtain such outside investments and thereby qualify for the Fast Track will (subject to qualifications described in the solicitation):

1. receive interim funding of $30,000 to $50,000 between Phases I and II;
2. will be evaluated for Phase II award under a separate, expedited process; and
3. are selected for Phase II award provided they meet or exceed a threshold of "technically sufficient" and have substantially met there Phase I technical goals.

This process is designed to prevent any significant gaps in funding between Phases I and II for Fast Track projects. Small companies have found the Fast Track program to be an effective tool for leveraging SBIR (or STTR) funds to obtain additional funds from outside investors. This is because, under the Fast Track, a small company can offer an investor the opportunity to obtain a match of between $1 and $4 in SBIR (or STTR) funds for every $1 the investor contributes.

How to Participate in the SBIR/STTR "Fast Track"

To qualify for the Fast Track, small companies and their outside investors must follow procedures set forth by the agency. The most important of these procedures are as follows. First, toward the end of a small company's Phase I SBIR (or STTR) project, the company and its investor submit a Fast Track application. In the Fast Track application, the company and investor:

1. State that the investor will match both interim and Phase II SBIR (or STTR) funding, in cash, contingent on the company's selection for Phase II award. The matching rates needed to qualify for the Fast Track are as follows:
    a. For small companies that have never before received a Phase II SBIR or STTR award from the federal agency, the matching rate is 25 cents for every SBIR (or STTR) dollar. (For example, if such a company receives interim and phase II SBIR funding that totals $750,000, it must obtain matching funds from the investor of $187,500.)
    b. For all other companies, the matching rate is one dollar for every SBIR (or STTR) dollar. (For example, if such a company receives interim and phase II SBIR funding that totals $750,000, it must obtain matching funds from the investor of $750,000.) The matching funds may pay for additional R&D on the company's SBIR (or STTR) project or, alternatively, they may pay for other activities (e.g., marketing) that further the development and/or commercialization of the technology. Certify that the outside funding qualifies as a "Fast Track investment," and the investor qualifies as an "outside investor," as defined in the agency's "Fast Track Guidance" outline. Outside investors may include such entities as another company, a venture capital firm, an individual "angel" investor, a non-SBIR, non-STTR government program; they do not include the owners of the small business, their family members, and/or affiliates of the small business.
2. The agency will notify each Fast Track company, no later than 10 weeks after the end of Phase I, whether it has been selected for Phase II award. Once notified, the company and investor must certify, within 45 days, that the entire amount of the matching funds from the outside investor has been transferred to the company.

Tips for Prospective Investors

The Fast Track policy offers prospective investors a major new opportunity to leverage their investments in small technology companies working on R&D projects of interest to the agency and which has commercial applications. If a prospective investor, is aware of promising small technology companies that are not yet participating in the SBIR or STTR programs. The following are some suggestions to such investors for taking full advantage of the new policy:

1. Encourage them to apply for a Phase I award (investor interest in a small company will lend credibility to its Phase I proposal); and during Phase I, qualify them for the Fast Track with investor commitment to match funds; and
2. If an investor is looking for small technology companies in which to invest, search the agency's list of ongoing phase I SBIR and STTR projects and if there are promising opportunities, invest in the company, thereby qualifying it for the Fast Track.
    Additional information is available at web sites or by phone from the respective agencies.
A brief summary is presented in table one and agency programs are set forth in table two.

Table one. Description of government agency small business programs.

SBIR	Provides up to $850,000 in early-stage R&D funding directly to small technology companies and individuals who form a company
STTR	Provides up to $600,000 in early-stage R&D funding directly to small companies working cooperatively with researchers at universities
Fast Track	Provides a higher chance of SBIR/STTR award, and continuous funding, to small companies that can attract outside investors. For the investors, Fast Track offers an opportunity to obtain a match between entrepreneurs and other research institutions; $1 and $4 in SBIR/STTR funds for every $1 the investor puts in.

Table two. List of federal agency programs.

Federal Agencies' SBIR/STTR Programs
Department of Energy SBIR Programs
National science Foundation SBIR/STTR Programs
Department of Agriculture SBIR program
Department of Transportation SBIR Program
Environmental Protection Agency SBIR Program
National Science Foundation SBIR/STTR Program
Department of Defense SBIR/STTR Program
    Army SBIR/STTR
    Navy SBIR/STTR
    Air Force SBIR/STTR
    Defense Advance Research Project Agency (DARPA) SBIR/STTR
    Defense Threat Reduction Agency SBIR
    Missile Defense Agency (MDA) SBIR/STTR
    U.S. special Operations Command (SOCOM) SBIR
    National Imagery and Mapping Agency (NIMA) SBIR

Cooperative Research and Development Agreement (CRADA)

CRADA is a written agreement between a private company and a government agency to work together on a project. By entering into a CRADA, the Federal government and non-Federal partners can optimize their resources and cost-effectively perform research by sharing the costs of this research. The collaborating partner agrees to provide funds, personnel, services, facilities, equipment or other resources needed to conduct a specific research or development effort while the Federal government agrees to provide similar resources but not funds directly to the partner.

The CRADA vehicle provides incentives that can help speed the commercialization of federally developed technology, making it an excellent technology transfer tool. The Government protects any proprietary information brought to the CRADA effort by the partner. This provides a true collaborative opportunity. Federal scientists can work closely with their non-Federal counterparts, exchanging ideas and information while protecting company secrets. Also, all parties can mutually agree, if they so desire, to keep research results emerging from the CRADA confidential and free from disclosure through the Freedom of Information Act for up to 5 years. CRADAs also allow flexibility in patenting and patent licensing enabling the government and the collaborating partner to share patents and patent licenses or permitting one partner may retain exclusive rights to a patent or patent license.

In summary, CRADAs offer the following benefits:

1. enable both partners to stretch their research budgets and optimize resources;

2. provide a means for sharing technical expertise, ideas, and information in a protected environment (The Federal government can protect from disclosure any proprietary information brought to the CRADA effort by the partner(s));

3. permit Federal and non-Federal scientists to work closely and offer non-Federal partners access to a wide range of expertise in many disciplines within the Federal government;

4. allow the partners to agree to share intellectual property emerging from the effort or to agree that one partner may retain exclusive license to patentable research; and

5. permit the Federal government to protect information emerging from the CRADA from disclosure for up to 5 years, if this is desirable.

CRADA partnerships are open to any non-Federal party that is interested in taking advantage of it. CRADAs must fall within certain criteria from the Federal government's perspective. For example, the CRADA effort must be consistent with the mission of the specific agency initiating the CRADA. CRADAs cannot adversely affect the scientific integrity of the agency and must be performed in the public interest. Agencies must also ensure that CRADA partners are selected fairly and that others interested in the effort have an opportunity to participate. This is often accomplished by placing notices of the CRADA opportunity in the Federal Register.

To enter into a CRADA, a prospective partner should contact the principal researchers involved in the agency's research opportunity or the Office of Technology Transfer. The CRADA opportunity will be discussed in terms of the work to be done and a written Statement of Work will be drafted by the agency in close coordination with a partner. The Statement of Work outlines the tasks to be performed in the CRADA, contributions of the parties involved, the duration of the effort, and anticipated outcomes or accomplishments.

Each agency has a standard, written CRADA document that accompanies the Statement of Work. This agreement contains the General Provisions of the CRADA, which describe the legal responsibilities of both partners. Although these provisions are flexible to some extent, Government regulations prohibit the agency from altering certain portions. Changes are discussed during the formal negotiation process.

Once a CRADA has been negotiated between both parties and an agreement has been made concerning the final document and Statement of Work, the document must be signed by authorized signatories of both parties. Once signed, the agreement is executed and the CRADA effort may begin.

INTELLECTUAL PROPERTY RIGHTS IN STTR LEGISLATION

There seems to be a conflict between the provisions of the Tax Reform Act and the STTR legislation. The STTR application requires an agreement between the company and the university that would explicitly set royalty rates "before" the research is funded. The question raised is whether this legislation specifically overrides the Tax Reform Act of '86 and the 501(c) 3 rules. For example, the ATP overrides Bayh Dole legislation.

This concern applies only to IP developed during the course of the STTR, not background IP. However, it is not known beforehand if any foreground IP will be created. Thus, it's difficult to pre-negotiate any royalties. However, the standard form agreement provided by the governmental agency is not mandatory and it is possible to create a revised version. The following are examples of language that might be considered depending on the situation.

Example one. "...The Participants shall have sixty days from receipt of the written disclosure of any Subject inventions to notify the Contractor in writing of an intent by the Participant to acquire an exclusive license for reasonable compensation in the field of use of _____ (TBD)."

Example two. "The small business must negotiate a written agreement with the research institution allocating intellectual property rights and rights, if any, to carry out follow-on research, development, or commercialization. The agreement must be finalized and assigned by both parties no later than 15 days after the small business receives notification that it has been selected for a Phase I STTR award. The small business must submit this agreement to the awarding agency on request and certify in all proposals that the agreement is satisfactory to the small business. The agreement should, as a minimum, state:

1. specifically the degree of responsibility and ownership of any product, process, or other invention or innovation resulting from the cooperative research. The degree of responsibility shall include responsibility for expenses and liability, and the degree of ownership shall also include the specific rights to revenues and profits;
2. which party may obtain U.S. or foreign patents or otherwise protect any inventions resulting from the cooperative research; and
3. which party has the right to any continuation of research including non-STTR follow-on awards.

GOVERNMENT RELATIONSHIPS

In the event the commercialization process involves government relationships either past, in the case of past research, or in current or future research it will be necessary to know what rights are to be retained by the government funding agency or what restrictions might be imposed. If markets reside in various countries, tax laws will vary and should be considered as part of the research and development and commercialization strategy is developed.

STRATEGIC ACQUISITIONS/ALLIANCES

Current research is often carried out with numerous inputs from individuals and sources, corporate, government or academic. It may be prudent to identify these past or preferred relationships upfront so appropriate agreements or commitments can be enacted before embarking on the arrangement under consideration in the event a conflict is encountered that may affect the research and its ultimate outcome. Alternatives exist for engaging these parties in the relationship and innovative bargaining and contractual relationships may be in order.

CLINICAL OR FIELD TRIALS

Securing government approval for new products requires extensive knowledge of government regulations. Failure to understand and comply with these regulations results in delayed product approval and hence, market introduction. A successful research relationship is often formed as a result of the party's interest and ability to comply with these regulations. Therefore, awareness of Good Manufacturing or Good Laboratory Practices, Standard Operating Procedures, Environmental Impact analysis reports, or agency (i.e. FDA, EPA, USDA) requirements benefit the collaboration and help assure success of the program.

For the foregoing reasons, it is important to recognize that the cost associated with clinical trials is therefore, more than what is usually associated with early stage laboratory experiments. On the other hand, this cost, and more importantly time, can be reduced by good long term planning involving appropriate team expertise.

Additional information is provided in Exhibit C in which questions and answers related to asset management and sponsored research are presented.

EXHIBIT A - PROJECT PROSPECTUS OUTLINE

PROJECT PROSPECTUS OUTLINE – EXAMPLE BIOLOGICAL SCIENCES

PROJECT:
DEPARTMENT:
PROJECT COORDINATORS:
PROJECT INITIATION DATE:
DATE:
SUMMARY: (GOALS, STATUS, TIMETABLE FOR SIGNIFICANT EVENTS, BUDGET, CONCERNS OR REDFLAGS)

I.   PROJECT GOAL
    A.   "PRODUCT" DESCRIPTION
    B.   PRODUCT STAGE

II.   PROJECT PROGRESS AND PLANS
    A.   PATENT/COPYRIGHT
        1.   PROGRESS
        2.   PLANS
    B.   EFFICACY
        1.   PROGRESS
        2.   PLANS
    C.   SAFETY/TOXICOLOGY
        1.   PROGRESS
        2.   PLANS
    D.   FORMULATION/PHARMACY
        1.   PROGRESS
        2.   PLANS
    E.   METABOLISM/RESIDUE ANALYSIS
        1.   PROGRESS
        2.   PLANS
    F.   MANUFACTURE/CONTROL SCALE-UP
        1.   PROGRESS
        2.   PLANS
    G.   PUBLICATIONS/PRESENTATIONS
        1.   PROGRESS
        2.   PLANS
    H.   REGULATORY
        1.   PROGRESS
        2.   PLANS

III. TARGET DATES FOR KEY DECISIONS (NETWORK)

IV.   MARKET CONSIDERATIONS (ESTIMATE)
    A.   FINISHED "GOODS"COST
    B.   POSSIBLE SELLING PRICE
    C.   PERCENT GROSS PROFIT
    D.   MARKET UNIVERSE
    E.   MARKET POTENTIAL
    F.   COMPETITION AND COMPARISON WITH THIS "PRODUCT"

V.   PROJECT FINANCING

VI.   PROJECT MANAGER

EXHIBIT B - DEVELOPMENT PLAN OUTLINE

DEVELOPMENT PLAN OUTLINE

A development plan of the scope outlined below shall be submitted to Licensor by Licensee prior to the execution of this agreement. In general, the plan should provide Licensor with a summary overview of the activities that Licensee believes are necessary to bring Products to the marketplace.

	Estimated Start Date	Finish Date

I. Development Program
    A.   Development activities to be undertaken (Please break activities into subunits, with the date of completion of major milestones)
        1.
        2.
        etc.
    B.   Estimated Total Development Time

II. Governmental Approval
    A.   Types of Submissions Required
    B.   Government Agency (e.g., FDA, EPA, etc.)

III. Proposed Market Approach

IV. Competitive Information
    A.   Potential Competitors
    B.   Potential Competitive Devices/Compositions
    C.   Known Competitor's Plans, Developments, Technical Achievements
    D.   Anticipated Date of Product Launch

Total Length: approximately 2-3 pages

DEVELOPMENT PLAN CRITERIA (EXAMPLE)

I. Development Program
    Development activities and time line or critical path
    Integration with current products or "stand alone"
    Alpha and/or beta testing
    Education/training of sales force
    Estimated development cost
    Estimated Total Development Time
    Projected product release date

II. Governmental Approval
    Required or not
    Types of Submission(s) required and to what agency
        (e.g. 510K, FDA, EPA, etc.)
    Proposed strategy to gain approval
    Estimated target dates for key events and total time for approval

III. Market Approach (3-5 year projections)
    Customer description and profile
    Market universe and projected penetration
    New markets or sale to existing customer base
    Domestic or global
    Product outlet system e.g. corporate, vendors, distributors, alliances
    Projected units sold and sales revenue over first 3-5 years
    Pricing strategy and projected sales revenue
    Proposed advertising material and schedule

IV. Competitive Analysis
    Potential Competitors
    Potential Competitive Devices/Compositions
    Known Competitor's Plans, Developments, Technical Achievements
    Comparative advantages/disadvantages (strengths/weaknesses)
    Anticipated Date of Product Launch

V. Projected needs from licensor
    Data for advertising
    Past publications and plans for future publications
    Conference, exhibits and meeting participation
    Development, clinical trials, beta testing, etc.

VI. License terms and/or expectations
    Exclusive vs. non exclusive
    Limited exclusivity e.g. field of use, geographic limits,
    Projected fee/royalty structure
    Government grants past/future if involved
    Intellectual property protection

VII. Anticipated Date of Product Launch

EXHIBIT C – TECHNOLOGY MANAGEMENT AND SPONSORED RESEARCH
Q AND A

(Following is for information only. Seek legal or accounting advice for your specific situation)

1. Material Transfer Agreement (MTA) rights - A company wants a MTA for a compound that grants them an exclusive, royalty free license under any rights resulting from the use of the sample. They have assured you that no inventions will result from the study, although results must of course be sent to the company and the agreement grants the company the sole right to determine whether and where patent protection will be sought. You dislike the language, and are concerned about the possibility of the company deciding there is patentable subject matter (despite the assurances of the investigator), but your supervisor (who is also the lab director for the post-doc requesting the materials) says sign it unless there is a legal impediment to doing so. What would your concerns be if accepting such terms, given Bayh-Dole or any other law or regulation?

The response to this query depends on these questions: Who is paying for the research and experimentation? What obligations are there to the sponsor?

The financial terms of this type of an agreement are not limited by anything except what the market will bear. Upfront fees vary from a few thousand to tens of thousands. Royalties are in the 5-15% range.

Companies usually do not pay royalties for unpatented biological materials unless they are an integral part of a product. Most biological materials are used as a research tool to help develop a product and are licensed for a one-time payment plus modest annual maintenance fees. The exceptions are licenses under programs that some drug companies have started to obtain exclusive rights to patented biological materials. These companies will pay royalties are usually no more than 2%.

Some organizations prefer to use a biological materials license agreement instead of a material transfer agreement. The two agreements are similar, but the biomaterials license agreement often extends its rights to progeny and mutations resulting from the use of the biological material. However, there are MTAs that do not extend their reach to progeny or mutations. It depends on what the parties are willing to agree to.

If it is the federal govt., then free dissemination of research results (especially tangible products) emanating from a federal grant is a major issue and exclusive rights run counter to that.

If the sponsor is a private entity, then check the sponsorship agreement before signing anything that would create a conflict. If you inadvertently double license, you will be sued.

There is the entire issue of fairness. If a mere donor of materials demands rights that normally are reserved for a full research sponsor, then where is the fairness? Offer a non-exclusive royalty free license for research purposes only and then negotiate from there.

It all comes down to need and greed. If you need the material from the company so much that you are willing to forego compensation of any type, then signing the MTA might be in the best interest of the researcher (provided they realize what they give up in the process). Companies that want royalty-free grant backs say they need them to protect against royalty stacking if the final product uses a combination of patented technologies developed with multiple partners who receive materials under MTAs.

You may want to ask the company if it was their intent to profit from the university-invented patent and share none of the benefit. If they said yes, you may either be dealing with a greedy, stupid, or posturing negotiator. The way it usually fell out was the offer of either a non royalty-bearing nonexclusive grant back license or an option for an exclusive royalty-bearing grant back license. If the company is motivated by greed, then admit that you are too, and propose a way for them to financially compensate you that does not produce royalty stacking. Although this is usually too complex for an MTA you could ask if they would be willing to fund research or pay a one-time milestone payment.

Companies act rationally by offering no compensation at first, because some people are willing to sign this type of agreement.

You might also want to have a senior level university person call a senior level person at the company. Embarrassment can sometimes help.

Lastly, remember that the company may have no real incentive to provide materials that are not on their terms if the material is their crown jewel and they really do not want others working on it.

MTA's can be the bane of academic's existence. The company cannot have a wholly exclusive license if government funds the research; government gets a royalty free, non-exclusive. Also, there is something inherently wrong with a party who does nothing but supply material, albeit valuable/costly/inventive stuff, getting all the rights in an invention made using it + inventor's expertise + other unique reagents + taxpayer dollars (and/or private dollars meant for research).

MTAs are means by which one can transfer proprietary material to another party without transferring any proprietary rights. There are several forms of MTAs, one of which is when payment is exacted to cover the costs of providing the material. If you were to charge much above the cost, then you may run the risk of establishing a first sale bar date if you have not filed a patent application for the material. Universities as well as nonprofit research organizations and commercial companies use material transfer agreements to control their downstream rights to the materials and may legally charge something for the materials as long as it is not excessive and is intended to cover their cost.

Bailment Another form of MTA that can be used is the Bailment Agreement which is used for proprietary material which is not likely to be patented because it is a biological material which will be used as a research tool leading to development usually of diagnostic kits within a year or two and then the products from its use will then be subject to a royalty under the bailment agreement.

The financial terms of this type of an agreement are not limited by anything except what the market will bear. Up front fees vary from a few thousand to 10s of thousands. Royalties are in the 5-15% range.

Bailment is an exception to university policy in that it requires that a trade secret be maintained, i.e., limited access to the biological material.

A bailment requires the recipient to exercise a certain degree of care over the transferred material but at least the same degree of care that they would exercise over their own material of a similar nature. Some universities prefer to use a biological materials license agreement instead of a material transfer agreement.

Agreements with bailments for unpatented, published biological materials can be enacted. Bailments do not always deal with proprietary objects. For example, you are creating a bailment when you park your car in a public parking lot for a fee or take your cleaning to a dry cleaner.

When material is accepted by a University and it is subject to a bailment agreement there may need to be an exception to University policy, to maintain as trade secret. You are addressing the degree to which to which the recipient must comply. It is also the responsibility of the university to also restrict its distribution. It may require a sign-off of a university official to make the exception to policy regarding publication restriction and maintenance of what amounts to a trade secret.

Fees/Price. MTA's terms are usually in the range of $2K-25K up front plus a 5-7% royalty on kits that were produced using biological material transferred under such agreements.

If biological materials are used as a part of the product a royalty is appropriate. Many fee-based MTAs or biological materials licenses are for drug targets used to screen candidate compounds. The drug targets are only used for R&D and not part of a product or used to develop a product so companies will not pay a royalty. The exceptions are those companies that have programs to grant exclusive licenses for patented drug targets. However, only unique patented targets pass their screens.

2. What kind of terms are being received for biomaterials agreements?
- Unpatented cDNA clones: $3,000 - 10,000
- Unpatented cell lines, including hybridomas: $5,000 - 10,000 plus an annual
maintenance fee of $3,000-5,000.

- Patented cell lines with unique properties used for drug screening: $30,000 - $50,000
     plus an annual maintenance fee of $5,000-$10,000.

     Some pharmaceutical companies have announced programs where they will pay much greater fees for patented biological materials used as drug targets. They will pay upfront payments of $50,000-100,000 milestone payments based on drug development, and a 1-2% royalty on sales. The challenge is having a drug target pass their initial screens

3. A large corporation contends that the reporting requirements under 37 CFR 401 provide for certain cases where inventions resulting from government sponsored research do not need to be reported, hence are not subject to the royalty-free, non-exclusive license to the federal government. The contention is based on 37 CFR 401.1.2b, which states, in part: "In accordance with 35 U.S.C. 212, no scholarship, fellowship, grant, or other funding agreement made by a Federal agency primarily to an awardee for educational purposes will contain any provision giving the Federal agency any rights to 37 CFR 401.1 inventions made by the awardee." The belief is that the value of the invention is diminished by the government having any rights to the technology. The academic institution feels strongly that all publications, patent applications, etc. note the federal sponsorship clearly and that this clause is relevant. What would you recommend for the academic organization? If a patent application was filed containing federally-funded claims and some non-federally funded claims, how would you promulgate this in the application?

     One can sustain the position that while students may not be obligated under their "own" funding, if the student chooses to work on a project that uses federal funding obtained by their mentor/principal investigator, then the public is paying for that specific research at least in part, and the student's potential inventions are subject to obligations under 37 CFR 401. The student is funded to learn how to do research, but when h/she chooses a project, they also implicitly agree to obligations that cover funding of that project, because otherwise they would be unable to do it.

     If you think about them clearly, you will see that the government rights are truly limited, and any effect they might ever have on the revenue stream would hit the licensor's revenue stream more than the licensee's. The greatest issue for companies in the 37 CFR 401 requirements is the substantial manufacture in the U.S. for U.S. markets requirement, but even that can be legitimately handled when the circumstances justify it.

4. A university has a large Federal cooperative agreement, the intent of which is to assist a major U.S. industry sector, of interest to the agency. About 1/3 of the funds get subcontracted to private companies in the industry (by RFP) for R & D; many of the subs require software development. An administrator wants to reserve - for the university - rights to IP developed by the private companies under the subcontracts. Subcontracted R & D sometimes involves creation of derivatives of software already developed and owned by the companies. In most cases there is no co-inventor at the university. Would the requirement be disadvantageous in contract negotiations between the university and private industry?

     This is overreaching and can be inequitable to the subcontractors. However, if the software would be a "subject invention" as defined in 37 CFR 401.2(d), it may also be unlawful. 37 USC 401.14(g) states that subcontracts of federal funds must flow down rights in subcontractor inventions to the subcontractor; and further states, "The contractor will not, as part
of the consideration for awarding the subcontract, obtain rights in the subcontractor's subject inventions."

     If the software is a derivative of IP owned and developed by the companies the U may be able to negotiate some rights in the developed software. But it seems that the U is engaging contract workers and not workers for hire. The contract workers are only obliged to present the work product to the contracting agent with a limited license for specific use by the contractor. There may be some royalty owed to the software creator who has developed a derivative, but that act should not obligate the creator to give up all rights in favor of a contract. Further if there is no U contribution, save the contract admin., it certainly is not a engaging a worker for hire and does not provide any technical supervision creating a U contribution to the work done under contract. It might be best for the outside provider to avoid doing business with the U. Does the administrator have an idea about what would be done with rights if obtained?

Federal funding doesn't necessarily provide a "blanket" claim to a third party's IP. Two points:

1. Look at the federal grant and review what IP rights are granted. DARPA and ATP programs often give the company full and total IP rights (for foreground inventions). Other programs vary and the specific working arrangement, like a CRADAs, give the private sector limited rights. Background IP lies with the

originator in all cases. However, reduction to practice on an existing invention(s) may transfer rights to the company if they reduce it to practice. Thus, read what the contract language is contained in the federal grant.

2. Most (a generalization) federal grants say "you can keep what you develop". Thus, if a company or university invents something then they may be able own it.

The university will generally own no IP if they only provide "pass through" funding and do no work. No company is going to subcontract (with you) if they will lose IP rights to their main products, which may be modified with federal funding. Thus, on software, I think you may have problems. Even if the university has ownership of the derivative work, any user would have to employ the main software, making a sale for the company, so this is a tricky situation especially if the software is more application orientated than shrink wrapped. If you are creating a consortium, then the IP will end up being shared by the consortium.

5. Does receipt of federal funding for a grant proposal count as a publication giving rise to a bar against future foreign filing? Also, would the publication date be the date of submission or the date of funding grant and subsequent publication. Second, does the submission of the proposal itself constitute an offer to sell, again giving rise to a bar against subsequent foreign filing and beginning the one-year U.S. clock?

The proposal itself may not be enabling and the funding request is not a proposal to sell the innovation but a request for funds. However, if experiments are described in such a clear and concise manner as to enable someone skilled in the art to which the invention pertains to make and use it the description might be considered enabling and be considered to be in the public domain. This would be especially true if the conception as disclosed was subsequently reduced to practice.

For that reason, and others, the provisional patent application process was created. This allows University researchers to file their grant proposal as a provisional application at a lower cost and preserve for one year their rights to pursue full patent protection later."

Funded proposals are not necessarily published but abstracts often are. An abstract is "accessible to the public" on the date of publication because it can be retrieved by a FOIA request. If the proposal when submitted identified specific sections regarded by the applicant as proprietary to the applicant, those sections can be redacted under FOIA (but that may not happen, given the high likelihood of a clerical oversight). So, if in fact someone does obtain an unredacted copy of the application under FOIA (whether or not he should have received it), that event could be held against the international patent if it is challenged. On or before the public is notified of the funding of a grant application, an abstract of the application is published electronically, and that will stand as prior art against the international patent. The argument that such disclosures are not enabling may not cut any ice in foreign jurisdictions because the enablement requirement is not a factor in patentability in the same sense as it is in the U.S. Submission of a grant application does not create an "on sale" bar unless by some peculiar circumstance the application has embedded within it an "offer" to make available to the granting institution an actual product that would embody the invention disclosed in the application. One thing to bear in mind is that there is no duty of disclosure to any patent office in any foreign jurisdiction. It is up to challenger to discover the prior art.

More patent-savvy faculty members will consider protection at the time they're developing the grant application. They've already conceived of the invention and perhaps have some confirmatory data; the grant is intended to get enough data to publish, which is usually more than is needed to get a patent). Ask grants administration personnel to provide a copy of the abstracts for all applications at the time they're submitted. In theory, you can contact the investigators before the grant is awarded. Time will be a key consideration.

As far as reduction to practice, the courts have consistently held that conception is the be-all and end-all of inventing; reduction to practice is only important inasmuch as it leads to a refinement in the conception. The act of filing a patent application constitutes "constructive" reduction to practice, which is sufficient under the law (provided, of course, that the application teaches how to complete the job). Filing a provisional would similarly constitute constructive reduction to practice. Conception of the complete and operative embodiment of the invention would constitute conception. Filing a provisional or utility patent application constitutes a constructive reduction to practice if it meets the requirements of Section 112. For mechanical and certain electronic inventions it may be possible to describe the invention so that it meets Section 112 requirements without an actual reduction to practice. However, the PTO has taken the position that the chemical (and biological) arts are unpredictable. For these arts, the patent application must contain actual data. Many journal articles and research reports do not provide enough data or experimental details to meet the burden of Section 112.

Advanced Technology Program (ATP). To add some further clarification or complexity, the authorizing statutes for some federal R&D programs, such as the ATP, explicitly exempt them from FOIA.

Cooperative research and development agreement (CRADA). CRADA data are legislatively protected for a period of 5 years after creation, and is treated by the National Laboratory as "confidential", is not released, and is not subject to FOIA until the 5-year period expires.

Proprietary information provided under a CRADA is protected not only by the CRADA statute but, more importantly, the Federal Trade Secrets Act. The Trade Secrets Act makes it a criminal offense for Federal employees to release defined proprietary information - the definition being very broad. Furthermore, the new FOIA legislation does not include a CRADA because a CRADA is not, by law a "funding" vehicle.

6. It is a standard requirement in an institutions clinical trial agreement that companies indemnify the organization for "Use of Study Results". Specifically the company shall defend, indemnify and hold harmless the Institution's, Principal Investigator etc. from any and all liabilities, claims etc. resulting from the Company's use of the study results. The Institution does include the standard provisions that the study is in accordance to protocol, there is no negligence on the Institution's part, etc.)

The Institution concern is that after studying a sample of 200 women who take the test drug and no adverse effects observed the drug goes to market, or the Company uses the results in a publication stating the results the population takes the drug and adverse effects occur. Those who have taken the drug, not only sue the company but those involved in the clinical trial.

However, the Company has indicated they no longer, although they have in the past, will indemnify for "use of results". They state that other universities and medical centers have agreed to forgo "use of results". They feel that the phrase is "use of results" is too broad and needs to be more definitive for them to accept. Questions are:

a. Is "use of results" as important and should it be included in clinical trial agreements?

b. Are there other potential problems which might occur if such indemnification is not obtained?

Insist on indemnification for use of results for clinical trials. The Institution has no control over what the company may do with results and Institution should not be held liable for what may happen.

7. What is the SBIR Program?

The Small Business Innovation Research (SBIR) Program is a highly competitive three-phase award system which provides qualified small business concerns with opportunities to propose innovative ideas that meet the specific research and research and development needs of the Federal Government.

8. What are the three phases of the SBIR Program?

Phase I is a feasibility study to evaluate the scientific and technical merit of an idea. Awards are for periods of up to six months in amounts up to $100,000.

Phase II is to expand on the results of and further pursue the development of Phase I. Awards are for periods of up to two years in amounts up to $750,000.

Phase III is for the commercialization of the results of Phase II and requires the use of private sector or non-SBIR Federal funding.

9. Do you have to be a Phase I awardee in order to be considered for Phase II of a project?

Yes.

10. What is the small business size standard for purposes of the SBIR Program?

A small business concern for purposes of award of any funding agreement under the SBIR Program is one which, including its affiliates, has a number of employees not exceeding 500.

11. How can a small business concern obtain funding under SBIR?

A small business can obtain funding under SBIR by being the recipient of a competitively awarded SBIR funding agreement.

12. What is an SBIR funding agreement?

An SBIR funding agreement is a contract or grant entered into between an SBIR participating Federal agency and a small business concern for the performance of experimental, developmental, or research work funded by the Federal Government.

13. Does the Small Business Administration make any awards under the SBIR Program?

No. The SBA has authority and responsibility for monitoring and coordinating the Government-wide activities of the SBIR Program and reporting its results to Congress.

The Federal agencies participating in SBIR have the responsibility for:

  a. selecting SBIR topics
  b. releasing SBIR solicitations
  c. evaluating SBIR proposals
  d. awarding SBIR funding agreements on a competitive basis

14. Who are the participants in the SBIR Program?

The following Federal agencies are eligible to participate:

Department of Agriculture
Department of Commerce
Department of Defense
Department of Education
Department of Energy
Department of Health and Human Services

Department of Transportation
Environmental Protection Agency
National Aeronautics and Space Administration
National Science Foundation

15. Can a firm go directly to a Phase II award without competing for Phase I?

No. The SBIR Program was created for NEW innovations to meet existing Federal R&D needs. The results of a Phase I are a determining factor in deciding whether there will be a Phase II award to continue the effort.

16. Does SBA designate any of the topics cited in SBIR solicitations or make any awards under SBIR?

No. The legislation governing the SBIR Program gives unilateral authority and responsibility for these functions to each of the Federal agencies participating in the program.

17. Since SBIR is a program to assist small business innovators, can SBA or the other Federal participating agencies provide direct funding for a project which a firm has initiated on its own?

No. SBA does not fund SBIR projects and such an endeavor would be considered an unsolicited proposal, which is outside the scope of the SBIR Program.

18. Is a small US firm still eligible to compete for an SBIR award if it forms a 50-50 joint venture with a nonprofit or foreign firm?

No.

19. Are foreign-based firms eligible for SBIR awards?

No. To be eligible for award of SBIR funding agreements, a small business concern has to meet the following qualifications:
- be independently owned and operated,
- principal place of business is located in the United States, and
- at least 51 percent owned or in the case of a publicly owned business, at least 51% of its voting
  stock is owned by United States citizens or lawfully admitted permanent resident aliens.

20. Are nonprofit concerns eligible for SBIR awards?

No.

21. May a portion of an SBIR award be subcontracted?

For Phase I, a minimum of two thirds of the research and/or analytical effort must be performed by the proposing firm, and for Phase II, a minimum of one-half of the research and/or analytical effort must be performed by the proposing firm.

22. Can a Federal agency other than the one originating the Phase I award make the Phase II award under the same SBIR topic?

No. Awards of this type would be the result of an unsolicited proposal, and therefore, would be considered outside the scope of the SBIR Program.

23. What is the difference between SBIR solicitations and the SBIR Pre-Solicitation Announcement?

SBIR solicitations are specific Requests for Proposals released by the Federal agencies participating in the program which may result in the award of Phase I SBIR funding agreements.
SBIR Pre-Solicitation Announcements, released by SBA, contain pertinent data on SBIR solicitations that are about to be released by the participating Federal agencies.

24. Will SBA provide funds for SBIR commercialization?

No. Private sources of capital should be used. However, SBIR awardees are encouraged to seek information on all of the services that SBA makes available to the small business community.

25. What is the STTR Program?

STTR is a highly competitive three-phase program that reserves a specific percentage of Federal research and development funding for award to small businesses in partnership with nonprofit research institutions to move ideas from the laboratory to the marketplace, to foster high-tech economic development and to address the technological needs of the Federal Government.

26. What are the three phases of the STTR Program?

Phase I is the startup phase for the exploration of the scientific, technical, and commercial feasibility of an idea or technology. Awards are for periods of up to one year in amounts up to $100,000. Phase II is to expand Phase I results. During this period the R&D work is performed and the developer begins to consider commercialization potential. Awards are for periods of up to two years in amounts up to $500,000. Phase III is the period during which Phase II innovation moves from the laboratory into the marketplace. There is no STTR funding in this phase.

27. Must you be an established business when you propose?

No. However, you must be organized as a business at the time of award.

28. Who can propose?

Only small for-profit businesses can propose.

29. What is size criteria?

A small business concern with 500 or fewer employees including subsidiaries and/or affiliates. The size of the nonprofit collaborator is not relevant.

30. How are future rights to projects developed under STTR determined?

The small business concern and the research institution must develop a written agreement prior to a Phase I award. This agreement must be submitted to the awarding agency if requested.

31. Who are the Federal participants in the STTR Program?

The following five Federal departments and agencies are eligible to participate: Department of Defense Department of Energy National Aeronautics and Space Administration Department of Health and Human Services National Science Foundation.

32. Can I skip Phase I and begin at Phase II?

No. Phase II awards can only be awarded to firms having successfully completed Phase I at the same awarding agency.

33. Does SBA make any STTR awards?

No. The five participating Federal agencies have unilateral procurement authority.

34. Can you subcontract in STTR -- either party or both?

Yes. Either party may subcontract or they may jointly fund a subcontractor.

35. Can a small business concern participate in both SBIR and STTR simultaneously at the same or differing agencies?

Yes, but they may not perform the same or essentially similar work under more than one contract or grant. Collecting funds more than once for the same work is fraud.

36. Must a successful Phase I small business concern use the same institution in Phase II?

No. The small business concern can change research institutions in Phase II.

37. Will an unsolicited proposal be accepted in the STTR Program?

No. Proposals must respond to the solicitation as published by one or more of the participating agencies.

38. Who is the prime contractor or grantee?

The small business concern.

39. Must the small business concern and/or the research institution be located in the United States?

Yes. Both the small business concern and the institution must be on U.S. soil.

40. Can a Phase III follow-on contract for funding be made, without competition, to the firm that successfully completes Phase I and II.

Yes, the firm may be given a sole source contract in Phase III for further work or production.

41. What is the minimum percent breakout for small firms and institutions in conducting research?

Small business concerns must perform at least 40% and research institutions must perform at least 30% of the work.

42. Who resolves problems concerning STTR topics, awards, audits, etc.?

The agency issuing the Program Solicitation. SBA handles program policy for across the board uniformity, reporting to Congress and program oversight.

43. Where can I go for further information on how I get started or if there is other assistance available?

Information can be obtained from SBA Online Bulletin Board; call: 1-800-697-4636.

MODULE VI - NEGOTIATION

Negotiation

- **Strategy**
- **Skills/methods**
- **Preparation - team, mock sessions, resources**

Negotiation strategy and procedures are reviewed and discussed with emphasis on impact of various intellectual property assets on the strategy and process. Impact of personnel involved in the process is also discussed.

INTRODUCTION

One of the key considerations when entering into negotiations is the time to reach agreement. Failure to conclude an agreement in a timely manner can result in loss of market position, lapse in asset protection or loss of key alliances. Therefore, it is important to recognize or be aware of the factors that could have an impact on consummation of an agreement and hence, business success.

"Homework" is of little value if one cannot effectively negotiate the win-win relationship. Negotiation strategy, tactics, planning and practice are critical to ensure a fair and reasonable return for your asset. Effective negotiators can make a difference in the "bottom line" and possibly even the future of the enterprise. Examples of strategies, tactics and negotiating tips will be discussed in the following sections.

The objectives of a negotiation might be: 1) reach a wise agreement; 2) efficient completion of the negotiation process; 3) enhance (or not damage) relationships and 4) ensure an equitable long-term relationship.

Remember, negotiation is problem solving and finding a formula that maximizes goals of both parties. It is not: 1) making mutual sacrifice in order to secure agreement; 2) giving in; 3) trying to win an argument; or 4) gamesmanship.

Negotiation strategy begins with: 1) first contact with outside party; 2) first with discussion about a secondary matter understanding that in the end you let the other party get most of what it wants providing you leverage when you bring the main issue to the table; 3) includes establishing a face to face meeting at critical points in the negotiation process; 4) involves determining what the other party wants by listening and asking leading questions and 5) avoids preconceived views or assumptions that prevent one from " hearing" true intent of the other party. Always assume someone in the room is smarter than you.

The negotiation model starts with high or low for licensee and licensor based on: 1) an array of considerations or variables judged to impact royalty; 2) reasonable estimates or dollar valuations of the variables impacting royalty; and 3) weights indicating the relative worth of the variables impacting royalty. One is a quantity consideration; two is consideration of relative importance i.e. importance of a dollar spent on the variable; and three provides for similar quantities of dollars to have varying degrees of importance for the royalty calculation.

Structuring a license agreement is the basic premise when negotiating a license arrangement. The lower the risk, the higher the value. (Figure one)

Figure one. Relationship of risk and reward.

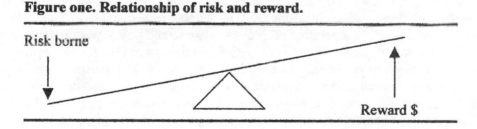

Good negotiators will apply as much creativity in structuring an agreement as possible. First, identify how each party perceives the risks involved and then, identify the factors, which are affected by the perceived risks. These factors include but are not limited to; market share, revenue, profitability, specific costs, production yields, manufacture, intellectual property protection and regulatory. Secondly, structure license payments to reflect allocation or assumption of risk. Factors varied might consist of lump sum, running royalty, equations, which compensate licensee based on achieving certain levels of performance (i.e. investment, development, revenue or units sold.)

Successful technology development requires completion of numerous activities and even after market introduction the product life varies. Cash flow of the project is related to the technology or product life cycle and is depicted in figure two. The cash flow variables are taken into account as the negotiation process progresses. Examples of items considered are; at what point in life cycle are negotiations taking place, how much upfront cash is required, or how should minimums be structured.

Figure two. Technology life cycle and cash flow.

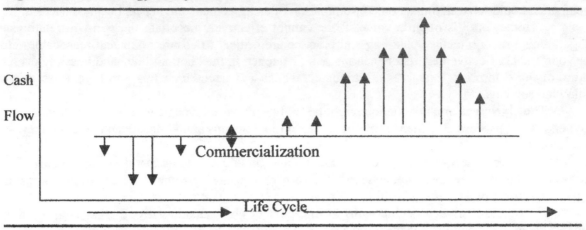

NEGOTIATION REQUIRMENTS

NEGOTIATOR TRAITS OR ATTRIBUTES

Negotiators are people with emotions, perceptions; feelings so reverse roles, i.e., put you in their shoes - what is important to them? Allow for "face saving" positions that facilitate compromise. Do not hide feelings and emotions and actively promote open communications. Position reflects interests. Try to understand the interests that lead to a given position and then focus attention on the interests. Tell the other party about your interests and then lead with reasoning, not conclusions.

A cooperative, reasonable person may need to become more assertive, confident and prudent in negotiations to be effective - especially in a confrontational negotiating situation. If this characteristic exists consider the following to improve one's bargaining performance: 1) avoid excess concentration on bottom line (spend time on goals and developing high expectations - a cooperative person worries about others peoples needs first); 2) develop specific alternative as a fallback; 3) get an agent and delegate negotiation task; 4) bargain on behalf of someone or something else - not yourself; 5) create an audience – if others are watching one tends to be more assertive; 6) say "you will have to do better than that because-----" – cooperative people are programmed to say yes to almost anything; 7) insist on commitments not just agreements – cooperative people tend to trust too much.

The opposite of the cooperative individual is the overly competitive person at the negotiation table and adjustments may be needed in this situation as well. Examples of personality considerations are: 1) think win –win; not just win; 2) ask more questions than you think you should-competitive people tend to sort out advantage and pounce –seek out what is important to others; 3) rely on standards – reasoned arguments work better than power plays; 4) hire a relationship manager – often prudent & wise; 5) be scrupulously reliable – keep your word; 6) don't haggle when you can negotiate – extended pursuit of each issue will result in leaving money on the table in complex negotiations; 7) identify issues fears and risks most important to other party and address interests and priorities in exchange for accommodations on things your want most; 8) package trade-offs using "if---then" e.g. if you give a and b we might consider concessions on issues x and y; and 9) acknowledge the other party – protect their self esteem; be respectful.

A negotiator or negotiation team must collect a much information as possible and convert this into as much competitive knowledge as possible, including the primary goals and interests of all

442

parties, product characteristics, market analysis, environment in which transaction is occurring, relevant legal principles and personalities or personal interest of people involved.

Besides core knowledge a good negotiator will posses' patience, tact, a sense of humor, ability to execute a clear rapid analysis of a situation and an ability and willingness to objectively consider other's ideas. The foregoing is further enhanced as a result of the negotiator's skill associated with identifying issues, communication and persuasion.

Personality issues can arise in any negotiation process. Sometimes one may think price is issue when in reality there are other concerns. Remember negotiators are people with emotions, perceptions, and feelings. A good negotiator is one who effectively separates people from a problem (some times referred to as positional bargaining), focuses on interests, not positions, generates alternatives before deciding what to do and insists that a result be based on an objective standard. Other traits a negotiator possess is the ability to: 1) reverse roles, i.e., put one's self in the other's shoes - what is important to them; 2) allow for "face saving" positions that facilitate compromise; 3) not hide feelings & emotions - actively promote open communication; and 4) not confuse personality with problem – avoid personal agendas & focus on problem; tell other party about your interests, then lead with your reasoning, not your conclusions; focus on where you want to be - not where you have been; and present options for mutual gain.

TIME FOR NEGOTIATION PROCESS

At the outset to increasing pace of negotiations consider; 1) using term sheets to establish a framework before contract language is exchanged and 2) establish a "closing date" for consensus in term sheet and takes it seriously.

The time to negotiate a license is highly variable and depends on such factors as: 1) different views on financial terms; 2) warranties, 3) representations, 4) liability, 5) sublicensing, 6) territory, 7) manufacturing, 8) grant backs, 9) delays within licensor's or licensees' organizations for legal reviews and internal approvals and 10) other key terms. Time to negotiate increases when terms are complex and contrary to what one might think the time is not highly correlated with type of inventions or technology.

There are also some who contend that philosophies and expectations between institutions involved in the negotiation process influence time to reach agreement. For example, there is a general view that agreement with academic and government organizations take longer. Some of the reason given are these institutions to use time as a negotiating tool, have little to loose from delay, sometimes are rather stringent about their expectations from the arrangement, and often have more "balls in air" than a company licensing office.

Examples of strategy and duration of negotiation are as follows: 1) range in time to negotiate a medical device license can be weeks to 2 years; 2) typically takes 3 to 6 months from initial interest to signed license; 3) progress depends on urgency felt on both sides (strong desire to complete can significantly reduce time; and 4) both sides might even agree to stay in same room until finished.

NEGOTIATION STRATEGY

A successful negotiator has knowledge of one side's primary goals and interests, the product, the other side, the environment in which the transaction is occurring, relevant legal principles, and the personalities and personal interest of the people involved. The attitude of a good negotiator is one of patience, tact, a sense of humor, clear rapid analysis, ability and willingness to objectively consider other's ideas. A certain amount of skill is required to identify issues, for communication and in persuasion.

Remember, the major objective is to reach agreement. You will have to live with each other for a long, long time after the agreement is in place. Breaking or terminating a contract is a lot harder than going into it - and only the lawyers get rich. The contract should end with good will intact.

Focus on provider strengths. How good is the technology? What is the strength of patent protection? What is or will be provider involvement? (What are provider's needs, expectations, and commitment?) At the same time you will need to understand the recipient's strengths that may be financial status, commitment, position in the market, whether they are to receive full or partial use of technology and if the company will mainly sublicense.

As one begins negotiations one must: be prepared, know the best alternative, understand what the bottom line/deal breaker is, determine maximal supportive value and assess what the other party wants. During the negotiating process focus on issues and interests, not positions or personnel, listen carefully; try not to develop a strong position; search for alternatives that provide mutual gains; be creative and open. The relationship is more important than the agreement; they will do business with this party again!

Know your walk away issues and limitations and do not be afraid to terminate the negotiations if dissatisfied with where they are leading you. Before you walk away consider other relationships you may have with the company and is the company the only leading candidate and what will happen if you begin again to seek a licensee, how much time and expense will be incurred and what are the odds of success.

There may be policy issues that affect the negotiations e.g.; due diligence, assignment or buyout; indemnification, compensation issues (cash, equity or a combination of the two); need for administrative or licensing office support that might in turn affect agreement terms; research support in lieu of cash; willingness to risk, for example, equity, up-front fee, milestones; extraneous factors - ongoing or other company relationships with your institution; favored "partner" – can you walk away?; publication restriction(s) or not; diligence commitments and governing law.

NEGOTIATION PLAN (DEVELOPMENT AND MARKETING PLANS)

The following are examples of items to be addressed in preliminary discussions as a relationship is considered. If intent is to identify key items that should be addressed to establish mutual understanding and which form the basis for future agreement. It is especially important that issues be identified that may require extended review and negotiation. In general, plans should provide licensor with a summary overview of the activities that licensee believes are necessary to bring a product to market. Report should be succinct and limited to 3 or 4 pages. An example of a development plan outline is presented in Module V, Exhibit E.

NEGOTIATION PROCESS

The negotiation process can be divided into three phases: analysis, planning and discussion. Steps within phases are; diagnose the situation, gather information, organize the information, think about it, identify possible people problems, identify conflicting interest(s) and assess known options.

Work for what you need – negotiate for what you want. To negotiate well, one must identify needs vs. wants. These may be indemnification release, no publication restriction, or certain diligence criteria. Plan and prepare. What is your situation and needs? First focus on needs and discuss financial terms last. Get everything else resolved first. Use a direct approach and understand marketplace economics; i.e. publications, industry norms, scientists, contacts.

Build a 5 to10 year pro-forma financial analysis, assess what kind of market share is anticipated and over what time period. Determine what other products the company has in the pipeline. Address what kinds of margins are expected in this market and what kind of market can be developed. Agree on the relative contribution of the licensed technology.

Look forward or look back to compare arrangements that have been enacted in the past, focus on mutual or common goals. Failure to address non-financial needs early in negotiation is likely to be counter-productive. Avoid positional bargaining. Use principled negotiation in which you separate the people from the problem, focus on interests, not positions, generate a variety of possibilities before deciding what to do and insist that the result be based on some objective standard. Focus on where you want to be - not where you have been and present options for mutual gain.

The objectives of negotiation are to arrive at a wise agreement, an efficient process to reach agreement and to enhance (or not damage) the relationship between the parties. Several suggestions for successful negotiation are: 1) use precise and definitive language; for example, avoid "we hope" or "we would prefer" or "it would be nice if"; 2) think about the negotiation site (a neutral site is usually best); 3) listen carefully and do not interrupt. Ask clarifying questions; write them down and ask when appropriate. Use silence if you wish more information; 4) find out as much as possible about the nature of the other party. Contact others who have been in negotiations with this party; 5) prepare an agenda. The agenda used is controlling the topics covered; 6) determine a settlement range, from least acceptable maximum supportable and 7) assemble a team (e.g. a leader, a recorder, an analyst, a technical consultant), define roles, and practice.

NEGOTIATION TACTICS

Following are some of the tactics that are employed in negotiation; limit authority, authority constraints limits other parties demands; change negotiators – sometimes done to compensate for poor position after initial negotiating round; introduce "add-ons" – usually best to introduce towards end of negotiations and may help reach settlement; make concessions, items should be traded rather than give; present threats, they will disrupt harmony, so usually used at the end as a last resort tactic, for example, threat of litigation; set deadlines, a self-imposed deadline can force you into a weak position; try to learn about the other parties deadlines; present the final offer, may not always be "final" but used to test other parties position resolve; it is usually better to have other party present the first offer; (If first, present logic and reasoning behind offer); and summarize, in writing, important agreed upon points as soon as possible and have other party verify.

Other tactics that are sometimes employed depending on the situation are; flinch - if told something is unacceptable flinch and grimace; the other party often backs off; reluctance - enthusiasm, once shown, puts a person at a disadvantage; constant trade-off. Never give a concession without getting one in return; always have multiple issues about which to bargain - if a person has only one issue and cannot win, there is nowhere else to go; do not offer to split difference - splitting difference gives away too much (Do so if the other side offers to split it.); keep boss behind scene, often they are too busy to know all & remain focused – once bosses agree there is no way out or change possible; take it or leave it, a negotiating ploy - test it immediately & broaden the issue (For example: ask how price might be affected by change in order size, quality, delivery practices, service, guarantees & so on. Test the other party by walking out or protesting to upper management or acting as if you did not hear offer and extend a counter offer.); simply ask for a better deal e.g., price, terms, quality, and service; be a bit unsettled e.g., show your resolve, act out of character and demonstrate commitment, glare, raise your voice, stamp your feet, and pound fist on table; leave yourself room e.g., aim higher with good reasoning, avoid aiming too high, may be good to "leave some benefits on table"; be stingy e.g., concede slowly and grudgingly and draw out negotiation by making small concessions; negotiate with limited authority e.g., saying "if it were up to me" can be useful - allows time to think, hold tight and get full story of opponents position, and provides opponent with face saving way to give in (can accept final position without looking like inadequate negotiator); bite your tongue - don't give out your motives, limitations & deadlines; use power of competition - do you
have choices?; call a time out e.g., use if headed for deadlock, gives other person opportunity to doubt and reconsider and you can come back with confirmation of your position or a concession; beware of quick deals - think before you talk; surprise e.g., sudden shift in method, argument or approach can make a point, unsettle opponent or force concession and may be mere change in tone of voice or a dramatic as flying off the handle; what are you going to do now - made bold move and wait for reaction - risky but can be effective (For example: if agreement is sent to you with a clause you dislike cross it out, sign & return - forces other party to accept amended agreement or reopen negotiation - often accepted; no pain, no gain e.g.; make other party work for every concession, people do not appreciate something for nothing, struggling will make other party likely to demand less and feel better about each concession won, and negotiator who gives freely will lose greatly; use budget tactic e.g., I want it, I like it and/or I can not afford it; nibble for extras e.g., seek small concessions - may be important to you and not other party; be patient e.g., do not expect instant acceptance of a new idea

445

and hold tight; do not corner your opponent e.g., leave room to save face, success is when everyone is satisfied, and no losers - only winners.

NEGOTIATION TIPS

PRE MEETING AND MEETING ETIQUETTE

In additions to the forgoing, several other suggested tactics and procedures are: use precise & definitive language (e.g. avoid "we hope" or "we would prefer" or "it would be nice if"); think about negotiation site - neutral site usually best; listen carefully! Do not interrupt! Ask clarifying questions (record & ask when appropriate); use silence if you want more information; find out as much as possible about the nature of the other party (contact others who have been in negotiations with this party); prepare agenda – use to control topics covered; and determine your settlement range - least acceptable to maximum supportable.

FIRST MEETING - TIPS

The first meeting set the stage for subsequent sessions. It is important to remember that first impressions are lasting impressions. The following are points to ascertain at the initial meeting:

- Who makes decision? – boss, lawyer, committee, etc. (Make that person a hero due to "wonderful business arrangement")
- What is decision-making process?
    1. How long does it take?
    2. Is a committee involved?
- Will tests/validation be needed before committing to license?
- Are products distributed WW?
- Have royalties, under similar circumstances been paid in past?
- Did inventor make money from that license? Who is/are other inventor(s)?
- Identify overall licensing conditions; e.g. upfront, minimum guarantee, exclusivity, etc.
    1. Observe if evidence of concern arises
    2. If so make sure they know you saw it (they're communicating)
    3. Acknowledge message was received by letting party know outcome will be mutually satisfactory
- Is there estimated marketing date if agreement signed before "end of next month"?
- What is estimated selling price for product?
- Is there a standard corporate formula for pricing the product?... standard margin?
- What is estimated number of units to be sold in 1st, 2nd years? ... In a typical year?
- Will help be needed to develop product? samples? drawings? consulting sessions?
- Important... do not resolve anything at first meeting ...rehearse phrase... "That sounds like a reasonable idea, I'll think it over."
- Do not get excited about rules that may thrown out (i.e.: a ridiculously low royalty rate as per corporate policy) ... rehearse the phrase... "That's not too encouraging, but I think we can come up with something that might make that work".
- Relax
    1. It's not over until the end
    2. You're allowed to change mind on certain issues
    3. Use your advisor as the bad guy
    4. Rehearse phrase... "gee that's something I just don't know anything about. I'll have to ask my advisor about that. I'll get back to you on it"
    5. Try not to use term "agent" or "attorney" (pretend mystery advisor is just a good friend who happens to give you advice from time to time)

- Use "we" when referring to success of project
  1. You're a team member throughout negotiation
  2. "We can make a very good agreement together ...I'm sure of that." (You're helping create a good business arrangement. Only hard nosed demands come from advisor who is looking out for your interest ... not from you.)
- Do not use term "contract" - refer only to an agreement
- Determine most compelling reason for interest in your project if not known (You will remind them of it later in negotiations)
- First meeting is only beginning of a process ...it's not a showdown! ...Be cool!

ROYALTY RATE NEGOTIATION

Royalty arrangements can be extremely complex. A number of issues that are important to keep in mind were presented in Module III.

Once all factors that may impact business terms of the license have been addressed the amount of compensation desired should be established. Since royalty is the most common form of compensation and generally is established so licensor shares in the income from product(s) based on some form of intellectual property, it is paramount that the rate be established based on the best valuation method(s). The negotiation outcome will reflect the time and effort spent to establish reasonable value along with various scenarios before the start of negotiations.

The author of a work (i.e., software, drawings, photographs, novels, etc.) owns, among other exclusive rights, the right to reproduce and market the work, as well as the right to create works derived from the original work, like movies from novels, or translating a novel from English to French, or software from a Macintosh to a Windows platform. The author may transfer all or a portion of these rights.

If the author is not marketing the work and has another person or company doing this, royalty payments will be the usual means of compensation to the author. A common example of royalty payments is where a publisher of a book pays to the author a percentage of the amount received on the sale of each copy of the book.

In the past, there was a limited universe of means to distribute works, and a limited number of works that could be derived from such works. Now, with communication technology evolving daily, the number of distribution means and derivations has greatly expanded. Furthermore, it is now extremely difficult, or impossible, to predict where future expansion will occur. However, the better these expansions can be predicted, the better an author will be able to protect his or her rights when transferred to a distributor.

Pre-negotiation

During the preparation for entering negotiations to arrive at agreement there is a need to: 1) be prepared – know what you want; 2) build your case – facts and authoritative data; 3) know your best alternative 4) what is the bottom line/deal breaker; 5) determine maximal supportive value; 6) assess other party wants; 7) strengthen relationships – trust and reciprocity; and 8) compare arrangements enacted in the past.

During Negotiation

Tactics a negotiator may follow or consider during the negotiation can be summarized as follows: 1) diagnose situation; 2) gather and organize information to establish sound intelligence; 3) establish acceptable alternatives and options; 4) identify conflicting interests; 5) strive for objective standards and decisions; 6) express feelings and emotions at appropriate times; 7) actively promote open communications; and 8) focus on the future not the past during the negotiation process.

Once preparation for discussion is completed there are numerous negotiation methods that affect the efficiency, effectiveness and ultimate success of the process. These items include but are not limited to: 1) focus on issues and interests, not positions or personnel; 2) listen carefully - try not to develop a strong position; 3) search for alternatives that provide mutual gains; 4) be creative & open; then relationship is more important than the agreement); 5) assert leverage – your alternatives and "walk away" criteria; 6) exchange information – elicit motivating factor(s) or subtle issues associated with other party e.g. desire to control or impress others or preserve self image; 7) try not to make opening or first offer – if you must seek best possible outcome and provide supporting reasons; 8) keep concessions small – large tradeoffs show extreme interest or weakness; 9) ask questions – what seems like budget issue might be timing; 10) get commitment – if oral, follow-up with written; 11) discuss financial terms last – not until everything else is resolved; and 12) use a direct approach.

For questions and answers related to negotiation see Exhibit A.

DIFFICULT ROYALTY RATE NEGOTIATION

Not all negotiations are simple or easy. In certain situations there is actually intent to create a negotiation impasse, "deal breaker" or raise issues that tend to result in conflict. In the event that issues do arise several tactics should be considered as one considers how to respond:

- Look beneath surface - typical conversation is not one but three conversations operating at same time:
    1. "What happened" conversation – each person's version of what took place; who said what, what should have happened, who is responsible, etc.
    2. "Feelings" conversation – how two people feel about situation
    3. "Identity" conversation - both parties are asking themselves "what does this situation say about me - about my competence & self-worth?'
- Begin conversation effectively - begin with fact and avoid personal points of view
- Look for contribution – not blame
    1. Blame is focused on judgment and punishment
    2. Contribution is focused on understanding – not punishment
    3. Problem solving works best when people examine contributions to problem
- Don't hide feelings
    1. Feelings creep in via tone of voice, & body language – so state them clearly
    2. Sharing emotions is not the same as getting emotional
    3. Sharing emotions can inspire cooperation
- Try hard to listen carefully
    1. Listening often leads to better understanding of other person's concerns
- Reframe other person's statement - if emotional statement, convert into a constructive one
- Be persistent
- Detection of false information hard if:
    1. Delivered over phone or electronically
    2. Little if any personal contact
    3. Presentation or public address format
- Barriers to arriving at right judgment
    1. Not enough time spent with presenter
        - First meeting or rushed encounter does not allow time for revealing personal traits; anxiety, nervousness
        -Lack of good expression may raise doubts about integrity
    2. Charm
        - One with charm may be liked instinctively providing the person an advantage.

448

- Charmers may have good integrity; however, harder to detect if they are not
- Be careful about intuition & integrity
  1. Cannot conclude that one who does not look you in eye is not truthful
  2. Nervousness does not always reflect lack of integrity
- Detecting lack of integrity
  1. No universal sign of deceit so establish a baseline
  2. Discuss non critical issues and note differences in mannerisms when critical items are discussed for which deceit may be attempted
- Expressions
  1. Fleeting expressions may suggest deceit
  2. May be seen on only one side of face
  3. Subtle, lasts longer than 5 seconds (genuine expressions flash on & off in about 1/4 of a second)
  4. May not be synchronized with the verbal statement
- Body movements
  1. Open or clenched hands (anger or denial)
  2. Shrugs, turning palm upward (I can't help it or what does it matter);
  3. Gestures (change in amount of gesturing, such as decrease, may indicate boredom or disinterest)
- Words
  1. Pauses are too long
  2. Many non-words e.g. ouch, ah etc.
  3. Partial words e.g. re-really, a-all
  4. Higher pitch to voice although often related to fear or anger and not deceit
  5. Good deceiver keeps voice quiet - it suggests truth
- Unethical tactics
  1. Threatening physical violence
  2. Lying about critical facts
  3. Not giving enough time to make a decision
- What if personal attacks are made against you?
  1. Party does not focus on issues but attempts to wear you down personally
  2. Don't play their game - don't respond to attacks
  3. Concentrate on the merits
- What to do in these situations?
  1. Immediately focus on the unethical behavior or problem, not unethical people
  2. Recognize the tactic
  3. If tactic used is good guy/bad guy routine, state the problem, but don't comment on other party's ethics.

EXHIBIT A – NEGOTIATION Q AND A
(Following is for information only. Seek legal or accounting advice for a specific situation)

1. In setting the "price" should one start with the highest proposal or start low?

Don't price high, hoping to get more than is actually sought - can scare other party due to the unreasonable request. Assume other party knows market. Best is not high - it is where one would like to be - so price within range of the market.

2. Is it prudent to make the 1st offer?

There may not be an advantage in going first or last - best is to know market, and make a reasonable proposal. This approach is more important when you go up against a more powerful party. Do not conclude money is the only issue. There may be other real issues .... what could they be?

For example, assume when negotiating a lease for a client/tenant the landlord does not want to give any more free rent, but you wanted to try to get more. They seemed adamant. However, you sensed that the real problem was that the agent for the landlord did not want to trouble himself with the number of changes throughout the lease that would have to be made in this case.

Figure out a way to make a minimal number of changes, visit the agent's office and show him how easy it would be to make the changes. The agent may accept the changes and you might save thousands of dollars. Here the issue really wasn't money, it was an administrative problem.

3. It is recommended that one should determine the true interests of each party. In addition it is suggested that one not rely on what the other party says their interests are because frequently there is much more going on than what meets the eyes or ears. How can you develop the skill of uncovering those unspoken interests?

One way is to generate a number of possible solutions before deciding what to do. Allow the parties to "brainstorm" in a pressure free environment. Sometimes you might want to use a facilitator for this purpose. But keep in mind that at the brainstorming meeting no decisions are being made. This session is to get people to communicate and not feel guarded about their thoughts.

4. Consider the following scenario: 1. The institution in question has a licensing staff who draft and negotiate, but do not sign, license agreements; 2. A practice of some licensing staff in this institution is to negotiate terms and conditions as would be normal — but with the notation, "THIS IS NOT AN OFFER." placed on all agreement drafts and related correspondence. As a licensee, what is your opinion regarding this approach and if you agree with it how would you enact or justify such an approach?

Organizations that do not allow negotiators to have the delegation of authority to negotiate, within proscribed and prescribed limits will come out second best, if they come out at all. The negotiator should be empowered and not just be a "figure head".

Consider a two-step approach, especially for a new licensing effort where there is little precedent. In the first step offer a Memorandum of Understanding (MOU) which is a bare license showing all the clause titles and only offer details to the preamble (the whereas), the grants clause, the compensation clauses, and perhaps one or two more if needed to get things started.

In the second step provide an essentially finished document that only needs dates and notice verification, and the sign-offs. Use of the MOU (which is not the agreement, but a memo to enable further negotiation and closure as expediently as possible. Make sure the preamble correctly identifies the players which might not be the immediate licensee but only a division of a larger entity who would stand behind the ultimate agreement, (it could be a bank). The real negotiation goes on in the MOU step, and step two can be the final act after the plot is known.

As a licensor, do not use the "NOT AN OFFER" qualification. It raises questions about creditability of the negotiator -- like the car salesman and the sales manager on the mezzanine scam.

Some negotiators sign every license draft sent out, indicating a willingness to be bound by the terms of the draft. It is not necessary to go that far, but one can send out drafts with the statement in a cover letter that one is prepared to sign the agreement as drafted.

Encountering situations in which one thinks they have reached agreement, only to have a licensee's negotiator relay that the boss wouldn't approve what had been agreed on. It's hard to take negotiations seriously after that.

5. You have a unique product and have been advised to start at the top of the industry with an offer of exclusivity, which you have done. You believe you have good legal advice but need good licensing information. What are the pros and cons of an attorney doing negotiations or yourself? How do you know fair value? What shouldn't you do?

Now is when you need some business info otherwise your negotiations are just guesses. Research on the market sizes and margins of similar type products will be useful in negotiating performance guarantee levels and royalty rates. Shoot for a performance guarantee that's about 25% of a conservative projection for sales—enough that it's "costly" if they just sit and pay the guarantee but not so high it isn't realistic to pay it if things go slower than they (and you) would like. If you are aiming for an exclusive license you can possibly get away with asking for more here but expect them to reduce any up-front amount and maybe even the royalty rate. Keep in mind that it's in their best interests to be wildly successful so all you are doing is guaranteeing that they have an active interest in getting there sooner rather than much later.

The higher the margins the higher the royalty percent of the wholesaling sales price should be. The net result should be you get about 20% of the "profits" after the overhead is factored in. In many cases this works out to a royalty of between 3 and 7% but this can vary tremendously. A quality window fashion treatment might even merit a 10-15% royalty under the right circumstances--especially if it's a high-end product. You'll need to evaluate your invention versus alternatives, etc. to figure this out. They are unlikely to tell you what margins they expect or what their overhead rate is so you'll need to do some research to get general industry info. The Robert Morris & Associates web site (www.rmahq.org) and/or their Annual Statement Studies Book (at large libraries with business collections), only $129 for non-members, are good places to start. They list over 500 SIC codes you can get average numbers for.

It won't hurt to have an attorney ASSIST with negotiations if that will make you more comfortable. If you can I highly recommend you be actively involved and focus the negotiations on the business deal (royalties, guarantees, up-front payment) and leave the "legal" technicalities to dotting i's and crossing t's till near the end. Where it gets interesting is in the in between areas such as who is responsible for pursuing patent infringers (my bias is to let them be responsible but with your cooperation and non-financial participation, then they get 95 or even 100% of any award/judgment). Some licensors even leave the issue out entirely on the grounds it can be decided if it ever comes up.

Know the whole industry size and major competitors. Know the product line and how well it fits with your product or product line. If your product would overrun a competitor's cash cow you should be prepared to explain its benefits. If it fills an obvious gap in a line and provides an edge over specific competitors your case will be further enhanced.

You should not expect to just make wild demands without being able to provide (or cite) evidence they will believe. You probably should not expect to close the deal in one session but if you are prepared and knowledgeable you shouldn't rule it out either. Regardless you'll likely want a "formal" signing of the final agreement documentation at a later date.

6. As an attorney involved in technology transfer, what constitutes the practice of law in representing private inventors in licensing their technology? Can a non-attorney/ non-law firm represent a private inventor in negotiating and structuring licensing agreements? At what point does this representation constitute or generate an attorney/client relationship?

Suggestions for a non-lawyer technology transfer agent:

a. specifically disclaim the practice of law,
b. do not discouraging the use of a lawyer by a business client,
c. avoid preparing contracts, especially ones involving great risk to clients and involving third parties, and/or
d. do not render opinions on matters involving the impact of the following on a business client's situation: case law, statutory law, civil procedures, contract law, court operations, etc.

Listen to lawyers and consider what they say but, unless they can site law on a point, do what you believe is right and advise clients to think for themselves. Many lawyers have less experience in intellectual property management and transfer than a professional technology transfer person so do not succumb to slavish adherence to opinions of lawyers. Recommend that lawyers be involved in final preparation of contracts, licenses, etc., particularly to assure the law of jurisdictions is correctly stated and observed. Not all technology transfer practice is the exclusive province of lawyers (or other trade unionists).

There is little difference between selling technology and selling real estate. Few would suggest that realtors "practice law" even though they fill out standard form contracts.

The job is negotiating terms, not resolving legal issues inherent in any contract. However, technology transfer people who are not representing employers can get into unauthorized practice trouble when legal issues arise, and they purport to resolve them without advice of counsel.

A patent agent with an active practice of writing patents for inventors helps sell inventions and provides advice on sales and marketing approaches. When an agreement is nearing conclusion the best licensing and litigation attorney should get involved to address legal questions. If activities fall outside a patent agent is licensed for, i.e. prosecuting patent applications with the USPTO, an attorney needs to get involved. A lawyer review of the final agreement is recommended.

Licensing is a different world than patent preparation and filing. Know what you want before you start negotiations. There is no conflict in employees negotiating and signing agreements for their employers but a real conflict exists when non-lawyers take on legal chores for individual inventors.

a. A license is a business document based in, and on the law. It is first and foremost a business document, and as such should be negotiated by business people in furtherance of their mutual business agenda.
b. Second, a license, as any new business venture, represents a risk. However, attorneys are paid to reduce risk as much as possible. Therefore one might conclude that a conflict exists between the business, risk-taking attitude required to market and license an invention, and the attitude of a risk averse attorney trying to do her/his best to protect the client.

Use marketing and business skills to create the business model for the license. You will need to learn a lot about the market and how things are done within it. Determine who has the most to gain, and who has the most to lose. Assess how the invention (or products based on the invention) will be sold, by whom, and in that chain identify the best link into which a license should be introduced. Sometimes this is a no brainier, and sometimes, as in the case where the invention creates a new market, or when the invention can be sold as either a component or finished system, things get a bit more complicated. Use business skills to open doors into companies who will potentially license the invention, and then make the business case for its adoption.

The forgoing seldom requires extensive legal knowledge but study the laws governing intellectual property and anti-trust (among other things), to make sure a business model is practical and based on law (principles of international exhaustion is one example).

When negotiating a license, discuss business needs and concerns with a fellow businessperson. Run the final draft of the license by an attorney and discuss key issues with he/she before and during the negotiation. They are there to make sure you don't get into trouble, and to inform you of risks. It is up to the businessperson to decide which risks to take.

453

Further evidence of the business lead with legal support is emphasized by the number of university technology transfer offices that substantially increased revenues once management of the technology transfer office changed from attorneys to business people. However, there are some already successful technology transfer offices being managed by very talented (business savvy) attorneys.

7. Equity deals in the licensing of technologies by universities to spin-offs have become more popular in many places. In Switzerland, we are just starting to do such deals. I am very interested to learn from you on how the following issues are handled and what experiences you have made with your policies:

A. Inventors usually get stock directly from the spin-off company as co-founders. If the university accepts stock as part of a licensing deal;

    a. do the shares fall under the normal revenue distribution scheme (inventors, institute, university, etc.) used for licensing revenues?

    b. does the university not give any shares to the inventor because he/she is compensated directly as a co-founder? If this is the case, what distribution scheme is applied instead?

B. What happens with the shares, i.e.;

    a. does the university keep them or are they held in trust by a third party due to concerns about conflict of interest issues, etc.?

    b. are the shares distributed (inventors, institute, university, etc.) or do you distribute the money after the shares have been sold?

    c. who decides about the exit strategy?

Try to follow these principles:

a. What the inventors did before the company formation was on behalf of the university. They share in the normal way (according to university policy at the time) in returns that arise from equity received by the university (in our case via the university research foundation). These shares usually are in the form of restricted stock which is not marketable. They then are held in trust by the foundation until they become unrestricted, or are swapped in a merger for unrestricted shares. At that point they are distributed. Otherwise, the foundation might incur fiduciary obligations for managing the inventors' investments. If the company is acquired and the stock is purchased, the cash received is distributed at that time.

b. What the inventors receive from the company in roles as consultants, founders, directors or officers really is for future contributions to the company, not what they have done in the past (which again is university-owned). Normally, they receive this equity compensation in the form of stock options, not stock grants. The options typically vest over time. Generally, we encourage inventors who will take an active role in companies to take fractional appointments or leaves of absence from the university. This greatly simplifies management of possible conflicts of interests.

c. Exit strategy is determined by the business plan in terms of what is acceptable to investors. In this case, the university (again via an autonomous research foundation in our case) is a de facto investor -- accepting shares instead of cash for at least partial payment under a license agreement. Investors need to agree with the exit strategy or they will not invest. In this case, no license will be granted, unless the deal makes sense to the university Obviously, the situation is much more complicated if shares are directly held by a university, and particularly by a public university. Having an outside, not for profit, foundation to hold shares and do the deals greatly simplifies matters and provides a measure of detachment of the university from liability issues that might arise in association with ownership or other involvement with a startup company. (Consult your legal advisor on such matters of course.)

Beware of complicating factors related to tax laws, Bayh-Dole law re: University inventions, export control laws regarding sensitive technology, as a few examples. What if an interested third party is not a national?

8. How should terms of the contract be negotiated?

Make sure someone on your team knows a thing or two about negotiations and has done their research on past cases with similar technologies/licenses.

Successful negotiation is both a science and art. The more that is known about the prospective party's needs, desires, business objectives, etc., etc. the better position one is in to negotiate. Also, you must have a very clear picture of your own expectations, bottom line requirements, etc., etc. We highly recommend that said negotiations be left on the hands of experts otherwise you risk killing any potential deal and/or leaving millions of dollars on the table.

MODULE VII - AGREEMENTS (LICENSES)

License

- **Checklist/Components**
- **Legal considerations**
- **Drafting do's and don'ts**
- **Boilerplate license review**
- **Boilerplate agreements**

Emphasis is on contractual terms and do's and don'ts depending on various situations. Discussion of strategy and negotiation of an intellectual asset license takes place. Examples of agreements or contracts are presented.

"Successful licensing requires presentation of an opportunity, not a threat."

INTRODUCTION

A license is an agreement not to assert licensor rights against the licensee in return for some consideration. For example, a license to a patent means the licensor will not assert patent rights against the licensee.

Universities usually consider the license granted as a "naked patent license"; i.e. the University is not the " source" of anything, but has agreed contractually with one or more parties not to assert University's patent rights against such parties for some consideration. The risk of liability from the act of entering a contract may exist, but it is significantly less than the relatively rare cases in which the University is actually the "Source".

When is licensing desirable or essential? A license is a good alternative for the licensor who does not want to get involved in the commercialization of an invention, idea, mark, or know-how. Hence, a domestic and/or international license offers alternatives to manufacturing and marketing an invention.

HISTORY

Licensing programs can generate good revenue for an organization. In recent years corporations, academic and government institutions are placing more emphasis on licensing activities.

For example, at IBM every IBM patent is available for licensing at rates from 1-5%. As of June '99 the company had 30K issued patents worldwide (Half from U.S.) and 26K patents pending. About forty-five percent (45%) of invention disclosures were not pursued, 35% of the invention disclosures were pursued for defensive purposes and 20% of the invention disclosures result in a patent application. Annual licensing revenue was $1.15 billion, all of which goes back into R&D. IBM receives about $1B from software licensing and about $800M from "hardware" licensing. It is important to remember that IBM is also usually the company with the most patents issued annually or very close to it.

In a survey completed in 1999 companies involved in licensing assets answered several questions. Results to the questions asked were as follows:

1. Which of the following approaches do you take when you compute royalty rates?

The responses show to compute royalty rate, the Market method for asset valuation was used most frequently, followed first by Income method and then by Excess earnings method. These percentages may be misleading since most participants indicate their choice of computation method depends on the type of the transaction, and a single method is seldom used independently. Special circumstances sometimes dictate special methods; for example when early technology is under consideration, the associated risks outweigh other issues in determining the royalty rate. In most cases, a combination of methods is used to ensure the validity of the numbers.

a. Market method

Dialog and Lexis-Nexus are two public databases cited the most. Knowledge Express (Data Quest, Corptech), Disclosure Inc., Recombinant Capital and SEC EDGAR are some other places, which are being used to gather information about prior transactions. A significant number of consultants have developed their own proprietary databases. Consultants also use their own prior deals, information gathered from publications such as *Les Nouvelles*, and *Licensing Economic Review*, from public news sources on the Internet and from competitive intelligence consulting agencies to gain insights on the subject. Sometimes the clients have researched the market values themselves prior to approaching the consultant.

Other points made by the participants: They use the market method when the other methods cannot be used for computing royalties. The amount of technology

459

contribution made by each party also plays a role in the determining the rate when using the market approach. The use of different types of market methods is even across all industries.

b. *Income Method*

Most consultants using an income method do so by using a method designed on their own. Usually the method is based partly on an established method such as the Discounted Cash Flow (DCF) analysis, or some accepted financial analysis principle.

Some examples of the methods in use: Value added approach - value could be added from newer technology that leads to savings/increased profits/entry into a new market; a percentage of savings experienced by the licensee/increased profits/net product sales are used for computing royalty rate in these situations. Net profit divided equitably based on the contribution of each party.

The true DCF method is used by 26% of the respondents, while 14% and 20% of respondents use Residual income and Postulated loss of income approach respectively. The 25% profit method is also one of the methods used, but it is employed only by a small number of survey respondents. There were no significant differences across industries.

2. *What percentage of transactions involved non-monetary consideration?*

A majority of respondents (34%) include this clause in 1 to 20% of agreements they put together. Only 8% of respondents put in the clause in 81-100% of the agreements they form. A significant number (24%), of respondents do not include a non-monetary consideration clause in any of their license agreements. It seems that the use and acceptance of this clause are dependent on the needs of the two parties.

Non-monetary considerations mentioned by the participants fall into three broad categories:

a. ***Sharing of present holdings:*** Equity. Cross licensing of existing technology, future improvements, or trade secrets. Trading of territorial rights. Extending visitation rights. Allowing use of facilities, raw material, or funding.
a. ***Sharing of work:*** Diligence, data gathering, marketing-promotion, development of channels-distribution, quids, tie-in contract work, providing technical assistance-consulting, patenting or defending the patent,
b. ***Clauses that guarantee specific performance:*** exclusivity, non-disclosure, non-competition, non-solicitation and covenants against reverse engineering, first refusal or option for licensing, marketing or manufacturing rights, marking obligations, requirement for prepaid royalties, upgrades of technology for a period of time. The pattern of including or excluding the clause is consistent across industries.

3. *What percentage of transactions involved transfer of know-how clauses in the agreement?*

The know-how clause is included in more than 80% of the agreements by a majority (47%) of the respondents which should not come as a surprise, but 6% of the respondents do not include this clause in agreements which is surprising.

The medical industry respondents include this clause more often than any other group does. One possibility considered was that the inclusion or exclusion of the clause could be dependent on the type of the industry. But, the five respondents who do not include the know-how clause are spread out across different industries (since these respondents represent clients from more than one industry, more than five industries are listed). The industries are Software, Hardware, Mechanical Engineering, Electrical Engineering, Chemical, Polymer, Food, Biotech, and Animal Health. Therefore, no conclusions could be drawn about the possible reasons for the practice of not including a know-how clause in the agreements.

4. What percentages of transactions involved transfer of show-how clauses in the agreement?

In contrast to the know-how clause, a majority of respondents (38%) do not include a show-how clause in the agreements. There is a clustering at the two extremities, this shows that the practitioners either routinely include this clause in the agreement or they do not. We can assume that the negotiation for the transfer of show-how is dependent on the characteristics of individual deals. There are no significant differences in the practices across industries.

5. What do you use for royalty calculation?

Net income from sales is the most common percentage basis method used to set the royalty rate. Gross sales are the second metric used most often as a base, which is surprising given the fact there is a known deficiency (the possibility of fraud by the licensee) in using this method. Some consultants indicated they base the calculation on a per part basis, which is a method that benefits both the licensor and the licensee. It helps the licensor because it bypasses the risks of fraud and deception by the licensee, which are possible when sales or income are used as a base; and it allows the licensee to include the license royalty payments in their COGS. A percentage of the savings experienced by the licensee, or a percentage of the added income contributed by the technology, $/ton of the product with an escalation provision using an appropriate index are some other Income methods in practice.

The most prevalent method of audit is an annual audit. Even though the respondents have a right to audit, they do so only when there is non-performance by the licensee or there is some other dispute. One respondent always audits unless the agreement is a flat dollar per year fee agreement.

Different audit practices reported: perform spot audits, audit one licensee per year, audit the licensee every three to five years, have audits performed by third party accountants (going back two years), use the licensee's annual audit data (generated by the outside auditors). No significant variation is observed across industries for either the type of percentage basis method use, or the audit interval.

6. What is the average time span in number of years for a license?

The most common response to this query was "the life of the patent", followed by decreasing responses for decreasing number of years. An interesting observation is that the number of responses for the <5year category does not remain consistent across industries. One would expect that this number would vary between the high-tech and low-tech industries, high tech having a larger number of responses. There is some indication this might be true since the Chemical and Consumer industries show no agreements in this category. The number of responses in the Software category is similar to the number of responses other industries. The reason for this could be that end-user agreements are often perpetual, and usually form a large portion of software agreements.

Some insights: This issue is usually resolved based on the useful life of the subject matter. The Trade Secret/Know-how agreements can be for a longer term (i.e. perpetual) than patent life. Agreements might contain a condition that there will be relief from royalties upon expiration of a patent, only if the licensee is faced with competition, otherwise the know-how license would yield royalties for a much longer period.

7. How soon after/before a patent grant do you/your clients normally enter into a license agreement?

The analysis indicates that the license agreement is made when the opportunity is right and the terms are agreeable. The time when licensors enter into the agreement depends on the product and the technology. It varies from "shortly after filing" to "40 years after the patent issue."

Some comments: Risk for grant before issue – therefore, if before issue, no royalties are paid until issuance. License, as soon after the first patent office action or allowance as possible during patent prosecution if possible, but not before disclosure. Depends on various factors such as infringement claims made by others and whether cross licensing is being considered. Try to license before the patent grant to shift the cost of patenting to the licensee. Do it before if you can use the existing base patents on the technology. License after the patent grant: when it is an early technology and there is limited evidence of need. It usually takes 3 to 5 years to develop the market for a technology.

8. In your estimation, how often do the licensees demand use of an escrow account to guarantee performance from the licensor?

Note: the qualitative answers were converted to percentages as follows: Never = 0%, Seldom/rarely = 1-20%, Often = 21-49%, Almost always = 50-99%, Always = 100%

The responses were similar across industries. Two things to note were that the percentages in the software industry were no higher than the rest, and there were no responses, which indicate that this clause is always included in Consumer and Medical industries. It was concluded that the practice of using escrow accounts is relatively new and may become readily accepted in coming years.

9. The breakdown of your clientele is...?

Corporations form the main client type of the respondents (39%), followed by independent inventors (26%) and then by universities (21%). Other types of clients which constituted 11% of the total responses, included Venture Capitalists, Start-ups, Federal and nonprofit research laboratories, government agencies, and private research institutes. Across industries, there was no significant difference in the representation. The other industry category included participants from:

Aerospace	Agriculture
Atmospheric science	Audio-computer, Internet, speech recognition, telephony
Automotive	Energy related industries e.g. nuclear & fossil utilities
Environmental	Household chemicals
Information & microelectronics	Materials and material processing
Microwave heating	Mineral and Earth sciences
Oceanography	Oil and Gas
Optical	Optical Fibers
Petroleum	Polymers
Road building	Telecommunications
Textile	Waste Recycling

The total number of responses for the consumer goods industry was low, so the answers in this category may not be a true representation of the industry. Medical Industry category includes participants from Pharmaceuticals, Medical Devices, and Biotechnology fields.

OVERVIEW

An agreement (contract) is a form of promise that is legally enforceable. Such promises are essential to trade and commerce. Every day people in business make and receive commitments.

Agreements are expressions of those commitments. They provide the basis for planning. Companies enter agreements to lease space, purchase parts, deliver services on time, hire key people, transport goods, and so on.

Contracts are central to building a business, any business. They give managers a level of certainty upon which to proceed. In a business context, the primary purpose of contracts is to protect the commercially reasonable expectations of the parties involved.

All promises are not legally enforceable. Only some are. To rise to the level of being an agreement (contract), a promise must meet certain requirements. Building a business is easier when managers understand those requirements and are comfortable with them. Such understanding includes an appreciation of the ramifications of a breach or default under a contract -- the source of much litigation.

When undertaking the responsibility for licensing assets several fundamental tactics and interests exist, including but not limited to: 1) emphasis on reduced "time to market"; 2) cost containment; 3) development expenses especially for biological technology requiring regulatory approval e.g. nearly $330M to reach market with a pharmaceutical; 4) profit margins are declining (price hikes are out); 5) elimination of me-too's; 6) need for steady source of novel chemistry; 7) fewer arrangements and more complex or broader; 8) more collaboration or cooperation (partner) - not "hand off"; 9) commercial terms are more complicated – share more risk and upside; 10) all parties must offer other contributions e.g. $ milestones, know-how, expertise, instrumentation; 11) need to act fast and be flexible; 12) requirement for creative entrepreneurial deals; 13) must communicate and avoid taking a position; 14) need to understand cross cultural differences; and 15) enact a win-win arrangement.

Technology licensing is becoming more complex as a result of stacked royalties, consolidation of multiple technologies in a product, combination products and the resultant need for cross licensing, and "fragmented" technology all of which contribute to the concern that the licensing process is or will become slow and/or inefficient.

In some cases, one will be seeking what is called profitable licensing. In this case, the best strategy to shorten time to market, for most inventions, is to share part or all of the commercialization process and risks with others who already have skills and resources in place. This requires that one: develop valuable intellectual property, license successfully and sustain a lasting business relationship. Building valuable intellectual property may require one to conduct some minimum development and to secure some protection. Successful licensing requires: effective protection, proper licensor-licensee match, skilled negotiation of the license, a profitable business relationship, focus on meeting each others' needs, continued follow-up and provisions for orderly termination of a license. In order to effectively achieve these objectives one must: establish sound strategy and transition points e.g. concept, prototype and production; set or "freeze" ideal prototype specifications; place business interests ahead of love for technology; identify product champion in firm; reduce risks outsiders perceive e.g. know market, production process, and financial needs; and emphasize overall business management.

There are several items that are sometimes more challenging or of more importance to the licensing team including but not limited to the following. 1) unrelated fees, e.g. upfront or milestone payments; 2) due diligence criteria; 3) ownership e.g. multiple, inventor only, restricted or limited rights, sublicense right, or future rights; 4) patent counsel e.g. accountability, responsiveness, or fee limit; 5) flexibility and ability to renegotiate terms if necessary; 6) trend awareness e.g. global business environment, corporate spin-outs; and 7) theft e.g. taking technology out "back door".

LEGAL

Although courts throughout the country vary somewhat in the specific language they use to define an agreement/contract, any definition would typically incorporate the following essential elements: An agreement/contract is: "One or more promises with regard to which the law imposes a duty to perform and for the breach of which the law provides a remedy."

The promise that provides the basic element of a given agreement typically starts as an offer or proposal to do something or to refrain from doing something. The offer or proposal may be in writing or it may be made orally. In either case, it must reflect intent to enter into and become bound by an agreement/contract; it must be more than mere discussion about possible arrangements.

In the U.S.A. the law of contracts is derived from court decisions, generally referred to as common law, and statutes, i.e., laws passed by legislatures. The primary statutory reference on contracts is the U.C.C. (Uniform Commercial Code), which has been adopted in practically all jurisdictions. The U.C.C. was created to bring about a degree of uniformity among American jurisdictions.

The first version of the U.C.C. was published in 1951; there have been several revisions since then. While different states have adopted different versions and added their own variations, the general principles and concepts of the U.C.C. are similar from state to state. The U.C.C. covers the sale of goods and a number of other topics including promissory notes and other commercial paper, bills of lading, and personal property secured transactions -- that is, the granting of interest in personal property to secure payment of a debt.

Copyright

Copyright and patents originate from Article 1, Section 8, Clause 8, of the constitution: "the congress shall have power to promote the progress of science and useful arts by securing for limited times to authors and inventors the exclusive right to their respective writings and discoveries." Further enactment of this provision was attained through passage of the 1976 Copyright Act in 1976.

Copyright notice is not necessary but the practical benefit is that notice facilitates recovery of damages and assists licensor in proving willful infringement possibly allowing pursuit of criminal and civil damages.

A copyright holder may retain right to copy, adapt, distribute for sale or otherwise or display copyrighted work; however, in more complex license situations one may give limited grant of rights, e.g. source code vs. object code; applicable notices; limited copying; government mandated disclosure requirements; obligation not to remove mandated legends; requirement to report third party misappropriation; license termination conditions; installation of metering software and/or license to use.

An example of copyright rejection is database vendors who copy the copy the white pages of a telephone directory. They are not entitled to copyright; "output contains only facts and arrangement in alphabetical order which are not "creative" enough.

Modifications (issues) that are considered when determining copyright; 1) if allowed vendor may not be able to provide/meet maintenance requirements; 2) if when applying ownership test "Does modification use the patented/licensed invention?" results in yes; and 3) leads to derivative work (copyright law grants copyright holder right to make a derivative work which can be licensed or assigned. (Exhibits D, E and F and Addendum III)

Creator of derivative work has only the rights granted by licensor but may modify for their own use. Court cases involving product liability demonstrate the competing interest of providing compensation to injured plaintiffs versus preserving freedom of speech and ideas.

In "Winter vs. Putnam" a mushroom enthusiast became ill from picking and eating mushrooms after relying on information published in a book the court found: "although there is always some appeal to the involuntary spreading of costs of injuries in any area the cost in any comprehensive cost/benefit analysis would be quite different were strict liability concepts applied to words and ideas." "threat of liability without fault (financial responsibility for our words and ideas in the absence of fault or a special undertaking or responsibility) could seriously inhibit those who wish to share thoughts and theories".

In "Walter vs. Bauer" - a student was injured while doing science project described in textbook and the court ruled: "a book is not product for purposes of product liability law". In "Lewin vs. McCreight" the court concluded, "publisher had no duty to warn of defective ideas" in a book published by it, in view of the "weighty societal interest in free access to ideas".

Products liability law applies to writings but not necessarily to copyrightable works containing the expression of ideas. Charts which graphically depict geographic features or instrument approach information for airplanes are "products" for purposes of product liability law.

Courts hold in favor of free expression of ideas but writings such as charts which fail to demonstrate "free" expression of ideas and had no competing constitutional or societal costs are products subject to product liability; not original works of authorship.

Patent

Patent must teach preferred method of use. Therefore, it describes invention and is a legal instrument by which the government grants right to patentee, which can be licensed, to another. A patent as an instructional document published by the government should be considered like a copyrightable work; in other words a "how to book".

Contention is that a patent licensor's liability is limited since: a) a patent contract authorizes use of an alleged patent; b) the product sold is usually not sold under trade name of licensor; and c) the public is not relying on licensor so as long as public does not rely on licensor for a product produced from rights granted; patent licensor generally falls outside scope of product liability law and further "safety" is achieved through well written, warrant disclaimers, non-use of names and hold-harmless/indemnification clauses.

Trademark

Trademark licensors face full exposure under product liability law. Academic institutions must evaluate transfer mechanisms in light of product liability law. Remember courts favor free expression of thoughts and ideas. The model uniform product liability act of 1979 also excludes intellectual property not introduced into the stream of commerce but only the products made available to the public from a licensee. Various states may have laws as well to provide protection. However, licenses that involve greater commitment by licensor to produce tangible products or in which reliance is placed upon licensor for the end product may result in potential for product liability, e.g., a) contract with licensee to perform additional product development; b) lends name for use in final product; c) starts a new company and participates in development of the final product; and d) license of software may be considered direct release of new product to end users.

Performance warranties may exclude modifications and require one to escrow fully annotated source code of most current version, complete description of program logic, and copy of program schematic. Statutes are only useful if the law is enforced. Some countries including, but not limited to, Taiwan, Brazil and India do little if anything to enforce intellectual property laws.

MINIMIZE LEGAL TROUBLES

Agreements are entered into to provide a reasonable degree of certainty to people building businesses. Executives and managers depend on contracts as they make and execute plans. Because contracts are so common and so essential, a given business has a competitive advantage if it is "good at contracts." An owner or management team good at contracts will minimize legal troubles for all the parties in the following ways:

1. *Identify the business objectives to be achieved by a given contract.* In advance of entering into negotiations, determine your specific interest. For example, if it is to be a contract for the sale of goods, are they to meet certain specifications? If so, whose specs? Are the goods to conform to models or samples and, if so, what deviations are permitted? What warranties and representations are required from the seller or, conversely, what warranties or representations will the purchaser permit the seller to disclaim, such as the warranty of merchantability or warranty of fitness for a particular purpose?

2. *Be clear about the details.* Many contract disputes are about the obvious: Who the parties are, the subject matter of the contract, the price or consideration, and the time for performance. The certainty sought via contracts is undercut when these subjects are not clearly and completely spelled out for all to see.

3. *Avoid oral contracts for anything vital.* Written documents reduce misunderstanding. While oral contracts can be enforceable, their use should be limited. No communication, written or oral, is as precise as it should be, at least from the perspective of an attorney representing a business in a contract dispute. But oral communication adds extra challenges since it is seldom complete and the parties often attach different meanings to the limited words that were used. Then, over time, witnesses disappear, memories falter and the differences may increase. Except in the simplest of circumstances, it is difficult to justify anything but a written contract.

4. *Read and understand before you sign.* This requirement may seem so obvious that its inclusion here is unnecessary, but failure to read and understand is a major cause of contract disputes. Further, most people have a tendency to read what they want the words to say, rather than what they actually say. Many contracts are not that simple and they are not easily read and understood, but this does not excuse failure to take the time to read with care. Defenses to enforcement of a contract based upon ambiguity or failure of the language to state what the parties intended are fairly weak. Occasionally such defenses might succeed, but the probabilities are low.

5. *Monitor contract compliance as you go along. Take action.* The sooner a potential problem is spotted the better. Early warning and prompt action is the best way to keep small issues small. This goes for meeting your own contractual obligations and for insuring that people owing you performance on a promise do what they are supposed to do. Once a small issue heats up into a default, managers usually lose some control over the process and their own destiny in the matter.

6. *Use contract amendments sparingly.* While anything (price, delivery date, specifications, etc.) might be addressed by an amendment to a contract, to become binding any amendment requires the agreement of the other party. Circumstances can change and the other party may refuse to make an amendment or will use it as an opportunity to extract a concession. In addition, except under the U.C.C., an amendment probably must itself be supported by adequate consideration.

7. *Use standard forms with care -- your own and those of other parties.* Often, in practice, one size does not fit all situations equally well. Significant transactions require well-conceived contracts. Standard forms should not be used for non-standard or complex matters.

Agreements are vital tools in building a business. They are, for example, fundamental to risk management in which business risks are passed off to other parties. However, agreements must be used well. Emerging companies each year as a result of broken promises and the ensuing agreement/contract disputes that are frequently the direct result of under-managed agreement-making processes wastes millions upon millions of dollars.

Agreements facilitate planning and the execution of plans. They help make sure one gets what one thinks they are getting. Without well thought out and well defined agreements, business builders would have to manage by hope -- a difficult task in these competitive times. Agreements are central to building a business; they deserve the same depth of attention given to the plans they support.

AGREEMENT/CONTRACT CONSIDERATIONS

INTELLECTUAL PROPERTY MANAGEMENT - AGREEMENTS

There are a variety of agreements that are involved in intellectual property management. The particular agreement depends on the technology, type of transfer, parties involved, and interests of the parties involved in the commercialization or transfer. A synopsis of the types of agreements and parties involved are presented in table one.

AGREEMENT TERMS

There is no magic involved in establishing the terms of an agreement. Standard economic and financial techniques are used many of which are the same tools as used for analysis of lease/buy decisions. It is important to understand economic issues from perspective of both buyer and seller; licensors and licensees. A significant amount of analytical evaluation will be associated with business terms whereas legal issues may also arise with respect to other agreement terms. Establishing acceptable terms involves taking into account all parts of the agreement and understanding the impact of language included in an agreement.

STRUCTURING A LICENSE AGREEMENT

Use creativity in structuring license agreement. Identify how each party perceives involved risks and factors which are affected by perceived risks, such as market share, revenue, profitability, particular costs and production yields.

Structure License Payments to Reflect Allocation/Assumption of Risk

Decide on lump sums, running royalty, equations, which compensate licensee based on achievements of certain levels of performance (i.e. cost, revenues or profit based) and other innovated compensation structures including equity or a combination of equity and cash.

As compensation and due diligence criteria are established one must be aware of and establish the appropriate model for market entry and resultant cash flow. An example of a technology life cycle and projected cash flow is presented in figure one.

Table one. Agreement types.

$ Source	R&D	Agreement considerations
Government	Screening Grants	MTA/bailment University rights to discoveries (Bayh Dole, 1984) Protection plan to coincide with publication schedule
Testing	"Work for hire"	Unique facilities/capabilities at University Preexisting established methodology Publication rights Full compensation for use of public resources*
Private	Sponsored Research Development Joint development	Data and discovery ownership Protection responsibility Publication Rights Business rights – time limitations
Sector	Clinical trials	Use of public resources Rights to outcome, options, license, joint venture Confidentiality/NDA Human rights MTA/bailment
Foundations	Grants	Ownership rights Revenue share MTA/bailment NDA

* Public resources cannot be used for private gain

Figure one. Technology life cycle and cash flow of a project.

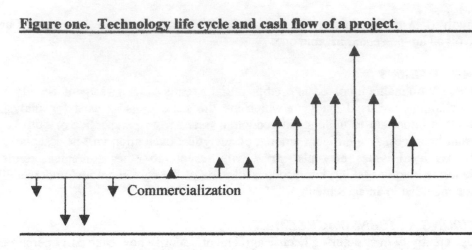

Commercialization

Project cash flow variables that will be taken into account is establishing license terms well depend on the stage of development or market activity. For example, at what point in life cycle are negotiations taking place? How much upfront cash is required? How should minimums be structured? What is the value of equity for the specific asset?

License Payments

Figure two depicts some of the factors to consider as one decides how to structure license terms. If a licensee wants to reduce risk or liability, there may be a desire to accept compensation as a lump sum payment for the asset. On the other hand, in order to share in the market return to the licensee, a licensor may prefer a running royalty, milestones fees and/or license maintenance fees.

Figure two. Type of compensation based on asset.

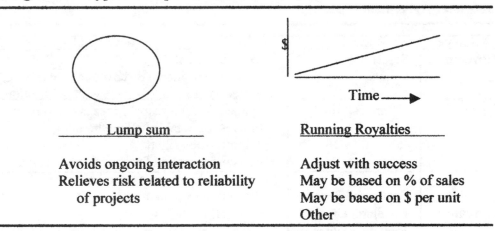

Time ⟶

Lump sum	Running Royalties
Avoids ongoing interaction	Adjust with success
Relieves risk related to reliability	May be based on % of sales
of projects	May be based on $ per unit
	Other

Customs may dictate form of royalty payments. Agreements do not have to fail as a result of monetary issues. Creative use of payments can often overcome potential monetary issues.

Balance Risk

Early stage technology may have a relatively low value when initially evaluated but this can change rapidly overtime. A rigorous valuation e.g. the risk adjusted net present value approach, would yield a much higher upfront price than most start-ups would pay.

Seek a low up-front payment but also obtain a share in the valuation increase as key development hurdles are progressively met. For example, if development milestone is to find a corporate partner, obtain a percentage of the arrangement.

It is important to express terms as percentage rather than as a fixed dollar amount since value is uncertain. It is an accepted theory of licensing, all the way up to patent infringement litigation, that the licensor should receive 25% of the value from selling products based on the technology licensed. The simplest way to do this would be for the licensor to receive a 25% equity stake in the licensee. With appropriate anti-dilution provisions, one can accept equity and waive all other financial components of the deal. Most license arrangements are a combination of equity, future value and shares of future arrangements. Structure the arrangement to balance risk (table two).

Table two. Risk considerations.

KNOWNS	PARTIAL KNOWNS	UNKNOWNS
Litigation is expensive	Likelihood of being in litigation	Outcome of litigation
Potential size of market	Superiority over prior methods market	Superiority over future methods share to be captured
Future cash flows are intended to justify current investment	Time to get product to market	Regulatory approval

LICENSE, AGREEMENT, AND CONTRACT TERMS

All preparation leads to consummation of an agreement. After all of the effort, it is essential that the agreement reflect the desires of the parties and is clear and precise. Language translation or work interpretation, customs, and ambiguity can easily affect the validity of an agreement. Failure to address all necessary and critical sections of an agreement can negate or modify all of the effort that was placed in getting to the point of drafting the agreement.

DRAFTING TIPS
Drafting do's and don'ts are subject to personal preference, in some cases, but there are certain statutory definitions that may not always correspond to personal interpretation of words or phrases. This is especially true if an international agreement is under consideration.

CHECKLIST AND CONTRACT COMPONENTS
In order to assure that all aspects of an agreement are taken into consideration as the drafting progresses, it is useful to have a checklist from which to select contract terms.

A contract checklist may contain the following items: parties and background, definitions, grant of rights, special aspects concerning patents, special aspects concerning trade secrets, special aspects concerning confidential information, special aspects concerning copyright, special aspects concerning trademarks, know-how and technical assistance, technical services and assistance, supply of raw materials, components, spare parts, equipment, etc., exploitation of licensed technology, the marketing phase, management services, monetary considerations, settlement of payment, release for past infringements, sublicensing and subcontracting, acceptance tests, warranties of quality, acknowledgement of validity, admission of infringement, enforcement of licensed patent, warranties of title, infringement, limitation of liability of licensor, indemnity, permits, insurance, safety measures, environmental matters, use of other party's name in promotions, term, termination, post termination, impossibility of performance - force majeure, settlement of disputes – arbitration, assignment, agency and similar relationships, notices, and miscellaneous clauses.

Be careful with form licenses unless they have been updated recently. New statutes are enacted over time, laws change, statute interpretation changes and business changes e.g. advent of e-commerce, importance and frequency of mergers and acquisitions, asset consolidation, etc. It may be necessary to rethink your approach to licensing, revisit and critically analyze the current form license and/or improve analytical skills and procedures.

The following are examples of perceptions and language in a software agreement that may seriously affect the validity and value of an agreement. Although focus is on software the examples can be applied to any license agreement.

Perception 1: When it is unclear what rights were exactly licensed, the interpretation that reserves the most rights for the licensor controls. However, the question is: Whose interpretation? – Licensor's, Licensee's or possibly third Party's interpretation – controls?

For example, new software has been developed that improves display of images and permits display of high-resolution motion pictures. A potential licensee is a media company that will use it to display motion pictures in theaters. A simple license with the media company has been enacted.

The grants clause reads, "Licensor grants to licensee a non exclusive license to use the software for the improved exhibition of motion pictures" in return for an upfront, paid-up royalty. An additional covenant is; "This is the entire agreement between the parties regarding the software and all prior representation, etc. have been merged into this document and are thus superseded in totality by this agreement."

While terms "use" and "exhibition" are undefined the Licensor believed the contract with ambiguous terms can work for licensor's benefit since it affords licensor some "wiggle" room and licensor believed that Licensors are always given the benefit of the doubt in a dispute over contract language.

After enactment of the agreement movies displayed in a theater with the software is a big success. However, licensor discovers that licensee released motion pictures also on video cassette and DVD formats along with the software and that the licensee also plans to distribute motion pictures over the Internet while utilizing the software

Licensee contends the term " exhibition" is not restricted to any particular venue and that the Licensor's more restrictive interpretation does not control. A reasonable interpretation of the term would permit the exhibition of motion pictures using the software in any venue and through any media.

On the other hand, Licensor continues to believe; 1) Licensee's preliminary discussions were related only to theater exhibition; 2) "wiggle" room exists and ambiguous terms will be read in Licensor's favor and 3) if not read in Licensor's favor court at least will be neutral and read ambiguous terms not necessarily in favor of anyone.

In reality, the Licensor's logic is based on tradition, not current case law, and ambiguous terms are now more likely to be read against the Licensor and are more likely to benefit Licensee than Licensor.

Historically, authors or licensors were favored because the court's logic was: Licensors are authors who are often impecunious, Licensees are often large business organizations and copyright law was enacted to nurture creativity by benefiting authors. See: U.S. Constitution, Article 1 Section 8: The congress shall have power... "to promote the progress of science... by securing for limited times to authors.... the exclusive right to their...writings." Therefore, this author favoritism resulted in the courts holding that: 1) only the "clearest language" will "divest authors from the fruits of their labors"; contract ambiguities are to be resolved in licensor's favor and 3) if the specific application of right is not specifically authorized, the right remains with the Licensor.

Today the new court recognition is as follows: "Intersection of copyright and contract law"...is "an area of law that is not yet well developed." Sun Microsystems Inc. V. Microsoft Corp., 51 USPQ2d 1825, 1830 (9th Cir. Aug. 23, 1999). Hence, many courts are now reevaluating prior practices or biases. The court's analysis now examines an agreement to ascertain intentions and this search for intent is within the "four corners" of the agreement. The advantage the Licensor and Licensee have is that intentions can be merged in a single document.

Failure to clearly expressed intent within the contract can result different views regarding undisclosed intent or alternatively, parties may have had no intent because new application of old technology didn't exist at the time of negotiations and agreement execution. Examples are presented in table three.

Table three. New applications forcing reevaluation of old licenses.

License grant	New Forcing Technology
Dramatic performance rights	Motion pictures
Motion picture rights	Sound motion pictures
Sound motion picture rights	Television
Magazine or newspaper publication rights	Internet distribution

Today's courts apply the following procedure to resolve disputes associated with missing intent. Courts identify the ambiguous terms(s) in grants clause and then take one of two different approaches to resolve ambiguity disputes. The definition for ambiguous term is: "capable of more than one reasonable interpretation".

The first approach is the strict construction approach: License grant to include only uses that fall within the unambiguous core. The second is the reasonable construction approach: any use that could be said to fall within any one of all the reasonable meanings of the ambiguous term is part of the grant.

Currently the preferred analytical approach is the second or reasonable construction approach. The logic for this preference is based on the following:

1. Courts are asked to determine what is reasonable and what is unreasonable;
2. Both parties agreed to the extended meaning of the term when they agreed to insert it into the document; and
3. Both parties had an opportunity to add restrictive language to narrow the interpretation but failed to do so.

If one applies this background to the situation herein "What are the reasonable limits of the term "exhibition"? Definitions that might be set forth are:

1. "Exhibition? Not limited to any method or means or technology;
2. Exhibition: " a display or show" Oxford American dictionary (1980); or
3. Motion picture: " a story recorded on film" Oxford American dictionary (1980): or " a series of pictures projected on a screen" Merriam Webster's dictionary (2000)

REASONABLE CONSTRUCTION

Video cassettes Theaters DVD Internet others

STRICT READING CORE

There are several means to resolve ambiguity issues including; 1) focus on wording in the grants clause, 2) building support for one's interpretation elsewhere in the agreement; and 3) incorporation of a reservation of rights clause.

In the grants, clause use terms that are: 1) not inherently ambiguous (for example, the term "use" by itself is inherently dangerous); 2) common or well know; do not rely on "terms of art"; 3) well defined; and 4) the same and consistent throughout grants clause and agreement.

Other sites in the agreement where support for an interpretation can be built are to state the specific intent of the license grant either as: a representation in the contract body or in the recitals clause or make sure the final agreement has a reservation of rights clause.

The reservation of rights clause might read as follows "all rights with respect to the licensed software, whether now existing or which may hereafter come into existence, including but not limited to {insert laundry list}, are reserved to licensor"

In order to build support for an interpretation elsewhere in an agreement make sure the final contract has a merger/integration clause such as; "This is the entire agreement between the parties regarding the stated subject matter and all prior representations, warranties, etc. have been merged into this agreement."

The question of ambiguity is depicted figuratively as follows:

Unambiguous grants clause has only one interpretation

Others are unreasonable

Perception 2: As long as an agreement contains the restrictive language that the licensor wishes to have, it doesn't matter where the language actually appears in the agreement. The question is: Should a Licensor try to get restrictive language in the grants clause or not? The belief that it doesn't matter where the language is located in an agreement, as long as it is there, is wrong. In reality, it is very important where restrictive language appears.

Restrictive language in the grants clause clearly defines the scope of the license. A licensee that exceeds the scope of the grant commits patent or copyright infringement, not simply a breach of contract.

An example of a license grant without clear restriction is "right to copy and sell licensed software". An additional covenant outside the grant clause might read "licensee shall pay licensor $/year minimum royalties". What if a licensee fails to make payments on a timely basis? Since the ongoing right to exercise granted rights doesn't hinge on prompt payment of the minimum royalties, one may have a legitimate breach of agreement claim but not a rescission of the contract and patent or copyright infringement.

On the other hand, the grant clause for a license with clear restriction might read as follows: *"Subject to the payment of the upfront payment no later than the effective date and the payment of the license maintenance fee on each anniversary of the effective date thereafter, licensee shall have the right to copy and sell licensed software"*. The scope of license formula is: $SL = SRG - R$; where: $SL =$ scope of license, $SRG =$ specific rights granted and $R =$ restrictions.

In general when specifying the specific rights granted one should avoid generalized language such as: "licensor grants licensee non-exclusive right to license patents and non exclusive right to licensed software" and get in the habit of identifying each specific right granted. Rights might be described as presented in table four.

Table four. Specific rights.

Patent rights	Copyright rights
Make	Copy
Use	Prepare derivative
Sell	Versions
Offer to sell	Distribute
Import into U.S.	Publicly perform
	Publicly display

Other forms of specific rights that might be granted are: trademark, trade secret, or right of publicity. Four examples of restriction language that might be included in an agreement are as follows:

First, modify each right granted. For example, if a right to copy is granted, define the purpose e.g. internal or external, that material may be copied. If a right to distribute is granted establish restrictions by asking; What? Approved copies? Copies that function to do.......? Through a specific method? Electronically? Photonically? In the event a right to prepare derivative versions is granted, identify the specific purpose?

Secondly, if one anticipates new technology applications, be careful with broad grants clause language not directed to specific right or limited subject matter. An example of such language: "right to reproduce, distribute, prepare derivative works, perform publicity, and display publicly software by any means or method now known or hereafter invented" Preferred alternative language will be worded so as to "restrict use of licensed matter in new technological contexts by selectively modifying one of the granted rights with the new technologies". Another restriction clause is "right to distribute content enhanced by licensed software by broadcasting by television or any other similar device now know or hereafter to be made known."

A third means to impose restriction are via performance standards or conditions. Performance conditions are more critical in a non-exclusive license. Best efforts should not be presumed. Instead provide minimum performance goals, minimum dollars spent on R&D, minimum dollars spent on foreign efforts, and consequences for failing to achieve goals that might be termination or conversion of exclusive to non-exclusive rights.

A fourth element associated with imposing restrictions in an agreement is to consider the existing position of the licensor. Take a neutral approach; neither licensor, nor licensee should be favored. The most common situation that will arise is that new assumptions arise. The licensor by permitting inclusion of ambiguous language in grant language agreed to broad interpretation of the scope of the license. Also if broad interpretation reasonably includes new technologies, licensee can use licensed property in new technological environment. Remember, the burden is on the licensor to frame, negotiate, and include limits in the license grant.

Perception 3: It doesn't matter whether a licensor can state a meritorious copyright infringement claim or meritorious breach of contract claim as long as the licensor has at least one. The question is: Should a businessperson try to construct a license that makes it easier to establish copyright infringement?

Frequently the position is taken that it doesn't matter to the businessperson. It is often concluded that is something for lawyers to worry about. This contention is incorrect. It is very important whether or not a meritorious copyright infringement claim can be presented. Advantages that accompany a meritorious copyright infringement claim and breach of contract are presented in table five.

Table five. Relative remedies: copyright infringement v. breach of contract.

Copyright	Breach of Contract
Injunction simplified	Injunction only after intentional or willful
Impounding/destruction	showing actual damages
Actual or statutory damages	
- Non-willful	
- Willful	
Attorney's fees	
Other costs	

A valid copyright infringement claim dramatically increases a licensee's risk because irreparable harm is presumed and therefore, preliminary injunction is easier to obtain than in breach of contract context. In addition the infringed party can collect actual or statutory damages, attorney's fees and litigation costs.

In summary, don't construct licenses linearly: i.e. from page one to end, build licenses from grants clause outward, consider a grants clause like patent claims (but in reverse) and remember that a clearly defined license scope will save time and money.

COPYRIGHT VS. PATENT LICENSE

There are some terms or considerations that differ between a patent and copyright license. Some select differences are as follows:
1. licenses for copyright might include shrink-wrap, integrated, site with varied numbers of derivative works are more common and there is need to address the definition and scope, authorship and related compensation;
2. sublicenses may also be necessary to consolidate, integrate or merge code. This bundling activity, derivative development and flow through of rights or compensation should be addressed when preparing the agreement; and
3. liability, warrantees, representation and Insurance may be different that would be included in a license for a pharmaceutical, for example. Therefore, there is a need to practice prudent selection of insurance providers. The end vs. intermediary use of the copyright will impact liability.

In certain situations a licensee will want software placed in escrow. The escrow agent, updates, duration, and payment for escrow activity will need to be addressed. Source code should be placed in an escrow account before a license enacted. This assures the parties of an understanding and record of the code subject to the license.

COPYRIGHT

If licensed as is source code usually must be provided. Treat source code as a trade secret with no sublicense rights and obligate everyone to keep methods and concepts as trade secret. Programming is critical and a valuable component of software. If there is a need for device independence, create an "interpreter".

An important software attribute is if it is used to establish the industry standard and this feature can add significant value when defining value and ultimately price. The following should be taken into consideration when licensing software:

1. offer "open" license and allow enhancement of object code and protect with copyright registration;
2. retention of source code results in control;
3. can license partial source code needed to meet specific need i.e. linkage to other devices;
4. royalty advance - recoupable only for sales of a specific unit and recoupable for only a limited period of time (adobe got six figure advance);
5. embed software affords protection especially if hard to duplicate;
6. if patent is a modification based on source code get grant back rights and state that licensee will not exercise rights of patent; and
7. do not agree to "most favorable nations" language in license.

MARKS

As for software there are important considerations to take into account when enacting a trademark license; several of which are:

1. allow use of trademark but set specifications if marketed by licensee; and

2. require use of trademark to increase awareness but remember obligations that accompany trademark

MULTIMEDIA

The definition of multimedia varies so begin by establishing the definition. If use of existing work is intended, determine who has rights; the producer, actor/actress, or musician. Examples of rights are:

1. rights of publicity - actor/actress;
2. rights of privacy - stand ins;
3. moral rights - licensing outside U.S.;
4. rights of attributes - attributed to person;
5. rights to architecture - buildings recognized in background;
6. rights to works of art - sculptures, art;
7. rights to sequel(s);
8. rights to synchronization;
9. rights to adaptation; and/or
10. rights to underlying works that predate home video and that may not be secured.

Licensing multimedia can be a complex process that requires knowledge of numerous factors, several of which are:

1. if use photography for any reason need right from actor or stand in or could pay treble damages (stand in gets $100k per day so damage for one days filming could be $300K;
2. cannot negotiate for photography rights at the same time as negotiating for filming rights;
3. if video games certain actor may not be in video till phase 5 so how do you set;
4. royalty negotiate intelligently - can have many hidden costs;
5. consents required are extensive;
6. rights required vary with product;
7. cover all forms of distribution i.e. CD-ROM, electronic means, TV, network;
8. interactive electronic;
9. royalty;
10. buyout;
11. running based on number of accesses, # of discs copied, CD ROMs made; and
12. if music synchronization and if change, need adaptation.

LICENSE THESAURUS

In Exhibit A is presented a special list of words and phrases that may have plural or different meanings in a contract or license. Suggestions are presented as to the most appropriate word or phrase to use to prevent misunderstandings and generally improve communications.

AGREEMENT TERMINOLOGY

Individual preferences for agreement terminology vary. However, in all cases legal and business requirements need to be well known and any agreement must conform to the statutes. As the terms are being drafted negotiations will be underway and terms will be the outcome of these negotiations. Agreement drafts can be a significant contribution to the negotiation process and need to be carefully prepared. The following is a summary of drafting suggestions. Details and reasoning are presented in Exhibit B (Terrible Terminology).

- do not let the word processor produce verbosity;
- recognize drafting as part of the negotiating process;

- use paragraph sculpturing for ease of reading and analysis;
- use definitions to achieve clarity;
- drafting laziness should not detract from precision;
- design definitions to limit and not expand the meaning;
- eliminate redundant words- less is more;
- verify cross references;
- forego use of imprecise old English words i.e. foregoing;
- phrase lists carefully;
- use user friendly language;
- keep it simple and succinct;
- use distinctive word to describe the parties; not licensor and licensee;
- do not use capitalized words; blocks communication flow;
- make document visually attractive;
- market, market, market!!!;
- remember words with specialized meanings i.e. sole and exclusive are contradictory;
- exclusive may eliminate licensor; sole grants rights to all except licensor;
- use early drafts to set out issues i.e. who provides support, installation and who delivers software and manuals;
- annotate, use footnotes, compare drafts;
- avoid term "best efforts"; its invitation to litigation;
- avoid phrase "reasonable efforts";
- specify minimum performance requirements;
- beware of vernacular; it may change legal context; i.e. sales refer to tangible property; but software may be licensed not sold;
- consider non-revenue producing use or distribution of the license product i.e. software distributed internally or to others for review and testing, or exchanged in joint venture;
- consider effect of non-cash consideration being included in royalty base;
- define revenues; fees for licenses to end users, sublicense to distributors who market to end users including payments for right to distribute and revenues earned from royalty by distributors;
- specify exemptions from gross revenues;
- state event that triggers right to royalty; i.e. when invoiced, receipt of payment, when shipped, when copied to disk;
- consider who bears risk for bad receivable; may depend on price of deliverable;
- be careful of "bundling" or combination products;
- do not allow affiliate to be placed between licensee and market;
- be careful of support price vs. license price – if you are paid on license and not support (predatory pricing);
- do not use word trust i.e. hold confidential information in trust - trustee must act to benefit of other party at the expense of his own interest - use contract;
- do not use word ensure i.e. ensure confidential information will not be disclosed it can lead to absolute liability - use endeavor to ...;
- clearly state secrecy obligation(s) not "hold in confidence as one does for its own secrets" - one may not do anything - have agreements put in place;
- make duration of secrecy correspond with economic life;
- define improvements - use words that have precise meanings or you may end up in court;
- tie improvements to term of underlying license;
- be careful of foreign ant-restraint of trade rules;

- specify standards of quality if product is software;
- state clearly the effective term i.e. automatic renewal every five years unless terminate by either party at the fifth year such notice must be given 12 months prior to termination;
- remember patent term can now be extended;
- clearly specify terminating events;
- consider consequences of termination i.e. sell inventory, audit rights, case use of marks, licensed matter; and
- strive for inclusive language not he/she - you, we, etc.

SOFTWARE AGREEMENTS

Terms in software agreements may differ from an agreement involving other types of intellectual property. Terms and examples of software agreements are presented in Exhibit D and Addendum III which is included with this book. Questions and answers related to contracts are presented in Exhibit E.

CONTRACT EXAMPLES

An example of an equity license is presented in Addendum III along with examples of other license agreements.

A list of other agreements that are associated with intellectual property management or technology commercialization process is presented in table six.

Table six. Examples of agreements relevant to intellectual property management.

1. Acknowledgement of required compromise
2. Alpha-beta test
3. Amendment
4. Assignment
5. Biological specimens and parts
6. Cease and desist
7. Certificate LLC
8. Click-wrap
9. Clinical trial
10. Consent to use name
11. Confidentiality/non disclosure
12. Conflict of interest
13. Consortium
14. Consulting
15. Cooperative research and development agreement (CRADA)
16. Creator – employer copyright
17. Data and database
18. Declaration
19. Employment
20. Employment of foreign national agreement
21. Engagement agreement
22. Equipment loan/lease
23. Escrow
24. Fellowship
25. Field trial
26. Gift
27. Interinstitutional

28. Intrainstitutional
29. Joint development
30. Joint development with marketing rights
31. Joint development with option
32. Landlord
33. Lease agreement
34. Lease purchases
35. Letter agreement
36. Liability
37. License (examples and components)
    a. Equity and sponsored R&D
    b. Equity
    c. Software business terms
    d. Thesis
    e. Non exclusive
    f. Exclusive
    g. Software
38. Letter of intent
39. Limits of liability and hold harmless
40. Loan
41. Materials transfer
42. Marketing
43. Marketing and distribution
44. Memorandum of agreement
45. Multimedia
46. Non disclosure
47. Non compete
48. Option
49. Patent counsel retainer agreement
50. Power of attorney
51. Pre-incorporation
52. Publishing agreement
53. Purchase order
54. Rescission
55. Release of intellectual property
56. Release of invention rights
57. Research support
58. Research support with option
59. Revenue distribution
60. Revenue share
61. Sale
62. SBIR/STTR
63. Seed/plant
64. Shared rights
65. Software development
66. Software escrow
67. Software marketing
68. Software release – evaluation

Table six (con't). Examples of agreements relevant to intellectual property management.

69. Software subscription
70. Sponsorship agreement
71. Standstill
72. Stock rights
73. Student – class project
74. Subcontract-3rd party
75. Teaming agreement
76. Term sheet
77. Test or screen
78. Trade secret
79. Trademark
80. Visiting scientist
81. Voting trust
82. Waiver and release
83. Website disclaimer
84. Work for hire

PROS AND CONS OF ASSIGNMENTS, PAID-UP LICENSES, & EXCLUSIVE LICENSES

First, if there is US government money in it, one will have to secure approval from the appropriate US agency if there is intent to assign the technology. Most US government agencies are reluctant to endorse assignment. If approval to assign is granted good reasons must be given such as they are very old and extensive marketing has taken place with no takers. In other words, as long as all else has failed assignment in order to commercialize is the last resort. Agencies also vary in their willingness to allow assignment.

The upsides to assignment are:

1. it removes one from the relationship (No follow-up is needed);
2. less worries regarding liability, since one is further removed from any cause for liability;
3. assignment is simpler than a license; and
4. university and inventor get money upfront and do not have to bear commercialization risks.

The downsides to assignment are:

1. it no longer belongs to original owner. (It would be hard to have it revert to a non-exclusive or anything else since rights no longer belong to the original owner.);
2. it is possible to require the company to warrant they would not use the newly assigned patent to sue someone for infringement within the first three years, and they did not intend any particular target(s) for infringement suits (If the warranty is violated, one might assert that the assignment was null and void but this approach may be rather difficult to enforce);
3. hard to know even approximately what it is worth? (With a royalty rate you are entitled to a share. If the technology is very valuable, the university gets a larger amount. If it is less valuable, the university doesn't get as much either.);
4. have to get the assignment approved by the U.S. agency;
5. have no guarantee that the tech will be commercially developed at all. (It might be sat upon, which is contrary to your Prime Directive (to borrow a Star Trek term) of bringing technology to the people.); and

479

6. may have to worry that the inventor will sue you for not asking enough and losing complete control over the technology (Of course as we've seen, inventors can and do sue for not asking enough anyway, assignment or license, but with an assignment or paid-up license the inventor doesn't even have a share if the tech makes a killing.).

Instead of an assignment, seek a paid-up license. One can still retain title, but the licensee doesn't owe any further money for the license. Performance requirements can be imposed and the license can be terminated if the licensee fails to abide by the performance criteria. Government approval is not required. Value can be estimated and the university and inventor get paid upfront and do not assume the risk of future sales (or lack thereof). The most reasonable approach is an exclusive license. However, many licensees prefer a paid-up or fixed yearly fee license to avoid accounting and reporting duties.

Many of the questions asked are provided in a commercialization or business plan a potential licensee should provide (sales, volume of material produced, milestones, etc.). An exclusive license with a lump-sum payment is still possible. Diligence criteria can still be imposed (e.g. producing so many tons of product a year) and reporting to ensure the technology is commercialized (and not kept off the market) based on numbers they provide in the business plan or if licensee is still paying only minimum royalties for two or more consecutive years at some point in the term. Retain some control in this fashion to ensure performance or, alternatively, that one can get the technology back and find a new licensee if the first arrangement turns out to be unsatisfactory. Certainly not meeting those diligences could default the license from an exclusive to a nonexclusive.

Seldom is exclusivity granted for an upfront payment especially for rights to patent claims over a 20-year period. A royalty arrangement would be more advantageous than a paid-up license. The paid-up often contemplates front loading the licensee's financial obligations, and one may end up with more earlier but less in the long run. Generally, seek royalties: one can still get an initiation fee to satisfy immediate need for cash, and by spreading payments out over time, get ahead in the long run.

The technology is subject to the "Bayh-Dole provisions" (23 USC202-212) because it was developed with Federal funds. Bayh-Dole requires agency approval before assigning ownership to an entity other than a patent management firm. It is unlikely the government would agree to an assignment of ownership without a compelling reason. Keep as much control as possible with an exclusive licensee to maximize return.

LICENSE WITHOUT A PATENT

Although it has been more common to associate a license with rights to patent claims there are also licenses to unpatented intellectual property. In fact, it may be of strategic importance to not patent but to grant rights to copyright, marks, plant material, trade secret or know-how. Most of the pros and cons related to licensing non patented intellectual property depends on specifics of the arrangement.

If an asset is readily reproducible, it may become available from unlicensed sources, while you are still forced to abide by the terms of your license. If access to the technology is tightly controlled (e.g. "secret formulas" that are not readily reverse engineered), this is less likely to be a concern, but keep in mind that what seems impossible today may become possible with evolving technology in the future.

Without a patent, and if there is no other detailed description of the technology, it may be harder to define the scope of the technology. For example, if there are internal undefined aspects of the technology or improvements over time, the parties may differ as to whether this is part of the original transfer that is subject to the license.

Also, it is possible to patent technology that is in use as long as it is not in public use or for sale. Since a license for other patent purposes is not a sale and the unpatented technology may not require public use or sale, as long as there is no protection for prior user rights, it is possible that someone could later patent the technology and prevent your use without a license.

In one form or another, one may be providing a "springboard" for someone else's efforts. This is the result of providing a competitor either; 1) the time advantage of information i.e., between the time of further creation or discovery and the information is published, they have access to the information and are able to use it for their purposes provided they handle it properly; or 2) the level of detail is greater than might otherwise be available, e.g., they have access to certain prototypes, drawings, software that embody the technical information.

The difficulties in these situations are: 1) arriving at a suitable value proposition and accompanying expectations on both sides - including access issues, and 2) defining the tangible representations of the information that form the basis for the license so that the agreement can be suitably focused and each party can say that the "technology" was delivered.

If the methodology has not been published and is not therefore generally known to the public, then at least during the time prior to publication, it may have standing as a trade secret. This does not mean that the licensor has to hold the information as a trade secret for the duration of any license: it means only that the licensee has privileged access to the information and agrees to behave in using it prior to its publication by the licensor.

Don't accept arguments that once the information is licensed, the licensee will be damaged if the information is subsequently published by the licensor. Non-patent methods can be hugely important in setting standards. The fact that they are not proprietary (once published) makes them potentially of great value to everyone. And many good things can come from being known as an organization that helps to establish standards. So you may want to publish freely, having provided a reasonable head start to selected commercial partners.

INTERNATIONAL LICENSING

Licensing of intellectual property rights outside the United States contains all of the challenges associated with such licensing in this country and a number of additional ones. The additional challenges have both cultural and legal aspects. Although this paper will concentrate primarily on legal issues, it is worth bearing in mind that some cultures have a very different attitude to the law and legal issues from ours. For example, throughout the Far East, where the influence of Confucius remains strong, there remains an underlying feeling that the need to resort to law is in some way "improper". One should be able to resolve problems by discussion and proper consideration of the other side's position. In other countries, where the importance of the law is fully recognized, but where reliance has traditionally been based on the wording of codes or legislation to define relationships between parties, one can still find a tendency to produce agreements that seem extremely skimpy by our standards and to do little more than state certain concepts. Nevertheless there has been a general tendency in recent years towards the adoption of detailed written contracts for licensing of intellectual property rights throughout the world. The basic reason for this has of course been that the more specific one can be in defining what an agreement is about at the time when the parties are keen to cooperate with each other, the less likelihood there is that there will be misunderstandings and disputes later on if the relationship becomes more problematical.

International licensing today is less fraught with difficulties than it has been previously. Nevertheless, one should still be cautious. In particular, the licensor must clearly have in mind the objectives to be achieved and thus be prepared to be flexible in crafting an agreement to secure those objectives. Above all, however, the differences between domestic licensing and foreign licensing lies in the need to make sure that you know who you are dealing with and the need to provide for an exit route if something goes wrong.

EXHIBIT A - LICENSE THESAURUS

Act of god

- An event beyond the reasonable control of the parties preventing the carrying out or delaying of an obligation.
- Words or phrases sometimes used for the same meaning: force majeure, catastrophic event or happening, event not under control of a party
- *Preferred phrase: force majeure*

Affiliate

- See subsidiary

Agreement

- A binding contract between parties such as a license, however some countries such as China interpret an agreement as nonbinding but a contract is considered binding.
- *Preferred term: agreement.*

Agreement date

- See execution date and effective date

Agreement not to license others

- See sole license

Arms-length transaction

- Idiomatic English, means a transaction between strangers who have no financial interest in each other or not ties. May present difficulties in translation.

Assign, assignment

- Used primarily in connection with the transfer of the tangible evidence of a right such as a patent or trademark or copyright. Words sometimes used for the same meaning: grant, transfer, convey.
- See exclusive license
- *Preferred word: assign or assignment*

Consisting of

- Means only those items mentioned-closed ended. Other phrase sometimes used for the same meaning: composed of.
- See comprising which is sometimes erroneously used to mean consisting of.
- *Preferred phrase: use the word "only" in conjunction with the above.*

Contract

- See agreement.

Convey

- Used in connection with real property and assignment, not often used in licensing.
- See grant and assign.

Corporate address

- See place of business.

Covenant not to sue

- See nonexclusive license.

Cross license

- Means when each party to an agreement grants a license to the other on the same subject matter. Term is used most often as a title and not as a technical licensing term in the body of the agreement.

Customer

- Usually a purchaser of goods or service. Term is generic in time-first purchaser such as distributor or last purchaser such as retail purchaser. Terms sometimes used for same meaning: end User or purchaser.

- *Preferred phrase: final customer, if end user is intended or intermediate customer or direct customer as appropriate.*

Domicile
- Means place of residence, used in connection with tax law, should not be used in licenses. Sometimes used to indicate place of incorporation
- See place of business

Down payment
- See lump sum.

Due diligence
- Term used by investment bankers. Means evaluating the situation or technology within a short period of time. Not used in licensing.

Effective date
- Means the date the agreement comes into full force and effect. Date may be before or after date of signing agreement by all parties. Words and phrases sometimes used and in some instances erroneously for same meaning: execution date, agreement date, commencement date, signing date.
- See execution date.
- *Preferred phrase: effective date.*

Election
- A requirement to make a choice. Word sometimes used for same meaning: option.
- See option
- *Preferred word: election when appropriate.*

Employment agreement
- An agreement between employer and employee usually including provision setting forth obligations of employee regarding confidential information, assignment of inventions, and obligations after termination of employment. Normally does not deal with monetary matters. Words and phrases sometimes used for same meaning; technical agreement, secrecy agreement, confidentiality agreement, assignment agreement.
- See secrecy agreement.
- *Preferred phrase: employment agreement.*

End-user
- Means final customer or purchaser. Is an idiomatic English term and maybe difficult to translate.
- See customer.
- *Preferred phrase: final customer.*

Exclusive license
- Means licensor grants the licensee the sole right to practice the invention or use trademark to the exclusion of licensor and others; may be limited to territory, field, product or time. Normally exclusive licensee has right to license others. Phrases sometimes used, and in some instances erroneously, for same meaning: sole license single license, assignment, and limited license.
- See sole license.
- *Preferred phrase: exclusive license.*

Execution date
- Means the date all parties have signed the agreement. Sometimes means the date an executory obligation has been fulfilled. Words and phrases sometimes used, and in some instances erroneously, for same meaning; agreement date, effective date of agreement.
- See effective date.
- *Preferred phrase: agreement execution date.*

Expiration date
- See term of agreement

Field of use
- Relates to the scope of license, such as a particular product for a particular use. Should define product and area of use.

First option
- See first refusal.

First refusal, right of
- Right of one party of an agreement to receive a right, commitment or license from another party of the agreement prior to being offered to any third party. Usually coupled with a time limit or a payment or both. Term per se not usually used in agreements but instead the specific terms of right are written out. Phrases sometimes used for same meaning: first option, right to improvement inventions, right to expand scope or to select other fields. In communication's, right should be clearly defined and specified.

Fixed fee or royalty
- See Lump sum and minimum royalty.

First class mail
- Does not have meaning in most countries outside the U.S.A. In international licensing use term regular mail or airmail as appropriate.

Force majeure
- An even beyond the reasonable control of the parties preventing the carrying out or delaying of an obligation. Words and phrases sometimes used for the same meaning: act of God, catastrophic event or happening, event not under control of party.
- *Preferred phrase: force majeure.*

Freedom
- See license and right.

Generally known to public
- Means information not confidential or secret. Information may, however, be subject to proprietary rights, such as information described in a valid, unexpired patent. Words and phrases sometimes used for same meaning: in the public domain, nonconfidential, not secret, available to public and publicly known.
- See public domain.
- *Preferred phrase: generally know to the public.*

Grant
Used primarily in connection with a license, such as "grant a license". Sometimes misunderstood to mean a warranty by licensor that no other licenses are required from
- third parties. Words and phrases sometimes used for meaning: convey, transfer, and assign.
- *Preferred word: grant.*

Guarantee
- See warranty and indemnification.

Hold harmless
- See indemnification ad nonexclusive license and warranty.

Immunity from suit
- See nonexclusive license.

Including
- See comprising

Indemnification
- Usually the licensor agrees to pay specified liabilities, such as repay any court awarded monetary damages, to licensee if he/she infringes another's patent or trademark in practicing licensed inventions or using licensed trademark. Words and phases sometimes used for same meaning: hold harmless, guarantee, liability, and warranty.
- See warranty.

- *Preferred phase: indemnification.*

Industrial property
- See intellectual property.

Initial payment
- See lump sum.

Intellectual property
- Ownership rights given by law in intellectual information such as inventions, patients, trademarks, trade names, logos, copyrights, know-how, trade secrets. Words and phrases sometimes used for same meaning: industrial property, proprietary information.
- See propriety information.
- *Preferred phrase: intellectual property.*

Know-how (information)
- Know-how may be confidential or non-confidential and it may be proprietary or nonproprietary (such as in a text book). It may be technical or non-technical.
- See confidential information, trade secret and proprietary information.

Letter of intent
- Have different meanings in different countries. In U.S.A., merely an outline of objectives for negotiations, usually not binding. In Japan, usually a binding agreement, with terms embodied in a letter of intent. Further negotiations focus only on terms not set out in letter. Unless intended to be a binding agreement, use and other term such as "non-binding proposal".

Liability
- See indemnification and warranty.

License
- Means permission to practice all or a part of a proprietary right. Words and phrases sometimes used for same meaning: right, right and license, permission, authorize, freedom.
- See nonexclusive license and right.
- *Preferred word: license*

License rights
- See proprietary rights.

Limited license
- See exclusive license.

Logo
- See trademarks.

Lump sum
- Idiomatic English. Means a single monetary payment. Words and phrases sometimes used for same meaning: down payment, initial payment or fee, fixed fee.
- *Preferred phrase: lump sum.*

Minimum performance
- See best effort and minimum royalty.

Minimum royalty
- Obligation to pay certain amount periodically, otherwise the license may be changed or terminated automatically or at option of licensor. Words and phrases sometimes used for same meaning: promise to pay, promissory notes, fixed royalty.
- *Preferred phrase: minimum royalty.*

Non-confidential agreement
- See secrecy agreement.

Nonexclusive license

- A license that does not prohibit the licensor from licensing others in the same field, or on the same product, or same territory, etc. Words and phrases sometimes used for same meaning: license, sublicense, and immunity from suit holds harmless, covenant not to sue.
- *Preferred phrase: nonexclusive license.*

Option

- Rights to make a choice, not a requirement. Word sometimes used for same meaning: election.
- See election.
- *Preferred word: option.*

Owned

- See proprietary rights.

Paid-up license

- A license which does not require further royalties because some considerations has been given in advance including cash but not necessarily cash. Phrase sometimes used for same meaning: royalty free license.
- *Preferred phrase: paid up license with no future royalty payments.*

Permission

- See license.

Personal license

- Idiomatic English, means a non-assignable, nontransferable license, usually license terminates on death of individual or dissolution for merger of corporation or firm.

Place of business

- Means principal place of business or corporate offices. Words and phrases sometimes used, and in some instances erroneously, for same meaning: domicile, corporate address, place of incorporation, location of corporate offices, principal place of business.
- See domicile.
- *Preferred phrase: a place of business.*

Place of incorporation

- Used primarily for identification purposes in license agreements.
- See place of business and domicile.

Principal place of business

- See place of business.

Promise of promissory

- See minimum royalty

Proprietary information

- Means information owned by supplier but not necessarily confidential. Misused to mean confidential information. Words and phrases sometimes used, and in some instances erroneously, for some meaning: confidential information, all rights and title in intellectual property, owned, controlled.
- See confidential information and intellectual property.
- *Preferred phrase; propriety information. Property rights*

Public domain

- Means free to use: free of patent, trademark and copyright right. Misnomer for generally known to the public. Words and phrases sometimes used for some meaning: non-confidential, not secret, publicly known, and available to the public. In the context of non-confidentiality, preferred phrase: generally known to the public or available to the public (something that is available to the public may not be generally known to public).

Rescind

- See terminate.

Right

- Means permission to practice all or part of a propriety right, Has different meaning in different countries. Sometimes broader than a license but with restrictions on grantor. Words and phrases sometimes used for same meaning: license, right and license, permission, authorize, freedom.
- See license.
- *Preferred word: license*

Rights conferred by law for ownership or control (generic)

- Words and phrases sometimes used for the same meaning: patent, trademark and copyright rights, license rights, intellectual property rights, right, proprietary information, title, confidential information.
- *Preferred phrase: proprietary rights*

Royalty-free license

- See paid-up license.

Scope

- See field of use. Sometimes refers to territory, type of license (e.g. nonexclusive), and subject matter. When used, it should be clearly defined. Seldom used alone.

Secrecy agreement

- An agreement between two or more parties setting forth conditions of accepting or not accepting confidential information. Words and phrases sometimes used for same meaning: confidential agreement, non-confidential agreement, employment agreement, and technical agreement. Preferred phrase: secrecy agreement when accepting confidential information, non-confidentiality agreement when not accepting confidential information.

Secret information

- See confidential information and proprietary information.

Semi-exclusive license

- See sole license

Service mark

- See trademark.

Signing date

- See execution date and effective date.

Single license

- See exclusive license and sole license

Sole license

- Means licensor grants licensee exclusive license except for retained nonexclusive license of licensor. Has different meaning in different countries and regions. Phrases sometimes used, and sometimes erroneously, for some meaning: single license, exclusive license, semi-exclusive license, and agreement not to license others.
- See exclusive license and nonexclusive license.
- *Preferred phrase: exclusive license except for a nonexclusive license retained by licensor*

Sublicense right

- The right of a licensee to grant licenses to others. Phrase sometimes used for some meaning: exclusive license right, sub-contract right.
- *Preferred phrase: right to grant licenses to others.*

Subsidiary

- Means a company at least partially owned by another company, the parent company. Should be defined in the license agreement. Words and phrases sometimes used for some meaning: affiliate, related company, and joint venture.
- *Preferred word: subsidiary with definition.*

Technical agreement

- See employment agreement.

Term of agreement

- Means length of agreement until it automatically terminates by an event for date certain. Not to be confused with right to terminate or cancel agreement before term of license agreement is up or termination of a specific right or obligation under the agreement. Words and phrases sometimes used for same or similar meaning: expiration of agreement, expiration date, and termination date.
- *Preferred phrase: term of agreement or the termination of a specific right or obligation under the agreement.*

Termination date

- See term of agreement.

Terminate or termination

- Termination of an agreement prior to its normal term as the result of an event or the option of one of the parties. Not to be confused with term of agreement. Words sometimes used for same meaning: cancel or cancellation, abrogate, default, rescind.
- *Preferred word: terminate or termination.*

Territory

- Refers to the geographical area covered by a license; may be territory of sale or territory of manufacture or both. Term must be defined in agreement.

Trade name

- Usually the name of a business enterprise. May or may not be protected by law.
- See trademark.

Trademark

- A mark, word or phrase for which the law has given the owner a right to exclude others from using. Often confused with trade mane. Words and phrases sometimes used, and in some instances erroneously, for same meaning: trade name, logo, motto, and service mark character.
- *Preferred word: trademark.*

Trade secret

- Means confidential information, which is protected by law. Has different meaning in different countries. Limited or no protection in some countries. Words and phrase sometimes used, and in some instances erroneously for same meaning: confidential information proprietary information, secret information, know--how,
- *Preferred phrase: confidential information or trade secret depending on use of term and jurisdiction.*

Transfer

- Used in connection with real property and assignment of title, not often used in licensing.
- See grant, assign, and convey.

Warranty, warrant

- Licensor's guarantee of ownership of license proprietary rights, right to grant license, no conflict with other licenses granted by licensor, non-infringement of other patents in practicing license, usefulness of information for purpose of agreement, practicability of information, operability, non-toxicity and non-hazardous. Type, duration, and monetary or other obligations must define the guarantee or obligations of licensor. Words and phrases used for same or similar meaning: guarantee, liability, damages, and indemnification.
- See indemnification.
- *Preferred term warrant with definition of scope and subject matter.*

EXHIBIT B - TERRIBLE TERMINOLOGY

DO'S AND DON'TS IN A LICENSE AGREEMENT

1. INTRODUCTION

Everyone has experienced the effects of Terrible Terminology, either as writer or reader. The following are drafting techniques related to a license. The goal is to minimize terrible terminology by the adoption of tactics designed to produce precise but understandable written agreements that set forth the parties' intended business and legal goals. Drafting is very personal; some of the following tactics may or may not be acceptable or unsuitable depending on the specific situation.

2. CASE STUDY

To assist in the review the following is a case study that may illustrate the tactics to be discussed. For the case study, assume the following facts.

1. Start is a small Canadian software developer[1] and has developed a complex scientific computer program (the "Licensed Software").

2. Ination is a large international corporation based in London, England and has a major office in Houston, Texas; it is a successful international distributor of scientific software.

3. Ination and Start entered into a license agreement in 1992 concerning an earlier version of the Licensed Software; recently there have been a number of disagreements about the interpretation of the 1992 license agreement.

Using all the negotiating skills known to him,[2] the President of Start has spent several weeks convincing Ination to market the latest version of the Licensed Software, rather than terminating their relationship.

The President of Start has written what he considers to be all the pertinent details of the new deal on the back of an envelope and delivers the envelope to our hero, Terrible Terminator. The details on the envelope are as follows:

(a) disputes are settled, it was an unfortunate misunderstanding;

(b) Ination gets all U.S. and England;

(c) best efforts in marketing;

(d) Ination gets source code so it can provide support;

(e) Start gets 5% royalty;

(f) Start gets rights to all improvements but Ination can use the improvements it makes;

(g) no warranties; and

(h) five year term, renewable.

Let's look over Terrible Terminator's shoulder as he wrestles with items on the President's list.

3. TERRIBLE TERMINATOR WRITES A "RELEASE"

The President's first note reads, "disputes are settled, it was an unfortunate misunderstanding". Terrible Terminator decides that he should make sure that the issues in dispute are not raised again between the parties. No disputes in the future should relate to anything arising out of the 1992 agreement. He decides that to implement this, a release will be required.

3.1   Terrible Terminator and his Word Processor's First Draft

Terrible Terminator, like most of us, has a library of precedents that are readily available through his word processor. He calls up a standard form of release, adapts it slightly and produces the following provision, which has a style familiar to all of us; it is a prime example of "lawyer-talk".

FIRST DRAFT

2.   Release. (a) Licensor releases, relinquishes, acquits and forever discharges Licensee, its officers, directors, shareholders, employees, agents, legal representatives, subsidiaries, affiliates, attorneys,

successors and assigns, of and from any and all debts, obligations, reckoning, promises, covenants, agreements, contracts, endorsements, bonds, specialties, controversies, suits, actions, causes of action, trespasses, variances, judgments, executions, damages, claims, demands, rights, titles, interests, charges, encumbrances, or liens of any kind or sort whatsoever or howsoever arising, in law or in equity, whether known or unknown, whether liquidated or unliquidated, whether in tort or in contract, which they or any of them had, now has, or in the future may have against Licensee, its officers, directors, shareholders, agents, legal representatives, subsidiaries, affiliates, attorneys, successors and assigns, arising out of, for, under, upon or by reason of or in connection with or relating to, directly or indirectly, the 1992 License Agreement or any of the following acts or omissions of Licensee, its officers, directors, shareholders, employees, agents, legal representatives, subsidiaries, affiliates, attorneys, successors and assigns, in connection with or relating to or arising out of or by virtue of any of the following: any loss, cost or damage relating to or arising out of any breach of fiduciary duty, breach of any duty of good faith or fair dealing, breach of confidence, undue influence, duress, economic, coercion, conflict of interest, negligence, bad faith, malpractice, intentional negligent infliction of emotional or mental distress, tortuous interference with corporate governance or prospective business advantage, breach of contract, deceptive trade practices, libel, slander, conspiracy, any claim of wrongfully marketing the Licensed Software, or the charging, contracting for, taking, reserving, collecting or receiving of interest in excess of the highest lawful rate applicable (i.e. usury) , or any violations of federal or state law, any violations of federal copyright rules, laws or regulations, or any violation of the federal antitrust acts; Licensor further agrees that neither it nor any of its legal representatives or successors, will institute, prosecute or in any way aid in the institution or prosecution of any claim, demand, action or cause of action now existing or hereafter asserted against Licensee, its officers, directors, shareholders, employees, agents, legal representatives, subsidiaries, affiliates, attorneys, successors and assigns, arising out of or by virtue of or in connection with or relating to any of the foregoing.

3.2   Terrible Terminator's Legalistic Style
The long sentence in this release contains 420 words. This sentence "not only talks about too many different things ... [it] says the same thing too many times, and - for good measure - adds the completely unnecessary. No one, not even the writer, can keep it all straight. . . ".

This peculiar style of legal writing is historic and is perpetuated by habit and standard legal forms. With the development of the word processor, it is all too easy to pull together strings of words without bothering to consider whether they make sense to the Terminator or the client.[5] By the third line the reader has fallen asleep, lost all hope of ever finishing the sentence or has let loose with every lawyer joke he knows.

Tactic: Do not let the word processor produce verbosity.

3.3   Terminator as Negotiator
Frequently a person will serve as deal negotiator as well as document producer. Terrible Terminator may have been an integral part of the negotiations during which he facilitate oral communication and interaction between the parties.[6] Unfortunately, all too often when he starts the draft he assumes a wholly different role, the objectives of which sometimes appear to be to obfuscate rather than facilitate. His written communication becomes verbose and stilted; "LBS" as one of my clients puts it (and the "L" stands for Legal").

3.4   Communication with Client
The first draft of a licensing agreement is often designed to communicate with the person instructing the Terminator.[7] The Terminator usually needs answers to many questions and concerns, for example:
(a) have I understood your instructions;
(b) have I expressed your instructions as you intended;

(c) there are some business issues I note were not discussed; please give me guidance;

(d) there are business and legal risks; please assess the risk/benefits involved; and

(e) there are some risks that we should perhaps not even consider at this time; they may be too remote or may even be insulting. Please assess and give guidance.

The Terminator normally does not have the authority to answer these questions; only the deal negotiators can answer them. It is obvious in our case study that the Start President has not fully addressed all the business issues, as we will see in more detail later.

The first draft released to the Start President must:

(a) be a document that he understands;

(b) communicate a request for answers to all the Terminator's questions; and

(c) clarify the unresolved issues.

The Start President will want the next draft to be designed to favorably but fairly communicate Start's business position with Intel-co as negotiators. The licensing relationship is a long-term affair; the negotiators want to keep the number of surprises to a minimum. Better that they spend their energies developing and marketing the Licensed Software than sorting out misunderstandings.

Unfortunately, with the style of the First Draft, the Start President will not easily understand what is being expressed and will have great difficulty explaining and selling to his negotiating counterpart at Ination the business issues which are expressed in the document.

Tactic: Recognize drafting as part of the negotiating process.

3.5   Terrible Terminator's Second Draft of the Release

It is clear Terrible Terminator needs help or he will face client rebellion. When the best precedent available is still incomprehensible to persons who must live with it, it is necessary to implement your anti-Terrible Terminology tactics. To determine what is the substance of this release, let us break it down into its individual parts as follows:

SECOND DRAFT

2.   Release

2.1 Licensor

(a)   releases, relinquishes, acquits and forever discharges

(b)   Licensee, its officers, directors, shareholders, employees, agents, legal representatives, subsidiaries, affiliates, attorneys, successors and assigns,

(c)   of and from any and all debts, obligations, reckonings, promises, covenants, agreements, contracts, endorsements, bonds, specialties, controversies, suits, actions, causes of action, trespasses, variances, judgments, executions, damages, claims, demands, rights, titles, interests, charges, encumbrances, or liens of any kind or sort whatsoever or howsoever arising, in law or in equity, whether known or unknown, whether liquidated or unliquidated, whether in tort or in contract,

(d)   which they or any of them had, now has, or in the future may have against Licensee, its officers, directors, shareholders, agents, legal representatives, subsidiaries, affiliates, attorneys, successors and assigns, arising out of, for, under, upon or by reason of or in connection with or relating to, directly or indirectly, (i) the 1992 License Agreement, or (ii) any of the following acts or omissions of Licensee, its officers, directors, shareholders, employees, agents, legal representatives, subsidiaries, affiliates, attorneys, successors and assigns, in connection with or relating to or arising out of or by virtue of any of the following:

(1) any loss, cost or damage relating to, or arising out of any breach of fiduciary duty,

(2) breach of any duty of good faith or fair dealing,

(3) breach of confidence,

(4) undue influence, duress,

(5) economic coercion,

(6) conflict of interest,

493

(7) negligence,

(8) bad faith,

(9) malpractice,

(10) intentional negligent infliction of emotional or mental distress,

(11) tortuous interference with corporate governance or prospective business advantage,

(12) breach of contract,

(13) deceptive trade practices,

(14) libel, slander, conspiracy,

(15) any claim of wrongfully marketing the Licensed Software,

(16) the charging, contracting for, taking, reserving, collecting or receiving of interest in excess of the highest lawful rate applicable (i.e. usury) , or any violations of federal or state law,

(17) any violations of federal copyright rules, laws or regulations, or

(18) any violation of the federal antitrust acts.

2.2 Licensor further agrees that neither it nor any of its legal representatives or successors, will institute, prosecute or in any way aid in the institution or prosecution of any claim, demand, action or cause of action no existing or hereafter asserted against Licensee, its officers, directors, shareholders, employees, agents, legal representatives, subsidiaries, affiliates, attorneys, successors and assigns, arising out of or by virtue of or in connection with or relating to any of the foregoing.

Now one can see what principles the release is addressing. This subdividing or sculpturing of the clause makes it, for the reader, both more visually appealing and easier to analyze.

Tactic: Use paragraph sculpturing for ease of reading and analysis.

3.6 Terrible Terminator's Third Draft

However, the reader still gets lost in the detail of each segment and will have difficulty finding the clause's essential purpose. Using essentially the same words, let us break the clause down even more, using definitions. The Third Draft follows.

THIRD DRAFT

2. Release

2.1 Licensor Releases Licensee of all Claims which it now has or in the future may have against the Licensee.

2.2 The Licensor shall not prosecute any Claim against the Licensee.

2.3 In this Article 2, the following words shall have the following meanings unless the context otherwise requires:

(a) "Licensor" means the Licensor, its officers, directors, shareholders, employees, agents, legal representatives, subsidiaries, affiliates, attorneys, successors and assigns.

(b) "Licensee" means the Licensee, its officers, directors, shareholders, agents, legal representatives, subsidiaries, affiliates, attorneys, successors and assigns.

(c) "Claims" means all debts, obligations, reckonings, promises, covenants, agreements, contracts, endorsements, bonds, specialties, controversies, suits, actions, causes of action, trespasses, variances, judgments, executions, damages, claims, demands, rights, titles, interests, charges, encumbrances, or liens of any kind or sort whatsoever or howsoever arising, in law or in equity, whether known or unknown, whether liquidates or unliquidated, whether in tort or in contract, arising out of, for, under, upon or by reason of or in connection with or relating to, directly or indirectly, the 1992 License Agreement or any of the following acts or omissions of, Licensee Related thereto:

(1) any loss, cost or damage to or arising out of governance or any breach of fiduciary duty,

(2) breach of any duty of good faith or fair dealing,

(3) breach of confidence,

(4) undue influence,

(5) duress,

(6) economic coercion,

(7) conflict of interest,

(8) negligence,

(9) bad faith,

(10) malpractice,

(11) intentional negligent infliction of emotional or mental distress,

(12) tortuous interference with corporate or relating prospective business advantage,

(13) breach of contract,

(14) deceptive trade practices,

(15) libel, slander, conspiracy,

(16) any claim of wrongful marketing the Licensed Software,

(17) the charging, contracting for, taking, reserving, collecting or receiving of interest in excess of the highest lawful rate applicable (i.e. usury),

(18) any violations of federal or state law,

(19) any violations of federal copyright rules, laws or regulations, or

(20) any violation of the federal antitrust act.

(d) "Prosecute" means prosecute, institute or in any way aid in the institution of prosecution.

(e) "Related" includes arising out of, by virtue of, under, by reason of or in connection with.

(f) "Releases" includes relinquishes, acquits and forever discharges.

Now our business decision-makers may understand the materials; it no longer has that peculiar "lawyer look" about it. At last we can see that the substance of this section is: "Licensor Releases Licensee of all Claims which it now has or in the future may have against the Licensee".

With our help, Terrible Terminator has a clause that can now be analyzed for its merits. Now that we can read the clause, let us analyze what tactics helped produce the Third Draft.

The use of definitions in the Third Draft allows the Terminator to isolate issues for the reader. We can now more readily see the substance of the release, and see who is doing the releasing, who is being released and what is released. Definitions can help the Terminator "achieve clarity and consistency without burdensome repetition".

Tactic: Use definitions to achieve clarity.

3.7 "Unless the Context Otherwise Requires"

Section 2.3 starts out "In this Article 2, the following words shall have the following meanings, unless the context otherwise requires". The last five words negatively influence the definition section. Every time a defined word appears the reader will be required to decide whether the definition applies or whether the "context" of the agreement here or in any other place otherwise requires another meaning. The goal of the use of definitions was to increase precision and the "ease of reading and analysis". Instead the words it unless the context otherwise requires" reduces precision and makes the agreement more difficult to read.

Tactic: Drafting laziness should not detract from precision.

3.8 "Expansive Definitions"

Some "definitions" do not define the meaning; i.e., confine the meaning of the word to certain specifics. Instead, statements often included in the definition section expand the meaning of the words used. The Third Draft indicates that the word "Releases" includes certain things. It does not say that the word "Releases" does not include any other things. The reader has to decide what the word "Releases" means and whether that word adds anything to the list of included items. Sometimes an expansive "definition" is appropriate; more often it gives rise to confusion.

Tactic: Wherever possible, design definitions to limit and not expand the meaning.

3.9 Coupled (Tripled?) Synonyms

The Third Draft clearly illustrates the long-standing use of strings of synonyms. Well-worn phrases such as "releases, relinquishes, acquits and forever discharges" are used. For many, standard strings of synonyms always appear and an incomplete feeling exists without presence of all the words. Sometimes, strings of synonyms are used by Terminators who are insecure about the meaning of the individual word, and, as a result of their insecurity they include them all Can we, as Dick suggests, safely reduce "releases, relinquishes, acquits and forever discharges" to if releases"? Similarly, can words that have larger scope be used (such as of affiliates") and eliminate companion words with a narrower but included scope (such as "subsidiaries")?

Terrible Terminator now should undertake the task of rewriting the release to keep the meat and throw out the filler.

Tactic: Eliminate redundant words - less is more.

3.10 Boilerplate Produces a Checklist

The Third Draft is now useful as a checklist of the issues to be considered in writing the next draft of the release.

Tactic: Precedents (however written) are a valuable source when developing checklists.

3.11 Long, Long Sentences Increase the Risk of Errors

The First Draft illustrates the significant risk of error due to its length and the resulting stress placed on the typist. In the definition of "Licensee" in the Third Draft, you can see that the word "employee" was omitted. Terrible Terminator will have difficulty noticing this error because the error is lost in the mass of words.

Will a court find that the Licensee's employees are not released due to the omission? It may have to if it follows the rule of law that every insertion and omission is done for a reason[16].

Tactic: Avoid, verbose, sloppy writing that may produce surprising results.
Tactic: Proof read long, long sentences carefully.

3.12 Cross References Must be Precise

In Section 2.2 of the Second Draft, Terrible Terminator provided that the "Licensor ... will not ... prosecute ... any claim ... against Licensee . . . arising out of. . . or relating to any of the <u>foregoing</u>". In the First Draft this word "foregoing" was the last word of the long, long sentence. Does it refer to the 20 causes of action that are listed in the description of a "claim" or does it refer only to some of them? Does it refer back to anything else? The word "foregoing" does not provide any precise reference back.

Cross-references within an agreement are always a potential source of error, particularly as a document is amended and the references change their position. There is no need to compound the problem by using words that are imprecise and which, many feel, should be dropped from the legal vocabulary.

Tactic: Verify Cross-references.
Tactic: Forego the use of imprecise old English words.

3.13 Lists

In Section 2.3(c) of the Third Draft, Terrible Terminator compiled a list of claims. This compilation must have exhausted Terrible Terminator's imagination; but is it sufficiently exhaustive? If anything is omitted, he may suffer from the application of the Latin maxim, *Inclusio unius est exclusio alterius*, (i.e., if you "specify something but not everything in the same category the reader may infer that the unspecified items have been deliberately omitted"). Notice that Terrible Terminator did not introduce his list with the saving words "including without limitation". Terrible Terminator using those saving words might now go through his list of 20 causes of action to see if he may safely delete the repetitious or inappropriate ones.

Tactic: Phrase lists carefully; avoid application of Latin maxims.

3.14 User Friendly Language

Software developers are making great efforts to produce user-friendly software and related manuals. Borland International, Inc. has endeavored to combine user-friendly language with complex legal issues in its standard license agreement. The following is an extract from one of Borland's licenses:

No-Nonsense™ License Statement

Both United States copyright law and international copyright provisions protect this software. Therefore, you must treat this software just like a book, except that you may copy it onto a computer to be used and you may make archival copies of the software for the sole purpose of backing-up our software and protecting your investment from loss.

By saying, "just like a book", Borland means, for example, that this software may be used by any number of people, and may be freely moved from one computer location to another, so long as there is no possibility of it being used at one location while it's being used at another or on a computer network by more than one user at one location. Just like two different people in two different places can't read a book at the same time, neither can two different people in two different places use the software at the same time. (Unless, of course, Borland's copyright has been violated or the use is on a computer network by up to the number of users authorized by additional Borland licenses as explained below.)

There is often an attempt to get the technical users to "buy into" the license agreement and push it through the legal department so there will be no delay before they can start using the software. User-friendly language permits the technical users to better assess the risks/benefits and guide the lawyers concerning the level of risk assumption that is acceptable.

Tactic: Use user-friendly language if possible.

3.15 Concise But Precise

Recently, I was involved in the development of a strategic Alliance of many parties where the goal of the drafting style had to be articulated to avoid inconsistency as the various Terminators proposed changes to clarify the business intent. Remember, drafting should be "not only concise, but precise, using business English without ambiguity".

Increasingly our clients are demanding "simple" documents. Too often this reflects a desire to remove all legal principles and legal language from the document. As Mellinkoff states in "Rule 5" of his superb book on drafting "Legal Writing: Sense & Nonsense"

RULE 5: WRITE LAW SIMPLY. DO NOT PUFF, MANGLE OR HIDE.

The only thing about legal writing that is both unique and necessary is law. To simplify legal writing, first get the law right. You can't simplify by omitting what the law requires or including what the law forbids. The better you know the law the easier to decide what law ought to go in, and what is overkill or window dressing.

Tactic: Simple is not stupid: simple expresses the substance of the business and legal intent succinctly.

3.16 Licensor/Licensee

In an earlier version of the Third Draft, Terrible Terminator noticed that Section 2.2 had been typed, "The Licensee shall not Prosecute any Claim against the Licensee. Despite repeated reviews, this error continued; "Licensor" and "Licensee" are not sufficiently visually distinct and errors are

497

almost invited. Occasionally on receiving a long document that uses "Licensee" and "Licensor", it may be optically scanned into a word processor and words with suitable names or acronyms can be replaced. Virtually every document will have "Licensor" and Licensee" switched at least once. With the present search and replace word processing facilities, there is no continuing reason to use indistinct words like "Licensee", "Licensor", "Lessee", "Lessor".

Tactic: Use distinctive words to describe the parties; avoid both "Licensor" and "Licensee".

3.17 Block Capitals

Many agreements use block capitals for every defined word, for example "LICENSOR" and "LICENSEE". These blocked words frequently BLOCK the communication flow; a feature that should be retained for emphasis has been squandered on a defined word. Using initial upper case letters serves the purpose of distinguishing defined words.

Tactic: Do not use BLOCK letters for defined words; it BLOCKS the communication flow.

3.18 Visual Appeal

With improved laser printers and libraries of available fonts, Terrible Terminator could make his document visually attractive as well as comprehensible. Visual appeal may overcome a reader's initial negative reaction to a complex document.

Tactic: Make your documents visually attractive.

To the greatest extent possible, the licensing documents should assist in the marketing of software rather than being a hindrance to the marketing. The marketing process should never stop.

Tactic: Market! Market! Market!

4. TERRIBLE TERMINATOR WRITES AN "EXCLUSIVITY" CLAUSE

Terrible Terminator looks again at his President's second instruction Start gets all U.S. and England and realizes that this refers to the exclusivity of Ination's distribution rights. Terrible Terminator writes, "Start hereby grants to Ination the sole and exclusive license to market the Licensed Software in the United States and England.

4.1 Use of Specialized Words

What does "sole and exclusive" mean to the reader? Does it mean that Start can market the Licensed Software in the United States and in England along with Ination? Can any of Start's other distributors market it in the United States or in England? Can Start license the Licensed Software to a company based in Canada for use in its U.S. offices?

The words "sole and exclusive" selected by Terrible Terminator do not resolve these issues. Indeed, under Canadian law they are a contradiction of terms. "An exclusive license gives the licensee the right to exercise the [intellectual property rights] as against all persons, including the licensor. A sole license gives to the licensee the right to exercise the intellectual property rights as against all persons except the licensor". It would be better if words such as "sole" and "exclusive" were not used in the grant clause since their specialized legal meaning is not apparent from their ordinary usage.

Tactic: Be careful with words that have specialized legal meanings.

4.2 Isolate Separate Business/Legal Issues

Instead of using legal "buzz words", Terrible Terminator could write a separate section setting out in detail the extent of the "exclusivity" which is granted to Ination. When isolated in a separate section, the business issues can be more fully communicated to the business decision makers. Examples of issues to be considered are:

(a) Will all licenses to Canadian companies require the user to be situated in Canada?

(b) If other distributors are appointed for other countries within the European Common Market, is it legally possible to restrict these distributors to specific territories within the European

Community or will such restrictions violate the "one market" principles set out in Article 85, the doctrine of exhaustion, or elsewhere?, and

(c) How will cross-referrals be dealt with by Start and all its authorized distributors? For example, who provides support installation, and who delivers the Licensed Software and the related manuals?

Tactic: Assist the business decision maker; write early drafts to set out the issues.

4.3 Consider Footnotes

In the first draft released to the Start President, Dreadful Terminator could use footnotes to discuss the risk/benefits of issues raised. This form of communication will let the President more readily understand what issues the Terminator is addressing and assess the merits of the various alternatives available.

Tactic: Use footnotes in early drafts to improve communication with business decision maker.

5. BEST EFFORTS

Terrible Terminator sees that his President had written "Best Efforts" in marketing and writes "Ination shall devote its best efforts to the promotion and licensing of the Licensed Software".

5.1 Best Efforts

"Best Efforts" is often used in agreements, and not always as a result of drafting laziness. It may be used because:

(a) the parties have developed a trust level between them and do not want to disrupt the relationship by pressing for more precision;

(b) the parties are unable to predict market acceptance of the product; and

(c) Terminators think it has well recognized meaning.

Unfortunately when the trust relationship collapses or the Licensor feels his product is not being adequately exploited, the parties will find out that, although the term "best efforts" has been the subject of frequent litigation, it is uncertain and ambiguous. A "party that signs a 'best efforts' contract has placed himself in a risky and uncertain situation."

Tactic: Avoid, the phrase "best efforts"; it may be an invitation to litigation

5.2 Reasonable Efforts

Instead of using "best efforts", Terrible Terminator decides to use reasonable efforts". Unfortunately, Terrible Terminator has made no improvement. There appears to be no Canadian case that defines "reasonable efforts"; likely this phrase is as uncertain and ambiguous as "Best Efforts".

Tactic: Use reasonable efforts to avoid the phrase "reasonable efforts" too.

5.3 Minimum Performance

The parties might be better served if they addressed what minimum performance" will be acceptable. This performance may be in terms of:

(a) media advertising to be undertaken;

(b) displays at trade shows;

(c) direct mail promotions;

(d) minimum number of licenses to be obtained in a year; and

(e) minimum revenue to be earned in a year.

Requesting "minimum performance" requirements cuts through the "puffery" of the Licensee; and they then realistically assess the product and the market place.

Tactic: Specify minimum performance requirements.

6. START GETS 5% ROYALTY

Terrible Terminator reads his President's notes concerning royalty "Start gets 5% royalty" and decides that instead of a fixed royalty, Start is to receive a royalty based on revenues. He writes "Ination shall pay to Start a royalty equal to 5% of net sales.

6.1   "Sales" versus "Revenues"

Terrible Terminator has used the word "sales". Start's sophisticated software will be "licensed" rather than "sold". Software developers often refer to grants of fully paid perpetual licenses in the vernacular as "sales", but this word is not an appropriate legal word. Start and perhaps Ination, will want to retain rights to the Licensed Software; a "sale" could deprive them of these rights. "Sales" may be appropriate in licenses of tangible property and probably Terrible Terminator too carefully followed a license agreement designed for tangible property; such a precedent could be very misleading in a license of software.

Tactic: Beware of vernacular; it may change the legal context.

6.2   Source of Revenues

Terrible Terminator tries again and this time uses "5% of gross revenue from licenses". He has not contemplated:

(a) Ination using the Licensed Software itself and getting revenue from its own use;

(b) Ination using the Licensed Software in a joint venture where others gain the benefits of its use;

(c) Ination providing copies to its staff to be used for marketing purposes; and

(d) Ination providing copies to third parties for the purpose of review and testing.

Tactic: Consider non-revenue producing use or distribution of the Licensed Software.

6.3   Non-Cash Consideration

Terrible Terminator has not considered non-cash consideration; such as, shares in a closely held corporation or a grant-back to Ination of the right to distribute the sub-licensee's software. How will Ination value non-cash consideration which it might receive from a sub-distributor at the time of granting the rights to that sub-distributor?

Tactic, Consider the effect of no-cash consideration being included in the royalty base.

6.4   Meaning of "Revenues"

Terrible Terminator has not defined "revenues". Revenues could include:

(a) all fees for licenses of the Licensed Software granted by Ination to end users; and

(b) consideration for sublicenses granted to distributors who will market to end users including:

(i) initial payments for the right to distribute;

(ii) revenues earned from royalties generated by these distributors.

Tactic: Define "revenues".

6.5   Exceptions from Revenues

Terrible Terminator did not specify what would be excepted from revenues. Will Ination be able to deduct amounts resulting from:

(a)   sales taxes;

(b)   packaging;

(c)   reproduction of user manuals;

(d)   transportation;

(e)   return allowances; and

(f)   commissions?

Tactic: Specify the exceptions from gross revenues.

6.6   Invoices vs. Receipts

The event that triggers the royalty right is not stated in Terrible Terminator's clause. It could accrue:

(a)   when the Licensed Software is copied, perhaps on to a compact disk or floppy disk;

(b)   when the Licensed Software leaves Ination's premises;

(c)   when Ination invoices the Licensee; or

(d)   when Ination receives payment.

The licensor will want to have the triggering event as early as possible in the distribution process such as the shipping of the product, particularly if the product has significant cost to the Licensor.

Tactic: State the event that will trigger the right to the royalty.

6.7   Who Bears Risk of Non-Payment

With software licenses, "receipt" of the consideration is often chosen as the triggering event. Although Start shares the risk of bad receivables with Ination, this may not be an unreasonable risk since the cost of each copy of software is minimal and this risk may allow wider dissemination of the Licensed Software.

Tactic: Consider who bears the risk of a bad receivable.

6.8   Bundling

Ination may want to market the Licensed Software as a unit with another product it has (i.e., "bundle" the two products). It there is a single price or license fee, can it be broken down easily to determine Start's share?

Tactic: Consider the allocation of unsegregate license fees generated by bundled products.

6.9   Hardware Bundles vs. Software Bundles

The Licensed Software could be bundled with Interco's hardware or with other software marketed by Ination. The profit margin in the hardware may be very different from the profit margin in the software. The royalty rate might vary depending on the nature of the products bundled.

Tactic: Consider different rates for different bundled products.

6.10   License Fee vs. Support Fee

Ination could decide to make more profit for itself by increasing the amount it receives for support and other services it provides, keeping all such revenues for itself, and correspondingly reduce the license fee for the Licensed Software. Terrible Terminator might require Ination to deal with the Licensed Software in good faith and prevent it from obtaining an unfair advantage.

Tactic: Avoid the Licensee gaining advantage, by predatory pricing.

6.11   Ination's Affiliates

Terrible Terminator should contemplate Ination placing a subsidiary between itself and the end user to reduce the royalty payable to Start. The license agreement might require Ination to deal as if at arm's length with its affiliates. If this is not likely to provide adequate comfort, the License Agreement might prohibit dealing with an affiliate. A solution that is practicable will have to be tailored for each situation.

Tactic: Prevent Licensee's affiliates from scooping Licensor's profits.

7. CONFIDENTIALITY OF TRADE SECRETS

Terrible Terminator looks at his President's next note which says "Ination gets source code so it can provide support".

Terrible Terminator recognizes that the source code is the version of the Licensed Software understandable by computer programmers. It contains all the program's trade secrets including the algorithms, concepts and underlying ideas, none of which are likely protected by copyright. The best available protection (apart from patent protection) is secrecy, and here Start is about to show all to Ination. Start needs to keep control over these secrets. Hence, Terrible Terminator writes "Ination shall hold all the confidential information in trust for Start".

7.1   Contract vs. Trust

The use of the word "trust" illustrates the clash between the law of trusts and the law of contracts. Under trust law, the trustee holds the property f or the beneficiary and may not use the property for his own benefit except as expressly permitted by the trust. A trustee is expected to act for the benefit of the other party at the expense of his own interest. Generally speaking, such a requirement does not fit the model of North American business reality.

If the trustee breaches his fiduciary duty a court will likely order him to restore the beneficiaries to the position in which they would have been had the duty not been breached. There is trust law that indicates that this would require the payment of restorative amounts no matter how remote or unforeseeable they may be. In contrast, in normal contract law, the awarded damages usually must be foreseeable and closely connected with the breach.

Thus, the use of the word "trust" increases the duties of Ination so that Ination is essentially a guarantor against unauthorized disclosure and, on a breach of the trust, exposes Ination to almost unlimited liability. It is rare that a licensee would be prepared to accept that level of responsibility and exposure to liability.
Tactic: Consider the appropriate remedies: contract vs. trust.

7.2   What is Fair?

Start knows that, even though it has taken all reasonable measures, there is still the possibility of disclosure of its confidential information occurring at its own offices. Should the obligations for retaining the 'information as confidential be any higher for Ination than they are for Start? When the goal is to produce a "win-win" agreement, does the licensing Terminator have the right to propose a clause that is patently wrong?
Tactic: In short fuse negotiations; design the first draft to produce a "win-win" result.

7.3   The Word "Ensure"

Intending to be fairer to the Licensee in his next draft of the confidentiality clause, Terrible Terminator writes, "Licensee shall ensure that the confidential information shall not be disclosed". He may not have lessened the duty of care. "Ensure" is defined to mean "to warrant; to guarantee ... to secure, make safe ... to insure".

Some Terminators use the word "ensure" as if it were equivalent to "endeavor" or "take reasonable measures". The dictionary definition seems to result in a very high duty of care, almost to the point that there will be absolute liability. Commonplace usage and the dictionary definition seem to be contradictory. Perhaps the Terminator should use a more precise word.
Tactic: Use "ensure" only when you mean "guarantee" or "insure"; better yet, don't use it at all.

7.4   Precautions to be Taken

Terrible Terminator tries again. He writes "Licensee shall take the same precautions to hold the confidential information in confidence as it takes for its own trade secrets "

Consider Start's reaction when it learns that Ination has lost its trade secrets as a result of its normal (but now proven inadequate) protective measures. To avoid this embarrassment, Terrible Terminator could select an objective standard combined perhaps with Ination's standards if they are known to be high. For example, "Licensee shall take all reasonable measures available to it, and in any event not less than those used to protect its own secrets to keep the confidential information in the strictest confidence".

Tactic: Secret obligations should include objective standards

7.5 What are the Reasonable Steps to be Taken To Maintain Confidentiality?

In a case of highly sensitive information or in the case of a Licensee in a foreign jurisdiction which may not have generally adopted standards of secrecy, you might want to set out the reasonable steps Start requires of Ination. For example, Terrible Terminator could provide that the reasonable steps shall be:

(a) physical security of areas where access may be gained to the Confidential Information;

(b) security measures for electronic storage and transmission of data including or derived from any Confidential Information;

(c) controls on access to any computer facility and tape or disk library where any Confidential Information may be stored;

(d) visitor control; controls over photocopying Confidential Information;

(e) document and computer network control systems which limit access to the Confidential Information to employees and agents who have a need to know, which control system provides for a secured method of protection of sensitive data; and

(f) confidentiality agreements with the Licensee's employees, agents or invitees who are permitted access to Confidential Information.

Tactic: Consider stating what secrecy measures are required.

7.6 Duration of Secrecy Obligations

Terrible Terminator has not stated how long Ination must maintain the secrecy. Ination will be concerned about the costs of maintaining secrecy and the risk of inadvertent disclosure particularly after an extended period of time. Frequently, Terminators pick a figure such as "five years" or "twenty-one years" without much justification. It would be preferable to pick a time period more in line with the anticipated economic life of the trade secrets, or at the minimum, the time it would have taken for Ination to independently develop the technology itself.

7.7.1 Terrible Terminator has not relieved Licensee's obligations of confidentiality for any portion of the confidential information which enters the public domain.

In Canada, it might be permissible to require continued confidentiality even if the secret has been disclosed. This may not be the case in the European Community. For example, grounds for objection under Article 85(1) of the Treaty establishing the European Economic Community will not arise from a covenant requiring a distributor "not to reveal manufacturing processes or other know-how of a secret character, or confidential information given by the other party during the negotiation and performance of the agreements, as long as the know-how or information in question has not become public knowledge".

Tactic: Establish and justify the duration of secrecy obligations.

The Licensee may want to restrict its liability if it has taken all reasonable steps to protect the confidential information but through some inadvertence there has been a disclosure without some clause limiting the Licensee's obligations, it could be exposed to a claim for significant economic damages.

Tactic: Consider limiting Licensee's liability for inadvertent disclosure.

8. IMPROVEMENTS

Terrible Terminator looks at his President's notes and sees the sixth instruction: "We get rights to all improvements but Ination can use improvements it makes."

Terrible Terminator writes the following clause (which appears to be enforceable in Canada) to give effect to these directions of his President.

"Ination shall communicate to Start details of all improvements to the Licensed Software during the term of the license granted by this Agreement. Intellectual property rights to such improvements shall belong to Start but, during the term of its license of the Licensed Software, Ination shall have the exclusive right to exploit the improvements in the United States and England."

8.1   Does the Word "Improvement" Have a Meaning?

There seems to be little case law on what constitutes an "improvement" and what case law there is provides few clear-cut principles.[37] Examples of improvements to the Licensed Software could be:

(a) an improvement that enhances the Licensed Software's speed of processing and analyzing the user's data,

(b) an improvement that provides processing and analytical features that the Licensed Software does not have, or

(c) a program that performs tasks similarly to the Licensed Software but in a different way.

These improvements range from something that could be included in the computer program, to something that could be a "stand-alone" product, to something that is a different but competitive product. How will Ination know what it is required to disclose and turn over to Start? What can it do in related areas without being subject to an infringement claim?

Unfortunately Terrible Terminator gives us no guidance as to what "improvements" Ination is required to disclose and turn over to Start.

Tactic: Use words that have precise meanings or document invites "creative misinterpretation".

8.2   An Improvement Must "Infringe"

Some licensing Terminators have chosen to say that an improvement that must be communicated is an improvement that infringes the intellectual property rights of the product involved in this case the Licensed Software. This solution may be appropriate for a product that is the subject of a patent, but may be of little help if the software is protected by copyright. Does the copyright protect:

(a)   only the literal code of the Licensed Software;

(b)   the structure sequence and organization of the Licensed Software; and

(c)   the Licensed Software's user interface?

The case law has established that the literal code is protected, but that protection provides little assistance. The Whelan v. Jaslow case indicates a desire to protect structure, sequence and organization, but there is no general consensus as to how far copyright will protect structure, sequence and organization. There are numerous cases now before the courts trying to establish to what extent copyright will protect user interface, and the cases seem quite contradictory.

Thus, this solution provides little certainty to the business decision-makers who are involved. It would seem that the word "improvement" will have to be tailored for each agreement. Dreadful Terminator should provide precise description of the improvements intended by the parties; otherwise court may be asked to imply what terms were meant by the use of the word "improvement".

Tactic: Define the word "improvement".

8.3   Communication of Improvements

As well, the draft clause does not state when or how details of improvements are to be communicated. Is the communication to be in writing addressed to a stated technical representative or will disclosure in a casual conversation over a beer be sufficient? Does Ination have to disclose details of the improvement as soon as rudimentary details of the improvement are developed or can it wait until it has developed the improvement sufficiently to establish substantial commercial advantage?

Start's ability to patent any improvement may depend on early disclosure. However Ination may be reluctant to disclose rudimentary ideas especially towards the end of the term of the license. **Tactic: Make the draft answer "how, who, when, what".**

8.4   Term of Use of Improvement

The improvement clause must address the term during which each party may use the improvement. Terrible Terminator stated that Ination had exclusive rights to the improvement in the U.S. and England "during the term of its license of the Licensed Software". Let us assume that the term of the license of the Licensed Software is ten years and the term of protection for the improvement under copyright rules is 50 years. As drafted, Ination will lose its rights to use the improvement at the end of the ten years. This could cause significant harm if the improvement was a stand-alone product with an economic life lasting well beyond the ten years fully protected by copyright and the right to use the improvement being lost on the termination of the right to use the unimproved technology.
Tactic: Co-relate the term of use of improvements with the term of the underlying license.

8.5   Only in Canada You Say

Earlier I mentioned that the improvement clause may be valid in Canada. This is not likely the case either in the United States or England due to their restraint of trade rules. These rules might invalidate any provision which does more than require Ination to grant to Start a world-wide non-exclusive royalty-free license with the right to grant sublicenses. In Canada, for example, it is necessary to be wary that many practices may be in violation of rules of other jurisdictions that are designed to promote competition.
Tactic: Watch foreign anti-restraint of trade rules.

9. WARRANTIES

Terrible Terminator sees that his President also has written on the envelope "no warranties". Terrible Terminator decides that a disclaimer of all warranties of quality[43] should be included and writes a clause which was (and still may be) a standard in the U.S. software industry:

"Start gives no warranties expressed or implied except as specifically provided in this Agreement. WITHOUT LIMITATION, ALL IMPLIED WARRANTIES OF MERCHANTABILITY AND FITNESS FOR A SPECIFIC PURPOSE ARE SPECIFICALLY DISCLAIMED."

9.1   A Warranty by Any Other Name

A disclaimer of "warranties" may be useful in the United States under Section 2 of the Uniform Commercial Code. However, in Alberta, the Sale of Goods Act (Alberta), if it applies, refers to implied "conditions" of merchantability and fitness for a particular purpose. The same words are used in Ontario's and England's sale of goods legislation.
Tactic: Design warranties that are "fit for the purpose"
Tactic: Avoid clauses drafted for the specific rules of other jurisdictions.

9.2   You Wanted it to Work?

It is a moot point whether any of the Sale of Goods Act (Alberta), Section 2 of the Uniform Commercial Code, or the English Sates of Goods Act, 1979 applies to computer programs which are not mass marketed.

None of these pieces of legislation was designed to cover software. The attempts to force software into the unaccommodating legislative schemes produce potentially absurd results. Is the software a it good" if conveyed to the client on a disk but not a "good" if conveyed electronically with no physical copy being delivered?

A prudent licensing Terminator might want to assume that the sale of goods legislation applies. It is rare that the implied warranties are appropriate for products (particularly computer programs) licensed by a specifically designed licensing agreement. Accordingly, Dreadful Terminator was correct to disclaim the implied warranties of quality but should structure the disclaimer using words appropriate for Alberta, the United States and England, and at least refer to all it representations, warranties and conditions (expressed or implied, oral or written)

Tactic: Tailor warranties for each technology transfer.

9.3 Disclaimer "Fundamentally Breaches its Essential Purpose"

The Start President said there shall be "no warranties". However, the courts in Alberta, United States and England are not favorably predisposed to accept complete disclaimers of warranties of quality of goods, particularly if the bargaining powers of the two parties are not equal. Alberta courts look to see if there is a "breach" going to the root of the contract. American courts speak of the agreement "failing of its essential purposes" or of "unconscionability", and English courts look to the Unfair Contract Terms Act, 1977, to see if the exclusion of warranties of quality are "reasonable".

Start will have to decide whether there are sufficient grounds to justify the exclusions of warranties of quality so it can survive arguments of breach going to the root of the contract, failure of essential purpose, unconscionability or unreasonableness. If there is any reasonable risk, Start should consider providing a few basic warranties designed to prevent opening the door wide to a damage claim.

Tactic: Be satisfied that a total disclaimer of warranties of quality is appropriate.

9.4 Basic Warranties of Quality

Terrible Terminator decides that he should provide some basic warranties of quality. He writes "Start warrants that the Licensed Software shall function if used in accordance with the user manual".

Terrible Terminator has not specified any standard of quality. Did he mean that it would function in accordance with the specifications expressed in the user manual? Or is use in accordance with the user manual a condition precedent to the warranty?

Terrible Terminator should precisely set out the standards of quality. He might want to consider:

(a) What standards of quality will be used?:
- (i) Are there presently developed functional specifications? Are these specifications clearly and precisely written?
- (ii) If the functional specifications are not yet developed, how will they be approved so they can be used as standards of quality?

(b) Will there be acceptance tests and if so, how will they be designed?

(c) Who will perform the acceptance tests? Where? At whose expense? What periods of rectification are allowed? What are the consequences of acceptance tests not being passed?

(d) Will there be conditions precedent to a warranty claim? Is it fair for the licensee to lose its remedies if a condition precedent is not satisfied?

(e) How will the parties resolve disputes over quality?

(f) What are the remedies of breach of warranty? Are there any limitations on liability?

9.5 Conditional Warranties

Let us assume that Terrible Terminator wanted to make the warranty conditional upon the Licensed Software being used in accordance with the user manual. Often the benefits of warranties are available only upon the satisfaction of various conditions precedent. All too frequently, however, the conditions precedent has no correlation with the error that is actually encountered. Did the failure to operate in accordance with the user manual actually cause the quality defect which was encountered? Is it unreasonable to have the warranty voided for the non-satisfaction of an irrelevant condition precedent?

Tactic: Correlate conditions precedent to a warranty to the quality defect.

9.6   Back-Up Remedy

Terrible Terminator might have written as his warranty "Start warrants that the Licensed Software, when installed, shall perform in accordance with the Functional Specifications [defined elsewhere]. All other warranties expressed or implied, including all implied warranties of merchantability and forms for a specific purpose, are specifically disclaimed."

Consider Start being unable to install the Licensed Software due to technical errors. A court will be eager to hold that the only warranty is ineffective, and therefore the disclaimer is ineffective. Terrible Terminator failed to provide any back-up remedy in the event that Start's warranties all proved to be ineffective.

Some agreements provide for the possibility that the basic warranties provided are found to be unreasonable or do not cover the breach that actually occurs.[57] This concern is especially significant when the only warranties provided are to repair or replace the defective product. These agreements go on to provide a "backup remedy", such as payment of an amount pre-agreed to be liquidated damages or payment of the Licensee's direct damages up to a maximum dollar amount.

Tactic: Consider providing a back-up remedy.

10. TERM AND TERMINATION

Terrible Terminator sees the last note from his President: "five year term, renewable" and writes "This agreement shall take effect as of February 1, 1992 and shall continue in effect until January 31, 1997 and thereafter for successive periods of five years." He then proceeds to include the usual provisions that the agreement will terminate on insolvency, unremedied breach, or "upon 12 months notice from either party."

Note that Terrible Terminator did not provide that the agreement would renew automatically after every five-year period unless terminated by either party at the end of the fifth year. Thus the five-year term is irrelevant; the term will not expire after five years but keep running for an indefinite period until either party gives the 12 months notice. The Courts will not read in different conditions of termination when termination has been provided for in a license.[59]

Frequently, agreements provide for a long term such as "five years" or "life of the patent" but subsequently provide for termination after the expiration of a shorter period following one of the parties giving notice to the other. In these agreements, for all practical purposes, the term that the parties can rely on for business purposes is only the shorter term. The business decision-maker could be deceived by the reference to the longer term.

Tactic: State clearly the effective term of the agreement.

10.1   License Exceeding Patent Term

Terrible Terminator should keep in mind that in Canada, pat-Lies may contract for the term of a license of technology to exceed the term of its patent protection.[60] In contrast, the U.S. anti-restraint of trade rules may limit the obligations under a simple patent license to the term of the patent protection.

Tactic: Determine if the applicable law will allow for the obligations under a license agreement to exceed the term of statutory (e.g., patent, copyright) protection.

10.2   Terminating Events

Terrible Terminator provided that the "agreement" itself shall terminate upon the happening of certain events. What happens to all the rights and remedies after termination of the Agreement? A better approach for Terrible Terminator might be to determine all the rights and obligations in the agreement that require termination and then draft a termination clause for each group of similar rights and obligations. The converse of this approach is to consider what provisions of the agreement shall "survive" termination of the agreement.

Tactic: Define the terminating events for each right and obligation.

10.3 Consequences of Termination

Terrible Terminator could now consider the consequences of the termination, including:

(a) the Licensee ceasing to use the Licensed Software;

(b) the Licensee ceasing to use the Licensor's trademarks and logos;

(c) the Licensee returning to the Licensor all copies of the License Software in its possession;

(d) if the Licensee does not have the right to return all copies of the Licensed Software which are on hand for the purposes of resale, consider what right the Licensee has to dispose of its inventory. Rules in the United Kingdom and the United States might require such a right of disposition;

(e) if the Licensee has the right to dispose of inventory on hand at termination, the Licensor might want to have the right to perform an audit of this inventory. Otherwise, the Licensed Software might be reproduced surreptitiously following termination, and the Licensor would have no way of separating pre-termination copies from copies made after the termination;

(f) the Licensee paying all royalties earned pre-termination and, if Licensee has the right to sell its inventory, after termination; and

(g) the Licensor having a right to audit the Licensee's books and premises to satisfy itself that it has been paid in full and that the Licensee has ceased to use and reproduce the Licensed Software.

Tactic: Consider the consequences of termination.

10.4 Bankruptcy

Most license agreements provide for termination in the event of bankruptcy of the licensee. Some bankruptcy legislation may render that type of termination provision ineffective and give the trustee in bankruptcy the right to assume or reject the license agreement.

Tactic: Draft termination on bankruptcy provisions specifically for the relevant applicable bankruptcy laws.

11. INCLUSIVE LANGUAGE

Terrible Terminator included in his boilerplate, at the end of the agreement, a standard provision with an interesting typographical error: "words importing the masculine gender shall include the feminine and neutered gender."

This word "neutered" might apply to my "Garfield" sized ex-Tom cat. It would seem to have little other application.

Increasingly, Terminators are endeavoring to use "inclusive" language to avoid a masculine bias. With today's word processing capabilities, there is no excuse to use the masculine when the feminine could just as easily be used. I am often surprised to see the masculine used when my client is feminine.

Unfortunately elimination of gender in writing English is very difficult and this bias may never be overcome. The use of "you" and "we" in documents may help.

Tactic: Strive for inclusive language.

12. CONCLUSION

Terminators of licensing agreements should facilitate open communication, prevent misinterpretation and prevent unintended business and legal results. Instead of Terrible Terminology, licensing Terminators can produce precise and comprehensible agreements.

EXHIBIT C – AGREEMENT CHECKLISTS

AGREEMENT (CONTRACT) CHECKLISTS

The following checklists are intended to serve as a reminder for persons skilled in licensing. They are not intended to be used, as a rigid listing of what should be included in a technology license agreement, but rather to pose questions in the mind of the user as to whether or not each of the items needs to be considered as an issue and addressed in any given agreement.

Abbreviated checklist

- Date of the Agreement
- Full legal name and address of all parties to the contract
- Date contract work will start
- Date contract work will be completed
- Any other important dates for contract events
- Paragraph that says, in effect, if the scheduled dates change you are entitled to additional compensation
- Contract amount and how it is going to be paid
- Paragraph that says you can stop work if you are not paid (*For example: If customer fails to make any payment when due, you on 3 days written or fax notice may stop work until paid. In the event of suspension of work under this paragraph you will have no liability to customer for delay or damage caused customer because of suspension of services and will be entitled to keep all money previously paid.*)
- Arbitration provision, if desired
- Warranty, if any
- Notice provision
- Waiver provision
- Entire agreement provision
- How to amend contract provision
- Severability provision
- Signatures

Extended checklist

1. PARTIES AND BACKGROUND
    1.1 Parties
        Identification
        Capacity or corporate authority, names and addresses
        Partnership titles, names and addresses of partners
        Legal capacity of foreign firms
    1.2 Effective Date of Agreement or Reference Date
    1.3 Place where Agreement is made
    1.4 Background/Recitals
        Licensed subject matter
        Prior relationship between parties
        What each party will contribute
        Statement of expectations
2. DEFINITIONS
    Accounting Year
    Affiliate
    Agreed Territory

Associate
Agreement
Acceptance Tests
Basic Technology
Components
Control
Confidential Information
Development
Documentation
Equipment
Exclusive Territory
Existing Process
Effective Date
Field of Use of Activity
Force Majeure
Improvement
License
Licensee
Licensor
Letter of Credit
Major Improvement
Minor Improvement
Maximum Liquidated Damages
Material Breach
Net Selling Price
New Process
Non-Exclusive Territory
Notice Period
Party, Parties & Parties Hereto
Patent(s)
Plant
Process
Product
Performance Guarantees
Standard of Quality
Start-Up Date
Subsidiary
Technical Information
Technical Services and Assistance
Third Person
Trademarks
Territory
Technology
Tribunal
Year

3. GRANT OF RIGHTS

3.1 Subject Matter of
    Patents
    Trademark
    Copyright
    Industrial design

Chip design
Know-how
Trade secret
3.2 Exclusivity
   a. Exclusive
      i. First right to negotiate for other exclusive territories
      ii. Duration of first to negotiate right
      iii. Matching offers of third party ("hard" first to negotiate)
      iv. Matching offer of Licensor before third party offers solicited ("soft" first to
           negotiate)
       v. Subject to licensor's rights
       vi. Subject to other license agreements
   b. Non-exclusive
3.3 Scope of Grant
   Make
   Use
   Sell
   Offer for sale
   Import
   Dispose
   Copy
   Modify
   Distribute
   Display
   Bundle
3.4 Field of Use
   a. Limited uses
   b. Solely in specified combination
   c. Style or size of product
   d. Sale or use limited to prescribed customers
   e. Sale or use through specified trade channels
3.5 Quantity Limitations
   a. Maximum
      i. Fixed number
      ii. Percent of industry sales
      iii. Percent of Licensor's sales
3.6 Price Limitations
3.7 Tying Arrangements
3.8 Territory
   a. Exclusive
   b. Limited exclusive
   c. Non-exclusive
3.9 Transferability
   a. Non-transferable
   b. Transferable
   c. Transferable to Affiliates
3.10 Additional Grants
   a. Affiliates - different locations
   b. Replacement (for equipment specific license)
   c. Relocation (for site license)
3.11 Most Favorable Terms & Conditions

a. Scope of clause
    i. All terms generally
    ii. Royalty terms only
b. Application of more favorable terms
    i. Automatically
    ii. At Licensee's option
c. Original Licensee entitled to
    i. Notification of later license
    ii. Copy of later license

3.12 Special Aspects Concerning Patents
  a. Maintenance in force of patent
  b. Duty to pay renewal fees
  c. Option of Licensee to acquire patents

3.13 Where Licensed Patent Invalid
  a. Right to terminate
  b. Effect on royalty payments
  c. Liability of Licensor to Licensee
    i. Limited to duty to cooperate
    ii. Arbitrary amount (e.g. not exceeding license fee)
    iii. Not in excess of compensation received from Licensee

3.14 Sublicenses
  a. Prohibited
  b. Permitted
    i. Affiliates
        A-So long as deals as if at arm's length
        B. Royalties guaranteed by Licensee
        C. Compliance guaranteed by Licensee
        D. Sharing of royalties
            (1) Lump sum payments
            (2) Running royalties
        E. Reporting of sublicense being granted
        F. Form of sublicense
        G. Effect of termination of license
            (1) Termination of sublicense
            (2) Right of Licensor to assume sublicense
            (3) Obligation of Licensor to assume sublicense

3.15 Improvements
  a. Definitions of "improvement"
  b. By Licensor - Licensor to Licensee
    i. Inclusion in license
    A. Automatic
    B. At option of licensee
    C. At option of Licensor
    ii. Exclusive
    A. Royalty free
    B. Compensation
    iii. Non-Exclusive
    A. Royalty free
    B. Compensation
    iv. Except out Improvements made under special contract to third parties
  c. By Licensee - "Grantback" license to Licensor

ii. After milestone is achieved
b. Fixed periodic payments
   i. Interest on overdue payments
   ii. Acceleration on default
c. Credit against future royalties
15.3 Fixed Sum Payment in Lieu of Royalties
15.4 Fixed Sum Combined with Royalties
15.5 Royalties for different Components of Licensed Technologies - Separate Pricing or Pricing as a Whole
a. Patent
b. Trademarks
c. Copyright
d. Mask works
e. Trade secrets
15.6 Variable Consideration
a. Rate
   i. Flat sum per unit
   ii. Flat percentage of gross or net sales
   iii. Rate decreases or increases with increasing sales
   iv. Differential
   v. Temporarily low
   vi. Flat sum per year
   vii. Flat sum for paid-up license
   viii. Dollar amount ceiling on annual payments
   ix. Dollar amount ceiling on aggregate payment
   x. Lower royalties if Licensee opts to make a lump sum payment
   xi. Annual or aggregate dollar amount ceiling on royalties to apply if Licensee opts to make a lump sum payment
   xii. Payment until a certain number of units are sold, then an increase or decrease in initial rate (or a fully-paid license)
b. Base
   i. Number of units
      A. Manufactured, sold or processed
      B. All units or patented only
      C. Definition of "sold"
      D. One payment per unit
   ii. Supplies or raw materials used
      A. Volume basis
      B. Cost basis
   iii. Use Compensation received by Licensee
   iv. Net sales of Licensee
      A. All articles or patented only
      B. Definition of "sold"
      C. Definition of "net sales"
      D. Effect of credit losses
      E. Sales to affiliates
   v. Profits of Licensee
15.7 Royalties for combination products
a. Any royalty relief
b. Simple algebraic reduction
c. Subject to floor rate

15.8 Royalties to continue past patent expiry during period of regulatory exclusivity

15.9 Nationality of parties

    a. Foreign Licensee/sublicensee to be responsible for withholding taxes

    b. Licensee to pay all royalties at full rate regardless of where the "sales" take place

    c. Licensee to provide Licensor certificate for withholding tax paid

15.10 Royalty Payment

    a. Payment mandatory

        i. In advance of each royalty period

        ii. At end of each royalty period

    b. Payment optional

        i. To retain exclusiveness

        ii. To maintain license

    c. In satisfaction of duty to exploit

    d. Carry over of payments from one period to another

15.11 Related Matters

    a. Allowance for royalties payable to others

    b. Exemption on sales to other Licensees

    c. Interest on overdue payments

    d. Effect of termination on obligation to pay accrued royalties

16. SETTLEMENT OF PAYMENT

    16.1 Reporting

        a. Frequency

        b. Content of royalty reports

    16.2 Maintenance and Inspection of Records

        a. Duty to maintain record--.

        b. Account for progress

        c. Right of Licensor to inspect

            i. Financial records

            ii. Production records

            iii. Inventory on hand

            iv. Measures implemented to maintain secrecy, quality control, etc.

        d. Inspection by Licensor

        e. Inspection by independent auditor

            i. Method of selection of auditor

            ii. Pre-agreement as to satisfactory auditors

        f. Time limitation

        g. Information confidential

    16.3 Cost of Audit

    16.4 Withholding of Taxes

    16.5 Designation of Currency of Obligation and Payment

        a. Currency of the obligation

            i. Local currency

            ii. Foreign currency

        b. Currency of the payment

            i. Local currency

            ii. Local currency - restricted circumstances

            iii. Foreign currency

        c. Rate of exchange

            i. Source

            ii. Date for determination

    16.6 Foreign Exchange Controls

18.5 Licensor reserves right to examine each assignee and withhold consent
    a. Unreasonably
    b. Within reason
18.6 Copy to Licensor
18.7 Rights and liabilities of licensor regarding royalties

19. ACCEPTANCE TESTS
  19.1 Performance of Tests
    a. Time period within which acceptance tests must be conducted
    b. Notification to Licensor of intention to conduct test
    c. Rights and obligations of Licensor
      i. To attend at testing
      ii. Right to conduct or participate in testing
      iii Obligation of Licensor to provide advisor or conduct tests
    d. Tests to be conducted
    e. Records of test results
    f. Raw materials, components or machinery, etc. obtained from source other than Licensor
      i. Licensee to supply
      ii. Allowance for pretest by Licensor to ensure these meet with specifications
    g. Performance test criteria
      i. Quantity of output
      ii. Quality of output
    h. Acceptance test condition precedent to payment
    i. Test almost passed
      i. Partial payment
      ii. No payment
    j. Test not passed due to Licensor's fault
      i. Extension period given to Licensor to attempt to remedy
      ii. Where remedied - penalty for delay or no penalty
      iii. Where not remedied - penalty or non-payment of retention amount
    k. Test not passed due to Licensee's fault
      i. Payment without penalty
    1. Where test not run within time set due to delays caused by Licensee
    m. Payment of retention amount without requirement of test
    n. Allowance for interruption of tests by force majeure
  19.2 Failure to meet performance guarantee
    a. Modifications at Licensor's cost
    b. Costs shared
    c. Departure from operating conditions - modifications by Licensee
    d. Failure resulting from engineering not part of technology
    e. Failure resulting from design information provided by Licensee
    f. Failure resulting from raw materials supplied by Licensee
  19.3 Repetition of tests
  19.4 Delay in commencement - extension
  19.5 Warranty
  19.6 Fulfillment of performance guarantee
  19.7 Deemed fulfillment of performance guarantee

20. WARRANTIES OF QUALITY
  20.1 Merchantability
  20.2 Fitness for Purpose
  20.3 Conformity with specifications
  20.4 Commercial utility

b. Initial training

c. Supervision

d. Provision of information for safe operation and handling

29.2 Duties of Licensee Relating to

a. Engineering

b. Installation

c. Process operation

d. Maintenance

e. Modifications

f. Training

g. Supervision

h. Establishment of safety and security check systems

29.3 Safety Tests

a. Initial testing

b. Periodic inspections

29.4 Development of Emergency Plan

29.5 Accident Investigation and Reporting

30. ENVIRONMENTAL MATTERS

30.1 Liability of Licensor for Environmental Damage

a. To Licensee

i. Full liability

ii. Limited liability

iii. No liability

b. To third parties

30.2 Representations and Warranties by Licensor

30.3 Disclosure

a. Right of Licensee to conduct environmental inspection at Licensor's facilities

b. No liability if full Disclosure and Right to Inspect

30.4 Insurance

31. USE OF OTHER PARTY'S NAME IN PROMOTIONS

31.1 Identification of Licensee in Licensor's Self-Serving Promotional Materials

31.2 Identification of Licensor in Licensee's Self-Serving Promotional Materials

31.3 No Disclosure of the Relationship or of this Agreement being Executed

32. TERM

32.1 Duration

a. Effective date

b. Term

i. Life of patent(s)

ii. Specified period

iii. Initial period subject to renewal

c. Option to cancel

i. At any time on notice

ii. Within an initial period

iii. After a stated period

33. TERMINATION

33.1 By licensor

a. Any default of Licensee

b. Bankruptcy or insolvency of Licensee

c. Ceases to carry on business

d. Non-payment of royalties

e. Non-payment of minimum royalties

EXHIBIT D - SOFTWARE AGREEMENTS NEGOTIATION CONSIDERATIONS

E-COMMERCE SOFTWARE AGREEMENTS FOR THE INTERNET

There is little question that the Internet's time as a marketing and retail pipeline has arrived. Once the exclusive realm of scientists and other techno-types whose vision of a powerful world economy driven by interconnected personal computers bordered on religious zealotry, the Internet - and the World Wide Web as its proxy - is fast becoming the sales medium of choice for many businesses.

In fact, no sector of the retail economy fails to be represented by virtual "storefronts," often located in virtual "malls". And, by all measures, the rush to go on-line continues apace: automobile, insurance, banking, brokerage, travel, entertainment and numerous other businesses are all expanding their efforts to enter into the already crowded digital marketplace. Not only are individuals increasingly ordering retail goods and services on-line1, businesses are doing an ever-increasing volume of business with other businesses via the World Wide Web. As certain key statistics suggest, the stage has been set for high growth in the electronic economy:

- the value of business-to-business commerce transacted over the Internet in 1997 was estimated by industry analysts to be $8 billion - a 10-fold increase from the prior year;
- 60 percent of respondents to a recent nationwide poll indicated that they have made a purchase of goods or services via the Internet;
- the value of on-line retail commerce is expected to reach 4.8 billion dollars in 1998 – double 1997's figure; and
- the value of Internet retail sales alone exceeded $17 billion in 2002

The use of "e-commerce software" by businesses engaging in Internet-based transactions has increased hand-in-hand with the dramatic increase in the volume of Internet commerce. One important key to the success of any on-line venture is the software applications designed to securely, promptly and efficiently handle on-line transactions.

Given the cyberspeed at which the Internet and the e-commerce landscape has evolved, any company that wishes to license or have developed on its behalf e-commerce software should be aware of certain concerns that may arise in addition to those that typically arise in a traditional software licensing or development arrangement. Accordingly, this article will examine key aspects of drafting and negotiating agreements for the licensing by a company of e-commerce software for use in its on-line business applications.

Putting the Bottom Line On-Line

Most e-commerce software for use in Web-based business applications will likely require some customization to meet the needs of a particular customer. The customer should, therefore, be sure to perform its due diligence on the software vendor itself, because the software will only be as good as the custom work performed by the vendor. There are a number of factors that companies should consider in selecting an e-commerce software vendor:

Compare "Bargains". Customers should comparison shop. Because the Web software industry is fairly new, costs for software to run similar Web applications may vary significantly. As with any other service business, you often get what you pay for; Web commerce software outfits offering low monthly fees often couple those low fees with a low level of service.

Think quality. A Website is only as good as its last hit. A vendor's reputation among its other customers for service and reliability should be a key factor in making your choice. As far as an on-line customer is concerned, your Website is your business; e-commerce software that operates slowly, poorly, inconsistently, or that is unavailable for significant periods will cause aggravation for the business and, more importantly, lost sales, customers and cash.

Consumer demand Another key factor in choosing an appropriate vendor is the need to strike a balance between the customer's needs and the vendor's capabilities. Businesses with established Web sites that purchase commercial, off-the-shelf e-commerce software and which require little more than application integration and occasional "break-fix" services may wish to avail themselves of the services of an independent software or Internet consultant and save the costs associated with obtaining the same services from a full-service vendor. Conversely, the economies of scale and the options for expansion in available services inherent in going with an end-to-end provider may augur in favor of signing up with a bigger provider.

Financial commitment. Customers should carefully investigate not only the vendor's reputation and technical capabilities, but also its financial wherewithal. E-commerce software providers range in size from industry giants like Microsoft and IBM to nimble start-ups managed from university dorm rooms by computer science majors with a Pentium chip and a dream. The trade-offs in choosing one over the other can be significant. Not only, as discussed above, will businesses licensing e-commerce software have to make a determination as to the scope of services they will need, but any business will want to make certain that its vendor (and the vendor's vendors) will be around to service and update the software – a commitment that will often require considerable financial and other resources of the vendor. There is also tremendous ongoing consolidation and reorganization occurring in the software industry. The vendor that the customer contracted with yesterday may be snapped up by the customer's competition tomorrow, and customers should therefore ensure that the provisions of the license help ensure that the customer will always be dealing with a vendor that it knows and can trust.

Customer Service. Customers should (apart from making sure that a vendor has a solid record of fixing bugs and providing timely service for and updates to the e-commerce software) investigate the best types of metrics for the customer's business to measure hits, drops, response times, return trips and the like, and ensure that the e-commerce software ultimately licensed provides useful feedback that is tailored to that customer's business needs.

Evaluating Contract Clauses

The customer should carefully review the terms of any contract provided by a vendor to be sure that the agreement appropriately addresses the customer's current and future e-commerce needs and business objectives. The following analysis highlights issues that typically will arise in such transactions:

Contract Basics

Scope of License: One of the key issues that the customer must negotiate with the vendor is the proper scope of the software's use. The software licensor will likely place certain use restrictions in the license and set the license fees accordingly. For example, software licensors may seek to impose restrictions on where the software may be physically located and who may access the software – an obvious set of considerations where the licensee has outsourced its Website to a third party or where the customer anticipates that third parties will have the right to use the software directly by logging on to the customer's Website.

Trial Periods, Testing and Acceptance: The customer should consider the desirability of licensing the software for a limited period of time to determine whether the software is appropriate for its intended use and will be compatible with the other systems of the customer. An obvious advantage of this approach is that the customer will be able to evaluate the software without having to incur the expense of entering into a long-term license arrangement. Many vendors will agree to license the software for a brief testing period – often 90 days – but any vendor that consents to this sort of arrangement will also typically not provide any warranties with respect to the software or its performance during the testing period.

Whether the software is purchased on a trial basis or licensed outright, the software license should provide for a period when the customer has the right to test the software to ensure that it – and any customizations made to it – function properly and in accordance with the functional, technical and performance specifications agreed upon by the parties prior to signing the license agreement. For

530

example, the specifications would typically address such details as response time – a key consideration for e-commerce applications. If the software fails to meet the acceptance test criteria, the customer should have the right to require the software vendor to resolve any problems within a specified period of time and resubmit the software for testing again. The agreement should also provide that the customer have the right to reject the software and terminate the license agreement without penalty in the event the acceptance testing has not been satisfactorily completed and the software installed and operating by a date certain. The purpose of this termination right is to create an incentive for the vendor to resolve problems quickly. The customer also may not want to be committed to a long-term license if the software has not been installed by a date certain. In addition, the inability of a software vendor to provide fully operational software within a reasonable time period may reflect poorly on the ability of the vendor to support the customer's needs over the term of the license.

Installation Assistance and Implementation Schedules: The customer should make certain that the agreement sets forth any assistance that the vendor will be required to provide the customer to install the software, particularly if the software will have to be modified to become compatible with the other operating system and application programs of the customer or a third-party Website host. If the installation services will be significant, the customer may want to consider negotiating a separate professional services contract. The customer should make certain that the scope of services, planned implementation schedules and fee structure for the installation and design services are clearly spelled out in the contract with as much precision as possible. The fee structure (fixed fee, per diem, time and materials, holdbacks, etc.) as well as the schedule for installation and any critical interim milestones should be clearly stated in the agreement or an exhibit. It also cannot be emphasized enough that if the Website on which the e-commerce software will be running is provided or supported by a third party, that third party may wish to be - and indeed, in some cases should be - included in the discussions with the e-commerce software vendor.

Training and User Documentation: The customer should make certain that it considers any initial and ongoing training that will be required by the customer in order to operate the e-commerce software. In the event that the software is be used by third parties the customer should make certain that the training obligation extends to these parties. The customer may also want to consider providing for a set training schedule or that at least a certain number of training hours be made available during a given period of time to ensure that the vendor will provide the training at time periods that are convenient for the customer. This approach also may help ensure that the vendor will not allocate training resources to its other customers to the disadvantage of the customer. The customer should also consider any specific documentation requirements that it may have. Ordinarily, a license agreement would also grant to the customer the right to use the documentation associated with the software. The customer should consider whether the user documentation is sufficient for its needs or whether it will require that the software licensor supplement the documentation with additional information or instructional materials.

Maintenance, New Releases and Updates: Because of the evolving nature of the e-commerce arena, most e- commerce customers will require ongoing maintenance services in connection with the software, as well as updates and new releases. This maintenance assistance could include items such as technical assistance, assistance in modifying the software to meet the specifications of the customer and extending the functionality of the software. The customer should note that software licensors frequently take the position that they not be required to provide maintenance services unless the customer updates the software for any new releases or updates within a period of time to be agreed. The customer should make certain in the license agreement that it will have the right to any new releases and updates to the software that are generally made available to the other licensees of the software. The right to receive new releases and updates should also grant to the customer the right to receive any associated changes in the documentation.

Term of the License: Software licenses for many non-Internet-based applications typically have a long term that would ensure that the customer would retain the right to use the software for a period of time sufficient to recoup its investment in the software. The dynamics of e-commerce over the Internet, however, can dramatically change this analysis: Many e-software licensees are wary of entering into long-term licenses because the medium is changing so rapidly that software becomes obsolete quickly. Customers should make certain that they carefully evaluate the appropriate term for the license and may want to consider protecting themselves against the obsolescence risk by entering into a relatively short-term license with customer renewal options at prices to be determined and set forth in the license.

Performance

One of the more important elements of any software license will be the warranty of the vendor that the software will perform in accordance with its specifications set forth in the user manuals or other appropriate documentation concerning the software. For this reason, as discussed above, the customer should review the user documentation carefully to ensure that it appropriately addresses the particular needs of the customer and, where necessary, the customer should modify the documentation to reflect its particular concerns.

Proprietary Rights

Right to Modify: The customer in any significant licensing transaction should consider whether it will have the right to modify the software to meet its own specifications. In many licenses for Website software, the customer should insist on receiving this right because it will likely have to adapt the software, either to its current transactional environment or to future environments. The licensee of the software should therefore insist that, at a minimum, the software license allow the licensee to effect modifications to the software during the term of the license. One significant wrinkle in this approach is that few licensors will allow third parties (such as Website developers) to modify their software and will require, at the very least, additional guarantees of confidentiality from such third parties. Moreover, many licenses provide that all warranties and indemnities are rendered void in the event that the licensee makes changes to the software. The customer should also consider what party should have ownership of the modified software, particularly in the event that the customer makes or finances the development of significant modifications. If the vendor is to own the modifications, the customer may wish to place certain restrictions on the use of the modifications by the vendor, particularly with respect to licenses to the customer's competitors.

Source Code and Escrow: The customer should consider in any significant software license whether it should have access to the source code for the licensed software. If the customer has the right to modify the software, access to the source code will be critical because without access to the source code, it will be much more difficult for the customer to modify the software. Without the source code, the customer would have to decompile or reverse engineer the software. In the event the software provider refuses to make the source code available to the customer, the parties may find that placing the source code in escrow would be an acceptable compromise. Software escrow arrangements typically provide that the software would be stored with and released from an escrow to the customer in the event of a material breach of the agreement by the licensor, or in the event of a bankruptcy, change of control or liquidation of the licensor. A software escrow may be particularly important if the customer licenses software from a small or start-up company.

Representations, Warranties and Indemnities

General Warranties: As discussed above, the software license should provide that the vendor will warrant that the software will function properly in accordance with its specifications for a period of time. The length of the warranty will vary, depending on the transaction, but will typically cover a period of at least 90 days from delivery or acceptance. In any event, the length of the warranty should be long enough for the customer to use the software under normal operating conditions to be able to identify any operating or other "bugs" in the software. The software licensor should also be required to rectify, at its cost, any problems with the software that prevents the software from performing in accordance with its specifications. The license should provide that any such problems be fixed within a certain period of time. If the problem is not resolved within the warranty period, the customer should insist that it have the right to terminate the license. Customers may wish to obtain covenants requiring the vendor not to insert, and to promptly remove, any viruses or disabling code from the software.

Intellectual Property: The customer should also ensure that the software license contains representations, warranties and indemnities regarding the infringement of any third party intellectual property rights by the software or documentation licensed to the company. This indemnity should not be subject to any cap or other limitation on damages that the contract may otherwise contain.

Damages

The damages and indemnification sections of any software license agreement may be some of the most heavily negotiated provisions of the license agreement. These provisions typically provide that each side will indemnify the other for any damages arising as a result of certain conditions or events to be agreed, such as a violation of the intellectual property rights of a third party or breach of representations. A vendor will often attempt to limit its liability for breach of the agreement to direct damages, subject to a cap or to mere replacement of the software and return of fees paid. In the event the customer agrees to a damage limitation of this type, it should insist that the limitation not apply to agreed indemnification claims and also exclude from the limitation any damages resulting from the gross negligence or willful misconduct of a party

Exit Rights

Software license agreements typically provide the parties the right to terminate upon the occurrence of certain events. The customer should have the right to terminate if the vendor breaches its obligations under the agreement and does not cure the breach within a period to be agreed. In establishing the applicable cure period, the customer should bear in mind that certain breaches of the agreement may be more critical than others and as a result may want to have shorter cure periods for certain failures. This may be especially the case with e-commerce software applications because the loss of the use of a Website even for a few hours could represent a critical failure for the company.

Nonsolicitation

As the demand for qualified information technology specialists - particularly in the area of e-commerce - has increased dramatically, the parties to information technology transactions are paying increasing attention to the nonsolicitation provisions in the agreement. If a customer agrees to an arrangement of this sort, it should make certain that the prohibition against soliciting employees is mutual and lasts only for a reasonable period of time.

Change of Control and Assignment

Parties negotiating software licenses sometimes neglect to address in detail the change of control and assignment clauses. A well-advised customer should insist that it have the right to approve assignments of the vendor's obligations under the license and also have a termination right in the event of a change in control of the vendor or its parent company. These clauses are assuming even greater importance in today's market, given the rapid consolidation occurring in the software and on-line industries. Customers should retain an effective veto over certain acquirors of the vendor's business to ensure that the customer does not end up licensing its software from an unacceptable party.

Conclusion

Given the enormous potential to reach large numbers of customers at relatively low cost through the Internet, it is no surprise that licenses for the software to manage such transactions raise key issues for customers. Customers who license e-commerce software should pay careful attention to both their needs and the complex new environment in which those needs (and the needs of their customers) will be served, and negotiate for such software licenses with care.

ENDNOTES

1 For example, about 4.5 million people now use some form of Internet-based banking as compared to 200,000 in 1995.

2 See Leslie Ayers, "Poll", PC Computing, June 1998 (citing Forrester Research). The $17 billion Internet sales figure may represent only a small slice of the e-commerce pie. Some analysts project that the aggregate value of electronic commerce could reach $300 billion within the next five to 10 years.

EXHIBIT E - AGREEMENT (LICENSES) Q AND A

(Following is for information only. Seek legal or accounting advice for specific situations.)

1. Should one allow a license to be assigned or serve as collateral? A license was granted to a spin-off company, who is negotiating a loan to finance commercialization of the licensed intellectual property. The licensee's lender is asking for consent by the licensor to allow the lender to reassign the license to a company of its choice in the event that the lender forecloses on the loan. The lender says it won't make the loan without obtaining the consent. Without the loan, the company will likely fold. Should the licensor grant its consent?

Relaxing diligent control over "ownership" of one's intellectual property in order to help finance its development is not recommended. It's best to keep control of the ownership of intellectual property. If the lender, upon foreclosure, has a new "licensee" in mind they can ask one to agree to the transaction. Often a licensee will want language allowing the license to be assigned or transferred to a company that acquires a controlling interest in the licensee. If the licensee is solely in the business of developing the intellectual property in question, then the lender's remedy upon foreclosure is to take control of the company and, with it, the technology. If the lender then wants to assign the intellectual property to a new company the new company would have to acquire the failed company. While this presents issues i.e. asset purchases vs. equity purchases, these are not the licensor's concern.

Mortgaging real property is one thing but intellectual property is not the same. In the past licenses were granted to a known licensee who sometimes had sublicensing rights, with approval of licensor, and some recursion rights if licensee defaulted or went bankrupt. Allowing a lender to assign the license to another entity of its exclusive choice, is foolhardy, considering the games played in today's volatile markets. It is better to sell the intellectual property to the spinoff, unless the licensor has other needs for continued ownership, and is positioned to pay maintenance fees and annuities. If one wants to retain control, and not have the intellectual property fall into hands adversarial to other potential licensees, then consider reassignment rights only after review of the new assignee, when known. It may be good business to grant a license to the new party, but not by way of a lender who will most likely treat the intellectual property as a book asset and not in the original licensor's interest!

The problem with assignment to a lender is that one will lose control of their intellectual property if the licensee defaults on the loan. However, if the licensee is facing a do or die situation, one should not unreasonably withhold agreement but try to add terms to the license that will not create a problem in the event of reassignment. For example, the assignee would have to assume all financial and non-financial covenants as they are, as licensor have a right to approve the assignee which approval will not be unreasonably withheld, and the assignee must pay any license payments in default. In addition, if the licensor has taken equity in the original licensee in lieu of cash payments, ask for certain "assumption fees" to compensate one for their loss.

A lender who is neither motivated nor equipped to develop the intellectual property or find a quality licensee, and for whom the intellectual property has more value as a tax loss than as a "going business".

Where there is valuable intellectual property involved consider registering one's interest under Personal Property Security Act legislation so you are the first creditor; not the last creditor.

2. What role should an academic institution play in current negotiations to minimize problems that may occur later and in the event a small company fails? Is there a standard approach to such a scenario? In this case the question is what role an academic organization needs to play in a sublicense. The third party client wants to license technology exclusively licensed to a small company by the academic institution - the license includes sublicense rights. Some payments on the license have been made, but there is concern that the small company may default on the license, at which time there would be a need to renegotiate directly with the academic institution.

Sublicensing has always been and still is an area of conflict. If a licensee makes a substantial return by sublicensing a technology either the licensee has added substantial value or the original licensor has mispriced the technology in the initial license agreement. When the university licenses a technology the university/licensee in free competition set the value and reach agreement. In a freely competitive market this is how price and value is established. Once the price is set in the license why should the original seller (i.e. the university) obtain any future value? Normally once any product is sold the initial seller obtains no further value if the buyer resells the product-whether the price goes up or down. Certainly if the value of the university technology goes down (the most common situation) the university doesn't give back to the licensee any of the initial price-does the university that prices the original sale to the licensee at full market value deserve an additional upside from sublicensing which is without risk - no downside. Probably not, so if the technology was priced correctly in the initial license then the increase in value was added by the licensee and they deserve the reward.

3. How can the university ensure that it gets part of this subsequent "sublicense" deal. What are the different mechanisms? For instance the university could ask for a percentage of "sublicense license milestone payments". What are the different types of milestone payments? What happens when payments to the biotech co. by the pharma co. are in the form of equity - can the university get a % of these payments?

The role played by the University will depend on whether the terms of the license granted to the small company (licensee) permit the University to control the terms of any sub-license. The University may, for example, be concerned with the dilution of royalties from revenues arising from the technology as a result of the sub-license (e.g. if the University is to receive say 3% of net revenue from the technology, it will want to ensure that this 3% is not diluted to 3% of 3% of royalties paid by the sub-licensee to the licensee).

In a transaction involving a sublicensee, consider a tripartite licensing agreement to be executed by the University, the licensee and the sub-licensee. In the event of the licensee's insolvency, or termination of the license by the University due to the default of the licensee, the University stands in the place of the licensee vis a vis the sub-licensee, with all other provisions remaining intact. This will depend on the University's willingness to their enjoinment to the agreement between the licensee and the sub-licensee.

Regarding royalties to be paid by sublicensees determine the sub-licensee's contribution to the process. Basically, the same royalty rate that applies to a licensee should apply to a sub-licensee. The more they add value, the more they should get to keep for themselves. If they are just passing on the licensing rights, then get the full amount received, and no less than what you would get if you were licensing this party directly (i.e., if you get 5% of your licensee's gross sales, you should get the same 5% of the sub-licensee's gross sales). Remember to also consider the licensing fees and other non-royalty amounts; otherwise, a licensee might think these fees belong to them. Seek at least half, or more, of such fees, depending on the relative contribution of the parties to the transaction. Furthermore, consider non-monetary transactions, e.g., a situation in which the licensee grants a sublicense to company X. Company X, in turn, provides the licensee with 10,000 hours of free consultation for the next year. Place a fair market value on these kind of transactions, what it would have cost to purchase them, and get a share.

As in any license, sublicensing terms are determined by negotiation. A range of 30-50% of sublicensing revenue is usually acceptable. Be careful how sublicensing revenue is defined. It should include all cash and non cash items not earmarked for specific purposes that are part of the sublicense transaction, especially equity investments in the licensee by the sublicensee.

Payments for equity investments by a sublicensee can be included in the definition of sublicensing revenue. Doing so would include them in the calculation for the percentage of sublicensing revenue that the licensee pays the licensor.

Avoid creating a disincentive for investment. If an investor knows that 50% of the cash will be going to the licensor, they may not invest.

These types of deals are common in the biotechnology industry. Investment by big pharma to biotechnology companies is usually done as a "cost of doing business." It also provides a validation of the biotechnology company and may help them attract investors for a new round of financing.

As a minimum require either a copy of the sublicense agreement, or a copy of the appropriate portion of the sublicense agreement, or sales reports and rights to audit, or a combination. Be aware of the Securities and Exchange statutes and liability concerns if a licensor provides too much input on how licensee runs their business.

4. University tech transfer office is trying to negotiate a licensing deal with a Japanese electronics company. The patents involved are mostly incremental improvements for which the company owns much of the background IP. The company appears to have cross-licensing arrangements with many of its main competitors, under which they have royalty-free access to each other's patents. They do not want a royalty-bearing licensing arrangement, but have offered a modest one-off payment for an exclusive license to each patent. They have said that the administrative burden of a royalty-bearing license would be too great for them, stating the main difficulties as: assessing the value of early-stage IP; assessing an appropriate royalty; identifying which products use a particular patent; calculating the total royalty in such a large company etc. Presumably it would also be difficult for them to pass on any royalty obligations to their cross-licensees. How should one structure a licensing deal with this type of company since a one-off payment doesn't seem fair?

Their points are consistent with the positions many US electronics companies take. Since they are cross licensing their own patents with competitors, there is really no-exclusivity in this business. Take the one-time payment but make the license non-exclusive. Since the company is offering the one-off in lieu of a royalty stream due to their burdens, presume a discount rate in line with the weighted average cost of capital of the technology transfer office rather than the WACC of the company. Presumably the technology transfer office cost of capital will be lower, allowing for a lower discount rate and yielding a higher NPV. Cash is nice and risk is gone, the day the check arrives.

An alternative approach is to place specific language in the agreement that clearly prohibits them from sublicensing and makes them positively assert that they agree that the license cannot be included in any cross-licensing agreements. There may be a complaint that their cross licensing agreements require that they get the right to sublicense their cross-licensees. Tell them that the price would be several times higher if they wanted such a right. This opens the door for you to ask for a copy of their cross licensing agreement. If they provide it, it normally is an interesting read. However, such a clause is rare in cross-licensing agreements and often one sees a clause that requires a cross-licensing party to extend to the others any rights which it has to a patent. If they don't have the right to sublicense, they can't extend that right. Tell them it puts their competitors on the same footing as them, since such competitors will need to pay for a license from you, rather than ride on the first licensee's coat tails.

5. Will a federal agency disclose the royalty a corporation pays for product sold that is subject to a license with the agency?

Usually not. The NIH recently won a lawsuit in which it was ruled that royalty amounts need not be disclosed.

Background: In July 2000, Public Citizen Health Research Group filed a Freedom of Information Act (FOIA) lawsuit against the NIH seeking royalty figures (including percentage of sale royalties) identifiable by company for each license the NIH Office of Technology Transfer executed from 1986-1998. Historically, NIH has taken the position that such information is protected from release under the confidential commercial/financial provisions of Exemption 4 of the FOIA.

Opinion: On March 12, 2002, Judge Colleen Kollar-Kotelly, United States District Court Judge, granted NIH's Motion for Summary Judgment and denied Public Citizen's Motion for Summary Judgment. The Court concluded that the NIH appropriately withheld the royalty information pursuant to Exemptions 3 and 4 of the FOIA. Public Citizen did not appeal the decision.

6. An IT unit in the organization has developed some software which probably has limited commercial potential in terms of licensing. However, they happened to come up with a very good name for the software and proceeded to get a decent amount of publicity for their work and the mark. A registration request has been filed. Several software companies who develop similar software are interested in licensing the mark for use with their product lines. Is there any advise you might give? What kind of royalties on products and services associated with the mark are customary?

Most of the product's value is in the trademark. The trademark provides market "branding"; provided that a market develops, and that market development sets the TM value in time. That is, for Gatorade, the TM provided the market branding strategy, so that when the patent ran out, the university could still claim on royalty on the TM based on brand reorganization. The Gatorade TM only had value because a market had developed and the product was worth something.

Thus, the royalty should be on the software plus TM, but the value is in the software, until, and if ever, the TM ever creates a branded value. It might be a mistake to think all the value is in the TM. There are a lot of "cool" TM names, but cool names don't make it unless the product makes it. A 15% royalty for both the software royalty plus TM might be reasonable.

Enact a "hybrid" license with two grants in the license agreement, with a specific amount of compensation for each part of the intellectual property package spelled out as what percentage of royalty you may be due. But Trademark and Copyright rights last much longer than patents. So the royalties can be paid for a very long period of time. On the other hand, Trademark licensing carries with it certain liability for the licensor. Defects in the software that may turn up from time to time can be attributed to the licensor's negligence in policing its trademark (this was the case in the consumer lawsuit against Levi Strauss). Indeed the trademark licensor has a duty to periodically check the quality of the products that it lends its trademark to. For software that is not hard to do but you do have set up a program that will obtain copies of the software and test the software for whatever performance characteristics are indications of quality for the software.

Value is proportional to actual value in commerce. Functional alternatives and workarounds diminish value considerably. The following are several scenarios or information that should be helpful in deciding what approach to take.

Most universities license their names and symbols for use on clothing for 7.5-8.0%. However, this is a case where the university has built all the value in the mark. On the other hand, clothing is a pretty low margin business.

Software obviously has much, much higher margins than clothing. But the licensee of the mark will be responsible for building most of the value. I keep thinking something like 15% or so might be appropriate as a target. Perhaps starting lower and then ramping up to 15%.

Seriously consider selling the trademark outright and take the payments in the form of installments payout per sale. The dilemma: why pay to build goodwill for a mark, when the prospective licensee can avoid you and create their own mark and save the 15% royalty?

The Pan Am logo and trademark sold for only $1.3M and it is one of the most famous marks of all time.

Another problem is that if the subject mark is sufficiently descriptive to have recognizable meaning e.g., "lowest fares", it may not be as enforceable as a more distinctive mark e.g., "orbitz."

7. A new startup company is being formed to commercialize software created at a (public) university. As the current deal stands, it will be an "exclusive, perpetual' license, and there will be no royalties. Instead, there will be 2-3 nominal (i.e., ~$25K) payments and the new startup will owned by my startup group of five and the university in an equity share. What should the ownership structure look like in this scenario? Should the start up include in the term sheet that

the fee payments will be paid only upon the university performing certain technology transfer related tasks?

The structure will vary depending on what each party brings to the table. They can range from 96/4 (company/university) to 50/50 depending on what the university provided with respect to the final product or how much the company will have to spend to develop the technology into a product.

Fee payments can be tied to completion of specified activities but be sure the activity is well defined and the criteria for completion well understood. Negotiation can follow.

8. A set of (copyrighted) CD-ROMs containing surface and gross anatomy video clips was created. They are designed as teaching materials for students in medicine, nursing, physical therapy, etc. The target market is universities with these types of course offerings. Some price targets are being considered but more advice on pricing levels and pricing structure with the following additional factors to consider:

- Simplicity is key. Goal is to minimize administrative and enforcement burdens for us and for the creators of the videos. Desire is a "ready-to-sign" license agreement with a one-time payment for an unlimited site license.
- some monitoring capability exists but password management is not of interest (Although the CD-ROMs are local, they are indexed via a web page that can be password protected).
- an updated version will be available in 18-24 months but the basic content is not likely to change soon.
- there might be individuals (e.g. private practitioners) wanting to buy the videos as a reference volume.

How should the private practitioner market be priced without creating a loophole for larger users?

How should the upgrade for new and existing licensees be structured?

Should the same price be charged to a large state university as to a local tech school?

Explore Microsoft's licenses page which gives details of volume licensing, non-profit institution vs. corporate licenses and other factors that might be relevant. See http://www.microsoft.com/licensing/Default.asp

9. How do you license or sell a database as either a training or research tool? The situation background: Rose Biomedical partnered with a private company and NIH to conduct a clinical study of algorithms designed to improve predictability and decision support in fetal monitoring. While the company's algorithms did not provide a statistically significant improvement in predictability, the two years of research did yield an extensive electronic database of 1300 cases (approximately 200 abnormals) that is richly detailed – fetal monitoring strips correlated to patient demographics, course of labor, delivery and outcomes. The database might serve as a valuable resource for a) fetal monitoring research, b) interactive or regular CME training on fetal monitoring interpretation and/or c) manufacturer research in product improvement, clinical use. Examples of questions are:

1. If fetal monitor manufacturers are approached how should this type of database be sold or licensed to CME course developers?
2. What price is suggested for license or purchase of all or part of a research database?
3. Are there any regulatory constraints (other than deleting patient identifiers such as names and dates) that should be factored into the equation?

Sell for use in training, because there is usually a clear case flow stream to support the database and everything else is pulling off overhead. On R&D use it may be easier to get a share of downstream royalties from outcomes and possibly some R&D money for development by the owner, ala a CRADA.

Pricing with databases is much like everything else. If comparables exist, use them. While the database is sometimes buried in the training software, etc., it is usually possible to get an estimate as to what percent of the value of the training is attributable to the database. Be sure the two databases are comparable and adjust percentages to differences in value

Determine the demand or need for CME training on fetal monitor interpretation and is there even a perceived need. If no comparables exist, survey end-users and experts to determine the value add or percent incremental a customer would buy and what would they pay for it.

Clearly patient identifiers need to be eliminated. Consent forms should be in place. Remember consent might be for research purposes only and not for commercial purposes.

10. What are the options a licensor has when a licensee files for bankruptcy with respect to a license?

If a licensee goes Chapter 7, full bankruptcy filing, then the license will be considered an asset of the company and is subject to the ruling of the bankruptcy judge as to what happens to it. It may even be sold or transferred to a sublicensee to satisfy the debts of the company.

Under Chapter 11, it is the same except that the company may continue to operate to pay its debtors and pay the licensor only a fraction, if at all, of licensor's royalty while it seeks to reorganize its debts. Again because it is an asset of the company a licensor may not be able to terminate it fully. The debtors usually get paid first.

The only thing to do is to terminate and file claim as soon as one becomes aware that a bankruptcy petition is filed or seek termination as soon as possible before bankruptcy is filed. By filing a claim one may at least be able to get back the license rights or get a royalty if a licensee continues to operate.

Many licenses are by their own terms non-assignable (i.e., terminate on transfer to a successor to the assets) and terminate automatically on bankruptcy. The bankruptcy code specifically addresses IP in bankruptcy, balancing the start-up's need to retain its IP, with the university's need to assure it gets paid. If the university structured the transaction as a "loan" secured by IP, then you can repossess. If the university simply has a royalty in the future, how will you file a claim for a debt certain - a fixed dollar amount due?

How can one prevent this from happening? First, place specific language regarding remedies for bankruptcy in the agreements. Place contingency language that says that obligations to pay royalties shall be continue if, in fact the license is dispositioned to another entity. Lastly and most important, make sure that you establish good diligence criteria in the license and monitor your license arrangement. As soon as there is any breech of contract initiate the termination process prior to the bankruptcy filing.

11. A license has been granted (on quite favorable terms) to a spin-off company, who is negotiating a loan to finance commercialization of the licensed IP. The licensee's lender is asking for consent by the licensor to allow the lender to reassign the license to a company of its choice in the event that the lender forecloses on the loan. The lender says it won't make the loan without obtaining the consent. Without the loan the company will likely fold, should the licensor grant its consent?

Grant consent - but cautiously. Some concerns are:
1. There is no benefit to putting the IP rights in the hands of bankers who are likely to be unfamiliar with the technology, disinterested in seeing it developed, incapable of finding a licensee and are only trying to recover what they can.
2. The bankruptcy process can take years. In the mean time, the technology is tied up and the market window is disappearing. Patent costs may also be accruing with no licensee to reimburse you. Technology can be tied up for years after a bankruptcy.

3. If company is financed mostly with debt, it may be much more prone to failure because it is an indication that an individual is trying to maintain too much control and financial interest.

If consent is granted, some suggestions to limit risk are:

1. look more closely at the financial structure of the company;
2. put a time limit on the lender's right (e.g. three months after bankruptcy);
3. obtain a candidate list of companies from the lender before granting consent and allow re-assignment to only those companies;
4. make sure the new licensee will be bound by all terms of the original agreement;
5. insist on a clause that the assignee must pay any license payments in default; and
6. if you took equity in the original licensee in lieu of cash payments, insist that the assignee pay you certain defined "assumption fees" to compensate you for your loss.

Instead of "limiting rights to three months after bankruptcy" change to "three months after filing for bankruptcy".

Bankruptcy judges have very broad powers, and when your licensee goes bankrupt & the court is taking over the assets, your agreements may get thrown out.

Mortgaging real property is one thing but IP is not the same. In the past licenses were granted to a known licensee who sometimes had sublicensing rights, with approval of licensor, and some recursion rights if licensee defaulted or went bankrupt. Allowing a lender to assign the license to another entity of its exclusive choice is foolhardy, considering the games played in today's volatile markets. It is better to sell the IP to the spin-off, unless the licensor has other needs for continued ownership, and is positioned to pay maintenance fees and annuities. If one wants to retain control, and not have the IP fall into hands adversarial to other potential licensees, then consider reassignment rights only after review of the new assignee, when known. It may be good business to grant a license to the new party, but not by way of a lender who will most likely treat the IP as a book asset and not in the original licensor's interest!

Refuse to grant rights to use IP as collateral to secure a loan - specifically prohibit it in a term in the license agreement. It is not in one's best interest to have a company fail or breech a contract. A 3rd party who obtains ownership of IP may not have the same business interest or see the same value for the IP.

Why is a spin-off company trying to finance development on a loan basis rather than giving up some equity? If the response is that the company is trying to avoid giving up equity to maintain control, a more fundamental problem may exist with the spin-off company. Excess control by individuals is a recipe for failure. If the founders of the company want to go the loan route to minimize the dilution of equity, they should be guaranteeing the loan as they presumably stand to gain the most from the leverage. Otherwise the asset is being used at no cost to the licensee, but a real cost to the licensor, while the 3rd party obtains the benefits.

Another approach is to register the licensor's under Personal Property Security Act legislation so that the University is the first creditor; not the last creditor.

12. IBM is a corporation that is usually in the top 10 companies for receipt of patents issued annually. What are some of the details related to the revenue from these patents?

In a report issued in June 1999 the following information was provided for IBM intellectual property and revenue therefrom:

- Every IBM patent is available for licensing at rates from 1-5%. (Of gross sales?)
- 30K patents worldwide. (Half from U.S.)
- 26K patents pending worldwide, "mostly from U.S."
- 50% of invention disclosures "closed," i.e., in the round file.
- 35% of invention disclosures published for defensive purposes.
- 20% of invention disclosures result in a patent application. (20+35+50 is not 100, but those are stats offered.)

- $1,150,000,000 (yes, $1.15 billion) annual licensing revenue, all of which goes back into R&D.

IBM gets even more from software licensing - $1B from Software & $800M from "hardware" licensing. It is important to keep this in perspective, that IBM is also the #1 patent holder (or close to it).

13. There is information being circulated that federal agencies are extending exclusive licensing terms. Is this possible?

Federal agencies are now required by statute to limit the scope of exclusivity to what is needed for development. For example, DDI, an HIV drug, was licensed on an exclusive basis for 10 years, which was more than enough. Cisplatin was licensed for 5 years on an exclusive license, which was more than enough for development. Life of patent exclusive licensing is in general irresponsible for government funded pharmaceutical inventions. The issue of extending the exclusive term comes up when a firm wants to continue the monopoly longer than what was given in the beginning. Under current law, agencies are supposed to make choices based upon the public interest.

Typically, a license expires upon the last to expire patent. The case law indicates that it is illegal to collect royalties pursuant to a license once the patent expires.

It is possible to confuse a federal agency's licensing authority with the FDA's regulatory authority. There is a provision that allows companies to request extension of patent term if the FDA approval process took "too long" and therefore cut into the company's ability to sell a product and take advantage of its full patent term.

A proposal is being made to make changes to the FTTA, which is the federal government's authority for conducting technology transfer that will give the government the right to conduct its licensing programs in a manner similar to universities. The public has a right to know what is being done with inventions that are funded with their tax dollars. However, the reality is "the public" does not make use of the notice and comment provision. Companies take advantage of the required notice and comment period to protect their own interest. Further, university technology transfer programs are not subject to the same notice and comment requirements even though they are granting licenses to inventions developed with federal funding. In addition to countering the bills being proposed to alter the way federal government does licensing, it is probably appropriate to suggest that Bayh-Dole be amended to include a notice and comment provision. A legitimate question is; why should the right to know about licensing terms, etc. only apply to government agencies when there are other entities, e.g. universities, that receive federal funds for the development of inventions?

14. In the section of the license dealing with enforcement of patent rights, a licensee (prospective) wants the right to approve before action is taken against potential infingers (such approval "not to be unreasonably withheld"). The licensee already would have the first right to take such action, but if they choose not to, the right falls to us, subject to their approval. The reasoning is that a licensee does not want the licensor to take action against a potential infringer if they believe the infringement is not that significant, and potentially risking a counter-suit seeking to invalidate the patent that the licensee has a major investment in.

The licensee's request is not unreasonable. Whether to pursue infringers is a business decision that includes factors such as the cost of litigation, prospect of winning, amount of damages likely to be recovered, and defenses that could be counterclaimed such as the patent is invalid.

One approach a licensor could use is insertion of language in the agreement such as "approval would not be required if the amount of infringement exceeds [a preagreed value]".

Logic that could be used against a licensee that wants to participate in infringement decisions might be:

a. licensee is not OBLIGATED to pursue infringers,

b. assuming normal discretionary termination provisions (not to mention termination for cause etc.), effectively, the licensee is renting the IP, if the licensee passes, and the licensor pursues, the licensee is under no risk except for counterclaim of invalidity, which probably hurts the licensor more. (This is especially true because, if the patent is invalidated, the licensor can still sell product and as a result, the licensor is probably in a better position to evaluate this risk), and if the licensee had final say, they could be incented to cut a side deal with the infringer.

Although a licensee could sell a product without paying royalties if a patent were invalidated so could anyone else and the licensee will have lost their exclusive franchise. This could be detrimental for certain products/industries.

Because conflicts between licensees and licensors are rather common, and because it is difficult for the licensor to know what other IP owned or controlled by the licensee could impact a licensee's decision, it may not be prudent for licensors to yield final authority on issues of patent prosecution, infringement etc.

If the licensee is concerned about third-party infringement that they might consider insignificant, perhaps they might agree to additionally pay the licensor a reasonable royalty for such infringement to prevent the undesired litigation. That way the licensor gets what it is looking for (money) in either case, and the licensee will have to think long and hard about standing in the way of enforcement for "insignificant" infringement. A potential downside is that the licensor could hurt its reputation for enforcement by accepting licensee payments to forgo litigation. It is possible that the licensee would be less and less willing to "buy out" enforcement as the infringements become less and less "insignificant."

The issue of how significant the infringement is often a consideration in deciding whether to pursue an infringer. For example, will the cost of litigation, assuming the case goes to trial, be more than one could recover in damages. It may also be more productive to settle infringement by a cross-licensing arrangement rather than litigation. Standard infringement clauses often do not allow for these possibilities.

15. A small business owns an underdeveloped proprietary technology for a working software product. An agency of the U.S. government wants a more developed version of the product and is willing to pay for the adaptation development of the existing product. The small business does not want to do the adaptation development itself, nor does the government agency. A third party government approved contractor is qualified and interested in doing the development. Is there a way for the development to be paid for by the government; performed by the third party government contractor – without the small business having to "give" a free license to the government? For example, how is technology ownership resolved in an SBIR or STTR grant so that the small business maintains full ownership of the technology and any resulting developments after the government spends money on development?

Presuming that the "original technology" was not developed under Federal funds, the government cannot acquire rights to the "original technology" under a funding agreement to further develop the technology. However, as a practical matter, it would be very helpful to have "original technology" clearly staked out in terms of a copyright or a patent application. The same principles apply to trade secrets, but if the trade secret subsequently becomes embodied as a copyright or patent only in the improvement it would be much harder to sort out what belongs to whom when the improved product is completed. Ideally (from the perspective of the small company) when the project is finished the government could not use the improved version without also buying/licensing the original technology from the small company.

There could be an advantage to the small company by having the funds flow from the government to the small business then on to the (presumably large entity) 3rd party contractor. This may not be practical for various reasons, but if it could be done the small business would be entitled to Bayh-Dole ownership rights to any inventions made either by them or their subcontractor (the 3rd party contractor). If the money flows directly to the 3rd party contractor, those Bayh-Dole rights would be lost. In either case the government will retain a government use right to the copyright or invention, but if the funds flow to the small business they could automatically elect title to any invention that is made (subject to granting the government its rights) rather than having to license those rights back from the government (and/or paying royalties to the 3rd party contractor).

Subcontractors enjoy the same Bayh-Dole rights as contractors - i.e. the subcontractor, not the contractor, has the right to elect ownership to their own inventions. SBIR involves the same IP rules/regulations as any other funding agreement - Bayh-Dole and the FAR. These do not vary from one Federal agency to another.

If the small business (SB) technology is proprietary and developed with private funds, then initially there is no "free" govt. license and this is SB background IP. The SB could hire to 3rd party contractor, and may use government money, to create the government needed technology. The SB could own any created IP (depending upon their agreement with the 3rd party contractor) and would make money by selling the original SB technology, plus the new technology at a profit which covers their manufacturing or other costs.

If one assumes that the SBIR is the funding mechanism for the SB to contract with the 3rd party the following scenario might be relevant. Generally IP originates with the SBIR or STTR grantee. STTRs mandate that a percentage of the grant go to a national lab, the inventor would own the invention (either grantee or national lab), but the STTR and CRADAs have a clause (Morella bill) which permits the national lab to license the national lab invention back to the SB exclusively, in a field of use, for fair and reasonable terms. The national lab gets no royalties if the product is made for the government (but the company can make a profit). The "free" government license applies to this invention and not the original, background SB technology. The government could take its government license and go to another contractor to make its product, but if the original SB IP is background to the government the government would have to work with the SB.

If the original SB IP has a "free" government license, and any new IP is also subject to a government license, the government can go anywhere to make the product. If the SB has unique special manufacturing equipment, then the government will probably go to the SB to keep costs low. The SB is still permitted to make a profit in manufacturing the product. The free government license means no royalties are paid to government agencies or national laboratories.

16. An organization has an exclusive license agreement with Company X (a small privately owned company). Company X is interested in licensing additional related technology; specifically, from some of the background material the inventor provided to them, as well as some new manuscript material. Their plan is to file "fencing" patents, which then provides them with more protection on the subject technology as well as provide the ability to pursue foreign rights. The original patents are U.S. only. There are some areas that are "new", that would not require rights to the original patent to practice. The firm is close to terms for the new license; they pay all patent costs, royalties with a capping provision by product and a minimum annual royalty fee. They agreed to a minimum fee for any "new" patent, but balked at paying a minimum royalty on any "fencing patent". Their argument is that as know-how it was part of the original package agreement and as stand-alone patents we could not license them to anyone else (unless the third party licensed from Company X). They will pay royalties, as the patent protection of the know-how is a value to them, but want it excluded from the minimum royalty provision. What is an appropriate position for the licensor?

Separate minimum royalties for different fields of use, not for different IP. Then it does not matter what patents or know-how are used for a given field. The company's position on "new" patent is hard to justify; however, the position and leverage for the licensor will depend on the terms in the original license grant. For example, does the original grant include related technologies, continuations, etc?

Whether the minimum applies to one patent or all patents is really just semantics. Set a minimum appropriate for the technology. As long as U.S. patents exist that have much of their life remaining, then by the time the U.S. only patents expire - either Company X will be living the good life and minimums won't matter or they will be struggling/terminated by then. Be sure to negotiate a fair minimum and call it whatever makes sense. Cash is king, not the technical terms of agreement although they should be definitive to avoid ambiguity.

Never tie minimums to specific patents or other IP, only to fields of use. This allows flexibility so the package can be licensed to others outside the field of use. It makes sense to license all IP needed for a given field, or use, as a package.

Have an annual minimum for the entire package of patents contained in the license. It's too difficult to monitor different annual minimums for different products or fields of use. From the Licensee's commercialization plan, how much do they project in annual sales? Set the annual minimum to be some percentage of projected total annual royalties.

17. One of the first decisions when licensing is whether to grant an exclusive licenses, field-of-use exclusive licenses, or non-exclusive licenses. Often that decision is dictated by such factors as the origin of the funding for the invention, industry norms, supply and demand, inventor's strong desires, etc. However, there are situation when the decision about exclusivity is not pre-destined or inherently obvious. To handle such cases a list of factors might be compiled to consider when making the decision. How often does the need to make a conscious decision about non-exclusive vs. exclusive licensing arise? How should a decision be made?

Consider the following factors that favor non-exclusive licenses:
- relatively low cost to complete the technical development and bring to market,
- relatively low cost of required production equipment to enter market,
- large market in which there are many known fields of use, but none of which by themselves is sizable,
- technology is well suited for use with, or will enable, proprietary complementary technology,
- technical workarounds are available or likely to develop,
- technology is something that companies will have to acquire to stay competitive,
     industry for this technology readily adopts new technology,
     - patent has weak claims or may be difficult to enforce (e.g. has process claims only), but companies will buy a cheap license rather than risk infringement, and
     - technology is platform or enabling (proprietary products are developed from these).

Factors favoring sole commercial licensing or sole commercial field of use licensing are:
     - relatively high cost to complete the technical development and bring to market,
     - high cost of required production equipment to enter market,
     - small market, or large market with many fields of use, each of which is quite sizable,
     - technology is stand-alone,
     - technical innovation is slow in this industry,
     - a startup needs this platform or enabling technology as a basis for their business, and
     - patent has strong, basic claims.

18. For an exclusive license with the right to sublicense, Licensor, a software development company, is requesting a license issue fee of $1 million plus 25% royalty for the period of 5 years. This seems rather high. What terms are reasonable with respect to the royalty range?

There is insufficient information provided to make a determination. What's the market over the next 5 years? What's the selling price and what's your added value to the product? What's the competition? Can you get similar software from another competitor at a lower rate, or can you write some new code yourself? Do you have additional add-on products to leverage off this license? If its $100M in sales over 5 years maybe its a good deal; if its $2 million in sales then its probably not worthwhile. However, it may be that the 25% royalty rate could be okay, although the upfront seems high. However, insufficient information is provided to be definitive.

19. A potential corporate licensee wants a provision in the agreement saying that rights granted under the license are, for the purposes of Section 365(n) of the US Bankruptcy Code, licenses of rights to "intellectual property" as defined under Section 101 of the US Bankruptcy Code; and that licensee "will retain and may exercise all rights and elections" under the Code. The company also want to include the following language " plus, in the event of bankruptcy proceedings by or against licensor, licensee shall be entitled to duplicate of the IP and any embodiments of the IP". What is the practical impact of this provision? Are there any issues to be aware of before signing off on such terms?

If any suspicions exist or licensor wants to hedge against them and potential bankruptcy potential exists, try to get a GSA (General Security Agreement) on the IP. This allows the IP owner or licensor to recover all rights and interest in case licensee fails. No receiver or anyone else can access the IP.

Usually if a licensee enters bankruptcy all bets are off and the licensor loses control over its IP. Control over everything shifts to the bankruptcy judge. Nothing you try works. In the past some licensors have tried to ex post facto terminate licenses by putting in clauses like:

a. "This Agreement automatically terminates upon bankruptcy of Licensee", or:
b. "If Licensee enters bankruptcy, this Agreement automatically terminates as of three months prior to such bankruptcy" or:
c. "Licensee must notify Licensor three months before entering into bankruptcy, at which time this Agreement shall automatically terminate. Failure to provide such three month notice will cause automatic termination of this Agreement effective three months before entering such bankruptcy."

All such clauses have been deemed ineffectual and bankruptcy judges have wide latitude in including any and all assets held by the company for months and months before the actual bankruptcy date.

One approach is to include this language in the agreement; "Plus, in the event of bankruptcy proceedings by or against licensee, licensor shall be entitled to duplicate of the IP and any embodiments of the IP" and/or a reciprocal of this language.

In the case of an academic or government it is unlikely that they will go bankrupt in contrast to a private company. Consider the following language; "In the event of bankruptcy proceedings by or against licensee, licensor shall be entitled to terminate the agreement and recover the licensed IP (knowing full well that the bankruptcy judge is almost sure to overrule that) and that pending decision by the bankruptcy judge and/or failing to recover the IP, licensor is entitled to change the grant to a non-exclusive grant. (Leaves at least a slim chance to license the IP elsewhere.)"

20. A licensor is in final stages of negotiation with a large medical device company for a unique orthopedic device. Overall, negotiations have gone well with respect to, fees, royalties, etc. and the general directions of the discussions. A sticking point however is the potential licensee's desire to include "commissions" in items deducted from gross sales to calculate Net Sales. Their standard line continues to be "This is how all our contracts are written". This could represent at least a 30% reduction in Net Sales, and the language is hard to accept. What would you recommend? Should the licensor "walk away"?

Do not get to concerned how "other" contracts are written; however, there is a need to be aware of how standard this practice is in the medical device industry and other industries as well. In the future define "net sales" in the term sheet.

This approach is not common at all. The issue might be best resolved by asking for a copy of one of the firm's typical Income Statements (if they are public, then just look at their 10k or 10Q). One will likely see that selling expense (typically including commissions) is part of SG&A and, therefore, subtracted from Net Revenues, i.e., commissions should be calculated above selling expense.

Another alternative, of course, is to increase the royalty rate to adjust for the difference.

A licensor might want to live with this approach in order to consummate an arrangement if accounting considers commissions to be an expense. However, it is very important that the basis for calculating royalties be unambiguous and not subject to manipulation etc. Therefore, carefully define how commissions are calculated. In most arrangements, the royalty basis is net revenues, where the deductions to calculate net revenues are items like shipping, volume discounts, and taxes that are reflected on the invoice and therefore not subject to manipulation.

21. A patent is pending on a hand tool and a license is being negotiated with a marketing firm to manufacture and distribute the product. They are requiring a liability insurance policy on the "design". Is this common?

It is uncommon to require insurance on a "design". An indemnification clause (likewise they will indemnify licensor from their responsibilities) is more common. In that event, licensor may be asked to indemnify licensee from any "specifications" or "engineering" data that licensor has given to licensee. Include disclaimer of reliance on licensor's information, if this is practical; and allow licensee to be responsible for all stress and strain matters.

However, a product liability lawsuit will include everyone having anything to do with the product ...including the designer. Be sure licensee names licensor as an "additional insured" on licensee's product liability policy. Negotiate "hard"; since the cost is only a few hundred dollars (additional) per year for millions of dollars of coverage for licensor.

Also remember it is licensee's responsibility to manufacture and present the product to the user with all legal indicia and hazard warnings.

22. Can know-how be licensed and if so what are the do's, don'ts, black holes, etc.?

Trade secrets, unlike patents, can be licensed in perpetuity (forever). The licensee can be obligated to continue paying royalties for the trade secrets license even if the information (subject to the trade secret license) has entered the public domain.

This fundamental principle of trade secrets law was illustrated in the famous "Listerine" formula case. Warner-Lambert Pharmaceutical Co. v. John J. Reynolds, Inc., 178 F.Supp. 655 (S.D.N.Y. 1959), aff'd 280 F.2d 197 (2nd Cir. 1960). In the early 1880s, Dr. J. J. Lawrence devised a formula for an antiseptic liquid compound which was given the name "Listerine." In 1881, J. W. Lambert signed a document that read as follows:

> "Know all men by these presents, that for and in consideration of the fact, that Dr. J. J. Lawrence of the city of St Louis Mo has furnished me with the formula of a medicine called Listerine to be manufactured by me, that I Jordan W Lambert, also of the city St Louis Mo, hereby agree for myself, my heirs, executors and assigns to pay monthly to the said Dr. J. J. Lawrence his heirs, executors or assigns, the sum of twenty dollars for each and every gross of said Listerine hereafter sold by myself, my heirs, executors or assigns. In testimony whereof, I hereunto set my hand and seal, Done at St Louis Mo. this the 20th day of April, 1881 Jordan W Lambert (Seal)."

Thereafter, Dr. Lawrence agreed to reduce the royalty to six dollars per gross and, on January 2, 1885, Lambert assigned his rights to Listerine to the Lambert Pharmaceutical Company.

For some 75 years, Plaintiff (Warner-Lambert Pharmaceutical Company) and its predecessors made periodic payments based on the quantity of Listerine manufactured or sold. By 1956, the payments totaled more than $22M.

In 1956, Warner-Lambert filed a declaratory judgment action to terminate the royalty payments because the "Listerine" formula was no longer a trade secret. The evidence revealed that there had been public disclosure of the Listerine formula by publication in the Journal of the American Medical Association at least as early as 1931.

The court held that the fact that the LISTERINE formula was no longer a trade secret was no bar to paying licensing fees:

Here, however, there is no such public policy. The parties are free to contract with respect to a secret formula or trade secret in any manner which they determine for their own best interests. A secret formula or trade secret may remain secret indefinitely. It may be discovered by someone else almost immediately after the agreement is entered into. Whoever discovers it for himself by legitimate means is entitled to its use. See, e.g. Rabor v. Hoffman, 118 N.Y. 30, 23 N.E. 12.

But that does not mean that one who acquires a secret formula or a trade secret through a valid and binding contract is then enabled to escape from an obligation to which he bound himself simply because the secret is discovered by a third party or by the general public. I see no reason why the court should imply such a term or condition in a contract providing on its face that payment shall be coextensive with use. To do so here would be to rewrite the contract for the parties without any indication that they intended such a result.

Possession of trade secret information, under a license, provides the licensee with a "head start" advantage in the marketplace:

At the very least plaintiff's predecessors, through the acquisition of the Lawrence formula under this contract, obtained a head start in the field of liquid antiseptics which as proved of incalculable value through the years.

In fact, as the District Court in Warner-Lambert observed: The case at bar illustrates what may occur in such cases. As the undisputed facts show, the acquisition of the Lawrence formula was the base on which plaintiff's predecessors built up a very large and successful business in the antiseptic or germicide field. Even now, twenty-five or more years after it is claimed that the trade secret was disclosed to the public, plaintiff retains more than 50% of the national market in these products.

The Listerine case illustrates the benefits of trade secret licensing. Even if a trade secret subsequently enters the public domain, royalty payments under trade secret licensing agreements can continue indefinitely.

Just to reinforce the preceding, know-how does not need to be licensed on an exclusive basis. A non-exclusive license of know-how is entirely consistent with the reality of academic institutions - an exclusive license would definitely create the problems that others have pointed out and could only be considered under exceptional circumstances if at all.. Of course the compensation terms would reflect the lack of exclusivity.

One concept to think about: "know-how" doesn't always equal "trade secret". It's possible for a transfer of know-how that's valuable. We have a few cases where a published screening technology could not be reproduced anywhere else, even though the paper was detailed. There's always a little "magic" in the lab that isn't always covered by the patent.

It should be possible to license know-how without any warranties that it be kept confidential. It's not trivial, but neither is it impossible. Seems like a one-time upfront payment. There might be some concerns about exclusively licensing know-how, but it could be for a limited period of time provided all parties involved agreed.

Remember, anything produced in a government lab outside of a CRADA and classified information is subject to the Freedom of Information Act. Thus even if government labs had the statutory authority to enter into a know-how license, the license would be worthless. Also, most government researchers are rated by their publications, as in academia.

23. In some cases academic institutions claim ownership of laboratory notebooks. They can license unpublished data as confidential information. However, the policy does not restrict a faculty member's use of their data or inventions including continued use if they accept employment at another non-profit institution. Should an academic institution be in the business of licensing know-how? What are the pros and cons of this approach?

First check the organizations policies and statutes to see if the institution even owns the know-how. It may not.

Secondly, even if the institution owns the know-how, who controls it? Some of it may reside in laboratory notebooks, but not all of it. What if it resides in the researchers head and that researcher

548

is not cooperative? Also, a know-how license may limit publication and if compensation has been received but the scientist publishes what impact will it have on the license? If the institution has agreed to provide the know-how it may result in a breach of contract.

It is especially important that whatever know-how is licensed be carefully & explicitly defined so there is clear definition of what is licensed.

There are two principal ways that universities license know-how:

1. one-time, one-on-one data dump of all written material which is usually part of a license agreement related to a patent. The know-how value is diminished over time and usually expires 10 years after the execution of the license, if no patent should issue. The value of the know-how is that the University will only do the know-how transfer one time.

2. MIT did a one-time, know-how transfer with several Japanese companies with regard to technology developed in its multimedia lab. They received about $20 Million for the transfer. Although most of the technology was unpatented and some was published at the time and most of it later, the value to the Japanese companies was that it was organized and came with technical assistance, increasing the rate of absorption by their scientists and engineers, thereby lessening the gap between US multimedia companies and the Japanese. The downside was that the US government was not pleased and some said at the time the MIT know-how transfer was a big reason why a coveted particle accelerator

project was awarded to Prairie View A&M instead of MIT.

In an academic setting most know-how is in the mind of the faculty. Most faculty (and maybe the companies, although perhaps not always) would be better off doing a consulting deal with the faculty member and cutting out the middle man (i.e., the institution). It is indeed touchy because it goes directly to the question of who owns what's in the employee's brain. Clearly, when something "rises" to the level of an invention, the institutional patent agreement/patent policy (and federal disclosure rules under grant regulations, if arising from federally funded research) comes into play.

24. A license is being negotiated for rights to compounds and targets that will be used for developing orphan drugs. An orphan drug will probably not generate the same revenue as might be expected for a non-orphan drug. What are some suggestions for license terms when an orphan drug is involved?

A good discussion about the economics of orphan products is the following: "Orphan products - pain relief for clinical development headaches" by C. Milne in Nature Biotechnology, Vol. 20, August 2002 pp780-784. Select points are as follows.

Orphan niches can represent a positive cash flow: "faster clinical development times, greater support from regulators, lower costs of development, and more significant, if smaller markets than products for common diseases." The article also states: "...active patient advocacy groups, the absence or scarcity of existing treatments, and close doctor-patient relationships with specialists actually facilitate enrollment in clinical trials for orphan products, despite patient populations that are small and geographically dispersed. ...Because orphan products address considerable unmet needs for relatively small patient populations for which care would otherwise be inordinately expensive (if available), managed care organizations can afford to reimburse... The combination of higher prices {charged and received for the orphan drug} but lower R&D costs (because fewer trials and smaller patient numbers are required mean healthier profit margins for the developers of orphan products"

Orphan drug status enables a clinical stage compound to obtain certain advantages in FDA review and approval. The general idea is to aid the review and approval of drugs indicated for fairly rare conditions. Just because a drug product is indicated for a fairly rare condition, however, does not mean that the drug product will not sell well. Rather, the reimbursement of the drug product for its indicated use may be quite high, and off label uses may significantly increase sales beyond this. For example, imagine that one of your professors discovers a drug that reverses age related cognitive impairment of any kind (everything from Alzheimer's disease to "old-timer's disease" or age related senescence). One has several options at the FDA. One may ask for approval for a label for a broad, common condition: "reverses age related cognitive impairment of any kind." Alternatively, one may take the Orphan Drug route and ask the FDA to approve a label for a more rare condition: "reverses age related cognitive impairment associated with early childhood exposure to cadmium," for example. The differences come in (1) the time & expense involved in getting regular vs. Orphan Drug approval; (2) the legal exclusivity accorded by the FDA; and (3) the marketing impact/value of the various labeled claims, and the concomitant likelihood of off label use.

25. License negotiations are underway with a company for technology developed by the licensor's scientist. The research was partially funded (90%) by the company. One of the issues that appears to be a stumbling block is patent expenditures. The proposed license agreement has an annual license maintenance fee and there is interest in having the company pay the patent prosecution expenditures. The company is willing to pay these expenditures but wants to deduct them from the annual license maintenance fee. The licensor has, in the past, allowed royalties to be deducted from annual license maintenance fees but not patent prosecution expenditures. What would you recommend to the licensor?

Place yourself in the company's position and determine how they view the patent: Is it an obstacle for which they need a license, or is it an opportunity to gain a valuable monopoly position? If the former, offer a nonexclusive license with no patent expenses; but if the latter, point out the value of investing in the asset.

Whether patent expenses are deductible from annual maintenance fees and the percentage of patent expenses that are deductible are business decisions. To help make the decision, estimate patent expenses, deduct them from the proposed maintenance fees and determine what is left. If little or no money is left, argue that unlike a corporation that can build certain expenses, including the cost of patenting, into its product prices, it is not possible to build patent expenses into licensing fees. Agreeing to the prospective licensee's request would create a situation in which licensor's benefits are reduced and it is not worth granting the license.

The recommendation will depend on the following; 1) is the license exclusive, and 2) what is the upfront and running royalty stream? If it is exclusive licensee should pay all patent related fees. If not, then some lesser fees are appropriate; or deduct all or some patent fees from royalties. Royalty stream is key. If the patent will bring in millions of dollars give credit for patent expense. Even if it brings in $100K/yr allow patent fee deduction (US only, not foreign). The problem is when does the royalty stream become small enough to not allow patent fee deduction? The worst case is probably when all patent fees are less than the royalty stream.

26. Company X licenses out a computer software program on a non-exclusive basis to academic and commercial institutions. The cost for an academic license is $1,500 and the cost for a commercial license is $5,000. A user is free to use the license in perpetuity (forever), but there is a yearly annual maintenance fee of $300 - $500 that allows the user to receive periodic upgrades and technical support. Company X does not offer site licenses. There are approximately 250 non-exclusive licenses for the program, and approximately 75 users pay for the yearly annual maintenance agreement. There are as many as seven individual paid license users of the program at a single institution. Company X understands that a site license will reduce the amount of time invested in billing and processing individual paperwork. Company X will continue to offer individual non-exclusive licenses to academic and commercial users. What are the advantages/disadvantages, if any, of offering a site license to groups of users? Is there a convincing argument as to why Company X should offer a site license and/or maintenance agreement to institutions/companies? Should a site license be offered at a savings to academic and commercial institutions, or should it be offered at an increased value and price? Are there any legal considerations that need to be addressed?

A good case can be made for site licenses.

   a.   It increases usage and sales with minimum licensing paperwork.

b. All large companies offer site licenses.

c. A price difference between university and commercial users makes sense.
   - universities may contend that as a nonprofit they cannot afford software if priced at commercial rates
   - provide a site license if the university dept. buys multiple copies i.e. if 3 copies additional copies can be made at no additional cost.
   - commercial companies make profits and can afford a larger licensing fee especially as they are probably making agreements in which the software is used for some analysis purpose.
   - the more sales made to an end-user, either university or commercial, should be provided at a discounted rate. It is not logical to seek an increased fee; unless for a site license the 1st copy is $1,500, the 2nd is say $1,250, the third is $1,000 ... The discount should be adjusted so that with more copies sold, the price per unit may decrease but the total purchase price increases.

d. An updated/maintenance fee still requires annual paperwork although it saves a single end-user license paperwork. There is no reduction in paperwork if a maintenance fee is requested. It might make sense to provide a discounted update fee for site licenses (less than $500 per end-user). For example, the 1st maintenance user fee is $500, the 2nd, $400, etc.

e. No legal problems are evident based on what has been presented.

27. An academic scientist seeks to let a company view source code to see if they want to develop it further. The scientist wants to prepare a non-disclosure agreement plus a licensing agreement at the same time, asking for 3% of the sales price. What would a reasonable price be? For example, should a lump sum fee be charged for letting the company see the code? Should there be a lump sum in addition to the royalty fee? What does "sales price" mean?

Is there a real need for the company to "see" the code? It seems that the capability of the software to do what it is supposed to do, should be sufficient for the company to establish a desire to secure rights to the technology.

In my opinion, an option may be appropriate, but an NDA may also work.

The most appropriate approach might be to offer a license "option" for which the company should pay a nominal price. This price of the option should not be reflecting the full value of the license. It could be credited towards the full license. The option should include:

a. the option price, nominal, say $10 000, credited toward a full license,

b. a time limit, i.e. 3 months, what happens to the source, return of the source, etc.,

c. what can and cannot be done with the source during this 3 months period, and

d. what happens if they want the license and what if they do not want.

The license will depend on the software itself -- what does it do, how would it be distributed, how is other software in the field generally distributed, etc. A royalty may or may not be in order. Will there be a sales price? Is the software going to be sold? Given away to gain visibility or market share for another product? Syndicated for others to use? Used widely? Used by a few companies in high value situations? You need to know more about the distribution before you can create an effective license.

Negotiate the license once there is interest in a license not at the time of evaluation. Indicate desire to negotiate in good faith and give a right to be the first to acquire or negotiate for rights to the asset during the option period or for a defined period after the option period but not for more than 3 months after the option expires.

An option fee is appropriate and should be related to the amount of time the option is in effect. Consider crediting the option fee toward payments a company would make under a license

The fee structure of a software license could mirror that of a patent license, e.g., license origination fee, annual maintenance fee until the first commercial sale, royalties, and minimum royalties.

Base royalties on net sales and use a definition of net sales that includes standard commercial deductions. For example, a 3% royalty on net sales of software, even when the licensee has to do some additional work, may be low for a program sold as a stand-alone product.

Many licenses for software have an up-front fee, and annual annuity payments, with steps up in the annuities at set events with only a few requiring royalty payments.

28. A company has developed a technology which it feels is beyond its capabilities to properly market. The company would like to hand the technology off to some other entity better able to commercialize it. The company intends to obtain a royalty from production revenues once the technology goes into production. A concern is that the other entity might decide to accept this license and then fail to make appropriate steps toward full marketing and commercialization. It is expected that this technology will have a slow market acceptance rate because of the nature of the industrial customers involved, so consistent early marketing is necessary and a commitment to be involved for a few years is important. Plus, there could be competitors two or three years later, so loss of lead-time could be significant. What options would help establish a greater obligation on the part of the technology accepting organization to proceed forward, in a timely and reasonably aggressive fashion with an appropriate technology commercialization plan? Is it appropriate to impose penalties for failure to capitalize the business as planned? What terms would you impose?

Require licensee to supply a business plan, and/or identify reasonable milestones (e.g., marketing expenditures, sales goals, regulatory approvals) and convert the license to a non-exclusive, or provide for termination of the license, if the milestones are not met. Allow licensees to buy additional time if they fail to meet milestones if licensor desires.

These suggestions require the ability to define clear milestones. If milestones are hard to define, then annual payments ("maintenance fees") or minimum annual royalties can be used to incentivize the licensee to diligently pursue sales. Make sure such annual payments are large enough to make it worth more to develop the technology than not, but not so large they threaten the company's survival (if a start-up) or cause them to drop the business prematurely if it doesn't take off as soon as expected.

29. A patent has just issued and now the need for writing a cease and desist letter has arisen. There are two U.S. companies that you contend are infringing the patent and the question is to whom this letter should be sent? Company #1 is manufacturing the infringing part but Company #2 has the exclusive license to sell it domestically. Although Company #1 does not sell it domestically, it does sell it internationally. Note: A PCT patent application has been filed. The patent is related to a part that attaches to a product made by Company #1 which is also exclusively licensed to Company #2 for domestic sale but again Company #1 sells the product internationally. That product is both companies main source of income and your part greatly enhances the utility of that product. You have compared your part in field tests with the infringing part and your part is superior in every way. The most important issue is that both companies involved are ideal licensees for your product, Company #1 for foreign markets and Company #2 for domestic, so professional action will be important. What strategy and correspondence outline would you deem appropriate?

More information is needed, however, it appears that the licensor has not granted rights to manufacture to Company #1 but has granted the exclusive right to sell in the domestic market to company #2. Since there is no issued PCT patent manufacture and sale in the international market cannot be restricted or controlled by the licensor.

The cease and desist letter should be sent to the president of Company #1 since they are manufacturing and incorporating licensor's product into their end product and selling the end product in the domestic market. They are also manufacturing licensor's product in the U.S., incorporating it into their end product and selling this end product in the international market. The act of manufacturing in the U.S. would infringe the U.S. patent.

30. A non-exclusive license is being considered for a technology, covered by a pending patent application. The technology is related to a biological molecule that (among other uses) is expected to have utility in a specific cell-based therapy; but the technology is "enabling" rather than central to the therapy. The molecule would be used in the early stages of developing the cell population for therapy, and could conceivably still be expressed in the final cell population, but it may be one of several molecules, factors, etc. that licensees

would use in this therapy. The technology is very early stage, but the licensees would get rights under the pending patent application, and the right to use biological materials and know-how. (In addition, the molecule is newly identified and so composition of matter claims are expected to be obtained. The intent is to license this technology in a field limited to cell-based therapy. Two companies are interested in the technology. A term sheet that features an upfront license fee, annual maintenance fees, milestone payments based on clinical development of products, and royalties on product sales has been drafted. In drafting these terms, it has been noted that the technology is an enabling technology (and is being non-exclusively licensed), and therefore the figures are being kept low; however, there is an desire not to be too conservative. What license terms should be considered in this situation?

This situation is typical for early stage technology. Some comments and recommendations are:
- not enough is known presently about the therapy product to establish value,
- the scope of the patent claims are unknown,
- use one set of terms, price the deal attractively, and move on, or
- use some deal flexibility, i.e. contingencies to capture value that may appear.

Establish a list of terms that address the key potential tracks development could take. For instance, use separate sets of contingent payments (milestones, royalties, success payments etc) for discoveries that have theoretical use as screening targets, gene therapy and therapeutic protein.

Always allow for blocking composition of matter claims as long as the patent has not issued. Prior licenses can be a problem if terms are prepared without forethought and a licensee can essentially got a free ride because the license did not anticipate composition of matter (the license assumed tool), but the grant was broad enough that it was included yet without a corresponding royalty provision. Remember that grant and field definitions are critical components in a license so make sure they are coordinated with payment provisions.

One way to proceed is to propose fees and royalties as though the intellectual property was the only one licensed to a licensee and include language that allows a reduction in royalties and/or fees if a licenses must also license third party intellectual property to make their product or perform their service. Set a floor for reductions in royalties and/or fees. The floor for royalties is usually 50% of the starting royalties. The floor for fees is negotiable. This approach doesn't require you to speculate about how low your royalties should be without knowing what and how many third party licenses a licensee will need.

31. An inventor establishes a start-up company with technology invented at an academic institution and remains on staff. The institution licenses the technology to the new start up company. When it is time to distribute net income from the license, does the inventor receive a share according to the institution's patent policy rate (say 50% of net income)? Is there any adjustment made to the inventor's share to offset the inventor's equity in the company? Should

there be? The inventor might be allowed to have equity in a company and not be penalized by having his share of net income diminished, but can this be considered "double dipping".

There are numerous arguments on both sides of this issue. Some are as follows.

Take the position that the inventor gets equity in the company for their contribution to the business apart from the technology. The institution (not the inventor) is compensated by the company for the technology via a license agreement. The institution shares compensation for its technologies with inventors in accordance with the patent policy. That the inventor is also a principal in the company does not mean they should not be compensated under this logic. Would you withhold inventor's share from a faculty member because they also had a consulting agreement with the company (that involved equity)? No. Think of the inventor as having a "super-consulting agreement" with the company that happens to cover the functions of a principal. However, be cognizant of other considerations, such as conflict of interest, that must be attended to.

Ask the inventor to waive all rights to compensation if they are associated with the company.

The University of Virginia allows inventors to receive their share of the royalties, even though they may possess equity in the start-up company (or established company) and manage the conflicts of interest in these cases.

U. of New Mexico's policy allows inventors with equity in startups to receive royalty portion (currently at 40% net) as well, so long as the Conflict of Interest committee is aware of the situation and the conflict is being managed.

32. A faculty member invented a technology that the University accepted, according to its Patent Policy. The faculty member has created a start-up company and wishes to become the exclusive licensee of the technology. (The company is located off-campus.) The University would like to encourage faculty inventiveness and entrepreneurial spirit. However, the University also wants to avoid conflicts of interest. How does one address the issue of further inventions by the faculty member relating to the technology licensed when any such inventions are created off-campus? Further, since a faculty inventor is granted a share of any royalties paid to the University, it would seem that a faculty inventor/licensee would have two bites at the royalty apple: one as the company owner, and one as the faculty member. Is a waiver of the faculty percentage payable under the Patent Policy appropriate? The University would want not to oppress the start-up with fees, but would also want to ensure some return on the resources spent in patenting, etc. In the case of such a start-up, having little current funding, is an equity position for the University in lieu of fees reasonable? Does a requirement for some payments/milestones act as a beneficial prod to the start-up? Or is it just an anchor around their necks? What pitfalls and benefits of faculty self-licensing University technology are possible?

This is always a dilemma where Academic Institutions get wrapped around an "ethics axel". Please consider that the "U" should become an investor in the licensee's enterprise, to have a voice in keeping everyone, including successors, honest. Do not inhibit further invention based on the licensed technology, or later unrelated technical products. By being an investor, but not a controlling interest, the "U" will be privy to the revenue status. Initial agreement on royalty for the basic licensed product(s) should be established. New and derivative product royalty would be also recognized but at a lesser rate to the "U". Technology partitioning is not easy but if a reasonable equity sharing is done, all benefit. Royalty producing products not based on "U" contributions should be accounted to the venture, with royalty to the inventors, who may not be investors in the enterprise. The "U" shares as a stockholder and can internally distribute funds as originally planned. So what if the faculty licensee gets more bites at the royalty apple? If the licensee takes the risk that person should get benefit. Royalties based on related product, net sales billed for a product and services are most equitable.

32(a). If you were the faculty licensee would you buy the proposed revenue distribution plan?

If the faculty member remains in the company, a full time employee of the company should negotiate all present and future transactions with the university. The faculty member should agree not to participate in the negotiations or ask about them. The company should agree not to discuss the transactions with the faculty member. This helps avoid conflicts of interest by keeping the conflicted party at arms length.

Different institutions view this matter differently. Some view it as "double dipping" and require the faculty member to waive their share. Others do not have this requirement.

Yes, provided you will have a mechanism for cashing out. The most likely mechanism will be the company doing an IPO at a future date and creating a public market for their stock.

It is not an anchor provided the payments are structured correctly. The first few payments could consist of cash and equity while the latter ones could be cash.

Absent a provision for this specific situation, compensation to a faculty member from the university presumes that the inventor is allied with the university, and contracts and employment law would back that up.

The burden of resolving the privity conflict should be on the faculty/ inventor as this person is seeking to change the relationship with the university. If the inventor is seeking to change roles to develop the technology, then this person would have to completely embrace the new role. 'Double dipping' would appear to be a problem.

However, as universities become more commercial oriented and as the entrepreneurial economy becomes hyper-energized, the bottom line may be that universities should specifically address this emerging possibility in their policies/contracts.

Although not formally enshrined in policy, at Kansas State University the practice is that inventions arising within a startup, that involve a university faculty member as an inventor or co-inventor, still go through the disclosure process, including review by our University Patent Advisory Committee. Precedents have been set by that Committee to determine the University has no claim on the invention. The process is critical to avoiding future complications, and so far is working well. If it truly is an invention outside the university, it will stand up as such. However, the potential for overlap between a faculty member's work in a startup and work in a university is fraught with issues that are best addressed upfront and in a forthright manner. Any faculty member with inventions truly outside the university should have no problem with the procedure. If they do object, one must ask why they object. In that case, they either don't trust the system, or are making an invalid claim of ownership.

33. A letter is sent to your institution, addressed to you, from a company. The letter refers to a specific research product and the company states that they are the exclusive worldwide licensee for human and mouse research applications. They go on to state there are several unlicensed cell lines being sold and transferred without their consent and if your organization is using any cell line to produce their product for use in research it may constitute infringement. Your Director of Research was not aware of anyone using the product and he wants you to alert all researchers. Your Executive Director disagrees with this and wants you to write to the company and indicate you are not aware of any infringement, but if they have a specific allegation please let you know. The Research Director disagrees; he feels to write such a letter "invites them into your research lab". You have never received a letter like this before, and don't know if it went to 1000 companies or just to you. What would you do and are there any legal obligations that might exist?

Do the usual checking and alerting and, if no potential infringement is found do not respond further. An alternative is to notify the company in writing that you are unaware of any potential infringement. On the other hand a technology transfer office cannot know all of the materials and reagents that its institute's researchers are using with out expending a considerable amount of time and effort. It is unfair to have to make such an effort in response to a nebulous charge of possible infringement, made wholly as a marketing ploy.

Think like the licensee. They have entered an exclusive contract, that on a very basic level they can only make money on if they enforce their rights. Specifically they want to sell a research product to research labs. You are a research lab. They don't want to shut you down. They just want to make you a customer.

One method of doing this is notifying you of their legal rights under the law. The company may be notifying research organizations, in a mass mailing, that are active in this particular research area merely to cast a broad net to see what they might catch. More importantly, such marketing practices may constitute an illegal use of a patent.

One way to deter such frivolous practices is to file a DJ (declaratory judgment) action against the accuser. This may be a bit excessive but would certainly have an impact on the party making a mass mailing such as this.

34. A company wants to deduct from net sales the interest that is earned against loaned funds as indicated in a letter of credit from an international bank. Is this a standard procedure? If so, want kind of language would be appropriate to make sure that the company is not deducting it up front to lower net sales, but then adding it back in later as some kind of adjustment to the income statement/balance sheet?

Although items included as deductions against net sales can be negotiated, interest earned against loaned funds is unusual. Do not accept it as a deduction since it is not an item separately invoiced to purchasers. It is part of the licensee's cost of doing business that should not be arbitrarily passed on to a licensor.

Common sense suggests that one should limit adjustments to costs directly related to the sale, but even then - what about commissions? They are related to the sale, but usually considered an expense (i.e. cost of doing business), and not used as an adjustment. The bottom line is that commissions are not an appropriate deduction from gross sales. Commissions are an expense that are, or should be, built into the licensee's gross profit and hence the selling price. If commissions are deducted from gross sales, a licensee recovers their costs twice: once from their customers and a second time from the licensee. In the latter case, the deduction from gross sales is pure profit to the licensee at the licensor's expense.

Net sales are usually a catalog price fob factory/source. Tax, shipping, insurance are not ordinarily in the royalty calculation. The basis for importation duty is CIF (cost, insurance, freight), or landed cost and is usually assumed by the buyer. Commission is a cost the seller or buyer can assume and it all depends on the sales representation agreement, and the seller's obligation to pay taxes on income produced elsewhere.

Since the instrument is sold both in the U.S. and foreign, you must adjust your thinking for two different scenarios. If produced in the U.S., the U.S. selling price is the
basis for all U.S. purchases. If the sale is bundled to include warranty costs-these are royalty bearing. Overseas the local basic selling price can be higher, if a published catalog price is available where sold. This is not unreasonable because the product sold outside the U.S. may require special packaging, local regulatory approvals, etc., which are comparable in a domestic sales cost build ups. The royalty, or commission, should be always based on the local cost where sold, less taxes, shipping and handling. Shipping does not usually include packaging costs.

Commissions on sales must be based on "catalog cost" and one must be aware of foreign sales practices. One can eliminate foreign commissions by selling FOB U.S. factory to buyers who are "resellers", and collect from the ultimate buyer whatever the traffic will allow. But be careful about warranty cost sharing. It is best to sell replacement parts which are commission/royalty bearing to the agent/licensor. The sales representative would ordinarily get a commission if all the payments went to the U.S. and the seller would compensate the agent. Is the foreign representative an agent or a reseller distributor? Who handles in/out warranty service? Who actually makes, sells, services the product in the U.S.? Are the inventors licensing their product to a licensee, who is the actual seller? Many small firms do not price their products or services for the actual market they are in, which in this case is a world market and not just local U.S. It is possible that the reality of too low pricing has now been

556

recognized and there is need for some kind of relief, which may be difficult once a world price has been set.

35. You are considering a license strategy for use of a certain technology. The technology involves use of a certain type of instrument and there may be multiple instruments at a given "site". Your contact is reluctant to give more information about the technology and its uses but is thinking of the PCR site license model which is a fee for each time the instrument is used. There has been some discussion as to how to define "site". Another aspect, with all the mergers and interrelationships, is how to define "multi-site". Because of the nature of the technology, licenses might be offered to universities and non-profit research organizations as well as corporations.

The mergers & acquisitions in the pharma industry have forced a re-evaluation of the definition of "site". In the past, a "site" used to be the location where software is loaded and deployed. One site received one copy of the software. With increased usage of the Internet, close collaborations between biotech and pharma companies and creation of international conglomerates from mergers & acquisitions, this resulted in the software being used as licensed (on one computer) but serving the needs of, in some cases, 5 or 10 potential licensees.

Therefore, licensing style has changed. (Who wants to limit potential market to 20 or 30 sales?) Although this is not applied consistently, "site" for large-scale bioinformatics software is defined as follows:

1. one site is each location where there are USERS, not each location where the computer and/or software is loaded,
2. if a licensor wants the software to be used by multiple sites, even over the internet and from a single computer, then they must have a multi-site license, and
3. multi-site license covers the number of locations where the licensor has users (Generally this is limited to locations within the same organization. If one of the multi-sites is at a collaborating organization, it is generally not allowed as a multi-site and the collaborating organization must get their own license).

Negotiation is key. Often some sites have more users than others. The licensor wants to have "legal" use at all sites, but, e.g., if one site has 500 users and another has 5 users, they are not considered equal. Consider the negotiation approach that 2 or 3 sites with only a handful of users are equivalent to one site for terms of pricing. Alternatively, use a model based on total number of users. This is precise, but can result in extra work/costs.

The Internet has impacted software licensing especially in pharmaceutical companies where virtually all are multi-site and have links with academia or smaller companies (i.e., organizations outside their own).

Many licensors have turned to per-user license fees. This is sometimes considered to be an economic "advantage" for the licensor as opposed to the revenue generated when a site license is issued. A " rule of thumb" is if the sites vary widely in number of users, then perhaps total number of users is a good indication of price.

However, if the number of users model is used and the licensee is providing any support at all, the number of sites will probably affect the support load as much as the number of users because each site will likely develop one "expert" user, who the licensee will be required to support. Another tactic is to specify one or two people as contact points to the licensee so that questions from the licensor do not get out of hand. While the lure of a precise pricing model for multi-site license is enchanting, especially to the licensor, be careful to check out the "real" costs and limit the extra work/liabilities that result from multiple sites.

36. Recent legislation appears to affect technology transfer out of government and academia. Are there any publications that summarize the impact?

TECHNOLOGY TRANSFER BILLS REDUCE COMPETITION, INCREASE SECRECY AND UNDERMINE PUBLIC ACCOUNTABILITY

(CPT comments on HR 209 and S.804)

Background

The National Institutes of Health has issued draft guidelines discouraging researchers from making pacts with companies for access to biomedical-research tools if those deals restrict dissemination of the resulting scientific findings. The agency last month invited public comment on the proposed guidelines, which followed many of the recommendations made last year by an advisory committee to the N.I.H. director, Harold E. Varmus. That panel found that deals had interfered with the progress of some scientific projects and the public release of useful scientific results.

University-based scientists rely on companies to supply a range of items used in research, including software, chemicals, living cells, and animals. Last year's report described widespread frustration among university researchers about the promises universities had made to companies for use of those tools.

The panel found that companies at times gained exclusive ownership of discoveries resulting from use of their tools. They also restricted the publishing of results and were viewed as seeking unreasonable prices for the tools. The deals were negotiated in a time-consuming, case-by-case fashion that university officials said posed a drag on their resources. Because the N.I.H. is a major supporter of basic biomedical research, the agency has an interest in solving such problems, the report noted. The new draft guidelines stop short of dictating exactly how users of research tools should negotiate agreements to acquire them, and propose no sanctions for anyone who refuses to follow the guidelines. Instead, the draft suggests general principles that any recipient of N.I.H. financing should follow.

Recipients of the agency's grants and contracts "should develop and implement clear priorities which articulate acceptable conditions" for acquiring the tools, "and refuse to yield on unacceptable conditions," the report said.

For example, the proposed guidelines would discourage universities from giving companies exclusive licenses to control the research tools, unless the license was limited to commercial applications of the item. Academic researchers should still have wide access to the tools at moderate costs. The guidelines also ask recipients of N.I.H. financing not to give companies licenses to control discoveries arising from the use of their tools. Exceptions include cases where the tool used by the university is unique, already patented, and not available from other sources. "The rights granted should be limited to inventions that have been made directly through the use of the materials provided," the guidelines state. In addition, the draft recommendations discourage universities from agreeing to delay publishing results for longer than 30 days. That finite amount of time is sufficient for a supplier of a research tool to redact proprietary information or, in certain circumstances, to file for a patent, the guidelines say. Comments on the draft guidelines are due by August 23 to the N.I.H.'s Office of Technology Transfer. View guidelines at http://www.nih.gov/od/ott/RTguide.htm and the advisory panel's report is on line at http://www.nih.gov/news/researchtools/index.htm.

MODULE VIII - CAPITAL FORMATION

Capital Formation

- **Due diligence – capital acquisition and provider**
- **Federal and state assistance programs**
- **Capital – amount and debt vs. equity**
- **Capital sources - ACENet, angel money, individual investor, venture capital, friends, banking industry**

Various kinds and sources of financing are available for different states of technology development and business growth, including start-up, seed, operating, venture capital, limited partnerships, and public commercial financial institutions. Emphasis is directed toward identifying the financial requirements related to financing a start-up enterprise, and possible sources of capital.

INTRODUCTION

Solicitation of investors requires preparation. A knowledgeable individual who has the proper information and a thorough understanding of the potential investor must make the presentation. A well-prepared business plan is crucial regardless of who is approached for investment capital. The presentation format will differ depending on who is being asked to invest.

Four key rules for raising capital are: 1) know how much is needed the first time around (it is difficult to go to the investor asking for more due to poor estimates upfront); 2) don't try to raise cash without an operating budget, short-term cash flow projections and 3-5 year business plan; 3) the capital structure must make sense from the beginning; and 4) be persistent, if fail at first - keep trying (See Module IX, Corporate Formation).

Good insight into what a venture capitalist needs or prefers not only impresses the investor but also leads to leverage for the party requesting capital. Several considerations when approaching the venture capital community are the following:

- What are the terms of debt incurred? (Debt restrictions usually impose limitations on the flexibility a venture capitalist may prefer),
- Is there opportunity for mergers? (Mergers may be a means to enhance and expand a business and may be a way for the investor to leverage other investments.),
- How strong are the intentions of the business owner? (An investor becomes very uneasy if the party seeking capital shows any hesitancy or change in business focus.),
- How much control is the capital solicitor will to give up? (The investor will likely want at a minimum a seat on the board of directors.),
- Is the party seeding capital willing to allow the investor a right to participate in the Initial public offering (IPO) i.e. give up 10% of the IPO? (It is hard to give up this much and if requested should be subject to negotiation with the basic objective not to agree to this condition.), and
- Who will assume responsibility for stock registration and what terms are acceptable in the registration rights agreement? (Company may register stock one year after the IPO; however, it may not be prudent to allow anyone to force registration. It is better to consent to a demand for a right to piggyback but avoid piggyback rights at the time of the IPO.)

BUSINESS CAPITALIZATION PROCESS

A well-formulated capital solicitation plan might be comparable to a product introduction plan. Preliminary feasibility will provide valuable information, which can be extremely useful as strategy; tactics and decisions are made to assure successful capital acquisition. The initial capital feasibility test should allow one to determine if it is prudent to invest in further preparation, revision or solicitation. The details related to capital needs may not need to be disclosed during this phase of solicitation and the presentations may be based on all available information not a full business plan.

A two to four page venture profile document can be used to ascertain initial interest and at the same time be a means to identify potential issues, yield ideas on presentation strategy and provide ideas for solicitation of capital.

The venture profile or feasibility test criteria should include at least the following: 1) scientific and technical concept principles; 2) a team view of market opportunities along with their credibility and significance; 3) a realistic projected market entry along with competitive strategy; and 4) an analysis of the strength of a proprietary position; description and credentials of management in place or to be acquired; and an assessment of actual or perceived operation plans including equipment, facilities and expense.

DUE DILIGENCE

REQUESTOR

As an investor determines interest in an investment, a detailed due diligence effort will be carried out. Examples of items that will be addressed along with samples of questions related to each are:

1. Management
   - Are they results and action oriented?
   - What complementary skills exist?
   - Do they have applicable experience?
   - What evidence is there of good integrity?
   - Are they effective communicators?
2. Target markets
   - Will market include US and/or International?
   - Is there potential for strong growth dynamics?
   - What evidence is there of a solid competitive structure?
3. Compelling business model
   - How significant is the proprietary technology, products, or services?
   - Will specialized distribution be required and is so what is plan?
   - Are there clear verifiable customer values?
4. Value creation
   - What opportunity is there for partnering or collaboration?
   - Is milestone based funding possible?
   - Are multiple exit opportunities possible?

Credibility of the entrepreneur or capital solicitor will need to be established. In order to gain respect the presentation should be complete (tell it like it is); accurate; without apology and contain a strategy designed to achieve success.

PROVIDER

The party soliciting an investment must also determine the qualifications and capabilities of the investor(s). This assessment is often related to the needs of the entrepreneur and may also be qualifications that add value to the entrepreneur's business venture if an investment is made. An investor provides; money, independent market knowledge, a business and financial network, mentoring capability, a sounding board for the entrepreneur or business management, a party to act as the devil's advocate, objectivity and; and independent or unbiased input and comments.

In addition, a potential investor must be in a position to provide the services and assistance the capital requestor needs or wants. Several factors affect what an investor is willing or can do in an investment relationship. These are:

1. What is health of current investments? A successful business portfolio suggests a good track record and no need to continue to "bail out" existing investments.
2. How much time and attention does the current portfolio require? The less time spent on exiting ventures, the more time available for the investor to dedicate to a new business venture.
3. Is there uncommitted investment money available? Remember institutions usually expect a venture to last for 10 years. If the venture fund is in its 8th year and you need 3-4 years to reach market the investor may not be a good or qualified candidate for you.
4. Does the investor invest in the industry you are in or what is the investor's focus? It is easy to indicate interest in preliminary oral discussion but if the venture fund is focused on

Internet businesses it is highly unlikely that interest in an unrelated industry will clear the investor's criteria necessary for commitment.

5. Is there a need to seek an acquisition or merger; i.e. fold a $300M competitor into your $500M company? If that is the case, one needs an investment banker or late stage venture capitalist. On the other hand, an early stage development firm will be more interested in an early stage business investor.

6. How does the venture capitalist locate investment candidates? Some firms rely on referrals, others examine cold submissions, and some may seek out candidate firms or technologies. Larger venture funds may have associations with asset and company evaluation and assessment organizations that carry out the due diligence and make recommendations to the venture capital firm. In any event early exposure through selective participating in key events or newsletters can be useful along with strategically timed press releases or other non intrusive ways to gain recognition and exposure. Some venture capital firms participate in meetings/conference designed to foster awareness of investment candidates.

In any event, due diligence will usually involve a technical, business and management analysis. This might be summarized as an assessment of strengths, weaknesses, opportunities and threats (SWOT) associated with the venture. The due diligence process is depicted in figure one.

Establishing capital need requires an in-depth knowledge of all facets involved in the development and marketing of an asset. Some items to consider as the strategy is established for capitalization are as follows:

1. Small biotech companies have less than 50 employees and have limited or no CGMP manufacturing facilities;
2. Venture capital investments are high risk and there is no guarantee of company success;
3. Do not rush to clinical trials as fast as possible without addressing all components involved in product development;
4. Business strategy is often to license or partner after Phase I or II clinical studies;
5. Overlooked details during product development require repeats e.g. cell line characterization, process validation analytical assay development, biological assay development, formulation development and early stability studies all increasing value of asset;
6. Establish a detailed product development overview (flow diagram i.e. PERT chart);
7. Need 2-3 years to finalize manufacture of clinical trial material;
8. Clinical trials will often require 4-7 years to complete;
9. Consider outsourcing stability, formulation development, toxicology and pharmacy-dynamic studies;
10. Choose outsource partner;
    - Outsourcer must define goals and deliverables of each outsourced activity to ensure success of development program
    - Consolidate as much as possible so one QA dept, one GMP manufacturing dept, one research dept, etc.
    - One senior manager from outsourcer
    - Establish standard operating procedures and exchange with responsible parties

    - Treat as partnership and business relationship with milestones for each partner to be successful
11. Must maximize chances of product success in order to assure business success;
12. Establish project plan and project team whether partnering or not; both are dynamic,
13. Communication is key to success;

14. Address assay development including process control, batch release, robust for both internal and external routine use, validated; reproducibility and precision, detection limits/ranges (time and cost often not precise);
15. Have backup outsource site; backup, competition; and
16. VC does not like to invest in manufacturing facilities.

Figure one. Due diligence process diagram.

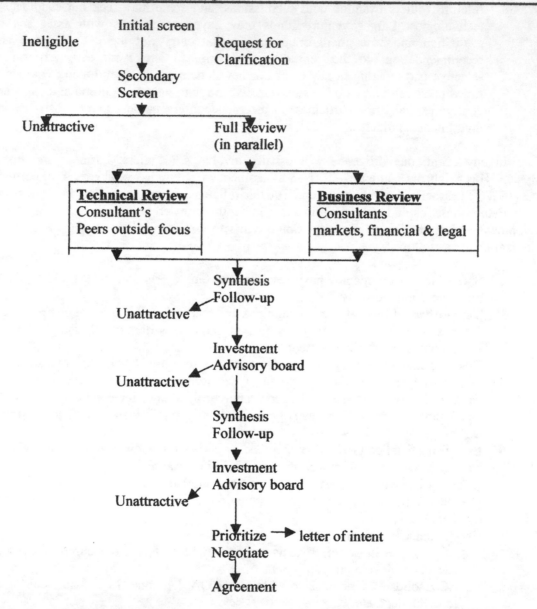

CAPITAL SOURCING STRATEGY

The financial life cycle stage of a business, from startup to fully mature, dictates the availability of the financing alternatives. Startups often begin with only ideas and enthusiasm. One of the many issues that every entrepreneur must address in starting a small business is the financial reality involved in deciding exactly what they want to do, when it can be done, and how it's going to be achieved.

New small businesses have trouble securing conventional financing because they present a tremendous risk to lenders and investors. The result is that nearly three-quarters of startup businesses are funded through the owner's own resources, such as personal savings, residential mortgages or consumer loans. Investments by family members, friends, and private contacts or "angels" provide most of the remaining "seed" funds for new small businesses.

The most common financial problem for startup businesses is a shortage of cash, and cash flow problems during a potentially long initial period can be fatal to the business, not to mention its owner. Any debt financing (loans) that the business can secure from traditional lenders, e.g., banks, is likely to be expensive because of the high risks assumed by the financier. Moreover, unless the business can boast a significant owner investment and marketable collateral, the availability of conventional debt financing can be almost nonexistent.

A "cash crunch" puts a tremendous focus upon things like inventory turnover, and the need for immediate revenue often becomes a daily crisis that takes priority over financing for sustained growth or development of new products. Perseverance and a willingness to investigate all sources of financing--from angels to government loan programs--are invaluable at this stage.

In contrast to starting a business from scratch (startup), when an existing business is purchased or capital is sought for business growth debt and equity vehicles are usually more available. In this case the target business has a credit history, existing assets, an established operating cycle and business goodwill. Therefore, lenders and investors can be approached in the same manner as if business expansion was intended.

The major distinction between financing to purchase an existing business and financing to raise funds for a growing business is the former offers the opportunity for seller-assisted financing. Entrepreneurs who are selling their small businesses usually realize they may need to participate in the buyer's financing of the business sale, and the buyer may be willing to negotiate a very favorable debt or equity arrangement.

A growing or mature business usually has sufficient stability in its operations so the cash flow problems are not a constant crisis. If the business is successful, internally generated money from sales and investments can fund many of the business's needs.

Typically, growing and mature businesses have more financing options available to them because of their operating history, established value, credit history, and availability of inventory and accounts receivable financing. In addition, the advantages of having established customers and suppliers, efficient internal operating procedures, more sophisticated marketing and advertising, realistic long-term business plans, and the company's emerging goodwill help improve the creditworthiness and investor appeal of the business.

Debt financing becomes increasingly feasible for a business as its track record supports creditworthiness. If the business has been profitable, debt financing is generally the preferred form of raising new capital for existing businesses. Nonetheless, a growing business may be stifled by inadequate capital for expansion that stems from the reluctance of an entrepreneur to dilute their ownership through equity financing.

Sometimes the decision simply comes down to whether the owner wants a profitable, growing business in which they share control or will cash out their interest at a given time, or whether they own a business that fails because they did not raise sufficient capital for the business to grow. Growing businesses can consider raising equity capital by private transfers of ownership interests; by using venture capital firms; or by selling ownership interests through formal, limited private offerings or an initial public offering.

An aging business is characterized by a conservative philosophy aimed at maintaining the business's internal bureaucracy and its market status quo. Some companies reach the point where innovation and creativity are limited to tinkering with current products and existing markets. Investment into new product lines and emerging markets represents a financial risk that a complacent ownership is unwilling to assume. Aging businesses tend to be cash-rich because less investment is being undertaken. Financing is rarely a problem for a business in this stage. The owners are generally more interested in conserving assets for the next generation and retiring to a life of leisure.

An example of the investment process, type of investment related to the business stage is presented in table one.

Table one. Investment process, type of investor and investment relative to business stage.

Passive[1]	Passive[1]	Active[1]	Active[1]	Active[1]
Family & Friends	Informal Investors	Informal Investors	Informal Investors	Venture Capitalists
$0-$50K	$50 – $100K	$100 - $500K	$500 - $2M	>$2M
				positive cash flow
Sweat Equity	*Seed Capital*		*Pre-venture Capital*	*Venture Capital*

Concept
Working model
engineering production product Market sales Breakeven
Prototype introduction

1. Investor role in business: Passive = little if any involvement; active = board and/or management role.

Business combinations are a way of leveraging business assets through contractual arrangements with other companies or organizations. Examples of cooperative arrangements with other businesses for sharing costs are mergers and acquisitions, bartering arrangements or R&D alliances.

FINANCING BASICS: DEBT VS. EQUITY

OVERVIEW

A brief overview of the basic types of financing may be helpful to understanding, which options might be most attractive and realistically available to your particular business. Typically, financing is categorized into two fundamental types: debt financing and equity financing. Debt financing means borrowing money that is to be repaid over a period of time, usually with interest. Debt financing can be either short-term (full repayment due in less than one year) or long-term (repayment due over more than one year). The lender does not gain an ownership interest in your business and your obligations are limited to repaying the loan. In smaller businesses, personal guarantees are likely to be required on most debt instruments; commercial debt financing thereby becomes synonymous with personal debt financing.

Debt and equity financing provide different opportunities for raising funds, and a commercially acceptable ratio between debt and equity financing should be maintained. From the lender's perspective, the debt-to-equity ratio measures the amount of available assets or "cushion" available for repayment of a debt in the case of default. Excessive debt financing may impair a firm's credit rating and ability to raise more money in the future. Excess debt, may lead to the conclusion that the business is considered overextended, risky and an unsafe investment. In addition, it might suggest that the firm may be unable to weather unanticipated business downturns, credit shortages, or an interest rate increase if loan's interest rate floats.

Conversely, too much equity financing may indicate that the business is not making the most productive use of its capital; the capital is not being used advantageously as leverage for obtaining cash. Too little equity may suggest that the owners are not committed to their own business.

Lenders will consider the debt-to-equity ratio in assessing whether the company is being operated in a sensible, credit worthy manner. Generally speaking, a local community bank will consider an acceptable debt-to-equity ratio to be between 1:2 and 1:1. For startup businesses in particular, the owners need to guard against cash flow shortages that can force the business to take on excess debt, thereby impairing the business's ability to subsequently obtain needed capital for growth. A discussion of equity basics is presented in Module IX.

DEBT OR EQUITY FINANCING
Debt

Debt financing usually originates from individuals, banks and/or saving and loan institutions that own debt securities that carry rights to receive interest and principal payments in the future. It is a loan and the debt investor is the creditor. This capital is usually obtained late in the product development cycle, when product is market entry or when expansion efforts are intended. The securities are usually "tied" to purchase or collaboration commitments or collateral that reduce the risk for the investing party.

Debt financing refers to what is normally called a loan. A creditor agrees to lend money to a debtor in exchange for repayment, with accumulated interest, at some future date. The creditor does not obtain any ownership claim in the debtor's business. Debt financing is attractive because there is no need to sacrifice any ownership interests in the business, interest on the loan is deductible, and the financing cost is a relatively fixed expense. Selecting a bank or conventional lender: what are your options and where are you most likely to obtain the best loan for your business?

Equity

Equity investors purchase ownership interests in a company and are stock or membership interest holders. Their return is based on dividends or stock price appreciation. These investors will generally have a right to vote at stockholder meetings and will seek a larger return on investment than would be the case for debt financing.

Equity financing describes an exchange of money for a share of business ownership. This form of financing results in obtaining funds without incurring debt; in other words without having to repay a specific amount of money at any particular time. The major disadvantage to equity financing is the dilution of ownership interests and the possible loss of control that may accompany a sharing of ownership with additional investors.

Equity financing requires the sale of an ownership interest in the business in exchange for capital. The most basic hurdle to equity financing is finding investors who are willing to buy into the business; however, the amount of equity financing that is undertaken may depend more upon willingness to share management control than upon the investor appeal of the business. An owner who sells equity interests in the business sacrifices some of their autonomy and management rights. The effect of selling a large percentage of the ownership interest in the business may mean that an entrepreneur's investment will be short-term, unless they retain a majority interest in the business and control over future sale of the business. Of course, many small business operators are not necessarily interested in maintaining their business indefinitely, and personal motives for pursuing a small business will determine the value placed on business ownership. Sometimes the bottom line is whether the entrepreneur or business owner would rather operate a successful business for several years and then sell their interests for a fair profit, or be repeatedly frustrated in attempts at financing a business that cannot achieve its potential because of insufficient capital.

The form of business organization will influence how willing others will be to invest in the business. While the choice of business form or "entity" for a small business involves a wide spectrum of other important issues; such as, the degree of personal risk involved in the type of business, tax considerations, and the need to attract good business managers there are certain financing considerations associated with different forms of business entities. The following is a brief summary of these factors:

1. Sole proprietorships are the simplest businesses to form, but equity financing is limited to the owner's assets;
2. General partnerships require at least two owners, so equity financing possibilities are greater than in proprietorships;
3. Limited partnerships can provide limited liability to some of the owners, if they're not active participants in the business;
4. Corporations provide the most flexible possibilities for investors; and
5. Limited liability companies/limited liability partnerships are relatively new forms of entity that combine favorable tax treatment with limited legal liability for the owners.

Exercise caution when making equity contributions of personal assets (cash or property) to the business. Usually the rights to that contribution become secondary to the rights of business creditors if the business goes bad. Alternatives to outright transfers of capital to the business may be secured loans or "straw man" transactions (the entrepreneur loans money to a third-party relative or friend who then loans the funds to the corporation). The insider then takes a secured interest in the property.

Performance oriented, flexible terms. May be called a "clawback" technique in which an equity investor receives a certain percentage of stock in return for a specified capital investment; but the terms can shift depending on how successful the company is in meeting agreed upon goals and deadlines. Performance is critical so this rewards recipient and provides satisfaction for investor.

Redeemable preferred stock. Once was a way to give investors guaranteed credit status in case of bankruptcy, now used to give investors extra consideration if a company's initial public offering and the deal's payoff get delayed. The preferred stock may be structured so if an IPO takes place in five years instead of two, investor will receive the full value of their original investment plus stock at exit time. This may cost more to build a technique like this into a deal but can make a closing take place. If the IPO market settles down quickly and the company goes public the financial cost may not be extensive.

CAPITAL SOURCES

MERGERS, JOINT VENTURES, OR ALLIANCES

Mergers, joint ventures, consolidations, acquisitions, strategic alliances, associations, and other combinations of business entities can also be employed to raise new funds for the business. The business climate of the '90s encouraged the use of joint ventures and alliances between businesses as a means of reducing costs and ownership dilution. Most of these arrangements are contractual, but no standard contract terms exist for all industries. The advantages of these joint ventures and alliances is that the business can finance certain services or production functions by sharing expertise, assets, expenses, and risk without necessarily incurring cash debt or trading equity.

RESEARCH AND DEVELOPMENT ALLIANCES

Alliances for research and development efforts are also quite common as a means of minimizing these long-term costs. In certain high-tech industries, the cooperation of other businesses is essential, not only from the standpoint of financing, but also for marketing, licensing, and distribution.

When choosing a business partner or alliance, make sure to research the operating and credit history of the potential candidate. Several credit-reporting agencies offer business financial reports on other businesses. These reports may include not only prior credit experiences, but also financial information from the potential partner's bank (e.g., account balance amounts) and personal background information regarding the principals of that business (e.g., education, relevant work experience, etc.).

In most cases, a strategic partner should benefit the small businesses by adding value, not just money. For instance, a business association with a well-recognized industry name can generate immediate credibility and also assist in advertising and marketing for the company. Networking ability plays a major role in locating and investigating strategic partnering opportunities.

Remember, although partnering arrangements are often with other businesses, relationships with trade associations, nonprofit groups, local community organizations, etc., may offer great opportunities for financing some advertising and distribution expenses. Moreover, it might be possible to work out arrangements with these groups that target a very specific, and important, consumer audience.

STRATEGIC PARTNERSHIPS

These partnerships are a very good alternative if traditional financing is unavailable. Cash infusion is usually smaller than with traditional financing but open the door for more capital options later on.

FRANCHISING

"Franchising" is the transfer of the right to sell a trademarked product or service through a system prescribed by a "franchisor," who owns the trademark. Franchising has been one of the fastest growing areas of new business development during the last 15 years and there are currently over half a million franchise businesses in the U.S. While traditional franchise businesses such as gasoline stations, auto dealers, and soft drink bottlers continue to grow, the most rapidly expanding industries for franchises are service businesses involving recreation and leisure activity and business services.

Franchise arrangements are usually either: (1) product and trade name franchises or (2) business format franchises. The former involves product distribution arrangements within a specified geographic territory. For example, a gas station can be a product and trade name franchise. A business format franchise includes not only a product and trade name, but also operating procedures such as facility design, accounting and bookkeeping procedures, employee relations, quality assurance standards, and the overall image and appearance of the business. For instance, restaurants and convenience stores are often business format franchises.

For the franchisee, franchising is a way to reduce the risks of a new business by buying into an established product or concept. For the franchisor, franchising is a way to expand the business more quickly, by sharing some of the costs, risks, and rewards with franchisees.

EMPLOYEE STOCK OWNERSHIP PLANS (ESOP)

Plans that allow employees to own a piece of the business can boost production and provide leverage for additional financing. An ESOP is a qualified retirement benefit plan in which the major investment is securities of the employer's company. In an ESOP, employees can purchase shares of stock in the company by paying cash or by agreeing to reductions from salary or benefits. The employees become part owners of the business and additional funds are available for other business purposes. In addition, the company contributes to the ESOP by either making an annual cash contribution to the plan for the purchase of company securities or by directly contributing stock to the plan. Either way, the company's contribution results in the cash price of the stock being returned to the company. The company gets a tax deduction for the ESOP contribution while effectively retaining the cash.

ESOPs may be of further benefit to the company because by giving employees a vested interest in the business it may promote productivity and a commitment to the long-term success of the company. Some ESOPs are also used as leverage for borrowing additional funds for the business. An ESOP can borrow funds from lenders in order to purchase additional securities in the employer's business. Alternatively, the employer can borrow from a lender and re-lend the funds to the ESOP; the ESOP would then purchase company stock with the cash. In both scenarios, the employer ends up with the cash price of the stock. ESOPs are sometimes used in this manner for large stock purchases when funding is necessary to finance mergers, acquisitions, or buy-outs. Because an ESOP requires that there be employees and because implementing an ESOP can be expensive and time-consuming, this financing tool may not be sensible for many startup and existing small businesses. Moreover, be aware that plan participants who terminate employment may demand distribution of stock itself, rather than simply the stock's cash value. A closely held business may not want former employees to own stock in the company or to be able to vote as shareholders. In addition, if the trustees of the ESOP are also the business's owners, they may occasionally face a conflict of interest between their duties to act in the best interests of the ESOP and their duties as directors and/or officers of the company. For example, if a takeover offer was tendered, the ESOP might profit from the takeover, but company management might oppose the possible change.

ESOPs are commonly used by business owners seeking to retire from the business. If the small business has grown to the point where there are a fairly large number of employees, an ESOP can provide an excellent way to, in effect, sell the business to the employees because the ESOP provides a ready-made buyer for the stock.

Because of the complexity involved in establishing and maintaining an ESOP, an attorney and/or accountant should be consulted for more details on an ESOP. General information is available from the ESOP Association, 1100 17th Street, NW, Suite 1207, Washington, DC 20036.

MICRO-LOANS

Range in size from hundreds of dollars to low six figures. Very popular if a small infusion of capital could make a difference in cash flow or growth related activities. Many lenders regard micro-loans as too small to be worth the effort.

THIRD PARTY LOAN GUARANTEES

Third party loan guarantees require a relative or close friend to cosign a credit line agreement if company's credit history is questionable. There are some financing intermediates that will cosign your corporate credit line for the right price, a fixed fee or a percentage of the face value of the loan. For contacts, check with your accounting, legal, or financial advisers.

BANK LOANS

Banks include traditional savings banks, savings and loans, and commercial banks, and are generally the first place small business owners think of when looking for institutional financing.

Investment or commercial banking links comes in handy when public equity offerings are unpredictable and offers a way to protect a company's short-term interests. The company links up with an investment banking or underwriting firm affiliated with a commercial bank and plan for an either or scenario. A firm should consider going public, if markets cooperate, but if not a banker can use their influence with the organization to negotiate an interim line of credit (bridge loan) to provide short term capital until an IPO can be consummated.

Select a small-preferred group of national banks seeking start-up deals such as Silicon Valley Bank and Chase and Fleet Bank. The company must have big scale growth plans to be considered. For example, one program at Chase and Fleet is Small Ticket Leasing, which allows business owners to finance $5,000 to $250,000 worth of equipment at competitive rates.

Bank Selection

A number of types of institutions offer small business loans, although each type of lender may be better suited to different lending situations.

Major Characteristics

Two major characteristics that vary among bank loans are the term of the loan and the security or collateral required to get the loan.

Loan term. The "term" of the loan refers to the length of time you have to repay the debt. Debt financing can be either long-term or short-term. Long-term debt financing is commonly used to purchase, improve, or expand fixed assets such as your plant, facilities, major equipment, and real estate. If you are acquiring an asset with the loan proceeds, you (and your lender) will ordinarily want to match the length of the loan with the useful life of the asset. Short-term debt is often used to raise cash for cyclical inventory needs, accounts payable, and working capital. In the current lending climate, interest rates on long-term financing tend to be higher than on short-term borrowing, and long-term financing usually requires more substantial collateral as security against the extended duration of the lender's risk.

Secured or unsecured debt. Debt financing can also be secured or unsecured. A secured loan is a promise to pay a debt, where the promise is "secured" by granting the creditor an interest in specific property (collateral) of the debtor. If the debtor defaults on the loan, the creditor can recoup the money by seizing and liquidating the specific property used for collateral on the debt. For startup small businesses, lenders will usually require that both long- and short-term loans be secured with adequate collateral.

Because the value of pledged collateral is critical to a secured lender, loan conditions and covenants, such as insurance coverage, are always required of a borrower. You can also expect a lender to minimize its risk by conservatively valuing your collateral and by loaning only a percentage of its appraised value. The maximum loan amount, compared to the value of the collateral, is known as the loan-to-value ratio. A lender might be willing to loan only 75 percent of the value of new commercial equipment. If the equipment was valued at $100,000, it could serve as collateral for a loan of approximately $75,000.

An unsecured loan is also a promise to pay a debt. Unlike a secured loan, granting the creditor an interest in any specific property does not support the promise. The lender is relying upon the creditworthiness and reputation of the borrower to repay the obligation. An example of an unsecured loan is a revolving consumer credit card. Sometimes, working capital lines of credit are also unsecured. If the borrower defaults on an unsecured loan, the creditor has no priority claim against any particular property of the borrower. The creditor can try to obtain just a money judgment against the borrower. Until a small business has an established credit history, it cannot usually get unsecured loans because of the business's risk.

An unsecured creditor is often the last in line to collect if the debtor encounters financial difficulties. If a small-business debtor files for bankruptcy, an unsecured loan in the bankruptcy estate will usually be "wiped out" by the bankruptcy due to no assets typically remain to pay these low priority creditors.

Specific or Alternative Loan Types

In addition to consumer loans and mortgages, the most common types of loans given by banks to startup and emerging small businesses are:

1. working capital lines of credit for the ongoing cash needs of the business;
2. credit cards: higher-interest, unsecured revolving credit;
3. short-term commercial loans for one to three years;
4. longer-term commercial loans: generally secured by real estate or other major assets;
5. equipment leasing for assets you don't want to buy outright; and
6. letters of credit for businesses engaged in international trade.

Loan Cost

What are the direct and indirect costs and demands of a bank loan? The final cost of borrowing money often involves much more than just the interest rate. A variety of other monetary and non-monetary costs should be considered in determining the real cost of borrowing. For example, a loan that requires maintenance of certain financial ratios may be unrealistic for the particular business. A checklist for reviewing the costs of a bank loan should include:

1. direct financial cost; i.e. interest rates, points, penalties, and required account balances;
2. indirect costs and loan conditions; i.e. periodic financial reporting, maintenance of certain financial covenants, and subordination agreements; and
3. personal guarantees needed to obtain the loan.

Bank Requirements

Whether applying to a bank for a line of home equity credit, a line of credit for business working capital, a commercial short-term loan, an equipment loan, real estate financing, or some other type of commercial or consumer loan, many of the same basic lending principles apply. The most fundamental characteristics a prospective lender will want to examine are:

1. credit history of the borrower;
2. cash flow history and projections for the business;
3. collateral that is available to secure the loan;
4. character of the borrower; and
5. loan documentation that includes business and personal financial statements, income tax returns, and frequently a business plan, and that essentially sums up and provides evidence for the first four items listed.

The first three of these criteria are largely objective data (although interpretation of the numbers can be subjective). The fourth item, the borrower's character, allows the lender to make a more subjective assessment of the business's market appeal and the business savvy of its operators. In assessing whether to finance a small business, lenders are often willing to consider individual factors that represent strengths or weaknesses for a loan.

COMMUNITY BANKS

Large institutions resulting from mergers and acquisitions offer a chance to build a bank relationship. Where there may or may not have much flexibility. Contact Independent Bankers Association of America for leads to community banks or visit www.ibaa.org or call 800 4222 8439 or email info@ibaa.org.

INVESTMENT BANKERS

Investment bankers are organizations or individuals that charge a fee for capital raised. They may assist with sale of stock to less than 35 people, which is a private placement. If more, offer to sell is to more than 35 people and stock is traded on the public market it is an initial public offering. The Investment Banker may assist with merger and acquisition in which funds are sought to help buy a company. An investment banker sells stock on public market and raises funds for companies.

These lenders are located mainly in large cities and focus on taking firms public. They usually prefer arrangements greater than $10M involving seasoned businesses that are profitable. The cost of capital raised is usually fifteen to twenty percent (15% to 20%) and there is a strong need to have a potential for "big winner".

MERCHANT BANKERS

Investment bankers that take finanical interest in their clients. The premise is that if a company is valuable why not own part of it.

ACCOUNTS RECEIVABLE

This form of financing uses the receivables as collateral. As the business collects the receivables, the proceeds are used to repay the loan or line of credit.

INVENTORY FINANCING

This is a similar type of loan similar to accounts receivable, using inventory as collateral, To generate working capital or to meet specific short-term cash needs, small businesses may use certain short-term assets as collateral for commercial loans. Collateral can be anything from a home equity line of credit or an SBA deal backed by a college savings account. (See GE Capital's "Guide to Asset Based Lending" or call 800 572 1838 for a free copy.

BARTER

For small businesses, strategic alliances often consist of simple "bartering" with customers, suppliers, and even competitors. For example, a manufacturing business might be able to get a better price for component parts if they propose using a label on the final product that includes the supplier's trademark.

Anything a company pays cash for is a candidate for barter. For example, trade computer repair or support services or legal accounting services for paper or advertising (Seminar service firm offers seminars to hotel employees in return for rooms). Direct barter would be when a bill is paid off through trade in kind. Effective bartering requires a sound knowledge of the economics of the business. Negotiate only with the company owner or sales manager. Barter can cut into a salesperson commission so keep exact records of barter arrangements for financial and accounting purposes.

FACTORING

A firm buys accounts receivable; however, cost may be about six percent (6%) of sales which is a substantial price to pay for money. Factorer assumes all credit risk, responsibility for credit checks and collections.

A classic cash crunch situation arises when employees are paid before a client pays the firm. A factoring company buys client receivables. The factorer is banking on the payment ability of a firm's customers, not the firm. The firm must be solvent, not credit worthy. One borrows on a client's credit. Factoring is unregulated and entrepreneurial. Factorers deal where banks often refuse to tread.

Factoring is expensive and the contracts are pretty one sided. The factorer advances the firm a percent of each invoice; the remaining reserve balance, less the factorer's discount is paid to the firm when the firm's customer pays the factorer. If a firm receives an 80 percent advance on money you would normally collect in sixty (60) days and pay a four (4) percent discount, annual interest is thirty (30) percent [(0.04/0.8) x (360/60)]. Can you afford to give up four (4) percent on invoices and remain profitable? Get proposals from at least three factorers and examine the contract closely. Is there a minimum invoice size, a minimum monthly volume, and administrative or setup fee or other interest or penalty costs? How long are you locked in with the factorer? Who assumes the bad debts? When and how are reserve balances paid to you?

Factorers operate nationwide; search the yellow pages. Ask your bank which factorers it deals with. Call trade association for a list of factorers interested in working with a select industry. Check Edwards Directory of American Factorers (Edwards Research, ~$200, 617 244 8414) or Commercial Finance Association's web site (ww.cfa.com).

LEASING

Leasing companies, as well as banks and some suppliers and vendors, will rent equipment and other business assets to small businesses. Some manufacturers have leasing agents who may be able to arrange lease terms or a credit arrangement with the manufacturer, a subsidiary company, or a specific leasor.

Leasing assets, rather than purchasing them, is a form of financing because it avoids the large down payment frequently required for asset purchases and it frees up funds for other business expenditures. However, be aware that leasing from conventional lenders may be difficult for startup businesses because traditional lenders require an operating history from prospective leasees.

This form of financing is generally available to firms that have already been granted institutional funds or are in midst of closing a deal with a venture capitalist or similar type of financier. The advantage is that lessees don't have to raise more capital for equipment or tie up venture funds to pay for equipment rather than growth activities. Venture leasing deals require payment of 100% of principal, plus 8% to 12% in interest charges over a 24 to 60 month lease horizon, plus the leasor gets the equipment when the lease period ends so deal is not cheap. However, venture leasing is cheaper than giving away more equity. Check with the company accounting and financing intermediaries to locate leasing firms and banks servicing this market.

Advantages

1. *Frees up cash.* Many leases require little or no down payment, maybe only first month's payment. Leasing thereby allows the firm to direct cash toward other business expenses and investments. An improved cash position can also help obtain additional debt in the following ways.

2. *Less debt appears on financial statements.* In a straightforward operating lease, in which assets are rented for a set time period without an ownership interest, neither the leased asset nor the cost of leasing appears on a balance sheet. Cash flow and expense-related financial statements will show only lease amounts as they come due. The relative absence of business debt will improve chances for conventional loans since it is more attractive to lenders.

3. *Tax treatment.* IRS does not consider operating lease as a purchase but a tax deductible overhead expense; so lease payments are deductible from corporate income. Also a lessee who is an inefficient taxpayer with certain tax challenges such as net operating loss carry-forwards or alternative minimum tax issues can mitigate such challenges by leasing equipment from a full tax-paying leasor.

4. *Customized solutions.* Variety of leasing products is available to customize a program to address select requirements such as cash flow, budget, skipped payments or step up and step down payments for seasonal businesses.

5. *Asset management.* Certain leases transfer risk of ownership and thus equipment obsolescence to the leasor.
   Allows more flexibility for equipment changes and upgrades. For businesses in which rapid technology changes or new equipment is common; leasing allows the firm to minimize cost of purchasing equipment that is quickly antiquated. If business grows and change is needed; a lease contract can be upgraded through add on schedules. Many leasing companies provide for lease upgrade options or termination fees. In addition, an option to purchase a leased asset is usually available if the firm wants to buy the asset at the end of the lease term. Risk of getting caught with obsolete equipment is lower due to ability to return the equipment to the leasor.

6. *Tax deductible.* Leasing costs are deductible expenses that immediately reduce taxable income. Compare the benefits of a lease deduction to the depreciation deduction the firm would obtain if the asset were purchased.

7. *Landlord may help.* If the firm is willing to enter into a long-term real estate lease for office or plant space, the landlord may be willing to finance certain improvements to the property

that are necessary for the business. The firm can pay for these improvements through added rent over the period of the lease. This arrangement saves up-front cash and equity and does not impair financial ratios for other financing.

Disadvantages

1. *Complexity.* Because more businesses are using leases, greater creativity in lease terms and purposes are becoming available. Leases can be drafted so that they resemble a long-term purchase of capital equipment. The term of the lease approximates the expected useful life of the asset and the total of lease payments is keyed to the underlying cost of the asset. The lessee pays insurance and taxes on the asset. The lessee may either be required to purchase the asset at the end of the lease, or a purchase option may be available at the end of the lease or for a stated price during the term of the lease. A service contract can usually be purchased for an additional charge.

2. *Asset purchase.* As ownership options/rights are increased in a lease agreement, financial statements may have to show the lease as an asset purchase, with an accompanying listing of the asset and a liability for the amount of the "loan." These changes will negatively affect debt/equity ratios and net income.

3. *Sale and leaseback.* A derivative form of lease financing, this type of arrangement requires the borrower to sell valuable, fixed assets, such as equipment or facilities, to a financier who then leases the asset back to the seller. The sale generates cash to the small business for short-term needs, allows continued use of the asset, and creates a tax deduction for rental expense. A purchase option at the end of the lease period allows the original owner to reacquire title to the asset at a later date.

Lease Contracts

A lease is a contract conveying use of equipment by one party (leasor) to another party (leasee) for a specific period of times.

Lease forms. Two lease forms are capital or true.

    a. *Capital.* These leases typically contain a series of rental payments and include an end of term purchase option of some nominal amount such as one dollar to ten percent of the original equipment cost.

    b. *True.* These leases contain a series of rental payments and an end of term purchase option of fair market value as well as an option to renew the lease or return the equipment to the leasor.

TRADE CREDIT

"Trade credit" is the generic term for a buyer's purchase of supplies or goods from a seller (supplier) who finances the purchase by delaying the date at which the price is due, or allowing installment payments. Vendors and suppliers are often willing to sell on credit and this source of working capital financing is very common for both startup and growing businesses. Suppliers know that most small business rely primarily upon a limited number of suppliers and that small businesses typically represent relatively small order risks; as long as the supplier keeps a tight rein on credit terms and receivables, most small businesses are a worthwhile gamble for future business.

Startup businesses may benefit from shopping for prospective suppliers as soon as the entrepreneur has a business location picked out. Many new businesses rely heavily upon a single supplier with whom they can reach a long-term understanding regarding credit purchases. Present a proposal to several possible suppliers, taking care to outline how much inventory is needed to get started and how much will be bought from the supplier in the future. Expect the supplier to demand a priority security interest in all goods provided to the firm on credit. A personal guarantee for some of the purchase price may be required, at least for initial inventory. The more business completed with a particular seller the better the negotiating position for arranging additional credit purchases.

When managing the amount of trade credit and other debt a business assumes, the critical feature is not the total amount of debt, but rather the ability of the business to make payments from its cash flow. The duration of the pay period and the repayment amounts, in relation to incoming cash sources are most important. Realistic cash flow projections and a strong cash flow history are consequently the primary interest of trade creditors.

The major advantages of trade credit, it is often readily available; it allows the company to spread payments over several months or years; and minimal, or no, down payment or interest charges are assessed.

Trade credit may be in the form of a simple delay in payment for purchases, sales on consignment, equipment loans, or a variety of different options to assist dealers in financing stock purchases. For instance, a supplier might agree to a promotion plan that allows the business to pay for specific items only as they are sold (supplier retains ownership of goods until paid for). This plan permits the supplier to continually monitor the mix of merchandise on the company's shelves and to adjust to changes in demand. Buying on consignment is also an inventory financing option in some industries, such as retail print products, electronic consumer products, or furniture. A purchase on consignment means that the purchaser pays the supplier for goods only if, and when, they are sold. The supplier keeps title to the goods and when they are sold, the selling business retains a portion of the sale and returns the balance to the supplier. There are no significant upfront costs and if not sold, the product is simply returned to the supplier.

The cost of trade credit is usually a higher purchase price. Keep in mind that vendors often experience the same cash flow pressures as small businesses and many sellers offer cash discounts for immediate payment. By purchasing on credit, a firm foregoes the cash discount price and pays a higher relative price for goods. It's a good idea to learn the rules of thumb on when to take a trade discount.

INSURANCE COMPANIES

If the company has substantial cash surrender value in a life insurance policy the firm can usually borrow up to that amount from the insurer. Ordinarily, the business would borrow against the policy and then re-lend the money to the business at the same interest rate. The business can then take an interest deduction on the loan and does not earn taxable interest income on the transaction.

When borrowing against the firm's policy, the company is not obligated to repay the loan principal, only to pay interest on the loan. Interest is typically due on an annual anniversary date. Most policies will allow the company to simply add the accumulated interest to the principal, as long as the cash surrender value of the policy has not been borrowed up. The rate of interest charged depends upon when the policy was purchased; rates on older policies might be very favorable. Of course, borrowing against the company's policy means the eventual death benefit of the policy will be diminished by the amount of the loan, plus the loss of interest.

As a source for loans that are not secured by an existing policy, insurance companies are not usually viable sources of financing for small businesses. Although insurers actively seek investments for unused premium income, the companies tend to invest in larger, established businesses. If security is available, such as real estate, insurance companies may provide some limited possibilities. Generally, insurance companies make secured term loans and mortgage loans. If a company borrows from an insurance company, expect terms and interest rates to be similar to those available from a commercial bank. Insurance companies can provide the business with a large amount of capital at market interest rates, but sufficient assets must be available to cover the debt, plus 20 percent to 30 percent extra.

GOVERNMENT FINANCING PROGRAMS

For many small businesses, government assistance can make the difference in getting the money they vitally need to start, continue, or expand operations. Government agencies may be a good source of funds. The technology, and business interests will be important considerations as you decide whether or not to submit proposals for such funds. Secure the request for proposal (RFP) and read it carefully. This capital might be called "low cost money".

"Low Cost Money" is grants, loans (micro loans) awards and prizes from government, corporate or philanthropic sources. Who can get "low cost money"- business people & entrepreneurs (especially high-tech and specialists; more difficult for traditional retailers), students, researchers, inventors, home buyers, bill payers, car buyers, veterans, the disabled, the disadvantaged, the elderly, the (ethnic, racial, gender & culturally) diverse, poets, writers, clubs, organizations, social services, not-for-profits, nonprofits to name a few.

To obtain the various types of "low cost money" use the sources listed below. Also research programs of interest and contact the program's organization. Ask for a description of the program, guidelines, deadlines and a copy of successful applications.

Before you actively go after the money, review this material carefully. You may also want to speak with a program representative to make sure you understand everything. Know what you are getting yourself into, e.g., is it a free grant or does it require remittance? Follow instructions to the letter. Send in your carefully completed application and anything else that's required as soon as possible. Send it to the proper person, address and office. Follow up after submission: call, write or even visit. Keep following up until you receive a reply. If favorable, you have what you want. If not, this time, reapply, and seek out new sources. "If at first you don't succeed, try, try again."

Obviously there's not enough room in this document to list every "low cost money," grant, loan, awards and prize resource available so here's a "low cost money" quick list:

- Government Agencies (Dept. of Agriculture, Dept of Commerce, Dept. of Health Education and Welfare, Dept. of Defense, Dept of Energy, Department of Housing and Urban Development, National Science Foundation, National Institute of Health, National Aeronautics and Space Association, etc.)
- The U.S. Government's "Catalog of Federal Domestic Assistance"
- The Foundation Center publications, i.e., "Foundation Directory"
- "Annual Register of Grant Support"
- Matthew Lesko's "Government Giveaways," "Info Power," "1001 Free Goodies and Cheapies," etc.
- Internet/World Wide Web

Remember, each agency will have different proposal conditions, requirements and formats. You can find these and many other "free money" sources without cost at your local Public Library and on the Internet. Also contact government agencies – Small Business Administration (SBA), Service Corp of Retired Executives (SCORE), Small Business Development Corporation, (SBDC), nonprofit organizations and groups you belong to.

Obtaining free money, grants and loans at the very least requires time, effort, postage, phone calls and follow-up. If you fail to follow instructions, send your application to the wrong sources or forget to follow up don't be surprised if you unconditionally lose out without hearing about it. Give yourself the best chance for success. Do the right thing!

Warning: Nothing is absolutely FREE. It may take a lot of time and effort just to find the right program for you (programs may not be listed or found in non-traditional areas).

The Small Business Administration (SBA) is responsible for the aiding counseling and protection interest of small businesses and works with intermediaries, banks and other lending institutions to provide loans and venture capital financing. Some of the programs for financial assistance are as follows:

- Small Business Investment Companies (SBIC) – licensed by SBA and receives SBA matching money if they invest in small business ventures.

577

- Minority Enterprise Small Business Investment Companies (MESBIC) – same as SBIC but oriented toward minorities.
- SBA's 7(a) Loan guaranty program – the primary lending program designed to meet majority of small business community's financing needs.
- 7(a) specialized loan programs (LowDoc) – designed to increase availability of funds under $100,000 and streamline/expedite the loan review process.
- Fa$tTrak – aimed at increasing the capital available to businesses seeking loans up to $100,000 but is currently offered as a pilot with limited number of lenders.
- CAPLines – an umbrella program to help small businesses meet their short-term and cyclical working capital needs with five separate programs.
- Export working capital – designed to provide short-term working capital to exporters in a combined effort of the SBA and the export-import Bank.
- Pollution control – aimed at providing loan guarantees to eligible small business for the financing of planning, design, or installation of a pollution control facility.
- DELTA – defense loan and technical assistance is a joint SBA and DOD effort to provide financial and technical assistance to defense dependent small firms adversely affected by cutbacks in defense.
- Minority and Women's Prequalification - a pilot program that uses intermediaries to assist prospective minority and women borrowers in developing viable loan application packages and securing loans.
- Qualified employee trusts – designed to provide financial assistance to Employee Stock Ownership Plans.
- SBA's Micro-loan Program – works through intermediaries to provide small loans from as little as $100 up to $25,000.
- SBA's Certified Development Company (504 Loan) program – makes long term loans available for purchasing land, buildings and machinery and equipment and for building modernizing or renovating existing facilities and sites.

Remember: 1) the time or year for submission or proposals varies with agency; 2) five agencies must reserve part of R&D dollars for Small Business Technology Transfer proposals (STTR) - Department of Defense (DOD), Department of Energy (DOE) Department of Health and Human Services (DHHS), National Aeronautical and Space Agency (NASA), National Science Foundation (NSF); 3) ten Agencies must reserve part of R&D dollars for small business innovative research proposals (SBIR) - Department of Agriculture, Department of Commerce (DOC), Department of Defense (DOD), Department of Education (DOE) Department of Health and Human Services (DHHS), National Aeronautical and Space Agency (NASA), National Science Foundation (NSF), Department of Transportation (DOT), Environmental Protection Agency (EPA), Department of Energy (DOE) and 4) in 1997 DOE received 1200 proposals and funded 200.

The SBA has offices located throughout the country. Consult the telephone directory under "U.S. Government," or call the Small Business Answer Desk at 1-800-8ASK-SBA or (202) 205-7064 (fax). For the hearing impaired, the TDD number is (202) 205-7333 or http://www.acq.osd.mil/sadbu/sbir. Additional information is presented in Exhibit B.

THE SMALL BUSINESS ADMINISTRATION (SBA)

This is a federal agency that offers a number of financing and operations assistance programs to small businesses. The programs include loan guarantees, training and educational programs, advisory services, publications, financial programs, and contract assistance. In fiscal year 1995, it's expected that nearly $11.5 billion in long-term credit and other financial assistance will have been provided to more than 67,000 small businesses through SBA's network of participating banks, non-bank lenders, certified development companies, and SBA-licensed companies.

SBA Loans

Governemnt agrees to guarantee up to ninety percent (90%) of bank loan and loan can be as high as $1M. The Small Business Administration (SBA) frequently offers private lenders a guarantee on loans made to qualified small businesses. That means that if the borrower fails to repay the loan, the lender can usually recover up to 75 or even 80 percent of the outstanding loan principal from the SBA.

A government guarantee encourages lenders to grant credit that otherwise would not be available on reasonable terms and conditions by giving them a couple of significant incentives. A federal guarantee not only reduces the lender's risks, but the bank has a readily available secondary market in which to sell the guaranteed portion of the loan. In addition, the guaranteed portion of the loan does not count against the federally mandated reserve funds that banks must maintain as protection against loan losses.

The major objective of an SBA loan guarantee is to make conventional financing available to a small business that might not otherwise qualify for the loan. Most often, an SBA guarantee is sought when a conventional lender feels that the prospective borrower has insufficient collateral to support the small business loan request. The SBA loan guarantee works as a substitute for the needed collateral and provides the lender with satisfactory security to support the loan. See Exhibit B.

There are a couple of strings attached. First, the agency limits the guaranteed portion of the loan to the leaser of $750,000 or 75 percent of the loan amount; for loans of $100,000 or less, the SBA will guarantee 80 percent of the loan. Secondly, the SBA prefers an owner's equity investment of at least 25 percent of the total cost of the project. While no fixed legal requirement actually exists, the SBA (and the lender) want proof that the business owner will not walk away from their business at the first sign of trouble.

Nonetheless, it is often possible for the owner to negotiate with the loan agent so a lower percentage of financing comes form the owner. The stated basis for granting an SBA loan guarantee is the borrower's character, credit, experience, and proof of a sufficient commitment to the business. Weaknesses in one area may be balanced by strengths in another area.

Another string is the concern about adequate collateral. The SBA states that a guarantee will not be denied merely because of inadequate collateral; however, in most instances, the private lender will still demand collateral, and the SBA's guarantee of an under-collateralized loan will be extended only if the business shows other favorable factors (e.g., solid cash flow) to support the creditworthiness of the borrower.

The most important consideration for the SBA is whether the loan is collateralized to the maximum capability of the individual business owner. An owner who has valuable personal assets may be requested to pledge those assets as security on the business loan before the SBA agrees to guarantee the loan. Unlike some of the other requirements, a personal guarantee by all owners having at least a 20 percent interest in the company is usually non-negotiable.

Sometimes the loan will cost more. A private lender can charge a slightly higher interest rate for an SBA-guaranteed loan than for a similar conventional loan. The SBA continues to put a maximum cap on the interest rate and prohibits extraneous fees. On loans for less than seven years, the rate cannot exceed 2.25 percent above the New York bank (Wall Street Journal) prime rate. For loans with maturities of seven years or longer, the rate cannot be more than 2.75 percent above the prime rate as reported in the Wall Street Journal.

To encourage banks to make relatively small loans to small businesses, an extra interest point (up to 3.75 percent over WSJ prime) can be charged for loans between $25,000 and $50,000, and an extra 2 points (up to 4.75 percent over WSJ prime) can be assessed for loans under $25,000. If the lender uses a floating rate, the rate can be adjusted periodically, pursuant to the guarantee agreement with the SBA; however, the spread between an adjusted rate and the WSJ prime cannot be increased. In addition, the SBA's guarantee fee (2 percent to 3.875 percent of the loan amount) can also be passed on to (ouch!) the borrower.

However, while these additional costs may sometimes make an SBA-guaranteed loan more expensive than a conventional loan, consider several counterbalancing factors. First, if the bank were to make the loan without the SBA guarantee, the lender might assess additional upfront points because of the higher risk; these points could equal the SBA guarantee fee. In contrast, SBA loans prohibit any points from being assessed in addition to the guarantee fee. Moreover, because of the SBA guarantee, many small businesses obtain a longer loan maturity term than they could otherwise obtain from a conventional loan.

Most small businesses have considerable difficulty obtaining long-term financing, because small business lending is so risky. One of the significant benefits of an SBA loan guarantee is that the government's backing will often support a longer-term loan. Instead of three- to five-year maximums on conventional bank loans for a small business, the SBA guarantee commonly covers loans up to 10 years, and some real estate loans have maturities up to 25 years. These longer terms provide much needed cash flow consistency so vital to a small business.

To be eligible for an SBA loan guarantee, a business must meet all of the following criteria:
1. be small enough to fit SBA's criteria;
2. be a type of business acceptable to the SBA;
3. be for-profit;
4. be independently owned and operated;
5. not be dominant in its industry; and
6. have applied for, and been denied, a conventional loan by a private lender.

However, if at least two conventional lenders have denied the loan application, rethink, or rework, your business plan. Try to assess whether the denials are based upon factors that can be realistically overcome or whether adjustments in the plan are necessary.

Recent Changes in SBA Programs

Although the SBA has been around for over 40 years, the agency is subject to frequent changes in funding and program policies. Among the most significant recent changes in the SBA was the creation of an expedited loan guarantee program for small business loans under $100,000 (the LowDoc guaranteed loan program), an increase in the cost to borrowers and banks for obtaining SBA loan guarantees (a result of the Small Business Lending Enhancement Act passed in October 1995), and a virtual elimination of the SBA's direct loan programs to small businesses. While these changes may affect the availability of SBA loan guarantees, the agency remains one of the best sources for assistance in obtaining financing for small businesses. An overview of the more significant trends and policy changes within the SBA are:

1. SBA financing for small businesses;
2. Recent law changes affecting SBA loan guarantees; and
3. Looking ahead for the SBA.

SBA Loan Guarantees

SBA loan guarantees provides a "nuts and bolts" explanation of how SBA loan guarantees work and what you should expect from a loan guarantee; it also gives a detailed discussion of each of the major SBA guarantee programs (LowDoc, CAPlines, and others) and the best options for qualifying for any particular program.

Commercial lenders often prefer a SBA-guaranteed small businesses loan because the federal guarantee not only reduces the lender's risks, but the bank has a readily available secondary market in which to sell the guaranteed portion of the loan. In addition, the guaranteed portion of the loan does not count against the federally mandated reserve funds that banks must maintain as protection against loan losses.

SBA Express

Bank qualified business owners can borrow up to $150,000 without going through the standard SBA application process and are guaranteed a loan decision within 36 hours. Loans are guaranteed at fifty percent (50%) of face value and many "preferred lenders, commercial banks and financing institutions, have yet to sign on. Locate active lenders in your area, via your SBA district office or visit www.sba.gov.

SBA Micro-loans

Small businesses needing small-scale financing and technical assistance for startup or expansion may be able to obtain up to $25,000 through short-term loans of public money called "micro-loans." These loans are administered through responsible nonprofit groups, such as local economic development organizations or state finance authorities that are selected and approved by the SBA. The SBA loans the money to the nonprofit organization which then pools the funds with local money and administers direct loans to small businesses.

These loans are administered much like a line of credit and are intended for the purchase of machinery and equipment, furniture and fixtures, inventory, supplies and working capital. The funds are intended to be dispersed with close monitoring of the recipient and a self-employment training program may accompany the loan. The maximum maturity for a micro-loan is six years. The loan cannot be used to pay existing debts.

The micro-loan program has received a fair amount of political attention as a model for government-sponsored assistance to local businesses, but the overall money allocated to this program is relatively limited.

A representative from one SBA-approved intermediary stated that their total annual allocation was $40,000 and those funds were gone within two months. Because your timing in applying for these loans may be important in some areas, checking with local sources prior to your actual need for the money may be the best plan for staking a claim to these limited funds.

Certified Development Companies (CDC)

Certified Development Companies explains the SBA's partnership with local lenders for a long-term, fixed-rate financing program, Section 504 Loan Program. The SBA 504 Loan Program provides long-term, and fixed rate financing for investment in fixed assets. The loans were intended to help small and medium-sized businesses avoid large down payment and floating interest rates that are typically associated with the purchases of "bricks and mortar" fixed assets. The program is also aimed at aiding local economies by increasing employment opportunities and the loans are tied to certain job creation mandates.

The majority of these loans are obtained by existing businesses that want to expand their operations. Startups occasionally use Section 504 if the type of business involves property ownership (rather than rental), as in the case of a manufacturer who determines that it would be cheaper to purchase real estate than to lease and possibly face relocation expenses, or a business that has a relatively low initial risk, and a significant equity base that reflects a long-term commitment. The program is also tied to job creation and typically a borrower is required to either create or retain one job for every $37,500 of total project cost.

Section 504 loans are extended through SBA-approved companies called Certified Development Companies ("CDCs"). A CDC is a private nonprofit corporation set up to contribute to the Economic development of its community or region. Typical CDC-financed projects range in size from $500,000 to $2 million, with an average cost of $1 million. The total size of projects using CDC financing is unlimited, but as with SBA loan guarantees, the maximum amount of CDC participation in any individual project is $750,000 (or $1 million for some public projects).

Participants in a CDC are usually banks, utilities, professional organizations, community groups, and private investors. For banks in particular, lending through a CDC is an opportunity for them to meet their bank regulatory requirements for community lending while spreading the risk from those investments among the separate CDC corporate members. The bank also need not consider their CDC participation against their loan loss reserves. CDCs can also minimize risks by selling 100 percent SBA-guaranteed debentures to private investors in amounts up to 40 percent of a project or $750,000, whichever is less. Finally, CDC investing by banks creates an attractive loan-to-value ratio; the bank usually contributes only about 50 percent of the CDC loan proceeds, yet is given a priority claim against the value of the project or collateral. If you're interested in obtaining a 504 loan, you'll also want to know about:

1. qualifying use of 504 funds - the purposes for which you can use loan proceeds;
2. eligibility criteria for 504 loans; and
3. obligations of a borrower under a 504 loan.

Export Financing

For those small businesses considering exporting outside the U.S., the SBA and several other government agencies offer special financing programs. Note, however, that while exporting may offer tremendous market potential for certain small companies, there will be additional research and preparation expenses necessary for developing and implementing an international business plan.

Among the additional considerations that may affect costs include: multinational legal compliance (labeling, packaging, product safety and liability laws, etc.), additional promotional material for different countries and languages, transportation costs for product/service delivery and personnel travel, and obtaining any required export licenses. Help in preparing the plan, and in finding more information about exporting, can be obtained through federal SBA and Department of Commerce assistance programs, state commerce departments, local chambers of commerce, international trade associations, export management and trade companies, and private consulting firms.

The SBA's financing programs include the Export Working Capital Program and the International Loan Program.

SMALL BUSINESS INVESTMENT CORPS (SBIC)

The federal government sponsors its own public venture capital organization through the Small Business Investment Corporation (SBIC) program. An SBIC is a privately owned and operated small business investment company that partners with the federal government to provide venture capital to small business. Using a combination of private funds and funds borrowed from the federal government, the SBICs provide equity capital, long-term loans (up to 20 years, with a possible 10-year extension), and management assistance to eligible small businesses. Loans and securities for less than five years are unusual and the Small Business Administration regulates the cost of money on loans and debt securities. See Exhibit B.

Like a VC firm, an SBIC is most commonly a source of financing for a fast-growing, existing business (rather than a startup) that needs a substantial amount of financing to keep up with its rapid expansion.

An SBIC must be federal licensed; however, almost anyone or any entity can be an SBIC owner if they have the minimum initial private capital of five million dollars and an SBA-approved full-time manager. Every SBIC is subject to annual financial reporting requirements and onsite compliance examinations by the SBA. Regulations control investment approvals and operating procedures. Most SBICs are owned by small groups of local investors, although commercial banks are often also owners.

SBICs operate like venture capital firms, although they may be more flexible in the terms of their investment arrangement. The SBIC may want to make an equity investment or may be interested simply in long-term lending on a fully secured basis. An SBIC is not permitted to control any small business on a permanent basis.

The SBA has offices located throughout the country and the agency staff will help locate the nearest SBIC. To reach your local SBA office, consult the telephone directory under "U.S. Government," or call the Small Business Answer Desk at 1-800-8ASK-SBA.

Recently, the SBA created a second category of government-operated small business investment companies, the Specialized Small Business Investment Company ("SSBIC"). Currently there are about 87 active SSBICs. They generally operate in the same manner as SBICs, but they can obtain additional government financial assistance by investing in, or loaning to, small businesses owned by people who are socially or economically disadvantaged.

STATE AND LOCAL PUBLIC FUNDING

In an effort to improve their local economies, most states, and many municipalities and counties, sponsor a variety of public funding sources for small business concerns. At the state level, nearly all states have some form of state economic development agency and/or state finance authority that make loans or loan guarantees to small businesses. State Commerce Departments often have direct or participating loan programs that may be even more attractive than SBA-guaranteed loan programs.

Although state programs and funding options vary, a popular form of program is a participating loan arrangement in which the state pools its public funds with money from a conventional lender to meet the needs of a small business borrower. For example, in Illinois, the state will loan up to 25 percent of the total cost of a small business project, with a maximum loan of $750,000. So, for example, if you needed a $100,000 loan, but a bank would lend only $75,000, the state "participates" in the loan by contributing public funding of $25,000 to the total loan package. The bank then processes the total loan of $100,000. The state is spared the administrative expenses of loan processing and the bank receives a priority lien on collateral.

States also receive federal money through federal Housing and Urban Development (HUD) block grants that can be used for a variety of local improvements, including small business financing programs. Urban development spending for larger cities, or smaller city community assistance programs, are oft-used purposes for the federal money. While the criteria for a small business to obtain a loan of grant money varies between states, the state will typically expect owner equity participation and evidence that a clear economic or social benefit to the local community will result from the funding. The amount of money made available at the local level will usually depend upon the perceived need for job creation in the area and the relative income level of that community.

In addition to state money, local county or municipal governments often loan small amounts of capital to local businesses. These local, "micro-loan" programs may be characterized by minimal (and sporadic) funding, so the timing of your request can be critical. Try to contact any local agencies as soon as possible, even if there is no need the money immediately, to determine the available funds at that time and when the program is expected to receive any additional money. Local programs can loan small amounts of money, e.g., under $10,000, for working capital, equipment or inventory purchasing, or property improvements.

Finally, don't forget to check local colleges, universities, or trade schools to see if they have any small business assistance programs. Some institutions, with the help of public funding, provide business "incubator" programs that can include consulting, marketing, services, facilities, and financing opportunities to local businesses as part of the institution's business education program.

In addition to loans, state and local governments have grant programs that could provide revenue with which to exploit a technology. Examples of specialized state programs are the Ben Franklin Fund (PA), Business Modernization and Technology (IN), Technology Development Fund (IL).

Certain consortia of trades are organized into centers or associations that may have an investment component associated with the organization. Be sure to identify all advocates, associations or benefactors of your asset and then determine if they might be interested in collaborating. The collaboration might take the form of monetary, expertise or in-kind e.g. equipment/service contributions.

The Small Business Innovative Research and Small Business Technology Transfer programs, SBIR and STTR respectively may be of interest. Two other government sources of support are the Advanced Technology Program (ATP) and Technology Development Program (TDP) programs offered by most of the federal agencies. It is necessary to gather the details and apply for the grants at defined times.

Most of the information is available over the web or from the Small Business Development Center (SBDC) offices. Many of the federal laboratories and government agencies also encourage cooperative research and development agreements (CRADA) in which the government and business collaborate in technology development. Many states have programs in which money is made available if there is a business match involved as well. This leveraging often appeals to the investment community as well. Federal Laboratories also offer technical assistance to the business that is developing technology or may have product on the market that requires the capabilities that reside at the laboratory. There is usually expertise and state of the art facilities that may be valuable for the business enterprise that has encountered technical difficulties during development or even after product is introduced to the market.

CREDIT CARDS

Not wise to rely on credit cards but Visa and American express have a range of unsecured credit line alternatives. If a banker refuses you, then contact major credit card suppliers to compare prices and options. Make sure you have opportunity to increase borrowing limit and add on other financing sources such as equipment leasing once you prove yourself.

Examine the on-line credit search engines. Many exist but the best search engine providers guarantee confidentiality, don't charge upfront fees, and can point to successful results in linking companies to lenders. See www.getsmart.com, which is affiliated with 17 banks and non-bank lenders such as American Express, Heller Financial, and First Union.

CREDIT UNIONS

Usually offer short-term arrangements for a limited amount of capital (<$25K) at a low interest rate. A credit union can offer generous terms to their members, but make mostly consumer loans.

FRIENDS AND FAMILY

Makes sense for company that is too new or small to get financing elsewhere. Arrangement should follow professional standards with appropriate contracts and commitments. Second stage investors will scrutinize terms of these "friendly" arrangements carefully and if poorly structured can delay future funding significantly.

ASSET SALE

A simple alternative to loans or equity deals. You sell one or more assets ranging from computer equipment to real estate to someone you know and trust. They then lease the asset back to the business a price that is fair to both parties. The friend gets the tax deduction and regular income stream, you get a one-time infusion of capital and better leasing terns that if you were dealing with an independent financier and your capital structure remains clean.

REVENUE SALE

Give investors what they want a share of revenue stream. This enables one to receive capital in the form of a loan that gets repaid as a percentage of product or service sales. It allows one to preserve equity and tap into a larger pool of potential investors attracted by a prospect of immediate cash return. This capitalization method also circumvents of all state and federal securities laws since advance on royalty deals is a loan not a sale of securities. Royalty financing works only if high margins and strong product or service sales or at least very high likelihood of strong sales exists.

INTERNATIONAL FINANCE

A means for U.S. companies to shelter cash flow from volatility abroad are international accounts receivable. International factoring may be advantageous if you're willing to pay a fee in return for quick cash infusion without the hassles of collecting receivables and letters of credit; but verify the soundness of banks issuing the letter of credit and financial health of your customers (e.g. countries like Russia and Brazil). Relay on your international accounting and legal experts. Some financing institutions will guarantee your company payment within a relatively short time while offering your customers the opportunity to extend their payment for several months or longer.

International strategic partnerships can be source of outright capital infusion and provide benefit when negotiating payment terms and receivable collection. Enhanced relationships with Int'l banker or private equity firm that views risk:reward ratio more optimistically than a cautious U.S. lender might help when negotiating payment terms and collection of receivables promptly.

INTERNET

The internet offers an ever expanding number of financing sites but often little cash but some sites; such as www.vfinance.com, provide information on numerous venture capital firms; as well as, frequent news updates about the industry. On line investment banking is new with an unproven track record. Wit Capital, www.witcapital.com, has concluded numerous offerings including IPOs, and public and private venture capital and other equity deals.

CAPITAL INTERMEDIARIES

An intermediary can be helpful but get references and check them out. They should have a history of success with companies and products that are similar to yours. History should consist of successes, customers, bankers and lawyers they have been associated with. If up front fees are required be careful although some very good firms require a retainer fee.

ENTREPRENEURSHIP PROGRAMS

These programs are often associated with economic development or a college or university that brings the small business and capital communities together in a matchmaking environment. Some programs provide advice on business formation and capital acquisition.

CUSTOMERS

A customer investment is useful if product demand is such that customers will provide a deposit or prepay. A beneficiary or customer may want to provide funds in order to gain an advantage e.g. market entry

SUPPLIERS

Payment delay can be low cost loans but if delay eliminates the discount rate be careful; it can be costly. Get money in return for granting manufacturing rights. This is off- balance sheet financing (debt not reported as liability since distinction between debt & equity is not clear-cut)

PROFESSIONAL ADVISORS/BUSINESS ASSOCIATES

Lawyers, accountants, etc. with interest in keeping firm adrift will provide "gap or transition" funding in some instances.

SALE OF DISTRIBUTION/MARKETING RIGHTS

An asset owner can license or establish agreement for others to manufacture and market. the price will depend on numerous factors including but not limited to product life cycle, pruduct demand, regional vs. national vs. international rights, profit margin, and fit in product line. Although it is possible to implement a franchise venture and/or grant regional rights for a fee but be sure to get preformance guarantees.

BUSINESS ANGELS OR PRIVATE INVESTORS
Seed and Early Stage Capital Market

Venture capital is commonly viewed as high risk capital involved in formation and launch of new companies with innovative technologies. Seed and start-up capital is considered synonymous with venture capital. In reality, seed and start-up capital (early stage capital) is only a small niche within the venture capital industry.

The venture capital industry is a small-specialized sector within the financial markets, managing between $40-$50B, and investing approximately $5-7B annually in the United States. Seed and start-up investments account for only about 15% of this amount or $750 million annually. Several factors have limited the availability of early stage capital:

1. More capital has been concentrated in fewer hands over the years. Many institutional investors that invest in venture capital funds want to invest at least $10 million in a fund and be no more than 10% of the fund's capital, thereby limiting their focus to funds of $100 million or more. Smaller institutions also perceive safety in investing in large funds. When a fund has $100 million under management, they need to invest $2 million to $5 million in a company over time. This leads them to favor the later stage deals. Seed and start-up companies are more people intensive than capital intensive. The early stage companies need smaller amounts of capital to hit the early milestones, and they require the active involvement of the investor to help fill the gaps in the founding management team.
2. Typical venture capital limited partnerships have a life of ten to twelve years. The life of funds under management typically overlaps, with the general partners out raising a new fund every four to seven years. A later stage investment opportunity takes three to five years on average from investment to exit, whereas an early stage company takes five to seven years to mature. If the General Partner plans to raise capital in four or five years, they are more likely to have results from the previous fund to show to prospective investors if they have a later stage focus.
3. The old adage in the venture capital industry is that the lemons ripen quicker than the plums. Failures occur in the early years of the investment's life, whereas the horizon to a successful exit is considerably longer. This typical fund's net asset value tracked over time is known as the J-curve. Total value decreases early in the fund life as losses are realized and gains are not yet recognized. Later in the fund life the gains are realized and the value grows significantly. The range of outcomes is far wider in the early stage sector. A higher percentage of these unseasoned entities fail, and the multiples on the success stories are far greater. Thus, the decline in value early in the fund life is deeper and the long-range value greater. However, if the general partners are raising the successor fund sooner rather than later, early stage investments are once again at a disadvantage.

The availability of early stage capital also varies more by region than in the later stage markets. Later stage transactions are with companies that have complete management teams, established market presence, and higher levels of predictability. Investor involvement is at the board of directors' level on a quarterly basis, with occasional consultation between meetings. In this sector, capital flows to where the best opportunities reside. The early stage market is characterized by a more narrow geographic focus. The management teams are incomplete and the companies can derive greater benefit from active investor involvement. The investor's network of advisors tends to be based in their immediate area. As a result, it is easier for them to be available for advice if the company is located close to the investor. The venture capital investor also has a greater need to closely monitor the progress of an early stage company because of the greater variability in performance. This also leads to a preference for investments that are geographically close to the investor. The combination of a geographic focus for early stage investors with the concentration of capital on the coasts and in select regional financial centers, results in large pockets of the country where it is extremely difficult to access early stage venture capital.

Value Add

Seed and start-up stage companies can benefit significantly from having an active investor. Early stage companies are typically formed by a few individuals with exceptional skills in a particular field. However, the management team is usually incomplete. In order to be successful in capitalizing and operating a new business carefully identify and select board members and advisors that can help fill these gaps in the early stages of a company's life. The gaps in expertise most frequently found in early stage companies are in sales and marketing, accounting and finance, and other general management matters. There are firms that specialize in providing assistance in procuring management personnel. Some key financial, marketing and team building needs for the small to midsize business that might be available from "outside" parties are:

Financial
1. Assistance in developing financial reporting formats,
2. Recommendations on size and timing for tapping into external financing sources,
3. Determination of company valuation with documented support of the pricing,
4. Identification and introduction to other financing sources,
5. Assistance in negotiation of the terms of the transaction,
6. Advice on packaging and presenting the company's plan to financing sources,
7. Development of strategy to build value on both a long term and short-term basis,
8. Advice on pricing and structuring strategic relationships,
9. Assistance in evaluating liquidity alternatives, and
10. Assistance in interviewing and selecting investment bankers.

Marketing
1. Strategic assessment of competitive environment and product focus,
2. Assistance in identifying and selecting target markets,
3. Advice on alternatives for channels of distribution, and
4. Assistance in structuring strategic relationships with marketing partners.

Team Building
1. Recruitment of senior management,
2. Identification of advisors in specific functional areas,
3. Recruitment of board members with specific skill sets, and
4. Selection and evaluation of key outside professional service providers.

Angel Description

Angel investors contribute a large amount of capital to business formation. In 1997 it was estimated that total capital invested in new business ventures was about $50B. The economy since '97 has lead to an increase in individual wealth, which has no doubt led to even a greater infusion of angel capital into the new venture business. Of the $50B, $40B was from family, friends and privately held small businesses.

Angel investors' reasons for committing funds to a new or growing business range from recreational (bragging rights) to sophisticated commitments (business venture). These investors like preferred or convertible notes, seldom accept common stock and usually invest where they have experience. They often like to operate in groups with a lead "archangel".

Sophisticated angels preferences resemble those of a venture capitalist; outstanding business plans and an impressive management team. The angel will provide or participate in the exchange of a term sheet (an offering or disclosure document at the outset is probably not necessary). On the other hand, consider providing a risk factor document rather than an offering document especially if less than five investors are involved. It is shorter and less costly to prepare than a full offering or disclosure document.

In the case of "recreational" investors a full offering or disclosure document is advisable. They seldom negotiate terms and prefer a final or set up "take it or leave it" offering. A capital solicitor should engage the recreational investor in informal conversations to ascertain interest before finalizing an arrangement.

Terms for the angel investor must be fair; recognizing that assuming a greater risk merits a larger reward. In addition, the earlier investor should probably be entitled to a better price or other advantages; e.g. warrants as a result of lower valuation, etc.

Angels can be located through personal contacts; networks e.g. accountants, lawyers, investment advisors; economic development organizations; bankers; government service units e.g. SBDC or SCORE; and web sites e.g. ACENet. Angels generally prefer investment in local areas and often like to remain anonymous. An angel may not be listed on web sites for various reasons security, publicity, recreational/non-business, etc.

Another type of angel is the corporate angel. Corporations invest in companies that fit into their corporate strategy. For example, in '97 Intel invested about $300M in 100 transactions with the investment ranging from $1M - $5M. A corporation can afford higher valuations since focus is on strategic rather than financial returns. Some seek early stage opportunities and want a company board seat while others prefer a passive role in a proven company.

Angel Capital

Angel capital is money provided by individuals or consortia of individuals. It is usually less than $500,000 and allows the business to add value or reach a point in development of the business that makes further investment more appealing or enables completion of product development and market entry (table two).

Table two. Comparison of angel and venture capital.

Angel	*Venture*
* cashed out entrepreneurs	* institutional $
* $250 – 500K investment	* invest later in company life
* economic downturn = lower valuation so more deals	* > $1M to keep early or mid stage co. going
* <$30B vs. $40B at economic peak ('00) expect IPO in 5-7 yrs not 1-2 yr as with dot.com	
* emphasis on liquidity event or cashing out is decreased so 1st few yrs is building company	

ACEnet is a relatively new government program designed to lead to matching of angel capital with business needs to post for solicitation of capital business must complete small corporation offering of registration (SCOR) forms (basic elements of business plan) which are reviewed by state securities organization and be classified as Reg. A (<$1M company) or Reg. B (<$5M company) Angel networks are in place to identify potential investors around the country.

Business and Angel Selection and Identification

Homework is necessary to locate and engage an angel. An angel should have: 1) contacts (suppliers, customers, human resources), 2) industry experience (understands business, worked in the industry), 3) experience with entrepreneurs (easier to work with and understand unforeseen delays), 4) experience with startups so expectations are realistic, and 5) deep pockets but not too deep (personal wealth of $2-50 million best; if more, startup may fall from radar screen). Locating angels can be achieved by word of mouth (track record, history of success), referral, presentation at a local angel group meeting, and a personal network (accountants, bankers, lawyers, brokers, consultants).

Opportunity Presentation

As mentioned earlier in this chapter, a party requesting capital from an investor must think like the investor. Therefore, when seeking capital make sure quality management is in place or described along with what stake they have in the company. Present details of the opportunity including the business model, market size, potential, customers, and timing. Be sure to place the business model in context and address external affecters, technology, customers, economy, regulations, and competition. Describe the preferred arrangement as well as price and structure. Price should be based on company valuation and structure will include terms of investment, board seats, salary units and all factors that might impact return on investment. All of the preceding should be addressed in the first meeting to secure interest on the part of the angel. The financial and business structure might be brought up late in the first meeting but usually delayed until later meeting or until serious interest has been established. Details are presented in Exhibits C and D.

Format. "Taylor" the presentation to the angel or talk about things that interest them. Focus on team formation. For example, if an angel wants 5 senior executives in place one cannot do it all and angel knows that. Offer to introduce the team at the next meeting. An investor may not understand technology but does trust a reputable team. They may assess the technology but will rely on people for successful implementation. Put forward realistic sales plan focused on "cash out" and return on investment for the investor. Identify exit strategy i.e. sale, IPO or buyout. Have the necessary documents in hand and be prepared to deliver then at the meeting including the business plan with financials, corporate bios, company documents. Be prompt, stay on schedule and provide succinct answers to questions. If the answer to a question is not known, say so and get the answer for later.

Valuation. Establish company worth, the amount of money needed and how much ownership stock or other securities will be given up in return for the investment. Remember Investors value of a company is based on potential financial return in the future. Consider time, reputation, contacts, opportunity costs (money that could be made doing something else), etc. Remember, angels may have intangible interests such as excitement about launching a start-up, pride in contributing to a successful business and a desire to give something to the entrepreneurial world. As expected angel's estimate of value will usually be less than the enterprise's estimate. Keep in mind that ideas are cheap and execution does not equal value; it is income that is important (table three). Also price can vary markedly but it must be taken seriously.

Table three. A thumb rule for estimating company value.

Item	Add to company value, $M
Sound idea	1
Prototype	1
Quality management team	1-2
Quality Board	1
Product rollout or sales	1
Total potential value, $M	1-6

Arrangement structure. Key business terms in the agreement between an investor and the venture will establish the type of capital involved (equity or debt), the kind of equity, cash disbursements, and the right of the angel to invest in future rounds of financing. In addition, the role of the angel in the future will be addressed. Define whether the angel will be a silent partner, be actively involved in the company business or act as an intermediate between silent and active. If an angel is involved in the business be sure the involvement is well defined at the outset.

Negotiation. The following are several points to take into account when engaging in negotiations with investors. Align everyone's interests so the end point is "Its you and me against world not you vs. me. Offer to keep CEO salary fixed till company exit and stress intentions to exit as soon as possible. Investors focus on numbers and specifically initial ownership stake. Angels have time and are usually not as intent on deal closure as the firm seeking capital. An investor has the option to have third party negotiators such as their lawyer, an investor not involved in the deal or a professional negotiator. On the other hand, some angels do not negotiate; their position is "take it or leave it". This tactic can also be applicable to the entrepreneur as well but be prepared to do so to avoid leaving the "table" too soon or erroneously.

Support. Plan to work together to maximize relationship and knowledge base. Investors can be a valuable source of customers, suppliers, human resources and/or follow on capital (next round of money). An angel also can provide leverage to enhance perceive economic value and be crucial when establishing strategic partnerships or engaging key or prominent accounts. An investor-owner relationship is a two-way relationship; the entrepreneur must update the investor regularly to elevate interest and foster the partnership.

Investment return. Several methods exist to harvest an investment and will be set forth in the angel-owner agreement. Examples are:

1. walking harvest - cash sent to angel on regular basis;
2, partial sale - angel sells stakes to company management, another shareholder or outsider;
3. strategic sale - competitor acquires company and angel gets negotiated share of acquisition price;
4. financial sale - buyer outside the industry buys company for its cash flow; angel gets negotiated share of acquisition price;
5. initial public offering - sell stock in public markets creating market for angel shares; and
6. negative harvest - bankrupt company.

Angel Offering Guidelines

Suggested guidelines to follow when soliciting angel capital are presented in table four.

High Points to Consider

Key features of an investment assessment are:

Required investment	Product/service obsolescence
Status of market	Competition
Perceived need of the product/service	Product/service expect lifetime
Suppliers (if any)	Product feasibility / product prototype
Government regulation (if any)	Proprietary rights
Labor requirements	Legal Entanglements (license, patent,
Gross margin	copyright violations etc.)
Frequency of purchase	Timing of revenue from customer
Tax treatment	Product/service liability
Distribution channel	PR worthiness of product/service
Product/service revenue dependence	Exit potential
on external factors (other than	
regulation, seasonality etc.)	

Table four. Guidelines for solicitation of capital.

I. Develop marketing plan
1. Solicitation method(s)
2. Investor demand for common or preferred stock or high yield notes (with or without warrants)
3. Amount to raise and planned use of proceeds

II. Private - if accredited investors are known by capital solicitor - follow Rule 506 of Regulation D of Securities Act of 1933

III. Public - if solicitation of strangers, advertising or seminars to attract investors:
1. Rule 506 does not apply and solicitor does not benefit from private placement exemptions contained in 1933 Act
2. It is considered a public offering subject to Rule 504 and in compliance with Small Corporate Offering Registration (SCOR) and state laws
3. Intent to raise less than $1M in 12 month period
4. Comply with Regulation A of 1933 Act or register offering with SEC

IV. General solicitation (SEC Regulation D) definition
1. Issuer and person acting on issuer's behalf shall not offer or sell securities by any form of general solicitation or general advertising including but not limited to following;
   a. Advertising, article, notice, or other communication published in newspaper, magazine or similar media or broadcast over television or radio.
   b. Seminar or meeting whose attendees have been invited by general solicitation or advertising.
2. Tailor marketing plan to comply with Rule 506 to avoid federal or state regulatory agencies and amount of capital to be raised is not limited.
3. If more than 35 non accredited investors – solicitor does not comply with 506 so; conform to Rule 504/SCOR which offers exemption designed as a "do-it-yourself" offering to facilitate raising small amounts of capital.

VENTURE CAPITAL
History

Venture capital ("VC") firms supply funding from private sources for investing in select companies that have a high, rapid growth potential and a need for large amounts of capital. VC firms speculate on certain high-risk businesses producing a very high rate of return in a very short time. The firms typically invest for periods of three to seven years and expect at least a 20-40 percent annual return on their investment.

When dealing with VC firms, keep in mind that they are under great pressure to identify and exploit fast growth opportunities before more conventional financing alternatives become available to the target companies. VC firms have a reputation for negotiating tough financing terms and setting high demands on target companies. Three suggestions when dealing with VC firms are; 1) make sure to read the fine print, 2) watch for delay maneuvers (they may be waiting for the financial position to weaken further), and 3) guard trade secrets and other proprietary information zealously. (Exhibit D.)

VC financing may not be available, nor a good choice of financing, for many small businesses. Usually, venture capital firms favor existing businesses that have a minimal operating history of several years; financing of startups is limited to situations where the high risk is tempered by special circumstances, such as a company with extremely experienced management and a very marketable product or service. Target companies often have revenues in excess of two million dollars and a preexisting capital investment of at least one million.

VC firms research target companies and markets more vigorously than conventional lenders, although the ultimate investment decision is often influenced by the market speculations of the particular venture capitalists. Due to the amount of money that venture capital firms spend in examining and researching businesses before they invest, they will usually want to invest at least a million dollars to justify their costs.

Be wary of "shopping" innovative ideas to multiple venture capitalists or private investors. Use caution in revealing any information considered proprietary. Even if intellectual property protection exists (e.g., a patent, trademark, or copyright), avoid the need to police rights that belong to the business. Limit the disclosure of details about the invention or creation and seek confidentiality arrangements for additional protection of any preexisting legal rights that belong to the company or the inventor.

The price of financing through venture capital firms is high. Ownership demands for an equity interest in 30 percent to 50 percent of the company are not uncommon even for established businesses, and a startup or higher risk venture could easily require transfer of a greater interest. Although the investing company will not typically get involved in the ongoing management of the company, it will usually want at least one seat on the target company's board of directors and involvement, for better or worse, in the major decisions affecting the direction of the company.

The ownership interest of the VC firm is usually a straight equity interest or an ownership option in the target company through either a convertible debt (where the debt holder has the option to convert the loan instrument into stock of the borrower) or a debt with warrants to a straight equity investment (where the warrant holder has the right to buy shares of common stock at a fixed price within a specified time period). An arrangement that eventually calls for an initial public offering is also possible.

Despite the high costs of financing through venture capital companies, they do offer tremendous potential for obtaining a very large amount of equity financing and they usually provide qualified business advice in addition to capital.

VC firms are located nationwide, and a directory is available through the National Association of Venture Capital, 1655 N. Fort Meyer Dr., Arlington, VA 22209, and (703) 351-5269). In addition, other sources for venture capital can be found through bankers, insurance companies, and business associations.

In a '98 survey, it was found that venture funds are more likely to go to companies developing Internet products and services for business-to-business market rather than for consumers. In the first quarter of '98, $460M was invested in 101 Internet related companies, a 54% increase over the 1st quarter of '97. Investments were equally divided among access and infrastructure, applications and services. Money flow is to firms developing products for network security, electronic commerce between companies, and vertical industries e.g. banking or construction.

Background Facts

It is important to recognize that venture capital is:

1. First and foremost a people business;
2. Only as good as the founding entrepreneur; who must be relentless in pursuit of goals, visionary, and a risk taker;
3. Especially important in high tech businesses;
4. A small industry when compared with other financial sectors such as mutual funds, real estate, leveraged buyout industries;
5. Directed toward high risk business;
6. Useful for developing a balance of people, business direction and operation; and
7. Often drawn to the entrepreneur who has a history of successful new business ventures.

Entrepreneur Prospective

One criteria investors use to measure probability of success is the type of person seeking capital. There are several definitions for an entrepreneur. The following is how some individuals describe an entrepreneur:

1. life style - want to own company, work for self, control;
2. directed life style - life is more important than the next $B company;
3. empire builder - likes to grow and rule the business; will not sell what they "own"; and
4. serial - desires to build, exit and/or cash out.

The bottom line is that venture capitalists and angels like serial entrepreneurs.

Solicitation

The search for venture capital is similar to the criteria to be considered for seeking angel investors. The reader is referred to the angel capital section herein. In addition, the following rules should be considered to increase the probability of a successful search for venture capital:

1. Develop a strong experienced management team for the company. Have a chief financial officer, finance person, a marketing executive, an operations manager and CEO. If CEO experience is limited, find someone who has experience and convince them to be part of the team. The most important factor in the decision to invest is the strength of the management team. If a CEO search is planned include the position description.
2. Don't rely on just one method of contacting investors. While it is a common belief that venture capital companies find most of their deals through referrals, that's just simply not true. Direct contact by the entrepreneurs themselves is tied in first place with referrals from accounting firms and intermediaries. Maximize the capital network.
3. Contact investors who are looking for what the firm offers. Research venture capital companies through Pratt's Guide, available at most public libraries, or by visiting venture capital web sites. If the company is a start-up in the consumer product industry don't bother contacting venture capital companies who invest in second stage software companies.
4. Make sure the business plan clearly explains the concept, why the company will succeed and what specific strategies will be implemented to achieve that success. Be realistic with financial projections and document assumptions. The most critical mistake entrepreneurs' make is presenting a sloppy, ill conceived, confused business plan. A business plan presentation gets one chance to make a first impression and the business plan represents the company. It's not location, location, location. It's competition, competition, and competition. Venture capital companies have stated that lack of competitive knowledge, underestimating the competition, or ignoring the competition is the most common mistake in business plans. Know more about the competition than potential competitors know about themselves! Never, never, never, suggest that a product or service has no competition.
5. Always enter the author's name, company name, phone number and address on the business plan's front cover, title page and contents page.

Investor Perspective

When searching for venture capital thinks like the capital provider. Become familiar with the questions they ask and are prepared to answer each. Examples of questions asked are:

1. How much can I expect to make on my money?;
2. When can I cash out?;
3. Why spend money on fixed assets like office equipment? (Take advantage of leveraging by leasing within reason.);

4. Will investment capital be used to repay loans to officers and affiliates? (If yes, it is a basis for rejection.);
5. Are other investors in line and if so who are they and what are their expected contribution and/or level of commitment?;
6. Who has been approached to invest and if rejection what were the reasons?; and
7. What are the existing contractual commitments including but not limited to service providers, employee agreements, or other investors?.

Investor Considerations

The investor will have certain items that are included in the list of critical issues when considering an investment. These need to be addressed in the business plan and/or should be included in the oral presentation material. A list of areas are:

1. staged investment;
2. management incentives;
3. experience;
4. time;
5. type of security;
6. full disclosure;
7. legal documents (proper organization, and good standing);
8. secured business and intellectual property rights;
9. third party guarantees;
10. absence of litigation;
11. affirmative action/words (shall/will);
12. insurance/taxes; and
13. financial health.

The Investment

A venture capital investment has no set formula and is not a perfect structure. Different needs and concerns of VC and entrepreneur are reconciled through negotiation and a desire to form a win-win arrangement. Three issues that are most common are: 1) the financial structure i.e. form of securities instruments used, 2) prices related to the arrangement and 3) agreement terms.

Financial structure (form of securities instruments used)

Company and venture firm needs are based on: a) stage of development for both product and company, b) risk assessment, c) ultimate potential, d) required inputs and e) philosophy of venture firm. Factors to consider when structuring an investment are:
1. protection from total loss in case of sale, liquidation or merger for the investor;
2. current yield for a Small Business Investment Company (SBIC) which has debt to service arrangement;
3. venture capitalist influence through board representation;
4. future liquidity from public offering or sale of company;
5. flexibility of structure including room for investment later, future management incentives, and retention of stock if management leaves;
6. minimizing tax exposure of entrepreneurs that buy cheap stock;
7. liquidity for outside investors if company goes "sideways";
8. voting control;
9. effect on future money raising ability;
10. balance sheet attractiveness to non-venture capital sources of debt financing as well as to suppliers;
11. management's relative contribution to capital; and

594

12. feasibility of paying dividends/interest.

Structuring process consists of the following:

1. define needs and concerns;
2. evaluate alternatives;
3. choose and negotiate a structure consistent with company's financial needs and capabilities;
4. provide liquidity; and
5. address investor control.

Securities instruments commonly used are straight debt, debt with equity features (convertible debt to debt with warrants) or common stock. Senior Debt is long tem financing for low risk companies or for mezzanine (late stage) financing. Subordinated debenture is debt subordinated to financing from other financial institutions such as banks. It may be unsecured and is usually convertible to common stock or accompanied by warrants to purchase common shares. Senior lenders accept this as equity and allow increased debt for other sources. Preferred stock is convertible to common stock and holders have a preference over common shareholders. This type of stock improves a company's debt to equity ratio but the disadvantage is that if dividends are associated with preferred stock they are not tax deductible. Common stock is the most expensive for a venture capitalist because it has the most risk and is the least flexible. It affords no protection and gives the venture capitalist the least amount of control over management. There is no dividend and so no return until the stock is sold.

Instrument Selection

This means choosing the preferred method of capitalization under the circumstances in question. Advantages for debt financing are: 1) it is preferred in case of liquidation, 2) there is some current income, 3) there are remedies in case of default, and 4) an SBIC that has used debt as leverage and thus has debt to service will prefer an income bearing security. For a company, excess debt can the strain credit standing and make future long term financing difficult and in a case of default places the venture capitalist in a position of control.

Common stock or straight equity on the other hand provides no extra advantage for the venture capitalist in contrast to any other investor awarded common stock; hence a VC may request preferred stock in return for their investment. The level of risk and potential return should be taken into consideration when negotiating with the VC community. Equity usually will cost the business more than if debt financing can be obtained. Common stock is usually the security offered by a larger successful company while senior debt with warrants is more appropriate in a turnaround situation.

Preferred stock structure is a compromise between common stock and note structures. It has more protection than common stock but less than subordinated notes and usually carries a dividend but it can only be paid if company is profitable. Preferred stock is a separate class of stock and so has certain rights established in the articles of incorporation that are stronger than rights of common shareholders but it is usually not as strong as note holders. This stock may be redeemable if sufficient capital is available for redemption.

Other combinations and unique hybrid structures can provide preference in sale, liquidation or merger and current income plus capital gain for the venture capitalist without weighting the balance sheet with too much debt. For example; no load convertible preferred stock has no dividend attached, has liquidation preference, converts to common stock at the option of the holder, automatically at a public offering votes as if common stock, is considered equity, and carries a right of first refusal for future financings. Convertible preferred stock is often used for startups and early stage financing. It is attractive to the entrepreneur because there are no dividend obligations.

Structure Flexibility

Flexibility is needed to enhance the possibility of finalizing an arrangement. Initial selection of the capitalization method affects the ability to take actions subsequently so is should be as flexible as possible at the outset. A right for the initial investor to participate in subsequent financing rounds should be established so as to provide as little of an obstacle as possible in later rounds of financing. Make provisions for providing stock that can motivate key management brought in subsequent to financing. Establish if management personnel leave the company should they retain some or all of their stock. Set up a class of stock different from that issued to investors. These reserves can be established for the management pool and stock issued can be escrowed. Be sure to take into account tax implications.

Remember, an early stage investor should not loose money while the entrepreneur makes money, so use a senior instrument to protect the investor's interest. These instruments should be considered equity and be leveraged as the firm grows. Preferred stocks are clearly equity even though they can have redemption requirements. Senior lenders easily handle it if or when the company is capable of acquiring debt. Subordinated debt can be designed to meet this need but issues arise for senior lenders as the company grows.

Venture capitalists prefer not to make outright purchases of common stock except when majority ownership exists for the investor group. Before taking a common equity position there can be a waiting period to determine if a company performs as expected and to establish compatibility of objectives of investor and company management. Remember, the venture capitalist's preferred exit is liquidity and this needs to be agreed to at the time of investment.

The structure of a transaction cannot make a bad investment good; but can influence results of investment that are not meeting initial expectations. The initial assumption is presumption of a high level of success; fact is only a small percentage is successful. Liquidity and/or return of capital and possible remedies available by using instruments other than common stock can be helpful to investment process and benefit both entrepreneur and venture capitalist. Keep the financial structure simple and flexible. Understand terms so relationship is considered to be a win-win for both parties.

Investment Pricing

Profit targets are set by venture capitalists some of which are presented in table five.

Table five. Venture capitalist profit targets.

Profit targets*	Compounded annual rates of return (pre-tax), %
3:1:3**	44
3:1:5	25
4:1:4	41
5:1:3	71
5:1:5	38
7:1:3	91
7:1:5	48
10:1:3	115
10:1:5	58

* Dollar return for each dollar invested within X years.
** Three times investment in three years.

Some venture capitalists use the following rules of thumb when pricing an investment.

Investment stage	Compound rate
Seed or startup	>50% compounded
Second stage	30-40% compounded
Late stage	25-30% compounded

Factors Affecting Price

Setting price for a venture is often considered to be an art rather than a science. The price will be based on risk assessment, the product definition, the market or markets and management. The potential reward must compensate for risk. The greater the perceived risk the higher the expected return; hence the more equity a venture capitalist will need to have in the company. Some analytical tools are used to assess risk and future potential but in dealing with unknowns the final determination of value will be judgmental based on knowledge, experience and intuition.

Quantitative analysis

Company potential will consist of the upside and downside. Items that will be assessed include; size, time to reach specific size, future revenues, comparison with others in the industry (leaders, midsize or small size firms), operating statistics for similar companies compared with projections, historic performance of second or greater stage company in terms of sales, operating costs, gross profits and margins, overhead, administrative expenses, net profit, net profit to sales ratio, net worth, return on equity, long term debt, current ratios, and price earnings ratios in current market. If stocks of leading firms are selling at 25 times, medium companies at 15 times and small companies at 8 times there will be hesitancy to consider a price earning s ratio of more than 10 –12 in estimating what the venture equity could be worth at the time of sale.

Accuracy of Financial Projections

It is important to be realistic and as accurate as possible. If the projections are too conservative the company value will be under priced but if they are too optimistic credibility will be impaired and investors will be hesitant to commit.

Future Dilution

Investors will want to consider the effect of additional rounds of financing on dilution of the company value especially their potential revenue.

Exit

The only way an investor will realize a return on investment is if the firm has an exit strategy. The venture capitalist will determine whether the firm is a good acquisition candidate has potential for a public offering or can survive as independent entity.

Elapsed Time until Profitable

A key consideration by any investor will be the time required until liquidity on an investment is probable or when return threshold expectations of the venture firm are met. This is closely tied to the exit strategy of the firm.

Performance to Date

Any good business venture will establish goals and milestones. Achieving these goals forms the basis for further funding. Acquiring this investment will often be based on whether or not prior projections or benchmarks have been met. On the other hand, unrealistic goals, if accepted, in the first round can lead to over valuation and if not met can result in lower evaluation in the second round. There is a definite need to increase corporate valuation in subsequent rounds of financing.

Capital Gains vs. Current Income

The investor will also want to know if the investment structure will provide some current income in the form of interest or dividends or is the return going to be based solely on eventual capital gain.

Management Analysis

Can the management team build product and exploit market if the product and market are viable? The investment team will determine how judgmental and intuitive management is and how critical thinking is practiced since it may affect investment pricing and perceived risk. The more relevant the accomplishments and experiences of management, the higher the valuation. Track records and credibility will be subjected to close scrutiny. Further the commitment of the management team will be based on the amount of net worth they commit to the venture. There is always a need to consider the personal chemistry between investor and management since it will be a significant contributor to comfort level and a good communication environment.

Fund Raising Environment

It is not always the business itself that has an impact on capitalization. The economic status of the public stock market, state of the venture capital community and entrepreneurial climate will influence the investor's decisions. If the stock market is high and speculative pricing tends to be higher. In the early 80's confidence level was high so valuations were high whereas in the mid 80's the market was less speculative and there was a dramatic drop in valuation when raising new money.

Venture industry and entrepreneurial climate The entrepreneur will find that the venture industry is cyclical and even regional. This is due to too much money chasing too few deals and can lead to high valuation. On the other hand, startup valuation and pricing is less subject to variation because business risk tends to dominate over financial and price risk.

Determining value The first step is to calculate company value. Price may not be negotiated in the first meeting but the venture capitalist may ask how much equity will be given up in return for the capital being sought. This strategy is an attempt to align expectations. Failure to respond to the request can jeopardize the chance of securing or maintaining investor interest. As discussed herein the following are factors that are taken into account to set price:

1. if business risk is high expected rate of return will be high;
2. for an early stage business, risk is high and pricing risk is low;
3. for mid to late stage business the risk is low or gone and the price risk is high; hence the investor may only be looking for a 3-5X ROI vs. 10 on a startup;
4. estimate Price/Earnings ratio based on comparable publicly held companies;
5. project market value by multiplying forecasted annual earnings by P/E ratio for comparable companies;
6. divide estimate of total dollar return venture capitalists want by projected market value of company yields percent of ownership venture capitalist will need as of future date to realize desired return; and
7. dilution from any additional equity financing required during interim period must be considered in making these calculations.

Valuation is dependent on: 1) quantitative analysis; 2) personal judgment; 3) venture capitalist bias; 4) money raining environment; 5) talent and skills of management team; and 6) desire for highest valuation or best investors. In any event confirm value projections with experienced professionals i.e. banker, accountant, and/or lawyer. Examples of company valuation are as follows:
Example 1:
ABC Company
   1. Startup
      2. Capital needed at outset = $500K
      3. Excellent product potential, BUT product unproven SO risky
      4. For initial investment investor wants 10 times investment in five years
      5. Management projects going public at 20 times earnings in five years

598

6. Post tax earnings for 5th year = $1.25M
7. Additional long term capital infusion at start of 3rd year = $500K
8. Second $500K is from same investor
9. Desired return for second round of financing is 10 times investment in 5 years (could be less if benchmarks up to this point met)

Estimate of total dollar return required

Total investment	$1,000,000
Estimate of return required	x____10
	$10,000,000

Projected market value in 5th year

Projected earnings	$1,250,000
Estimated P/E ratio	x____20
	$25,000,000

Percentage ownership needed in 5th year

a. Estimate of total dollar return required	$10,000,000
b. Projected market value of company in 5th year	$25,000,000
Ratio of a to b	40%

Example 2: A second investor provides the second round of financing.
ABC Company
1. Startup
2. Capital needed at outset = $500K
3. Excellent product potential, BUT product unproven SO risky
4. For initial investment investor wants 10 times investment in five years
5. Management projects going public at 20 times earnings in five years
6. Post tax earnings for 5th year = $1.25M
7. Additional long term capital infusion at start of 3rd year = $500K
8. Second $500K is from NEW INVESTOR
9. Desired return for second round of financing is 10 times investment in 5 years (could be less if benchmarks up to this point met)

Estimate of total dollar return required

Total investment	$ 500,000
Estimate of return required	x____10
	$5,000,000

Projected market value in 5th year

Projected earnings	$1,250,000
Estimated P/E ratio	x____20
	$25,000,000

Percentage ownership needed in 5th year

a. Estimate of total dollar return required	$ 5,000,000
b. Projected market value of company in 5th year	$25,000,000
Ratio of a to b	20%

However; ownership given up by initial investor for 2nd round financing by another investor will cause dilution of ownership position so he wants more that 20% ownership initially. For example, it is assumed that 15% ownership will have to be given up for subsequent financing and so initial financier would need 23% (.20x.15) ownership initially to end up with 20% in the 5th year.

Agreement Terms

The following is an outline of items to consider in the legal process of securing a venture capital investment presented in "Pratt's Guide to Venture Capital Sources." Ninth Edition 1985 edited by Stanley E. Pratt and Jane K. Morris. These terms are meant to be guidelines only. An attorney should be involved in the finalizing the agreement. Legal counsel is also recommended at the investment solicitation strategy is established and during the investment procurement process. The cost for upfront legal advice can be minor in contrast to litigation expenses in the event that an invalid or poor agreement is consummated.

I. Common set of documents in transaction
    A. Term sheet – summary of principal financial and other terms of investment
    B. Investment agreement – terms of purchase and provisions of securities (equity or debt) being acquired
    C. Stockholders agreement – restrictions on the transfer and voting of securities by management and occasionally investors
    D. Employee stock purchase or stock option agreement – current and future allocation of equity in business to key employees
    E. Employee confidentiality and proprietary rights agreement – assurance that business shall retain valuable intellectual property and business rights
    F. Legal opinion

II. Term Sheet or Letter of Intent
    A. Reflects agreed upon valuation of business and quantifies proposed allocation of that value between entrepreneurs and investors
    B. Summarized key financial and legal terms that will serve as basis for definitive legal documents
    C. Impose enforceable legal obligations on parties e.g. payment of expense in event investment does not proceed or prohibits negotiation with other pending completion of this transaction
    D. Sets forth or elicits issues or concerns that can be deal killers later
    E. Valuable to entrepreneur who has never seen venture terms – establishes some commonality between parties;

III. Investment Agreement
    A. Principal purposes and legal consequences
        1. Detailed substantive terms
        2. Basic disclosure document; history, business, financial, legal data
        3. Conditions precedent to closing; issuers "stop action" conditions to be met before closure
        4. Defines business parameters for future – "shalt's" and "shalt not's"
        5. Consequence of breach – investor withdrawal
        6. Remedies – specific performance and injunctive relief
            -   Most severe are ratchet down provisions in an antidilution formula or extraordinary voting rights granted to a class of preferred stock holder
            -   Less severe is repayment of debt securities required
    B. Description of transaction;
        1. Type of securities
        2. Purchase price
        3. Requirement that securities be properly authorized
        4. If investor acquires a note (convertible or not) or stock purchase warrant for of security is attached as exhibit to investment agreement
        5. If stock other than common terms of this class set forth in corporate charter should be attached as exhibit
        6. If more than one investor participates
            -   List or reference in exhibit
            -   Investor may require identical investment agreements executed simultaneously

600

with others along with no amendments, in full force at closing date and minimum amount of money has been raised by company
7. Staged investment common
    - Incentive to management
    - Gives venture capitalist impact on business development
C. Specific Representations and warranties of company
    - Full disclosure of company operating details - identifies relevant issues for conduct of biz
    - Preceded by affirmative declaration or affirmation of compliance (exhort company to undertake normal actions in course of business)
    1. Organization and authority- properly organized, in good standing, legal authority to conduct business
    2. Corporate action – all actions taken to authorize transaction and to issue securities based on corporate charter and by laws
    3. Governmental approvals – compliance with securities laws
    4. Absence of litigation – exiting or threatened that would impact business
    5. Employment of key personnel – no restrictions on key employees e.g. non compete clauses
    6. Compliance with other agreements – no violations of corporate charter, by laws or agreements exist or would exist if investment went forward
    7. Ownership of properties and assets – business and intellectual property rights secured
    8. Financial information – audited and internal unaudited financial statements in place using generally accepted accounting principles with fair presentation of financial condition of company
    9. Transactions with insiders – disclosure of direct or indirect transaction between company and its directors, officers and stockholders.
    10. Third party guaranties or investments – absence of continuing financial involvement with third parties
    11. Compliance with federal securities laws – certification that transaction complies with federal and state securities laws
    12. Disclosure – business plan is accurate and complete and all material disclosures related to transaction have been made
    13. Brokerage – disclosure of any finders or brokers fees or commission associated with transaction
    14. Capitalization
        - Description of authorized capitalization and status of outstanding securities including warrants, options and convertible securities
        - Description of transfer restrictions repurchases rights or preemptive rights
D. Covenants and undertakings of company (Stated in affirmative form – "will or shall")
    1. Payment of taxes and claims - Pay all lawful taxes, assessments and levies on income or property prior to default
    2. Property and liability insurance - Maintain insurance against hazards and risks and liability to persons and property as necessary
    3. Maintenance of corporate existence – all rights, license patents, copyrights trademarks etc. useful in business maintained and type of business presented in business plan will be pursued
    4. Legal compliance- comply with all laws and regulations
    5. Access to premises – investor or its representative may inspect facilities, books and records subject to confidentially provisions
    6. Accounts and reports- investor may request general y accepted accounting principles be applied and to keep full and complete financial records

7. Repair and maintenance – need to maintain equipment and property in good condition
8. Approval of budgets - may require budget or budget revisions to be approved by investor of board of directors.
9. Protection of proprietary rights – includes employee confidentiality, proprietary rights agreements
10. Compliance with key agreements – includes stockholder agreement and need for future stockholder to join agreement
11. Life insurance – key officers and employees, amount may be face amount of securities purchase price, proceeds may go to investor particular if investor holds debt securities
12. Board of Directors – investor representation often required, notice of meeting if not on board, frequency and financial arrangement may be defined
13. Financial and operating statements
    - Sales, production, profits cash balances, receivables payables and backlog reports
    - SEC or other agencies statements
    - Lawsuits or other legal proceedings
    - Certificate from CEO or CFO as to compliance with investment agreement
14. Current ratio, working capital, or net worth
    - Usually only in debt financings
    - Keyed to company projections
15. Use of proceeds – can be related to business of company or narrowly defined to specific financing plan

Negative covenants

1. Limit company from actions it otherwise might be inclined to take unless investors have consented in advance
2. Often subject to sharp negotiation since they relate to fundamental nature of business or alter balance of control between investor and entrepreneur
3. Mergers, consolidations and sale or purchase of assets – prohibited without investor approval
4. Dealings with related parties – no transaction with offices, directors or stockholders but if approved terms no less favorable than for unrelated parties.
5. Change in business – no deviation from business plan
6. Charter amendments – no amendment of charter or bylaws
7. Distributions and redemption's
8. No dividend distribution or limited to fixed percent of profits
9. Not to repurchase or redeem securities except according to terms of securities by investor (redeemable preferred stock), employee plans (forfeiture of stock upon termination of employment or agreements with stockholders (right of first refusal)
10. Issuance of stock or convertible securities – no issuance if investor position diluted
11. Liens and encumbrances – restrictions on liens pledges or other encumbrances except for real estate mortgages (may cover leases of real property or equipment)
12. Indebtedness – limits further debt (usually in case of debt securities)
13. Investments – only in wholly owned securities and not other companies
14. Employee compensation – may set maximum term and compensation
15. Financial covenants – limitation on losses.

Other undertakings imposed on company

1. Registration rights – right to register securities for public sale (critical for investor who is dependent upon liquidity to realize a return on investment)
2. Securities available for registration
    - Limited to common stock

- Pooled or coordinated registration rights with subsequent or earlier rounds of financing
3. Piggy back registration rights
   - Investor guaranteed minimum anticipation in piggyback registrations
   - Inclusion of additional shares of stock in a registration
4. Demand registration rights
   - Right to require an issuer to register their shares upon demand and without regard
   - To registration of shares for account of any other parties
   - Assure investor of access to public market- enable investor to force a company to
   - Go public but rarely used this way but can be influencing factor
5. Marketing rights
   - Related to underwriters to alter shares to be registered, if necessary in order to market the public issue effectively
6. Indemnification – each party indemnifies the other against liability for which it is responsible arising out of a registration
7. Procedural covenants – defined procedures exist for registration; need to follow
8. Availability of Rule 144 – one public company must file all reports and action required in rule 144 of Securities Act of 1933
9. Expenses of registration – Cost to register can be high; investor will require company to agree to bear expenses

Rights to future financings
1. Right of first refusal to assume entire financing
2. Preemptive rights to participate in financing on a pro rata basis with other security holders of company
3. Rights of prior negotiation to discuss and negotiate financing opportunities with company prior to company making offers to others

Indemnification for breach of agreement
1. In startup investor may require founders or top management to share personal responsibility for representations and warranties made by company in investment agreement and to indemnify investors for any breaches thereof
2. Effective means of assuring complete and accurate disclosure of all material business information (be sure entrepreneur's responsibilities specifically identified e.g. proprietary materials only)

Conditions to closing
1. Counsel opinions for investor and company
2. Employment, noncompete, and stock restriction agreements
3. Elections and resignations of directors
4. Compliance certificates by senior management

VENTURE CAPITAL LETTER OF INTENT (LOI)

High Points to Consider
The letter of intent is intended to establish an understanding between the investor and capital recipient. The following are features of the LOI:

1. first official document from an investor
2. 99% are non binding BUT it serves as blueprint of the deal and moves negotiations from an indication of interest to the closing table

3. many deals die at LOI stage because it is where precise terms and conditions of investment are presented
4. previously finer points have not been addressed
5. a LOI actually leads to the due diligence and exchange of information that makes or breaks a deal
6. signed LOI is first step toward closing.

Key errors in creating a LOI that should be addressed are:

1. Absence of time frame
   a. typically 90 days after which deal is off
   b. a LOI often requires solicitor to refrain from seeking other financing so need termination date or condition
2. Letting investor take over hunt for $
   a. investor puts up part and makes deal contingent on syndicating the rest among other investors, and
   b. commitment of entrepreneur and VC may not be the same
3. Not taking ratchet provisions into account
   a. each round of financing should put a higher value on company
   b. BUT a LOI often contains provisions that put onus on entrepreneur if a later found is done at a lower valuations
   c. ratchet provisions mean if value of company goes down, ownership stake of the VC goes up to compensate for loss they experience (declining values may be fact of life BUT should not be born solely by entrepreneur
   d. best tactic; be sure all shareholders, VCs and founders take a weighted averages portion of the decline
   e. be sure Legal Counsel reviews and has experience with VC LOIs.

VENTURE OPPORTUNITY PROFILE

Criterion	Highest Potential	Lowest Potential
Industry and Market		
Market: Need	Mkt driven; identified recurring revenue niche; meets existing customer need	Unfocused; one-time revenue
Customers	Reachable; receptive	Loyal to others or unreachable
User benefits	Less than one year payback	Three years plus payback
Value added	High; advance payments, identifiable, repeatable, and verifiable	Low; minimal impact on market
Product feasibility	Working and feasible prototype	No prototype
Product life	Durable; more than one product to bring to market; life of product great enough to recapture initial investment plus profit	Perishable
Market structure /competition	Imperfect, fragmented competition or emerging industry	Highly concentrated or mature or declining industry
Market size	$100+ million to $1 billion sales potential	Unknown, less than $20 million or multibillion sales
Growth rate	Growth at 30 to 50% or more	Contracting or less than 10%
Market capacity	At near or full capacity	Under capacity
Market share attainable -Yr.5	20% or more; leader	Less than 5%
Cost structure	Low-cost provider; cost advantages; economies of scale are insignificant	Declining cost

Economics		
Profits after tax	10-15% or more; durable	Less than 5%; fragile
ROI potential	25% or more; high value	Less than 15 to 20%; low value
Capital requirements	Low to moderate; fundable	Very high; un-fundable
IRR potential	25% or more per year	Less than 15% per year
Tax treatment	Favorable	Unfavorable
Free cash flow characteristics	Favorable; sustainable; 20-30 + % of sales	Less than 10% of sales
Sales growth	Moderate to high (15 + % to 20 + %)	Less than 10%
Asset intensity	Low/sales $	High
Spontaneous working capital	Low, incremental requirements	High requirements
R&D/capital expenditures	Low requirements	High requirements
Gross margins	Exceeding 40% and durable	Under 20%
Time to breakeven - cash flow	Less than 2 years; breakeven not creeping	Greater than 4 years; breakeven creeping up
Time to breakeven - P&L	Less than 2 years; breakeven not creeping	Greater than 4 years; breakeven creeping up
Harvest Issues		
Value-added potential	High strategic value	Low strategic value
Valuation multiples and comparables	p/e 20+ x; 8-10+ x EBIT; 1.5-2+ x revenue free cash flow 8-10+ x	p/e = 5x, EBIT = 3-4x ; revenue = .4
Exit mechanism and strategy	Present or envisioned options	Undefined; illiquid investment
Capital market context	Favorable valuations, timing, capital available; realizable liquidity	Unfavorable; credit crunch
Competitive Advantage Issues		
Fixed and variable costs	Lowest; high operating leverage	Highest
Control over costs, prices, and distribution	Moderate to strong	Weak
Barriers to entry: Proprietary protection	Have or can gain	None
Response/lead time (tech., product &, market innovation, people, location, resources, or capacity)	Competition slow; napping	Unable to gain edge
Regulatory issues	Advantage	Disadvantage
Product liability	Little or none	Great
Supply source (materials and labor)	Accessible	Not accessible
Legal, contractual advantage	Proprietary or exclusivity	None
Contacts and networks	Well-developed; accessible	Crude; limited
Key people	Top talent; an A team	B or C team
Management Team		
Entrepreneurial team	All-star combination; free agents; proven P&L experience in the same technology, market, and service area	Weak or solo entrepreneur
Industry & technical exper.	Top of the field; super track record	Underdeveloped
Integrity	Highest standards	Questionable
Intellectual honesty	Know what they do not know	Do not want to know what they do not know
Fatal-Flaw Issue	Non-existent	One or more

Personal Criteria		
Goals and fit	Getting what you want; but wanting what you get	Surprises, as in The Crying Game
Upside/downside issues	Attainable success/limited risks	Linear; on same continuum
Opportunity costs	Acceptable cuts in salary, etc.	Comfortable with status quo
Desirability	Fits with lifestyle	Simply pursuing big money
Risk/reward tolerance	Calculated risk; low R/R ratio	Risk adverse or gambler
Stress tolerance	Thrives under pressure	Cracks under pressure
Strategic Differentiation		
Degree of fit between founders & team, opportunity and resource requirements	High	Low
Team	Best in class; excellent free agents	B team; no free agents
Service management	Superior service concept	Perceived as unimportant
Timing	Rowing with the tide	Rowing against the tide
Technology	Groundbreaking; one-of-a-kind	Many substitutes or competitors
Flexibility	Able to adapt; commit and exit quickly	Slow; stubborn
Opportunity orientation	Always searching for opportunities	Operating in a vacuum; napping
Pricing	At or near leader	Undercut competitor; low prices
Distribution channels	Accessible & receptive; networks in place	Unknown; inaccessible
PR value	Great PR angles	Not news worthy
Room for error	Forgiving strategy	Unforgiving, rigid strategy

INITIAL PUBLIC OFFERING (IPO)

Going public simply means that a company that was previously owned by a limited number of private investors has elected, for the first time, to sell ownership shares of the business to the general public. The public sale of ownership interests can generate funds for working capital, repayment of debt, diversification, acquisitions, marketing, and other uses. In addition, a successful public offering increases the visibility and appeal of a company, thereby escalating the demand and value for shares of the company. Investors can benefit from an IPO not only because of the potential increase in market value for their stock, but also because publicly-held stock is more liquid and can be readily sold if the business appears to falter or if the investor needs quick cash. The availability of a public market for shares will also help determine the taxable values of the shares and assist in estate transfers.

Publicly traded stock can also make a business more attractive to prospective and existing employees if stock option and other stock compensation plans are offered. Employee stock-based programs are worth more if transfer restrictions, such as that normally accompanying private company stock, are not placed on the stock.

The use of IPOs has increased in popularity during the '90s, but despite the IPO hype, most small companies are not going to "go public". IPOs largely remain a financing option limited to rapidly growing, successful businesses that generate over a million dollars in net annual income.

The use of IPOs is limited primarily because: (1) there is a very high cost and much complexity in complying with federal and state laws governing the sale of business securities (the cost for a small business can run from $50,000 - $500,000); (2) offering the business's ownership for public sale does little good unless the company has sufficient investor awareness and appeal to make the IPO worthwhile; and (3) management must be ready to handle the administrative and legal demands of widespread public ownership. Of course, an IPO also means a dilution of the existing shareholders" interests and the possibility of takeovers or adjustments in management control is present. Additional information on IPOs is presented in Exhibit A.

Securities laws are complicated. The sale of "securities" to the public is regulated by federal and state laws that have two primary objectives: (1) to require businesses to disclose material information about the company to investors, and (2) to prohibit misrepresentation and fraud in the sale of securities. Under federal law, a "security" is broadly defined and would include stocks, notes, bonds, evidence of indebtedness, and most ownership interests. The law defines a "public offering" of a security not by the number of investors to whom the stock is offered, but by the classification of whether the investors are considered "sophisticated" or not. However, state law definitions of a "security" and of a "public offering" can vary from the federal law.

Many small businesses can sell stock to insiders or to a small group of investors without being subject to securities laws; in effect, they can take advantage of alternatives to going public. However, it's not always clear where the exemptions end, so consult a knowledgeable attorney before selling any stock in the company. The process of soliciting money from the public through the issuance and sale of securities requires a working knowledge of the state and federal registration statements concerning the securities to be sold, complex disclosure documents about the company with detailed information for potential investors, and financial statements. Employing professionals (attorney, accountant, and sometimes a stock underwriter) to assist in the process is a practical necessity.

See Exhibit C for more information on capital acquisition.

LIMITED PRIVATE OFFERINGS

While many small businesses sell interests in their companies that are "securities," as defined by federal or state laws, the transactions are often exempt from registration regulations because the offerings are sufficiently small in dollar amount, and they are restricted to a limited number and/or type of investors. These exempt offers of securities are called "limited private offerings" and they can avoid much of the cost and delay of a public offering. Unfortunately, to qualify for any of the exemptions, certain federal and state security law criteria must be met.

Limited private offerings can be either debt or equity instruments, or a hybrid of both. For instance, a convertible debt warrant would be a debt instrument that allowed the holder to convert the debt into an equity interest at a certain time. These alternative offerings allow the business to tailor the amount of immediate equity (ownership and control) that it relinquishes, and the amount of debt (cash outflow) that it can safely assume. In this section, discussion of the use of limited private offerings is largely confined to equity financing.

FEDERAL EXEMPTIONS

At the federal level, the most popular exemption from registration requirements for small businesses is Rule 504, commonly known as "Regulation D." Under this provision, private companies that are selling less than $1 million worth of securities to any number of investors within a 12-month period are exempt from federal registration requirements.

Solicitations of investors by a private business may be made through almost any means, including advertisements and seminars, and no specific disclosure requirements regarding the stock or the company are required. Most startups and smaller businesses would fall within this exemption.

Even if a securities offer is exempt from the registration requirements of federal or state law, the anti-fraud provisions of those laws may still apply. Therefore, avoid misrepresentations or omissions in the offering that create an overly optimistic picture of the investment. The investor should be provided with sufficient information to make an informed decision regarding the investment.

Another exemption may be available to either private or publicly held companies that sell less than $5 million within a 12-month period, if the sales are made only to "accredited investors" and no more than 35 such investors are involved. Accredited investors include institutional investors (e.g., banks, brokers and dealers, insurance companies), company insiders (e.g., officers and directors), and wealthy investors ("wealthy" meaning they have more than $200,000 individual annual income or, individually or jointly with their spouse, have a net worth of over $1 million).

A lesser degree of exemption from regulation exists for a private or publicly-held company that sells an unlimited issuance of securities to an unlimited number of accredited investors, or to no more than 35 non-accredited but "sophisticated investors" (sophisticated investors have sufficient knowledge and experience so that they understand the risks of the sale, or the issuer reasonably believes the investors have these qualifications). Finally, an exemption exists for private offerings of stock that is sold only to persons living in the same state where the company is both incorporated and does significant business, although reliance upon this intra-state exemption is subject to continual policing because the securities must remain within the state.

STATE EXEMPTIONS

Because each state also has securities regulations, the local exemptions must also be checked. Just because a sale may be exempt from federal registration does not mean state registration is not required. State securities laws are commonly referred to as "blue sky" laws because the regulations were originally enacted to prevent unscrupulous issuers from selling "speculative schemes that have no more basis than so many feet of blue sky."

The state laws need not match the federal regulatory exemptions and even though a Uniform Securities Act exists for states to follow, that Act has not been adopted by each state nor is it consistently interpreted in those states which claim to follow it. The result is that consultation with a qualified professional is a practical necessity before soliciting investors for sales of securities. Forty-one states currently have relaxed their securities regulations for small business by offering a Small Company Offering Registration (SCOR) procedure. Even if the business is not based in one of these states, it is still possible to register and sell securities in the states, which have adopted SCOR. For a current list of eligible states, contact the North American Securities Administrators Association at 202-737-0900.

LEVERAGED BUYOUT

The definition of Leveraged Buyout (LBO) is the use of debt or leverage to recapitalize or buy technology companies; hence, "leveraged buyout". LBO is a deal that uses financing of at least 70% debt to buy all of a company's assets BUT some use the term to refer to leveraged "recaps" in which investors use equity and debt to purchase a controlling share of a public company. An LBO is hard to engineer even without added risk of new technology and there is a need to raise a huge amount of money from debt markets. The amount of debt depends on cash flow or EBITDA (earnings before interest, taxes, depreciation, and amortization of the business. IN most cases the amount needed is 3-6 times the annual cash flow of target company. Once the company is healthy, LBO firm makes money by selling the entire company or pieces of it at a premium. The firm also gets a fee of 1-2% of the total capital it manages. The LBO firm often holds the company for an average of 5-10 years. A major task for the LBO firm is finding talented management.

New capital funds are being formed with a focus on technology buyouts. For example, Accel Partners, Brentwood Venture Capital, Oak Investment Partners and Worldview Technology Partners formed Meritech Capital; Institution Venture Partners (IVP), and Texas Pacific and Seset; Sequoia Capital; and Thomas Weisel Partners, a technology investment bank, have established funds of as much as $1B focused on buyouts or late-stage financing. Interest in late stage or buyout is due to several factors including the astronomical valuations of Internet firms based on projected huge returns at every stage of investment, less risk for late stage investments and history of success i.e. Softbank which made significant profit on its $106M investment in Yahoo on the eve of the firm's IPO.

Technology companies are high-risk ventures since debt markets consider their cash flows less reliable than for mainstream businesses like manufacturers or vendors of packaged goods. Short product life cycles also contribute to business risk. Only 23 technology LBOs took place in '97 and '98 vs. 500 traditional LBOs in the same period. The technology industry is becoming more and more important for economic development. For example, the technology sector in '98 accounted for 6.9% of US gross output and is expected to account for 55% of real growth and for 30.8%of gross output in 2002. More than 1000 publicly traded technology companies with $25M plus market capitalization represented almost $3T in market capitalization, 26%of the S&P 500's total market capitalization. Technology companies generated $806B in total revenues in '98 with stable cash flows; low price/earnings and price/sales ratios and almost 2/3 of public technology companies have valuations of 3 times revenues or less. LBO returns are usually in 30-50% range.

A consultant for a management buyout would receive about 1% of the sale upfront, a management fee of ~ $150K/yr, an annualized return of 30-35% or stake in business when company is resold, 3-5 yrs later; therefore, deal flow is important. The management equity interest in the business would be about 17-22% (17% = average) and vest over 4 yr. Pre-economic slowdown companies sell for 7.0-7.5% times cash flow; but during the slowdown era a company sells for 6.00-6.55 times cash flow; therefore, debt needed to finance buyout is 20% less than during the "good" economic times.

Buyout valuations are down due to the economy and prior overvaluations. Investment money is abundant (500 buyouts firms with $150B) but skilled experienced management is scarce. Therefore buy the business you work for!! Several reasons are given for the reduced capital necessary for the buyout are: 1) good management is in place so no learning curve is required, 2) secrecy can be assured due to no need for marketing of the business and 3) it takes less time to finalize the buyout but it still takes 6-12 months to finalize an arrangement. It is essential that both the buyer and seller know the value of the enterprise. For example value is 1.5 to 2.00 times revenue so business valued at $7.5 – 10M could be sold to management for $11.25 to 20M. In order to "reserve legacy" of owner an owner could "stay around" to help with company management.

A buyout firm will carefully assess the firm's management. Where does responsibility reside and who has been successful? What tangible records of success exist? Does management have 10 or mores years of experience? Do management candidates have experience in a similar size organization i.e. if they have run a $10M company the new company cannot be > $20M or if they ran a finance division they cannot hope to run a retail company unless a retailer is involved on the management team.

The buyer should approach the negotiations with the following in mind: 1) if after three meetings there is a stalemate, move on; 2) do not talk money at the 1st meeting but do so by the 3rd meeting, and remember the owner's company is their baby and it is hard for them to decide to sell.

In addition to the foregoing, be aware of seller- buyer conflict. A seller may like a management buyout to "preserve legacy". On the other hand company management may attempt to sabotage the business to get an advantage in setting up the arrangement. Company management has an obligation to the employer (owner) so put cards on table & bring in a professional negotiator. If selling a business "shop" the company and don't negotiate one on one. Be objective; if sell low get warrant that says "if buyer sells at more then $X million seller gets 15%"

Parties involved in a buyout also need to recognize and understand the significance of logic and statements associated with the transaction. Examples of this are presented in table six.

Table six. A comparison of language and meaning in buyout negotiations.

Buyout firms says	Buyout firm means
On plan	Revenue shortfall of 25%
Ahead of plan	Hit plan in 1 of last 3 months
Entrepreneurial CEO	CEO uncontrollable: borders on maniacal
Ingredients there	Given 2 yr; might find workable strategy
Long selling cycle	No customer who likes product yet
Niche strategy	Small time player
Turnaround opportunity	Lost cause
Working closely with management	Talk on phone once/ month

The negotiators involved in buyouts have challenges and conditions similar to any negotiator. Several suggestions points are:

1. be confident and realistic (value);
2. find or create opportunity;
3. have sound business plan;
4. strike agreement with seller;
5. strike arrangement with equity investor;
   - Buyout firm gets 3-5% of sale price therefore $50M deal requires $1.5-2.5M extra
   - Buyer and new CEO get avg. of 15% of company in stock or stock options (CEO or manager usually asked to put up $ to get this i.e. $250-500K; if low liquidity get $15K)
   - If fired in < 1 yr 25% of CEO equity vests or 1 yr salary as severance
6. arrange bank financing – can borrow 2.5 – 3 times cash flow;
7. complete due diligence;
   - Litigation
   - Contracts
8. close arrangement -30-40% of deals have an 11th hour issue arise; and
9. build company;
   - 20% are big winners
   - 30% die
   - 50% breakeven

Questions and answers related to capital formation are presented in Exhibit G.

SECURITIES ACT OF '33
(Amended in 1996)

An entrepreneur or individual seeking investment from others often attempts to secure investments with out the assistance of financial consultants. The structuring of an investment arrangement needs to be well-prepared and appropriate agreements enacted. Legal and/or accounting consultation is recommended. The business and financial arrangement will likely be subject to Securities and Exchange Commission (SEC) guidelines. A brief synopsis of the Securities Act (SA) guidelines in outline and table formats related to capital procurement is as follows.

Two main provisions are covered in the Act; 1) registration and 2) antifraud, which is associated with, full disclosure and risk factors. The following is an outline of SA rules:

Private placement choices (no general solicitation and qualified investors with whom preexisting relationship exists)

A. 505
1. Advantages
   sell to 35 unsophisticated people
   sales to unlimited # of accredited investors
   no federal review required
2. Disadvantages
   limited to $5M over 12 month period
   no general solicitation permitted
   professional investors may extract onerous terms because of nonliquidity
   must comply with state securities laws

B. 506
1. Advantages
   unlimited $ amount can be sold to 35 sophisticated and experienced investors and an unlimited number of accredited investors
   no federal review
   registration provisions of state securities laws are preempted, provided notice is given (if required by state)
2. Disadvantages
   no general solicitation is permitted
   professional investors may extract onerous terms because of nonliquidity

C. Required per Rule 506 and 505
1. Disclosure of certain information unless all purchasers are accredited
   although antifraud rules may not relieve one of disclosure
2. Restrictions on resale of securities
3. Notice filed with SEC and state "blue sky" regulators

Public offering choices
Registered with SEC

Advantages
   better terms for founder than private placements
   unlimited marketing where "blue skied"
   no investor qualification

Disadvantages
   cost (underwriting firm = $350-$500K)
   self underwritten ($100 - $250K)
   underwriting discount and commission and expense allowance
   audited financials required

Public intrastate offering registered in one state (exempt from federal but not state registration)

Advantages

same as 1

no federal review required

Disadvantages

can market in one state only

must comply with state registration requirements

Public regulation A offerings (exempt from federal registration but federal review required)

Advantages

can test waters before filing in select states

audited financials *not* required for federal review

less disclosure required than if SEC registered

can use question and answer format

unlimited marketing where "blue skied"

Disadvantages

limited to $5M in 12 month period; no more than $1.5 M in non issuer resales

still must be reviewed by both federal and state regulators

professional help required

cost in excess of $75K (range = $75 - $150K)

Public rule 504/SCOR

Advantages

same as Regulation A BUT no federal review required and unaudited financial statements permitted in most states

can be completed without professional help so less expensive

Disadvantages

limited to $1M in 12 months

must be reviewed by state regulators

higher risk of defective disclosure and personal liability if prepared without professional help

Private Offering
(No general solicitation; qualified investors, preexisting relationship)

R - 505	R - 506
Advantages	
N = < 35 unsophisticated Unlimited # accredited No federal review	N = < 35 unsophisticated Unlimited # accredited No federal review No St. compliance IF notice given Unlimited $
Disadvantages	
Limited to $5M/12 mo. period No general solicitation Prof. investors - onerous terms (non-liquidity) State securities laws compliant	No general solicitation Prof. investors - onerous terms (non-liquidity)

Required per R - 505 and R - 506

Disclosure of certain information unless all purchasers are accredited although antifraud rules may not relieve one of disclosure

Restrictions on resale of securities

Notice filed with SEC and state "blue sky" regulators

Public Offering

1. R - 506 Public offering Registered with SEC	*Advantages* Better founder terms vs. private Unlimited marketing where "blue skied" No investor qualification
	Disadvantages Cost (underwriting firm = $350-$500K) Self underwritten ($100 - $250K) Plus underwriting discount + commission/expenses Audited financials required
2. registered in one state	*Advantages* *Public intrastate offering* *Same as 1* exempt from federal but not state registration
	Disadvantages Can market in one state only Must comply with state registration requirements
3. Public regulation A offerings	*Advantages* exempt from federal registration & federal review required Can test waters before filing in select states Audited financials <u>not required</u> for federal review Less disclosure required than if SEC registered Can use question and answer format Unlimited marketing where "blue skied"
	Disadvantages Limited to $5M/12 mo. period No more than $1.5 M in non issuer resales Reviewed by both federal and state regulators Professional help required Cost in excess of $75K (range = $75 - $150K)
4. Public rule 504/SCOR	*Advantages* Same as Regulation A BUT no federal review required Unaudited financial statements permitted in most states Can complete without professional help - less expensive
	Disadvantages Limited to $1M in 12 months Must be reviewed by state regulators Higher risk of defective disclosure and personal liability if prepared without professional help

Accredited/qualified investor
1. Net worth or joint net worth with person's spouse at time of purchase is >$1M
2. Income > $200K in two most recent years or >$300K jointly with spouse and reasonable chance to have the same in next year.

In addition to knowledge of the SEC guidelines and statutes other suggestions to consider are:

Type of offering – factors to consider

Amount of money =?

Does marketing plan require that you generally solicit potential customers?

Where do you intend to sell securities?

Most important factor = method of marketing

If approaching strangers or advertise in newspapers - cannot use offerings that prohibit general solicitation

In private offerings, SEC prohibits solicitation of investor with whom company or its broker does not have a preexisting relationship

If soliciting strangers or investors in more than one state must register offering with SEC or seek a Regulation A offering

Most self underwritten and best efforts public angel offerings are for less than $5M so practical choices are to use Regulation A or an intrastate offering registered with one state

If offering is for < $1M over 12 month period SCOR offering may permit you to avoid federal Registration; BUT need to file a Q&A SCOR form with state in which offering is made

Control personal liability

If one violates registration or antifraud provision of federal securities laws:

- they could be held personally liable even if they formed company to receive sale proceeds

-Federal securities laws and some state laws impose personal liability on people in control

The best defense against liability when securing investment in a business is to always act in good faith and after reasonable investigation.

EXHIBIT B - SMALL BUSINESS ASSOCIATION PROGRAMS

S.B.I.C.s - Program Funds Businesses With High Growth Potential

If a company is looking for financing, do not overlook the opportunities available through one of the country's most successful public/ private sector partnerships, Small Business Investment Companies, or SBICs. SBICs are privately organized and managed investment firms that provide venture capital to small independent businesses, both new and established, by way of equity capital, long-term loans, and expert management assistance.

What Is An SBIC? The SBIC program was formed by the Small Business Administration (SBA) in 1958 to help small businesses and entrepreneurs secure financing. SBICs are typically formed by a group of people experienced in venture capital financing who have at least $5 million in capital they want to invest. They pool their money together, and apply to the SBA for an SBIC license. There are very few restrictions on the ownership of SBICs. Many commercial banks also own SBICs. Current laws allow banks to invest up to 5% of their capital and surplus in an SBIC. Banks are interested in SBICs because they allow them to invest in higher risk business ventures than possible under federal banking regulations. For every dollar an SBIC invests in a company, the SBA matches that investment (up to 300 percent). With that money, the SBIC forms SBA-guaranteed debentures that are sold to investors.

How do SBIC's Invest? It is the function of SBICs to act as a financier for small business concerns. There are three main ways SBICs can do this:

1. LOANS. SBICs make long term loans to small businesses for growth, modernization, and expansion. This can be done independently, or in cooperation with other public or private lenders. These loans normally have a maturity of no more than 20 years, though many loans have a much shorter maturation period. The minimum period of financing is five years.

2. DEBT SECURITIES. Debt securities are asset-backed securities for which the small business issues a security, which may be convertible into or have rights to purchase equity in the small business. These securities may also have special amortization and subordination terms.

3. EQUITY SECURITIES. By law, SBICs must provide equity capital to small businesses. In this scenario, the SBIC has some say over management concerns. However, according to law, SBICs may not become general partners or otherwise liable for the general obligations of a business. This means they cannot purchase enough equity to gain controlling interest status.

Who Qualifies For SBIC Funding? Any small business in the development, start-up, or growth stage may qualify for SBIC funding. However, there are a few restrictions on types of businesses in which SBICs may invest. SBICs may not invest in: other SBICs; finance and investment companies; finance-type leasing companies; unimproved real estate; companies with less than one-half of their assets and operations in the US; passive or casual businesses (defined by the SBA as those not engaged in a regular and continuous business operation); and companies that plan to use the proceeds to acquire farmland. Investments in real estate are limited to one third of the SBIC's portfolio, and combined investments in real estate related activities are limited to two thirds of a SBIC's portfolio investments. Lastly, SBICs may not invest in companies whose primary business activity involves providing funds to others, purchasing debt obligations, factoring or leasing equipment.

What SBIC's Typically Fund Similar to venture capitalists, SBICs like high-risk, high-growth, high-tech, high-potential businesses. If your company or product is first in the marketplace (a proprietary product), is patent-pending, or involved in any high-tech arena, an SBIC may take interest in you. It is also be beneficial if your product offers an extreme competitive advantage that allows you to dominate or control the market. SBIC's typically prefer a return on investment of 30 percent, with a high potential that after five years the investment is worth twelve times what they paid for it. Other factors they consider are your current financials and their perceived notion that with proper funding you will be successful.

Where to Find an SBIC There are numerous SBICs in every major US city, but they are not always easy to find. Remember that it's not as important to find an SBIC geographically close to you as finding one who fits with your company's style and product line. Using the Financing Sources Databank V4.7, you can find about 300 SBICs. When searching the Databank, focus on financing stage and industry for best success. Each SBIC profile will tell you what kind of projects they like to fund, typical financing amounts, and how much money is available.

SBA *Express* Loan Program Expanded - Simplifies Loans for Small Businesses

The Small Business Administration has just announced changes in the SBAExpress pilot loan program that will significantly expand the number of lenders participating in the program and increase access to capital for small businesses. The modifications will allow an estimated 2,400 lenders already delivering other SBA loan products to participate in the SBAExpress program. Many of these are small and rural lenders that serve small businesses in remote areas. As an additional measure, the SBA will open up the program to other lenders across the country experienced in small business lending but that have not participated with SBA.

To meet the needs of new and startup small businesses requiring smaller loan products, SBA will offer certain incentives to lenders to increase the availability of smaller loans, especially loans of $50,000 or less. At the same time, SBA will raise the maximum limit of an SBAExpress loan to $250,000, from $150,000, to allow more small business borrowers to take advantage of the program's expedited loan process.

The program, which is aimed at simplifying access to SBA loan products, allows lenders to use their own forms and processes to approve loans guaranteed by SBA. Minimal paperwork is required for the SBA, and the agency generally provides an immediate response on most SBAExpress applications. SBA encourages the use of technology to expedite the loan process.

"The program is innovative in its approach to providing delivery mechanisms for SBA-guaranteed loans to suit the specific needs of a diverse array of small businesses," SBA Administrator Hector V. Barreto said. "The agency has looked at new ways to work with its lending partners in order to expand service to small business borrowers and provide greater capital access opportunities.

"These enhancements will expand the program's reach to more small businesses and represent a major step in the agency's continuing efforts to increase efficiency and better meet the needs of both its lending partners and small business owners."

For additional information about SBA lending programs visit the SBA web site at http://www.sba.gov, or contact local SBA, SCORE, or SBDC offices.

EXHIBIT C - MONEY PROCUREMENT

There are numerous sources of information on how to construct a business plan and an present the request for business capital. See the resources presented in Addendum II that accompanies this book. Also refer to America's Business Funding Directory at http://www.businessfinance.com to locate "Potential Funding Sources" that are offering the type and criteria of capital being sought. America's Business Funding Directory, http://www.businessfinance.com. Gather as much information as possible and then embark on preparation of the plan.

Businesses Need Capital

Successful businesses are well planned and well capitalized. Being well capitalized, is having the ability to access capital when you need it. Being well planned, will help you to be well capitalized. This book is designed as a workbook to assist in planning and ultimately to result in sound capitalization.

Entrepreneurs often miss good opportunities because they believe the cost of capital is too high. Excess time is spent negotiating over the cost of money, while the window of opportunity goes by. Try to cut a good arrangement, but the cost of capital should be considered along with the losses sustained by not having it. Simply, if it costs one dollar in order to make two, are you ahead or behind?

The follow material addresses:

1. What information to present to Lenders or Investors;
2. How to package the request in order to get attention;
3. The format a presentation package should take; and
4. Where to find the Funding Source to provide the capital.

Statistics show that 90% of all new businesses fail. This is usually a direct result of the failure to plan effectively. Entrepreneurs cannot be successful if they are a "loner" but solid preparation and relationships can make business plan development and capital acquisition much easier and can increase the odds of success.

The topics presented herein are as follows:

1. Plan for Success - Executive Summary, History, Stage, Structure...
2. Management - Ownership, Management, Consultants...
3. Strategic Position - Nature of Market, Specific Niche...
4. Market Strategy - Market penetration, market domination...
5. Set Goals - Every successful business has set goals...
6. Competition - Why are you better, smarter, faster, cheaper...
7. Amount Requested - Present a supported overview...
8. The Terms - Know what you are looking for and can afford...
9. Use of Funds - R&D, start-up costs, advertising, be specific...
10. Repayment Plan - Massive sales, sell the business, go public...
11. Pro Forma Financial Projections - Don't do the math, you won't get the money...
12. Preparing the Presentation - The format and additional information...
13. Type of Capital Desired - Debt, equity, asset based, venture...
14. Find a Funding Source - America's Business Funding Directory...
15. The Internet Factor - If your not there, you're already behind...
16. Negotiating the Deal - First learn to say "No", then...

"Nothing is quite so embarrassing as watching someone do what you told them couldn't be done."

1. *Plan For Success*

Capitalizing a business is a full time endeavor. Developing a business plan is the single most important step to be taken toward success. To maximize potential to receive capital, it is vital that a business plan be developed that will guide the company and allow outsiders to picture where the business is going and how it will get there. Take great care in preparing the plan, it is the road map that will lead the company to wherever it wants to go.

Lenders or Investors, which way to go? They tend to look at transactions from very different perspectives. Lenders are concerned with "Can the company repay?" While investors are more interested in "How far can the firm go?" Some information is common to both and will be the information disclosed at the start.

Executive Summary

Get interest at this point and the odds of success are improved markedly. This summary is an overview description of the product or service, its market, the niche, the management, the mission, company structure, pro forma highlights, funding request, use of funds and proposed terms. No more than two pages, sell the sizzle not the steak.

EXECUTIVE SUMMARY WORK SECTION

Give a brief yet concise explanation of the following items. Remember, details and support for each of these will be presented later in the plan, so keep it short.

Desired Amount: _____

Desired Terms: _____

Company Name: _____

Industry Type: _____

Time in Business: _____

Principals: _____

Use of Funds: _____

Collateral Offered: _____

Narrative. Briefly describe what your company is all about.

History. The reader needs a summary of how this venture came to be. Where did the idea come from? How did it evolve? Who is responsible? Be concise; give dates, background, etc. Paint a short picture from how you started, to where you are today.

Mission Statement. One sentence defining what the company is all about. Think about it and *"make it mean something"*. Don't just write a bunch of flowery words.

Stage. Clearly identify what stage of funding the firm is at. Is the business a start-up, initial growth, positioning for going public, seeking a strategic partner, looking for near future acquisition or sale?

Market Niche. It is important for any funding source to know where the company fits in the economic food chain. What niche is the business exploiting that will make it jump over the competition? What it the company doing that is better, faster, or newer than what everyone else is doing? For this part details are needed. Remember the investors know nothing about the business. One must prove to them that an individual knows what is being done or what the firm's focus is.

Market Research. This is the research that supports a determination that there is a market and a need for the product or service. This will form the backbone of support for the price points and revenue assumptions contained in the pro forma projections indicating to investors or lenders how the company can turn a substantial profit.

Financial Overview. Here is where briefly highlights, graphics and preview of outstanding financial projections are made. This provides a glimpse into where gross sales, net income, net worth, etc. should be in years one, two and three. Remember this is only an overview. It should contain no details

618

or support information. That will come later in the financial pro forma section.

"Business is the art of extracting money from another person's pocket without resorting to violence."

2. Management

Funding Sources are going to want to know with whom they are dealing. Important issues become; what are the qualifications, experience, goals and most of all the character of those in the management of this venture?

Personal. Lenders and Investors are both concerned with whether or not the company has what it takes to be successful. Highlight information that demonstrates that management has the ability to make this business a success. Detail education, past successes or failures that made the management stronger. Indicate how the business was started and what will make it a success.

Character. Who is management? Take a deep look inside. Character is not only about winning. It's about getting up again and again when management has been knocked down. Will they panic in a crisis? Will they run for cover when things get rough? Are they the Captain that brings the ship in against all odds? Character is staying power!

To be a successful entrepreneur you must not only be able to start well, but you have to be able to finish strong. For most, running a business is a hard road and not an easy one. Search your soul. If you don't have this kind of character, do yourself and others a favor and don't even start.

Management. Good management is essential. Funding Sources desire to see that the company understands the market and has the skills to succeed. Are you a stand alone player, or are there others helping you? If alone, do you plan to keep it that way? Who will comprise your management team? Give detailed resumes of all those involved, along with a description of the vital roles they will play in the business' success. If your management skills or your team is weak, take on the task of building it up in order to support your own success, as well as the success of your funding request.

Third Party Professionals. Listen to "GOOD" advice, and forget "BAD" counsel. Carefully seek out and select professionals who can help. Do homework in advance of the need to avoid delays. These legal, financial, tax, marketing, etc., professionals may be willing to advise the company for a piece of the glory to come or can act as consultants once you have the money to pay them.

Survivorship. What plans have been made to ensure the business will continue to survive without certain management? Have others been trained take over? Is there going to be key man insurance in place for the possibility of illness, disability or death? Without you, can the business continue to survive? Describe how the management team will step up and work the plan.

"The closest to perfection a person ever comes is when they fill out their resume."

3. Strategic Position

Assume that your reader knows nothing. Even if you know they are experts, remember that the Lenders or Investors want to see that you know more about the industry and your market than they do.

Market Overview.
General industry definition
Current size and demand
Potential target market
Potential market growth
Market share of competitors
Technical evaluation of industry
Direction of industry
Current condition of industry

Market Approach.
Initial plan to obtain a market share

Resources available or allocated to market penetration
Clearly defined long range market strategy
Support assumptions on ability to hold market share

Market Analysis.

Who are the customers?

	Percentage of Business
Private sector	_____
Wholesalers	_____
Retailers	_____
Government	_____
Other	_____

We will target customers by:

Product lines or services	_____
Geographic area	_____
Sales	_____

Feasibility.

How successful will the product or service be?

What is the total potential market?

Is there really a market at all?

Does the company have the strength to get the job done?

Let outsiders know why this will work and be able to support what the beliefs are!

Product Protection. What measures have been taken or will be taken to insure the proprietary nature of the product? Patents, Trademarks, Copyrights, Trade Secrets, Proprietary Contracts, etc.

Product or Service Analysis. If the product or service is of a proprietary nature, take steps to protect it. Have a non-disclosure/non-circumvent agreement for partners or investors to sign. **Keep it simple.** If it is too long or contains too many legal words, no one will sign it.

What is the product/service and what does it do?

What advantages does the product/service have over those of the competition?

What are the unique features, patents, expertise, etc.?

What disadvantages does the product or service have?

Where will the materials and supplies come from?

Outside Factors. List the important economic factors that will affect the product or service. Consider things such as country growth, industry health, economic trends, rising prices, etc.:

What are the legal factors that will affect the market?

What are the government factors?

What factors, that cannot be controlled, will affect the market?

Commercial Viability. Look for outside opinions on the commercial prospects of your product or service. There are numerous low cost or no cost organizations, such as retired executives or small business network groups to run your ideas by.

"Business is like an automobile. It won't run by itself, except downhill." Henry Ford

4. Market Strategy

If you don't know where you are going and how you will get there, you are already lost.

Market Position. What kind of image do you have? Are you; inexpensive, exclusive, customer service oriented, high quality, convenience, or fast?

List the features you will emphasize:

What pricing strategy will you use?

% Markup on cost	_____
Competitive	_____
Below competition	_____

Premium price   _____
Are your prices in line with your image?
What is the percentage of profit margin have you allowed for?
What customer services will you provide?
What are your sales/credit terms?
Advertising/Promotion. Write a short paragraph that best describes your business:
What advertising/promotion sources will you use?

Television	_____
Radio	_____
Direct mail	_____
Internet	_____
Magazines	_____
Newspaper	_____
Personal contacts	_____
Trade associations	_____
Yellow Pages	_____
Other	_____

What are the reasons you consider the chosen media to be the most effective?
What features will you promote?

Applications	_____
Price	_____
Performance	_____
Delivery	_____
Reputation	_____
Service	_____
Exclusive	_____
Components	_____
Colors	_____
Sizes	_____
Uses	_____
Rugged	_____
Design	_____
Availability	_____
Installation	_____
Terms	_____
Workmanship	_____
Other	_____

What rationale will you appeal to?

Accurate Performance	_____
Increased Profits	_____
Economy of Purchase	_____
Increased Production	_____
Durability	_____
Labor Saving	_____
Economy of Use	_____
Time-Saving	_____
Simple Construction	_____
Simple Operation	_____
Ease of Repair	_____
Ease of Installation	_____
Space Saving	_____

Other _____

What buying motive hot buttons will you use?

- Bigger Savings _____
- Increased Sales _____
- Greater Profits _____
- Reduced Cost _____
- Time Saved _____
- Prestige _____
- Greater Convenience _____
- Uniform Production _____
- Economy of Use _____
- Reduced Upkeep _____
- Continuous Output _____
- Leadership _____
- Ease of Use _____
- Reduced Inventory _____
- Low Operating Cost _____
- Simplicity _____
- Reduced Waste _____
- Long Life _____
- Other _____

What emotional responses can you use to your benefit?

- Pride of Appearance _____
- Pride of Ownership _____
- Desire of Prestige _____
- Desire for Security _____
- Desire for Recognition _____
- Desire to Imitate _____
- Desire to be Unique _____
- Desire for Variety _____
- Fear _____
- Desire to Create _____
- Convenience _____
- Curiosity _____
- Other _____

Initial Market Penetration. How long will it take? What capital resources will be required to acquire the initial share?

"Doing business without advertising is like winking at a girl in the dark, you know what your doing, but nobody else does."

5. Set goals

Written short and long-term goals is one attribute of all successful entrepreneurs.

Benchmarks/Milestones. These are critical development stages the company has set to meet. Without these visible and obtainable milestones your company and your investors may lose their way. What are the first ten priority items to be accomplished as soon as your company gets the money? How long should it take to complete them?

Priority   Time

1._____ _____

2._____ _____

3._____ _____

4._____   _____
5._____   _____
6._____   _____
7._____   _____
8._____   _____
9._____   _____
10._____   _____

Short Term. Near future...One year success points. Define levels of projected success that must be obtained in order to allow the pro forma to come true. Establish obtainable goals that will show investors how the company will reach goals.

Long Term. Lenders/Investors don't know the company vision. Define it them. This is the written series of events that will occur in the next five years that are depicted in the pro forma.

Exit Strategy. Funding Sources want to know how the will recover their investment. Will the business generate a cash flow large enough to support the debt? Is the product or service demand such that the company will go public? Answers to these questions and more will not only help determine success, but also narrow the search for a lender most likely to fund the company.

Personal. While personal goals may not matter to potential Lenders or Investors, they do matter to management and the company. Define personal goals, discuss them with your family and take time to find out what business associates expect of you.

"Building a business is no small task. It will affect all parts of your life, so consider well what you do." J. Corey Pierce

Competition

Know the competition. They can help or bury a business.

Complementary Products. Identify and analyze companies that offer competitive or related products. Define those that offer complementary products in the same or similar industries. Explain how competitive relationships can be turned into joint ventures, strategic partnerships, buyouts, acquisitions, etc. in the future. Lenders or Investors like to know what the possible exit solutions are if things don't go as planned.

Who are your three major competitors?

Competitor #1 _____

Address   _____

               _____

Years in Business   _____
Market Share   _____
Price/Strategy   _____
Product/Service   _____
Advantages/Disadvantages:

Competitor #2 _____

Address   _____

               _____

Years in Business   _____
Market Share   _____
Price/Strategy   _____
Product/Service   _____
Advantages/Disadvantages:

Competitor #3 _____

Address _____

_____

Years in Business   _____
Market Share   _____
Price/Strategy   _____
Product/Service   _____
Advantages/Disadvantages:

Compare the company's strengths and weaknesses with competition's. Consider such things as location, size of resources, reputation, services, personnel, etc.

Strengths:

Weaknesses:

Current Market Share. It is vital to demonstrate a solid understanding of the industry. Where is the industry going?

What is the current condition of the industry?

Why are the current market distributions the way they are?

What has competition done to achieve their market share?

What advertising media is most effectively used by the competition?

Trade Associations. Give a reference to all trade associations that cover the industry. Use material supplied by these organizations to support statements and assumptions made in the funding request. List trade associations that service the industry of interest.

"Efficient executives find machines that can do half their work, and then buy two."

7. Amount Requested

Conservative Request. It is extremely important that financial projections fully support the amount of funds sought. If debt financing is preferred – say so. Lenders dislike continuous requests for more capital due to poor estimates of need. This is a reflection of poor management and can result is loss of investors.

Downside Planning. Plan for the downside. It is better to over estimate capital requirements than to run short and be forced to go hat in hand back for more.

Supportable Assumptions. Both Lenders and Investors want to know that estimated costs and revenue are reasonable. The financial pro forma should include detailed information and trade references on the costs of each expense listed.

Association Documentation. In income projections include Trade Industry support information or other market information that lends credibility to conclusions drawn. Most associations publish reports of standard industry costs, margins and financial ratios.

8. *The Terms*

Know what the wants are, what can be afforded and what can be given up.

How Long? This should be based on the financial pro forma or useful life of the asset being financed. Receivable and contract financing are less than 12 months, equipment normally one to five years, real estate and other long-term assets 5 to 20 years.

Amortized versus Interest Only. Most ventures require some time before making money. New equipment or other acquired assets take time to begin paying for themselves. Think about an initial period of interest only or skip payments to offset lack of cash flow.

Interest Rate. Profitablility is directly affected by the rate paid for needed capital. However, it it is necessary to pay 50% interest for 100% profitability it may be okay.

Fixed or Adjustable. A fixed rate of interest is a known. Adjustable rates are subject to the future and are unknown. Normal is Prime plus one to three percent or LIBOR (London Index) plus three to five percent. Rates vary as you add or subtract risk.

Points and Fees. Most, if not all, funding sources charge points (percentage of amount funded) and fees (costs of putting your transaction together). These can run from 1% to 10% depending on terms of the arrangement and the degree of risk. Fees are sometimes payable 50% at commitment and 50% at closing. Try to get 100% at closing or at least deposit the 50% into a trust or escrow account. Beware of those sources that require money from the company before they put up money. Always consult Legal Counsel.

Prepayment Penalties. Funding sources spend time, energy and money selecting deals to invest in. Once they lend or invest they want to stick with it. Pre-payment penalties are one way to insure that funds are left in place. Try to negotiate these away, or limit them to one or two years.

Blanket & Specific Liens. Blanket means "all". Specific is just that. Blanket liens will restrict ability to raise cash in the future. Always attempt to have specific liens. Don't let them have blanket!

Personal Guarantees. How committed is the person seeking money? If the person seeking money will not sign personally, an investor may not provide the capital. If the person seeking money does not believe in their own success, why should anyone else? As success is achieved personal guarantees should be released.

Covenants & Conditions. Be very careful. These spell out just what can and cannot do. No management or ownership change, quarterly filing requirements, no borrowing from anyone else, deposits maintained, collateral pledges, etc. Carefully read and evaluate the fine print. Seek legal review and assistance.

% Ownership to be Offered. What's fair? 80%, 50%, 20%... only the person requesting money knows; define, support and defend the request. While most lenders won't ask, most investors will demand. Be prepared by doing homework on potential funding sources and know what the company or idea is worth.

Stock Repurchase Agreement? What happens if incompatibility arises with the investor? Are the parties committed forever? Try to negotiate escape clauses that will allow a way out if a need arises and what is the cost of terminating a relationship. Be able to buy stock back at a predetermined price, if possible.

Management Controls? Most entrepreneurs are in business to make decisions for themselves. Some investors desire a partnership. Once again, pre-plan, know what is needed and wanted. They are not the same. What can be given up?

Collateral Anyone? What level of risk is acceptable? Lack of personal believe means others will also not believe.

Accounts Receivable

Contracts

Equipment
Inventory
Marketable Securities, CD's, T-Bills
Purchase Orders
Real Estate
Patents
Name Recognition
OP (Other Peoples Investment; Family, Friends, etc.)

"No business opportunity is ever lost. If you lose it, your competitor will find it."

9. Use of Funds

Entrepreneurs tend to spend too much time looking for money and not enough time making it. This problem stems from the lack of adequate pre-planning given to the initial use of funds. In order to determine what short and long term capital needs are going to be, accurate financial projections are rquired. Those projections must consider:

- Immediate Need For Capital (Bills to pay)
- Research and Development (Estimate, then double)
- Capital Asset Acquisition (Required equipment, etc.)
- Inventory Floor Planning (Necessary raw materials)
- Working Capital Requirements (Payroll, payables, etc.)
- Market Penetration (When will the cash flow begin)

The cash flow model is the best tool for determining what capital needs will be. Don't be overly optimistic or conservative. Know what factors will affect projections to the downside, (sales, costs, price breaks, etc.). Work closely with third parties, financial advisors, accountants, industry consultants, retired executives, etc., to keep from having tunnel vision and missing the big picture. The cash flow model should be month-to-month for one year and quarterly for the next four years.

"Anyone who thinks the customer isn't right, should try doing without them for ninety days."

10. Repayment Plan

Repayment is tied directly to success. In order to repay a Funding Source, it is necessary to clearly define how and how much money is going to be made.

R&D Requirements. How much research and development remains before market entry? Does the product require regulatory approval? What about manufacture? What is the timetable? What delays are foreseeable that could affect the timetable? Are there any alternative plans if tests, approvals, patents, licenses, etc., don't go as planned?

Break Even Analysis. Exactly when will it be achieved? How much product must be sold; 10 or 10,000 units? What effect will price breaks have? Can the salespeople survive on the commission structure? What about material price increases? This is one way to demonstrate a knowledge of the product, market, costs and the industry.

Current or Projected Debt Coverage Ratio. Remember 1.25 to 1. For lenders if net income is below 1.25 to 1, it may mean no loan, a higher rate or more collateral. It is a reflection of ability to service debt. Net income should be 1.25 times higher than the debt payment committed to. Analyze the debt coverage ratio and be sure the projection is much higher. If it is not reconsider the business commitment or plan.

Investors, no debt, are concerned about profit margins and retained earnings. The projections should support ratios of better than 2.0 to 1 to generate serious investor interest.

Amortization or Dividend.
>Return on investment
>Return of investment

These are terms all funding sources want to know. What is the projected timetable for an investor to get their investment back? When does the return on the investment start?

Pre-Planning. Arrange for funding before it is needed. Entrepreneurs are famous for seeking capital in a crisis. When the need is great (payroll, taxes, sales drop, etc.) rates seem to go up or capital is not available. Forecast capital requirements at least six months in advance.

"Good entrepreneurs hire optimists as salesmen and pessimists to run the credit department"

11. Pro Forma Financials

Projection Information. Being able to present a clear, concise, logical and supportable financial projection is probably the most important key to having a chance of obtaining the capital you desire. If you don't have financial forecast ability, hire someone who does. Have your pro forma give a month-by-month breakdown for the first year and then annually for the next four years. Include and fully support:

>Sales Estimates
>Administrative Costs
>Production Costs
>Sales Costs
>Capital Expenditures
>Gross Margin by Product Line
>Sales Increase by Product Line
>Interest Rates on Debts
>Income Tax Rate
>Accounts Receivable Collection Plan
>Accounts Payable Schedule
>Inventory Turnover
>Depreciation Schedules
>Usefulness of Assets

The Income Statement (Profit & Loss). The income projection enables the owner/manager to develop a preview of the amount of income generated each month and for the business year, based on reasonable predictions of monthly levels of sales, costs and expenses.

1. Total Net Sales (Revenues). Determine the total number of units of products or services realistically expected to be sold each month in each department at the expected prices. Use this step to create the projections to review pricing practices. What returns, allowances and markdowns can be expected?

2. Costs of Sales. The key to accurately calculating cost of sales is not to overlook any costs that have been incurred. Calculate the cost of sale of all products and services used to determine total net sales. Where inventory is involved, remember transportation costs and any direct labor.

3. Gross Profit. Subtract the total cost of sales from the total net sales to obtain gross profit.

4. Gross Profit Margin. The gross profit is expressed as a percentage of total sales (revenues). It is calculated by dividing the gross profits by the total net sales.

5. Controllable Expenses.
   a. Salary expenses - Base pay plus overtime.
   b. Payroll expenses - Include paid vacations, sick leave, health insurance, unemployment insurance and social security taxes (employer paid portion).
   c. Outside services - Include costs of subcontracts, overflow work and special or one-time services.

d. Supplies - Services and items purchased for use in the business.
e. Repair and maintenance - Regular maintenance and repair, including periodic large expenditures such as painting.
f. Advertising - Include desired sales volume and classified directory advertising expenses.
g. Car delivery and travel - Include charges if personal car is used in business, including parking, tools, buying trips, etc.
h. Accounting and legal - Outside professional services.
i. Dues and subscriptions.
j. Utilities.

6. Fixed Expenses
a. Rent -- List only real estate used in business.
b. Depreciation -- Amortization of capital assets.
c. Insurance -- Fire or liability on property or products. Include workers' compensation.
d. Loan repayments -- Interest on outstanding loans.
e. Licenses and permits.
f. Miscellaneous -- Unspecified; small expenditures without separate accounts.

7. Net Profit (or Loss)
(before taxes) - Subtract total expenses from gross profit. Taxes - Include inventory and sales tax, excise tax, real estate tax, etc.
(after taxes) - Subtract taxes from net profit (before taxes)

Income Projection Worksheet

Revenue Projection

Total net sales (TNS)	$_____
Costs of sales (COS)	$_____
Gross profit (TNS-COS=GP)	$_____
Gross Profit margin (GP/TNS)	_____%

Controllable expenses

Salaries/wages	$_____
Payroll expenses	$_____
Legal/accounting	$_____
Advertising	$_____
Automobile	$_____
Office supplies	$_____
Dues/Subscriptions	$_____
Utilities	$_____
Other	$_____

Fixed Expenses

Rent	$_____
Depreciation	$_____
Insurance	$_____
License/permits	$_____
Loan payments	$_____
Other	$_____

Total expenses	$_____
Net profit (loss) before taxes (GP-Expenses)	$_____
Taxes	$_____

Net profit (loss) after taxes $_____

This form should be used to project month-to-month income and expenses for year one and then to provide annual projections for the next four years.

The Balance Sheet

Assets

List anything of value that is owned or legally due the business. Total assets include all net values. These are the amounts derived when you subtract depreciation and amortization from the original costs of acquiring the assets.

Current Assets

Cash - List cash and resources that can be converted into cash within 12 months of the date of the balance sheet (or during one established cycle of operation). Include money on hand and demand deposits in the bank, e.g., checking accounts and regular savings accounts.

Petty cash - If your business has a fund for small miscellaneous expenditures, include the total here.

Accounts receivable - The amounts due from customers in payment for merchandise or services.

Inventory - Includes raw materials on hand, work in progress and all finished goods, either manufactured or purchased for resale.

Short-term investments - Also called temporary investments or marketable securities, these include interest - or dividend yielding holdings expected to be converted into cash within a year. List stocks and bonds, certificates of deposit and time-deposit savings accounts at either their costs or market value, whichever is less.

Prepaid expenses - Goods, benefits or services a business buys or rents in advance. Examples are office supplies, insurance protection and floor space.

Long-term Investments - Also called long-term assets, these are holdings the business intends to keep for at least a year and that typically yield interest or dividends. Included are stocks, bonds and savings accounts earmarked for special purposes.

Fixed Assets

Also called plant and equipment. Includes all resources a business owns or acquires for use in operations and not intended for resale. Fixed assets may be leased. Depending on the leasing arrangements, both the value and the liability of the leased property may need to be listed on the balance sheet.

- Land - List original purchase price without allowances for market value.
- Buildings
- Improvements (Including leasehold improvements)
- Equipment
- Furniture
- Automobile/vehicles

Liabilities

Current Liabilities

List all debts, monetary obligations and claims payable within 12 months or within one cycle of operation. Typically they include:

- Accounts payable - Amounts owed to suppliers for goods and services purchased in connection with business operations.
- Notes payable - The balance of principal due to pay off short-term debt for borrowed funds. Also includes, the current amount due of total balance on notes whose terms exceed 12 months.
- Interest payable - Any accrued fees due for use of both short-and long-term

629

borrowed capital and credit extended to the business.

- Taxes payable - Amounts estimated by an accountant to have been incurred during the accounting period.

Payroll accrual - Salaries and wages currently owed.

Long-term Liabilities

Notes payable - List notes, contract payments or mortgage payments due over a period exceeding 12 months or one cycle of operation. They are listed by outstanding balance less the current position due.

Net Worth

Also called owner's equity, net worth is the claim of the owner(s) on the assets of the business. In a proprietorship or partnership, equity is each owner's original investment plus any earnings after withdrawals. In a corporation it is the capital investment paid for the issuance of stock, plus the surplus paid in by the principals, and the after tax retained earnings.

Total Liabilities and Net Worth

The sum of these two amounts must always match that for total assets.

The Balance Sheet Worksheet   As of _____, 20___

Assets

Current Assets (Net Values)

Cash	$_____
Petty cash	$_____
Accounts receivable	$_____
Inventory	$_____
Short-term investment	$_____
Prepaid expenses	$_____

Long-term investments $_____

Fixed assets

Land	$_____
Buildings	$_____
Improvements	$_____
Equipment	$_____
Furniture	$_____
Automobile/vehicles	$_____

Other Assets

1.	$_____
2.	$_____
3.	$_____

Total Assets $_____

Liabilities

Current Liabilities (within 12 months)

Accounts payable	$_____
Notes payable	$_____
Interest payable	$_____

Taxes Payable

Federal income tax	$_____
State income tax	$_____
Self-employment tax	$_____
Sales tax (SBE)	$_____

Property tax	$_____
Payroll accrual	$_____
Long-term liabilities (over 12 months)	
Notes payable	$_____
Total Liabilities	$_____
Net worth (owner equity)	$_____
If Proprietorship or Partnership	
(name's) equity	$_____
(name's) equity	$_____
(name's) equity	$_____
(name's) equity	$_____
If Corporation	
Capital stock	$_____
Surplus paid in	$_____
Retained earnings	$_____

Total Net Worth $_____

Total Liabilities and Total Net Worth $_____

(Total assets will always equal total liabilities and total net worth)

Cash Flow Projections. Having a model of how much cash it is going to take and when that cash must be available, is just like having a road map. Detailed first year cash flow projections, followed by a summary overview of how the next four years will flow, are a must.

1. Cash on hand (beginning of month) $_____
Cash on hand same as (7), Cash position, and previous month.

2. Cash receipts –

(a) Cash sales   All cash sales. $_____
Omit credit sales unless cash is actually received.

(b) Collections from credit accounts $_____
Amount to be expected from all accounts.

(c) Loan or other cash injection $_____
Indicate here all cash injections not shown in 2(a) or 2(b) above.

3. Total cash receipts (2a+2b+2c=3) $_____
4. Total cash available (before cash out)(1+3) $_____

5. Cash paid out –

(a) Purchases (merchandise) $_____
Merchandise for resale or for use in product (paid for in current month).

(b) Gross wages (excluding withdrawals) $_____
Base pay plus overtime.

(c) Payroll expenses (taxes, etc.) $_____
Include paid vacations, paid sick leave, health insurance, unemployment insurance, social security (employer portion). These might be 10 to 45% of 5(b).

(d) Outside services $_____

(e) Supplies (office and operating) $_____
Items purchased for use in the business (not for resale).

(f) Repairs and maintenance $_____
Include periodic large expenditures such as painting or decorating.

(g) Advertising $_____
This amount should be adequate to maintain sales volume.

(h) Car, delivery and travel $_____

(i) Accounting and legal $_____

(j) Rent $_____

Real estate only (See 5(p) for other rentals).

(k) Telephone $_____

(l) Utilities $_____

(m) Insurance $_____

Coverage on business property and products (fire, liability); also worker's compensation, fidelity, etc. Exclude executive life (include in 5(w)).

(n) Taxes (real estate, etc.) $_____

Plus inventory tax, sales tax, excise tax, if applicable.

(o) Interest $_____

Interest on loans as it is injected (See 2(c)).

(p) Other expenses (specify each) $_____

Unexpected expenditures may be included here.

Equipment expenses during the month should be included here (non-capital equipment). When equipment is rented or leased, record payments here.

(q) Miscellaneous (unspecified) $_____

Small expenditures for which separate accounts would be practical.

(r) Subtotal $_____

This subtotal indicates cash out for operating costs.

(s) Loan principal payment $_____

Include payment on all loans, including vehicle and equipment purchases on time payment.

(t) Capital purchases (specify) $_____

Non-expensed (depreciable) expenditures such as equipment, building purchases on time payment, leasehold improvements, etc.

(u) Other start-up costs $_____

Expenses incurred prior to first month projection and paid for after start-up.

(v) Reserve and/or escrow (specify) $_____

Example: insurance, tax or equipment escrow to reduce impact of large periodic payments

(w) Owner's withdrawals $_____

Should include payment for such things as owner's income tax, social security, health insurance, executive life insurance premiums, etc.

6. Total cash paid out (5a through 5w) $_____

7. Cash position (end on month) (4 minus 6) $_____

Enter this amount in (1) Cash on hand following month

Essential operating data (non-cash flow information)

This is basic information necessary for proper planning and for proper cash flow projection. Also with this data, the cash flow can be evolved and shown in the above form.

A. Sales volume (dollars) $_____

This is a very important figure and should be estimated carefully, taking into account size of facility and employee output as well as realistic anticipated sales (actual sales, not orders received).

B. Accounts receivable (end of month) $_____

Previous unpaid credit sales plus current month's credit sales, less amounts received current month (deduct "C" below).

C. Bad debt (end on month) $_____

Bad debts should be subtracted from (B) in the month anticipated.

D. Inventory on hand (end on month) $_____

Last month's inventory plus merchandise received and/or manufactured current month minus account sold current month.

E. Accounts payable (end of month) $_____

Previous month's payable plus current month's payable minus amount paid during month.

F. Depreciation $_____

Established by your accountant, or value of all your equipment divided by useful life (in months) as allowed by Internal Revenue Service.

Monthly Cash Flow Projection Worksheet

1. Cash on hand (beginning month) $_____
2. Cash Receipts $_____
2. (a)   Cash sales $_____
   (b)   Collections from credit accounts $_____
   (c)   Loan or other cash injections (specify) $_____
3. Total cash receipts $_____
4. Total cash available (before cash out)(1+2+3) $_____
5. Cash paid out $_____
   (a)   Purchases (merchandise) $_____
   (b)   Gross wages (excludes withdrawals) $_____
   (c)   Payroll expenses (taxes, etc.) $_____
   (d)   Outside services $_____
   (e)   Supplies (office and operating) $_____
   (f)   Repairs and maintenance $_____
   (g)   Advertising $_____
   (h)   Car, delivery and travel $_____
   (i)   Accounting and legal $_____
   (j)   Rent $_____
   (k)   Telephone $_____
   (l)   Utilities $_____
   (m)   Insurance $_____
   (n)   Taxes (real estate, etc.) $_____
   (o)   Interest $_____
   (p)   Other expenses (specify each) $_____
   (q)   Miscellaneous (unspecified) $_____
   (r)   Subtotal $_____
   (s)   Loan principal payment $_____
   (t)   Capital purchases (specify) $_____
   (u)   Other start-up costs $_____
   (v)   Reserve and/or escrow (specify) $_____
   (w)   Owner's withdrawal $_____
6. Total cash paid out (5a through 5w) $_____
7. Cash position (end of month)(4 minus 6) $_____

Essential operating data (non-cash flow information)

A. Sales volume (dollars) $_____
B. Accounts receivable (end of month) $_____
C. Bad debt (end of month) $_____
D. Inventory on hand (end of month) $_____
E. Accounts payable (end of month) $_____
F. Depreciation (in months) $_____

Key Indicators and Ratios. Being able to summarize important financial points allows the Lender/Investor insight into whether or not the requestor understands how the money world operates. Provide support for: sales revenue, price points, fixed costs, gross margins, and net income. The financial industry judges potential success by RMA (a lending trade association) standards and ratios. If not well understood ask an accountant to calculate the following ratios:

Current Ratio (1 to 1 or better)   Current
    assets divided by current liabilities.

Quick Ratio (0.5 to 1 or better)   Current
    assets less inventory divided by current liabilities.

Debt to Worth Ratio (3 to 1 or better)   Creditors
    capital to owners capital.

Gross Profit Margin (60% or better)
    Gross sales less cost of goods sold.

Net Profit Margin (10% or better)
    Gross sales to net income.

Debt Coverage Ratio (1.25 to 1 or better)
    Net income divided by debt payment (Principal & Interest).

A/R Turnover Ration (as close to 12 as possible)
Gross Sales divided by accounts receivable.

"SIC" Standard Industrial Code (know yours)

Lenders will compare the business ratios to those of other businesses in the industry. There are many good computer financial programs available to assist in formatting projections. Seek the services of someone who is computer literate if necessary. Once the numbers have been estimated have an accountant look them over.

"I can't be out of money, I still have checks." A Great Bumper Sticker

12. Preparing Your Presentation

Carefully prepare all items cited above. The party seeking funding usually gets one shot per funding source, so make it the best possible.

Have Additional Information Packaged and Ready

    Schedule of Assets
    Personal Financial Statements
    Credit Report Releases
    Business Tax Returns
    Personal Tax Returns
    Articles of Incorporation
    Copies of Orders or Invoices
    Customer Testimonials
    Trade References
    Banking References
    Title Reports (equipment, real estate, etc.)
    Asset Appraisals
    Patents, Trademarks or Licenses

Presentation

    First impressions are lasting, make a good one.
    Use a color product brochure as a cover.
    Bind the material in such a way that allows for easy reading.
    Tab each section for direct access.
    Keep information concise and to the point.
    Pictures are worth a thousand words, include good ones.
    Support assumptions with facts, not more assumptions.

"Education is learning from teachers and books. Experience is learning from your mistakes."
George Miller, My Grand Father

13. Type of Capital Desired

Debt Versus Equity. Debt funding is normally cheaper and easier to find than equity funding. Debt typically carries the burden of monthly payments, whether or not positive cash flow exists.

Equity investors expect little or no return in the early stages, but require much more extensive reporting as to the company's progress. They have invested on the gamble of very high returns. Therefore, investors anticipate that goals and milestones will be met.

Debt financing is usually available to all types of businesses. Equity is generally restricted to businesses with fast and very high growth potential.

Debt Considerations.

> For what type of debt financing can the company qualify?
>
> How much debt can be afforded?
>
> Can payments be made if cash flow is off?
>
> What happens if interest rates rise?
>
> Can company and personal assets be pledged?
>
> What about a personal guarantee?
>
> Debt lending is more analytical than personal. Are the ratios right? Who has the assets? How is personal credit history?

Equity Considerations.

> What type of investors are to be targeted?
>
> Can control and future profits be shared?
>
> Is it acceptable to have investors as partners forever?
>
> How much of a share can be given up?
>
> Can required reports be made?
>
> What about disclosing company secrets to potential investors?
>
> Investors will want to take a much larger share of a start-up venture, than they will of a company with a two or three year track record of success.

Angels. Angels are individual private investors who make up a large portion of "informal" venture capital. These investors usually keep their money close to home (50 miles or so). They tend to invest small amounts ($25,000 to $250,000), and they can be difficult to locate because they usually don't belong to networks or trade associations.

Angels are found among friends, family, customers, third party professionals, suppliers, brokers and competitors. For the most part, once they invest in two or three deals they are out of money. There are a few private investor-locating services available. Beware of those who charge large ($1,000 or more) advance fees in order to identify an investor. Do homework, check these people out and negotiate a commission if a request is placed.

> *Caution: Don't advertise in the local paper for investors until discussing the opportunity with a securities attorney to avoid any SEC issues.*

Venture Capital. These investors are out looking for huge returns not just good ones. Venture capital is extremely hard to get and the competition is fierce. These funding sources get thousands of requests each year and only invest in three or four.

The managers who invest these funds are great at finding oysters that will produce pearls. They usually are very bright, well educated and extremely arrogant. Tread lightly, exhaust all other capital sources and be well prepared for the negotiation process.

Joint Ventures/Strategic Partnerships. A personal favorite. This is where two companies with parallel interests get together based on their mutual needs:

> * Money vs. plan
>
> * Product vs. distributors.
>
> * Seek companies with parallel interests. This requires much more research than simply asking for a loan. Most of these partners will settle for 20% to 40% equity in a company. Be careful to protect ideas by having any potential partners sign a non-circumvention document.

Small Business Administration (SBA). A tremendous resource, but the paperwork can be tiring. This is a great place to look. The SBA has many different programs. Local banks should have an SBA loan officer who can explain them. The most aggressive SBA lending sources nationwide are AT&T Capital, The Money Store and GE Capital, look them up in the local phone book.

If $100,000 or less is needed and excellent credit rating exists the SBA Low Doc program could be of interest. It is a simple application and a response is received in about 72 hours.

Small Business Investment Corporation (SBIC). These firms leverage their private capital into government money to form a sort of venture capital fund. Most SBICs are part of commercial banks. They offer both long-term loans and equity participation. They are conservative investing mainly in established companies for management buyouts, funds to go public, strategic partnerships and bridge financing.

Commercial Paper. This is a short term debt instrument typically issued from 2 to 270 days. An issue is normally a promissory note that is unsecured and discounted from its face value. The issue is usually backed by a letter of credit or some other from of credit guarantee. The company may pledge assets to obtain a credit guarantee which is then leveraged into an issue of commercial paper.

Letters of Credit. Issued to a funding source on a persons behalf, as a guarantee that they will pay. If the loan recipient does not pay the issuer does. A bank might issue the L/C based on the customer's pledge of a receivable or other hard asset.

Receivable Factoring. An age-old method of financing. Funds are advanced against goods sold, accepted and not yet paid for. Normal advances on accounts receivable are 80% to 90%. The lenders are looking for ninety (90) days or less to be paid. Funding is available for older accounts receivable, but the rates take a dramatic turn upwards.

Purchase Order Advances. Leveraging the future. If purchase orders are in place with the customer base, it may be possible to get advances towards their completion. The typical advance is less than 50%, and the rates are very high. Don't choose this one unless there's no other way.

Equipment Leasing. Essentially renting assets. The leasee gains the capital equipment needed and agrees to pay rent for a specific period of time. There is no interest rate here, but the rates tend to be higher than commercial loans. Some of that is offset by being able to expense 100% the payments (pretax). Check with a tax accountant to be sure.

Asset Sale Lease-Backs. If cash poor and asset heavy, this may work. The asset is being sold for cash to a funding source that leases it back (typically with a lease end purchase option). The downside of this approach may be capital gains or sales tax.

Private Placements. A do it yourself stock offering. A great way to raise small amounts of capital ($500,000 or less) with a few investors (typically less than 35). These are now available in a boilerplate format in most states. Contact the state's Department of Corporations for information on what is required to stay out of trouble.

Public Offerings. 504, 505 & 506 Offerings. Forms of stock offerings that let one raise more money and have more investors than private placements. These are great vehicles if time is taken to figure them out. Contact the SEC, they will be happy to send the rules and the forms.

Limited Partnerships. Search for one or form one. Limited partnerships usually exist for the purpose of investing. The general partner has all the exposure and management duties, while the limited partners have put up all the money. There are numerous Limited Partnerships that have been formed to invest in businesses. Search for them or inquire within the State as to the requirements for forming one.

Convertible Debt. This is normally a loan than can be converted (at the lender's option) into an ownership position in the company. These are most common with seed or start-up funding where the lender would like a piece of the rock in the event you become a tremendous success.

State Bonds. Most states have revenue bonds. These bonds are usually designed as debt instruments, where the company issues the bond and the state agency underwrites it. These bonds are generally issued to promote manufacturing facilities that will create jobs.

Line of Credit. A revolving account that is continuous in its nature. The funds are available as draw downs against the total line. These types of accounts are most commonly secured with accounts receivable and inventory as collateral.

"Even if you're on the right track, you'll get run over if you just sit there." Will Rogers

14. Find the Funding Source
America's Business Funding Directory

Connecting entrepreneurs who are searching for capital, directly to Funding Sources with capital available to place. That's really the whole point, isn't it? This service is designed to match a specific funding request with the lending or investing criteria of thousands of Funding Sources nationwide.

It is far better to go directly to a Funding Source whose criteria already match the requestor's, then to try to make a request match. Don't waste valuable time talking to sources who can't help. Get the request in front of those Funding Sources that are pre-qualified to match a specific funding request.

This service is provided by Business Funding Services, Inc.. It contains the criteria of Funding Sources world wide, with entries from every type of funding category listed in the previous chapter and the service is free.

Remember, Funding Sources come and go, and along the way they change what they are looking for. Printed material tends to get out of date. Consider use of America's Business Funding Directory to locate business capital funding sources that match your specific request for capital.

Venture Capital. Investments are normally more than $500,000 placed in industries and businesses that exhibit extremely high growth potential. Find a fit from thousands of these companies.

Commercial Finance. Commercial Lending is normally renewable short-term loans to finance the working capital needs of a business. Qualifying for this type of capital typically involves the pledging of some form of asset or equity. Take a look, there may be assets never thought of!

Investment Funds. There are many sources for investment in a business. Directories of equity or other types of offerings exist. Do some research.

Equipment Finance. Is equipment acquisition a major part of the need for business capital? Equipment finance and leasing sources are also presented in numerous directories or can be located on the Internet.

Government Funds. The government is one of the major sources of small business capital. We have listed those Funding Sources that are outlets for U.S. Government programs.

Real Estate Finance. Need Funding for a Real Estate project? Funding sources for every type of real estate project can be found.

A Directory? Get to the Internet, visit a local computer store, try the local Chamber of Commerce, local library or local college or university and access a directory at http://www.businessfinance.com

"Being a good entrepreneur is not knowing everything, it's knowing where to find everything."

15. The Internet Factor

If not already on-line, get there. A wealth of the world's information is available at the click of a mouse. The Internet is expanding by quantum leaps everyday. There has never been anything like it. The opportunity to do business and locate customers here is worldwide.

If the company isn't on the Internet, they are already behind the competition. Pick up one of a dozen magazines for the Internet. Most of these publications will tell how to get a "Web Site" for the company. It should cost about a $1,000 in total for very basic design work or $5,000 to $50,000 for complicated work. Select an Internet service provider that will bill a flat rate, typically no more than $19.95 per month. A home page (or website) address on somebody else's server unit should cost no more than a couple of hundred dollars per month. This is the fastest growing media the world has ever seen, don't be left behind.

"America's Business Funding Directory" is available on-line at Internet address http://www.businessfinance.com. Submit a funding request. Specific Funding Source matches are provide and a summary of the funding request may be posted for anyone to examine for thirty days.

America's Business Funding Directory also contains a valuable index to hundreds of Internet sites that are available to post or advertise your company's product, service or funding request. Most of these sites are free or for a very low cost. If more information is needed about promoting a business on the Internet visit http://www.businessfinance.com/busres.htm. This unique Internet resource may help with expansion of a business.

"Looking for money is like searching for the Holy Grail. It would be easier if someone just told you where it was."

16. Negotiating The Deal

First learn to say NO. Now you're ready to negotiate. Most Entrepreneurs approach the issue of negotiating with great stress and anxiety. This leads directly to weak negotiations or becoming defensive about being asked too many questions. Either way, you lose! In order to avoid this happening, reexamine section eight "Terms" and make sure a clear definition of what is sought has been made before negotiations begin. Then...

- Determine which points are worth fighting for.
- Express any objections and questions to any point.
- Get it in writing, leave nothing to verbal agreements.
- Subject everything to one's long-range goals.
- Pay close attention to what triggers default.
- Establish ceilings and caps. It is not wise to be stuck with huge payments if rates go up.
- Plan for the downside. Attempt to have an "interest only" clause or "skip payment" provision in the event of slow downs.
- Look for no pre-payment penalty or the right to buy back stock at a fixed price.
- Pay attention to covenants, conditions, ratios, restrictions or other clauses which can have serious long term effects.
- Try to minimize pledging collateral. You may need those assets in the future to raise additional capital.
- Seek professional counsel before you sign anything. Lawyers and accountants may not help fund the deal, but they can help spot small details that may be a burden down the road.

Close. This is a good place to do just that. Remember to sell management and the company. Be a closer! Only accept "No", as being one step nearer to "Yes".

"I cannot give you a formula for success, but I can give you the formula for failure: try to please everybody."

638

EXHIBIT D - INDIVIDUALS VIEW OF VENTURE CAPITALISTS

Author unknown

I have worked with more than 30 startups as founder, advisor, engineer, executive, and board member. I've formed opinions along the way. VCs know how to deal with engineers but engineers do not know how to deal with VCs. VCs take advantage of this situation to maximize their return for the venture funds' investors. Engineers are getting short changed.

My first experience with VCs was as an engineer starting a microprocessor-design company; VCs were the gods of money. The other founders and I told the VCs what we thought we could do and how long it would take. We believed it; they believed it; we were all naive. I had designed two microprocessors, had written a textbook on the topic, and had taught at a well-known university. They thought I knew what I was talking about. We landed money from premiere firms on Sand Hill Road in Palo Alto, Calif. We told them a year; it took something like seven years and it took major changes in strategy to get there.

I wasn't the CEO; I hired and managed the engineering teams that eventually reached the goal. I wasn't there for the finish. I had a run-in with the other founders, including the CEO, over how to manage engineers. It was micromanagement versus laissez faire. (Their attitude: "Turn your back on them and they'll sit on their hands." My attitude: "Turn these particular engineers loose and they'll work themselves to physical ruin.") We were in danger of losing good engineers to morale problems. I suggested to the board that firing all of the founders, including me, might solve the problem. A new team might manage more consistently.

The board member from our largest VC firm invited me to his house in Woodside for a chat about the morale problems. Acres, opulence, wealth. We sat in leather chairs on a black marble floor. Behind him, through the glass wall, I saw major excavation and construction work going on up the hillside. "It's too bad someone is building a resort hotel so close to your house," I said. "That's my new house," he said. "This one will be torn down when that one's finished."

We talked about the situation at the start-up. I outlined my concerns. I handed him a list of names. "Here's contact information for some of the project engineers. The first four will tell you what I have told you. The fifth will say the following things...." To his credit, he interviewed the engineers. Also to his credit, he called to tell me the result. "Everything you said is as you said it was." I felt relief. I had struggled with a deteriorating situation for a year and a half.

We agreed on the problem; we agreed on the circumstances--a solution was on the way. They told me: "We think you should resign." I left; the problems didn't.

Guide to venture capitalists

The VC connects wealthy investors to nerds. There are few alternatives. You can self-fund by consulting and by setting aside money for your venture. That doesn't work. You could go to friends and family, but that risks friendships. You could find "angel" investors, but that only delays going to VCs.

The VC community is a closed one. It caters to a restricted audience. In fact, you don't get to meet a VC unless you have a personal introduction. Don't send them your business plan unless the VC has personally requested it.

VCs don't sign nondisclosure agreements

That affords them protection if they like your ideas, but they want to fund someone else to do them. At least two of my friends have had their ideas stolen and funded separately. One case was blatant theft--sections of the original business plan were crudely copied and taped into the VC-sponsored plan. My friend sued and won a moral victory and a little money. The start-up based on the stolen idea went public and made lots of money for that start-up's VCs. Most entrepreneurs don't have the time, the means, or the proof to sue. In the second case, venture firm D sent its expert several times for additional "due diligence" regarding the possible investment. My friend got funding elsewhere, but D funded its expert with the same ideas.

VCs are sheep
The electronics industry is driven by fads, just as the fashion and toy industries are. The industry is periodically swept by programming language fads: Forth, C++, Java, and so on. It's swept by design fads such as RISC, VLIW, and network processors. It's even swept by technical business fads such as the dot-coms. No area is immune. If one big-name VC firm funds reconfigurable electronic blanket weavers, the others follow. VCs either all fund something or none of them will. If you ride the crest of a fad, you've a good chance of getting funded. If you have an idea that's too new and too different, you will struggle for funding.

VCs aren't technical
Mostly, they aren't engineers--even the ones with engineering degrees. An engineering degree is a starting point. If you design and build things, you can become an engineer; if you work on your career, you can become an executive or a venture capitalist. VCs in Silicon Valley are as technically sophisticated as VCs come. As you get geographically farther from technical-industry concentration, investors become more finance-oriented and less technically-oriented.

Like all people, they dismiss what they don't understand, your novel ideas, and they focus on what they know, usually irrelevant marketing terms or growth predictions.

Experts aren't very good
The VC will send at least one "expert" to evaluate your ideas. Don't expect the expert to understand what you are doing. Suppose your idea implements a cell phone. The VC will send an expert who may know all there is to know about how cell phones have been built for the last 10 years. As long as your idea doesn't take you far from traditional implementations, the expert will understand it. If you step too far from tradition--say, with a novel approach using programmable logic devices instead of digital signal processors--the expert will not understand or appreciate your approach.

One company I worked with had an innovative idea for a firewall: build it with programmable logic and it works at wire speed. Wire speed meant no buffering, no data storage, and therefore no need for a microprocessor or for an IP (Internet Protocol) address. Simple installation, simple management, but so different that experts--even those from programmable logic companies--didn't understand it. To them, proposing a firewall without a microprocessor and an IP address was like proposing a car without an engine. No funding. Back to work at a big company. Worse for them; worse for us. The industry loses. Progress is delayed.

VCs don't take risks
VCs have a reputation as the gun-slinging risk-takers of the electronics frontier. They're not. VCs collect money from rich people to build their investment funds. Answering to their investors contributes to a sheep mentality. It must be a good idea if a top-tier fund invested in a similar business. VCs like to invest in pedigrees, not in ideas. They are looking for a team or an idea that has made money. Just as Hollywood would rather make a sequel than produce an original movie, VCs look for a formula that has brought success. They're not building long-lasting businesses; they're looking to make many times the original investment after a few years.

When VCs build a venture fund, they charge the fund's investors a management fee and a "carry." The carry, which is typically 20 to 30 percent, is the percent of the investors' profit that goes directly to the VC. The VC, who gets a healthy chunk of any venture-fund profits, may have no money in the fund. Even a small venture fund will be invested across a dozen or so companies, spreading risk. Also, the VC, as a board member, will collect stock options from each start-up the fund invests in.

The rich investors take some risk, though their risk is spread across the fund's investments. The real risk-takers are the entrepreneurial engineers who invest time and brain power in a single start-up.

Venture funds are big

Too big. If your idea needs a lot of money, say $100 million, then you have a better chance of getting money than an idea that promises the same rate of return for $1 million. The VCs running a $1 billion fund don't have the time to manage one thousand $1 million investments. It won't even be possible to manage two hundred $5 million investments. It's better to have fewer, bigger investments. In such an environment, if you need only $5 million, your idea will struggle for funding.

VCs collude

VCs collect in "bake-offs" that are the VC's version of price fixing. They discuss among themselves funding and "pricing" for candidate start-ups. Pricing sets the number of shares and the value of a share, and is typically expressed in a "term sheet" from the VC to the start-up. VCs optimize locally. It wouldn't do for several of them to fund, say, six companies in an industry wedge. Limiting the options to two or three limits competition and makes the success of the few more likely. The downside: limiting competition stifles innovation and slows progress. As in nature, competitive environments foster healthier organisms. Innovation is the beneficial gene mutation to the current technology's DNA.

I attended a recent talk by a VC luminary, who gloated over the state of the venture industry, after money for technology start-ups was scarce. Here's my summary of the VC's view:
"A year ago there was too much money available, so there was too much competition to fund good ideas. Valuations for pre-IPO (initial public offering) start-ups were too high. Start-ups could get term sheets from several venture firms and select the most favorable. Too many ideas were getting funded. With too many rivals, markets might never develop. The current market is much better. Valuations are reasonable and, with few rivals in each sector, new markets will develop--as they might not have with many rivals."

This is nonsense. Look, for example, at hard disks and floppy disks. In the hard-disk business, there have been as many as 41 rivals fighting for market share. Only three major manufacturers competed in floppy disks. The hard disk has improved much faster technically; the floppy disk is stagnant by comparison. I'm not talking about market size or market opportunity (the hard-disk business versus the floppy-disk business); I'm talking about rates of innovation.

VCs don't say no

If the VC is interested, you can expect a call and, eventually, a check. If the VC is not interested, you won't get an answer. Saying "no" encourages you to look elsewhere--that's not good for the VC, who prefers to have you hanging around rather than going elsewhere for funding. Fads change; the herd turns; your proposal may look better next year. In addition, the VC may want more due diligence from you--to add your ideas to a different start-up's plan.

If VCs think you have few alternatives, they will string you along: "I love the deal, but it'll take time to bring the other partners along." "We need more time to get expert opinions." "We're definitely going to fund you, but we're closing a $500 million fund, and that's taking all our time." "I'll call you Monday." Once your alternatives are gone, they negotiate their terms.

VCs have pets

The VC's version of a pet is the "executive in residence." Many venture firms keep a cache of start-up executives on staff at $10 000 to $20 000 per month (a princely sum to an engineer, but just enough to keep people in these circles out of the soup kitchens). Start-up executives, loitering for an opportunity, may collect these fees from more than one venture firm, since the position entails no more than casual advising. These executives have "experience" in start-ups. When you show your

641

start-up to the VCs, they will grill you about the "experience" of your executive team. It won't be good enough, but not to worry, the VC supplies the necessary talent. You get a CEO. The CEO replaces your friends with cronies.

The VCs' pets are like Hollywood's superstars. Just like Julia Roberts and Tom Cruise, the superstar CEOs command big bucks and big percentages (of equity)--driving up the cost of the start-up--but are "worth it" because they give investors and VCs a sense of security.

Your idea, your work, their company

The VC's CEO gets 10 percent of the company. VC-placed board members get 1 percent each. Your entire technical team gets as much as 15 percent. Venture firms get the rest. Subsequent funding rounds lower ("dilute") the amount owned by the technical team. Venture firms control the board seats. The VC on your board sits on 11 other boards. Board members visit once a month or once a quarter, listen to the start-up's executives, make demands, offer suggestions, and collect personal stock options greater than all of the company's engineers hold, with the possible exceptions of the chief technology officer and the vice president of engineering. The VC's executives control the company. You and the rest of the engineers do the work.

One company I know got a good valuation a year ago. Over the year, it grew rapidly, developed its product, met or exceeded its milestones, and spent its money according to plan. When it was time to get money again, the funding environment had changed. Last year's main investor wouldn't "price" the shares or "lead" the new funding round. The "price" declares the number of shares and the valuation of the company. Think of the company as a pie. It is a certain size (valuation) and it is cut into a number of slices (shares). An investor "leads" by offering a specific price for shares for a large percentage of the next round. Other investors follow at the same price. Even though the company's engineers had executed flawlessly, the round came in at less than a third of last year's valuation.

As a part of closing this "down" round, the last year's investors renegotiated the previous round, effectively saying, "Since this round is lower, we must have overpaid in the last round. We want more equity for the last investment." If there had been fraud by the entrepreneurs instead of flawless execution, renegotiating the previous round might have been reasonable. Imagine the opposite scenario: "In light of market developments, it's obvious that your idea is worth much more than we thought, so we're returning half the equity we took for last year's funding." It's so ridiculously improbable that you can't read it without laughing out loud. That we accept the converse highlights the entrepreneur's weak position.

Values at variance

The VCs know money and they don't care about the technology; the entrepreneurs know technology and they need money. Money knowledge applies across all the start-ups; the technical knowledge is unique to each. The VCs don't care about any single technology because they spread their investments across the opportunities. Knowing money isn't the same as knowing value. A year ago, VCs were lining up to give money to Internet dog-food companies; this year, they wouldn't back an inventor with a working Star Trek transporter.

It's financial; it's not technical or personal. To the VC, the engineer and the ideas are commodities. The venture firm squeezes the technical team because it can. VCs believe that they are exercising their responsibility to maximize return for themselves and for the fund's investors.

Reducing the engineers' share of the pie is counterproductive, however: they become demoralized; productivity suffers; eventually, they leave. Engineers are not commodities. Replacing a chip designer one year into a complex design delays the project six months while the replacement engineer learns and then redesigns the work-in-progress.

VCs don't appreciate that the electronics revolution is built on the backs and brains of engineers, not of executives. Moore's law and engineering talent drive the electronics revolution. Tremendous market pull for its products builds momentum. The pull is so great that the revolution is indifferent to the talents and decisions of its executives (legendary blundering causes only ripples), but it depends on the talent and the work of its engineers. The engineers are the creators of wealth; the VCs are the beneficiaries.

Fixing the problem

The engineers building the future deserve a fair equity share in the value they create; today they don't get one. For them to get their share, wealthy engineers must fund start-ups. And they don't have to be Bill Gates to do so. "Qualified investors" can participate in pre-IPO funding. This means your net worth (exclusive of your home) must be at least a million dollars or you must meet minimum annual income requirements. These days, the millionaire's club isn't all that exclusive. Many engineers arc qualified investors.

If you are a qualified investor, participate in start-ups as an "angel" investor. An angel investor participates in early or "seed" funding rounds. Don't do it with more money than you can afford to lose, however, because it is risky. To change the situation I'm describing, start-ups need your money and they need your advice. More money and more start-ups bring faster progress and create more wealth. Creating wealth isn't only about money; it's about quality of life and it's about raising the standard of living for everyone (but that's another essay).

Engineers should band together to form venture funds. Start-ups need more angel funding and they need better-organized angel funding. I'd like to see a dozen or so $100 million venture funds run by nerds. These nerd-based venture firms would work at the seed round and at the next funding round (called the A round). They provide initial funding and advice and they, with the benefit of professional financial advice, represent their start-ups in future funding negotiations with traditional venture firms.

Here's a third suggestion. I'd like to see an engineer-run start-up whose goal is to raise $100 million in a public offering. The money becomes a fund for sponsoring start-ups. It's a public venture firm and it sells shares to raise money. Investing in start-ups wouldn't be exclusively for rich people; anyone who could buy stock could be investing in start-ups. Ideally, the public VC firm would be managed and run by nerds with empathy for nerds in the start-ups.

I wanted to publicly thank more than a dozen people for help on this essay, but they all said "NO!" None can afford to have the VCs find out that they contributed.

Some of the nuggets:

1. It's financial; it's not technical or personal. To the VC, the engineer and the ideas are commodities. The venture firm squeezes the technical team because it can.

2. When you show your start-up to the VCs, they will grill you about the "experience" of your executive team. It won't be good enough, but not to worry, the VC supplies the necessary talent. You get a CEO. The CEO replaces your friends with cronies.

3. If the VC is not interested, you won't get an answer. Saying "no" encourages you to look elsewhere--that's not good for the VC, who prefers to have you hanging around rather than going elsewhere for funding.

4. The VC community is a closed one. It caters to a restricted audience. In fact, you don't get to meet a VC unless you have a personal introduction. Don't send them your business plan unless the VC has personally requested it.

5. VCs like to invest in pedigrees, not in ideas.

EXHIBIT E – CAPITAL FORMATION Q AND A

(Following is for information only. Seek legal or accounting advice for your specific situation)

1. How do I get funds to "test-drive" my business idea?

Risks are much greater when investing in an "idea" that is not yet a working company. Numerous things can change the risk exposure of an up-and-running business, so capital for development of a business "concept" becomes even more risky given the lack of validation of the business model as viable in that particular market space.

It's important to do a quick review of the stages in a company's life cycle and understand the use of funds for each stage. There are four stages: the pre-launch, the launch, the ramp-up and the viability stages. Questions pertaining to the pre-launch cover two unique sub-phases. First, interest in raising money could be to conduct "concept feasibility" work. The work would be to develop working prototypes and working models or various versions of the product or service to see if it does what it is supposed to do. In addition there may be a need for funds to "market test" which would involve surveys, focus groups and field tests of beta versions.

It's during the concept period that research and development happens for a brand-new product or service to determine all aspects of the ultimate manufacturing, distribution and support processes. Funds invested here have very little substantive expectations because no one can be sure if the feasible solution can be put together and the kinks worked out in a satisfactory manner. Funds used to do market testing is also risky because, while trying to determine price points, potential sales volume and viable buying patterns of targeted customers, results could be very negative and point toward a lack of support for the idea/concept in the industry.

Some basic rules to follow when trying to find capital for the pre-launch areas follows. First, because of the high risk for the investor and lender be reasonable in expectations on the potential investors. If they don't immediately show enthusiasm for the plan, be open to working with them on identifying what can be done to alleviate some of their risk concerns. Always remember that this effort could end without any plan on how to proceed further and actually open for business.

Second, money used for "getting ready" will almost certainly be tied to the likelihood that there will in fact be a business doing business after all the testing and R&D is finished. Investors will want to have a significant stake in that enterprise that follows, because they recognize that without their money now, there can never be a company later. But remember that the person with the idea and expertise to make the concept a reality, counts for something, too. When deciding on percentage stakes in the ultimate firm, keep in mind that it is a mutual relationship, in which, almost equally, the money needs the idea and the idea needs the money.

Finally, there is a need to clearly demonstrate an expected path from pre-launch to launch; otherwise, investors will view their funds as going into a black hole. Product testing, lab research, surveys collected and focus groups polled could all result in no forward momentum. Outline strategic vision at each stage, and show the benchmarks that will define success or failure at each critical juncture. Get agreement that "if we do this and this and that, then we will proceed to do these nest steps."

What complicates this type of funding is that during this pre-launch stage, there is no revenue - only development expense. Therefore ask yourself: "Would I provide funds for this idea in its current state? If the answer is no, then what things need to be tighten up before approaching real investors? If the answer is yes, get two or three other people to provide an objective opinion as to whether you're ready to ask for money. If a clear path to a launch date and eventual sales is evident, then there are investors who will provide funding to do these pre-launch activities.

2. How do I determine how much of my company I should give to an investor?
Beauty Is In The Eye of The Stockholder

Rather complex financial analysis tools are used to establish the value of a business and its stock. Although the tools seem to apply a degree of scientific accuracy to the subject, they do not produce automatic results. In the case of an established company, it is possible to use three or four different methods and arrive at three or four radically different results. It is then up to the person doing the valuation to find an "average" among the results. For an early stage company, the valuation question is even more problematical, because the valuation is typically done based on projected future cash flows and what you can sell the business for in 3 or 5 or 7 years, which are inherently subjective in the first place.

Entrepreneurs, being naturally enthusiastic people, tend to get carried away with their projections and assume there will be no obstacles to the company becoming a roaring success. Venture capitalists, being naturally skeptical people, will take these same projections and discount them (lower them) based on the degree of risk the venture capitalist sees that the projections will not turn into reality. The more skeptical the venture capitalist is, the greater the percentage of the company he will want for a given level of investment.

Reaching an agreement on the price of the company's stock depends on how this natural gap can be bridged. A valid question for the entrepreneur to pose is, "If this investment is so terribly risky that you need 80% of my company, why do you want to get involved at all?" The investor's counter argument is then, "My investment will cause your company to be larger and more valuable. Wouldn't you rather own 20% of a large, successful company, than 100% of what you have now?"

A Little Analysis Is Better Than None At All

Occasionally we have seen an entrepreneur propose a deal based on absolutely no financial analysis, instead using this logic(?): "I need $5 million. I don't want the investor to have control of my business, but I need to give them a nice chunk. How about 40%?" Despite the imperfections in the process of trying to project future cash flows in a growing business, it is better to at least try to tie your valuation of the company back to the projections instead of using this non-valuation method of business valuation.

Never Listen to Someone Who Says Investors Have To Have Control

You should never assume that you must give up control of your company to investors in order to secure financing. Some of the larger venture capital firms, in fact, prefer to have a minority share because they believe that a management group with a higher equity stake is more likely to put their full energies into building the company.

The Fine Print Can Be Hazardous to Your Wealth

One of the most perilous parts of structuring a venture capital investment involves the performance criteria set for the existing owner/managers. These parameters are set in to protect the investors in the event the company under performs relative to what was projected. This fine print of the agreements could specify that the investors receive more shares, giving them control for example, or may say they have the right to bring in their own management team, or even sell the company out from under the original owners in order to recoup their investment. You, the entrepreneur should assume that actual results will vary from what had been forecast, and be very cautious when agreeing to the performance criteria that will be used to trigger any of these changes.

We heard of one wealthy individual investor who never objected to puffed-up projections, but set the management performance criteria based on them, knowing full well that management could not achieve the results and he could take over the company.

He let them hang themselves by their own spreadsheets.

My Advice Is To Get Advice

Although it is possible to read books on the subject of valuing a business and setting the price for an investment, being able to usefully employ these analytical tools only comes through experience of having been through the process many times.

If you are negotiating with professional venture capitalists, you are at a distinct disadvantage, because they have put deals together many times, and know how to structure them in their favor. You, then, need people on your team who have seen many deals put together. Among the options available to you:

- CPAs who work on corporate finance transactions.

- Business valuation consultants (and have professional accreditation.)
- Investment bankers who specialize on smaller or mid-market companies.

Don't assume these professionals are completely out of your price range. They may be willing to defer part of their advisory fees until the deal is closed, especially if you have reasonable prospects of getting investors interested in your company, or are in discussions with investors at the present time.

3. Does anyone know how to go about obtaining Seed Financing for product development, market research etc.?

Seed money is the most difficult of all to obtain. The reason, of course, is that the promise of success very seldom matures into an invention that pays back a profit.

Here are a few ways to go about getting seed money:

1. Form a close corporation, and sell shares in a high risk venture to friends and relatives. Do not ask for loans; this creates hard feelings in the majority of cases. A corporation places each investor on equal footing. Be sure to get an attorney experienced in startups to do the incorporating. The key here is to reserve enough stock for future investors (venture capitalists and the like). If this isn't done right, you can stall at the very point that success is near.

2. Locate successful persons in the same line as your invention fall into, and ask for a grant to proceed. The grantor must know more about your field than you do, or at least as much, or the probability of attracting him/her is zilch. Sometimes a bored lawyer, doctor, dentist, etc., may act as an angel in the early stages. But go back to point 1 above in any case in dealing with any such persons.

3. Locate vendors who will eventually manufacture your invention, and form a strategic partnership that includes yielding manufacturing rights and/or royalties etc. to the vendor.

All of these methods require a lot of effort to put in place, but it can be done. See www.inventorhelp.com

4. What are some recommendations that you would make for raising venture capital?

The Challenge

For the past fourteen years I have been raising venture capital, either as an entrepreneur or as a venture capitalist. This has included raising capital for my own businesses and helping others to raise capital for their new or existing businesses.

Raising venture capital is both a marketing and a sales challenge in that, to insure your success, you must both develop a product that a large enough market wants to buy, and you must have the selling skills to convince the dogs that they should eat your particular brand of dog food. Most professional venture capitalists are essentially in the business of screening, qualifying, and selecting venture capital investments from as large a source of quality deal flow as they can muster. A few venture capitalists are essentially entrepreneurs themselves and can work with an entrepreneur to start and develop a new company.

Increasingly, the start up variety of venture capitalist is hard to find, in that over the past decade most venture capitalists now have so much money to manage that they cannot afford the time or effort required to help develop and then invest in a start up. For all but the very few, start up capital will not come from the professional V.C., but rather from the D.D.F. market - Doctors, Dentists, and Friends, or from personal savings, credit, or family members. Some states have incubator programs or incubator venture funds which will provide small amounts of capital ($100,000-$200,000), but once again generally only the few, the persistent, and the lucky will qualify.

To successfully raise professional venture capital, particularly for a start up, your venture will need to address a large, rapidly growing market with a unique product, which is very tough to duplicate and for which there is little or no known present competition. Your product needs "compelling economics" - twice as fast, twice as cheap, twice the margins, and twice the appeal. If the potential product is likely to gain rapid favor in the stock market after in IPO, all the better. The good news is that the D.D.F. market is about $25 billion annually. The professional V.C. market is only $3-$5 billion. There are more friends and family than Venture Capitalists.

Use the following checklists as guides to raising venture and to assess the likelihood of success.

Obtaining A State Of Mind Conductive To Raising Venture Capital

Several authors, combining the best of the ways of Eastern mysticism and relaxation techniques with Western competitiveness, present approaches to obtain your goals which permit the participant to "go with the flow" rather than against the grain. This "on ness with what you are doing" approach permits the objective, in this case raising venture capital, to be obtained with a minimum of hassle, anxiety, and difficulty. Those who are successful in raising venture capital obtain a state of mind as well as an understanding of the process which promotes and permits success. Administer this self-awareness review to determine whether your stuff is right:

- I would rather be rich than be the big cheese.
- While I want to be rich, I would rather build a successful company.
- While I want to build a successful company, I would rather be creative and effective in what I do everyday.
- I work effectively with peers, but not well for another.
- I want the best around me in my products, employees, investors, and other supporters, but if they are not available I will on occasion compromise, but not too much.
- I am afraid to fail and admit it, but succeeding is okay.
- I will work both very hard and very smart to obtain my goals.
- I accept that in this life it is difficult to have everything, at least at one time, and that it will be necessary at times to surrender personal life for business success.
- I know in what way I am truly unique, and what it is that I want to bring to the world.
- I will let my family and friends know that it's not that I am not interested in them, but that this is just something that I have to create for a time.
- I will never give up.
- If forced to give up by adverse circumstances, I will start over.

Steps in Successfully Raising Venture Capital

Successfully raising venture capital is an established process and your chances of success are enhanced if all bases are covered in a logical progression.

Develop a unique product, concept, or service.

Develop an outline of what is required in people, money, organization, strategy and tactics, and other assets to build this particular business.

Assemble a management team with the ability to successfully build and operate this business.

Prepare, with the assistance of the members of the management team, a clear, concise business plan representing the "game plan" of how the business will be operated and financed.

Identify those venture capitalists who are most likely to review a business plan in your

industry and stage of development.

Mail the plan, with a cover letter indicating why the plan is unique to four or five selected venture capitalists.

Call the venture capitalist in several weeks to determine the status of your plan if a reply has not yet been received.

Meet with the venture capitalist to initially present your deal.

Prepare for "due diligence" meetings with the venture capitalist to continue to you're your deal.

Negotiate with venture capitalists over deal structure and price.

Complete investment syndicate formation by entrepreneur and lead venture capitalist.

Obtain commitment by all venture capitalists in the deal. Prepare legal documents of closing (time to involve your deal-making attorney).

      Officially close the deal.

      Work with the venture capitalist after the sale.

      Cash out for the venture capitalist through a sale, merger, or public offering.

5. How much money do I need to get my business off the ground?

To help you estimate the amount of financing you will need to get your business off the ground, use the following checklist. For each item, estimate a monthly amount needed.

Monthly Expenses:

      Salary of owner-manager (if applicable)

      All other salaries and wages

      Rent

      Advertising

      Delivery expense

      Supplies

      Telephone

      Utilities

      Insurance

      Taxes, including Social Security

      Interest

      Maintenance

      Legal and other professional fees

      Miscellaneous

One-Time Start-Up Costs:

      Fixtures and equipment

      Decorating and remodeling

      Installation of fixtures and equipment

      Starting inventory

      Deposits with public utilities

      Legal and other professional fees

      Licenses and permits

      Advertising and promotion for opening

      Accounts receivable

      Cash

      Other

TOTAL

Your total will depend on how many months of preparation you want to allow for.

6. Is there "free" money and if so how can I get it?

Free Money" is grants, loans (micro loans, low doc), awards and prizes from government, corporate or philanthropic sources.

Who can get "free money"- business people & entrepreneurs (especially high-tech and specialists; more difficult for traditional retailers), students, researchers, inventors, home buyers, bill payers, car buyers, veterans, the disabled, the disadvantaged, the elderly, the (ethnic, racial, gender & culturally) diverse, poets, writers, clubs, organizations, social services, not-for-profits, nonprofits, etc.

To obtain the various types of "free money" use the sources listed below. Also research programs of interest and contact the program's organization- ask for a description of the program, guidelines, deadlines and a copy of successful applications.

Before you actively go after the money review this material carefully. You may also want to speak with a program representative to make sure you understand everything. Know what you are getting yourself into, e.g., Is it a free grant or does it require remittance?

Get the money

Follow instructions to the letter. Send in your carefully completed application and anything else that's required as soon as possible. Send it to the proper person, address and office. Follow up after submission: call, write or even visit.

Keep following up until you receive a reply. If favorable, you have what you want. If not, this time, reapply, and seek out new sources. "If at first you don't succeed, try, try again."

Obviously there's not enough room in this book to list every "free money," grant, loan, award and prize resource available so here's a "free money" quick list:

- Government Agencies (Dept. of Agriculture, Dept. of Education, Dept. of Education, HUD, SBA etc.)
- The U.S. Government's "Catalog of Federal Domestic Assistance"
- The Foundation Center publications, i.e., "Foundation Directory"
- "Annual Register of Grant Support"
- Matthew Lesko's "Government Giveaways," "Info Power," "1001 Free Goodies and Cheapies," etc.
- Internet/World Wide Web (see "Internet Resources" in the Computer Info chapter of "THE Self-Employment Resource Guide," see resource box below)

These and many other "free money" sources without cost can be found at the local Public Library and on the Internet. Also contact government agencies - SBA, SCORE, GSA, nonprofit organizations and groups you belong to. See "Your Info Quick List" and the "Free Information From Your Government" chapter earlier in this book ("THE Self-Employment Resource Guide" see resource box below).

WARNING: Nothing is absolutely FREE. It may take a lot of time and effort just to find the right program (programs may not be listed or found in non-traditional areas).

Obtaining free money, grants and loans at the very least requires time, effort, postage, phone calls and follow up. If you fail to follow instructions, send your application to the wrong sources or forget to follow up don't be surprised if you unconditionally lose out without hearing about it. Give yourself the best chance for success. Do the right thing!

This information was excerpted from Arthur A. Hawkins II's book "THE Self- Employment Resource Guide" ($25 US) (c)Copyright 1996.

7. Can you tell me about factoring and when should I consider such a financing method for my business?

Dealing with cash flow is a common problem. If a product is involved, competition will likely take a "wait and see" approach for a while – if the product takes off, then the gross revenue will attract competition. One might pursue a line of credit (LC) with their bank based upon orders from the retailer to take care of this concern.

Because of the short time in the manufacturing business, it's more likely that one would rely on factoring - selling his receivable (invoice) to a factoring house the day orders are shipped. This is arranged in advance of shipping with a factoring company (some banks offer factoring services).

Factoring *discount* rates depend on the quality of the receivable (invoices to "Joe's Home Handyman" would not likely be factorable, because Joe could skip out on the payment - go out of business - and the factoring house looses). However, Home Depot would be a low risk receivable. Therefore, figure on possibly 4-6% discount on the invoice amount to get your money *today* verses in 90 days.

Factoring – cash in return for receivables with hefty interest charge; may be good for short-term capital. For information see: "Finding money: the small business guide to financing", K. Lister and T. Harnish, Wiley & Sons, 800 225 5945 $17.95

1. Commercial Finance Assoc. -info on factoring and commercial credit industry; http://www.cfa.com.

2. The International Factoring Assoc. – matches businesses with factors; http://www.factoring.org.
3. Commercial Finance Online - factors & brokers specializing in factoring; http://www.factoring.com.
4. Hoovers; company's history & financial report; http://www.hoovers.com.

If cash flow is a serious problem for your small business or you're looking for quick cash to expand your business, you may want to consider factoring your accounts receivables.

Are you familiar with factoring? If not, it's a form of financing for small and medium-sized businesses whereby you "sell" your accounts receivable to a factoring company at a discount. It's a $70 billion industry in the U.S. and a $250 billion industry worldwide. Although the terms you'll get will vary from company to company, factoring contracts all have the following elements in common:

1. Advance rate. The advance rate is the percentage of your accounts receivables that companies will advance to you. Some companies will advance the full 100 percent up front. Others will advance 70 percent and then will pay you the balance once the receivables are collected. The typical range for how much they'll pay in cash up front is 60 percent to 90 percent of your account receivables.
2. Discount rate. The discount rate is the fee charged by the factoring company for the financing. The typical range is 2 percent to 7 percent of your accounts receivables, although I have seen as low as 1 percent.
3. Recourse vs. no recourse -- In a no recourse agreement, the factoring company bears the burden of collecting the accounts receivable. In a recourse agreement, the small business owner bears the burden (in other words, if they are uncollectable, they will be charged back to you). Obviously, for a small business owner, the no recourse agreement is preferred, although the rates you'll get won't be as good as with a recourse agreement.

You'll have to weigh one against the other. Just make sure that you understand whether your agreement is recourse or no recourse before you agree to the terms.

As with most financial arrangements, the terms and rates depend upon what the lending institution views as your credit worthiness. Small businesses with higher sales volumes or with what are viewed as stronger account debtors get better rates than those with small sales volumes or more questionable account debtors. Thus, the smaller the business, typically the worse the terms.

If you're interested in factoring, the first question you should be asking yourself is: Why don't I just get a bank loan and use the accounts receivables as collateral? The answer is "you should" -- if you can get a bank to loan you the money. Bank fees will typically be much lower than factoring fees, and you should definitely pursue that option if it is available to you.

But factoring companies are betting that most small businesses can't easily get loans from banks these days, particularly those with a troublesome cash flow history. And judging from the size of the industry, they appear to be winning their bet.

The factoring companies also believe they can outperform the banks in one other area -- speed. "Factoring provides cash in 48 hours or less after an account is set up," says Paul Chapman, founder and president of American Certified Factors, a worldwide factoring company based in New York. "The account set-up typically takes about seven days, but often we can provide access to funding immediately."

You'll just have to crunch the numbers to figure out if factoring makes sense for your business. Ask your lawyer or accountant what they think about factoring. And ask some of your business associates for their experiences.

If you're interested in pursuing this further, here's a short list of factoring companies with web sites where you can find more information. The list is by no means exhaustive. There are literally hundreds of factoring companies all around the world, and many of them have web sites. Before you choose a company, make sure that you shop around for the best rates.

1. American Certified Factors   members.aol.com/AmericanCF/index.htm
2. Stratford Funding, Inc.   choicemall.com/newyork/ny169-01

3. Business Funding Services   www.busfund.com/busfund
4. Hilldun Corporation   www.hilldun.com
5. 21st Capital Corp.   websites.earthlink.net/~21stcapital

Factors measure viability of a business by looking at what it does, how well it does it, and the financial strength of its customers Not by financial ratios, equity, profitability or years in business.

If account is viable they purchase the invoice and advance cash to the business. Comparable to credit cards for payments factor acts a s a commercial credit card service that gives a business the ability to sell its receivables in return for immediate funds, albeit for a much higher fee than those imposed by credit card companies.

Factors buy the receivables on a monthly basis or carry them until they are paid. Gees can be huge from two to seven percent a month. Fee is only paid as long as the receivable is outstanding and typically such receivables are paid within 30-60 days BUT still expensive proposition.

8. What kind of company does receivables factoring?

Factoring is when the financier is essentially buying a book of actual debtors. Based on his review of the quality of the debtors, he might pay 90% of face value and the balance less fees within 90 to 120 days. A purchase order is an offer to buy, not a debt. The debt crystallizes when the product is sold, not before it is manufactured.

The range of purchase order value that is necessary for obtaining "purchase order" order financing or factoring can be as low as $75,000 of purchase orders whereas some investors may want $1-5M in valid PO's. Shop around!

9. Does anyone have an opinion about the advisability of a university non-profit tax exempt tech transfer office's taking an "ownership interest" in an LLC as opposed to an S Corp or C Corp?

For some reason that is not entirely clear to me, most of our faculty spin-offs are opting for the LLC type of organization. This gives me heartburn, because we often take equity in these start-ups but we do not want to be a "member" of the LLC. We do not get involved in the choice of entity by the spin-off although they do often ask us our opinion. To the extent that we have an opportunity to influence this decision, does anyone have any advice to share? (Multiple responses to question.)

The only reason for a startup to take the LLC route is if the members are looking for the tax losses on their personal incomes in the first few years. Membership for an institution would be interesting.

You do an S or C corporation (usually C) because your rights in the company are generally fungible with cash, i.e. if you want to sell it's a straight up exchange of cash for equity. Makes the attorneys and tax counsel happier too. Add to it that any company with an eye to the public markets will eventually incorporate and the formation of the LLC is pointless.

The primary reason lawyers would advise against using an LLC form has to do with the fact that stock ownership legal issues are more settled (more case law to provide a basis for a court ruling) as opposed to those involving member units in LLCs (which is a relatively new form of business entity). As to the benefits to the founders (choosing between LLC vs. Corp.), there is no easy answer as demonstrated by the fact that there are very large complex LLCs out there and very small corps out there. Although it largely depends on the specific needs of the parties, I certainly would not suggest you write off an LLC just because it's owners have ownership interests that appear dissimilar to that of a corp. LLC interests can be as fungible as stock in a startup (which btw is generally NOT very fungible).

LLCs are considerably less costly to set up and you can generally start with a clean sheet of paper without being hamstrung into "traditional" structures and requirements, e.g., reporting requirements.

Another benefit that may apply here is the ability to structure the tax losses of early stage development against the parties that put hard cash into the LLC while the NPO has no particular interest in the tax write-offs.

While the S corporation's special tax status eliminates double taxation, it lacks the flexibility of an LLC in allocating income to the owners.

For example, the owner of 25% of an S corporation normally pays 25% of the taxes on reported income. On the other hand, LLC owners are free to divide income and tax liability among themselves within the constraints of IRS regulations for distribution of partnership income. Equal partners may change the allocations of profit or loss from year to year to benefit their individual tax needs.

In addition, LLCs have no ownership restrictions. An S corporation limits the number of owners to just 35 and prohibits corporate and foreign ownership.

Regarding the issue of being a "member," it is not a problem. There may be a desire not to be a "managing member" or a "manager" of the LLC, but being a member is really no different than being a shareholder - different words for comparable rights.

The most experienced and astute investors seem to rely heavily on the LLC. Even though an IPO is the exit strategy, it is well accepted that the LLC provides sufficient advantages in the early stages to start with an LLC and convert it into a C-Corp when the time is right. Most states are working on improving the "rollover" capability to C-corps as well.

The big downside that most attorneys will warn one about is that LLC is a state device and the risk is that other states may not recognize your state's LLC as you would like them to. Since they have now been around for a decade with interest and implementations only continuing to increase annually, probably not a serious concern. Also, most will have been rolled over prior to doing any serious transactions across state lines.

We just set up an LLC and there is not much difference, except there is no stock. The ownership interest entitles you to a pass through of whatever income there is distributed to the members. Note that there are different classes of members, such as voting and nonvoting, not to mention various ownership transfer rights, so you definitely want to have an attorney who knows LLC's to look at the agreement.

Note also that since there is no stock, there is no appreciation, nor is there something you can sell later on, so you either have to do a deal with royalties as well, or put language in your agreement that forces the LLC to distribute a certain amount or percentage of net to the members. Otherwise the other members (who are usually the people running the company) can pay themselves $1M a year and distribute nothing to the membership at large, so you would get zilch.

It's a clean sheet of paper at the start. If there are "different classes of members..., etc., " it is because the architect wanted to have those complexities. If you don't, then negotiate them out of the way.

A "member interest" is virtually identical to a share of stock. Write the LLC Operating Agreement so that there is a measurement system comparable to shares of stock. They can be called "Equity Units" or more appropriately "Member Interest Units." These are merely means of measuring change and shared ownership and valuation as new investors enter downstream. Everything can be made to look as much like a corporation share company as the architect wishes.

Dealing with dilution is far easier using such a measurement system than merely using percentages.

Again, if all eyes are directed towards making the company a C-corporation then why do anything other than set up a C-corporation? A VC will not invest in a company that isn't looking for entry in the public markets. The company may get sold before then, but the intent is to exit via IPO and cash in the chips.

In the context of a university-based startup funded by venture capital, it makes little sense to do anything but the C-Corp.

Faculties are as protected from personal liability in an LLC as they are in corporations. That is one of the key benefits of the LLC. The beauty of the LLC is that the tax losses can all be applied to the folks who put in the capital. Since they are likely to profits they seek to shelter (or their investors seek to shelter), then they generally appreciate an investment opportunity that allows them to do that concurrently with making a sound, albeit risky, investment. Faculty typically put in their IP and some time (and often get fees for their time). They generally are not seeking the tax sheltering effects. Again, this is the beauty of the LLC vs. corps.

At the end of the day, the business is selling IP to the best bidder. Although a bit brutish... "If you want to kill rats, feed them rat poison." If you want to attract quality VCs and "sophisticated" investors to your IP licenses, then be prepared to bend to their desires, interests, and needs.

10. What are the differences between the Dept of Commerce SBIR and STTR programs?

Department of Commerce -Small Business Innovation Program (SBIR) and Small Business Technology Transfer Program (STTR)

Criteria	SBIR	STTR
American owned & independent operation	Y	Y
For profit	Y	Y
Principal Investigator employed by company	Y	N or Y
Company size < 500	Y	Y
Phase I, $ (can vary by agency)	<$100K	<$100K
Phase II, $ (can vary by agency)	<$750K	<$500K
Phase III, $	$0K	$0K
Duration of phase I	0.5 yr	1yr
Duration of phase II	2yr	2yr

Small business Administration (SBA) phone # 202 205 6450 or 1 800 382 4634 (http://www.acq.osd.mil/sadbu/sbir). Time or year for submission varies with agency.

Five agencies must reserve part of R&D dollars for STTR - Department of Defense (DOD), Department of Energy (DOE) Department of Health and Human Services (DHHS), National Aeronautical and Space Agency (NASA), and National Science Foundation (NSF).

Ten Agencies must reserve part of R&D dollars for SBIR - Department of Agriculture, Department of Commerce (DOC), Department of Defense (DOD), Department of Education (DOE) Department of Health and Human Services (DHHS), National Aeronautical and Space Agency (NASA), National Science Foundation (NSF), Department of Transportation (DOT), Environmental Protection Agency (EPA), Department of Energy (DOE). In 1997 DOE received 1200 proposals and funded 200.

ACEnet - matching of angel capital with business needs to post for solicitation of capital business must complete small corporation offering of registration (SCOR) forms (basic elements of business plan) which are reviewed by state securities organization and be classified as Reg. A (<$1M company) or Reg. B (<$5M company).

11. What are some guidelines when addressing debt and company value?

IPO or sale within 3-5 years?
- Must ratchet up company growth rapidly
- Credit line essential
- If too new or too small to qualify for a credit line find way to pair an equity financing deal with a bank loan (odds good for co. with investments from established venture capitalists, private equity funds or repeat angel investors with contacts in banking community

Is debt justified?
- If lack of funds from cash-flow problems that require corrective measures i.e. in accounts receivable or payable systems; do not expect outsider to applaud unnecessary borrowing
- A fast growing service company or company with few assets that can serve as collateral? A problem exists. Can use some debt but unless personal financial position strong it's unlikely that banker will give a loan

- Rely entirely on equity deals to bring capital in, pursue other sources of financing with a goal to move to traditional credit line as soon as you have a track record and cash flow steam (start with credit line from you credit card company or with a contract financing deal from a non bank lender.)

Can you control your company's hunger for capital?
- This is a major concern for growth company.
- Some debt is good - too much is catastrophic (if you owe too much; it is coming due and prospective buyer has reason to worry; then debt is big strike against company.
- Walk line between abstinence and self-destruction; layer debt and equity arrangements into your growing company's capital structure.

MODULE IX - CORPORATE FORMATION

Corporate

- **Entrepreneur description**
- **Pre-formation diligence**
- **Legal structure of company e.g. S, C, LLC**
- **Corporate management criteria**
- **Equity types and distribution in business**
- **Business plan**

Emphasis is on a discussion of personal characteristics necessary for an entrepreneurial business venture. Certain technology may be a candidate for a business start-up. Discussion is focused on what type of asset is a candidate for a start-up business in contrast to licensing to an existing business. Focus is on factors to consider in the start-up process including case studies. Business plan strategy and content is addressed.

ENTREPRENEUR DESCRIPTION

Many people mistakenly believe they are either born creative or they are not. They envy "Idea People" and are amazed at the ideas they seem to come up with so effortlessly. Actually, everyone is creative. Creativity consists of coming up with many, many ideas. Oliver Wendell Holmes once said "A human mind once stretched to a new idea never goes back to its original dimensions." Creativity is not only profitable, it should be fun. What are the key traits of an entrepreneur? What does it take to have a successful business? Consider the following:

1. *View Yourself As Creative and Give Yourself the Freedom to Be Creative.* If you have never thought of yourself as creative, you have probably created barriers and obstacles in your mind about idea generation. Give yourself permission...the freedom...to consider new and sometimes wild ideas and possibilities. Empower yourself to begin immediately to stretch and use your dormant creative muscles!

2. *Listen To Your Sub-Conscious and Your Dreams.* Our subconscious mind is often at work solving problems and coming up with ideas while we are consciously off doing something ordinary like working, playing or sleeping. Key ideas times occur just as we are falling asleep and beginning to awaken. Keep a small notebook and pen handy at all times to record those flashes of creativity. When you are fully awake, aware and distracted by the real world you may have difficulty recalling those great ideas.

3. *Create an Idea Friendly Environment.* Work at creating an environment that invites and inspires creativity. Drab and dreary workspaces and living space with poor lighting, inadequate ventilation, no plants, no music or artwork inhibit creativity and innovation. Clear out the clutter. Improve lighting and bring in some living plants. Research shows that live plants improve air quality and are good for health and ideas! Invest $5.00 or $500.00 for something for your desk, coffee table or nightstand that provide inspiration, enhance vision, and create an inventive environment.

4. *Break Out Of a Rut!* The more something is done the same way, the more difficult it is to think of new and better ways (ideas). Make it a point to do at least one thing every day that takes you out of the usual comfort zone. Drive home a different way and enjoy new scenery, spend $25.00 on magazines and newspapers you have never read, tune in a different radio station, watch a unique documentary on the Learning Channel. Creative opportunities are endless.

5. *Set Aside Time to Brainstorm.* Set aside time weekly or daily to brainstorm. Meetings of five to seven participants are optimal idea generators. However, don't overlook the benefits of flying solo. The same rules that apply to group brainstorming apply to solo brainstorming. The objective is to generate many ideas then later eliminate the losers, and combine and refine the winners. Always start with a warm-up, the wackier the better, to loosen up the brain and get the creativity juices flowing. A good rule of thumb is that 20% of every meeting should be devoted to active brainstorming. This time may very but can become the most productive part of a meeting.

6. *Borrow and Adapt Good Ideas.* Set up an idea file and whenever an article, ad, or direct mail piece is read or good ideas heard, add it to the file and look for ways to use it. Take periodic idea field trips and study competing and non-competent businesses for ideas on everything from customer service to marketing. Don't plagiarize, just get inspired and develop novel ideas.

7. *Ban Negatives*...Killer Phrases...Downers. It is rare when a new idea is proposed that someone doesn't shoot it down with a phrase such as "we've tried that before"...."that will never work"...."it's not in the budget." Sometimes, we are our own worst enemy when we allow our doubts and fears to overshadow creative ideas. When we say to ourselves "I'm not smart

enough, old enough, young enough, fast enough, brave enough or creative enough to do that" we are using internal "killer phrases". Identify the "killer phrases" commonly heard in the organization and from clients. Learn to diffuse them by asking "Why and What If?" Establish penalties for use of killer phrases and internal downers and watch the use of negatives decline as awareness of them grows.

8. *Ask A Lot of Questions.* Whenever there is a need for a lot of ideas to solve a problem the best way to get a lot of answers (ideas) is to ask a lot of questions. Try the old traditional WHO, WHAT, WHEN, WHERE, WHY and HOW. When it comes to creativity the most important question to ask is WHAT IF -------------? Plug in an action and then try its opposite. For example: What if I raised my fees? or What if I gave away my time? What if I combine it or what if I separate it? Ideas always come from comparing opposites.

9. ***Don't Stop With the First Right Answer Or The First Good Idea.*** Throughout our school years we were taught to look for the "right" answer. It's a hard habit to break. For maximum creativity, the best way to get a good idea is to gets lots of ideas. So, we need to change our frame of mind from looking for the right answer to looking for as many right answers as possible. The first idea may be a great one, but the fifth or thirty-fifth idea may be even greater.

10. ***Be A Lifelong Creative Learner.*** Attend creativity workshops and tele-classes. Buy books on creativity such as "A Whack On The Side Of The Head", by Roger Von Oech and "What A Great Idea", by Charles Thompson. Invest in creativity software such as Inspiration by Ceres Software or Idea Generator from Experience in Software, Inc. The more you learn about creativity and innovation the more ideas you will have.

Personality features

Technology often requires further development and additional time to reach market. Many entrepreneurial traits will be practiced for a long period of time before a return on investment is realized. Perseverance, patience, and problem solving traits will be especially important. Entrepreneurs often have their own set of (always evolving) rules and strategies. Many entrepreneurs are successful in spite of themselves. The key in working with, and enjoying entrepreneurs is to fully understand their weaknesses, which are often their biggest strengths, although others may not think so! An entrepreneur questionnaire and analysis are presented in Exhibit A. The following is a list of entrepreneurial traits:

1. *Problem Solver.* Entrepreneurs have an uncanny ability to find solutions for difficult problems. The start up company business environment results in many unique problems. A prompt solution to these problems is required.

2. *Calculated Risk Taker.* A successful entrepreneur is a good judge of acceptable risk levels. They always research a topic before trying to make decisions and leave no stone unturned. They tend to be an adventurous group but always minimize their risk with alternate plans should something unexpected arise. Starting a business is inherently risky, so research and plan before committing.

3. *Innovator.* Most entrepreneurs will start several businesses during their lifetime. This is because they always seem to have new business ideas and often start a company and then move on to the next project. It is rare for a true entrepreneur to actually "run" a company past the start up phase.

4. *Delegate Tasks.* One key to becoming an excellent entrepreneur is ability to delegate tasks to others. When starting a business, it's impossible to know how or have the time to do everything. One has to delegate tasks and focus on those parts of the business that one excels in.

5. *Handle Rejection Well.* Dealing with rejection is part of being an entrepreneur. Starting a business will likely result in opposition from friends, family, creditors, business associates,

and soon to be ex co-workers. In certain instances, people will not want the entrepreneur to succeed. It will be necessary for the entrepreneur to believe in the business and persist until success is achieved.

6. *Generalist (Can't Focus but has lots of ideas that run in circles).* The entrepreneur's currency is ideas, often a flood of ideas. This is good. Encourage more ideas; don't try to pin them down. When they feel your support in challenging them to come up with more and better ideas, the flow is restored and they'll find the one to really naturally focus. The reason they can't focus is that they haven't yet flushed out all of the half-baked ones.

7. *Not good with details.* It would great if they would focus on details, and in fact, many entrepreneurial-types fail or have lots of stress specifically because they won't or cannot address details. However, given many won't deal with details well, suggest they give up even trying and challenge the entrepreneur to solve the mess as if the mess was a new business!

8. *"Loner" (Feel odd, different, alone, strange).* Entrepreneurs are simply wired differently. Help the entrepreneur to relish their unique, contrary, leading edge ways; you'll increase the flow of ideas and potential for success. Educate the entrepreneur to understand not just themselves as individuals but to understand about the species called Homo- entrepreneurs.

9. *Good at starting business, bad at running them.* This is true of many entrepreneurs, but many entrepreneurs think they have an obligation to run their businesses and become a great manager. Ninety percent (90%) will never be great managers; they shouldn't even try! The solution: Help the entrepreneur set a "sell date" right now, so they know they're getting out and when! This forces the entrepreneur to create a sell-able company vs. one that is just a monument to ones ego. Selling is not failure; it's good business.

10. *Chaos reigns in the company.* First, the entrepreneur likes chaos and is unlikely to attract or be able to hire a manager that is cross-platform, one who is able to both manage the people/operations and also be able to put up with the personality or constant flow of ideas and changes that the entrepreneur is likely to have. A solution is to design the company so that it can afford the chaos and the financial stress that chaos usually brings. A second solution is to educate the entrepreneur and staff that chaos can be good business and not to worry about it. Another solution is to ask the entrepreneur to solve the chaos problem by thinking of it as a floundering business the entrepreneur has purchased and needs to be turned into a profit center. A fourth solution is to help the entrepreneur create fully automated and foolproof systems, usually managed by outside contractors or vendors who are not in the business day to day. This works well, because it forces the employees/owner to use the systems, which are mostly computer based.

11. *Persistent (They fail and fail again).* Like a child learning to ride a bike, an entrepreneur has to fail a couple of times as they learn how to be successful. Remember, it's the spark the entrepreneur has that is the real source of profitability. There is often a learning curve as the entrepreneur learns to compensate for his/her weaknesses by delegating, outsourcing, maturing, and learning new skills. The spark usually wins in the end.

12. *Exaggerate and often too optimistic.* This is good! Encourage the entrepreneur to exaggerate as much they want to. This is a reverse way to get them to tell the truth. Exaggeration and pipe dreaming are as important to the entrepreneur. It comes with the lifestyle. Entrepreneurs are so out in front of the rest of us they need to exaggerate how well things are going, in order to keep the faith. Exaggeration, pipe dreaming and denial are the tools and comforts of the trade of entrepreneurs.

13. *Always at the edge financially.* Causes "unnecessary" stress on the entrepreneur, the business, employees, and families. Educate the entrepreneur who is always at the edge there is an emotional dilemma they are trying to heal, via their business. The psychological source of this "always at the edge" may be an addiction to adrenaline, the pleasure/high of "pulling it off" at the last minute, of the high that victory brings, the need to be better than everyone else/compensate and even the inability to establish a reserve of cash and time so that they

function without this stress. Being at the edge financially can be a strength because the entrepreneur has proven, time and time again, they are resourceful, can survive and bounce back from adversity. Direct the entrepreneur to focus this energy into creating a healthy savings account instead of leveraging.

COMPANY FORMATION

PRE-FORMATION

Technology commercialization might be defined differently for different situations. It can be achieved when the technology:

1. belongs to an existing enterprise;
2. originates from a research institution that does not develop and market technology but establishes relationships or alliances; and
3. the basis for a company start-up.

By the time a business is established the conditions that warrant the need for a startup as well as the business focus of the company, should already have been assessed. For example, determine if the need for an operating company is to develop, manufacture, package, warehouse/distribute, serve as a retail outlet (slotting fees), and/or market products. Is the firm going to private label products act as an original equipment manufacturer (OEM), integrate into OEM products, or create a partnership? Maybe the business will be one of service or consulting. The cost to setup and operate must be determined along with the time necessary to form the business.

EXISTING COMPANY

The commercialization activity in an existing company is usually associated with expanded use or markets related to the company business. The company probably has experience and capability to establish a strategic plan for the commercialization, although often one of the major challenges is how to efficiently and effectively satisfy the demands associated with the expanded market and corporate growth with existing business assets. Certainly, the type of technology will contribute to the strategic plan in a high growth situation.

ALLIANCES – PARTNERSHIP, FRANCHISE, MERGERS AND ACQUISITIONS

Business Partnership or Alliance

There can be disastrous results when care is not taken to build a solid foundation under which a new business partnership or alliance can safely develop strength and stability. The following list offers some basic steps to consider when moving forward into a business partnership and alliance, which can decrease the chances for negative results, and can increase the chance for a successful partnership to be established:

1. After choosing one another as potential partners, establish mutual ideas, goals, and operating philosophies. Look for enough compatibility to challenge and stimulate one another over time as well as the presence of mutual trust.
2. Choose a partner whose strengths complement the limits of the other partner, and vise versa.
3. Establish the project or core focus of the partnership being created.
4. Determine the kind of partnership that will be created. Will it be equal, or possibly an associate relationship, or any other possible combinations in between? Factors such as level of financial risk, availability of time and energy for the project, and prior existence of any intellectual property related to the project are examples of key items to consider.

Hire a coach that has expertise in this area during the formative stages of the partnership and in the future, can be a good investment with long term benefits.

5. Develop a sound financial compensation plan for profits received, which each partner agrees to in a signed document or contract. Legal representation for the partnership may be appropriate at this juncture.
6. Clearly determine and define the roles each partner will play during the course of the project. Be accountable to a specified role, until both partners change the structure of roles established.
7. Create and support the intent to continually place a plan of action, review the results, and make expedient and necessary shifts that will support the health of the partnership over the life span of the alliance.
8. Develop an immediate support system before entering into a partnership. Educate them about expenditures of time, money, energy and other resources that will be needed to successfully launch the project(s) the partnership represents.
9. Have regularly scheduled weekly meetings. These meetings will be set up for the purpose of discussing progress and challenges, what's working and what is not, areas of discord and mutual planning for future growth and expansion.
10. Set a minimum time period that the partners will agree to a "no exit" clause. New ventures take time to be planted, watered and nourished, weeded and ultimately harvested.

Franchise

A franchisee is no longer the middle-aged manager who fills out endless reams of paperwork and does what the franchiser tells them to do. The International Franchise Association (IFA) identifies 70 categories in franchising and estimated that franchising brought $1 trillion into the U.S. economy in 2000. This indicates there are a lot of choices that may fit business objectives. The franchisee can own their own business and enjoy the benefits of experience, pooled resources and a well-known name or mark. A franchise has three legal elements in the business transaction; license to a trademark, substantial assistance with business operations and payment of franchise fee. The business definition of a franchise reflects a continuing, almost symbiotic relationship between a franchiser, who owns intellectual property and know-how, and the franchisee who investment money to develop a business based on that intellectual property and experience. By using a proven program, risk is reduced and the provider of this property and experience receives a fee and/or royalty.

Some franchisers offer direct financing to help with start-up costs and have preferred relationships with banks and commercial lending companies. Talk to other franchisees and see how they financed their start-up.

The Federal Trade Commission (FTC) provides a free package of information about the FTC Franchise and Business Opportunity rule, which regulates the sale of franchise and business opportunities. Write to Public Reference Branch, Federal Trade Commission, Washington, DC 20580; call 202 326 8128 or visit http://www.ftc.gov.

Check with the Better Business Bureau and consumer or franchise regulators in the state to see if there are any complaints on file against the company or if there are any lawsuits involving fraud or violation of Federal Trade Commission regulations. Seek a Dunn and Bradstreet report (800 234 3867) for financial and business information. Refer to Entrepreneur Magazine's Annual Franchise 500, the best and most comprehensive rating of franchises in the world (www/entrepreneurmag.com). Also, fourteen states regulate franchises and contact can be made through the state franchise authority to see if the company complies with registration requirements (CA, HA, IL IN, MA, MI, MN, ND, NY, RI, SD, VA, WA and WI)

Mergers and Acquisitions

Mergers and acquisitions are on the increase throughout the world. In any technology commercialization strategic plan, there will be an assessment of business relationships that are necessary or preferred to achieve successful asset research, development and/or marketing. As the complexity of technological advances and the need to consolidate numerous inputs into a single output or product increases, the need to merge or acquire providers of these inputs increases.

Factors affecting the merger or acquisition strategic environment have been the end of the "cold war", ushering in a new era of political stability and expanding capitalism, leading to new European and Asian markets. U.S. companies have had to strengthen themselves to exploit new opportunities abroad to compete overseas. In the last 3 years of the 20th century, approximately 27,600 companies joined with each other; so there were more mergers in three years than in the entire decade of the 80's.

The merger activity affects nearly every industry from telecommunication to banking to aerospace to accounting. In 1997, about one trillion dollars was involved in mergers of U.S. companies. The total monetary value of mergers was 50 percent greater than those in '96. In 1997 there were 156 mergers of $1 billion or more; 60 percent higher than in '96 ('97 exceeded $1 billion). Competition drives the merger and often involves large business entities. However, size alone is not a reason to challenge a merger although it seems that mergers often involve the larger enterprises or niche market entities.

INCUBATOR, BUSINESS CLUSTER, OR RESEARCH PARK

BUSINESS INCUBATION

Business incubation is considered to be one method for business and economic development. Currently there are about 600 incubators in the U.S. Some statistics suggest that the success rate of businesses in incubators is nearly 90% (www.nbia.org). On the other hand, more and more e-business Internet companies are considered to be "bricks and clicks" with little need for "bricks and mortar" leading to the advent of "virtual incubators".

Critics say incubators offer little, since a strong company already has good management and capability to raise money. However, this concern often arises when incubator management is made up of individuals who have limited private capital and investment experience.

Often the service incentive of incubators may "cloud" the need to make sound business and investment decisions e.g. whom to incubate. For example, the recent dot.com closings and associated incubators, who often have stakes in dot.coms, are in trouble. CMGI, an Andover, MD based incubator, whose portfolio included AltaVista and PlanetOutdoors.com, stock plunged from $163.50 early in 2000 to $11 late in 2000 (lost $664M in 3rd qtr of 2000).

Divine Intervention Inc., a Chicago incubator, in which CMGI has a 5% stake, went from $12 to <$2. Issues involved excess investing too quickly and a 41-person board, some of whom had conflicts of interest. Divine Intervention has now decided not to work with startups but mergers and acquisitions of existing businesses. Idealab, a Pasadena CA incubator with a $1B private fund, has abandoned an IPO.

Certain assets may merit a startup effort and fit well with the incubation concept such as life science technologies, which take time to develop but also require significant investment for development. These technologies then become good candidates for incubation. Tax breaks, grants and subsidy are often cited as major determinants where a company locates but these are not always valid reasons. For example, necessary support services can be more important for success than where the funds come from.

General considerations when considering an incubator for a business are as follows:

<u>FACILITY SIZE, ft^2</u>	2K - 12K
<u>COST/ft^2</u>	100 - 1000
<u>MANUFACTURING SPACE</u>	3%

<u>OVERALL COST (options and needs)</u>
- Construction/remodeling
- Rental
- Taxes and other government costs
- Transportation
- Services
- Insurance
- Housing
- Plant start-up or moving costs
- Availability and affordability of land
- Cost of living
- Affordable housing
- Proximity of research with main offices.
(Administration efficiency)

<u>INDUSTRY SPECIFICS</u>
- Staffing talent (educated/skilled)
- Proximity to research or medical center e.g. university
- Local image/perception (areas intellectual, business & living environment
- Accessibility (less then 1 hour from major airport)

<u>CRITICAL MASS</u> (provides employee security)
- Biotechnology Centers
- Clusters of companies

<u>FINANCIAL</u>
- Bank financing
- Venture capital
- Early stage financing ("seed" capital)

<u>STRATEGIES</u>
- Takes time
- Buyers market
- Early Stage Company seeks talent
- Manufacturing emphasis will be oriented toward low costs and tax incentives
- Lab space
- Lab tech job training
- Total business & research support
- State/city backed

<u>INCUBATOR PROVISIONS</u>
- Expansion room
- Scale-up equipment
- Scale-up plant & real estate leases
- Stable job base & tax revenues

In some cases, consolidation of businesses in a select area is referred to as business clusters. These can be low technology or high technology "clusters". The cluster environment may offer the same advantages as an incubator. These are natural competitive advantages; mutual reinforcement; information flow among similar companies; environment for innovation; existing suppliers versus new suppliers; personnel exchange; and community relationships expand in schools, colleges, and local businesses.

Clusters usually start as a result of a nurturing environment, supplier base, and university research or government laboratory. Manufacturing and production are not generally as good for cluster formation as the center or core technology. Needs for success of incubators and clusters are a critical mass of expertise, specialized skills and technical resources, environment in which to organize, publicize and promote; along with existing capabilities.

A frequent model that is cited is Silicon Valley and Stanford. One of the myths is that Stanford's technology dominates in Silicon Valley. In a recent 3000-company survey, one in twenty use Stanford technology either directly or indirectly. The key to success was considered to be access to educated and talented employees. Science does not recognize state, nation or country boundaries – it is capability. Large long-term projects are common and the main success criteria other than personnel are financial, big company commitment or alliance/partner relationships, and ability to leverage federal money (basic research) with corporate money (development). Another outcome of the survey was the consensus that information technology services are exploding WW: $265B in '97--- $317B in '99 and E commerce sales are projected to be $1.3T in 2003.

In the past decade, universities have been shifting gears to meet their traditional missions in new ways. Technology commercialization was not even in past vocabularies, and now it is on the agenda alongside academics and research. Business schools went from an exclusive focus on corporations to embracing entrepreneurship. Internships programs have blossomed from negligible to necessary. Business incubators and research parks have appeared in the panoply of programs that fulfill commitments to students, alumni, faculty and community. The question is how to integrate all these efforts for maximum gain.

Some top universities are building dynamic engines with entrepreneurship education, technology commercialization, business incubators, research parks, and internship programs as the working parts. The returns have been substantial, and in some cases unexpected (table one).

Table one. Academic institution benefits related to an incubator, cluster or research park.

Increased enrollment
Enriched educational experiences
Improved faculty recruiting
Increased sponsored research
Enhanced regional economic development
Increased royalty and licensing revenue
Increased student funding and sponsorship
Enhanced academic reputation
Future benefactors
Increased alumni, foundation & corporate support
Increased employment opportunities for graduates

RESEARCH PARK

The role of research parks varies with the institution. The following are the results of a survey of forty-six research parks:

What is the mission?

1.	Economic development	46%
2.	Technology transfer	24%
3.	Advanced research by sponsor	22%
4.	Promote cooperation with private sector	22%
5.	Advance high technology firms	13%

What University assets are of interest to company?
1. Facilities
2. People

What does a Research Park setting offer a business?
What does a Research Park setting offer a business?
1. Technology Transfer
   A. Conflict of Interest
   B. Public Rights
   C. Academic Careers
2. Public/Private Relationships
3. Coordination of University Research Strategies
4. International Collaboration
5. Facility Recruitment (spouse)
6. Capital acquisition

What are Park requirements or issues?
1. Parking
2. Environment (site)
3. Social centers
4. Security (family)
5. Flexible leases
6. Shorter leases
7. Multi user - corporate style buildings
8. Proximity to airport/highway
9. Proximity to research labs
10. Location
11. Space
12. Amenities
13. Continued improvement
14. Support economic development
15. Restrictions
16. Image

Are there market advantages?
1. Products on demand
2. Cheaper
3. Added functionality
4. Life cycle accountability

Can value creation or enhancement be realized?
1. Organize science
2. Abundant resources
3. Focus on problems/needs

What are advantages of multiple business environments?
1. Speed to market
2. Harness necessary skills
3. Alliances

Identify keys to success
1. Relationships
2. Hard work
3. Commitment
4. Management
5. Flexibility (change with needs)
6. Synergism

Advantages an incubator, cluster, research park provide a new business from their perspective are:
1. Conserve cash reserve
    - Minimize initial expense
    - Greater return on investment (15% is good)
    - No real estate value reduction upon relocation
2. Lower total occupancy cost
3. Less staff time spent on real estate matters
4. Minimal down time upon relocation
5. Can expect 2-year cycle but leases of 5-10 year requested
    - No need to buy
    - Option to expand or acquire
    - Lease
6. Research park development strategy
    - Start as not-for-profit
    - Go to combination of for profit and not for profit
    - Design so not for profit can accept gifts
    - Design so for profit can engage in investment
7. Financing guidelines
    - Loan $5 - 20M
    - Building 40K - 140K square feet
    - Interest Rate 150 - 300 basis points above T-bills
    - Amortization 15 - 25 year schedule
    - Loan to value 75% maximum
    - Loan to cost 90%
    - Debt coverage, 1.2 - 1.3

TECHNOLOGY TRANSFER OR COMMERCIALIZATION OFFICE

Technology transfer offices vary in size and scope. There may be a single person who is responsible for the intellectual property that is disclosed to offices with people focused on specific areas of technology and with a support infrastructure that serves the individuals responsible for the select technology area.

Generally, the unit that is involved in the technology transfer provides a service function to the organization and organization's employees. The objective would be to educate the employee and administration on intellectual property policy and procedures. This education would be achieved through appropriate written and electronic communications. In addition, the transfer unit might be responsible for notification to funding organizations when intellectual property creators or authors disclose. The office would be in charge of evaluation, protection and licensing an intellectual property asset. All or part of this responsibility could be performed by organizations external to the originating organization. Therefore, the strategic plan will take into account the financial and personnel commitment needed or available for effective technology commercialization.

Most of the transfer from research institutions is to the small or start-up business community for which protection of intellectual property assets is often critical. It is often prudent to focus on protection strategy as soon as possible or enter into corporate relationships and establish protection strategy in cooperation with the corporate partner. This is especially true in an academic setting in which publication is of primary interest. On the other hand, it is also prudent to assess intellectual property before a transfer and protection strategy is designed and implemented.

Technology commercialization business model

The personnel in the technology transfer or commercialization office will depend on the goals of the office. A small office focused on assuring that discoveries are recognized, disclosed and protected by the organization will be comprised of personnel that may not be as market oriented as an office that is dedicated to marketing intellectual property. Larger offices may focus on internal and external efforts and employ people with different characteristics or personality traits. Others may be technology oriented and personnel will be focused on a select technology from disclosure to market.

In a corporate setting there is significant interest in the asset base of the company and careful attention is usually given to asset disclosure and protection. Therefore, support services may be given the research community in the form of assistance with data retention and disclosure. The industrial approach will also be focused on extending the range of protection or what is sometimes called patent defense or stockade and limiting the publication of information. Hence, the intellectual property protection or technology commercialization strategy will reflect corporate policies and goals.

There is increasing interest in reducing the time to market for all discoveries that can be commercialized. Embarking on the marketing effort can be important in a university environment that does not have development or marketing interest or expertise. However, there is a need to consider the effect of further investment in expertise, research and development to advance a discovery and ultimately enhance the asset's value.

There are numerous reasons given for interest in startup companies some of which are entrepreneurial venture, success, publicity, corporate job instability, corporate downsizing, public offering frenzy, broaden the tax base, active involvement in commercializing a target technology, equity within a venture, product-market diversification, and decentralization or expansion of an organization. However, along with the real or perceived startup benefits, there are risks, such as options usually do not vest for a set period; stock awards dwindle as company grows; salary may be better than salary plus equity; benefit packages may have more value in established firm; management and timing are usually more important than "sexy" technology; need substantial investors with exit strategy- track record with start-ups vs. semi-rich group passing the hat; must be prepared for delays - is there enough sustaining dollars; and family may have to adapt to different life style. Pressure is immense in a startup and it is necessary to be prepared and able to handle it.

DEVELOPMENT OF A TECHNOLOGY-BASED COMPANY

PRE-FORMATION DILIGENCE

There are numerous sources of information available in either hard copy or electronic form that addresses all aspects of starting and growing a business. Anyone involved in a business venture must review as much of the information as possible before embarking on formation of a new or expanded business.

SUCCESSFUL START-UP HISTORY

In a recent U.S. business survey, results indicate that 15 of 19 million businesses are sole proprietorships. Further 90% of all businesses have 19 or fewer employees and 98% of all businesses have less than 100 employees. However, only 7% account for virtually all job growth. As the business progresses there is a 50% turn over every 5 years. Only 2.5% of gazelles (fast growth companies) are high tech and the growth for any given fast growth company is extremely volatile over a 2-3 year period.

"What are the real issues in a new business venture?" Data from the survey suggest the following are key hurdles: policies, regulations, information and interpretation, manufacturing, management (small business people), and employee selection or satisfaction.

A recent survey by Inc. led to the conclusion that there are at least seven habits of effective start-ups. These are presented in table two. The survey also led to the conclusion that prior industry experience was not a significant factor in success. However, the investment community does not always accept this conclusion.

Table two. Habits of effective startups.

1. Founder is ready, willing and able to learn on job.
2. An unusually large amount of time and effort is devoted to established suppliers and subcontractors.
3. Close attention is paid to new entrants and potential competition.
4. Business position and identity need to be established at outset.
5. Ready access to capital.
6. Customized products or services offered.
7. Business is part of a growth industry.

The complexity of a technology impacts the way a technology-based company performs. It is important to provide the organization a steady flow of up-to-date information. In the rapidly changing technology environment, it is critical that the latest information and knowledge are made available to the employees for sustained success. Information flow and keeping current must transcend the boundaries of the company. It is important that individual employees can contact or interact and discuss technical problems with others whether they are within or outside the technology-based company. In a successful technology-based company, the individual's effectiveness is measured by results and credibility, perceived reputation and networks of relationships, rather than formal authority, job description or position in the hierarchy. Technology-based company employees are often more sensitive to peers than to management and therefore, it is important to provide opportunities, challenges, and growth as both individuals and professionals. Remember, compensation and benefits attract but do not retain employees in the technology-based company environment.

With knowledge comes awareness of scientific "tools". State of the art research equipment and services increase employee satisfaction, efficiency and effectiveness in the technology-based company. It is necessary to provide the best and it usually pays off in the long run. Be prepared for change and more importantly try to anticipate change. Scientific information is doubling every five years or less and creating the need to constantly review and possibly change technology and market strategies or tactics. Staying networked and informed are important for success.

What will keep the business successful for the long term? A business needs the flexibility to change and grow with emerging markets, technology, and opportunities. The flexibility to stop what no longer works, to change what can be better, and to develop what's needed is critical. The business also needs a reserve of cash to make immediate changes, bring in new equipment, and to develop employees. Profits must be reinvested to keep the products current and well stocked.

The trend in business development is toward relationship-based marketing. This includes networking, referrals, developing a niche, value-added sales, and being customer-driven. The business owner's idea is no greater than the market's ability and desire to purchase it! There is a need to find out everything possible about what current customers want or need and send the message they want to hear...rather than what the company wants to deliver. Communicate with individuals, and do not shot gun markets. Build a database! Attraction marketing is inter-developmental, that is, the business and the customer act, react, and interact for the benefit of both.

In many businesses, too much attention is placed on reacting to day-to-day problems and not on growing the business. The following contribute directly to sustained profitability: monthly and accurate financial statements, letting go of old ways that reflect the past more than the future, adding product or service lines, automating procedures, having a plan for reinvesting profits, establishing a tight budget, and achieving high employee retention (turnover is very expensive).

Where do businesses spending money needlessly? Is inventory high as a result of poor tracking systems and lack of purchasing controls? Are discounts lost due to late payment or missing discount deadlines? Is advertising in the wrong media or the wrong message portrayed? Is outmoded technology used to run the business? Are costs increased due to poor buying of insurance, supplies, and equipment by not shopping around, providing excessive benefits, and excessive decor? Being over-staffed or poorly staffed will always cost money, and finally, being slow to market by waiting too long to develop new lines or products can be disastrous. What is the mission statement? How is the company to be perceived by its customers? What are the company's values and goals? Has customer loyalty been strengthened by management's reputation for mastering the profession, service, or product line, and do they really understand who the customer is and what they need?

Worthwhile profit uses include; investing in the next product, investing in staff training for better customer service and increased productivity, commitment to keeping up with technology for automation and for developing a customer database, maintaining and attracting good staff with raises, benefits, and sales incentives, expansion either geographically or by increasing inventory levels and maintaining a money reserve for a rainy day...equipment failure, bad judgment, dry spells.

Don't give people a reason to stop buying products being sold. The most common reasons are: 1) changing the packaging or delivery of a product, 2) increasing the price without adding value, 3) ignoring changing customer tastes and needs, 4) lack of innovation and new ways to use a product or service, 5) downscaling the quality of the product and assuming the customer will continue to purchase from the company.

No one becomes successful by accident. Success requires making a plan and sticking to it. It is simple, but does require commitment; it is not hard to do, but does require hard work. The good news is that once begun, the results start coming almost instantly. The miracle of successful living is that the smallest step towards success attracts more success! A brief outline of key points that will help achieve the highest levels of success follows:

1. Look into the nearest mirror - the person staring back is the only person responsible for your success. Smile! No one else is the cause of success or to blame for shortcomings. Successful people take full responsibility for their actions.
2. Smile back at the reflection. Successful people are cheerful, optimistic, and forward thinking. If there is nothing to smile about, smile anyway. Positive thoughts drive out negative thoughts. It's hard to have a negative thought while smiling!
3. Positive self-esteem is the foundation for success. Develop a sense of personal pride in ones abilities, achievements and potential. Don't dwell on mistakes. Remember past accomplishments and develop confidence in making decisions related to future objectives.
4. Believe in yourself and have a purpose. Find a mission and begin working to fulfill it.
5. Strive for success. Be determined to be successful and commit to being successful.
6. Associate with successful people. Do what they do. When faced with choices, make the choice a successful person would make.
7. Avoid unsuccessful people. Do not under any circumstance associate with negative people. Negative people are toxic; they destroy, they do not build. They are vampires that can live only by draining the life from others. The odds are greater that they will pull a person down before they can be lifted up. Avoid whiners, complainers, and blamers.
8. Do what one is best at and what one gets the most satisfaction from. There is no reason to be stuck doing things that are frustrating, boring, unhealthy, unproductive, demeaning or unfulfilling.
9. Record a vision of how one wants to live their life. Be specific; i.e. where one wants to live, what kind of carpet, the type of friends desired, the pony's name, what the new church recreation hall one funded looks like, etc. Make a "future scrapbook"; paste in pictures, drawings, essays, and clippings. Make up news headlines about achievements. Every day visualize yourself, as you would like to be - and then act that way!
10. Record one's biggest goal, the most important one to be fulfilled. Write it in the present tense, "I am...", "I have...", "I contribute...". Success is the result of a personal decision, so start the goal with "I". Read goals aloud every morning and night. Inform others of goals and formulate plans to achieve goals and stick to them.

11. Study the science of success. Read books; listen to tapes, watch videos and positive TV programming. Talk to successful people and ask them how they became successful. Maintain positive thoughts and positive self-affirmations.
12. Every day do something that brings you closer to your goal. Never give up. Failure is due in many cases to a failure to continue to try. Persist. Achieving success requires following a system. Begin today by putting these twelve points into daily practice.

Everybody experiences fear of failure, uncertainty, insecurity, low self-esteem, indecision, depression, nervousness and embarrassment. Successful people master these temporary conditions by taking positive action, by sticking to their plan, by maintaining their vision of the future, by learning from setbacks and by rededicating themselves to the pursuit of their mission. By following these simple steps you will become successful and achieve all that you desire.

Start a business you care about. Before committing to start or buy a business, be sure you're genuinely interested in what the business does. If not, you are unlikely to succeed in the long run-no matter how lucrative the business could be. A few questions to ask before taking the leap are:

1. How will the principal tasks of the business be accomplished? (Don't open a transmission repair shop if one hates cars, or a restaurant if one can't cook.)
2. If the business involves working with others, are the parties good communicators? If not, consider a one-person business.
3. Are basic business principles and tasks understood, such as bookkeeping and financials including profit-and-loss forecasts and cash-flow analysis? If not, learn before, not after, a business is started.

Does the business fit a person's personality? If a person tends to be a shy introvert, stay away from businesses that require extensive personal selling. If the individual is easily bored, find a business, which will require work with new material on a regular basis (publishing a newsletter, for example).

Strategic plans are usually not in place for many startups. Market need is critical even if the technology is good. The key is that a market or markets be identified and in place. Competencies may make an abrupt shift leading to a tendency for the company to drift in its search for markets. When competencies, products and markets are being addressed an incremental assessment based on select goals is necessary to avoid impulse changes in direction. At the same time incremental change may not be preferred if the business becomes tangled with business problems rather than addressing cutting edge technology or product needs that are impacting the business. Generation of ideas is not necessarily creation of business.

A business must be basically strong and then branch out to alliances (must be able to survive on its own). Remember, 70% of alliances end in failure for at least one of the partners, hence, the greater the dependency on alliances the lower the success rate. In the case of a software company, patents may not be of major interest. In a recent survey of 116 software companies, that were less than 8 years old, external alliances were more critical.

PRE-BUSINESS FORMATION SUMMARY

No matter what type of business is being formed there are some practical and legal issues that need to be addressed including choosing a name and location for the business, deciding whether or not to hire employees, writing a business plan, choosing a legal structure, establishing a system for reporting and paying taxes, and adopting policies to deal with customers. Don't be discouraged by the details. If the business is exciting to the creator, a good business plan is in place, and profit potential is highly likely much of the planning is in place. A brief synopsis of items to take into account when planning a business should involve consideration of the following:

1. be committed and excited about the business,
2. write and continually adjust or update a business plan,
3. pick a memorable name for the business,
4. confirm that marks selected for the business are legally available,
5. business location: Let common sense and a clear knowledge of zoning rules,
6. know how to negotiate a good lease,
7. understand and establish employment plans and policies before hiring,
8. define the risks and plans to protect personnel and the businesses,
9. know legal issues related to products and services sold directly to the public,
10. identify information and service providers i.e. related books or software, and/or
11. use the Internet

START-UP CONSIDERATIONS

Business start-up costs will vary with the type and location of the business, but there are certain start-up activities that need to be taken into account. These are presented in the following checklist. Since laws vary by state and type of business, be sure to check with local authorities and your legal counsel to determine if there are any additional legal steps that need to bee taken.

Not every business will have to complete each step. For instance, it may not be necessary to register your trademark with state or federal officials or there may not be interest in publishing a notice of intent to do business.

1. Choose a business based on skills and interests;
2. Research the business idea;
    - What will be sold?
    - Is it legal?
    - Who will buy it and how often?
    - Are you willing to do what it takes to sell the product?
    - What will it cost to produce, advertise, sell & deliver?
      What laws will need to be complied with?
    - Can a profit be made and how much?
    - How long will it take to make a profit?
3. Write a business plan and market plan;
    - Choose a business name
    - Verify right to use the name
4. Reserve corporate name if you will be incorporating;
5. Register or reserve state or federal trademark;
6. Register copyrights;
7. Apply for a patent if intent is to market an invention;
8. Check zoning laws;
9. Choose a location for the business or make space at home;
10. File partnership or incorporation papers;
11. Register business name and get a business certificate;
12. Get required business licenses or permits;
13. Order required notices (advertisements) of intent to do business in the community;
14. Have business phone or extra residential phone lines installed;
15. Check into business insurance needs;
16. Find out about health insurance;
17. Apply for sales tax number;

18. Get tax information such as record keeping requirements, information on withholding taxes if employees are involved, information on hiring independent contractors, facts about estimating taxes, forms of organization;
19. Call Department of Labor to determine labor laws if employees involved;
20. Apply for employee identification number if employees hired;
21. Find out about workers' compensation for employees;
22. Open business bank account(s);
23. Have business cards and stationery printed;
24. Purchase equipment or supplies;
25. Order inventory;
26. Order signage;
27. Order fixtures;
28. Have sales literature prepared;
29. Get adequate business insurance or a business rider to a homeowner's policy;
30. Send out publicity releases;
31. Place advertising if the business will benefit from paid advertising; and/or
32. Publicize the business to friends and acquaintances.

Other startup considerations are presented in a checklist presented in Exhibit C. An example of a software company startup is also presented in Exhibit F.

OVERVIEW

At the outset, structure an organization to grow. Design proper legal and structural aspects for the select business and plan for future growth of the product line, profits, and personnel. Prepare a good business plan including detailed market analysis, sales forecasting, staffing, cost projections, projected financial statements, capital requirements, and financing. The following is an overview of the general consideration and process one might follow as business strategy and planning progresses.

How much money is needed and when which yields the cash flow requirements? This assessment required estimates of expected sales, when and how much, collections e.g. deposits, progress payments, and timing of payments (30-120 days post invoice). One will ignore non-collectables but more important will be the estimation of the amount of non-collectables that will vary for the industry and the particular business venture. What kind of business is anticipated and hence, what type of plan will need to be prepared? Is it a technology rollout, market positioning, sales oriented, manufacture based, acquisition oriented, issue or problem solving or refinancing situation?

Of course a key consideration will be the "stage" of the company. There are several ways a company may be classified. The seed stage company is one with; 1) a promising technology position or business opportunity, 2) compelling commercialization strategy, little if any revenue, or/and 3) a key visionary or business manager who has founded company. An early stage firm has; 1) completed proof of concept; 2) revenue which is less than cash flow breakeven; 3) developed a business plan with defined market opportunity and development strategies; 4) has a core management team in place and/or 5) has a technology leader or experienced manager in place. In other cases, the company classification tends to be more investment oriented.

The first stage company has expended its initial capital and/or need funds for true commercial activities e.g. scale-up, manufacturing and sales. A second stage company is; 1) producing and shipping products; 2) needs additional capital to support growing accounts receivable and inventories and 3) often is not yet profitable. Third stage investment for a company is associated with a firm that; 1) has increasing sales volume; 2) is breaking even or profitable; 3) needs further plant and market expansion needed; 4) requires working capital; and/or 5) is interested in development of an improved product, new technology or expanded product line. Another type of investment is called bridge financing which is capital required in the next 6-10 month period prior to the initial public offering.

ROLE OF BOARDS

Each company will usually have one or more boards associated with it. An investor will be interested in the quality and expertise that makes up a board. Company management will select board membership based on business mission, goals and objectives.

The board of directors will have certain legal and fiduciary responsibilities i.e. policy, major decisions. It is available at www.directorshandbook.com. Members of a board often are or have been associated with business enterprises that operate in a similar or related industry as the company's board in question. A unique document that can be helpful for selecting or for members of a board of directors is "Directors Handbook of Questions" by Scott Pickard.

An advisory board is oriented toward providing advise to the company management related to; 1) technological assessment; 2) strategic plans; 3) are operations reasonable; 4) what "unknowns" need to be considered; 5) "blue sky" or future anticipation and 6) assignments between meetings. The advisory board tends to be more tactical oriented than the board of directors and should not be a substitute for professional advisors or consultants to address specific needs.

FIRST CONTACTS

At the outset there will be several business functions that need to be addressed. Two types of legal needs exist. Corporate (business) counsel will be needed to set up the company, assist with equity arrangements, and help with contract enactment. The goals will be to ensure a high quality firm that has addressed all potential or anticipated legal issues that may arise. The assets of the company will require review and development of a strategy for the company to maintain a proprietary market position. An experienced intellectual property counsel, individual or firm, can assist with strategic planning and procurement of property protection. An accountant will also be critical in establishing the company especially with respect to the basic accounting principles that need to be applied to the type of business, applicable accounting and tax statutes.

A business consultant can also be an important participant in the business venture. Their experience and advice can often enhance the knowledge base and contribute to the success of the business. The role of these advisors may change as the business grows. Further and possibly the main contribution might be advise that keeps the business out of litigation or making business decisions that are not prudent. As one might expect, litigation and business failures are extremely costly to a new or growing enterprise.

Initially the company management may want to seek one hour of consultation with these business and legal advisors. This initial discussion will be the time to establish compatibility and assess capabilities of the consultant/advisor and will usually not be subject to a fee for service. The following should be ascertained during this initial discussion: 1) review of your background; 1) what is the company and its mission?; 2) "what can consultant/advisor do for the company?"; 3) does consultant/advisor have clients similar to your business and who you might know (get references)?"; 4) what preliminary suggestions does consultant/advisor have; 5) what can you do; 6) what role would consultant/advisor want to play; 7) what will this cost? (Do not pay in stock – a fired advisor who holds stock can be bad.); 8) when should the next meeting be scheduled and what would the agenda items be; and 9) what should be done in the event issues arise in meantime?

FOR-PROFIT COMPANIES

Questions frequently arise for lawyers who counsel small business owners concerning the form a business should take. The choices may vary slightly from state to state but generally include a sole proprietorship, a partnership, a corporation or a limited liability company. The analysis applies to the start up as well as an on-going business. A comparison of business entities is presented in Exhibit B. The threshold question which needs to be addressed is: Will the business be owned by one person or more than one person? If an individual owns the business, it may be owned as a sole proprietorship, a corporation or a limited liability company (LLC).

Ownership of a business by an individual is usually set up as a sole proprietorship. A sole proprietorship can exist either under the owner's real name or under a fictitious name (commonly referred to as a "dba", an acronym for "doing business as"). It is not important or significant as to which of these two forms of sole proprietorship is used. It is important to consider whether the sole proprietorship either has one or more employees or uses independent contractors in conducting its business. If a sole proprietorship has no employees and does not use independent contractors to assist in doing its work, changing the form of business from sole proprietorship to any other form of business rarely makes sense.

The vast majority of small business people begin as sole proprietors, because it's cheap, easy and fast. With a sole proprietorship, there's no need to draft a partnership agreement or go to the trouble and expense of registering a corporation or limited liability company (LLC) with your state regulatory agency. All it usually entails is getting a local business license, and unless you are doing business under your own name, filing and possibly publishing a fictitious name statement. But there are several reasons why doing business, as a sole proprietor is not appropriate for everyone. First, the owner of a sole proprietorship is personally responsible for all business debts, whereas limited liability companies and corporations normally shield their owners' assets from such debts. Second, a sole proprietorship is possible only when one person or a husband and wife own a business. And finally, unlike a corporation, which is normally taxed separately from its owners (something that can actually result in lower taxes for many small businesses-sees below), a sole proprietor and her business are considered to be the same legal entity for tax purposes.

One big advantage of a partnership is that it is not necessary to register with the state and pay a registration fee. In addition, because a partnership is a "pass through" tax entity (the partners, not the partnership, are taxed) filing income tax returns is easier than it is for a regular corporation, where separate tax returns must be filed for the corporate entity and its owners. However, because business-related acts of one partner legally bind all others, it is essential partners completely trust each other. Prepare a written partnership agreement establishing, among other things, each partner's share of profits or losses, day-to-day duties and what happens if a partner dies or retires.

A major disadvantage of doing business as a partnership is that all partners are personally liable for business debts and liabilities (for example, a judgment in a lawsuit). While it's true that a good insurance policy can do much to reduce lawsuit worries and that many small, savvy businesses don't have debt problems, it's also true that businesses, which face significant risks in either of these areas should probably organize themselves as a corporation or LLC. There are only two reasons one would ever use a corporation or LLC for such a business: for tax reasons or to limit one's personal liability.

It is uncommon that such a business would benefit for tax reasons. In fact, in many instances it would cost more to operate a business as either a corporation or LLC than it would as a sole proprietorship. An accountant should provide advice as to if and when it would be beneficial to change the form of business for tax reasons. The other reason for using a corporate or LLC form of business is to limit personal liability. Many people believe if they incorporate their sole proprietorship business, they can protect themselves against their own mistakes. Nothing could be more incorrect. One cannot exculpate him - or herself from their acts by doing business as a corporation or LLC. If the business is either a corporation or LLC, you are the sole owner (i.e., shareholder), if you do not have employees or use independent contractors, and you do something that creates a liability; the law will hold both the business and you personally responsible for your conduct. The way to protect the individual financially from mistakes in this situation is to have both proper and adequate insurance.

A sole proprietorship with either employees or independent contractors may be best changed to a corporation or an LLC. As an example, consider a swimming pool company, which is a sole proprietorship but has a few employees and also uses certain sub-contractors. In a hypothetical situation in which one of the employees (not the owner) or sub-contractors does something that causes injury to someone using the pool, that victim may sue the swimming pool company as well as the employee or sub-contractor who made the mistake. If the owner is operating the business as a sole proprietorship, not only will all of the company's assets be exposed but all of the owner's personal assets will also be exposed. Of course, insurance could help protect the owner and there should also be insurance for the business entity. But, there are instances when the amount of damage exceeds the policy limit or where a circumstance is unusual and the policy does not provide coverage for such an event. However, if that same hypothetical arose and the business was either an LLC or a corporation, while the individual employee or the sub-contractor would still be exposed, as would the LLC or corporation, the owner and the owner's personal assets would be protected.

One might incorporate as a subchapter S, close corporation that would be taxed like a sole proprietorship and would also minimize virtually all-corporate formalities, which would have to be followed in a general corporation. Then, lease office space, including furniture and equipment from oneself to their corporation, and also lease all business vehicles from oneself to the corporation. The corporation owned pens, pencils, paper, forms and similar things but leased or rented everything else. Then, all that is exposed is the company's insurance policy limits and the few things the company actually owned. Personal home and other personal holdings, commercial building and furnishings, and business vehicles would not be exposed as assets.

When more than one person owns a business, it may be operated as a partnership, an LLC or a corporation. In general, the problems, which exist for a sole proprietorship, which uses employees or independent contractors, also exist when there are two or more owners of a business. One also has the additional problem that both partners are jointly and severally liable for the partnership debts or other obligations. What this means is that one partner can unilaterally commit to an obligation on behalf of the partnership, later go bankrupt and the remaining partner will wind up being personally liable on the obligation. A very careful analysis should always be made concerning the best form in which to do business when there are multiple owners of that business. Whatever the form of business with multiple owners, it is critical that the business be set up and operated properly. If a business is operated as a corporation or LLC, certain paper work must be prepared and processed with the state to create the entity.

While this can be done without the assistance of legal counsel, to save money by doing it yourself is frequently "penny wise but pound foolish". Preparation of articles of incorporation and by-laws is only a small part of what a lawyer does in setting up a corporation. Knowing what questions to ask and what recommendations to make for the business is the more difficult part of forming the business. Issues such as pooling agreements as to shares of stock or first right of refusal in a stock sale may be important but not even recognized by the do-it-yourselfer. Operation of a corporation is also important. Failure to operate the business properly could result in destroying the protection afforded through corporate shield. There is even a legal doctrine used by lawyers to get beyond the protection usually afforded by the corporate structure called "piercing the corporate veil." It is simply stupid to go to the trouble of forming a corporation to shield one's self from personal liability and then destroy that protection by improper operation of the corporation.

One of the most common problems, which arise in the small business setting, involves partnerships. Typically, when two or more people begin a new business venture as a partnership, everything is cordial and exciting, and everyone trusts everyone else. Most of the time, very little is put in writing and even more rarely, is a partnership agreement prepared and signed. Inevitably, things go wrong somewhere in the future. It is common for animosity and distrust to arise. When this happens without a proper and adequate written partnership agreement in place, it is almost always a disaster. In fact, in most cases, if the parties have not provided the terms and conditions of the partnership, the state has provided them by default. Virtually, all states have adopted some version of a model law known as the Uniform Partnership Act. This act provides for the terms and conditions of a partnership agreement when the parties themselves fail to provide for such an agreement. Many partners learn about this law the hard way: After it is too late!

Pay now or pay later - People starting a new business typically have limited resources to start the business. When faced with the option of having foil embossed stationery and business cards but not being able to "afford" a consultation with a lawyer, or saving money by having plain cards and stationery and being able to afford the legal consultation, people starting a business usually opt for the upgraded stationery and forego legal advice. This occurs, in part, from the simple fact that most people starting businesses fail to recognize their need for legal advice. Most lawyers do not mind. They may earn a few hundred dollars to $1,500 in advising a start-up business and preparing the proper legal papers but will make many times more from the do-it-yourselfer who later needs a lawyer to extricate him from his own mistakes caused by not getting legal advice in the beginning. Remember, that one can pay a few hundred dollars now or greater than $60,000 later to resolve a bad situation which occurs as a result of no legal advice to begin with.

EXIT STRATEGY, FINANCING NEEDS AND ENTITY FORM

No single entity is perfect for every business venture; there are a number of different factors that favor one entity over another. In dealing with a technology or Internet start-up business, however, two very important factors in deciding which form of entity to choose are (a) expectation of the most likely exit strategy, if any, and when; and (b) expected financial needs, particularly venture capital.

Exit strategy is the plan, if any, to sell the business, how, and when. While it may seem odd to focus on an exit strategy at the start of a technology or internet business, in the technology and internet world where a year is 5 weeks and companies are born and sold (or go public) in a span of months and not years, give some thought up-front to which, if any, exit strategy is most likely and when.

Companies that expect to go public and/or will need a significant amount of venture capital financing may be best suited with a C Corporation. Companies that don't anticipate going public or will not need much, if any, venture capital financing, may be best suited with a limited liability company (LLC). Work closely with an attorney to decide which entity is most appropriate for the particular business. Exit strategy examples are:

1. *Asset sale.* Sale of some or all of the company's assets to a buyer (either another company or individual(s).
2. *Private equity sale.* Sale of ownership interests (stock or membership interests) in a private sale to another company or to one or more individuals.
3. *Initial public offering (IPO).* Sale of ownership interests through an IPO on a public stock exchange like the NASDAQ or NYSE.
4. *Merger.* A corporate reorganization, such as a merger or combination with another company. (For example, in the Time Warner/AOL merger Time Warner was merged into AOL and Time Warner shareholders gave up Time Warner stock for AOL stock).

INCORPORATION AND TAXES

Taxation of business income is complicated; and only the high points are presented herein. First, understand that most types of businesses-sole proprietorships, partnerships, the great majority of limited liability companies and corporations that have qualified for Subchapter S status-are known as pass through tax entities, meaning that all business profits are reflected on the individual tax returns of the owners. For example, if a sole proprietor's convenience store turns a yearly profit of $85,000, this amount goes right on their personal tax return. By contrast, a regular profit corporation (often called a C corporation, after the applicable section of the Internal Revenue Code) is a separate tax entity from its owner(s)-meaning that the business files a tax return and pays its own tax.

But this doesn't necessarily mean profits of a C corporation will be taxed twice. That's because owners of most incorporated small businesses are also employees of those businesses; with the result that money they receive in the form of salaries and bonuses is tax deductible to the corporation as an ordinary and necessary business expense. In short, after surplus money is paid to owners in the form of salaries and bonuses, a corporation often shows no profit and therefore pays no corporate income tax.

In some situations there can be tax advantages to incorporating. That's because corporations pay federal income tax at a far lower rate than do most individuals for the first $75,000 of their profits-15% of the first $50,000 of profit and 25% of the next $25,000. By contrast, in a sole proprietorship or partnership, where all profits are taxed to the business owner(s), up to 39.6% could be subject to federal income tax. What this amounts to is that a corporation can often reduce taxes by paying its owner-employees a decent salary (which, of course, is tax-deductible to the corporation but taxable to the employee), and then retaining additional profits in the business (say, for future expansion).

S CORPORATION AND TAXES

S corporation tax status will benefit those corporations that will not save taxes by splitting income between the corporation and its owners. The election will also benefit corporations that expect losses in the early years of operation. If losses are passed through to individual shareholders, they may be able to deduct these losses against other income on their tax returns. Since the wide legal acceptance of limited liability companies, S corporations have become less popular. That's because LLCs often more easily accomplish the same goals.

Unlike S corporations, there are no limits on the number or type of members in an LLC. S corporations must divide profits and losses according to stock percentages--with owners' interests limited to their capital contributions. In an LLC, profits and losses can be split up in any manner. For example, a person making a 10% capital cash contribution could get a 30% interest in the profits of the LLC. LLCs also allow investors to make any sort of capital contributions--such as cash, property, services, or a later promise to pay cash (a promissory note) or provide services (an employment contract). In some states, such as New York, corporations cannot be capitalized with the promise to pay cash or perform services in the future.

Tax consequences are often of most concern to a not-for-profit organization that must be careful about unrelated business income tax. The tax consequences for a corporation and LLC are summarized in table three.

Table three. Tax consequences of select business forms.

Corporation	LLC
Separate taxable entity	flow through treatment*
2nd level of tax on dividends	members report income, gain and losses of LLC
No flow through of losses	loss limitations; passive loss rules

* Flow through does not appeal to a not-for-profit entity and can affect the not-for-profit status. It also does not appeal to foreign investor due to tax consequences. When setting up business consider investor exit. It is possible to switch partnership to corporation tax-free but cannot switch corporation to partnership tax-free.

WHERE TO FORM ENTITY

Selection of the state in which to incorporate will also be a consideration in setting up a business. The choices are within the state where the business is located or incorporation in Delaware. Delaware has been a popular state for incorporation because of the good case law and court system (good anti-takeover provision in statutes), investor preference and stock prices of Delaware corporations seems to have performed better. A more detailed checklist related to forming a business is presented in Exhibit D.

BUSINESS INCORPORATION

The incorporation process for a business involves primarily three steps:

1. performing a preliminary name check;
2. preparing and filing articles of incorporation with the state; and
3. paying all state filing fees.

The name check is performed at state level to determine if the name selected is already in use by an existing business entity in the state. If the name is already in use, the state will require a different name be used to avoid confusion.

The next step is to prepare articles of incorporation. Articles of incorporation are filed with the state and must comply with state law. Articles of Incorporation are the most important corporation document and usually contain five to seven clauses stating basic information about the company.

Start by understanding that it usually makes the most sense to stay put and incorporate in the state where you do most of your business. If you form an out-of-state corporation (such as in Delaware or Nevada, two of the current favorites), you will end up having to qualify to do business in your home state anyway. Unfortunately, this process is similar to incorporating in your state, and costs the same. It will be necessary to pay any state corporate income taxes levied in the businesses home state for income earned there. Even if another state has more modern or flexible corporation laws, these mostly favor large, publicly held corporations, not the smaller type of privately held corporation most small business owners form.

It's easy to incorporate as long as founders, close associates and family members own all stock and none is sold to the public. Necessary legal documents-principally Articles of Incorporation and Corporate Bylaws-can usually are prepared in a few hours. The first step is to check with the state's corporate filing office (usually either the Secretary of State or Corporations Commissioner) and federal and state trademark registers to be sure the company name is available for use. Then fill in blanks in a preprinted form (available from commercial publishers or your state's corporate filing office) listing the name of the corporation, purpose of corporation, its principal place of business and the number and type of shares of stock the corporation is authorized to issue and the name of the corporation registered agent.

These documents are filed with the appropriate office, along with a registration fee, which is usually between $200 and $1,000, depending on the state. Corporate Bylaws will need to be completed, but not filed. These outline a number of important corporate housekeeping details such as when annual shareholder meetings will be held, who can vote and the manner in which shareholders will be notified if there is need for an additional "special" meeting.

The state approves articles and the corporation comes into existence after review to make certain they comply with state statutes and collects fees due.

A certified copy of the articles is sent back to the person forming the corporation to prove corporation has been formed with the state. This along with a federal tax identification number (also known as a federal employer identification number) will be needed to set up a bank account.

There are firms that provide incorporation services such as "Business Filings Incorporated". The firm offers a "turnkey" service designed to complete all necessary steps to obtain approval from the state as quickly and cost effectively as possible. Business Filings charges about $100 plus state fees. (http://www.bizfilings.com/)

If the corporation has not sold stock to the public, conducting corporate business is remarkably straightforward and uncomplicated. Often it is no more than recording key corporate decisions (for example, borrowing money or buying real estate) and holding an annual meeting. Even these formalities can often be completed by written agreement and may not necessitate a face-to-face meeting.

Self-help books exist in many states, which make it easy and safe to incorporate your business without a lawyer and, once incorporated, operate your corporation. See the directory in Exhibit C, Forms and Bylaws in Exhibit E, Addendum I (Glossary of Terms) and Addendum II (References and Resources).

BUSINESS NAME SELECTION

Select a memorable name for the business. Products or services will likely be marketed under a business name. Assume there will be competitors and the business name will be a significant part of the marketing identity. For marketing purposes, the best names are those that customers will easily remember and associate with your business. Also, if the name is memorable, it will be easier to stop others from using it in the future (See module II - intellectual property)

Most memorable business names are made-up words, or are somehow fanciful or surprising, such as Exxon and Kodak (made-up words), Double Rainbow ice cream (fanciful) and Penguin Books (surprising). And some notable names are cleverly suggestive, such as The Body Shop (a store that sells personal hygiene products) and Accuride tires.

Names that tend to be forgotten by consumers are common names (names of most people), geographic terms and names that literally describe some aspect of a product or service. For instance, Steve's Web Designs may be a name that delights Steve, but it's not likely to help Steve's customers remember his company when faced with competitors such as Clever Spider Web Designs and even Left Bank Web Designs. Similarly, names like Central Word Processing Services or Robust Health Foods are not particularly memorable.

While it's true that over time even a common name can occasionally become memorable through widespread use and advertising, as with Ben and Jerry's Ice Cream, it's also true that most small business people can't afford the advertising it takes to accomplish this. A word of caution; professionals face special rules and customs. Although change is in the air, custom and the rules of some professional licensing groups often restrict the names that their members can use. For example, lawyers, physicians and CPAs are limited in many states to using the names of one or more of the licensed professionals who own the business. If a different name is desired i.e. "The Evergreen Accounting Group," check with the state licensing board to see if this is permitted.

Can the chosen business name be legally used? The first step depends on whether the plan is to incorporate the business. Check with the Secretary of State's office in the state capital to see whether the proposed name is the same or confusingly similar to an existing corporate name in that state, if it is, choose a different name. If incorporation is not planned, check with the county clerk to see whether the proposed name is already on the list maintained for fictitious or assumed business names in the county. In the few states where assumed business name registrations are statewide, check with the Secretary of State's office. (The county clerk should be able to indicate whether there is a need to check the name at the state level.) If the chosen name (or a very similar name) is listed on a fictitious or assumed name register, do not use it:

1. A business name may be a trade name that describes the business for purposes of bank accounts, invoices and taxes,
2. A business name may be a trademark used to identify and distinguish products sold by the business (for example, Ford Motor Co. sells Ford automobiles), and
3. A business name may be a service mark used to identify and distinguish services sold by the business (McDonald's Corporation offers McDonald's fast food services).

While a state's corporate or assumed business name registration offices can legally clear the name for the first purpose, they do not speak to the second and third. For example, a green light from the Secretary of State to use IBM Toxics as a business name (if no other corporation in the state is using it or something confusingly similar), it may not be possible to use that name in the marketplace and if it is used there may be trouble with the IBM general counsel's office.

To find out whether a proposed name can be used as a trademark or service mark to identify and market products and services, conduct a trademark search. If the name is available and the service or product will be marketed in more than one state (or across territorial or international borders), it is wise to file an application with the U.S. Patent and Trademark Office to reserve the name for federal registration.

BUSINESS LOCATION

Commercial real estate brokers are fond of saying the three most important factors in establishing a business is location, location and location. While true for a few types of businesses-such as a retail sandwich shop that depends on lunch time walk-in trade-for most, locating in a popular high-cost area is a mistake. For example, if the business designs computer software, repairs tile, imports jewelry from Indonesia, or does any one of ten thousand other things that doesn't rely on foot traffic, the best bet is to search for convenient, low-cost, utilitarian surroundings. And even if yours is a business that many people will visit, consider the possibility that a reasonably priced offbeat location may make more sense than a high-cost trendy one. Remember, businesses that pay a comparatively low rent have lots of money to spend on other important aspects of their business or can pass some of their savings along to their customers in the form of lower prices.

But no matter what location is chosen, never purchase property or sign a lease without being absolutely sure operation of the business is permitted. If the business will be located in a non-shopping center area, especially an off-beat one is sure the business meets applicable zoning rules, which typically divide a municipality into residential, commercial, industrial and mixed-use areas. Determine if any other legal restrictions will affect operations. For example, some cities limit the number of certain types of business-such as fast food restaurants or coffee bars-in certain areas, and others require that a business provide off-street parking, close early on weeknights, limit advertising signs or meet other rules as a condition of getting a permit. Fortunately, many cities have business development offices, which help small business owners understand and cope with restrictions.

LEASE NEGOTIATION

Almost all small businesses start out in leased premises and many use leased space throughout the life of the business. By leasing rather than owning, valuable working capital is not tied up. It is also easier to move to new quarters if space needs change. Securing space will usually mean examination of a typed or printed lease prepared by the landlord or the landlord's lawyer. Rule one is to understand that the terms almost always favor the landlord. Rule two is to know that with a little effort significant improvements in the lease can be negotiated.

Obviously, one big issue to consider is how much rent is required. Commercial space is usually priced by the square foot and figured by the year; $20 a square foot, for example, means $20 per square foot per year. Space is sometimes priced by the month; $1.60 a square foot would mean $1.60 per square foot per month, or $18 a square foot figured yearly. Either way, it's sensible to check out rates for comparable spaces and ask for a reduction.

When "shopping around" look carefully at who is required to pay taxes, insurance, repairs and utilities. With a "gross lease," the leasee pays for none of these. By contrast, with a "triple net lease" the leasee pays for them all--potentially a large sum. In fact, the best approach may be to pay a relatively higher amount for rent in exchange for eliminating these extras. But don't just focus on what is to be paid each month. Other concerns can be more significant. For example, if improvements are needed (called build outs), use the lion's share of your bargaining power to have the landlord provide them at no cost. Or if the move will be costly, resulting in a temporary cash flow problem, ask for a few months of reduced rent.

The negotiating power on these and other issues depends on whether the local rental market is hot or cold. If plenty of commercial space is available, it is probable that landlords will make concessions but if the rental market is tight or unique space is needed leverage is reduced or non-existent. One area of the lease to focus on is the length. Occasionally, a small business that's just starting out wants a month-to-month tenancy, permitting the tenant to move on with 30 days' written notice. The majority of small businesses, however, prefer the protection of a written lease that lasts a year or more.

If the business isn't particularly location-sensitive (a mail order business or software testing lab, for example) and plenty of commercial space is available in the area, a short-term lease probably makes the most sense. Even if the landlord doesn't renew the lease, finding comparable space won't be a problem. But if an especially favorable location for a retail shop, restaurant or other business is found in which location is key, deciding on how long a lease to ask for is far more problematic. If the business does well, it may be advisable to get the right to stay on for an extended period. On the other hand, if business uncertainty exists, being bound to a four-year lease could be problematic in the event of business failure or lack of success.

A good solution is to bargain for a short initial lease with one or more options to renew; i.e. a one or two-year lease with an option to renew for two or three more years. Typically, an option gives the right to exercise an option to stay by notifying the landlord in writing a certain number of days or months before the lease expires.

If asking for an option, expect the landlord to want a higher rent for the renewal period. If the property is particularly desirable, the owner may also want an extra fee in exchange for giving the choice to stay or leave.

HUMAN RESOURCE PROCUREMENT AND DISMISSAL
Plan Before Hiring Employees

At some point during the business venture, there will be a need to hire people to help manage the workload. The company or individual will be held accountable to a host of state and federal laws that regulate the owner-employee relationship. Among the legal rules that will need to be thoroughly understood before becoming an employer is:

1. wage and hour laws (including the minimum wage and when overtime pay is required), as well as the laws that govern retirement plans and healthcare benefits;
2. properly classifying independent contractors (and avoiding illegally treating part-time or full-time employees as independent contractors);
3. proper hiring practices, including how to write appropriate job descriptions, conduct interviews and respect employee privacy rights;
4. workplace safety rules and regulations;
5. how to avoid sexual harassment as well as discrimination based on sex, age, race, pregnancy, sexual orientation and national origin; and
6. how to avoid trouble if there is a need to fire an employee.

Consider carefully what the potential liabilities are if someone is injured or suffers an economic loss if a product is defective or the service substandard. For example, suppose a copy shop is operated in leased premises with ten employees. There is a heavy walk-in trade, and deliveries are made to important customers. Potential legal risks include:

1. customers being hurt on the premises;
2. a delivery vehicle accident;
3. the possibility that an employee may lose or damage a customer's original documents, storage and disposal of toxic chemicals;
4. problems with lease, and if it ends soon, legal and practical aspects of renewing it; and
5. the possibility an employee will quit and open up a similar business across the street, having stolen the confidential customer list.

NOT-FOR-PROFIT ASSOCIATIONS/ORGANIZATIONS

OVERVIEW

Nonprofit corporations, by definition, exist not to make money but to fulfill one of the purposes recognized by federal law, charitable, educational, religious, scientific or literary activities. A nonprofit corporation is a group of people who join together to do some activity that benefits the public, such as running a homeless shelter, an artists' performance group or a low-cost medical clinic. Making a profit from these activities is allowed under legal and tax rules as long as the money is used for nonprofit purposes, but the primary purpose of the organization should be to do good work, not make money.

PROFIT DEFINITION

Making a profit from related activities should be well understood and carefully managed to assure that the associations does not loose its non-for-profit status and become subject to taxation.

An example of a non-profit organization is a group called Friends of the Library, Inc. It's a 501(c)(3) nonprofit (that means it has a federal tax exemption) organized to encourage literary appreciation in the community and to raise money for the support and improvement of the public library. It can make a profit from its lecture series featuring famous authors and from its annual sale of donated books.

Because these activities are educational, they do not jeopardize the group's tax-exempt status. It may use its tax-free profits for its own operating expenses (including salaries for officers and staff) or for the benefit of the library. What it cannot do is distribute any of the profits for the benefit of officers, directors or employees connected with Friends of the Library--as dividends, for example.

UNRELATED BUSINESS ACTIVITY

Nonprofits can also make money in ways that aren't related to their nonprofit purposes. Such unrelated business income is permissible and often essential to the survival of nonprofit organizations. But it is subject to taxation, under state and federal corporate tax rules.

It's best not to let unrelated business activities reach the point where the group starts to look like a regular commercial business. Unrelated business activities shouldn't absorb a substantial amount of staff time, require additional paid staff or volunteers to run them, or produce much more income than the exempt-purpose activities and services generate. For example, assure that many thousands of books are donated to Friends of the Library for its annual book sale, one of its major fund raising events. Although the sale is always highly successful, thousands of books are left over, and Friends decides to sell the more valuable ones by advertising in the rare and out-of-print books classified sections in various magazines.

The response is overwhelming, and soon there are six employees cataloguing books. In addition, Friends begins a business buying books from other dealers and reselling them to the public. Such a situation could attract attention from the IRS and prompt it to reconsider Friends' 501(c)(3) tax-exempt status. Finally, although it's not typical for the average group, a nonprofit corporation may make money from "passive" sources such as rents, royalties, interest and investments. This income is non-taxable in some cases.

TAX EXEMPTIONS

What type of exemptions do most nonprofits get? Most nonprofit organizations obtain a federal tax exemption under Section 501(c)(3) of the Internal Revenue Code for charitable, education, religious, scientific or literary purposes. States typically follow the federal lead and grant state tax-exempt status to nonprofits recognized by the IRS as 501(c)(3)s. To apply for federal nonprofit tax status, get an IRS Package 1023 exemption application. This is a lengthy and technical application with many references to the federal tax code. Most nonprofit organizers need help in addition to the IRS instructions that accompany the form but it can be accomplished. A self-help resource is available from Nolo titled "How to Form Your Own Nonprofit Corporation" by Anthony Mancuso, which shows how to complete an application line-by-line.

Generally the following conditions must be met to qualify for a 501(c)(3) IRS tax exemption:

1. Assets of the nonprofit must be irrevocably dedicated to charitable, educational, religious or similar purposes. If the 501(c)(3) nonprofit dissolves, any assets it owns must be transferred to another 501(c)(3) organization. It is not necessary to name the specific organization that will receive the assets. A broad dedication clause will suffice.
2. The organization cannot campaign for or against candidates for public office.
3. Political lobbying activity is restricted.
4. If nonprofit makes a profit from activities unrelated to its exempt-purposes activities, it must pay taxes on profit (but up to $1,000 of unrelated income can be earned tax-free).

INCORPORATION – WHY?

Five reasons to incorporate a nonprofit association are:

1. desire to solicit tax-deductible contributions;
2. association makes a taxable profit from its activities;
3. intent is to apply for public or private grant money;
4. members want some protection from legal liability; and/or
5. advocacy efforts might provoke legal quarrels.

If an organization becomes a tax-exempt nonprofit corporation, donors can deduct their gifts to the group on their federal and state tax income returns. Assume that a group, For Shore United, wants to sponsor monthly cleanup drives to pick up and haul away trash left along the local bay shore. A sufficient number of enthusiastic volunteers have been enlisted but funds are needed to rent a truck, buy gas and pay for volunteers' meals. Many in the local community would be willing to chip in and help fund the effort, but only if the group was a recognized public charity eligible to receive tax-deductible contributions. The decision is to incorporate as a nonprofit corporation and apply for tax-exempt status to accomplish this objective.

The association makes a taxable profit from its activities. If a profit is made from its activities, incorporating as a nonprofit can yield a great benefit: There will not be a need to pay income tax on the money made. For example, an educational nonprofit association, Better Books and Learning, which began as a part-time effort by a few dedicated individuals who led book-reading groups for disadvantaged youth. The volunteers paid all expenses out-of-pocket, and the group never made a profit. But now, a board member of a local junior college has heard about the good work and asks the group to submit a bid for a consulting contract to the college. The group would be paid for administering and running book reading and discussion groups as part of the college curriculum. The board of the college accepts the bid and the group will now show a profit from its educational activities. It decides to incorporate as a nonprofit and seek tax-exempt status with the IRS to avoid paying income tax on money generated by the consulting contract.

There is a desire to apply for public or private grant money. Sorry, but without being recognized as a tax-exempt nonprofit by the IRS, the group is unlikely to qualify for grants. A nonprofit, tax-exempt association could be formed, rather than a corporation, but preparing and filing the standard incorporation forms is simpler and easier. (Tax-exempt associations require a customized charter and set of operating rules.) Further, the IRS generally has an easier time approving tax exemptions for nonprofit corporations. This is the normal type of nonprofit legal entity.

Members want some protection from legal liability. If there is the possibility of a lawsuit, incorporation can provide welcome peace of mind. Nonprofit corporations can still be sued; but their individual members are generally protected from personal liability. That's not true of an unincorporated association. For example, Engineers for the Environment is a nonprofit, educational consulting firm that helps developers prepare environmental impact reports for nonprofit housing and ensure compliance with state and federal regulations. To avoid legal liability if projects are denied approval or if unforeseen federal and state guidelines cause costly delays with client projects, they decide to incorporate their organization.

Advocacy efforts might provoke legal quarrels. Nonprofits may engage in political advocacy only to an insubstantial degree, unless they elect to follow special federal political lobbying rules. These rules limit the amount of money spent to further political causes, such as sponsoring or opposing federal, state and local legislation.

The primary purpose of No Smoke United, an anti-smoking nonprofit group, is to inform the public the health hazards of secondary smoke from cigarettes. But it also sometimes enters the political fray. One of its recent efforts is a campaign for local legislation banning cigarette advertising on billboards in the community. It expects rapid and sure-fire response from cigarette advertisers and the ad agencies they employ, including the filing of spurious, but expensive and time-consuming, lawsuits against their organization and its directors and officers personally. The embers decide to incorporate before beginning the campaign, to insulate their directors and officers from personal liability and to allow the corporation to approve indemnification provisions in its Bylaws. These provisions will permit directors and officers to be advanced or repaid expenses by the nonprofit corporation for any personal expenses they incur for appearing in and defending lawsuits.

Most helping groups start out as small, loosely structured organizations. Volunteers perform the work, and the group spends what little money it earns to keep the organization afloat. Because there is no profit, the group does not file tax returns. Formal legal papers (such as a nonprofit charter or bylaws) are rarely prepared at this stage. Legally, groups of this sort are considered nonprofit associations, and in legal theory-but rarely in practice-each member can be held personally liable for organizational debts and liabilities.

Once a nonprofit association starts to take in money, or wishes to obtain a tax exemption to attract public support and qualify for grant funds, it usually formalizes its structure. Typically a decision is made to incorporate, but adopting a formal charter and operating bylaws for an unincorporated association is an alternative. Most groups form a nonprofit corporation because it is the more traditional legal structure and one the IRS and grant agencies are very familiar with it. Once incorporated, the individual members of the nonprofit are not personally liable for debts of the organization-a big legal advantage of the corporate form over the unincorporated association.

To form a nonprofit corporation, one of the organization's founders prepares and files standard Articles of Incorporation; a short legal document that lists the name and directors of the nonprofit plus other basic information. The Articles are filed with the Secretary of State's office for a modest filing fee in the state where the nonprofit has its operations or headquarters. In addition, the nonprofit will want to apply for and obtain a federal and state nonprofit tax exemption which frees you from having to pay income taxes on profits made from engaging in your nonprofit activities, makes you eligible for charitable tax deductible contributions from donors and qualifies the firm for local real and personal property tax exemptions. It's often best to obtain the state tax exemption before filing Articles with the Secretary of State. This approach allows one to file the Articles without making the tax payments that the state requires of nonexempt corporations. For example, in California, if nonprofit Articles are filed after getting the state tax exemption, the fee is just $80; but if filing is before the exemption is received, the fee is $880 (one pays the extra $800 required to form a nonexempt corporation).

HOME-BASED BUSINESSES

With the rapid advances in communications technology, it becomes more and more efficient and economical to operate a business from home. Depending on local zoning rules, as long as the business is small, quiet and doesn't create traffic or parking problems, it's usually legal to do so. But as with any other business endeavor, it pays to know the rules before beginning.

Home-based businesses aren't legally different from other businesses. The basic legal issues, such as picking a name for the business and deciding whether to operate as a sole proprietorship, partnership, limited liability company or corporation, apply to all businesses whether they operate from a garage or the Sears Tower. Similarly, when it comes to signing contracts, hiring employees and collecting from customers, the laws are identical.

What laws govern a person's right to operate a business from home? Municipalities have the legal right to establish rules about what types of activities can be carried out in different geographical areas. For example, they often establish zones for stores and offices (commercial zones), factories (industrial zones) and houses (residential zones). In some residential areas especially in affluent communities local zoning ordinances absolutely prohibit all types of business. In the great majority of municipalities, however, residential zoning rules allow small non-polluting home-businesses, as long as any home containing a business is used primarily as a residence and the business activities don't negatively affect neighbors.

To find out whether residential zoning rules allow the home-based business, get a copy of the local ordinance from the city or county clerk's office, the city attorney's office or the public library.

Keep in mind, when reading it, that zoning ordinances are worded in many different ways to limit business activities in residential areas. Some are extremely vague, allowing "customary home-based occupations." Others allow homeowners to use their houses for a broad-but, unfortunately, not very specific-list of business purposes (for example, "professions and domestic occupations, crafts or services"). Still others contain a detailed list of approved occupations, such as "law, dentistry, medicine, music lessons, photography, cabinet making." If after reading the ordinance it is still uncertain whether the business is acceptable, it may be tempting to ask for a meeting with zoning or planning officials. But until the exact rules of the locality are known and plans have been adjusted to comply with them, it can be a mistake to call attention to home business plans. One way to cope with this problem is to have a friend who lives nearby, but who doesn't plan to open a home-based business, make detailed inquiries.

In many cities and counties, if a planning or zoning board rejects a business, an appeal can be made to the city council or county board of supervisors. While this can sometimes be an uphill battle, it is easier if support of all affected neighbors is in place. It is also possible to get an overly restrictive zoning ordinance amended by the municipality's governing body. For example, in some communities, people are working to amend ordinances that prohibit home-based businesses entirely or only allow "traditional home-based businesses" to permit those that rely on the use of computers and other high tech equipment-businesses that are usually unobtrusive, but far from traditional.

What should be done if a business to be run from home is not specifically allowed or prohibited by local ordinance? Start by understanding that in most areas zoning and building officials don't actively search for violations. The great majority of home-based businesses that run into trouble do so when a neighbor complains-often because of noise, parking problems or even because of the unfounded fear that the business is doing something illegal such as selling drugs. It follows that the best approach is often to explain business activities to neighbors and make sure the activities are not worrying or inconveniencing them. Another way to think about this problem is to consider that many zoning ordinances-especially those which are fairly vague as to the type of business that can run from home may restrict how the business is carried out. The most frequent rules limit the use of on-street parking, prohibit outside signs, limit car and truck traffic, and restrict the number of employees who can work at the house on a regular basis (some prohibit employees altogether). In addition, some zoning ordinances limit the percentage of a home's floor space that can be devoted to the business. Again, study the local ordinance carefully to see how these rules will impact business activities.

How do planned development rules affect a home-based business? In an effort to protect residential property values, most subdivisions, condos and planned unit developments create special rules-typically called Covenants, Conditions and Restrictions (CC&Rs)-that govern many aspects of property use. Rules pertaining to home-based businesses are often significantly stricter than those found in city ordinances. But as long as the rules of the planned development are reasonably clear and consistently enforced, they must be followed. Because many planned developments enforce their rules more zealously than municipalities do, it's essential that a home-based business fully comply.

It's a mistake to rely on a homeowner or renter's insurance policy to cover a home-based business. These policies often exclude or strictly limit coverage for business equipment and liability for injuries to business visitors. For example, if a computer is stolen or a client or business associate trips and falls on the steps, the business may not be covered. Fortunately, it's easy to avoid these nasty surprises. Sit down with the insurance agent and fully disclose the planned business operation. It is relatively inexpensive to add business coverage to a homeowner's policy and it's a tax-deductible expense. However, be sure to check prices-some insurance companies provide special cost-effective policies designed to protect both homes and home-based businesses.

Almost all ordinary and necessary business expenses (everything from wages to computers to paper clips) are tax-deductible, no matter where they are incurred-in a factory or office, while traveling or at home. In addition, if the business is operated from home and qualifies under IRS rules, it may be possible to deduct part of the rent from income taxes or take a depreciation deduction if the same person as the business owner owns the home.

In addition, a portion of the total utility, maid, home repair and maintenance, property tax and house insurance costs, can be deducted based on the percentage of the residence used for business purposes. To qualify to take this deduction, the IRS requires that three legal tests be met:

1. The home must be the principal place where the business is conducted. If the business is conducted in more than one place, it is necessary to evaluate the relative importance of the activities at each location, and the amount of time spent at each location.
2. The business must occupy a separate and identifiable space. To qualify for a home office deduction, the office must be apart from the rest of the home. The easiest home office to prove to the IRS is one in a separate structure—for example, a detached garage converted to an office. But many individuals convert a spare bedroom to a legitimate home office by removing the bed. This is acceptable as long as the space set aside for the business is really used for the business.
3. The business space must be regularly and exclusively used for business purposes. The word "regular" is hard to precisely define but it's clear that it isn't enough to use it just occasionally--one or two days a month--for business. If customers or clients are met regularly at the home office, keep a record of appointments, in case an IRS auditor ever questions the tax return.

The term "exclusive" is more straightforward. It means the space is used exclusively for business. It is not possible to claim the kitchen table or the room where TV is watched. Examples of how the IRS applies this rule are as follows:

Example 1: A schoolteacher spends 25 hours per week at school, but 30 hours at home grading papers and preparing for class. The IRS denies a home office deduction even though she spends more time at home than school, because the essence of her business is teaching students at another location.

Example 2: A plumber works out of his home office and keeps a full-time employee there. The plumber is at his home office 10 hours a week and in the field 40 hours a week. The IRS says that he is not entitled to a deduction for rent or depreciation. (He could deduct other ordinary business expenses, such as the employee's salary.)

Example 3: A home-based jewelry businessperson sells goods by mail and at craft shows. She spends 25 hours a week at home and 15 hours working outside of the office. A home office deduction is allowed.

If a home office deduction is possible determine how much can be deducted. First, divide the number of square feet used for the home business by the home's total square footage. This percentage of business use determines how much can be deducted. Determining a home office deduction is simple for a renter. Multiply the annual rent payment by the percentage of the total space occupied by the office. Example: Lois, who makes ceramic frogs at home, rents a 900-square-foot apartment for $8,000 per year. One 200-square-foot room (22% of the total) contains a kiln and working tables. Lois is entitled to deduct 22% of the rent, $1,778, as a home office expense.

If the home is owned take a deduction for "depreciation". That is, a deduction that reflects the gradual wearing-out of the office space. The tax code declares that a building wears out over a certain number of years. For buildings bought before 1994, this period is 27.5 years; for buildings bought since then, it is 39 years. Deduct the entire cost of the space used for business over that length of time.

How much deducted each year depends on the depreciation method used. There are several. If the property was bought after 1987, deduct the same amount each year ("straight-line" depreciation). For property bought earlier, larger deductions can be taken in the first few years ("accelerated" depreciation).

The last step is to determine the values of the building and the land it rests upon, because any part attributable to the land cannot be deducted. (Land never depreciates in the eyes of the tax law.) An allocation of 80% to structure and 20% to land is common in most of the country. Example: Katie uses 400 of her home's 1,800 square feet (22%) for her business. Katie bought her home for $100,000 in 1987 and hasn't modified it or taken any depreciation deductions. The local property tax assessor says the lot is worth $20,000 and the structure $80,000. Katie calculates her depreciation deduction this way: $80,000 / 27.5 years = $2,909/year 22% business usage x $2,909 = $646 per year deduction for the office.

Can a tax deduction be claimed for a part-time, home-based business? For purposes of claiming a tax deduction it makes no difference if work is only part-time at the home-based business or if the party has another occupation. The business must be more than a disguised hobby. It has to pass the test with the IRS as a real business. The IRS defines a business as "any activity engaged in to make a profit." If a venture makes money-even a small amount-in three of five consecutive years, it is presumed to possess a profit motive. (IRC 183(d).) However, courts have held that some activities that failed to meet this three-profitable-years-out-of-five test still qualify as a business if they are run in a business-like manner. When determining whether a non-profitable venture qualifies for a deduction, courts may look at whether thorough business records were kept, a separate business bank account was maintained, advertising or other marketing materials were prepared and any necessary licenses and permits were obtained (a business license from the city, for example).

BUSINESS PLAN

A business plan is a written document that describes the business to be started and how it will become profitable. The document usually starts with a succinct statement outlining the purpose and goals of the business and how the plan will be achieved. It should also contain a formal profit-and-loss projection and cash-flow analysis designed to show that if the business develops as expected, it will be profitable. The business plan enables one to explain business prospects to potential lenders and investors using the financial language and tools they have been trained to understand. Even more important, the intellectual rigor of creating a tight business plan will help one determine whether the business is likely to meet personal and financial goals. Many times when budding entrepreneurs take an honest look at their financial numbers, they see that hoped-for profits are unlikely to materialize. Or, put another way, one of the most important purposes of writing a good business plan is to convince one not to start a bad business.

BUSINESS PLAN WRITING

If this is the first business plan to be written, don't be overwhelmed! It's quite comprehensive, and may require some hard work and research. It may seem stressful and overwhelming, because the answers are not always easy. It forces one to discuss rationally a lot of things that seem intuitive.

Writing a business plan is one of the most difficult things that entrepreneurs have to do, because it challenges one in areas in which one may have little or no knowledge or experience--and funding success may depend on knowledge in these areas. Keep researching to find answers to items most important for success of the business. It will take time to gather all the information and prepare it for the plan. Business plan guidelines are presented in more detail in Exhibit D.

Good news is a plan or idea exists and it is thought that money can be made! The bad news is there is a lot of work to do to get the idea ready to present to potential investors. Writing a business plan is hard work. It will take longer than one thinks and, in the end, forces one to do the things they would really rather avoid right now; i.e. research and financial projections and identifying the strengths of the management team in a convincing way.

A company's business plan is the single most important business piece to be written. There are as many ways to write a business plan, as there are to write a resume. Some will end up in the trash; others will just be "filed". There are several key elements that will make the difference between being told, "We read the plan and have decided not to invest at this time," and "We think the company is on the right track -- when can we get together to discuss funding for the company in further detail?"

Before writing a business plan, do some research. There are countless guides, books and articles on how to write the perfect plan. Find the style that is best suited to the company's needs so it is prepared right the first time. For a high technology type company, and a simple business or idea, 8-10 pages may be adequate. However, there is a need to address each of the following topics, even if only to show why it's "not" important for the business. Write as if the business is already in place. Do not write about what has been completed unless it's important to show progress or for what one plans to do.

Packaging is important. With today's technology, it is not difficult or expensive to insert color images or accent color to make the final product more appealing, distinguish your company, and improve content retention. Print the business plan on good quality laser or color printer and bind copies in attractive covers. Use a nice text layout and effective headlines to make the document look more professional. Invest some time in the appearance of the finished product.   Proofread carefully.

Dale Carnegie said, "Most of the important things in the world have been accomplished by people who have kept on trying when there seemed to be no help at all." There will be times when management starting a new business and soliciting funding will feel this way.

It is necessary to work hard on a business plan and there are no other options if success is to be achieved. If a major business report or proposal or strategic plan has never been written consider hiring a business or technical writer to help with that part in order to leave time to gather and organize information. The following will be needed to prepare for writing the plan.

BUSINESS PLAN WRITING TIPS

A business plan gives prospective investors the facts about a concept and ability to deliver, but it also demonstrates how a problem is analyzed and solved. This is important to investors who are not familiar with management. Rewrite resumes to emphasize the skills needed to make the venture succeed. A business plan is like a management team resume with financial projections. An investor wants to know that the people behind the idea have the expertise to make it happen.

Give a structured and factual presentation. Even if the idea involves creativity or leading edge technology or a radically new concept, the people with the checkbooks still need a document that is full of substance, easy to read and simple to understand. In this case the rule is substance over form. That is why it is important to put time into preparation of the business plan. To write an effective business plan considers the following to improve content and presentation:

1. *Know the competition.* Be prepared to identify the competition and tell what makes the business different (and better) than each of them.

2. *Know the audience.* Several versions of the business plan might be necessary; one for bankers or venture capitalists, one for individual investors, one for companies that may want to enter into a joint venture rather than fund the business. Determine the audience and get facts to support the ideas that will be important to the audience of potential investors. The Greek poet Ovid said, "Everyone is a millionaire where promises are concerned." It takes proof, not claims, to convince an investor to write a check.

3. *Back up claims with proof.* If the company expects to be the leader in the field in six months, explain why. If the product will sweep the market by storm, support the statement with facts. If the management team is fully qualified to make the business a success, be sure their resumes demonstrate the experience needed.

4. *Financial projections.* Be conservative in all financial estimates and projections. If 50% of the market can be captured in the first year, say why and estimate the financial return and expense but be sure they are realistic. Think conservatively. A 10% market share is much more credible.

5. *Time and resources.* Be realistic with time and resources available. Progress is usually slower than expected. Over-optimism with time and resources is a common error entrepreneur's make. Being realistic is important because it lends credibility to the presentation.

6. *Be logical.* Think like a banker and write what he/she would want to see, in an order that makes it easy to find the information.

7. *Credentials and expertise.* Make sure management has good credentials and expertise. They don't have to have worked in the field, but there is a need to draw parallels between what they have done and the skills needed to make the venture succeed. If all of the skills needed are not currently present consider adding an advisory board of people skilled in the field and use their resumes. Discuss the shortcomings factually in the business plan, showing how and when they will be addressed getting the right people on board to fill in the gaps in the management team.

8. *Documentation.* Document why the idea will work. Have others done something similar that was successful? Is a prototype available? Include all the variables that can have an impact on the result or outcome of the idea. Show why they don't apply to this situation or explain how to overcome them or make them better.

9. *Facilities.* Describe facilities and location for performing the work. If expansion is needed, discuss when, where and why.

10. *Payout options.* Discuss payout options for the investors. Some investors want a hands-on role, some want to put associates on your Board of Directors, some don't want to be involved in the day-to-day. All investors want to know when they can get their money back and at what rate of return. Most want out within three to five years. Provide a brief description of options for investors, or at least mention that you are ready to discuss options with any serious prospect.

Business plans that don't inform and excite often end up in the trash. To make sure the plan "hits the bull's-eye," follow these six steps.

1. *Focus on the product ("Wow, what a terrific product!").* Furnish all pertinent details about the product or service, including any research conducted. What development stage is it in? How is it unique? What are the distribution methods? Who will use the product and why? What does it cost to manufacture, and what is the selling price? Describe future plans for updates and new releases. Involve the lender in the product or service so they will be as excited about it as you are. Try to describe everything in simple terms; items and attributes that are clearly to some may not always be clear to others. The goal is not only to convince the lender that the product will revolutionize the world, but that the facts in the plan prove it!

2. *Applaud the competition - then rise above it.* ("Impressive! This company offers a unique advantage that will have customers beating a path to their door!") Analyze the competition in great detail. Who are they? How do their products work? How are they similar to and different from the company product? What are their marketing tactics? Define each competitor in terms of sales volume, gross margin, income and market share. Then discuss your company's competitive advantage over each one. Do this without dragging names or products through the mud. Instead, show how a customer will chose the product over the competitor's because of its quality, delivery time, location, price, etc. Convince the reader that the company will be not only a worthy competitor, but will be setting industry standards in the future. Make the lender aware that risks related to competitors are known and how the business will overcome each one.

3. *Know the markets. ("This market analysis leaves no pebble unturned!").* Provide an in-depth analysis on how your company perceives its target markets. What are the economic, geographic, occupational and psychological profiles of the people who will buy the product and how will each benefit? Develop and include a preliminary marketing plan. List sites in which to advertise, promote and publicize. Make sure to include budgets and project revenue for each. Also include an outline of the sales strategy. Will outside sales reps or an in-house

force be used? Are resellers, distributors or franchises to be involved? What sort of sales training will be provided? Again, details are paramount.

4. *Present the course of action ("This plan of action is bullet proof!").* How exactly will the product be brought to market? How is the product being assembled? What materials will be used? What production resources are owned or needed? What are the costs for equipment and manufacturing? Are facilities leased or owned? Explain both the fixed and variable costs related to assembling, storing and delivering the product.

5. *Show off the management team ("Look who they have lined up! If this company was a baseball team, they would be headed straight to the World Series!").* The key to turning an idea into a successful venture is to have a strong management team. The team must have in-depth technical knowledge, managerial skills and years of experience. It is management's responsibility to plan, organize, control and direct the activities of a company towards its goals. Describe the team and its responsibilities as a whole first. Then break down each member's special skills, attributes, and accomplishments, indicating how each will benefit the company. Describe management objectives and include organizational charts to support claims.

6. *Make the executive summary shine ("This company is going to be huge. I can't wait to read the rest of their plan!").* Does the executive summary leave the reader intrigued and thirsty for more information? It should, because it will leave a lasting impression. It will be the last thing submitted but the first thing the lender will read, and should summarize the most pertinent details from the plan. Include a brief yet captivating overview of the writer's position within the company, the company's capabilities and limitations, the competition, marketing and financial strategies, and the management team. This is the company's cover letter, so make it good.

A business plan is the most important document to be written. Take the time to do it correctly. The goal is to have the business expand and grow far beyond projections...maybe even dreams! When writing a business plan avoid:

1. *Form over substance.* If it looks good but doesn't have a solid basis in fact and research, save your energy.

2. *Empty claims.* If facts are presented, back them up in the next sentence with a statistic or fact or quote from a knowledgeable source that supports the claim.

3. *Rumors about the competition.* If a competitor is going out of business allude to it, but avoid listing their weaknesses or hearsay. Stick to facts.

4. *Superlatives and strong adjectives.* Words like major, incredible, amazing, outstanding, unbelievable, terrific, great, most, best, and fabulous don't have a place in a business plan. Avoid "unique" unless it can be demonstrated with facts that the product or service is truly "one of a kind". Seldom is an opportunity truly unique.

5. *Long documents.* Keep it under 25 pages total. Write what is necessary, but keep it at home. If investors want details, they will ask.

6. *Over estimating on financial projections.* It is good to appear optimistic, but resist excess optimism. Use half of what might be considered reasonable. Better to underestimate than set expectations that aren't fulfilled.

7. *Overly optimistic time frames.* Ask around or do research on the Internet. If it takes most companies 6-12 months to get up and running, this is probably true of this business. If prototype development is expected to take 3 months, double it. Delays are inevitable and hard to control.

8. *Gimmicks.* Serious investors want facts, not hype. They may eat the chocolate rose that accompanies the business plan for your new florist shop, but it won't make them any more interested in investing in the venture.

9. *Typos and misspelled words.* Use a spell checker, hire an editor or have four people read the document from back to front, but get those errors out of there if the plan is to be taken seriously.
10. *Amateurish financial projections.* Spend some money and get an accountant to do these. They'll help one think through the financial side of the venture, plus put them into a standard business format that a businessperson expects.

BUSINESS CHALLENGES (TURNAROUND)

In many business situations it is well to remember the 80:20 rule that is that 20% of customers generate 80% of income so focus on the top 20% customers. This will include product management and sales and sales force strategies. Identify those firms responsible for the top 20% of sales and focus on reducing cost to generate sales.

Corporate management usually attempts to establish teams that have the responsibility for various corporate activities. An effective team can be a valuable asset for the organization. On the other hand teams fail or are ineffective as well. In a survey of corporate management reason why teams failed were identified (table four).

Table four. Reasons cited for team failure in corporations. *

Reason	%
Unclear goals	55
Changing objectives	55
Lack of accountability	51
Lack of mgnt support	49
Lack of clarity about roles	47
Ineffective leadership	45
Low priority given to team	40
Lack of team – based pay	30

*Response of managers from 243 companies

In addition to team issues, corporate management contends that the problem most often encountered is inadequate planning followed by insufficient initial capital, mistaken estimate of market demand, lack of management ability, failure to select and use appropriate outside professional advisors, inability to market effectively, over dependence on an individual or on a predicted specific event, failure to understand capital requirements for growing business, poor timing of expenditures as a result of poor planning and expedient rather than reasoned decision-making. Remember the company board of directors has a responsibility to keep the company "on track".

Remember the economy is like a two cylinder engine. First, job creation prospers through new products and emergence of new industries. Growth continues until the market is saturated. Secondly, intense price and efficiency competition sets in and jobs are eliminated even though wealth creation continues. Technical and process improvements eliminate people.

People characteristics have a significant impact on success of the business; "intuitive" create, "extroverts" relate to people and thinking, judging people are hard drivers, often singular in purpose. If they can keep their company from rebelling or quitting because of their perceived harsh personality, they probably are suited to deal with the critical issues of innovation, finance, organization and marketing.

Major underlying reasons why businesses have internal problems are: the right people are not in the right slot and systems or processes cause people to behave adversely or poorly. Jobs and wealth are generally created due to local environment. World markets, competitors, money flow, buffet the wealth creation process but do not drive it.

Industry starts, saturates market and the result is an employment decline. Wealth increases as knowledge increases until distribution extends to regions, national worldwide markets and competition increases and then levels off and finally declines unless new ideas/communications increase. A successful business must create, modify or adjust the environments for complexity i.e. innovation, jobs and wealth.

Demographics, money supply and national investments make some difference but highest correlation is between economic growth and ideas. Demographics provide surge and sags in the cycle as does monetary policy but long-term trend is ideas from economies such as from agriculture to industrial and eventually to an informational economy. Only a small percentage of companies actually produce significant growth in product or service, employment and wealth creation. Common characteristics based on a recent survey are: reliance on team efforts, leadership is by people who know their line of work (10 years experience) and/or who have started other businesses (which often failed); top management is by men (93%); a disproportionately number are high tech manufacturers; companies better financed, although not by much; are not owned by the founders alone and markets are not just local.

BUSINESS ENTERPRISE CAPITALIZATION

Governments usually get most of their funds from taxation. Universities and religious and service organizations generally rely on the charitable instincts of people who share their interests. By definition, business enterprises are funded by private capital. These enterprises cannot rely on taxation or on charitable solicitation. Instead, they must find investors or lenders. The most fundamental source of financing for private enterprise is equity capital (selling stock), which is further described later in this section.

In order to persuade people or financial institutions to invest their savings in a business enterprise, that enterprise must offer the promise of a financial reward, or return. While the profiles in this database are full of stories of successful enterprises, others here have not been good investments.

When industry began evolving from individual crafts-people and cottage industry, requiring larger groups of people to maximize the technology of the Industrial Revolution, business was usually financed by people who already had a great deal of capital: often those who had inherited land from their feudal ancestors.

As more and more individuals, such as small merchants and skilled craftspeople, began to prosper from this revolution, there was no way for them to readily participate in large business ventures, other than by working for a paycheck. Members of this new middle class, with modest savings, could not become part owners of a major enterprise. While they were interested in participating in the profits of these enterprises, they could not afford to take the risks involved.

INDUSTRY COMPARISON

Each industry has its own unique set of characteristics that go beyond basic demand and that affect every company in the industry. The home-building industry goes up and down with mortgage interest rates and other cycles. Stockbrokers prosper in good markets and lose customers after crashes. On the other hand, the demand for toothpaste and shoes is pretty reliable. The cyclical company must be prepared for the natural cycles it will experience, but Coke is more worried about market share and Pepsi than about year-to-year swings in total soft drink demand.

The skills required by Walt Disney are vastly different from those required by Caterpillar. Selling millions of $6 movie tickets or $24.95 videocassettes is a radically different proposition from selling bulldozers at $500,000 apiece. Caterpillar requires fewer but longer sales calls; Disney announces its products with ads and opens the doors. Disney doesn't even know the names of all of its customers. Some companies with expertise in selling to businesses have tried and failed to sell to individual consumers, and vice versa. There is also a big difference between selling $10,000 cars and

$50,000 cars and between selling $300 washing machines and rolls of toilet paper. Marketing skills demonstrated in one area may not be successful at different price points. Higher-priced items usually require more effort per sale on the part of both buyer and seller than small, inexpensive things.

When gasoline is bought the product is known. Commodities are simple products, often made in huge quantities by many firms. Usually, the most important factor in selecting the product is price. Texaco couldn't sell gas at $5 a gallon next door to a Shell station selling it for 50 cents. At least Texaco wouldn't sell much. However, determining the difference between Levi's 501s and Wrangler boot cuts is much trickier. Individual emotions and tastes come into play. The two products do not appear the same to the consumer. Novels by James Michener are not exact substitutes for those of Sidney Sheldon. Most companies in this database try to differentiate their products from those of the competition; some are successful and some are not.

There are many other ways that industries differ; those above are among the most common. There is nothing inherently good or bad about a cyclical industry or a commodity-producing company. But a company's odds of prospering are greatest if demand is predictable and growing and if that company has successfully differentiated its products or services from those of the competition.

Any understanding of a company must first start with a basic grasp of the industry in which the company competes. And that industry perspective starts with the demand for the products or services produced by the industry. In looking at any company, consider these three questions first:

1. How much of the product or service do people (or other companies) buy?
2. How much of it do they buy from the enterprise under consideration, compared to what they buy from competitors (what is their market share)?
3. How easily can customers substitute some other product?

All products, from diamonds to bread, have unique characteristics, but none is as important as these three. All companies have their own attributes, as discussed in the following section, but none is as critical as these three. The nature of the soap company, whose products almost everyone uses, is different from that of the jet engine maker who sells to a few.

The maker of specialized orthopedic shoes looks at the world differently than the mass producer of sneakers; he or she faces a different world. If your company has a market share leader like Kodak film or Heinz ketchup, the challenges are vastly different from those for a new, young competitor. Most business enterprises have products that are well established, as well as new, experimental products. The makers of slide rules found out the hard way that their product was replaceable when the more powerful but inexpensive pocket calculator came into being.

What answers should we look for to these 3 questions? While each case is unique, a company is generally in pretty good shape if everybody uses lots of the product, doesn't buy it from anybody else, and can't substitute anything for it. Aside from government-endorsed monopolies like electric utilities, we can't think of any case in our company database in which a company can respond to all 3 questions with such strong answers. That is what makes business such a challenge for the people who manage it.

Of equal importance to the three answers is the trend in the answers: in other words, for each question, is the answer this year the same as the answer last year? Is the answer getting better or worse? A lot better or a little better? A lot worse or a little worse? To understand the direction of change over time (better or worse) and the rate of change over time (a lot or a little), the three questions can be rephrased:

1. Are people buying more or less of the product or service each year?
2. Is this firm's market share rising or falling? and
3. Are people more often substituting other products, or is the product becoming more entrenched?

The direction of change (up or down) is the starting point here. A company with rising demand for its products, such as one that makes personal computers, has a more promising future than the maker of black-and-white TV sets. The company with a rising market share (Toyota) is headed in a better direction than the firm that's losing share (Renault). At one time the telegraph and the telephone were competitors; railroads and airlines fought over passengers. In each case, correctly picking the survivor paid off for investors, suppliers, and employees alike.

Any analysis of trends must also pay attention to the rate or relative size of change. For example, suppose a company shipped 9,000 items last year and 10,000 this year and crows about the increase of 1,000 to all with-in earshot. But what about the competitor who went from 1,000 to 2,000 in the same period of time? Next year, will they just gain 1,000 again, or will they double again, to 4,000? Any analysis of change must focus on the percentage rate of change, which was 11% (increased by 1-9) for one firm but 100% (doubled) for their smaller competitor.

Whether interest is in the absolute level (how much) or the rate of change (what percent), understanding demand is the starting point for understanding any enterprise. For those charged with the task of managing an enterprise, this means that nothing is more important than understanding the customer and the customer's needs.

Managers of the successful enterprises in a company database generally follow simple rules with regard to their customers. They: 1) put themselves in the shoes of their customers and follow the Golden Rule ("treat the customer the way you would like to be treated"); 2) use and believe in their own products (when the president of GM starts driving a Ford, it's time to sell your GM stock); 3) go out of their way to know the characteristics of their customers (Where do they live? How old are they? How much money do they make? How much schooling do they have? Are they single or do they have families? If customers are individuals or families, the answers to these demographic questions are discovered by conducting market research (e.g., surveys) and by studying the census. If customers are other businesses, many of the answers are in the company database); and 3) do everything in their power to ensure that potential customers know that the company's products and services exist, and know where to find them. Once a person understands the demand for a company's products and whether the firm is gaining or losing market share (and at what rate), they can look at the other ways in which industries and companies differ.

COMPANY COMPARISON

Within any industry, each company may take any number of approaches. Which approaches it takes are what managers are paid to decide? The individual characteristics of a company include attributes relating to strategy, financing, and management. Every company has a strategy, whether expressed or not. Those firms with no apparent strategy can be considered to have haphazardness as a strategy. Companies can also have the same strategy year after year or change strategies periodically, sometimes falling into haphazard phases. Perhaps more than any other aspect of a company, strategy is a direct reflection of the views of top management. In general, the most successful companies in this database are those that have kept a clear vision in place for many years. Southwest Airlines (23 years old) sticks to its original principles: low fares, no meals, and fast, friendly service. It reduces costs by flying only Boeing 737s.

At the same time, it is pointless to stick to strategies that time has passed by. When the railroads first lost their passenger business to airlines and then most of their small freight business to truckers, they were forced to review their status. The successful ones have emerged as huge haulers of bulky commodities such as grain and coal and of heavy products like automobiles. Many of our older industries have had to develop creative strategies to adjust to changing times, new technologies, and foreign competition. Probably the single most common method of shifting strategy is to diversify. While diversification generally connotes moving into whole new fields of endeavor, it can also take other forms. One of the most fundamental forms of growth is to take a good idea to new territory. Holiday Inns started in Memphis and worked outward; Wal-Mart began in Arkansas and expanded from there. Coca-Cola early in its history began peddling its product in Mexico and Canada and now sells worldwide.

Horizontal, from economics, means to diversify by buying competitors or similar companies in other locations. The giant trusts of the late 19th and early 20th centuries (for example, U.S. Steel) were formed by combining most of the major companies in an industry. Buying up local and regional mom-and-pop operations originally formed the largest trash collectors, Browning-Ferris and WMX Technologies. Vertical is more commonly referred to as vertical integration. This means buying up your customers and/or your suppliers. At one time, Henry Ford's River Rouge plant in Detroit made its own steel and glass, and finished Fords rolled off the other end of the production line. Integrated oil companies are those with wells, refineries, and filling stations. Geographical, horizontal, and vertical diversification is all well established strategies for increasing the size and competitiveness of a company. In the 1960s and 1970s, it became more common for companies to diversify into vastly different fields.

The term conglomerate came into use in the 1960s to describe firms that operated in several unrelated industries. Managers of these firms came to believe that they could manage anything, that the basics of running a steel mill were no different from those of running an airline. While managers undoubtedly will continue this debate, the companies in this database indicate that prosperity is easier to achieve when an enterprise is focused, or at least sticks to fields with something in common. While Sears' retail stores seem different from Allstate car insurance, the company originally sold the insurance to its retail customers. Sears' later introduction of the Discover credit card was a natural outgrowth of its experiences with its own Sears credit operation.

The Company Profile database contains fewer than 24 enterprises that were so diversified that we could not assign them to some broad industry group. While almost all the firms have diversified to one degree or another, most have remained in fields that are in some way related, such as mass-marketed consumer products. Most of the diversified companies are in two or three industries. General Electric stands out as one company that is an industry leader in several businesses. But even this great company has shown the difficulty of achieving excellence in unrelated businesses. GE's stock brokerage business has lost hundreds of millions of dollars.

Each company can also take any number of roads with regard to innovation. Fred Smith at Federal Express created a whole new industry. Some companies take a good idea and apply it in a different way: Home Depot is the application of the Toys "R" Us concept of giant, low-priced specialty stores to home-improvement retailing. Other companies are based on cloning: Amdahl was founded to make copies of IBM mainframe computers for a lower price. While successful innovators can reap substantial rewards, they also entail substantial risk. The first successful large computer was the UNIVAC, made by a predecessor of Unisys. A late entrant to the field, IBM, made more money from the idea. Small, entrepreneurial companies created the large general merchandise discount store. But no one executed the idea as successfully as Kmart, until the even-later entry of Wal-Mart.

While innovation often comes from small, entrepreneurial enterprises, this is not always the case. Minnesota Mining and Manufacturing (3M) is an unusual company that seems to specialize in innovation, from Scotch tape to Post-it notes. This tradition continues even as 3M grow larger and larger. Whether we look at technology in computers, in chicken growing, or in toy stores, the management of each company must decide whether it will be a leader or a follower, which technologies to bet on, and how much to bet.

This database includes successful companies that have taken many routes with regard to innovation. The one common denominator of the successful enterprises is that they make quality products, year after year after year.

Business corporations have a number of choices as to how they finance themselves. Their first choice is whether to sell shares of stock (equity) to raise money or to borrow the money (debt). While all companies have stock, they can have no debt, some debt, or a great deal of debt. The companies in this book range from zero indebtedness to several billion dollars of debt. This debt can take many forms, including bank loans and direct loans from individual or corporate investors (e.g., bonds, debentures, commercial paper, mortgages). The heavy use of debt (called leverage) can increase the returns to shareholders but also entails substantial risk. Another decision is whether to operate as a public or a private company. Most corporations are private, also called privately held or closely held corporations. Most, but not all, of the biggest corporations are public companies, or publicly held.

Private companies do not sell stock to the general public; while they may have thousands of shareholders, most are owned primarily by family members, managers, or employees. You cannot call a stockbroker and buy or sell shares. It is harder to get your money out of an investment in a private company (an illiquid investment). Private companies cannot raise money as easily as public companies, since they do not have access to the public stock markets. On the other hand, private companies are not required by law to reveal information about them, and some are indeed very secretive.

Public companies, since their stock is available to anyone who calls a stockbroker, are required by the Securities and Exchange Commission (SEC) to report their sales and profits quarterly and to produce a full report to shareholders annually. When you call a broker and buy or sell stock in a public company, the transaction is normally executed in a matter of minutes; therefore, common stocks of public companies are "very liquid." Stocks can be traded on the New York Stock Exchange (NYSE, or Big Board), the American Stock Exchange, or the Over-the-Counter (OTC) market, the most important part of which is NASDAQ (National Association of Securities Dealers Automatic Quote system). Most of the largest US companies are listed on the NYSE, though many companies that have become large recently (e.g., Microsoft and MCI) have elected to remain on the NASDAQ system.

Most companies begin life as private companies; when and if they decide to sell stock, they are said to "go public" through an Initial Public Offering (IPO). At that time the SEC requires that they publish a prospectus detailing virtually every aspect of their business and management. Because these documents are so revealing, smart investors pore over prospectuses.

Public companies can also "go private," a practice virtually unknown 15 years ago. This recent financing strategy most commonly occurs in the form of the leveraged buyout (LBO). In an LBO a small group of investors borrows enough money to buy all the stock in a company on the stock market. This investor group often includes an investment firm specializing in LBOs (for example, The Carlyle Group L.P.). The group often includes the management of the company being bought out. LBOs require huge amounts of debt - up to billions of dollars. Often the debt is in the form of "junk bonds" sold directly to the public. Because of the rise of LBOs, there are now some companies whose stock is privately held (by the investor group) but whose bonds (debt) are publicly held. Montgomery Ward is a good example of this. While technically not publicly held, such companies are required by the SEC to release substantial information because the public can loan money to these enterprises (that is, buy bonds issued by the companies).

Perhaps the most important differences among the companies in this book are their management styles. While strategies and financing methods reflect management, there are also more direct ways to compare managers. One of the most common ways of dividing types of management is into centralized and decentralized management. The idea is that, prior to Alfred P. Sloan's innovations at General Motors in the 1920s, most companies were run "from the top down," with all key decisions made by very few people at headquarters, often by one person. Sloan developed the idea of passing authority and responsibility "down the line." Heads of divisions and other operating units were considered closer to the customer and were entrusted with more power. Sloan's ideas were widely copied in organizations worldwide.

Today, the distinctions have become blurred: it is not uncommon for a company to have highly centralized financial controls, while production and other decisions are decentralized. Other companies change their approach periodically, and yet others give decentralization lip service without much reality behind it. Also, answers about management structure are not readily found in annual reports and other company literature; you really have to talk to the people who work in the organization. Another difference among these companies is their corporate culture. It has become very stylish to talk about corporate culture. This very broad subject can cover everything from dress (blue jeans or pinstripes) to reward systems (based on seniority or contribution to sales and profits). An enterprise's culture is usually a direct reflection of the personalities of its leaders.

An aspect of management that is less discussed is the profession of the people at the top. While, as top executives, they are defined as "management," these people worked their way up through more specific fields: finance, marketing, engineering, law, operations, production, etc. Years ago, people were classified in broad groups, such as doctors, lawyers, and businessmen. But to call a printer or a broadcaster or a car maker a businessman or businesswoman is not very useful. These are very different professions.

Companies that really understand their own strengths often have clear ideas about what skills are most important for top management. A journalist runs Dow Jones; Disney is run by an entertainment professional; and Coke is run by a lifelong Coke marketer. We believe that much of the success of these companies flows from having the right type of people in the top jobs.

ENTERPRISE PROSPECTIVES

Before clearing the fog that surrounds accounting, there are two additional viewpoints that are critical to a broad understanding of business: 1) the view that each enterprise evolves over time; and 2) the view that enterprise is a human activity. While these two perspectives may seem obvious, it is not uncommon for analysts to financially study a company "six ways to Sunday" without having completed the big picture; these two brief sections put the final touches on that picture.

Natural evolution of enterprises

As can be seen from the above comments, every enterprise is unique. And yet, they do share one process: like living organisms, they grow, evolve, and mature. Each enterprise begins as an idea, usually on the part of one person or a small group of people. This idea, or invention, can be a product or a way of doing things, from service to production. In order to succeed, it should represent a better or more efficient way; it should add value. This is often described as "finding a need and filling it."

Many of the companies in our company database took roundabout routes to their "destinies" - Armstrong made bottle corks before floors; Cummins Engine was based on the tinkerings of a banker's chauffeur. Other creative products were discovered by accident. Once a company "hits stride," mass-producing a commercially viable product or service, early growth is usually rapid.

As an enterprise ages, this growth slows, eventually to very low growth (no higher than the growth of the overall economy). This fast growth-medium growth-slow growth cycle is called the S-curve. As companies evolve along this curve, they become more established, more structured, and usually more bureaucratic. As they grow, they can become more focused on protecting their assets than on inventing new products and services. In this way they become vulnerable to the attacks of the next generation of entrepreneurs coming along, who have less to lose and more to gain through innovation. While it has become in vogue to praise achievements of entrepreneurs, we often forget that managing a mature enterprise can be a very difficult challenge. At the same time that a company is at its wealthiest, with the largest number of jobs and lives depending on it, it is often also at its most vulnerable, and perhaps about to "die."

Death comes to enterprises differently than it does to living organisms. It often takes many years and is at first unrecognizable. Those closest to the company may refuse to face up to the realities. Companies with big bank accounts, many offices, and established reputations may rest on their laurels for many years before they are forced to admit that their time has come. Death, for a business enterprise, is more often a period of confusion, of selling and closing facilities, and perhaps of selling the whole company, rather than a sudden, single event. Even companies that have entered bankruptcy often re-emerge, usually in a much smaller form.

The large corporation, unlike a living organism, can be reborn. The S. S. Kresge company of 1960 was a tired chain of variety stores, 3rd in the industry after Woolworth and W. T. Grant. Sales and earnings were going nowhere. A manager named Harry Cunningham convinced top management to try a new concept: Kmart. Thirty years later, Grant is gone (fatal bankruptcy) and Woolworth is a fraction of the size of the renamed Kmart Corporation. Today, that enterprise must in turn react to relative newcomer Wal-Mart.

Sears, Roebuck was a mail-order giant selling to rural and small-town America. If it had stayed like that, it would be gone today. As an encore it became a dominant retailer for America's suburbs. The icing on the cake was its successful entry into financial services, first by insuring cars. Today, Sears is at another crossroads: its giant retail chain is losing market share to dozens of new competitors and struggling to find a role to play in the marketplace of the 1990s. In the last few years, Sears' general merchandise retail operations fell from #1 in the world to the #3 position and in 1993 bounced back to #2. While Sears is showing signs of turning around its decline, whether Sears will again revitalize itself is one of many unfinished corporate life stories.

It is easy to become over focused on the strategies of businesses and on the ways we measure their performance. It is equally easy to forget that each enterprise is fundamentally a human endeavor. No computer can plan strategies, no computer can hire and fire people, and no computer can motivate people. Balance sheets and profit and loss statements do not tell the underlying story of the people in an organization. Each organization really consists only of people and tools for people to use.

As a successful enterprise evolves, more people must be attracted to "the cause." In order to maintain leadership, the corporation must attract and keep talented people. These people must remain creative and responsive to their ever-changing environment. Whether Sears survives is up to the people of Sears. Whether 3M continues to develop innovative products depends on 3M's people. Every enterprise reflects the people of that enterprise: the people of the past, the present, and the future.

Composite data by industry group should play an essential part in stock selection whether you use a "top-down" approach, studying the economy as a whole and then researching which industries may perform well, or a "bottom-up" approach, developing a list of prospective stocks and comparing each stock's performance to its respective industry group.

SUMMARY

As presented herein numerous factors need to be considered when forming a business enterprise. The basic decision to be made is whether or not a technology is the type that justifies creation of a company that will eventually yield a satisfactory return for the investor. Many times individual create "paper" businesses that are designed to generate grants or capital necessary to complete specific projects or functions which affords the owner an income but does not satisfy the needs of an investor. Savvy investors will detect this lack of foresight and hence the odds of acquiring capital are nearly nil.

A list of business forms and an example of by-law terms are presented in Exhibit E. Questions and answers related to corporate formation are presented in Exhibit G.

Suggested reading: See the book "Zero Time" authored by Dr. Raymond Yeh who is also co-chairman of the new venture "Zero Time Labs," a virtual incubator organization for developing 21st century companies (www.businessincubatorinc.com).

EXHIBIT A - ENTREPRENEUR ANALYSES AND INTERVIEW

The Small Business Administration conducted a survey of more than 100 California business owners. Their comments about small business success were used in creating the following quiz. Choose the answer you think is best for each question. Use the sheet at the end to determine your total point score and then see where you stand in the Success Quotient Ratings. There are no "wrong" answers.

Each answer listed represents a segment of the responses to survey questions--and the final rankings correspond with the importance successful owners gave to different answers.

Questions 1 - 5

1. What is the key to business success:
    a. business knowledge
    b. market awareness
    c. hands on management
    d. sufficient capital
    e. hard work

2. If a relative ever asks me for advice about starting a business I will tell them to:
    a. work for someone else in the field first
    b. write a business plan
    c. study marketing
    d. give up the idea
    e. learn about budgeting

3. Which is the largest potential trouble spot:
    a. too much growth
    b. too little growth
    c. too fast growth
    d. too slow growth
    e. sporadic growth

4. I trust: (select as many as apply)
    a. nobody
    b. myself
    c. my partner
    d. a few key employees
    e. my customers

5. I am unhappy when my employees are:
    a. late
    b. unhappy
    c. abrupt with customers
    d. resigning
    e. less dedicated than me

Questions 6 - 10

6. My customers are: (select as many as apply)
    a. always right
    b. too fussy
    c. demanding
    d. worth listening to
    e. dumb

701

7. Rank these in order of importance for small-business marketing success:
   a. word-of-mouth
   b. advertising
   c. signs
   d. location
   e. community events
8. When it comes to money I am:
   a. careful
   b. too carefree
   c. emotional
   d. shrewd
   e. hardnosed
9. Financially my firm:
   a. has trouble with cash-flow
   b. has a good line of credit
   c. is financed totally by receipt--no credit
   d. is making better profits this year than last
   e. knows exactly where it is all the time
10. In hiring people:
   a. I take far too long
   b. I look for the cheapest person
   c. personality is more important than experience
   d. I look for the best person, and am willing to pay
   e. I only hire at the trainee level

Questions 11 - 15
11. With my employees:
   a. I treat everybody the same
   b. I try to talk privately to everybody once a week
   c. To whatever extent possible I tailor assignments to personalities
   d. I encourage them to talk to me about the business
   e. I try to work alongside them whenever possible
12. The real key to business success is:
   a. hard work and perseverance
   b. fine products and service
   c. advertising
   d. knowing the fundamentals of business
   e. employees
13. Competition is:
   a. dumb
   b. smart
   c. cunning
   d. everywhere
   e. a constant threat
14. The best competitive advantage is:
   a. experience
   b. understanding what the market wants
   c. confidence
   d. conducting a business ethically
   e. a detailed plan

15. I keep:
  a. careful financial records
  b. in touch with my customers
  c. in touch with my employees
  d. trying new techniques
  e. wanting to retire

Questions 16 - 20
16. My dream is:
  a. to grow the business until someone else can run it
  b. to work until I drop
  c. to give up these headaches and have more fun at work
  d. to try another business
  e. to take a vacation
17. I think business plans are:
  a. for the birds
  b. nice but not necessary
  c. something I can do with my accountant
  d. useful and informative
  e. essential--wouldn't do business without them
18. What makes a terrific entrepreneur?
  a. creativity
  b. discipline
  c. consumer orientation
  d. technical proficiency
  e. flexibility
19. What does a business need most?
  a. money
  b. market research
  c. help
  d. time
  e. a solid business plan
20. What is essential to marketing?
  a. "a sixth sense"
  b. market research
  c. customer awareness
  d. experience
  e. testing

Quiz Results.
  Find each question in the scoring box. Write the score for the answer you selected in the margin next to every question, (If you didn't select the highest scoring choice, take a look at that one and try and figure out why it scored so well.) When you've worked through the entire quiz, go back and add up your points. Then compare your total with the Success Quotient table to see how you compare with some of California's most successful business people.

SCOREBOX (Question Points)
1. a = 5, b = 4, c = 3, d = 2, e = 1
2. a = 5, e = 4, b = 3, c = 2, d = 1
3. c = 5, a = 4, b = 3, d = 2, e = 1
4. b = 5, e = 4, d = 3, c = 2, a = 1
5. b = 5, d = 4, c = 3, a = 2, e = 1
6. d = 5, c = 4, a = 3, b = 2, e = 1
7. a = 5, d = 4, c = 3, b = 2, e = 1
8. a = 5, d = 4, e = 3, b = 2, c = 1
9. e = 5, d = 4, b = 3, a = 2, c = 1
10. d = 5, a = 4, c = 3, b = 2, e = 1
11. c = 5, d = 4, e = 3, b = 2, a = 1
12. e = 5, d = 4, a = 3, b = 2, c = 1
13. e = 5, d = 4, c = 3, b = 2, a = 1
14. a = 5, b = 4, c = 3, e = 2, d = 1
15. b = 5, a = 4, c = 3, d = 2, e = 1
16. e = 5, a = 4, b = 3, c = 2, d = 1
17. e = 5, d = 4, c = 3, b = 2, a = 1
18. c = 5, a = 4, b = 3, e = 2, d = 1
19. b = 5, e = 4, a = 3, d = 2, c = 1
20. c = 5, b = 4, e = 3, d = 2, a = 1

Score: Your Business Success Quotient

75-100 You're a successful entrepreneur whose operations reflect tried & true business practices.

50-74   Your business is probably headed for long-term success. But success will come sooner if you sharpen your awareness of solid management skills and marketing techniques.

25-49   While you may be enjoying customer loyalty and repeat business, never forget that savvy competition is always looking for ways to take the lead. Don't let comfort lull you into false security. Be creatively assertive!

0-24   You may well have the right product; but to sell it successfully, you need to increase your market awareness and improve your operating philosophy. Reach out for practical classes, seminars and advice from people who have good business track records. And - keep persevering. It's the key ingredient to winning!

ENTREPRENEUR RELATIONSHIP ANALYSIS

How likely are you to thrive as an entrepreneurial couple? What about the strain it might put on your marriage and family? Up front consideration of the impact your business will have on your primary relationships will help protect the people closest to you from unwelcome circumstances that can destroy your marriage and uproot your family. A recent survey of over 125 entrepreneurial couples led to the conclusion that the following indicators predict how well you and your spouse (or intimate partner) will endure the challenges of entrepreneurship. Score your relationship from (1) to (4), for each of the following questions, according to the following scale: (1) that doesn't describe us at all; (2) that somewhat describes us; (3) that describes us most of the time; and (4) that describes us completely.

QUESTION 1. We've done our homework and thoroughly researched the business option we're considering. It's a good match for our skills, passions, and our family's needs. We've put together a solid, realistic business and family plan, that enables us to forecast how much time, money, and personal sacrifice our enterprise requires and how the business will impact, in detail, our day-to-day home life. Though we hope for the best, we've planned adequately for how we'll handle the worst-case scenario.

QUESTION 2. Both of us are incredibly flexible and creative people. If something isn't working in our relationship or our lifestyle, we take stock, talk it out, and find another way. We don't get stuck in one-track thinking, and we're willing to make the changes necessary along the way to achieve success. People could compare us to two willow trees standing side by side: Strong at the roots, but able to bend with the weather.

QUESTION 3. We are committed to one another "for better or worse." Our relationship has withstood the test of time, and the ups and downs that life brings. We're able to keep our eyes on the big picture, and to keep perspective when going through rough times. We've got a rewarding, strong, supportive relationship heading into this entrepreneurial venture.

QUESTION 4. For us, romance is a daily attitude, not just something we do on Valentine's Day and our wedding anniversary. We express love and appreciation daily to one another, even when time or money is short. We aren't likely to neglect or take for granted our relationship, even if business needs absorb a lot of our attention. We understand that it's good for our business, as well as our marriage, to take good care of one another.

QUESTION 5. We share a joint vision and are both headed in the same direction. When we verbalize and perhaps even write down, our personal, family, and business goals, we see that these goals are in harmony and congruent with one other. We are each willing to sacrifice personally in order to support our partner's life dreams.

QUESTION 6. We approach conflict looking for a win/win solution. Getting my way is an empty victory if it results in distance between my spouse and me. If we were ever to have difficulty resolving differences between us, we wouldn't hesitate to get outside support and professional advice before our relationship hits a breaking point.

QUESTION 7. We can keep our sense of humor and look at the bright side of things, even during the roughest times. We figure, if we're going to laugh about it later, we might as well laugh about it now! We're pros at making lemonade out of lemons, and finding the silver lining in the clouds. When we start taking our work or ourselves too seriously, we can take a step back and lighten up.

QUESTION 8. One or both of us was raised in an entrepreneurial family, so we're accustomed to the erratic income and schedule, and the high demands that come along with it. Our parents were excellent role models for us for starting and managing a small business well. If our parents are still alive, they are very supportive of us following in their entrepreneurial footsteps.

Total your score and check the analysis table below:

24 - 32 Your relationship should make it! Your foundation is strong and your attitude upbeat and positive. You seem to be realistically prepared for the challenges of entrepreneurship and though your relationship will be tested along the way, the signs are positive that you can withstand the challenge and come through.

16 -23 Warning - entrepreneurship could endanger your relationship! Expect plenty of growth opportunities along the entrepreneurial path! If you prioritize sustaining a strong healthy marriage, you should be OK, but it will require enormous commitment on your part. What doesn't kill your relationship will probably make it stronger, but realize the risks you are taking before setting out on the journey.

8-15 Danger - entrepreneurship could land you in divorce court! Before going forward with any entrepreneurial venture, strengthen your relationship with some outside counseling, or you may find yourself in divorce court before your business dreams are realized. Though you may be the exception to the rule, research shows that you lack several of the essential components to thriving on the entrepreneurial journey.

EXHIBIT B - BUSINESS ENTITY COMPARISON

BUSINESS ENTITY COMPARISON

Entity	Sole Proprietorship	General Partnership	S Corporation
Limited Liability	Sole Proprietor has unlimited personal liability	Partners are jointly and severally liable for partnership debts and liabilities	Shareholders have limited liability even if they participate in management of the corporation
Number & Type of Permissible Owners	One, although husband and wife can sometimes be treated as sole proprietorship for income tax purposes	Must be at least two partners with no limitation on the type of entity that can be a partner	No > than 75 shareholders. Only individuals, estates & certain trusts can be shareholders. Partnerships and corporations cannot be shareholders. Only citizens or residents of USA can be shareholders
Federal Tax Treatment	Not a separate taxable entity. All income tax items reported on Schedule C of sole proprietor's Form 1040	No tax at partnership level. Almost all income tax items flow through to individual partners by way of a k-1. Partnership files Form 1065	Generally no corporate level tax (some exceptions) but S-corp required to file form 1120-S. Shareholders report income tax items distributed to them pursuant to 1120-S on personal income tax return. If there is distribution of appreciated property, tax treatment not as favorable as for LLC.
Management Method	Sole proprietor manages	By all partners	Shareholders elect Board of Directors who select officers
Cost of Formation	None unless doing business under assumed name. Then an assumed name publication has to be made at cost of $5 paid to county clerk + cost of publishing the notice one time/week for 3 weeks in a newspaper	None unless doing business under assumed name. Then an assumed name publication is made at cost of $5 paid to county clerk plus cost of publishing notice 1 time per week for 3 weeks in a newspaper	$75 filing fee + franchise tax in amount of $1.50 per $1K of paid in capital with a minimum franchise tax of $25
Cost of Filing Annual Report	None required	None required	$25 filing fee + a franchise tax that is at least $25 more depending on amount of paid in capital
Special Issues with Respect to Raising Capital	Only method to raise capital would be a loan on which the sole proprietor has personal liability	Most investors prefer not to invest in a general partnership due to partner being personally liable for partnership debts	Limitation on types of entities which may invest & limitation to a single class of stock provides significant limits on ability to raise capital through angel investors & venture capital firms
Different Classes of Investors Allowed	No	Yes	No

BUSINESS ENTITY COMPARISON (CONTINUED)

Entity	C Corporation	Multiple Member Limited Liability Company	Single Member Limited Liability Company
Limited Liability	Shareholders have limited liability even if they participate in management of the corporation	Members have limited liability even if they participate in management of the LLC	Members have limited liability even if they participate in management of the LLC
Number & Type of Permissible Owners	No limits	No limits except that must be at least two members	Limited to one member. Allowed in most states. Check with your state.
Federal Tax Treatment	Corporation's income taxed at the corporate level plus dividends to shareholders are taxed at the shareholder level ("double level tax")	Treated same as a partnership	No tax at LLC level. Single member reports all income tax items on the member's income tax return
Method of Management	Shareholders elect Board of Directors who select officers	By members or managers depending on how LLC is structured	By single member or by manager, who would be selected by a single member
Cost of Formation	$75 filing fee + franchise tax in amount of $1.50/$1K of paid in capital with a minimum franchise tax of $25	$400 filing fee paid to Sec. of State (IL) when Articles of Organization filed	$400 filing fee paid to Sec. of State (IL) when Articles of Organization filed
Cost of Filing Annual Report	$25 filing fee + a franchise tax that is at least $25 but can be considerably more depending on amount of paid in capital	$200	$200
Special Issues with Respect to Raising Capital	Most VC firms require entity to be a C corp. Pass through tax treatment is not desired by VC firms because many of their investors are not for profit entities which do not want to have pass through tax treatment associated with a S corp. or LLC. C corporations are required to do an IPO	Lack of limits on who may invest in LLC is favorable to raising capital. Pass through tax treatment can be very favorable for early stage investments if there is desire to pass through early stage losses to investors who can use those early stage losses to offset other gains. Startups frequently utilize LLC initially during angel investment stage but then convert to C corp. VC round of financing	
Different Classes of Investors Allowed	Yes	Yes	No, unless converts to multiple member LLC

EXHIBIT C - BUSINESS START-UP CHECKLIST

BUSINESS START-UP CHECKLIST

The list below is meant to be a reminder of tasks to perform when starting a business. Not every business will have to complete each step. For instance, it may not be preferable to register a trademark with state or federal officials. Or, it may not be required to publish a notice of intent to do business.

Since laws vary by state and by type of business, be sure to check with local authorities to determine if there are any additional legal steps that need to be taken.

- Choose a business based on your skills and interests
- Research the business idea based, in part, on the following questions:
  1. Is it legal?
  2. What will be sold?
  3. Who will buy it and how often?
  4. Are commitment and methods in place to do what it takes to sell the product?
  5. What will it cost to produce, advertise, sell & deliver?
  6. What laws will need to be complied with?
  7. Can a profit be made?
  8. How long will it take to make a profit?
  9. Write a business plan and market plan?
  10. Choose a business name?
- Verify right to use the name
- Reserve corporate name if you will be incorporating
- Register or reserve state or federal trademark
- Register copyrights
- Apply for patent if you will be marketing an invention
- Check zoning laws
- Choose a location for the business or make space in the house for it
- File partnership or corporate papers
- Register business name and get a business certificate
- Get any required business licenses or permits
- Order any required notices (advertisements you have to place) of your intent to do business in the community
- Have business phone or extra residential phone lines installed
- Check into business insurance needs
- Find out about health insurance if you will not have coverage under a spouse
- Apply for sales tax number
- Get tax information such as record keeping requirements, information on withholding taxes if you will have employees, information on hiring independent contractors, facts about estimating taxes, forms of organization, etc.
- Call Department of Labor to determine labor laws if you have employees.
- Apply for employee identification number if you will have employees
- Find out about workers' compensation if you will have employees
- Open business bank account(s)
- Have business cards and stationery printed
- Purchase equipment or supplies
- Order inventory

- Order signage
- Order fixtures
- Have sales literature prepared
- Get adequate business insurance or a business rider to a homeowner's policy
- Send out publicity releases
- Place advertising if yours is the type of business that will benefit from paid advertising
- Call everyone you know and let them know you are in business
- Check "Legal Guide for Starting and Running a Small Business" for following information (Nolo Press, 2 volumes, $29.95 each)

  1. Business structure – S, C, LLC or LLP with pros and cons

  2. Written documents – lease, purchase agreements, employee contracts, etc.

  3. Co-ownership agreements – what if partner wants out, buy/sell agreement for partner's interest, non compete terms, etc.

  4. Licenses and ordinances – does your industry require you to be bonded or insured, professional or product liability insurance, etc.

  5. Employee relations – handbook with policy and procedures for trade secrets, intellectual property, and copyright

  6. Future planning – will, trust if disabled, benefit plan, retirement plan, etc.

EXHIBIT D - BUSINESS AND DEVELOPMENT PLANS

DEVELOPMENT PLAN OUTLINE

A development plan of the scope outlined below shall be submitted to Licensor by Licensee prior to the execution of a license or development or marketing agreement. In general, the plan should provide Licensor with a summary overview of the activities that Licensee believes are necessary to bring Products to the marketplace.

	Estimated Start Date	Finish Date

I. Development Program

    A.   Development Activities to be Undertaken
           (Please break activities into subunits, with the
           date of completion of major milestones)
           1.
           2.
           etc.
    B.   Estimated Total Development Time

II. Governmental Approval
    A.   Types of Submissions Required
    B.   Government Agency (e.g., FDA, EPA, etc.)

III. Proposed Market Approach

IV. Competitive Information
    A.   Potential Competitors
    B.   Potential Competitive Devices/Compositions
    C.   Known Competitor's Plans, Developments, Technical Achievements
    D.   Anticipated Date of Product Launch

Total Length: approximately 2-3 pages

ONE PAGE BUSINESS PLAN

Key word description of project	Name	Phone number

Overall venture concept	
Market opportunity	
Technology specialized process, or know-how	
Protection program for intellectual property and proprietary rights	
Appropriate manufacturing or production program	
Marketing program	
Selling procedure	
Distribution program	
Team members: credentials, experience and roles	
Required venture resources	
Expected results	
List of additional documentation that is available	

MILESTONE – BASED OPERATIONS

Milestone Events				
Milestone 1 Proof of concept demonstration	Brief description of a major event that has occurred	brief description of the impact or already significance of achieving this Milestone	resources (or other kinds of input or col- laboration) associat- ed with achieving this Milestone	Month 20__
Milestone 2 Competitive analysis: assessment of proprietary rights	Brief description of a major event that has already occurred	Brief description of the impact or significance of achieving this Milestone	Resources (or other kinds of input or col- laboration) associat- ed with achieving this Milestone	Month 20
Milestone 3 Planning for Commercial Development and Applications	Brief description of a specific activity that is currently Underway	Brief description of the impact or significance of achieving this Milestone	Resources (or other kinds of input or col- laboration) associat- ed with achieving this Milestone	Month 20__ to Month 20__ (or "ongoing" or current)
Milestone 4 Key words only	Brief description of specific acti- vities required For Milestone	Describe the significance of achieving this Milestone	Resources associat- ed with achieving this Milestone	Month 20__
Milestone 5 Key words only	Brief description of specific acti- vities required for Milestone	Describe the significance of achieving this Milestone	Resources associat- ed with achieving this Milestone	__ months following funding
Milestone X Key words only	Brief description of specific acti- vities required for Milestone	Describe the significance of achieving this Milestone	Resources associat- ed with achieving this Milestone	__ months following funding

Milestone-based thinking helps explain priorities at each stage of a company's development, operations and growth. It helps in communication with potential investors.

Milestone Events			
	Required Work	*Significance*	*Required Resources*	
Milestone 1				___200__
Milestone 2				__200__
Milestone 3 *Current focus:*				__200__ to __200__
Milestone 4				__ months after funding
Milestone 5				__ months after funding
Milestone 6				__ months after funding
Milestone 7 Cash flow break- even operations				__ months after funding

BUSINESS PLANNING WORKSHEET

Before going into a business attempt to learn as much about the business (and yourself!) as possible. This worksheet--if actually completed and all questions are answered honestly -- will help collect and evaluate essential information about yourself and the business to be started. While it won't give all the facts needed to determine if a business idea should be pursued, it will help answer some very fundamental questions and help identify possible pitfalls.

List the reasons for going into business for yourself.

_____

_____

_____

Are you willing to work long hours even if this business doesn't make money immediately? _____
Have you ever worked in a similar business? _____
Have you ever worked as a foreman or manager? _____
Have you taken any business courses in school? _____
Describe what you plan to sell in one or two sentences? _____

_____

_____

Describe the typical customer to be sought?
    Consumer sales: _____
    Age: _____
    Sex: _____
    Family income: _____
    Geographic location: _____
    Buying habits: _____
    Frequency of product use: _____
    Business Sales: _____
    Industry: _____
    Purchasing/decision maker: _____
How big is the market? _____
Is the market growing, static, or declining? _____
How much of the market can you reach? _____
In what geographic areas are those kinds of businesses and/or consumers located?

_____

_____

How will you get your products or services to them, or how will they (customers) get to you?

_____

Who are the competitors?

_____

_____

_____

How well are they doing? _____

_____

_____

_____

How will you distinguish your products or services from theirs?
    Price: _____
    Performance: _____
    Quality: _____

Strength: _____

Speed: _____

Size, color: _____

Other: _____

Is there really a need for another business like the one you are planning to start? _____

How will you advertise your business? _____

_____

_____

Who will prepare your ads? _____

Where can you get help with your ads? _____

How do other businesses like the one you are considering get customers?

_____

_____

Do you know how to price the products or services you plan to sell? _____

Do you know what other businesses are charging for products and services like those you plan to sell?

_____

What have you done to find out what your potential customers really want to buy? _____

_____

_____

_____

If you will be selling products, do you have a system devised for tracking inventory and determining when to reorder? _____

Where will you get your stock if you are selling a product? _____

Who will actually do the selling? You, or a salesperson? _____

Do you have any sales training, or have you studied books on salesmanship?

_____

Do you like selling? _____

How much money do you have now to put into this business? $_____

How much money do you need to start this business? $_____

Where will you get the rest of the money you need to start this business? (list sources and amounts)

_____

_____

_____

How much credit will you be able to get from suppliers (people you will have to buy goods or services from)? $_____

How much money do you expect to make per year from this business (salary and profit on investment)? $_____

What is the minimum amount of money you need per year to meet living expenses? $_____

Have you discussed business loans with a banker or an accountant? _____

Will you need a partner to supply money or business know-how? _____

If you will need a partner, do you know someone who would be appropriate and with whom you are sure you could get along? _____

Have you investigated the pros and cons of working on your own (sole proprietor), with a partner, or as a corporation? _____

Have you discussed your plans with a lawyer? _____

Are most businesses in your community doing well? _____

Are other businesses like the one you want to start doing well in your area? _____

Are other businesses like the one you want to start doing well in the rest of the country? _____

Where will you find employees if you need them? _____

Are other businesses in the area having difficulty finding qualified help? _____

_____

What salary will you have to pay to get reliable help? _____

How will you train your employees? _____
_____

Do you know how long it normally takes to get paid in your line of business? _____

Will you accept credit cards? _____

Have you investigated the requirements of credit card companies and the benefits and drawbacks of accepting credit cards? _____

Could you make more money working for someone else? _____

Are you sure you will have the support of your family? _____

Do you read trade journals or other sources of information about new ideas and products in the field?
_____

Have you investigated how the Small Business Development Center or SCORE might be able to assist with formulating and implementing your plans? _____

BUSINESS PLAN OUTLINE

I. INDUSTRY/COMPANY/PRODUCTS OR SERVICES
- A. INDUSTRY
- B. COMPANY
  1. Management and personnel
  2. Legal structure
  3. Location
  4. Methods of record keeping
  5. Insurance
  6. Security
- C. PRODUCT OR SERVICES
  1. Description
  2. Proprietary Position

II. MARKET RESEARCH
- A. CUSTOMER
  1. What are the customers' needs
  2. How can I meet those needs
  3. What is unique about my business
- B. SIZE/TRENDS
- C. COMPETITION (See Exhibit A)
  1. Is company publicly owned or privately owned/closely held? (directory of companies required to file annual reports with the SEC)
  2. Does company have parent company or subsidiaries? (directory of corporate affiliations; international directory of corporate affiliations; Americas corporate families)
  3. Do you know the company's type of business, executive officers, number of employees, annual sales? (Standard and Poor's register of corporations; Dun and Bradstreet's million dollar directory; Ward's business directory of largest U.S. companies; career guide: Dun's employment opportunities directory standard directory of advertisers)
  4. Do you need the company corporate background and financial data? (Standard and Poor's Corporate Records; Moody's manuals; Thomas Register of Am Manufacturers; Best's Insurance Reports; Standard Directory of Advertising Agencies; USA Oil Industry Directory; Who's Who in Electronics; Fairchild's Financial Manual of Retail Stores; World Aviation Directory Medical and Healthcare Marketplace guide)
  5. How does the company rank in the industry? (Annual issues of Fortune Forbes, Inc. and Business Week; Dun's business rankings)
- D. ESTIMATED MARKET SIZE/ SHARE /SALES
- E. ONGOING MARKET EVALUATION

III. MARKET PLAN
- A. STRATEGY
  1. Activity
  2. Market entry, quarter/year
  3. Commence with publicity related to scientific achievements related to product(s).
  4. Third party arrangements to test, evaluate, manufacture, produce, etc.
  5. Beta test with key clients
  6. Establish market outlets and contractual relationships
- B. SALES TACTICS

1. Target market/customer
   - economic level
   - sex
   - age
   - psychological makeup (lifestyle)
   - buying habits
2. Location
   - where do my customers live
   - where do they work
   - where do they shop
3. Methods of distribution
4. Product design
5. Timing of market entry

C. PRICING
D. SERVICE WARRANTY POLICY
E. ADVERTISING/PROMOTION
F. INDUSTRY TRENDS

IV. DESIGN/DEVELOPMENT PLANS
A. DEVELOPMENT STATUS AND TASKS
B. DIFFICULTIES/RISKS
C. PRODUCT IMPROVEMENT/NEW PRODUCTS
D. COSTS

V. MANUFACTURING - OPERATING PLAN
A. GEOGRAPHIC LOCATION
1. Address
2. Name, address, phone number of realtor/contact person
3. Square footage/cost
4. History of location
5. Location in relation to your target market
6. Traffic patterns for customers
7. Traffic patterns for suppliers
8. Availability of parking
9. Crime rate for the area
10. Quality of public services
11. Notes on walking tour of the area
12. Neighboring shops and local business climate
13. Zoning regulations
14. Adequacy of utilities
15. Availability of raw materials/supplies
16. Availability of labor force
17. Labor rate of pay for the area
18. Housing availability for employees
19. Tax rates
20. Evaluation of site in relation to competition

B. FACILITIES/IMPROVEMENTS
C. STRATEGY/PLANS
D. LABOR

VI. MANAGEMENT TEAM
A. ORGANIZATION
B. KEY MANAGEMENT
C. MANAGEMENT COMPENSATION AND OWNERSHIP

D. BOARD OF DIRECTORS
E. MANAGEMENT ASSISTANCE/TRAINING NEEDS
    1. Scientific/business advisory committee
F. PROFESSIONAL SERVICE SUPPORT

VII. SCHEDULE

VIII.RISKS/PROBLEMS

IX. FINANCIAL PLAN
A. SUMMARY OF FINANCIAL NEEDS
B. DISPERSAL OF LOAN FUNDS STATEMENT
C. PROFORMA CASH FLOW ANALYSIS (BUDGET)
    1. Assumptions
    2. Cash flow sensitivity
D. THREE YEAR INCOME PROJECTION
E. BREAK-EVEN ANALYSIS (CHART)
F. PROFORMA BALANCE SHEET
G. PROFIT AND LOSS FORECAST
H. LOAN APPLICATION/FINANCIAL STATEMENT ANALYSIS

X. EXIT STRATEGY/PLAN (COMPANY OFFERING - IPO)

BUSINESS ORGANIZATIONAL PLAN

- Description of business
  - A. Products or services
  - B. Management and personnel
  - C. Legal structure
  - D. Location
  - E. Methods of record keeping
  - F. Insurance
  - G. Security
- Location analysis
  - A. Address
  - B. Name, address, phone number of realtor/contact person
  - C. Square footage/cost
  - D. History of location
  - E. Location in relation to your target market
  - F. Traffic patterns for customers
  - G. Traffic patterns for suppliers
  - H. Availability of parking
  - I. Crime rate for the area
  - J. Quality of public services
  - K. Notes on walking tour of the area
  - L. Neighboring shops and local business climate
  - M. Zoning regulations
  - N. Adequacy of utilities
  - O. Availability of raw materials/supplies
  - P. Availability of labor force
  - Q. Labor rate of pay for the area
  - R. Housing availability for employees
  - S. Tax rates
  - T. Evaluation of site in relation to competition

MARKETING PLAN

- Target market
- Competition
- Methods of distribution
- Promotion
- Pricing
- Product design
- Timing of market entry
- Location
- Industry trends

TARGET MARKET WORKSHEET

- Who are my customers
  - A. economic level
  - B. sex
  - C. age
  - D. psychological makeup (lifestyle)
  - E. buying habits
- Location
  - A. where do my customers live
  - B. where do they work
  - C. where do they shop
- Projected size of market
- What are the customers' needs
- How can I meet those needs
- What is unique about my business

COMPETITION EVALUATION WORKSHEET

- Competitor
- Location
- Product or services offered
- Methods of distribution
- Image
  - A. packaging
  - B. promotional material
  - C. methods of advertising
  - D. quality of product or service
- Pricing structure
- Business history and current performance
- Market share (number, types and location of customer's strengths)
- Weaknesses

COMPETITION REFERENCE LIST

Is company publicly owned or privately owned/closely held?

   Directory of companies required to file annual reports with the SEC

Does company have parent company or subsidiaries?
    Directory of corporate affiliations
    International directory of corporate affiliations
    Americas corporate families
Are company's type of business, executive officers, number of employees, annual sales known?
    Standard and Poor's register of corporations
    Dun and Bradstreet's million-dollar directory
    Ward's business directory of largest U.S. companies
    career guide: Dun's employment opportunities directory
    standard directory of advertisers
Are company corporate background and financial data needed or known?
    Standard and Poor's Corporate Records
    Moody's manuals
    Thomas Register of American Manufacturers
    Best's Insurance Reports
    Standard Directory of Advertising Agencies
    USA Oil Industry Directory
    Who's Who in Electronics
    Fairchild's Financial Manual of Retail Stores
    World Aviation Directory
    Medical and Healthcare Marketplace guide
How does the company rank in the industry?
    Annual issues of Fortune Forbes, Inc. and Business Week
    Dun's business rankings

FINANCIAL DOCUMENTS

- Summary of financial needs
- Dispersal of loan funds statement
- Cash flow statement (budget)
- Three-year income projection
- Break-even analysis
- Balance sheet
- Profit and loss statement
- Loan application/financial statement analysis

U.S. TAX INFORMATION

Schedule c (1040)
Schedule SE "social security and self-employment (1040)
See free IRS publications 1 800 tax form, 1 800 829 3676
Request #334, 910 for basics; then 15, 17, 463, 505, 508, 509, 510, 533, 534, 535, 536, 538, 541, 542, 547, 551, 557, 560, 583, 587, 589, 594, 596, 908, 911, 925, 937, 946, 947, 1544

EXHIBIT E - BUSINESS FORMS AND BY-LAW OUTLINE

BUSINESS FORMS

These documents are free to download and customize for professional use, and are subject to terms of use agreement. http://www.officedepot.com/inbusiness/hot/index.asp

Ready-to-use business tools to help you get the job done faster and easier, including:
- Model business documents and financial spreadsheet templates
- Sample letters, contracts, forms, and policies
- Checklists and a variety of information-at-a-glance tools

Business/Finance
- Balance Sheet Template
- Cash Flow Budget Worksheet
- Customer Statement of Account
- Daily Cash Sheet
- Income Statement Template
- Loan Application, Bank Review Form
- Monthly Bank Reconciliation
- Personal Statement Package
- Present Value Tables
- Sample Collection Letters
- Trial Balance Worksheet
- Unsecured Promissory Note

Compensation & Benefits
- Compensation Work Chart
- Initial Notification of COBRA Rights
- Overtime Guidance
- Privacy Policy
- Profit-Sharing Plan
- Simplified Employee Pensions
- Time-Off Policies
- Workers' Comp Policies

Employee Management
- Comprehensive Job Satisfaction Survey
- Electronic Funds Transfer Authorization
- Employee Coaching Script
- Employee Disciplinary Action Form
- Drug Test Policy
- Employee Discipline Aids
- Employee Feedback Script
- Employee Work Rules
- Long Distance Call Log
- Noncompete Agreement
- Employee Time Sheets
- Sample Absence Policies
- Sexual Harassment Policy
- Smoking Policy

Firing & Termination
- Employment Reference Release
- General Release for Employment Termination
- Termination Checklist and Form

Marketing
  Business Plan Components: Sample Plans Illustrate Required Content
  Customer Satisfaction Survey Form
  Customer Service Action Form
Recruiting & Hiring
  Applicant Information Release
  Applicant Rejection
  Driving Record Check
  Drug Testing Consent Form
  Educational Record Check
  Employer Reference Check
  Employment Reference Phone Script
  Employment Reference Release
  Fair Credit Disclosure Act Notice
  Job Analysis Questionnaire
  Job Description Form
  Job Requirements Checklist
  Personal Reference Check Letter
  Reference Checking Documentation Form
  Sample Employment Application Form
  Sample Independent Contractor Agreement
  Sample Interview Script
  Temporary Help Agency Checklist
Starting Your Business
  Business Selection Checklist
  Cash Flow Sensitivity Analysis
  Cost Assessment Checklist
  Equipment Lease Checklist
  Family Monthly Budget Form
  Franchise Agreement Checklist
  Projected Staffing Schedule
  Real Property Lease Checklist
  Start-Up Checklist
  Strengths/Weaknesses Assessment Checklist
Vehicles &Equipment
  Annual Lease Table
  Checklist for Evaluating Used Cars
  Equipment Inventory List
Worker Safety
  Hazard Communication Program Package
  OSHA Form 101 - Supplemental Illness and Injury Log
  OSHA Form 174 - Material Safety Data Sheet
  OSHA Form 200 - Illness and Injury Log
  Sample Emergency Procedures
  Sample Safety Policy
  Sample Workplace AIDS Policy
  Sample Workplace Violence Prevention Policy

CORPORATION BYLAWS OUTLINE

ARTICLE 1 OFFICES & CORPORATE SEAL
    SECTION 1 PRINCIPAL OFFICE
    SECTION 2 OTHER OFFICES
    SECTION 3 CORPORATE SEAL
ARTICLE 2 SHAREHOLDERS
    SECTION 1 SHAREHOLDERS' MEETINGS
    SECTION 2 ANNUAL MEETINGS
    SECTION 3 SPECIAL MEETINGS OF THE SHAREHOLDERS
    SECTION 4 LIST OF SHAREHOLDERS
    SECTION 5 NOTICE OF SHAREHOLDERS' MEETINGS
    SECTION 6 CLOSING OF TRANSFER BOOKS OR FIXING RECORD DATE
    SECTION 7 QUORUM & ADJOURNMENT (A-C)
    SECTION 8 VOTING
    SECTION 9 ACTION WITHOUT MEETING
    SECTION 10 WAIVER OF NOTICE
ARTICLE 3 DIRECTORS
    SECTION 1 NUMBER
    SECTION 2 VACANCIES
    SECTION 3 POWERS
    SECTION 4 REMOVAL OF DIRECTORS
    SECTION 5 PLACE OF MEETINGS
    SECTION 6 ANNUAL MEETINGS
    SECTION 7 REGULAR MEETINGS
    SECTION 8 SPECIAL MEETINGS
    SECTION 9 QUORUM
    SECTION 10 ACTION WITHOUT MEETING
    SECTION 11 COMMITTEES OF THE BOARD
    SECTION 12 COMPENSATION
    SECTION 13 WAIVER OF NOTICE
ARTICLE 4 OFFICERS
    SECTION 1 DESIGNATION & TITLES
    SECTION 2 ELECTION, TERM OF OFFICE, QUALIFICATIONS
    SECTION 3 SUBORDINATE OFFICERS
    SECTION 4 REMOVAL
    SECTION 5 VACANCIES
    SECTION 6 CHAIRMAN OF THE BOARD
    SECTION 7 THE PRESIDENT
    SECTION 8 VICE PRESIDENT
    SECTION 9 THE TREASURER
    SECTION 10 THE SECRETARY
ARTICLE 5 RESIGNATIONS
ARTICLE 6 CONTRACTS, LOANS, CHECKS & DEPOSITS
    SECTION 1 CONTRACTS
    SECTION 2 LOANS
    SECTION 3 CHECKS, DRAFTS, ETC.
    SECTION 4 DEPOSITS
ARTICLE 7 CERTIFICATES FOR SHARES AND THEIR TRANSFER
    SECTION 1 CERTIFICATES FOR SHARES
    SECTION 2 TRANSFER OF SHARES
ARTICLE 8 FISCAL YEAR
ARTICLE 9 DIVIDENDS
ARTICLE 10 INDEMNIFICATION OF OFFICERS, DIRECTORS, EMPLOYEES, & AGENTS
ARTICLE 11 REPEAL, ALTERATION OR AMENDMENT

EXHIBIT F – SOFTWARE START-UP SCENARIO

SOFTWARE ENTREPRENEUR AND BUSINESS START-UP – A CASE STUDY

LEGAL STRATEGIES FOR STRIKING DEALS

The general legal strategy is to have credibility in all communications with potential investors such as the business plan, presentations and due diligence. Some elements of credibility will add value to your business while others will help avoid a discount on value. The key action points covered in this presentation are:

- Feature intellectual property as a key value.
- Design your capital structure to look normal.
- Try to avoid unconventional financings and business transactions.
- Demonstrate an understanding of current software licensing trends and their impact on revenues.
- Address the legal issues in international markets since such markets are an increasingly important source of revenue.

FEATURE INTELLECTUAL PROPERTY AS A KEY VALUE

A. Be prepared to demonstrate that your company owns its software products. Problems with this issue can kill a deal.

1. Pitfalls in Development. The relationships described below will be carefully examined by a potential investor. You need to be prepared to answer questions and demonstrate that such situations have been properly handled.

2. Duties to previous employers. The work of one or more of your software developers may be tainted relative to a former employer even if there was no written employee confidentiality and invention assignment agreement with the former employer. Key factors from a legal point of view are: (a) the similarity of the product line of the former employer and the new company, (b) where the developer did the development, and (c) whether any of the former employer's proprietary technology was used. These factors differ from state to state.

3. Use of contractors/consultants. Your company must obtain written assignments of all right, title and interest in all software work product. Otherwise, under the U.S. copyright law, the contractor will own the software even if you paid for it. Also, determine if consultants are tainted by prior work for other clients in the same technology area.

4. Use of university technology. Your company needs to identify and follow the university's policies and procedures for commercially exploiting the technology. Rights are likely to be nonexclusive so speed to market is very important.

5. Use of federal government technology. Obtaining such technology seems to take forever and may result in acquiring vaguely defined nonexclusive rights. Vagueness is generally not good. Investors want to see crisply and clearly defined rights.

6. Assignment or license. At the time of company formation, founders may consider hedging by licensing rather than assigning ownership of software to the company. There is significantly more value to a potential investor in a company with "ownership" of its key asset.

7. Independent development. Independent development is not a defense to a patent infringement claim. It is a defense to copyright and trade secret claims.

B. Featuring IP as a key value.

1. Major forms of intellectual property protection for your software products are patent, copyright, trade secret and trademarks.

2. Consider global protection not just U.S. protection. Copyright protection is easy and inexpensive to implement on a worldwide basis. No action is needed. Enforcement is always an issue. Patent and trademark protection are more expensive to secure and action is needed for

727

implementation.

C. Investors look for at least the beginning of a patent portfolio for key products.

　1. Patent protection (as well as copyright) provides statutory protection which means no signed agreement is needed to implement protection. This is very important because of the mass-market sales trend in software.

　2. It is estimated that about 8000 software related patents will be issued in the U.S. during 1996 and that about 20,000 software related patents will be issued in the U.S. during 1993-1996. Even if you are philosophically opposed to patents for software-related inventions, you must be strategic and consider patents at least for defensive purposes.

　3. Pitfalls - offer for sale and public disclosure bars. A "bar" is an action or event that means patent protection is no longer feasible. An "offer for sale" of an invention can occur even if the invention has not been reduced to practice and even if a nondisclosure agreement ("NDA") is implemented. An NDA will prevent the public disclosure bar from being triggered. In the U.S. there is a one-year grace period for both the offer for sale and public bars. Other countries have a public disclosure bar and no offer for sale bar, but have no grace period.

　4. Following are estimates for planning purposes of costs of filing patent applications and prosecution in U.S. and elsewhere. Keep in mind that there are two stages, filing and prosecution. It would be a rare case in which the PTO says "good job," here is your patent. You normally have to fight for the patent to issue during the prosecution stage which causes added expense.

　　a. Drafting and filing the application. In the U.S.: $4,500-$10,000 for attorneys' fees (for simple to moderate cases); $10,000-$23,000 for attorneys' fees (for complicated cases), plus $500-$2500 for Patent Office filing fees and drawing fees.

　　　In foreign countries, after filing first in the U.S.: $4,500-$6,500 (in a country where translation of the U.S. application is required); $1,500-$2,500 (in a country where no translation is required): $7,800-$8,800 (in the European Patent Office).

　　b. Prosecution costs. In the U.S.: $1,000-$10,000 (without interferences, appeals or extraordinary proceedings).

　　　In foreign countries: $3,000-$5,000, without opposition being filed by third parties.

　　c. The general approach is to file a U.S. patent application first. The U.S. filing provides a 12-18 month hedge for filings in certain other countries. This provides time to make an initial commercial viability determination of your product.

　　d. Estimated time from filing to issuance in the U.S. for software related inventions is 2-3 years. First office action can be anticipated in about 18 months. A patent may not be enforced until issued.

　5. Business plan credibility - "The company has consulted with a patent attorney concerning filing of several patents in the U.S. and other important markets which will be funded from the proceeds of the financing." Compare this approach to "I haven't done anything."

D. Trademark

Trademark use can be an early area of legal exposure. Plan ahead for this visible symbol of your business so time can be spent on positive marketing activities. Words that describe your product may be good from a marketing point of view but may have little protection as a trademark. Do not go to a lawyer for the first time on the day before you go to the printer with promotional and packaging materials containing the trademark you've selected. You also do not want to have to explain to a potential investor why a trade name or mark is being changed.

E. Mark markings

Make sure your product and packaging have proper intellectual property markings (©,TM,®, etc.) as a key indicator of intellectual property credibility. Ask your lawyer to review these items before they are out in the market.

F. Confidentiality

Investors will observe your discipline in using nondisclosure agreements for products and other sensitive information. There is no such document as a "standard NDA." They are all different and must be read and possibly negotiated. Some are labeled "Confidentiality Agreement" but say that everything you are given is confidential but nothing you disclose is confidential. There is often a balance between maintaining confidentiality and having opportunity. If you are too rigid on confidentiality there is no opportunity. A balance is needed.

II. DESIGN THE CAPITAL STRUCTURE TO LOOK NORMAL

A. Keep it simple. Both investors and the public market like a simple capital structure.

B. Standard Pattern.

	Authorized	Outstanding
Founding	10 million c/s	2-4 million c/s (founders)
	4 million p/s	1 million c/s (stock plan)
Immediately	25 million c/s	8 million c/s and equivalents
Prior to IPO	4 million p/s	

1. If all goes according to plan, based on overall company value and the desirable per unit share price, about 8 million common stock equivalents (common stock, preferred stock plus options) are generally outstanding moving into the IPO stage. Working backward from this stage, it generally means that 2-4 million common stock ("c/s") are issued in the founders round and 1 million c/s are reserved for the stock option plan.

   The number of shares outstanding at the time of an IPO is driven by:
   - company value at IPO;
   - amount to be raised in the IPO; and
   - IPO per share range

2. The "pattern" for the business value at the time of the IPO can be reached by forward or reverse stock splits. For example, if a company has a market valuation at IPO time of $120 million, it would not be feasible for 40 million shares to be outstanding. A reverse stock split is needed. No one likes reverse stock splits from excess dilution which reduce the number of units held and, therefore, potential return from the IPO. On the other hand, forward stock splits are welcomed since they add units to holdings.

C. Keep the c/s price as low as possible as long as possible to provide greater stock incentives to attract and keep key employees. Tax and state corporate laws generally require option grants to be made at current fair market value.

1. Using preferred stock ("p/s") is a way to keep c/s at a lower price. A 5-10x value ratio (p/s to c/s) is generally acceptable to avoid bargain pricing for tax purposes. This is not guaranteed but is common practice in the Silicon Valley.

2. If you try to use c/s to raise large amounts of capital, there is usually a material dilution impact. Compare raising $1 million in c/s priced at $0.25 per share to using p/s priced at $1 per share.

	Shares Outstanding Prior to Financing	After	New Ownership Percentage
$0.25 c/s	4 million (100%)	8 million	50% each
$1.00 p/s	4 million (100%)	5 million	80% founders
			20% investors

3. Reward the entire software development team with stock incentives not just the Vice President of Engineering. Inequities in stock holdings and other compensation will be very visible at the time of an IPO and can create a potential destructive force. This is part of leadership and management.

B. Use of S Corporation/Limited Liability Company (LLC). The benefit of electing S corporation tax status is to avoid double taxation. An S corporation is taxed like a partnership. A LLC can also be taxed like a partnership but does not have the eligibility restrictions of an S Corporation. The LLC is not generally perceived as an investment vehicle with the possibility of traditional liquidity events.

1. An S corporation may not have two classes of shares outstanding (as opposed to merely authorized). Other eligibility requirements are:
   - No non-resident aliens permitted as shareholders
   - No corporations as shareholders
   - No more than 35 shareholders
   - All shareholders must elect to be an S corporation

2. The S corporation's tax year (calendar year) is truncated if p/s is issued.

3. Only C corporations and noncorporate investors are eligible for the Qualified Small Business Corporation capital tax break. A loss of lower capital gains rates on S Corporation stock is not likely acceptable to investors. This benefit of this QSBC tax break is that if the stock is held for at least 5 years, 50% of any gain on the sale on exchange of stock may be excluded from gross income.

4. With respect to LLCs, an acquisition of an LLC generally may not be done on a tax-free basis and the expenses of formation are higher than for forming a corporation.

C. There are pitfalls of hedging on the timing of forming corporation to save on expenses. The longer you hedge the more difficult it is to keep the founders price at a minimum level if a financing is imminent.

D. The best reason for using a Delaware corporation at startup is the ease of dealing with the Delaware Secretary of State in financings and other transactions. Otherwise, there is probably no compelling business reason to have a Delaware corporation at the outset if operations are in California or a state other than Delaware. Delaware law benefits are of the most value to public companies. About 75% of California corporations which go public reincorporate in Delaware at the time of the IPO.

1. A Delaware corporation will result in taxation in Delaware as well as the state of operations.

2. Many provisions of California corporation law are applicable in any event if primary operations of a private company are in California and at least 50% of its shareholders are here. A corporate name doesn't otherwise become available for use in California because the business has been incorporated in Delaware.

3. The advantages of a Delaware corporation are:
   - p/s protective provisions are primarily defined in the certificate of incorporation rather than certain protections being required by statute;
   - more flexibility for directors and officers to act without shareholder approval;
   - slightly more protection of directors and officers from monetary liability to shareholders; and
   - more flexibility with respect to implementing anti-takeover provisions.

III. TRY TO AVOID UNCONVENTIONAL FINANCING AND BUSINESS TRANSACTIONS.

A. Conventional financing pattern.

1. Pattern is succeeding rounds of p/s which are sold at higher prices in each round and which have superior rights over prior rounds of p/s financing. P/s is convertible into c/s (initially at 1-1) and, at a minimum, has liquidation and dividend preferences. Depending on your leverage, the p/s will likely have other features to benefit and protect the investor.

2. Even if a "bootstrap" financing is needed, keep in mind what venture capital investors may want. Avoid small p/s financings because of the statutory veto authority over future financings. Cal. Corporations Code §903 requires approval of the initial series of p/s (even without voting rights) of a new round of p/s if the new p/s will have superior rights to the

existing p/s. Also avoid using c/s at a price that inflates value too quickly. Again, a general approach is to keep the c/s price as low as possible as long as possible as an incentive to attract and retain key employees.

3. Avoid debt service--go for equity or at least debt which is automatically convertible into equity upon a successful event. A short-term loan secured by your proprietary intellectual property could result in disaster.

B. Comply with federal and state securities laws.

The general rules are that: (1) full disclosure must be made to prospective investors, and (2) offerings of securities must be registered with applicable authorities. The rules apply to both offers and sales. "Debt" is a security unless the lender is in the business of lending.

1. Must make full disclosure regarding material matters. Usually done primarily through the venture's business plan.

2. Must register all securities offerings unless an exemption from registration is available. Lawyers always look for exemptions based on the dollar amount of the offering and/or business sophistication of potential investors. Requirements differ between federal and state law.

3. An investor has a money back guarantee if securities laws are not followed. Legal opinions regarding exemptions are not possible if securities are sold without regard for such laws. An opinion may be required in venture capital investments or an acquisition.

4. Multi-state offerings require compliance with the laws of each applicable state.

C. Pitfalls in contract financings such as software development or license agreements.

1. Distribution, license and other commercial relationships will have an adverse impact on future financings if you give away too much in terms of revenue generation or the ability to compete. A strategic partner is often a likely acquirer unless the initial commercial deal is so "sweet" to the partner that there is minimal value left to be acquired.

2. In a development project, if ownership cannot be acquired, your company needs to be granted the scope of license rights needed for commercial exploitation. Any right not expressly granted in a license is reserved so your company does not have the right if the agreement is silent on the activity. The right to prepare derivative works is a key right that is often missed.

IV. DEMONSTRATE AN UNDERSTANDING OF CURRENT SOFTWARE LICENSING TRENDS AND THEIR IMPACT ON REVENUES

A. Licensing and deployment must be market driven to fit current computing environments - network, distributed processing. Client-server is a key trend in business computing.

B. You must understand the licensing impact on revenues. How did you establish your pricing? The market size and ability to obtain and sustain a share of revenues in the market is a key factor to potential investors. There are price points for many types of software (not just mass market software) and these points are generally moving downward. Concurrent, floating, enterprise, site licensing all have various meanings and related revenue impacts.

C. Do not assume there is a standard meaning. Consider and define licensing rights and related revenues for your distribution model.

D. The mass market trend and competitors' actions may force a move to shrinkwrap (as opposed to signed licenses) sooner than ever before. This shift is also driven by the platform and pricing. The goal is to speed up deals and revenues while maintaining a fundamental level of protection.

E. Be prepared to address how you are using or could use the Internet in marketing and distribution. Early on, the Internet was thought to be a great equalizer, a way for small software companies to avoid the shelf space/cost of distribution problem. Today, with the proliferation of World Wide Web sites, the problem is how to get people to your Home Page to learn about your products.

V. ADDRESS THE LEGAL ISSUES IN INTERNATIONAL MARKETS SINCE SUCH MARKETS ARE AN INCREASINGLY IMPORTANT SOURCE OF REVENUE.

A. International revenues comprise a high percentage of the revenues of many software companies.

B. Try to create channels in parallel not domestic first and international later. Do not wait until your domestic market is "fully developed" because the global window of opportunity may be closed. A World Wide Web home page is an immediate window to international business.

C. Demonstrate knowledge of dealing with critical international issues to support credibility of revenues in the business plan and discussions with investors.

1. Making the right choice of a foreign partner is crucial as a practical matter. Does the prospective partner have distribution capability and enforcement clout in the territory?

2. Create the right type of legal relationship to avoid unexpected tax and other liability (distributor, sales representative, OEM, etc.). A vaguely defined relationship is also bad business.

3. You need to learn about international payment mechanisms such as the letter of credit to create certainty for your revenue streams. Avoid the open account method until at least a track record of payments is established. The point of changing to open account is also vulnerable.

4. There is also always the risk of non-enforcement of intellectual property protection in foreign markets. You will want to go into foreign markets any way because your competitors are there and practical actions can minimize risk. The right foreign partner with practical clout can help protect intellectual property.

5. Withholding and other tax planning issues are very important economic factors. Foreign tax credits are not likely usable in the early stages of a company so withholding taxes on royalties could have revenue impact. A gross-up is the likely solution. The ROC and Singapore are market countries without a U.S. tax treaty which means there is a 30% withholding tax on license revenues. The solution for mass-market software is to "sell" units since withholding tax is not applicable to sales.

6. Most commercial software, particularly mass market software, is currently exportable to major market countries under the U.S. export controls except for software containing a file encryption feature. There is much discussion about relaxing export controls on software with file encryption features but it hasn't happened yet.

(Following is for information only. Seek legal or accounting advice for your specific situation)

1. How should I divide my shares?
    a. I'd like to better understand how share works and how I divide them among investors, employees, and how much I should keep in reserve for the future? I believe I requested during incorporation an issue of 1,000,000 shares at $1.00 par value.
    b. I am currently starting an Internet service business which is different from my incorporated business above. Should I include this entity as a DBA to the incorporation or create a separate INC or LLC?

        Corporations are required to have at least one class of voting shares of stock. These shares represent the right to receive assets upon dissolution of the corporation. To conform with this requirement, most corporations authorize at lease one class of common stock with one vote per share. The attributes of the shares as well as the number that can be issued are set forth in the articles of incorporation.

        Authorizing a large number of shares of stock has both advantages and disadvantages. The main advantage is the large number of shares that can be issued to potential shareholders of the corporation. There are more pieces of the pie to divide up amongst the owners. The negative is that many states charge base initial filing fees and annual taxes upon the number of shares that a corporation is authorized to issue. The more shares, the higher the fees. The number of shares of a corporation can always be changed by filing an amendment with the state.

        When issuing shares, most jurisdictions provide that shares may be issued in return for any tangible or intangible property or benefit to the corporation, including cash, promissory notes, services performed, contracts for services to be performed or other securities of the corporation. The board must determine the adequacy of the consideration for shares and so the values that are set must be reasonable. Thus, the board must decide how to issue the shares of stock.

        The par value of a stock is simply the stated minimum value of a share stock and has no relationship to the actually value of the shares. Stock must be sold for at least this value or the owner of the stock can face liability. The actual value of the shares will be determined by book value or simply what someone is willing to pay for the stock.

        A corporation can operate many different businesses and use many different names as DBAs. If this is down however, there is no separation between the businesses because no legal entities are formed. Thus, the assets of one the businesses could be used to pay the debts of the other businesses. If a new corporation is formed, the businesses would be separated, and, in most circumstances, the assets of one business (corporation) would not be used to satisfy the debts of the other corporation.

2. Is there an established process or standard formula for determining how much stock you would take (in lieu of a license fee) for a startup?
        The standard value of technology for exclusive licensing is a 5% gross royalty plus a $30K origination fee, which needs to be adjusted upwards on downwards depending on many case factors.

        As risk increases, so must reward. So... If there is no obligation for the company to pay dividends, and if the stock is non-liquid (at least until an IPO) then increase the equity. If there is no origination fee, then increase the equity some more. The end result is about a 20% stock position.

        Take a rather pragmatic view. First, take equity as the up-front fee -- never instead of royalties. Start by deciding what up-front fee would be if it were in cash. For a pharmaceutical, one might ask for $200,000 up front. With a start-up, simply ask for equity and dilution protection that would value your share to be equal to or greater than that up-front target; e.g., 10% equity, not subject to dilution at any time the total stockholder's equity is less than $2 Million or, 5%, not subject to dilution if TSE > $4 Million.

Downside of this approach is that it ignores the time value of money, and also ignores the risk the stock is worthless. Upside is that it is easy to explain (even to entrepreneurs), and is quite palatable to venture capital investors.

Issue with statement below that "we all . . . agree that the standard value of technology for exclusive licensing is a 5% royalty plus a $30k origination fee which needs to be adjusted . ". depending on many case factors". Not as much issue with the 5% running royalty as a fairly popular benchmark for certain kinds of technologies (but certainly not most software, where 5% would be considered quite low, or many pharmaceuticals, where 5% would be considered too high), but who says that a benchmark upfront fee is $30k? Why not $10k, $50k, or $100k? For determining up-front fees, I think we are much safer starting with a blank piece of paper and trying to make an estimation of what to ask based on some realistic assessment of the technology.

Appraising a technology is no different than appraising a piece of real estate or other business asset. In appraising residential and some commercial real estate, start with comparable sales ("comps") --known, closed deals. These are iron-clad facts off which you work. Take the house that you are appraising (the 'subject' property) and adjust it up or down in value. If it has a swimming pool, you adjust it up. If it has an extra or corner lot, you adjust it up again. If it is in a worse neighborhood, you adjust it down, etc. Our comps are much harder to get. We have fewer data points. So, we use what we got. 5% may be an average figure --again AVERAGE. It really doesn't matter.

Adjust for the industry, e.g. FDA approvals, development stage, cash flow, patent costs, etc. etc. 5% and $30K is not the end point. It is the starting point. A startup situation is riskier than licensing to an existing Fortune 500, so the equity compensation (potential payout) needs to be higher.

3. I am setting up a corporation and want to know the differences between C corp., S corp. and the new LLC as it affects future business, complications in filing returns, and write-offs - you want to be able to use losses if any against my personal taxes.

The types of entities that allow losses to be deducted against personal income are "pass through" tax entities. Income to the entity is not taxed. Instead the income is "passed through" to the individual shareholders or interest holders. S corporations and LLCs are both pass-through taxation entities.

Corporations that make the subchapter S election with the IRS and Limited Liability Companies (LLCs) do possess similarities: they offer their owners limited liability protection and are both pass-through tax entities. Pass-through taxation allows the income or loss generated by the business to be reflected on the personal income tax return of the owners. This special tax status eliminates any possibility of double taxation for S corporations and Limited Liability Companies.

However, that is where the similarities end. The ownership of an S corporation is restricted; however, a limited liability company does not possess these same restrictions. An LLC can have an unlimited number of members (owners) while a subchapter S corporation is restricted to no more than 75 shareholders. Non-US citizens can be members of an LLC while an S corporation may not have non-US citizens as shareholders.

Also, S corporations cannot be owned by C corporations, other S corporations, many trusts, LLCs, or partnerships. Limited Liability Companies are not subject to these restrictions. LLCs are allowed to have subsidiaries without restriction. S corporations are not allowed to own eighty percent or more of another corporation's shares.

An LLC is more flexible in distributing profits than an S corporation. With an S corporation, the corporation can have only one class of stock and your percentage of ownership determines the percentage of pass-through income. On the other hand, an LLC can have many different classes of interest and the percentage of pass-through income is not tied to ownership percentage. The pass through percentage can be set by agreement of the members in the LLC's operating agreement.

S corporations are not without advantages. One person can form an S corporation, while in about 5 of the states at least two people are required to form an LLC.

A corporation's existence is perpetual. Conversely, an LLC typically has a limited life span. Most states require that an LLC list a dissolution date in its articles of organization and certain events such as the death or withdrawal of a member can cause the LLC to dissolve.

The stock of an S corporation is freely transferable while the interest (ownership) of LLC is not. This free transferability of interest means that the shareholders of S corporation are able to sell their interest without needing the approval of the other shareholders, while a member of an LLC would need the approval of the other members in order to sell his or her interest. Be sure to seek advise from a competent attorney or accountant.

4. How do I structure my LLC so it will be a partnership for federal income tax purposes?

1.Applicable Factors

    a.   The analysis of whether an LLC is a partnership or corporation is made by applying the Morrisey factors. The Morrisey factors were established by the U.S. Supreme Court in Morrisey v. Commissioner, 296 U.S. 344 (1935). These factors are now embodied in Treas. Reg. §301.7701-2.

    b.   The tax law uses the term "association" to refer to an organization whose characteristics requires it to be classified as a corporation for tax purposes. The basic analysis looks at six factors:

        1. associates,

        2. objective to carry on a business and divide the gains therefrom,

        3. limited liability,

        4. centralized management,

        5. continuity of life, and

        6. free transferability of interest.

        The first two factors are generally disregarded because they are present in both a corporation and a partnership. The final four factors are analyzed to determine whether there are more corporate than non-corporate characteristics. Because the test is whether there are more corporate than non-corporate characteristics, an entity with three or more of the corporate characteristics will be deemed to be a corporation. However, if an entity has two or fewer of the corporate characteristics, it will be classified as a partnership for federal income tax purposes.

    c.   The following discussion analyzes each of the primary factors:

        1.   Associates (necessity of two or more). This factor is generally ignored because associates are common both in a partnership and a corporation. However, this factor is a problem in some cases. Some states' LLC statutes permit the formation of a single member LLC. The use of a single member LLC can raise some serious tax concerns. While one can argue that a single member LLC should be taxed as a sole proprietorship, the IRS has not yet conceded this point. The IRS position is that a single member LLC is a corporation for tax purposes because the LLC does not have associates and because of the effect on the other factors of having only one member.

        2.   Objective to carry on a business and divide the gains therefrom. This factor is present in both partnerships and corporations so it is generally ignored.

        3.   Limited liability. An organization has the corporate characteristic of limited liability if, under local law, there is no member who is personally liable for the debts of, or claims against, the organization. Personal liability means that a creditor of an organization may seek personal satisfaction from a member of the organization to the extent that the assets of such organization are insufficient to satisfy the creditor's claim. Under the terms of the LLC statutes, a member is not liable for the debts of an LLC merely as the result of being a member or manager. Therefore, an LLC will have the corporate characteristic of limited liability.

4. Centralized management. An organization has centralized management if any person (or any group of persons which does not include all of the members) has continuing exclusive authority to make the management decisions necessary to the conduct of the business for which the organization was formed. Thus, persons who are vested with such management authority resemble in powers and functions the directors of a statutory corporation.

   Under most state statutes, an LLC is permitted, if it so chooses, to be operated by its members. However, the company may be operated by managers who are appointed under the terms of the Operating Agreement. Therefore, an LLC may or may not have centralized management. If an LLC has managers, the LLC will likely have centralized management. If the LLC does not have managers (i.e. it is member-managed), it will not likely have centralized management.

5. Continuity of life. An organization has continuity of life if the death, insanity, bankruptcy, retirement, resignation or expulsion of any member will not cause a dissolution of the organization. On the other hand, if the death, insanity, bankruptcy, retirement, resignation or expulsion of any member will cause a dissolution of the organization, continuity of life does not exist. An agreement by which an organization is established may provide the business will be continued by the remaining members in the event of the death or withdrawal of any member, but such agreement does not establish continuity of life under local law if the death or withdrawal of any member causes dissolution of the organization.

   Continuity of life is one of the key areas around which the LLC has been structured in order to provide partnership tax treatment. Most state statutes have essentially adopted the events of dissolution described in the Treasury Regulations as the events which will cause an LLC to dissolve. When any of these events occur, there is a technical dissolution of the LLC. A technical dissolution does not mean the entity must be wound up or its affairs terminated. The members may include a provision in the LLC's formation documents which permit the remaining members to continue the operation of the LLC by agreement. Under the currently prevailing tax authorities, an agreement which requires approval of at least a majority in interest of the members of the LLC to continue the business of the LLC should not cause an LLC to have continuity of life.

6. Free transferability of interest. An organization has the corporate characteristic of free transferability of interest if each of its members or those members owning substantially all of the interest in the organization have the power, without the consent of other members, to substitute for themselves in the same organization a person who is not a member of the organization. In order for this power of substitution to exist in the corporate sense, the member must be able, without the consent of the other members, to confer upon his substitute all the attributes of his interest in the organization. Thus, the characteristic of free transferability of interest does not exist in the case in which each member can, without the consent of other members, assign all his rights to share in profits but cannot sell or assign his rights to participate in the management of the organization. Most LLC statutes are structured to avoid free transferability of interest. Some state statutes specifically prohibit a transferee from succeeding to any rights to participate in management of an LLC unless the admission of such transferee to the partnership is approved by all the members. Other state statutes permit the operating agreement for the LLC to control the conditions for the admissions of a transferee to membership. In these states the draftsman needs to be careful to assure that he requires sufficient approval to avoid the characteristic of free transferability of interest.

7. Other factors. In addition to the factors described above, the IRS may consider additional factors to determine whether an entity is more like a partnership or more

like a corporation. Although the IRS has made several comments in this regard, the IRS has not identified what other factors it might consider.

   d. In summary, the analysis of whether an entity is a partnership or a corporation for tax purposes revolves around four primary factors. These factors are (1) limited liability, (2) centralized management, (3) continuity of life and (4) free transferability of interest. As described above, limited liability almost always exists in an LLC. Centralized management may or may not exist. However, if it does exist, that is only the second corporate factor. The key factors are continuity of life and free transferability of interest. If these factors are not present, the entity should be a partnership for tax purposes. A carefully structured LLC can avoid the existence of continuity of life and free transferability of interest and, therefore, should be capable of classification as a partnership for tax purposes.

2. IRS Rulings

   a. Rev. Rul. 88-76. In Rev. Rul. 88-76 the IRS finally conceded that it would recognize a Wyoming LLC as a partnership for tax purposes.

   b. Private Letter Rulings. Following the release of Rev. Rul. 88-76, there was a slow trickle of private letter rulings on the tax classification of LLCs.

   c. New Published Rulings. In January of 1993, there were several published rulings issued by the IRS which classified LLCs formed under various state statutes as partnerships for federal income tax purposes. Several additional published rulings have been added since then. These rulings have established a clear intent on the behalf of the IRS that LLCs will be classified as partnerships for tax purposes. It is important to note that these rulings applied to specific LLC statutes and specific provisions included in the LLC formation documents. An improperly structured LLC can be taxed as a corporation. A drafter of LLC formation documents needs to use caution in forming an LLC.

   d. New Revenue Procedure. The IRS has recently issued Rev. Proc. 95-10 which describes the factors that are required to be present before a ruling will be issued that an LLC is classified as a partnership.

   e. Notice 95-14. The IRS has recently issued Notice 95-14. This notice announces that the IRS is considering making the partnership versus corporate income tax classification elective. If adopted, LLCs could become much less complex.

3. Other Tax Considerations

   a. There are a number of other important tax considerations in deciding to operate as an LLC. Tax practitioners are generally taking the position that the word "limited liability company" is inserted for the word "partnership" and the word "member" is inserted for the word "partner" in all provisions of the Internal Revenue Code. However, there is no clear authority for such a position.

   b. The lack of clarity on this point has raised a number of collateral tax issues. One example is whether the LLC may use the cash method of accounting. This question has been examined in a private letter ruling which went through a convoluted analysis of whether the LLC was a "tax shelter" as defined in certain provisions of the Internal Revenue Code. Another issue which has raised questions is whether income from an LLC should be treated as self-employment income. New Proposed Regulations have been issued to address these issues. A review of these issues and other tax considerations is beyond the scope of this outline. For a detailed discussion of these issues see Thomas and Morgan on Limited Liability Companies, by James C. Thomas III and John C. Morgan (Harcourt Brace Professional Publishing 1995).

4. State Tax Considerations

   Since federal taxes are generally much higher than state taxes, the state tax considerations are often overlooked. State taxes can be significant and should not be ignored.

   Each state is different. Some states tax income of LLCs at the entity level even though the LLC is a partnership for federal income tax purposes. For example, Florida imposes an income tax on an LLC and Texas has a franchise tax on LLCs.

5. I am looking to begin an Internet-based home furnishing business. What incorporation status and business structure best fits e-business? Are there special legal considerations for a business that is entirely web-based?

No one entity is perfect for every business venture; there are a number of different factors that favor one entity over another. In dealing with a technology or internet start-up business, however, two very important factors in deciding which form of entity to choose are (a) your expectation of the most likely exit strategy, if any, and when; and (b) your expected financing needs, particularly venture capital financing. By exit strategy, I mean your plan, if any, to sell the business, how, and when. Companies that don't anticipate going public or will not need much, if any, venture capital financing, may be best suited with a limited liability company (LLC). You should work closely with an attorney to decide which entity is most appropriate for your business.

6. You just formed a new corporation, and now need to put together the bylaws. Where can you get a sample copy of simple corporate bylaws as examples to structure yours?

There are several Internet sites that offer legal forms. You should be able to download a sample form off one of these sites. One such site is Business Filings Incorporated, https://www.bizfilings.com that offers a corporate forms disk for $35. The corporate forms disk has been designed to make complying with corporate formalities easy. It contains all of the necessary forms to properly hold every type of corporate meeting including: organizational directors' meeting, annual directors' meeting, special meeting of directors and annual shareholders' meeting. The forms disk also contains bylaws and resolutions. All forms included on the disk can be used as are or with minor changes or additions.

An informational booklet is included that explains how and when to hold corporate meetings. The booklet also contains an index of all of the forms included on the disk.

7. I plan to incorporating my business in California. What do you estimate it will cost and what type of corporation is best?

A1: Incorporating is fairly straightforward. The papers can be filed by an individual entrepreneur. But there are usually considerations regarding what type of corporation is best and how much stock to initially authorize. If there is a plan to have offices in other states the amount of authorized shares, not issued shares, can mean a substantial tax on the corporation for doing business within that state. However, it is possible to authorize enough shares so there is no need to get stockholder approval to authorize new stock as the company grows. Issuing new shares can then be done solely with board approval.

Incorporation in California cost is about $115, so the cost is not that much. A C corporation is the simplest, most straightforward form of organization. It provides the flexibility to do many things that would be much more difficult if the company was an S or LLC. This is especially true if there is intent to do a private offering. S types are limited by the number of total shareholders and LLC shares issued to each member are valued at par and taxable to each member of the LLC.

A2: A difference of opinion also exists when comparing C and LLC companies. LLC's are highly flexible, and are now the most common form of initial legal format used in most states for startup businesses. They have pass through of profits and losses to shareholders which in many cases is very appealing to the investors because they get early advantage of the startup tax losses rather than having to wait some years to offset against potential profits.

They are governed by their operating agreement which can be tailored to the negotiated needs of the founders and the angel investors. They are now available in all states. In Wisconsin, they expect to modify them soon for easier "rollover" into corporations which will help startups around the corner. Such a rollover can be accommodated currently, but from a tax accounting standpoint they are not as easy as they should be, and will be in Wisconsin. Due to the prominence of LLCs it is likely that they are easy to "rollover" in all states.

Be careful of listening to an attorney who does not give a fair and reasonable review of LLCs. For one's particular situation another format may be better, but attorney's have been having a field day with LLCs for the last half dozen years. One example of their simplicity relative to corporations, is reporting. Reporting, as are most components, is a function of what the owners define it will be in the operating agreement versus corporate reporting which is specified by law and far more detailed, typically. Remember, if the owners fail to follow the corporate reporting requirements, they may be piercing their own veil.

A3: There are a lot of pluses for LLCs, particularly the flexibility it gives the owners regarding the reporting of profits and losses, and the resulting tax implications.

However, because of the flexibility, they can be difficult to structure properly, especially making sure the capital accounts balance (that is, stay consistent with the investors intentions) after allocation of profits and losses. Good attorneys and good accountants are needed to avoid later regrets. Flexibility, complexity and legal costs tend to go together. Administration of an LLC can be trivial or a disaster, depending on how it is set up.

The bottom line for universities is: if flexibility is not needed, don't push for it. Simpler can be better. If outside investors want it, fine, but get them to pay for the legal and financial advice. It won't be cheap. And, don't forget to get advice.

A4: LLCs give flexibility to owners, but university license deals involving equity in LLCs are not easy to be structured properly for several reasons:

1. *Regulatory/policy issues.* LLCs are classified for federal income tax purposes as partnerships. Therefore, income earned from active businesses conducted by LLCs is taxable to the university as UBTI ("Unrelated Business Taxable Income"). Tax-exempt universities are usually allowed to only have a small percentage of UBTI. Please make sure that your university allows you to take equity in LLCs before you structure equity deals with LLCs. Exempt organizations generally would have UBTI when the LLCs earn the income, not the LLCs distribute the income to the exempt organizations. It is irrelevant that the exempt organizations may not take any active role in the LLCs' business.

2. *Special skills are needed to structure equity deals with LLCs.* There are alternatives for exempt organizations to get around UBTI. However, technology managers need to thoroughly understand financial instruments other than equity and be familiar with tax/business laws. For example, to avoid having equity in LLCs, an exempt organization could receive warrants from the LLC. Receipt of the warrants should not be a taxable event to the organization if the LLC's income is not allocated to the warrant holder. The organization could exercise the warrants when the LLC is converted to a C corporation because the LLC-to-C conversion can usually be designed as a tax-free transaction. Thereafter, the dividends from the C corporation would not be UBTI.

3. *Economics of UBTI.* An exempt organization may be willing to incur UBTI if the after-tax economic return is high enough and its tax-exempt status is not endangered. An example follows.

Assumption:
> -An exempt organization has a 5% equity in a business. The business earns $1M of net income, and gives the exempt organization a $50K share. The exempt organization's UBTI tax rate is 34%.
> -A C Corporation paying tax on its income at the rate of 34% and paying the exempt organization a dividend out of after-tax income ($660k)
> -An LLC paying no income tax and distributing the full $1M to the LLC members. The exempt organization gets $50K (5% ownership).

Consequences:
> - The C Corporation pays $340K to the IRS and issues $660K as dividends. The exempt organization gets $33K and pays no tax. Thus, the exempt organization having no UBTI receives $33K after tax.

- The LLC distributes everything to its members and the exempt organization gets $50K. The exempt organization owes IRS $17K at the tax rate of 34% and will be left with $33K. Thus, the exempt organization receives $33K after tax. Economically, there is no difference between holding equity in the C and in the LLC in this scenario.

However, if the $1M business income consisted of income that would NOT be considered UBTI (such as interest income), the exempt organization could be better off holding equity in the LLC than in the C. For example, if the $1M consists 10% of interest income, the exempt organization would receive the same amount ($33K) after tax if it holds 5% in the C because the C pays tax on interest income. However, the exempt organization would be left with $34.7K after tax if it holds 5% in the LLC because interest income would be tax-exempt. The math reads as follows:

- Income distributed to LLC members: $1M
- The exempt organization's share: $50K
- The amount subject to UBTI: $50k-$50k x 10% =$45K
- Tax paid: $45K x 34%=$15.3K
- The exempt organization's net worth of the 5% equity in the LLC: $50K-$15.3K=$34.7K

In summary, LLC deals are more complicated than people think, but an exempt organization could be better off economically if the technology transfer (TT) office's performance is measured by economic return on TT deals. Please be aware that the above examples are simplified hypotheticals. There are more facts that need to be considered to determine whether you would like to have an LLC deal or a C deal. Generally speaking, TT people prefer to have a C deal for two reasons: a) limited skill sets in TT offices; b) most successful LLCs convert to C corporations eventually.

8. Where did LLCs originate?

LLCs have their roots in the "partnership association" of 1874 and 1881 in Pennsylvania, Michigan, New Jersey, and Ohio. Although the partnership association did not survive as a viable business entity because too many restrictions on its structure hindered it, not so with LLCs. Today, Germany's GMbH and the "limitada" entity in Latin American countries are variations of the LLCs existing worldwide.

9. When were the first LLCs formed?

When Wyoming passed its LLC Act in 1977, the first LLC statute was enacted. But between 1977 and 1988, states were slow to adopt LLC legislation. In those early years, LLCs were not popular mainly because business persons were uncertain about how the Internal Revenue Service (IRS) would treat the LLC's tax status. In 1980, the IRS issued proposed regulations that would have denied taxation as a partnership to LLCs because their members lacked personal liability. The originally proposed regulation was subsequently withdrawn, and after several years of consideration, the IRS enacted Revenue Ruling 88-76, which set forth the regulations under which an LLC could be taxed as a partnership rather than a corporation.

In the meantime, Florida became the second state to adopt an LLC statute, and it designed its statute to allow greater flexibility than Wyoming's statute. After Revenue Ruling 88-65 was enacted, Colorado, Kansas, Virginia, Utah, and Texas enacted LLC statutes. To date, 47 states and the District of Columbia have enacted LLC legislation. The remaining states are either in the process of drafting LLC legislation or are considering it. The American Bar Association has drafted a proposed Uniform LLC Act that is now being ratified by the states.

10. Why did LLCs originate?

The original Wyoming statute was written specifically for an oil company that required a special form of ownership interest similar to the Latin American limitada. Both require management by an administrator, limited liability, and a minimum 20-year life continuity.

11. Who are the parties to an LLC?

The LLC owners are called members. These LLC members may also be its managers, or they may elect managers who have the ability to bind the LLC and who are responsible for the LLC's operations.

12. What are an LLC's characteristics?

Because one of an LLC's purposes is to preserve the pass-through tax advantage found within the partnership structure, an LLC's characteristics are dictated by IRS regulations, specifically Treas. Reg. Sec. 301.7701. According to the Treasury regulations, six characteristics determine if an entity is taxed as a corporation or a partnership:

- associates,
- an objective to carry on business and divide the gains derived from that business,
- continuity of life,
- centralized management,
- liability for debt, and,
- transferability of interest.

The IRS assumes an LLC will automatically contain associates, plan to to carry on business and divide its gains, and maintain debt liability. So, to be taxed as a partnership and not as a corporation, the LLC must lack two of the remaining characteristics. To assist LLCs in complying with these regulations, states have adopted two approaches to qualifying an LLC for pass-through taxation. The "bulletproof" statutes, such as those in Wyoming, Colorado, Virginia, and Nevada, mandate certain LLC characteristics, such as limits on the LLC's life duration and restrictions upon free transfer of interest. On the other hand, states such as Florida and Utah have adopted a "flexible" approach about how they will deal with LLC life duration and interest transferability. Most states provide flexibility about LLC management-management power vested in all members unless otherwise stated. But, those drafting LLCs formed under those statutes must carefully draft their agreements to avoid violating IRS regulations and incurring corporate tax liability.

13. How do LLC's compare with partnerships and corporations?

An LLC's purpose is to combine the limited liability for its members usually found in the corporate structure (and to limited partners in limited partnerships) with the pass-through tax advantages of the general partnership. So, an LLC has some, but not all, of the characteristics of each entity.

LLCs' formation and liability characteristics are similar to corporations: To form a corporation, the necessary documents must be filed with the designated state agency and corporations must otherwise comply with state laws. The corporation is liable for debt: Shareholders are not personally liable. Other characteristics may be similar to or differ from corporate characteristics, depending upon how the LLC members wish to structure the entity and comply with IRS regulations to receive favorable tax treatment.

LLCs have also been compared to the Subchapter S corporation. A Subchapter S corporation is a corporation that allows the pass-through taxation feature of a partnership but maintains the corporate structure. Using a Subchapter S corporation holds one major disadvantage: restrictions exist on the number and type of ownership. The Subchapter S corporate form is limited to 35 shareholders, and those shareholders are limited to natural persons. In other words, no other business entity can be a shareholder in a Subchapter S corporation.

LLCs may be similar to general partnerships in all aspects except formation and liability, again, depending upon how the LLC elects to structure itself. That is, as in a general partnership, financial interests may be freely assigned. Like general partners, LLC members may withdraw and receive their interest, and they manage the entity. An LLC's continuity of life parallels a general partnership's: it continues until the death, bankruptcy, withdrawal of a partner (member), or after a period of time the agreement sets forth.

Similarly, LLCs may parallel limited partnerships in the same aspects as they do general partnerships, but members have the same kind of limited liability that limited partners enjoy. LLC members, however, are able to participate in the LLC's management without the threat of losing their limited liability status.

14. How is an LLC formed?

An LLC may be formed by just one person, but it more commonly requires two or more "persons." As in many states, in Ohio, an LLC is formed by two or more persons who sign and file Articles of Organization (Articles) with the appropriate state office, such as a Secretary of State. The Articles must include the following information:

- the LLC's name,
- the period of the LLC's duration,
- the LLC's address, and in many states, and
- the name and address of a statutory agent for the LLC.

The LLC's name must also include the words, "Limited Liability Company," or one of the following abbreviations: "Limited," "Ltd.," or "Ltd" (with no period at the end).

15. What other documents are necessary?

Along with the Articles, which are necessary to establish the LLC of public record, the Operating Agreement (Agreement) sets forth the particulars of how the LLC will be governed. To be valid, the Agreement's terms may be either written or oral. If all of the governing terms of the Agreement are intended to be included within the Agreement, this should be specifically stated in the Agreement.

16. What information does the agreement contain?

The Agreement, comparable either to a corporation's by-laws or a partnership agreement, provides the framework within which the LLC will be governed. It is crucial to properly draft the Agreement, especially in those states with flexible statutes. An improperly constructed Agreement will result in the loss of the LLC's pass-through tax status. Some of the more important provisions that the Agreement should include are the following:

- Management. Most state statutes do not provide specific management requirements. So, the Agreement must detail how the management is to be structured. Management can be either direct: all members are managers and hold authority to act on the LLC's behalf-or centralized: members elect a manager or managers who are then authorized to act on the LLC's behalf.
- Purpose. LLCs " . . . may be formed for any purpose which individuals may lawfully associate themselves . . . "
- Capital contributions. Each member must make some form of capital contribution. Members are not restricted to contributing only cash, but they may make contributions in the form of services rendered, property, or other forms of capital.
- Allocations and distributions. Periodic allocations of income or distribution if a member withdraws will be aligned with a member's capital contribution, unless the Agreement specifies otherwise.
- Transferability of interest. A member's interest is treated as personal property. This permits members to assign their financial interests in the LLC but prohibits members from assigning management authority, unless the Agreement states otherwise. Take great care in structuring this part of the Agreement: This is one area that the IRS will examine if it questions the LLC's tax status.

- Dissolution and termination. Again, as in the transferability of interest, this section of the Agreement is very important. Some state statutes mandate a specific duration to the LLC's life. Others do not. If not contemplated by statute, this is another area the IRS will examine to determine if the favorable pass-through tax is appropriate.

17. Who may be an LLC member?

Any "person," partnership, business trust, or any other viable business entity may be an LLC member. Because corporations are considered "persons" under the law, a corporation may also be an LLC member. Likewise, an LLC may also be a partner of a partnership or a stockholder of a corporation.

18. What are the advantages of forming an LLC?

Very definite advantages make forming an LLC attractive. An LLC provides its members limited liability and yet allows members to escape the double taxation pitfall found with the corporate structure. The LLC is also becoming more common as a business entity because any "person," either natural or legal, can be a member. Further, the members may actively manage the LLC without incurring personal liability as would a limited partner of a limited partnership.

19. What are the disadvantages of forming an LLC?

The greatest disadvantage to an LLC is the uncertain tax status surrounding it. IRS regulations are very exacting about how an LLC must be structured to gain the favorable partnership-tax treatment. Plus, not only does the lack of unity among state statutes make drafting the Agreement a difficult chore, many business persons do not know how to deal with LLCs because they are so new.

20. Can LLCs do business outside home states?

Most states will allow a foreign LLC to perform business within their borders. But the LLC must register to do business in that state with the appropriate state office, usually the Secretary of State. One problem here (that is now diminishing) is whether a state that has not enacted an LLC statute will recognize an LLC. But the main concern is whether such a state will recognize LLC's limited liability aspect. It probably will, under "comity," the legal theory requiring a forum state to recognize and admit the laws of the state of the LLC's organization, when those laws do not run contrary to the forum state. States may also resolve this problem by reasoning:
- the forum state recognizes the LLC's limited liability because it already recognizes the limited liability of corporations and limited partnerships, or
- the forum state reasons that the state's public policy is to recognize the LLC's limited liability by express statute.

21. What does a lender think about LLCs?

The LLC is an increasingly popular form of business entity. Since Ohio's LLC statute became effective (July 1, 1994), 1,270 domestic and 50 foreign LLCs have filed Articles with the Secretary of State's office. Because an LLC may own assets and do business in its own name, the entity is relatively easy to deal with as a lender. Initial concerns are is the entity a legal entity? If so, who is authorized to bind the LLC? If research reveals an LLC is a legal entity, examine the LLC's Articles to see if it has been duly registered in its domicile state, and in the state where it intends to borrow money. Examine the Agreement to determine who is authorized to bind the LLC.

Ask for certified copies of the Articles and Agreement to verify these concerns. Then, ask the LLC's attorney to prepare an opinion of counsel letter.

22. How Do LLCs work? When is this form of company structure appropriate? Are there pros and cons to such a business structure?

For many years, many small business people have been torn between operating as a sole proprietor (if several people are involved, as a partnership) or incorporating. On the one hand, many owners are attracted to the tax reporting simplicity of being a sole proprietor or partner. On the other, they desire the personal liability protection offered by incorporation. For many years it was possible to achieve these dual goals only by forming a corporation at the state level and then complying with a number of technical rules to gain S-corporation status from the IRS. Then a few years ago the limited liability company (LLC) was introduced. LLCs, which are recognized by all states can have many of the most popular attributes of partnerships (pass through tax status) and corporations (limited personal liability for the owners). In some states, an LLC requires at least two owners, meaning they are not suitable for sole proprietors except where a spouse is included as a co-owner. You can establish an LLC by filing a document called an Article of Organization with your state's corporate filing office (often the Secretary of State or Commissioner of Corporations).

There are few drawbacks to organizing your business as an LLC, beyond the fact that it requires a moderate amount of paperwork at the outset. These papers include the Articles of Organization and an Operating Agreement. You must file the Articles with your state's Secretary of State, along with a filing fee that will range from a few hundred dollars in some states to almost $1,000 in others.

Here are the main features of the LLC, which make it so attractive to many small business owners:

Limited liability. Until the LLC came along, business owners were personally on the hook for all the business debts, including liability from most lawsuits, unless they incorporated. But LLC owners are not personally liable for business debts, such as court judgments or legal settlements obtained against the business. They risk losing only the amount they paid into the business to get it started. (If however, you personally co-sign a loan, you are personally liable, no matter how the business is set up.)

Flexible management. The owners of an LLC are called members. Small LLCs are normally member-managed--after all, most small business owners want and need to have an active hand in running the business. Members can, however, elect a management group, which may include nonmembers. This flexibility can't be found in a standard corporation, where owners must split up decisions among directors and shareholders. Even if the same people fill all positions, corporate rules require the owners to don both director and shareholder hats when approving major decisions. A limited partnership is less formalistic, but has its own built-in restrictions: generally, limited partners are not allowed to manage the business without losing their limited liability.

One-level taxation. The LLC, like a partnership, is normally recognized by the IRS as a "pass-through" tax entity (you can also elect to have it taxed like a corporation). Unless you choose corporate tax treatment, the profits or losses of the business are not reported and taxed at a separate business level, as are corporate profits. Instead, they pass through the business and are reflected and taxed on the individual tax returns of the owners. (Sole proprietorships and corporations that have elected Chapter S status with the IRS (S corps) are also pass-through entities.)

Flexible distribution of profits and losses. When a business is co-owned, the owners may or may not wish to split profits and losses of the business proportionately to capital contributions. Different business forms have different rules about how business profits, losses and assets can or cannot be split up. The corporate form is generally the most rigid, and partnerships the most flexible. The LLC is treated like a partnership for tax purposes, and this applies to the division of profits and losses of the LLC.

23. I am trying to determine what a company is worth. What are some criteria to consider as the determination is made?

See Venture Opportunity Profile. Points to Consider when forming or setting value for a business entity:

Required investment	Product feasibility / product prototype
Status of market	Proprietary rights
Perceived need of the product/service	Exit potential
Suppliers (if any)	Labor requirements
Government regulation (if any)	Gross margin
Frequency of purchase	Tax treatment
Distribution channel	Timing of revenue from customer
PR worthiness of product/service	Product/service liability
Product/service obsolescence	Competition

Product/service expect lifetime

Product/service revenue dependence on external factors (other than regulation - seasonality etc.)

Legal Entanglements (license/patent/copyright violations etc.)

NOTES

NOTES

NOTES

NOTES

NOTES

ADDENDA, CASE STUDIES & PRESENTATIONS REQUEST FORM

Addendums I, II, and III are included with the ebook and Addendum IV (software) is available at no cost to those who purchase an ebook. Addendums I, II, III, and IV are also available to those who purchase a POD book. Complete this Addenda Request Form and send the original to the address below. **Only an original form with an original signature will be accepted.**

1. ADDENDUM I - GLOSSARY OF TERMS
2. ADDENDUM II - REFERENCES AND RESOURCES
3. ADDENDUM III - FORMS AND AGREEMENTS
   - i. FORMS
   - ii. AGREEMENTS
4. ADDENDUM IV - SOFTWARE
   - i. TECHNOLOGY EVALUATION SOFTWARE (TES - I) – PHASE ONE
   - ii. TECHNOLOGY EVALUATION SOFTWARE (TES - II) – PHASE TWO
   - iii. TECHNOLOGY PRICING MODEL™ (TPM)

COMPLETE THE FOLLOWING (PLEASE PRINT ALL BUT SIGNATURE)

I purchased an ebook. ___ yes ___ no (**must be completed**)

Signature: _____

Name: _____

Address: _____

_____

_____

Phone #: _____

Email: _____ (required for electronic return)

Addenda will be sent electronically to the email address provided unless a compact disk with material is desired. Check here to have addenda sent on a compact disk (CD). _____

Over 100 situation analysis are available for Modules I through IX. Highlights from each Module are summarized in over 1200 PowerPoint slides which can be adapted to individual needs.

Select the Module of interest and identify which item is desired. Fee for each item is $5.00. Send this completed form along with a check or money order to the address below. Make checks payable to Med-Launch. Items checked and paid for will be sent to the email address provided unless a compact disk with the material is desired. Check below to have items sent on a compact disk (CD). Include your address with this form. **SEND COMPACT DISK.** _____.

| Item available for each module | Modules*(check items desired) | | | | | | | | | | Subtotal, $*** |
	1	2	3	4	5	6	7	8	9	Σ,$	
Case studies/situation analysis**										45	_____
PowerPoint presentations****										45	_____

Total, $ _____

---

* Modules are 1 (Introduction), 2 (Intellectual Property), 3 (Evaluation), 4 (Marketing), 5 (Technology Management & Sponsored Research), 6 (Negotiation), 7 (Agreements), 8 (Capital) and 9 (Corporate Formation). ** Fee for all cases in each module is $5; minimum of 5 cases/module. *** If cases and PowerPoint slides from modules 6, 7 and 8 checked total cost is $30 ($15 + $15 = $30). ****Fee for each set of slides in each module is $5; minimum of 27 slides/module.

Print, photocopy or remove form from a textbook or ebook, complete, and send to the address on the form or see www.tclearningcenter.com to place an order.

Return address

____

____

____

Stamp

Med-Launch, Inc.
2813 Woodhaven Dr.
Champaign, IL
61822